ANATOMY & PHYSIOLOGY

The Unity of Form and Function

Ninth Edition

KENNETH S. SALADIN

Distinguished Professor of Biology, Emeritus
Georgia College

Digital Authors

CHRISTINA A. GAN

Highline College

HEATHER N. CUSHMAN

Tacoma Community College

BSC 2086
Volume 2
Broward College

Mc Graw Hill Education

1 2 3 4 5 6 7 8 9 0 SCI SCI 23 22 21 20

ISBN-13: 978-1-265-95887-9
ISBN-10: 1-265-95887-4

Solutions Program Manager: Steve Tomecek
Project Manager: Jennifer Bartell
Cover Photo Credits: Mike Kemp/Rubberball/Getty

BRIEF CONTENTS

© Tim Vacula

KENNETH S. SALADIN is Distinguished Professor of Biology, Emeritus, at Georgia College in Milledgeville, Georgia. He received his B.S. in zoology at Michigan State University and a Ph.D. in parasitology at Florida State University, with interests especially in the sensory ecology of freshwater invertebrates. He joined the Georgia College faculty in 1977. His courses included human anatomy and physiology, introduction to medical physiology, histology, general zoology, parasitology, animal behavior, biomedical etymology, study abroad in the Galápagos Islands, and premedical seminars, among others. Ken was recognized as "most significant undergraduate mentor" nine times over the years by outstanding students inducted into Phi Kappa Phi. He received the university's Excellence in Research and Publication Award for the first edition of this book, and was named Distinguished Professor in 2001. Ken is a member of the Human Anatomy and Physiology Society, American Association for Anatomy, American Physiological Society, Society for Integrative and Comparative Biology, Authors' Guild, and Textbook and Academic Authors Association. He served as a developmental reviewer and wrote supplements for several other McGraw-Hill anatomy and physiology textbooks for a number of years before becoming a textbook writer. Ken has used the earnings from his textbooks to support the Charles Darwin Research Station and fund ecosystem conservation and restoration in the Galápagos Islands, to remodel and equip the Georgia College anatomy laboratories, to fund the Honors Program, and to endow student scholarships, the William Harvey Chair in Biomedical Science, the Annual William Harvey Lecture in Medicine and Society, and the William P. Wall Museum of Natural History. Ken and his wife Diane have two grown children and a nature-loving grandson in North Carolina.

© Chris Gan/Yuen Lui Studios

CHRISTINA A. GAN, digital coauthor for Connect®, has been teaching anatomy and physiology, microbiology, and general biology at Highline College in Des Moines, Washington, since 2004. Before that, she taught at Rogue Community College in Medford, Oregon, for 6 years. She earned her M.A. in biology from Humboldt State University, researching the genetic variation of mitochondrial DNA in various salmonid species, and is a member of the Human Anatomy and Physiology Society. When she is not in the classroom or developing digital media, she is climbing, mountaineering, skiing, kayaking, sailing, cycling, and mountain biking throughout the Pacific Northwest.

© JC Penney Portraits/Lifetouch Portrait Studios, Inc.

HEATHER N. CUSHMAN, digital coauthor for Connect®, teaches anatomy and physiology at Tacoma Community College in Tacoma, Washington, and is a member of the Human Anatomy and Physiology Society. She received her Ph.D. in neuroscience from the University of Minnesota in 2002, and completed a postdoctoral fellowship at the Vollum Institute at Oregon Health & Science University in Portland, Oregon, where she studied sensory transduction and the cellular and molecular mechanisms of muscle pain. She currently resides in Tacoma, Washington, and enjoys climbing, camping, and hiking with her husband Ken and their daughter Annika.

CONTENTS

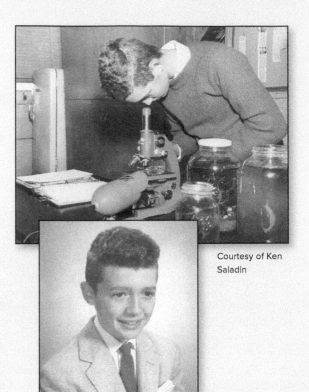

Courtesy of Ken Saladin

Ken Saladin's first step into authoring was a 318-page paper on the ecology of hydras written for his tenth-grade biology class. With his "first book," featuring 53 original India ink drawings and photomicrographs, a true storyteller was born.

When I first became a textbook writer, I found myself bringing the same enjoyment of writing and illustrating to this book that I first discovered when I was 15.

—Ken Saladin

Ken in 1964

Ken's "first book," *Hydra Ecology,* 1965
Courtesy of Ken Saladin

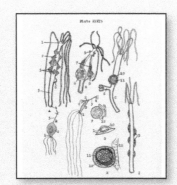

One of Ken's drawings from *Hydra Ecology*
Courtesy of Ken Saladin

Ken began working on his first book for McGraw-Hill in 1993, and in 1997 the first edition of *The Unity of Form and Function* was published. In 2020, the story continues with the ninth edition of Ken's best-selling A&P textbook.

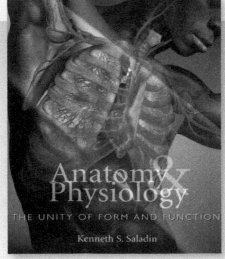

The first edition (1997)

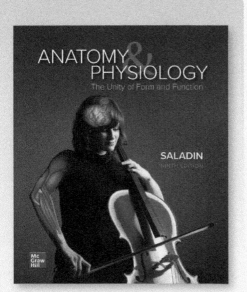

The story continues (2020)

PREFACE

Anatomy & Physiology: The Unity of Form and Function tells a story comprised of many layers, including core science, clinical applications, the history of medicine, and the evolution of the human body. Saladin combines this humanistic perspective on anatomy and physiology with vibrant photos and art to convey the beauty and excitement of the subject to beginning students.

To help students manage the tremendous amount of information in this introductory course, the narrative is broken into short segments, each framed by expected learning outcomes and self-testing review questions. This presentation strategy works as a whole to create a more efficient and effective way for students to learn A&P.

Writing Style and Level

Saladin's text is written using plain language for A&P students who may be taking this course early in their curricula. Careful attention has been given to word selection and paragraph structure to maintain the appropriate writing level for all students.

CHANGES TO THE NINTH EDITION

New Science

This edition draws on recent literature and scientific conferences attended by the author to update many topics, including but not limited to molecular, vascular, and brain imaging techniques; peroxisome and mitochondrial behavior; the DNA damage response; gene regulation; epigenetics; the tissue interstitium; regenerative medicine; osteoporosis; prosthetic joints; fibromyalgia; sleep physiology; trigeminal neuralgia; pain physiology; endocrine functions of osseous and adipose tissue; diabetes mellitus; cord blood transplants; thrombopoiesis; AIDS; prostate diseases; breast cancer; aging; life expectancy; and assisted reproductive technology.

New Deeper Insight sidebar essays have been added on cardiac tamponade; biopsy; stem-cell therapy; regenerative medicine; osteomalacia and rickets; vertebral disc herniation; rotator cuff injury; carpal tunnel syndrome; shinsplints; calcaneal tendon rupture; plantar fasciitis; brain connectomics and diffusion tensor imaging; lumbar puncture; stroke; blindness; alcoholic ascites; diverticulosis and diverticulitis; colorectal cancer; and cleft lip and palate.

While new science has been added, keeping up with such growth also means pruning back topics discredited by newer literature. For this edition, these include adult cerebral neurogenesis; endorphins and runner's high; human pheromones; pineal tumors and precocial puberty; prophylactic use of low-dose aspirin; myocardial regeneration; female ejaculation; and the free-radical DNA damage theory of senescence.

In consideration of user and reviewer suggestions to reduce detail in a few areas, this edition has more concise discussions of some topics: chromatin coiling; apoptosis; skin grafting; the hair cycle; calcium and phosphate homeostasis; and spinal cord tracts.

New Art and Photography

This edition features new drawings of epidermal histology, flat bone structure, lever mechanics, Parkinson disease, lumbar puncture, hand innervation, Bell palsy, the vagus nerve, olfactory pathways, erythropoiesis, cardiac innervation, regulation of cardiac output, air embolism, colonic histology, lipoprotein structure, cleft lip and palate, and senescent muscle atrophy.

New photos in this edition include digital subtraction angiography, molecular-scale cryo-EM imaging, diabetic gangrene, embryonic stem cells, albinism, jaundice, osteocyte SEM, rickets, muscle fiber histochemistry, diffusion tensor imaging of the brain connectome, shingles, cataracts, glaucoma, forelimb veins used for phlebotomy, kidney stones, gallstones, hepatic cirrhosis, MRI of obesity, and intracytoplasmic sperm injection.

Organizational Changes

For improved readability, narrative descriptions of some systems are moved from tables into chapter text; selected illustrations are moved outside of the tables; and tables are distilled to more concise summaries. These include the skeletal muscles (chapter 10), spinal nerve plexuses (chapter 13), cranial nerves (chapter 14), and blood vessels (chapter 20). A detailed list of changes by chapter follows.

Detailed List of Changes

Chapter 1, Major Themes of Anatomy and Physiology, now includes digital subtraction angiography among the common clinical imaging techniques.

Atlas A, General Orientation to Human Anatomy, has an added Deeper Insight A.1 on cardiac tamponade in relation to body cavities and membranes.

Chapter 2, The Chemistry of Life, has added the Nobel-winning new technique of cryo-electron microscopic imaging of biological structure at the atomic level.

Chapter 3, Cellular Form and Function, has enhanced discussions of limitations on cell size, the origin of peroxisomes, mitochondrial fusion and fission, and clinical mitochondrial transfer and three-parent babies.

Chapter 4, Genes and Cellular Function, updates protein processing by the Golgi complex, epigenetics, the DNA damage response, and the role of the nuclear lamina in gene silencing.

Chapter 5, The Human Tissues, has a new perspective on the tissue interstitium, updates on stem-cell therapy and regenerative medicine, and a new Deeper Insight on biopsy methods.

Chapter 6, The Integumentary System, has a new drawing of epidermal histology, new discussion of the evolutionary genetics of apocrine glands, an update on skin-grafting technology, and a simpler description of the hair growth cycle.

Chapter 7, Bone Tissue, gives a less detailed overview of calcium and phosphate homeostasis, adds a Deeper Insight on osteomalacia and rickets, and updates the pathology and treatment of osteoporosis.

Chapter 8, The Skeletal System, conforms the description of normal and pathological spinal curvatures to orthopedic terminology and has a new Deeper Insight on herniated discs.

Chapter 9, Joints, improves the discussion of joint biomechanics and updates the discussions of temporomandibular joint dysfunction and engineering of prosthetic joints.

Chapter 10, The Muscular System, pulls illustrations and narrative descriptions from the muscle tables, converts the narrative to easier-to-read normal text, and condenses the tables to more concise summaries. It updates inguinal hernias and adds new Deeper Insights on rotator cuff injury, shinsplints, calcaneal tendon rupture, and plantar fasciitis.

Chapter 11, Muscular Tissue, adds a photo of the histochemistry of fast glycolytic and slow oxidative muscle fiber types and updates the discussion of fibromyalgia.

Chapter 12, Nervous Tissue, includes updates on astrocyte functions, beta-endorphin and enkephalin, mutations affecting neurotransmitter reuptake and neurological disorders, and the implication of lipofuscin in some diseases. It introduces the frontier neuroscience of brain connectomics and the use of diffusion tensor imaging to visualize the connectome. There is now an illustration of the midbrain histological change and body posture characteristic of Parkinson disease.

Chapter 13, The Spinal Cord, Spinal Nerves, and Somatic Reflexes, adds a new Deeper Insight and illustration of lumbar puncture, reduces detail on spinal cord tracts, reformats the tables of spinal nerve plexuses, illustrates regional innervation of the hand by the major forearm nerves, and adds a photo of a shingles lesion.

Chapter 14, The Brain and Cranial Nerves, now adopts the concept of brainstem as excluding the diencephalon. It adds Deeper Insights on stroke and diffusion tensor imaging, and updates the Deeper Insight on trigeminal neuralgia and Bell palsy, adding an illustration of the latter. It updates sleep physiology and the functions of the midbrain colliculi and pretectal nuclei. It corrects a common misconception about the subdural space. The discussion and table of cranial nerves are reorganized.

Chapter 16, Sense Organs, has an updated discussion of pain physiology and includes phantom limb pain. It updates the genetics and functions of some taste sensations and flawed assumptions about human olfactory sensitivity. It deletes discredited or dubious views of endorphins and runner's high and human pheromones. It enhances the figure of olfactory projection pathways; adds the dorsal and ventral streams of visual processing pathways; adds photos of cataracts and glaucoma; adds macular degeneration and diabetic retinopathy to the Deeper Insight on blindness; and has better insights into the functions of the cornea, choroid, and vitreous body.

Chapter 17, The Endocrine System, updates the histology and cytology of the thyroid gland and pancreatic islets and the effects of melatonin; adds new information on hormones of osseous and adipose origin; updates the enteroendocrine system; and adds effects of lipocalin 2 on insulin action. It deletes the now-questionable idea about pineal tumors and precocial puberty. It updates the pathologies of Addison disease and myxedema, and the genetic, immunological, and treatment aspects of diabetes mellitus.

Chapter 18, The Circulatory System: Blood, now explains how blood is fractionated to obtain plasma and then serum, and the uses of blood serum. It has an enhanced explanation of the functional significance of the discoidal shape of erythrocytes, and includes cell proliferation in the illustration of erythropoiesis. It reports updated clinical research on the number of known blood groups and RBC antigens, cord blood transplants, other methods of bone marrow replacement, and pharmaceutical anticoagulants. It adds the surprising new discovery of abundant platelet production by megakaryocytes in the lungs and megakaryocyte migration between the lungs and bone marrow.

Chapter 19, The Circulatory System: Heart, is reorganized at section 19.1 to place figures closer to their references. Cardiac innervation is moved to section 19.6 on regulation of cardiac output, with a new illustration. The electrocardiogram is described with more detailed attention to interpretation of each wave, segment, and interval, with an added table. The section on cardiac arrhythmias includes a fuller explanation of atrial fibrillation.

Chapter 20, The Circulatory System: Blood Vessels and Circulation, has improved discussions of the vasa vasorum and metarterioles; describes the measurement of blood pressure in more depth; adds photos of edema, circulatory shock, and upper limb veins most often used for phlebotomy; and has a new drawing of air embolism. It discusses the difficulty of pancreatic surgery in light of the complex, delicate branches of the celiac trunk. The Deeper Insight on ascites is rewritten to relate it to alcoholism. The tables of blood vessels and routes of flow are now converted to normal, easier-to-read text.

Chapter 21, The Lymphatic and Immune Systems, updates bone marrow histology; the sources of macrophages; T cell diversity; asthma and AIDS mortality; and the obstacles to treating AIDS in pandemic countries. It adds the risk in splenectomy and the role of ATP and ADP as inflammatory chemoattractants.

Chapter 22, The Respiratory System, enhances descriptions of the nasal epithelium; the cricothyroid ligament in relation to emergency tracheotomy; the Deeper Insight on tracheotomy; cor pulmonale; and squamous cell carcinoma. It adds a mutational cause of Ondine's curse; discovery of pulmonary platelet production; and the potential of electronic cigarettes and legalization of recreational marijuana as emerging risk factors for lung cancer.

Chapter 23, The Urinary System, adds to the function of glomerular mesangial cells and has an improved Deeper Insight on kidney stones, with a new photo.

Chapter 24, Fluid, Electrolyte, and Acid–Base Balance, has further information on sodium and the effects of hypernatremia, and has added a new table summarizing the major electrolyte imbalances.

Chapter 25, The Digestive System, includes additions on the immune role of the omenta; dental proprioception; aspirin and peptic ulcer; the cell-signaling function of the intestinal mucous coat; anatomical variability of the colon and a new drawing of its histology; an updated Deeper Insight on gallstones, with a photo; a new Deeper Insight on diverticulosis and diverticulitis; a new Deeper Insight on colorectal cancer; and an improved description of intestinal lymphatic nodules.

Chapter 26, Nutrition and Metabolism, includes new MRI images of a morbidly obese individual compared to one of normal BMI; a new drawing of lipoprotein structure and chart of composition of the lipoprotein classes; new information on the effects of leptin on sympathetic nerve fibers and lipolysis; and a new photo of hepatic cirrhosis.

Chapter 27, The Male Reproductive System, has a new table and discussion of the composition of semen and function of the bulbourethral preejaculatory fluid, and updates on benign prostatic hyperplasia and prostate cancer. It adds discussion of zinc deficiency as a cause of infertility, hypothalamic maturation and GnRH in relation to the onset of puberty, and andropause in relation to declining androgen secretion.

Chapter 28, The Female Reproductive System, has improvements in hymen anatomy and the figure of ovarian structure; a new perspective on morning sickness as a possible factor mitigating birth defects; and updates on contraception and on breast cancer genes, risk factors, and mortality.

Chapter 29, Human Development and Aging, adds the role of the sperm centrosome in fertilization; chromosomal defects as a leading cause of first-trimester miscarriages; and the formation of monozygotic twins. It adds a new Deeper Insight and illustration of cleft lip and palate. It updates the telomere theory of senescence but deletes the now-doubtful theory of DNA damage by endogenous free radicals. It adds a new, MRI-based drawing of muscle atrophy in old age and a discussion of pineal gland senescence as a factor in the insomnia experienced by some older people. It updates statistics on human life expectancy and the major causes of death. The final Deeper Insight is retitled Assisted Reproductive Technology and has a new photo of intracytoplasmic sperm injection.

Appendix D, The Genetic Code and Amino Acids, now adds a table of the 20 amino acids and their symbols, and the structural formulae of the amino acids.

ACKNOWLEDGMENTS

Peer review is a critical part of the scientific process, and very important to ensure the content in this book continues to meet the needs of the instructors and students who use it. We are grateful for the people who agree to participate in this process and thank them for their time, talents, and feedback. The reviewers of this text (listed here) have contributed significant comments that help us refine and update the print and digital components of this program.

Christina Gan and Heather Cushman have updated the question bank and test bank to closely correlate with the intricate changes made in this ninth edition and have greatly increased the educational value of these books through their work to create self-assessment tools and align McGraw-Hill's Connect resources with the textbook. This has contributed significantly to student and instructor satisfaction with our overall package of learning media and to the students' success as they master A&P en route to their career aspirations.

I would also like to extend appreciation to members of the Life Sciences Book Team at McGraw-Hill Education who have worked with me on this project, including Matthew Garcia, Senior Portfolio Manager; Valerie Kramer, Marketing Manager; Donna Nemmers, Senior Product Developer; Vicki Krug, Senior Content Project Manager; Lori Hancock, Lead Content Licensing Specialist; Brent dela Cruz, Senior Content Project Manager; Egzon Shaqiri, Designer; and Jeanne Patterson, freelance copy editor. Their efforts have yielded another great edition of the text and its companion media suite of Connect products.

Timothy A. Ballard
University of North Carolina—Wilmington

Barry N. Bates
Atlanta Technical College

Christopher I. Brandon Jr.
Georgia Gwinnett College

Nickolas A. Butkevich
Schoolcraft College

John W. Campbell
Oklahoma City Community College

Jennifer Cochran Biederman
Winona State University

Mary B. Colon
Seminole State College of Florida

Abdeslem El Idrissi
College of Staten Island, City University of New York

Bagie George
Georgia Gwinnett College

Kyle P. Harris
Temple University

Karen L. Kandl
Western Carolina University

Stephen A. Kash
Oklahoma City Community College

Stephanie Matlock
Colorado Mesa University

Deborah T. Palatinus
Roane State Community College

Jeffrey Alan Pence
Excelsior College

Carla Perry
Community College of Philadelphia

Franz Sainvil
Broward College–Central Campus

Brian Stout
Northwest Vista College

Andrew Van Nguyen
The City University of New York–Queensborough Community College

Kimberly Vietti
Illinois Central College

Beth L. Williams
Wallace State Community College

Delon Washo-Krupps
Arizona State University

Samia Williams
Santa Fe College

INNOVATIVE CHAPTER SEQUENCING

Some chapters and topics are presented in a sequence that is more instructive than the conventional order.

Early Presentation of Heredity

Fundamental principles of heredity are presented in the last few pages of chapter 4 rather than at the back of the book to better integrate molecular and Mendelian genetics. This organization also prepares students to learn about such genetic traits and conditions as cystic fibrosis, color blindness, blood types, hemophilia, cancer genes, and sickle-cell disease by first teaching them about dominant and recessive alleles, genotype and phenotype, and sex linkage.

Urinary System Presented Close to Circulatory and Respiratory Systems

Most textbooks place this system near the end of the book because of its anatomical and developmental relationships with the reproductive system. However, its physiological ties to the circulatory and respiratory systems are much more important. Except for a necessary digression on lymphatics and immunity, the circulatory system is followed almost immediately with the respiratory and urinary systems, which regulate blood composition and whose functional mechanisms rely on recently covered principles of blood flow and capillary exchange.

Muscle Anatomy and Physiology Follow Skeleton and Joints

The functional morphology of the skeleton, joints, and muscles is treated in three consecutive chapters, 8 through 10, so when students learn muscle attachments, these come only two chapters after the names of the relevant bone features. When they learn muscle actions, it is in the first chapter after learning the terms for the joint movements. This order brings another advantage: The physiology of muscle and nerve cells is treated in two consecutive chapters (11 and 12), which are thus closely integrated in their treatment of synapses, neurotransmitters, and membrane electrophysiology.

BRIEF CONTENTS

THE STORY OF
FORM AND FUNCTION

LEARNING TOOLS

Engaging Chapter Layouts

- Chapters are structured around the way students learn.
- Frequent subheadings and expected learning outcomes help students plan their study time and review strategies.

Deeper Insights highlight areas of interest and career relevance for students.

Chapter Outlines provide quick previews of the content.

CHAPTER 7

BONE TISSUE

A bone cell (osteocyte) surrounded by calcified bone matrix
Eye of Science/Science Source

CHAPTER OUTLINE

7.1 Tissues and Organs of the Skeletal System
  7.1a Functions of the Skeleton
  7.1b Bones and Osseous Tissue
  7.1c General Features of Bones

7.2 Histology of Osseous Tissue
  7.2a Bone Cells
  7.2b The Matrix
  7.2c Compact Bone
  7.2d Spongy Bone
  7.2e Bone Marrow

7.3 Bone Development
  7.3a Intramembranous Ossification
  7.3b Endochondral Ossification
  7.3c Bone Growth and Remodeling

7.4 Physiology of Osseous Tissue
  7.4a Mineral Deposition and Resorption
  7.4b Calcium Homeostasis
  7.4c Phosphate Homeostasis
  7.4d Other Factors Affecting Bone

7.5 Bone Disorders
  7.5a Fractures and Their Repair
  7.5b Other Bone Disorders

Connective Issues

Study Guide

DEEPER INSIGHTS

7.1 Medical History: Bone Contamination

7.2 Clinical Application: Achondroplastic Dwarfism

7.3 Clinical Application: Rickets and Osteomalacia

7.4 Clinical Application: Osteoporosis

Anatomy & Physiology
Module 5: Skeletal System

198

CHAPTER 3 Cellular Form and Function   **75**

BRUSHING UP

- The transport of matter through cell membranes follows the principles of flow down gradients (see section 1.6e).
- To adequately understand the structure of the cell surface, it is essential that you understand glycolipids and glycoproteins, as well as phospholipids and their amphipathic nature (see sections 2.4c and 2.4d).
- The proteins of cell membranes have a great variety of functions. To understand those depends on an acquaintance with the functions of proteins in general and how protein function depends on tertiary structure (see "Protein Structure" and "Protein Functions" in section 2.4e).

All organisms, from the simplest to the most complex, are composed of cells—whether the single cell of a bacterium or the trillions of cells that constitute the human body. These cells are responsible for all structural and functional properties of a living organism. A knowledge of cells is therefore indispensable to any true understanding of the workings of the human body, the mechanisms of disease, and the rationale of therapy. Thus, this chapter and the next one introduce the basic cell biology of the human body, and subsequent chapters expand upon this information as we examine the specialized cellular structure and function of specific organs.

3.1   Concepts of Cellular Structure

Expected Learning Outcomes
When you have completed this section, you should be able to

a. discuss the development and modern tenets of the cell theory;
b. describe cell shapes from their descriptive terms;
c. state the size range of human cells and discuss factors that limit their size;
d. discuss the way that developments in microscopy have changed our view of cell structure; and
e. outline the major components of a cell.

3.1a Development of the Cell Theory

Cytology,[1] the scientific study of cells, was born in 1663 when Robert Hooke observed the empty cell walls of cork and coined the word *cellulae* ("little cells") to describe them (see section 1.2). Soon he studied thin slices of fresh wood and saw living cells "filled with juices"—a fluid later named *cytoplasm*. Two centuries later, Theodor Schwann studied a wide range of animal tissues and concluded that all animals are made of cells.

[1]*cyto* = cell; *logy* = study of

Schwann and other biologists originally believed that cells came from nonliving body fluid that somehow congealed and acquired a membrane and nucleus. This idea of *spontaneous generation*—that living things arise from nonliving matter—was rooted in the scientific thought of the times. For centuries, it seemed to be simple common sense that decaying meat turned into maggots, stored grain into rodents, and mud into frogs. Schwann and his contemporaries merely extended this idea to cells. The idea of spontaneous generation wasn't discredited until some classic experiments by French microbiologist Louis Pasteur in 1859.

By the end of the nineteenth century, it was established beyond all reasonable doubt that cells arise only from other cells and every living organism is composed of cells and cell products. The cell came to be regarded, and still is, as the simplest structural and functional unit of life. There are no smaller subdivisions of a cell or organism that, in themselves, have all or most of the fundamental characteristics of life described in section 1.6a. Enzymes and organelles, for example, are not alive, although the life of a cell depends on their activity.

The development of biochemistry from the late nineteenth to the twentieth century made it further apparent that all physiological processes of the body are based on cellular activity and that the cells of all species exhibit remarkable biochemical unity. The various generalizations of these last two paragraphs now constitute the modern **cell theory.**

3.1b Cell Shapes and Sizes

We will shortly examine the structure of a generic cell, but the generalizations we draw shouldn't blind you to the diversity of cellular form and function in humans. There are about 200 kinds of cells in the human body, with a variety of shapes, sizes, and functions.

Descriptions of organ and tissue structure often refer to the shapes of cells by the following terms (**fig. 3.1**):

- **Squamous**[2] (SKWAY-mus)—a thin, flat, scaly shape, often with a bulge where the nucleus is, much like the shape of a fried egg "sunny side up." Squamous cells line the esophagus and form the surface layer (epidermis) of the skin.
- **Cuboidal**[3] (cue-BOY-dul)—squarish-looking in frontal sections and about equal in height and width; liver cells are a good example.
- **Columnar**—distinctly taller than wide, such as the inner lining cells of the stomach and intestines.
- **Polygonal**[4]—having irregularly angular shapes with four, five, or more sides.
- **Stellate**[5]—having multiple pointed processes projecting from the body of a cell, giving it a somewhat starlike shape. The cell bodies of many nerve cells are stellate.

[2]*squam* = scale; *ous* = characterized by
[3]*cub* = cube; *oidal* = like, resembling
[4]*poly* = many; *gon* = angles
[5]*stell* = star; *ate* = resembling, characterized by

Tiered Assessments Based on Key Learning Outcomes

- Chapters are divided into brief sections, enabling students to set specific goals for short study periods.
- Section-ending questions allow students to check their understanding before moving on.

Each chapter begins with **Brushing Up** to emphasize the interrelatedness of concepts, which is especially useful for adult students returning to the classroom, and serves as an aid for instructors when teaching chapters out of order.

Each major section begins with **Expected Learning Outcomes** to help focus the reader's attention on the larger concepts and make the course outcome-driven. This also assists instructors in structuring their courses around expected learning outcomes.

Questions in figure legends and **Apply What You Know** items prompt students to think more deeply about the implications and applications of what they have learned. This helps students practice higher order thinking skills throughout the chapter.

---

separation between the bones and length of the fibers give these joints more mobility than a suture or gomphosis has. An especially mobile syndesmosis exists between the shafts of the radius and ulna, which are joined by a broad fibrous *interosseous membrane*. This permits such movements as pronation and supination of the forearm. A less mobile syndesmosis is the one that binds the distal ends of the tibia and fibula together, side by side (see fig. 9.2c).

9.1c Cartilaginous Joints

A **cartilaginous joint** is also called an **amphiarthrosis**[7] (AM-fee-ar-THRO-sis). In these joints, two bones are linked by cartilage (fig. 9.4). The two types of cartilaginous joints are *synchondroses* and *symphyses*.

Synchondroses

A **synchondrosis**[8] (SIN-con-DRO-sis) is a joint in which the bones are bound by hyaline cartilage. An example is the temporary joint between the epiphysis and diaphysis of a long bone in a child, formed by the cartilage of the epiphysial plate. Another is the attachment of the first rib to the sternum by a hyaline costal cartilage

[7]*amphi* = on all sides; *arthr* = joined; *osis* = condition
[8]*syn* = together; *chondr* = cartilage; *osis* = condition

(fig. 9.4a). (The other costal cartilages are joined to the sternum by synovial joints.)

Symphyses

In a **symphysis**[9] (SIM-fih-sis), two bones are joined by fibrocartilage (fig. 9.4b, c). One example is the pubic symphysis, in which the right and left pubic bones are joined anteriorly by the cartilaginous interpubic disc. Another is the joint between the bodies of two vertebrae, united by an intervertebral disc. The surface of each vertebral body is covered with hyaline cartilage. Between the vertebrae, this cartilage becomes infiltrated with collagen bundles to form fibrocartilage. Each intervertebral disc permits only slight movement between adjacent vertebrae, but the collective effect of all 23 discs gives the spine considerable flexibility.

▶▶▶ **APPLY WHAT YOU KNOW**

The intervertebral joints are symphyses only in the cervical through the lumbar region. How would you classify the intervertebral joints of the sacrum and coccyx in a middle-aged adult?

[9]*syn* = together; *physis* = growth

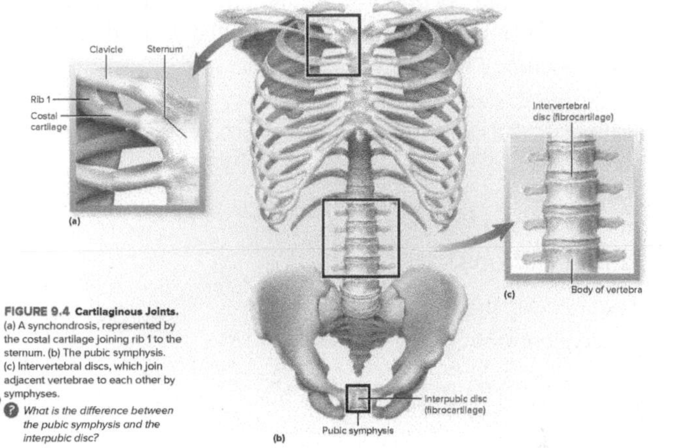

FIGURE 9.4 Cartilaginous Joints. (a) A synchondrosis, represented by the costal cartilage joining rib 1 to the sternum. (b) The pubic symphysis. (c) Intervertebral discs, which join adjacent vertebrae to each other by symphyses.
❓ *What is the difference between the pubic symphysis and the interpubic disc?*

The end-of-chapter **Study Guide** offers several methods for assessment that are useful to both students and instructors.

Assess Your Learning Outcomes provides students a study outline for review, and addresses the needs of instructors whose colleges require outcome-oriented syllabi and assessment of student achievement of the expected learning outcomes.

End-of-chapter questions build on all levels of Bloom's Taxonomy in sections to
1. test simple recall and analytical thought;
2. build medical vocabulary; and
3. apply the basic knowledge to new clinical problems and other situations.

What's Wrong with These Statements? questions further address Bloom's Taxonomy by asking the student to explain *why* the false statements are untrue.

Testing Your Comprehension questions address Bloom's Taxonomy in going beyond recall to application of ideas.

▶ **Assess Your Learning Outcomes**

To test your knowledge, discuss the following topics with a study partner or in writing, ideally from memory.

9.1 Joints and Their Classification

1. The fundamental definition of *joint (articulation)* and why it cannot be defined as a point at which one bone moves relative to an adjacent bone

3. Three essential components of a lever
4. The meaning of *mechanical advantage* (MA); how the *MA* of a lever can be determined from measurements of its effort and resistance arms; and the respective advantages of levers in which the *MA* is greater than or less than 1.0
5. Comparison of first-, second-, and third-class levers, and anatomical examples of each

12. The same for flexion, extension, hyperextension, and lateral flexion of the spine, and right and left rotation of the trunk
13. The same for elevation, depression, protraction, retraction, and lateral and medial excursion of the mandible
14. The same for dorsiflexion, plantar flexion, inversion, eversion, pronation, and supination of the foot

▶ **Testing Your Recall**   *Answers in Appendix A*

1. Internal and external rotation of the humerus is made possible by a _____ joint.
   a. pivot
   b. condylar
   c. ball-and-socket
   d. saddle
   e. hinge

2. Which of the following is the least movable?
   a. a diarthrosis
   b. a synostosis
   c. a symphysis
   d. a synovial joint
   e. a condylar joint

3. Which of the following movements are unique to the foot?
   a. dorsiflexion and inversion
   b. elevation and depression
   c. circumduction and rotation
   d. abduction and adduction
   e. opposition and reposition

▶ **Building Your Medical Vocabulary**   *Answers in Appendix A*

State a meaning of each word element, and give a medical term from this chapter that uses it or a slight variation of it.

1. ab-
2. arthro-
3. -ate
4. cruci-
5. cruro-
6. -duc
7. kinesio-
8. men-
9. supin-
10. -trac

▶ **What's Wrong with These Statements?**   *Answers in Appendix A*

Briefly explain why each of the following statements is false, or reword it to make it true.

1. More people get rheumatoid arthritis than osteoarthritis.
2. A doctor who treats arthritis is called a kinesiologist.
3. Synovial joints are also known as synarthroses.
4. Menisci occur in the elbow and knee joints.
5. Reaching behind you to take something out of your hip pocket involves flexion of the shoulder.
6. The cruciate ligaments are in the feet.
7. The femur is held tightly in the acetabulum mainly by the round ligament.
8. The knuckles are amphiarthroses.
9. Synovial fluid is secreted by the bursae.
10. Like most ligaments, the periodontal ligaments attach one bone (the tooth) to another (the mandible or maxilla).

STUDY GUIDE

▶ **Testing Your Comprehension**

1. All second-class levers produce a mechanical advantage greater than 1.0 and all third-class levers produce a mechanical advantage less than 1.0. Explain why.

2. For each of the following joint movements, state what bone the axis of rotation passes through and which of the three anatomical planes contains the axis of rotation. You may find it helpful to produce some of these actions on an articulated laboratory the first interphalangeal joint of the index finger. (Do not bend the fingers of a wired laboratory skeletal hand, because they can break off.)

3. In order of occurrence, list the joint actions (flexion, pronation, etc.) and the joints where they would occur as you (a) sit down at a table, (b) reach out and pick up an apple, (c) take a bite, and (d) chew it. Assume that you start in anatomical arm. Imagine a person holding a weight in the hand and abducting the arm. On a laboratory skeleton, identify the fulcrum; measure the effort arm and resistance arm; determine the mechanical advantage of this movement; and determine which of the three lever types the upper limb acts as when performing this movement.

5. List the six types of synovial joints, and for each one, if possible, identify a joint in the

ARTWORK THAT INSPIRES LEARNING

The incredible art program in this textbook sets the standard in A&P. The stunning portfolio of art and photos was created with the aid of art focus groups and with feedback from hundreds of accuracy reviews.

Vivid Illustrations

Rich textures and shading and bold, bright colors bring structures to life.

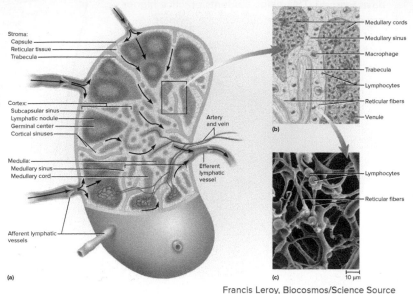

Francis Leroy, Biocosmos/Science Source

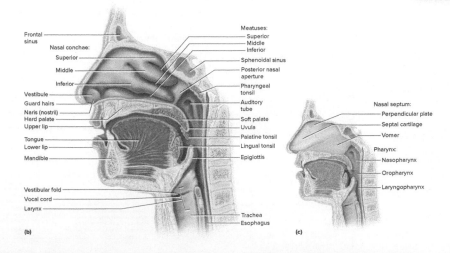

Rebecca Gray/McGraw-Hill Education

Cadaver dissections are paired with carefully drawn illustrations to show intricate human detail.

Orientation Tools

Saladin art integrates tools to help students quickly orient themselves within a figure and make connections between ideas.

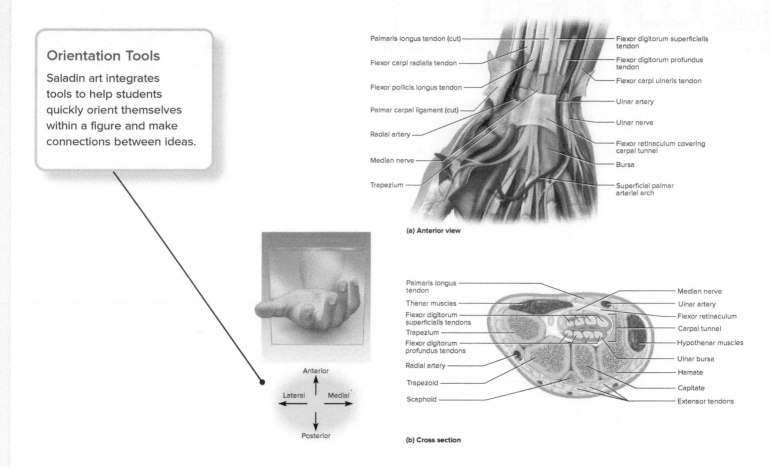

Palmaris longus tendon (cut)

Flexor carpi radialis tendon

Flexor pollicis longus tendon

Palmar carpal ligament (cut)

Radial artery

Median nerve

Trapezium

Flexor digitorum superficialis tendon

Flexor digitorum profundus tendon

Flexor carpi ulnaris tendon

Ulnar artery

Ulnar nerve

Flexor retinaculum covering carpal tunnel

Bursa

Superficial palmar arterial arch

(a) Anterior view

Anterior

Lateral — Medial

Posterior

Palmaris longus tendon

Thenar muscles

Flexor digitorum superficialis tendons

Trapezium

Flexor digitorum profundus tendons

Radial artery

Trapezoid

Scaphoid

Median nerve

Ulnar artery

Flexor retinaculum

Carpal tunnel

Hypothenar muscles

Ulnar bursa

Hamate

Capitate

Extensor tendons

(b) Cross section

Conducive to Learning

- Easy-to-understand process figures
- Tools for students to easily orient themselves

Process Figures

Saladin breaks complicated physiological processes into numbered steps for a manageable introduction to difficult concepts.

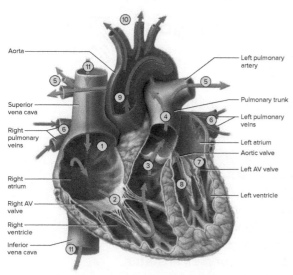

Aorta

Left pulmonary artery

Superior vena cava

Pulmonary trunk

Right pulmonary veins

Left pulmonary veins

Left atrium

Aortic valve

Left AV valve

Right atrium

Right AV valve

Left ventricle

Right ventricle

Inferior vena cava

1. Blood enters right atrium from superior and inferior venae cavae.

2. Blood in right atrium flows through right AV valve into right ventricle.

3. Contraction of right ventricle forces pulmonary valve open.

4. Blood flows through pulmonary valve into pulmonary trunk.

5. Blood is distributed by right and left pulmonary arteries to the lungs, where it unloads CO_2 and loads O_2.

6. Blood returns from lungs via pulmonary veins to left atrium.

7. Blood in left atrium flows through left AV valve into left ventricle.

8. Contraction of left ventricle (simultaneous with step 3) forces aortic valve open.

9. Blood flows through aortic valve into ascending aorta.

10. Blood in aorta is distributed to every organ in the body, where it unloads O_2 and loads CO_2.

11. Blood returns to right atrium via venae cavae.

You're in the driver's seat.

Want to build your own course? No problem. Prefer to use our turnkey, prebuilt course? Easy. Want to make changes throughout the semester? Sure. And you'll save time with Connect's auto-grading too.

65%

Less Time Grading

Laptop: McGraw-Hill; Woman/dog: George Doyle/Getty Images

They'll thank you for it.

Adaptive study resources like SmartBook® 2.0 help your students be better prepared in less time. You can transform your class time from dull definitions to dynamic debates. Find out more about the powerful personalized learning experience available in SmartBook 2.0 at **www.mheducation.com/highered/connect/smartbook**

Make it simple, make it affordable.

Connect makes it easy with seamless integration using any of the major Learning Management Systems—Blackboard®, Canvas, and D2L, among others—to let you organize your course in one convenient location. Give your students access to digital materials at a discount with our inclusive access program. Ask your McGraw-Hill representative for more information.

Padlock: Jobalou/Getty Images

Solutions for your challenges.

A product isn't a solution. Real solutions are affordable, reliable, and come with training and ongoing support when you need it and how you want it. Our Customer Experience Group can also help you troubleshoot tech problems—although Connect's 99% uptime means you might not need to call them. See for yourself at **status. mheducation.com**

Checkmark: Jobalou/Getty Images

Effective, efficient studying.

Connect helps you be more productive with your study time and get better grades using tools like SmartBook 2.0, which highlights key concepts and creates a personalized study plan. Connect sets you up for success, so you walk into class with confidence and walk out with better grades.

Study anytime, anywhere.

Download the free ReadAnywhere app and access your online eBook or SmartBook 2.0 assignments when it's convenient, even if you're offline. And since the app automatically syncs with your eBook and SmartBook 2.0 assignments in Connect, all of your work is available every time you open it. Find out more at **www.mheducation.com/readanywhere**

"I really liked this app—it made it easy to study when you don't have your textbook in front of you."

- Jordan Cunningham, Eastern Washington University

No surprises.

The Connect Calendar and Reports tools keep you on track with the work you need to get done and your assignment scores. Life gets busy; Connect tools help you keep learning through it all.

Calendar: owattaphotos/Getty Images

Learning for everyone.

McGraw-Hill works directly with Accessibility Services Departments and faculty to meet the learning needs of all students. Please contact your Accessibility Services office and ask them to email accessibility@mheducation.com, or visit **www.mheducation.com/about/accessibility** for more information.

Top: Jenner Images/Getty Images, Left: Hero Images/Getty Images, Right: Hero Images/Getty Images

McGraw-Hill Connect® empowers students to learn and succeed in the Anatomy and Physiology course with user-friendly digital solutions.

SMARTBOOK®

SmartBook 2.0 provides personalized learning to individual student needs, continually adapting to pinpoint knowledge gaps and focus learning on concepts requiring additional study. The result? Students are highly engaged in the content and better prepared for lecture.

LEARNSMART PREP®

LearnSmart Prep helps students thrive in college-level A&P by helping solidify knowledge in the key areas of cell biology, chemistry, study skills, and math. The result? Students are better prepared for the A&P course.

Practice ATLAS

Practice Atlas for A&P is an interactive tool that pairs images of common anatomical models with stunning cadaver photography, allowing students to practice naming structures on both models and human bodies, anytime, anywhere. The result? Students are better prepared, engaged, and move beyond basic memorization.

Stop the Drop!

50% of the country's students are unable to pass the A&P course*

 **Anatomy & Physiology Revealed® 4.0**

Anatomy & Physiology Revealed® (APR) 4.0 is an interactive cadaver dissection tool to enhance lecture and lab that students can use anytime, anywhere. The result? Students are prepared for lab, engaged in the material, and utilize critical thinking.

Ph.I.L.S.

Ph.I.L.S. 4.0 (Physiology Interactive Lab Simulations) software is the perfect way to reinforce key physiology concepts with powerful lab experiments. The result? Students gain critical thinking skills and are better prepared for lab.

Concept Overview Interactives are groundbreaking interactive animations that encourage students to explore key physiological processes and difficult concepts. The result? Students are engaged and able to apply what they've learned while tackling difficult A&P concepts.

*Statistic courtesy of *The New England Journal of Higher Education*

When I was a young boy, I became interested in what I then called "nature study" for two reasons. One was the sheer beauty of nature. I reveled in children's books with abundant, colorful drawings and photographs of animals, plants, minerals, and gems. It was this esthetic appreciation of nature that made me want to learn more about it and made me happily surprised to discover I could make a career of it. At a slightly later age, another thing that drew me still deeper into biology was to discover writers who had a way with words—who could captivate my imagination and curiosity with their elegant prose. Once I was old enough to hold part-time jobs, I began buying zoology and anatomy books that mesmerized me with their gracefulness of writing and fascinating art and photography. I wanted to write and draw like that myself, and I began teaching myself by learning from "the masters." I spent many late nights in my room peering into my microscope and jars of pond water, typing page after page of manuscript, and trying pen and ink as an art medium. My "first book" was a 318-page paper on some little pond animals called hydras, with 53 India ink illustrations that I wrote for my tenth-grade biology class when I was 16 (see page viii).

Fast-forward about 30 years, to when I became a textbook writer, and I found myself bringing that same enjoyment of writing and illustrating to the first edition of this book you are now holding. Why? Not only for its intrinsic creative satisfaction, but because I'm guessing that you're like I was—you can appreciate a book that does more than simply give you the information you need. You appreciate, I trust, a writer who makes it enjoyable for you through his scientific, storytelling prose and his concept of the way things should be illustrated to spark interest and facilitate understanding.

I know from my own students, however, that you need more than captivating illustrations and enjoyable reading. Let's face it—A&P is a complex subject and it may seem a formidable task to acquire even a basic knowledge of the human body. It was difficult even for me to learn (and the learning never ends). So in addition to simply writing this book, I've given a lot of thought to its pedagogy—the art of teaching. I've designed my chapters to make them easier for you to study and to give you abundant opportunity to check whether you've understood what you read—to test yourself (as I advise my own students) before the instructor tests you.

Each chapter is broken down into short, digestible bits with a set of Expected Learning Outcomes at the beginning of each section, and self-testing questions (Before You Go On) just a few pages later. Even if you have just 30 minutes to read during a lunch break or a bus ride, you can easily read or review one of these brief sections. There are also numerous self-testing questions in a Study Guide at the end of each chapter, in some of the figure legends, and the occasional Apply What You Know questions dispersed throughout each chapter. The questions cover a broad range of cognitive skills, from simple recall of a term to your ability to evaluate, analyze, and apply what you've learned to new clinical situations or other problems. In this era of digital publishing, however, learning aids go far beyond what I write into the book itself. SmartBook®, available on smartphones and tablets, includes all of the book's contents plus adaptive technology that can give you personalized instruction, target the unique gaps in your knowledge, and guide you in comprehension and retention of the subject matter.

I hope you enjoy your study of this book, but I know there are always ways to make it even better. Indeed, what quality you may find in this edition owes a great deal to feedback I've received from students all over the world. If you find any typos or other errors, if you have any suggestions for improvement, if I can clarify a concept for you, or even if you just want to comment on something you really like about the book, I hope you'll feel free to write to me. I correspond quite a lot with students and would enjoy hearing from you.

Ken Saladin
Georgia College
Milledgeville, GA 31061 (USA)
ksaladin2@windstream.net

THE ENDOCRINE SYSTEM

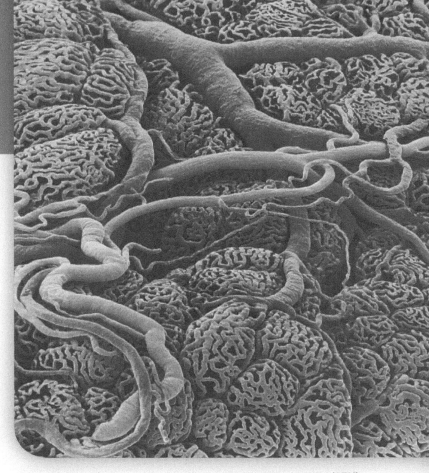

Vascular corrosion cast of the blood vessels of the thyroid gland (SEM)
Susumu Nishinaga/Science Source

Anatomy & Physiology Revealed 4.0

Module 8: Endocrine System

I f the body is to function as an integrated whole, its organs must communicate with each other and coordinate their activities. Even simple organisms composed of only a few cells have mechanisms for intercellular communication, suggesting that such mechanisms evolved very early in the history of life. In humans, two such systems are especially prominent—the nervous and endocrine systems, which communicate with neurotransmitters and hormones, respectively.

Nearly everyone has heard of at least some hormones—growth hormone, thyroid hormone, estrogen, and insulin, for example. At least passingly familiar, too, are some of the glands that secrete them (such as the pituitary and thyroid glands) and some disorders that result from hormone deficiency, excess, or dysfunction (such as diabetes, goiter, and dwarfism).

This chapter is primarily about the *endocrine* (hormonal) *system* of communication. We will start with the relatively familiar and large-scale aspects of this system—a survey of the endocrine glands, their hormones, and the principal effects of those hormones. We will then work our way down to the finer and less familiar details—the chemical identity of hormones, how they are made and transported, and how they produce their effects on their target cells. Shorter sections at the end of the chapter discuss the role of the endocrine system in adapting to stress, some hormonelike *paracrine* secretions, and the pathologies that result from endocrine dysfunction.

17.1 Overview of the Endocrine System

Expected Learning Outcomes

When you have completed this section, you should be able to

a. define *hormone* and *endocrine system;*

b. name several organs of the endocrine system;

c. contrast endocrine with exocrine glands;

d. recognize the standard abbreviations for many hormones; and

e. describe similarities and differences between the nervous and endocrine systems.

The body has four principal avenues of communication from cell to cell:

1. **Gap junctions** join unitary smooth muscle, cardiac muscle, epithelial, and other cells to each other. They enable cells to pass nutrients, electrolytes, and signaling molecules directly from the cytoplasm of one cell to the cytoplasm of the next through pores in their plasma membranes (see fig. 5.28).

2. **Neurotransmitters** are released by neurons, diffuse across a narrow synaptic cleft, and bind to receptors on the surface of the next cell.

3. **Paracrines**[1] are secreted by one cell, diffuse to nearby cells in the same tissue, and stimulate their physiology. Some call them *local hormones.*

4. **Hormones,**[2] in the strict sense, are chemical messengers that are transported by the bloodstream and stimulate physiological responses in cells of another, often distant, tissue or organ. Certain hormones produced by the pituitary gland in the head, for example, act on organs as far away as the pelvic cavity.

This chapter is concerned mainly with hormones and, to some extent, paracrine secretions. The glands, tissues, and cells that secrete hormones constitute the **endocrine**[3] **system;** the study of this system and the diagnosis and treatment of its disorders is called **endocrinology.** The most familiar hormone sources are the organs traditionally recognized as **endocrine glands,** such as the pituitary, thyroid, and adrenal glands, among others **(fig. 17.1).** Growing knowledge of endocrinology has revealed, however, that hormones are also secreted by numerous organs and tissues not usually thought of as glands, such as the brain, heart, small intestine, bones, muscles, and adipose tissue.

17.1a Comparison of Endocrine and Exocrine Glands

In section 5.5b, we examined another category of glands, the *exocrine* glands. The classical distinction between exocrine and endocrine glands has been the presence or absence of ducts. Most exocrine glands secrete their products by way of a duct onto an epithelial surface such as the skin or the mucosa of the digestive tract. Endocrine glands, by contrast, are ductless and release their secretions into the bloodstream (see fig. 5.30). For this reason, hormones were originally called the body's "internal secretions"; the word *endocrine* still alludes to this fact. Exocrine secretions have extracellular effects such as the digestion of food, whereas endocrine secretions have intracellular effects—they alter cell metabolism.

---

[1] *para* = next to; *crin* = to secrete
[2] *hormone* = to excite, set in motion
[3] *endo* = into; *crin* = to secrete

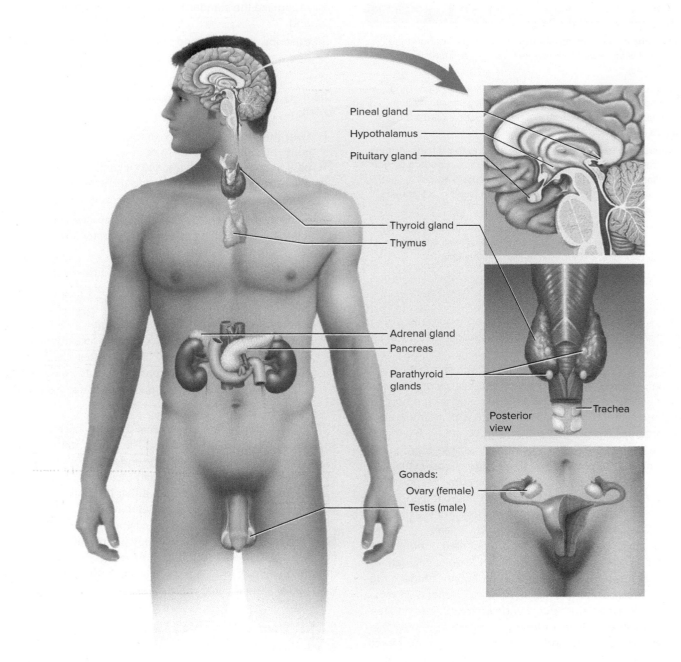

FIGURE 17.1 Major Organs of the Endocrine System. This system also includes gland cells in many other organs not shown here. **APR**

❓ *After reading this chapter, name at least three hormone-secreting organs that are not shown in this illustration.*

As we see in this chapter's opening photo, endocrine glands have an unusually high density of blood capillaries; these serve to pick up and carry away their hormones. Often, these vessels are an especially permeable type called *fenestrated capillaries,* which have patches of large pores in their walls allowing for the easy uptake of matter from the gland tissue (see fig. 20.5b).

Some glands and secretory cells defy simple classification as endocrine or exocrine. Liver cells, for example, behave as exocrine cells in the traditional sense by secreting bile into ducts that lead ultimately to the small intestine. However, they also secrete hormones into the blood, and in this respect they act as endocrine cells. They secrete albumin and blood-clotting factors directly into the blood as well. These do not fit the traditional concept of exocrine secretions, because they're not released by way of ducts or onto epithelial surfaces; nor do they fit the concept of endocrine secretions, because they're not hormones.

Liver cells are just one of nature's myriad ways of confounding our impulse to rigidly classify things into the fixed categories of our imagination.

17.1b Comparison of the Nervous and Endocrine Systems

The nervous and endocrine systems both serve for internal communication, but they're not redundant; they complement rather than duplicate each other's function **(table 17.1).** One important difference is that an efferent nerve fiber innervates only one organ and a limited number of cells within that organ, so its effects are usually precisely targeted and relatively specific **(fig. 17.2a).** Hormones, by contrast, are secreted into the bloodstream and circulate throughout the body **(fig. 17.2b).** Some of them, such as growth hormone and epinephrine, have more widespread effects than any one nerve fiber does.

Another difference is the speed with which the two systems start and stop responding to a stimulus. The nervous system typically responds within a few milliseconds, whereas it takes from several seconds to days for a hormone to act. When a stimulus ceases, the nervous system stops responding almost immediately, whereas hormonal effects can last for days or even longer. On the other hand, under long-term stimulation, most neurons quickly adapt and their response declines. The endocrine system shows more persistent responses.

But these differences shouldn't blind us to the similarities between the two systems. Both communicate chemically, and several chemicals function as both neurotransmitters and hormones—for example, norepinephrine, dopamine, and antidiuretic hormone (arginine vasopressin). Thus, a particular chemical such as dopamine can be considered a hormone when secreted by an endocrine cell but a neurotransmitter when secreted by a nerve cell. Another similarity is that some hormones and neurotransmitters produce identical effects on the same organ. For example, both norepinephrine and glucagon stimulate the liver to break down glycogen and release glucose. The nervous and endocrine systems continually regulate each other as they coordinate the activities of other organ systems. Some neurons trigger hormone secretion, and some hormones stimulate or inhibit neurons.

Some cells defy any attempt to rigidly classify them as neurons or gland cells. They act like neurons in many respects, but like endocrine cells, they release their secretions (such as oxytocin) into the bloodstream. Thus, we give them a hybrid name—**neuroendocrine cells.**

TABLE 17.1	Comparison of the Nervous and Endocrine Systems	
Nervous System	**Endocrine System**	
Communicates by means of electrical impulses and neurotransmitters	Communicates by means of hormones	
Releases neurotransmitters at synapses at specific target cells	Releases hormones into bloodstream for general distribution throughout body	
Usually has relatively local, specific effects	Sometimes has very general, widespread effects	
Reacts quickly to stimuli, usually within 1–10 ms	Reacts more slowly to stimuli, often taking seconds to days	
Stops quickly when stimulus stops	May continue responding long after stimulus stops	
Adapts relatively quickly to continual stimulation	Adapts relatively slowly; may respond for days to weeks	

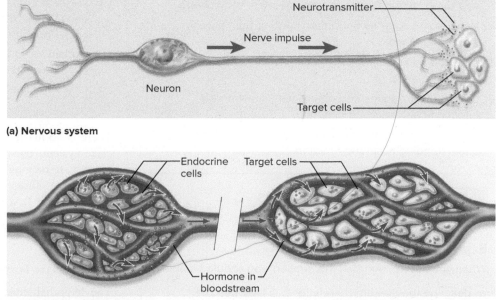

(a) Nervous system

(b) Endocrine system

FIGURE 17.2 Communication by the Nervous and Endocrine Systems. (a) A neuron has a long fiber that delivers its neurotransmitter to the immediate vicinity of its target cells. (b) Endocrine cells secrete a hormone into the bloodstream (left). At a point often remote from its origin, the hormone leaves the bloodstream and enters or binds to its target cells (right).

We have seen that neurotransmitters depend on receptors in the receiving cell; they can't exert any effect unless the receiving cell is equipped to bind and respond to them. This is true of hormones as well. When a hormone enters the bloodstream, it goes wherever the blood goes; there is no way to send it selectively to a particular organ. However, only certain **target organs** or **target cells** respond to it. Thyroid-stimulating hormone, for example, stimulates only the thyroid gland. In most cases, such selective responses are because only the target cells have receptors for a given hormone. They can also occur, however, because the circulating hormone is inactive and only the target cells have the enzyme needed to convert it to active form. Circulating testosterone, for example, is relatively inactive, but its target cells have an enzyme that converts it to dihydrotestosterone, which is much more potent.

17.1c Hormone Nomenclature

Many hormones are denoted by standard abbreviations that are used repeatedly in this chapter. These are listed alphabetically in **table 17.2** for use as a convenient reference while you work through the chapter. This list is by no means complete. It omits hormones that have no abbreviation, such as estrogen and insulin, and hormones that aren't discussed much in this chapter. Synonyms used by many authors are indicated in parentheses, but the first name listed is the one used in this book.

TABLE 17.2	Names and Abbreviations for Hormones	
Abbreviation	**Name**	**Source**
ACTH	Adrenocorticotropic hormone (corticotropin)	Anterior pituitary
ADH	Antidiuretic hormone (arginine vasopressin)	Posterior pituitary
CRH	Corticotropin-releasing hormone	Hypothalamus
DHEA	Dehydroepiandrosterone	Adrenal cortex
EPO	Erythropoietin	Kidneys, liver
FSH	Follicle-stimulating hormone	Anterior pituitary
GH	Growth hormone (somatotropin)	Anterior pituitary
GHRH	Growth hormone–releasing hormone	Hypothalamus
GnRH	Gonadotropin-releasing hormone	Hypothalamus
IGFs	Insulin-like growth factors (somatomedins)	Liver, other tissues
LH	Luteinizing hormone	Anterior pituitary
NE	Norepinephrine	Adrenal medulla
OT	Oxytocin	Posterior pituitary
PIH	Prolactin-inhibiting hormone (dopamine)	Hypothalamus
PRL	Prolactin	Anterior pituitary
PTH	Parathyroid hormone (parathormone)	Parathyroids
T_3	Triiodothyronine	Thyroid
T_4	Thyroxine (tetraiodothyronine)	Thyroid
TH	Thyroid hormone (T_3 and T_4 collectively)	Thyroid
TRH	Thyrotropin-releasing hormone	Hypothalamus
TSH	Thyroid-stimulating hormone (thyrotropin)	Anterior pituitary

---

BEFORE YOU GO ON

Answer the following questions to test your understanding of the preceding section:

1. Define the word *hormone* and distinguish a hormone from a neurotransmitter. Why is this an imperfect distinction?
2. Name some sources of hormones other than purely endocrine glands.
3. Describe some distinctions between endocrine and exocrine glands.
4. List some similarities and differences between the endocrine and nervous systems.
5. Discuss why the target-cell concept is essential for understanding hormone function.

b. distinguish between the anterior and posterior lobes of the pituitary;
c. list the hormones produced by the hypothalamus and each lobe of the pituitary, and identify the functions of each hormone;
d. explain how the pituitary is controlled by the hypothalamus and its target organs; and
e. describe the effects of growth hormone.

17.2 The Hypothalamus and Pituitary Gland

Expected Learning Outcomes

When you have completed this section, you should be able to

a. describe the anatomical relationship between the hypothalamus and pituitary gland;

There is no master control center that regulates the entire endocrine system, but the pituitary gland and hypothalamus have a more wide-ranging influence than any other part of the system, and several other endocrine glands cannot be adequately understood without first knowing how the pituitary influences them. This is therefore an appropriate place to begin a survey of the endocrine system.

17.2a Anatomy

The hypothalamus, shaped like a flattened funnel, forms the floor and walls of the third ventricle of the brain; we studied its structure and function in chapter 14 (see figs. 14.2 and 14.12b). It regulates primitive functions of the body ranging from water balance and thermoregulation to sex drive and childbirth. Many of its functions are carried out by way of the pituitary gland, which is closely associated with it both anatomically and physiologically.

The **pituitary gland (hypophysis**[4]**)** is suspended from the floor of the hypothalamus by a **stalk (infundibulum**[5]**)** and housed in a depression of the sphenoid bone, the sella turcica. The pituitary is usually about 1.3 cm wide and roughly the size and shape of a kidney bean; it grows about 50% larger in pregnancy. It is actually composed of two structures—the *anterior* and *posterior pituitary*—with independent origins and separate functions. The anterior pituitary arises from a pouch that grows upward from the embryonic pharynx, while the posterior pituitary arises as a bud growing downward from the brain **(fig. 17.3).** They come to lie side by side and are so closely joined that they look like a single gland.

The **anterior pituitary,** also called the *adenohypophysis*[6] (AD-eh-no-hy-POFF-ih-sis), constitutes about three-quarters of the pituitary as a whole; its main part is the large, bulging *anterior lobe* **(figs. 17.4a, 17.5a).** It has no nervous connection to the hypothalamus but is linked to it by a complex of blood vessels called the **hypophysial portal system** (hy-POFF-ih-SEE-ul) **(fig. 17.4b).** This system consists of a network of *primary capillaries* in the hypothalamus, a group of small veins called *portal venules* that travel down the stalk, and a complex of *secondary capillaries* in the anterior pituitary. The hypothalamus controls the anterior pituitary by secreting hormones that enter the primary capillaries, travel down the venules, and diffuse out of the secondary capillaries into the pituitary tissue. The hypothalamic hormones regulate secretion by various types of pituitary cells that we will study shortly.

The **posterior pituitary,** also called the *neurohypophysis,* constitutes the posterior one-quarter of the pituitary. The stalk that connects the pituitary to the hypothalamus is part of the posterior

[4]*hypo* = below; *physis* = growth
[5]*infundibulum* = funnel

[6]*adeno* = gland

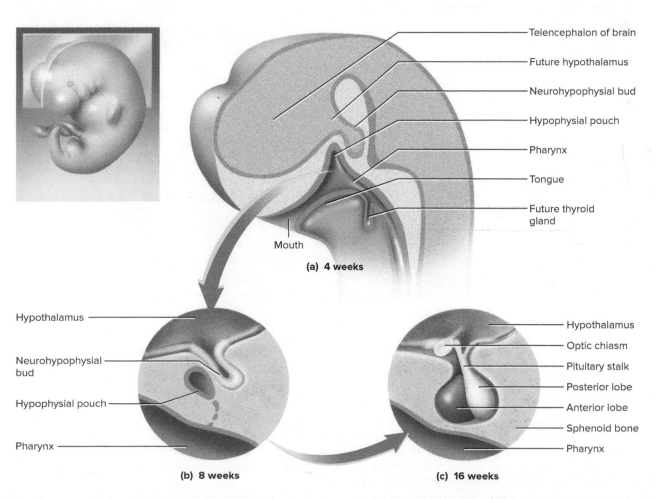

FIGURE 17.3 Embryonic Development of the Pituitary Gland. (a) Sagittal section of the head showing the neural and pharyngeal origins of the pituitary. (b) Pituitary development at 8 weeks. The hypophysial pouch, destined to become the anterior pituitary, has now separated from the pharynx. (c) Development at 16 weeks. The two lobes are now encased in bone and so closely associated they appear to be a single gland.

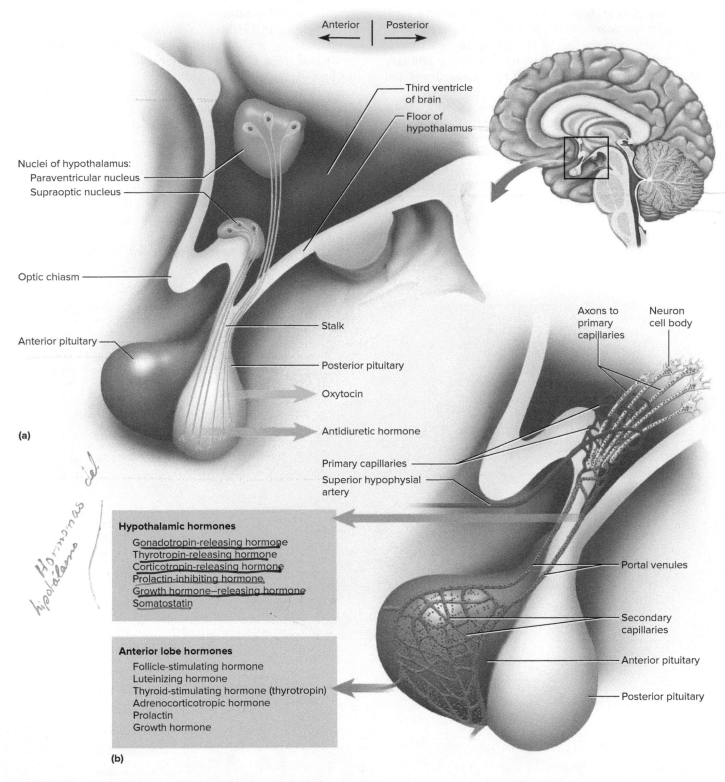

Anterior | Posterior

Third ventricle of brain

Floor of hypothalamus

Nuclei of hypothalamus:
Paraventricular nucleus
Supraoptic nucleus

Optic chiasm

Stalk

Anterior pituitary

Posterior pituitary

Oxytocin

Antidiuretic hormone

(a)

Primary capillaries

Superior hypophysial artery

Axons to primary capillaries

Neuron cell body

Portal venules

Secondary capillaries

Anterior pituitary

Posterior pituitary

Hypothalamic hormones

Gonadotropin-releasing hormone
Thyrotropin-releasing hormone
Corticotropin-releasing hormone
Prolactin-inhibiting hormone
Growth hormone–releasing hormone
Somatostatin

Anterior lobe hormones

Follicle-stimulating hormone
Luteinizing hormone
Thyroid-stimulating hormone (thyrotropin)
Adrenocorticotropic hormone
Prolactin
Growth hormone

(b)

FIGURE 17.4 Anatomy of the Pituitary Gland. (a) Major structures of the pituitary and hormones of the neurohypophysis. Note that these hormones are produced by two nuclei in the hypothalamus and later released from the posterior lobe of the pituitary. (b) The hypophysial portal system, which regulates the anterior lobe of the pituitary. The hormones in the violet box are secreted by the hypothalamus and travel in the portal system to the anterior pituitary. The hormones in the pink box are secreted by the anterior pituitary under the control of the hypothalamic releasers and inhibitors. **APR**

❓ *Which lobe of the pituitary is essentially composed of brain tissue?*

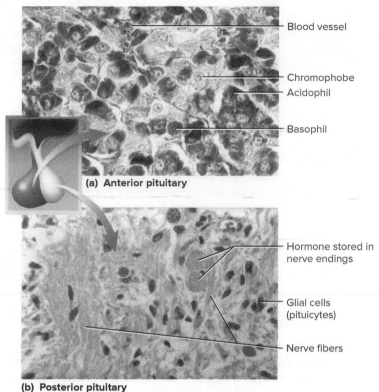

(a) **Anterior pituitary**

- Blood vessel
- Chromophobe
- Acidophil
- Basophil
- Hormone stored in nerve endings
- Glial cells (pituicytes)
- Nerve fibers

(b) **Posterior pituitary**

FIGURE 17.5 Histology of the Pituitary Gland. (a) The anterior lobe. Basophils include gonadotropic, thyrotropic, and corticotropic cells. Acidophils include somatotropic and prolactin cells. These subtypes are not distinguishable with this histological stain. The chromophobes resist staining; they may be either stem cells or cells that have been temporarily depleted of hormone. (b) The posterior lobe, composed of nervous tissue.

a: Victor P. Eroschenko; b: Biophoto Associates/Science Source

pituitary; the bulging part of the gland below the stalk is called the *posterior lobe*. The posterior pituitary is actually nervous tissue (nerve fibers and neuroglia, **fig. 17.5b**), not a true gland. Hormones of the posterior pituitary are made by certain neuroendocrine cells in the hypothalamus. Their axons pass down the stalk as a bundle called the **hypothalamo–hypophysial tract** and end in the posterior lobe (fig. 17.4a). Hormones are made in the neurosomas and move down the nerve fibers by axoplasmic flow to the posterior pituitary. Here they are stored in the nerve endings until a nerve signal coming down the same axons triggers their release.

17.2b Hypothalamic Hormones

To understand the physiology of the hypothalamic–pituitary system, we must begin with the hormones produced in the hypothalamus. There are eight of these (fig. 17.4)—six to regulate the anterior pituitary and two that are stored in the posterior pituitary and released on demand. Among the first six, those that stimulate the pituitary to release hormones of its own are called *releasing hormones;* those that suppress pituitary secretion are called *inhibiting hormones* (**table 17.3**). The releasing or inhibiting effect is identified in their names. *Somatostatin* is also called growth hormone–inhibiting hormone, though it also inhibits secretion of thyroid-stimulating hormone. Its name derives from *somatotropin,* a synonym for growth hormone, and *stat,* meaning to halt something (in this case, growth hormone secretion).

The other two hypothalamic hormones are *oxytocin (OT)* and *antidiuretic hormone (ADH).* These are stored and released by the posterior pituitary. OT comes mainly from neurons in the right and left **paraventricular**[7] **nuclei** of the hypothalamus, so called because they lie in the walls of the third ventricle. ADH comes mainly from the **supraoptic**[8] **nuclei,** named for their location just above the optic chiasm. Each nucleus also produces small quantities of the other hormone. ADH and OT are treated as posterior pituitary hormones for convenience even though the posterior lobe doesn't synthesize them.

17.2c Anterior Pituitary Hormones

The six main hormones of the anterior pituitary are as follows (**table 17.4**). The first two are collectively called **gonadotropins**[9] because they target the ovaries and testes (gonads). Their individual names (FSH and LH) refer to their female functions, although they are equally important in males.

1. **Follicle-stimulating hormone (FSH).** FSH is secreted by *gonadotropic cells.* In the ovaries, it stimulates the secretion of ovarian sex hormones and the development of the bubble-like *follicles* that contain the eggs. In the testes, it stimulates sperm production.

2. **Luteinizing hormone (LH).** LH is also secreted by the gonadotropic cells. In females, it stimulates *ovulation,* the release of an egg. It is named for the fact that after

---

[7] *para* = next to; *ventricular* = pertaining to the ventricle
[8] *supra* = above
[9] *gonado* = gonads; *trop* = to turn or change

TABLE 17.3	Hypothalamic Releasing and Inhibiting Hormones That Regulate the Anterior Pituitary
Hormone	**Principal Effects**
Thyrotropin-releasing hormone (TRH)	Promotes secretion of thyroid-stimulating hormone (TSH) and prolactin (PRL)
Corticotropin-releasing hormone (CRH)	Promotes secretion of adrenocorticotropic hormone (ACTH)
Gonadotropin-releasing hormone (GnRH)	Promotes secretion of follicle-stimulating hormone (FSH) and luteinizing hormone (LH)
Growth hormone–releasing hormone (GHRH)	Promotes secretion of growth hormone (GH)
Prolactin-inhibiting hormone (PIH)	Inhibits secretion of prolactin (PRL)
Somatostatin	Inhibits secretion of growth hormone (GH) and thyroid-stimulating hormone (TSH)

ovulation, the follicle becomes a yellowish body called the *corpus luteum*.[10] LH also stimulates the corpus luteum to secrete progesterone, a hormone important in pregnancy. In males, LH stimulates the testes to secrete testosterone.

3. **Thyroid-stimulating hormone (TSH),** or **thyrotropin.** TSH is secreted by pituitary cells called *thyrotropic cells*. It stimulates growth of the thyroid gland and the secretion of thyroid hormone, which has widespread effects on metabolic rate, body temperature, and other functions detailed later.

4. **Adrenocorticotropic hormone (ACTH),** or **corticotropin.** ACTH is secreted by cells called *corticotropic cells*. Its target organ and the basis for its name is the adrenal cortex. ACTH stimulates the cortex to secrete hormones called glucocorticoids (especially *cortisol*), which regulate glucose, protein, and fat metabolism and are important in the body's response to stress.

5. **Prolactin[11] (PRL).** PRL is secreted by pituitary cells called *prolactin cells*. The hormone and these cells are named for the role of PRL in lactation. During pregnancy, the lactotropes increase greatly in size and number, and PRL secretion rises proportionately, but it has no effect on the mammary glands until after a woman gives birth. Then, it stimulates them to synthesize milk.

6. **Growth hormone (GH),** or **somatotropin.** GH is secreted by *somatotropic cells,* the most numerous cells of the anterior pituitary. The pituitary produces at least a thousand times as much GH as any other hormone. The general effect of GH is to stimulate mitosis and cellular differentiation and thus to promote tissue growth throughout the body.

You can see that the anterior pituitary is involved in a chain of events linked by hormones: The hypothalamus secretes a releasing hormone; this induces a type of pituitary cell to secrete its hormone; that hormone is usually targeted to another endocrine gland elsewhere in the body; and finally that gland secretes a hormone with an effect of its own. For example, the hypothalamus secretes thyrotropin-releasing hormone (TRH); this induces the anterior pituitary to secrete thyroid-stimulating hormone (TSH); TSH, in turn, stimulates the thyroid gland to release thyroid hormone (TH); and finally, thyroid hormone exerts its metabolic effects throughout the body. Such a relationship between the hypothalamus, pituitary, and another downstream endocrine gland is called an **axis**—the *hypothalamo–pituitary–thyroid axis,* for example. **Figure 17.6** summarizes these relationships between the hypothalamus, anterior pituitary, and more downstream target organs.

17.2d Posterior Pituitary Hormones

The two posterior lobe hormones are ADH and OT (table 17.4). As we have already seen, they are synthesized in the hypothalamus, then transported to the posterior pituitary and stored until their release on command. Their functions are as follows:

1. **Antidiuretic hormone (ADH).** ADH increases water retention by the kidneys, reduces urine volume, and helps prevent dehydration. ADH also functions as a brain neurotransmitter and is usually called *arginine vasopressin (AVP)* in the neuroscience literature. This name refers to its ability to cause vasoconstriction, but this effect requires concentrations so unnaturally high for the human body that it is of doubtful significance except in pathological states. The ADH name refers to its more common function in everyday human physiology.

2. **Oxytocin (OT).** OT has a variety of reproductive functions in situations ranging from intercourse to breast-feeding. It surges in both sexes during sexual arousal and orgasm, possibly aiding in the propulsion of semen through the male reproductive tract and stimulating uterine contractions that help transport sperm up the female tract. OT also functions

---

[10]*corpus* = body; *lute* = yellow
[11]*pro* = favoring, promoting; *lact* = milk

TABLE 17.4	Pituitary Hormones	
Hormone	**Target Organ or Tissue**	**Principal Effects**
Anterior Pituitary		
Follicle-stimulating hormone (FSH)	Ovaries, testes	*Female:* Growth of ovarian follicles and secretion of estrogen *Male:* Sperm production
Luteinizing hormone (LH)	Ovaries, testes	*Female:* Ovulation, maintenance of corpus luteum *Male:* Testosterone secretion
Thyroid-stimulating hormone (TSH)	Thyroid gland	Growth of thyroid, secretion of thyroid hormone
Adrenocorticotropic hormone (ACTH)	Adrenal cortex	Growth of adrenal cortex, secretion of glucocorticoids
Prolactin (PRL)	Mammary glands	Milk synthesis
Growth hormone (GH)	Liver, bone, cartilage, muscle, fat	Widespread tissue growth, especially in the stated tissues
Posterior Pituitary		
Antidiuretic hormone (ADH)	Kidneys	Water retention
Oxytocin (OT)	Uterus, mammary glands	Labor contractions, milk release; possibly involved in ejaculation, sperm transport, sexual affection, and mother–infant bonding

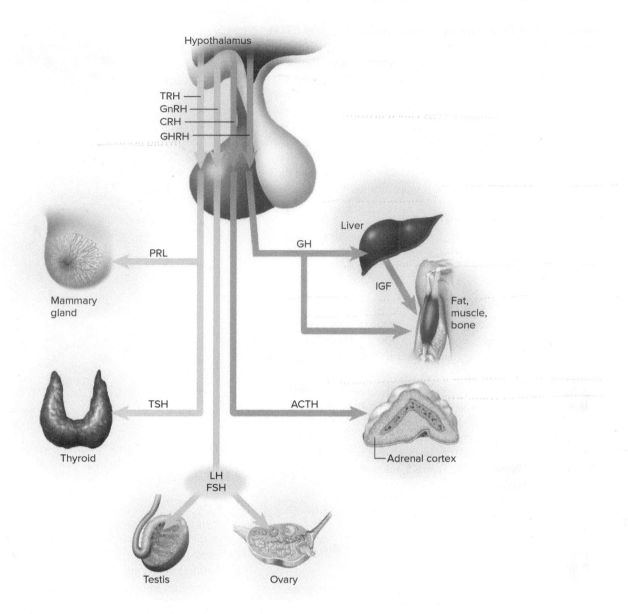

FIGURE 17.6 Hypothalamo–Pituitary–Target Organ Relationships. Hypothalamic releasing hormones, shown at the top, trigger secretion of all of the anterior pituitary hormones (bottom).

in feelings of sexual satisfaction and emotional bonding between partners. In childbirth, it stimulates labor contractions, and in lactating mothers, it stimulates the flow of milk from deep in the mammary gland to the nipple, where it is accessible to the infant. It may also promote emotional bonding between the mother and infant. In the absence of oxytocin, other female mammals tend to neglect their helpless infants, even allowing them to die.

17.2e Control of Pituitary Secretion

Pituitary hormones are not secreted at constant rates. GH is secreted mainly at night, LH peaks at the middle of the menstrual cycle, and OT surges during labor and breast-feeding, for example. The timing and amount of pituitary secretion are regulated by the hypothalamus, other brain centers, and feedback from the target organs.

Hypothalamic and Cerebral Control

Both lobes of the pituitary gland are strongly subject to control by the brain. Hypothalamic control enables the brain to monitor conditions within and outside the body and to stimulate or inhibit the release of anterior lobe hormones in response. For example, in times of stress, the hypothalamus triggers ACTH secretion, which leads to cortisol secretion and mobilization of materials needed for tissue repair. During pregnancy, the hypothalamus induces prolactin secretion so a woman will be prepared to lactate after the baby is born.

The posterior pituitary is controlled by **neuroendocrine reflexes**—the release of hormones in response to nerve signals. For example, dehydration raises the osmolarity of the blood, which is detected by hypothalamic neurons called *osmoreceptors*. They trigger ADH release, and ADH promotes water conservation. Excessive blood pressure, by contrast, stimulates stretch receptors in the heart and certain arteries. By another neuroendocrine reflex, this inhibits ADH release, increases urine output, and brings blood volume and pressure back to normal.

The suckling of an infant also triggers a neuroendocrine reflex mediated by oxytocin. Stimulation of the nipple sends nerve signals up the spinal cord and brainstem to the hypothalamus and from there to the posterior pituitary. This causes the release of oxytocin, which stimulates the release of milk. Neuroendocrine reflexes can also involve higher brain centers. For example, this lactation reflex can be triggered when the mother simply hears a baby cry—any baby—and emotional stress can affect gonadotropin secretion, thus disrupting ovulation, the menstrual rhythm, and fertility.

▶▶▶ APPLY WHAT YOU KNOW

Which of the major themes at the end of chapter 1 is best exemplified by the neuroendocrine reflexes that govern ADH secretion?

Feedback from Target Organs

The regulation of other endocrine glands by the pituitary isn't simply a system of "command from the top down." Those target organs also regulate the pituitary and hypothalamus through various feedback loops.

Most often, this takes the form of **negative feedback inhibition**—the pituitary stimulates another endocrine gland to secrete its hormone, and that hormone feeds back to the pituitary or hypothalamus and inhibits further secretion of the pituitary hormone. **Figure 17.7** shows this in the hypothalamo–pituitary–thyroid axis as an example. The figure is numbered to correspond to the following description:

① The hypothalamus secretes thyrotropin-releasing hormone (TRH).

② TRH stimulates the anterior pituitary to secrete thyroid-stimulating hormone (TSH).

③ TSH stimulates the thyroid gland to secrete thyroid hormone (TH).

④ TH stimulates the metabolism of most cells throughout the body.

⑤ TH also *inhibits* the release of TSH by the pituitary.

⑥ To a lesser extent, TH also *inhibits* the release of TRH by the hypothalamus.

The negative feedback inhibition in this process consists of steps 5 and 6. It ensures that when the TH level is high, TSH secretion remains moderate. If thyroid hormone secretion drops, TSH secretion rises and stimulates the thyroid to secrete more hormone. This feedback keeps thyroid hormone levels oscillating around a set point in typical homeostatic fashion.

▶▶▶ APPLY WHAT YOU KNOW

If the thyroid gland was removed from a cancer patient, would you expect the level of TSH to rise or fall? Why?

Feedback from a target organ isn't always inhibitory. As noted earlier, oxytocin triggers a positive feedback cycle during labor (see fig. 1.9). Uterine stretching sends a nerve signal to the brain

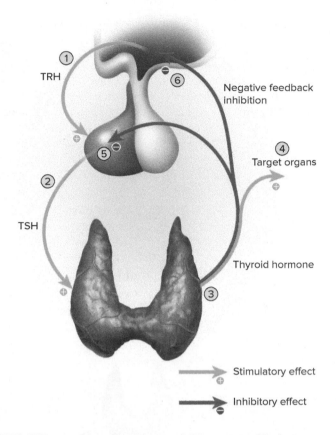

FIGURE 17.7 Negative Feedback Inhibition of the Pituitary Gland by the Thyroid Gland. See text for explanation of numbered steps.

that stimulates OT release. OT stimulates uterine contractions, which push the infant downward. This stretches the lower end of the uterus some more, which results in a nerve signal that stimulates still more OT release. This positive feedback cycle continues and intensifies until the infant is born.

17.2f A Further Look at Growth Hormone

The ultimate effects of most pituitary hormones are exerted through endocrine glands farther downstream, such as the thyroid, adrenal cortex, and gonads. Thus, we will study those effects in the following section as we survey those glands. Growth hormone is a different matter and warrants further exploration at this point.

Unlike the other pituitary hormones, GH is not targeted to just one or a few organs but has widespread effects on the body. In addition to directly stimulating diverse tissues such as muscle and bone, it induces the liver and other tissues to secrete growth stimulants called **insulin-like growth factors (IGF-I and IGF-II), or somatomedins,**[12] which then stimulate other target cells (fig. 17.6). Most of these effects are caused by IGF-I, but IGF-II is important in fetal growth.

One effect of IGF is to prolong the action of GH. All hormones have a **half-life,** the time required for 50% of the hormone to be cleared from the blood. GH is short-lived; its half-life is only 6 to

[12]acronym for *somatotropin mediating protein*

20 minutes. IGFs, by contrast, have half-lives of about 20 hours. The mechanisms of GH–IGF action include the following:

- **Protein synthesis.** Tissue growth requires protein synthesis, and protein synthesis needs two things: amino acids for building material, and messenger RNA (mRNA) for instructions. Within minutes of its secretion, GH boosts the translation of existing mRNA, and within a few hours, it also boosts the transcription of DNA and thus the production of more mRNA. GH also enhances amino acid transport into cells, and to ensure that protein synthesis outpaces breakdown, it suppresses protein catabolism.

- **Lipid metabolism.** To provide energy for growing tissues, GH stimulates adipocytes to catabolize fat and release fatty acids and glycerol into the blood. By providing these fuels, GH makes it unnecessary for cells to consume their own proteins. This is called the **protein-sparing effect.**

- **Carbohydrate metabolism.** GH also has a **glucose-sparing effect.** Its role in mobilizing fatty acids reduces the dependence of most cells on glucose so they won't compete with the brain, which is highly glucose-dependent. GH also stimulates glucose synthesis by the liver.

- **Electrolyte balance.** GH promotes Na^+, K^+, and Cl^- retention by the kidneys, enhances Ca^{2+} absorption by the small intestine, and makes these electrolytes available to the growing tissues.

The most conspicuous effects of GH are on bone, cartilage, and muscle growth, especially during childhood and adolescence. IGF-I accelerates bone growth at the epiphysial plates. It stimulates the multiplication of chondrocytes and osteogenic cells as well as protein deposition in the cartilage and bone matrix. In adulthood, it stimulates osteoblast activity and the appositional growth of bone; thus, it continues to influence bone thickening and remodeling.

GH secretion fluctuates greatly over the course of a day. It rises to 20 nanograms per milliliter of blood plasma (ng/mL) or higher during the first 2 hours of deep sleep, and may reach 30 ng/mL in response to vigorous exercise. GH secretion rises sharply in response to trauma, physical or emotional stress, hypoglycemia (low blood sugar), and other conditions. Small peaks occur after high-protein meals, but a high-carbohydrate meal tends to suppress GH secretion.

Another stimulus to GH secretion is **ghrelin**[13] (GRELL-in), a hormone secreted by the stomach, especially when it is empty. Ghrelin acts on the hypothalamus to produce the sensation of hunger as well as to stimulate release of growth hormone–releasing hormone (GHRH). This, in turn, stimulates a spike in GH secretion, priming diverse target organs to take advantage of the nutrients one is presumably about to consume.

GH level declines gradually with age. The serum level averages about 6 ng/mL in adolescence and one-quarter of that in very old age. The resulting decline in protein synthesis may contribute to aging of the tissues, including wrinkling of the skin and reduced muscular mass and strength. At age 30, the average adult body is 10% bone, 30% muscle, and 20% fat; at age 75, it averages 8% bone, 15% muscle, and 40% fat.

BEFORE YOU GO ON

Answer the following questions to test your understanding of the preceding section:

6. What are two good reasons for considering the pituitary to be two separate glands?

7. Briefly contrast hypothalamic control of the anterior pituitary with its control of the posterior pituitary.

8. Name three anterior lobe hormones that have reproductive functions and three that have nonreproductive roles. What target organs are stimulated by each of these hormones?

9. In what sense does the pituitary "take orders" from the target organs under its command?

10. The liver does not secrete growth hormone, but does promote its action. How? How does GH affect the metabolism of proteins, fats, and carbohydrates?

17.3 Other Endocrine Glands

Expected Learning Outcomes

When you have completed this section, you should be able to

a. describe the structure and location of the remaining endocrine glands;

b. name the hormones these endocrine glands produce, what stimulates their secretion, and their functions; and

c. discuss the hormones produced by organs and tissues other than the classical endocrine glands.

17.3a The Pineal Gland

The **pineal gland** (PIN-ee-ul), named for its pine cone shape, is attached to the roof of the third ventricle of the brain, beneath the posterior end of the corpus callosum (see figs. 14.2 and 17.1). The philosopher René Descartes (1596–1650) thought it was the seat of the human soul. If so, children must have more soul than adults—a child's pineal gland is about 8 mm long and 5 mm wide, but after age 7 it regresses rapidly and is no more than a tiny shrunken mass of fibrous tissue in the adult. Such shrinkage of an organ is called **involution.**[14] Pineal secretion peaks between the ages of 1 and 5 years and declines 75% by the end of puberty.

We no longer look for the human soul in the pineal gland, but this little organ remains an intriguing mystery. It seems "wired" to respond to information from the eyes about the relative hours of light and darkness in the environment. Some optic nerve fibers, instead of going to the visual cortex of the brain, lead to the superior colliculi of the midbrain and synapse here with other neurons that, in sequence, carry the signal down the spinal cord, out through sympathetic nerve fibers to the sympathetic chain ganglia, and finally back into the head and specifically to the pineal gland. The pineal may play a role in establishing 24-hour *circadian rhythms* of

---

[13]named partly from *ghre* = growth, and partly as an acronym for *growth hormone–releasing hormone*

[14]*in* = inward; *volution* = rolling or turning

DEEPER INSIGHT 17.1
CLINICAL APPLICATION
Melatonin, SAD, and PMS

There seems to be a relationship between melatonin and mood disorders, including depression and sleep disturbances. Some people experience a mood dysfunction called *seasonal affective disorder (SAD),* especially in winter when the days are short and people get less sunlight, and in extreme northern and southern latitudes where sunlight may be dim to nonexistent for months at a time. SAD thus affects about 20% of the population in Alaska but only 2.5% in Florida. The symptoms—which include depression, sleepiness, irritability, and carbohydrate craving—can be relieved by 2 or 3 hours of exposure to bright light each day *(phototherapy).* Premenstrual syndrome (PMS) is similar to SAD and is also relieved by phototherapy. The melatonin level is elevated in both SAD and PMS and is reduced by phototherapy. However, there is also evidence that casts doubt on any causal link between melatonin and these mood disorders, so for now, "the jury is still out." Many people take melatonin for jet lag or as an aid to sleep, and it is quite effective, but it is also risky to use when we know so little, as yet, about its potential effect on reproductive function.

---

physiological function synchronized with the cycle of daylight and darkness. At night, it synthesizes **melatonin,** a monoamine, from serotonin. Melatonin secretion peaks about 3 to 5 hours after the onset of sleep each night, and fluctuates seasonally. In other animals with seasonal breeding, it regulates the gonads and sets the annual breeding season. Melatonin may suppress gonadotropin secretion in humans; removal of the pineal from animals causes premature sexual maturation. Some physiologists think that the human pineal gland may regulate the timing of puberty, but a clear demonstration of its role has remained elusive. Melatonin receptors are widespread in the body, including in the pancreatic islets. Melatonin receptor defects are correlated with a higher incidence of type 2 diabetes, and low melatonin levels reduce the body's insulin sensitivity. Melatonin has been implicated in jet lag and some mood and sleep disorders, although the evidence is inconclusive (see Deeper Insight 17.1).

17.3b The Thymus

The **thymus** plays a role in three systems: endocrine, lymphatic, and immune. It is a bilobed gland in the mediastinum superior to the heart, behind the sternal manubrium. In the fetus and infant, it is enormous in comparison to adjacent organs, sometimes extending between the lungs from near the diaphragm to the base of the neck (**fig. 17.8a**). It continues to grow until the age of 5 or 6 years. In adults, the gland weighs about 20 g up to age 60, but then it too, like the pineal, undergoes involution and becomes increasingly fatty and less glandular. In the elderly, it is a small fibrous and fatty remnant barely distinguishable from the surrounding mediastinal tissues (**fig. 17.8b**).

The thymus is a site of maturation for certain white blood cells called T cells that are critically important for immune defense. It secretes several hormones (**thymopoietin, thymosin,** and **thymulin**) that stimulate the development of other lymphatic organs and regulate the development and activity of T cells. Its histology and immune function are discussed more fully in chapter 21.

17.3c The Thyroid Gland

The **thyroid gland** is the largest adult gland to have a purely endocrine function, weighing about 25 g. It lies adjacent to the trachea immediately below the larynx, and is named for the nearby shield-like thyroid[15] cartilage of the larynx. It is shaped like a butterfly wrapped around the trachea, with two winglike lobes usually joined inferiorly by a narrow bridge of tissue, the **isthmus (fig. 17.9a).**

Histologically, the thyroid is composed mostly of sacs called **thyroid follicles (fig. 17.9b).** Each is filled with a protein-rich colloid and lined by a simple cuboidal epithelium of **follicular cells.** These cells secrete about 80 micrograms (μg) of **thyroid hormone (TH)** daily. About 90% of this is in a form called **thyroxine, T_4,** or **tetraiodothyronine** (TET-ra-EYE-oh-doe-THY-ro-neen), because its

---

[15]*thyr* = shield; *oid* = resembling

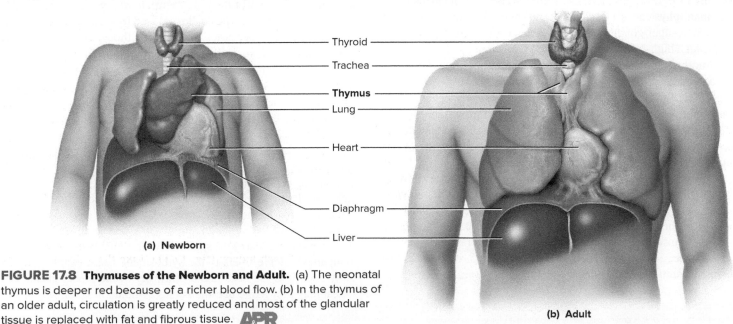

FIGURE 17.8 Thymuses of the Newborn and Adult. (a) The neonatal thymus is deeper red because of a richer blood flow. (b) In the thymus of an older adult, circulation is greatly reduced and most of the glandular tissue is replaced with fat and fibrous tissue. **APR**

(a) Newborn

(b) Adult

Thyroid
Trachea
Thymus
Lung
Heart
Diaphragm
Liver

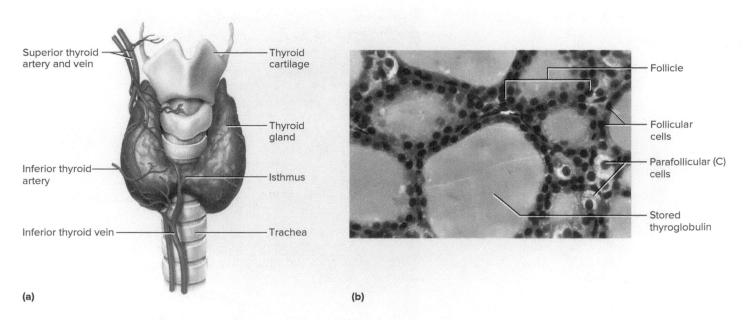

(a)

(b)

FIGURE 17.9 Anatomy of the Thyroid Gland. (a) Gross anatomy, anterior view. (b) Histology, showing the saccular thyroid follicles (the source of thyroid hormone) and nests of C cells (the source of calcitonin). **APR**

b: Biophoto Associates/Science Source

structure includes four iodine atoms. The other 10% is a form with three iodine atoms, called **triiodothyronine** or **T$_3$.** That is, the expression *thyroid hormone* refers to T$_3$ and T$_4$ collectively.

Like other endocrine glands, the thyroid releases these hormones directly into the bloodstream. Each follicle is surrounded by a basketlike network of capillaries, the globular clusters of blood vessels seen in this chapter's opening photo. These are supplied by the superior and inferior thyroid arteries seen in figure 17.9a. The thyroid receives one of the body's highest rates of blood flow per gram of tissue and consequently has a dark reddish-brown color.

Thyroid hormone is secreted or inhibited in response to fluctuations in metabolic rate. The brain monitors the body's metabolic rate and stimulates TH secretion through the action of TRH and TSH as depicted in figure 17.7. The primary effect of TH is to increase one's metabolic rate. As a result, it raises oxygen consumption and has a **calorigenic**[16] **effect**—it increases heat production. To ensure an adequate blood and oxygen supply to meet this increased metabolic demand, thyroid hormone also raises the respiratory rate, heart rate, and strength of the heartbeat. It stimulates the appetite and accelerates the breakdown of carbohydrates, fats, and protein for fuel. Thyroid hormone also promotes alertness and quicker reflexes; growth hormone secretion; growth of the bones, skin, hair, nails, and teeth; and development of the fetal nervous system.

The thyroid gland also contains nests of **parafollicular cells,** also called **clear (C) cells,** at the periphery of the follicles. They respond to rising levels of blood calcium by secreting the hormone **calcitonin.** Calcitonin antagonizes parathyroid hormone (discussed shortly) and stimulates osteoblast activity, thus promoting calcium deposition and bone formation. Calcitonin is important

mainly in children, who have 10 times as many C cells as adults; it has little effect in adults (see section 7.4b).

17.3d The Parathyroid Glands

The **parathyroid glands** are ovoid glands, usually four in number, partially embedded in the posterior surface of the thyroid. Each is about 3 to 8 mm long and 2 to 5 mm wide, and is separated from the thyroid follicles by a thin fibrous capsule and adipose tissue **(fig. 17.10).** Often, they occur in other locations ranging from as high as the hyoid bone to as low as the aortic arch, and about 5% of people have more than four parathyroids. They secrete **parathyroid hormone (PTH),** which regulates blood calcium levels. Unlike the thyroid gland, the parathyroids are not regulated by the pituitary, but directly monitor blood composition and secrete PTH when the calcium level dips too low. PTH raises the calcium level by stimulating calcium reabsorption from the bones and reducing calcium losses in the urine. Calcium homeostasis is so crucial to neuromuscular and cardiovascular function that a person can die within just a few days if the parathyroids are removed without instituting hormone replacement therapy. This often happened to patients shortly following thyroid surgery before surgeons realized the existence and function of the tiny, nearly hidden parathyroids.

17.3e The Adrenal Glands

The **adrenal**[17] **(suprarenal) glands** sit like a cap on the superior pole of each kidney **(fig. 17.11).** Like the kidneys, they are retroperitoneal, lying outside the peritoneal cavity between the

---

[16]*calor* = heat; *genic* = producing

[17]*ad* = to, toward, near; *ren* = kidney; *al* = pertaining to

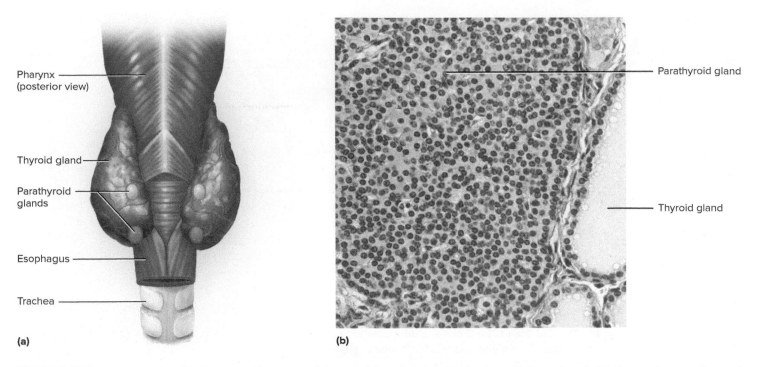

(a)

(b)

FIGURE 17.10 The Parathyroid Glands. (a) Location of the usual four parathyroid glands partially embedded in the posterior surface of the thyroid gland. (b) Histology of a parathyroid gland in relation to its fibrous capsule and adjacent thyroid and adipose tissue. **APR**

b: Victor P. Eroschenko

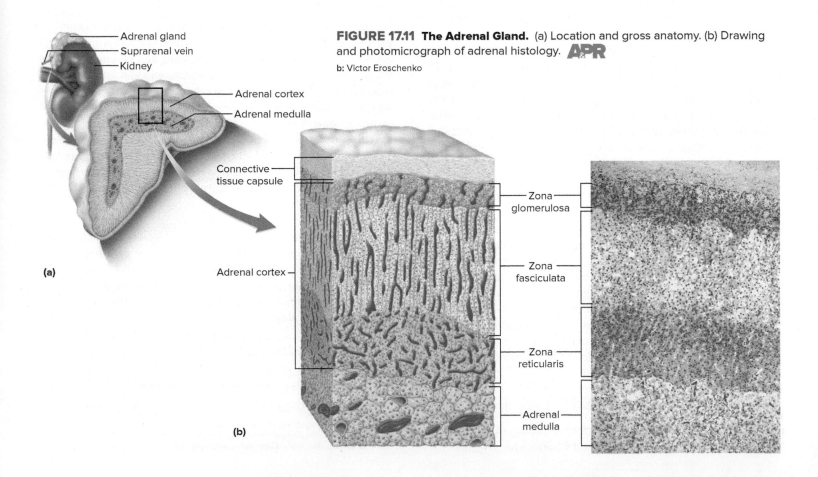

FIGURE 17.11 The Adrenal Gland. (a) Location and gross anatomy. (b) Drawing and photomicrograph of adrenal histology. **APR**

b: Victor Eroschenko

peritoneum and posterior body wall. The adult adrenal gland measures about 5 cm vertically, 3 cm wide, and 1 cm from anterior to posterior. It weighs about 8 to 10 g in the newborn, but loses half of this weight by the age of 2 years, mainly because of involution of its outer layer, the adrenal cortex. It remains at 4 to 5 g in adults.

Like the pituitary, the adrenal gland forms by the merger of two fetal glands with different origins and functions. Its inner core, the **adrenal medulla,** is 10% to 20% of the gland. Depending on blood flow, its color ranges from gray to dark red. Surrounding it is a much thicker **adrenal cortex,** constituting 80% to 90% of the gland and having a yellowish color due to its high concentration of cholesterol and other lipids.

The Adrenal Medulla

The **adrenal medulla** has a dual nature, acting as both an endocrine gland and a ganglion of the sympathetic nervous system (see section 15.2b). Sympathetic preganglionic nerve fibers penetrate through the cortex to reach **chromaffin cells** (cro-MAFF-in) in the medulla. Named for their tendency to stain brown with certain dyes, these cells are essentially sympathetic postganglionic neurons, but they have no dendrites or axon and they release their products into the bloodstream like any other endocrine gland. Thus they are considered to be neuroendocrine cells.

Upon stimulation by the nerve fibers—as in a situation of fear, pain, or other stress—the chromaffin cells release a mixture of catecholamines that we previously encountered as neurotransmitters (see fig. 12.22): about three-quarters **epinephrine,** one-quarter **norepinephrine,** and a trace of **dopamine.** Now we find them acting as hormones. They increase alertness and prepare the body in several ways for physical activity. They mobilize high-energy fuels such as lactate, fatty acids, and glucose. The liver boosts glucose levels by **glycogenolysis** (hydrolysis of glycogen to glucose) and **gluconeogenesis** (conversion of fats, amino acids, and other noncarbohydrates to glucose).

Epinephrine is said to have a **glucose-sparing effect.** It inhibits the secretion of insulin, so the muscles and other insulin-dependent organs absorb and consume less glucose. They fall back on alternative fuels such as fatty acids, while the blood glucose is left for use by the brain, which is more glucose-dependent but not insulin-dependent.

Adrenal catecholamines also raise the heart rate and blood pressure, stimulate circulation to the muscles, increase pulmonary airflow, and raise the metabolic rate. At the same time, they *inhibit* such temporarily inessential functions as digestion and urine production so that they do not compete for blood flow and energy.

The Adrenal Cortex

The **adrenal cortex** surrounds the medulla on all sides. It produces more than 25 steroid hormones, known collectively as the **corticosteroids** or **corticoids.** All of them are synthesized from cholesterol; this and other lipids impart a yellow color to the cortex. Only five corticosteroids are secreted in physiologically significant amounts; the others are either negligible in quantity or, if more abundant, are in chemically less active forms. The five most important corticosteroids fall into three categories: **mineralocorticoids,** which regulate the body's electrolyte balance; **glucocorticoids,** which regulate the

metabolism of glucose and other organic fuels; and **sex steroids,** with various developmental and reproductive functions.

The adrenal cortex has three layers of tissue (fig. 17.11b), which differ in their histology and hormone output.

1. The **zona glomerulosa**[18] (glo-MER-you-LO-suh) is a thin layer, less developed in humans than in many other mammals, located just beneath the capsule at the gland surface. The name *glomerulosa* ("full of little balls") refers to the arrangement of its cells in round clusters. The zona glomerulosa is the source of mineralocorticoids.

2. The **zona fasciculata**[19] (fah-SIC-you-LAH-ta) is a thick middle layer constituting about three-quarters of the cortex. Here the cells are arranged in parallel cords (fascicles), separated by blood capillaries, perpendicular to the gland surface. The cells are called **spongiocytes** because of a foamy appearance imparted by an abundance of cytoplasmic lipid droplets. The zona fasciculata secretes glucocorticoids and androgens.

3. The **zona reticularis**[20] (reh-TIC-you-LAR-iss) is the narrow, innermost layer, adjacent to the adrenal medulla. Its cells form a branching network for which the layer is named. Like the preceding layer, the zona reticularis also secretes glucocorticoids and androgens.

Aldosterone is the most significant mineralocorticoid, and is produced only by the zona glomerulosa. Falling blood pressure leads to increased aldosterone secretion by a mechanism called the *renin–angiotensin–aldosterone (RAA) system.* In brief, blood pressure sensors (baroreceptors) in major arteries near the heart detect falling blood pressure and activate a sympathetic reflex. This leads to the production of a hormone called angiotensin II. Among its other effects, angiotensin II stimulates the adrenal cortex to secrete aldosterone (see fig. 23.15 and the associated text for details). Aldosterone stimulates the kidneys to retain sodium. Water is retained with it by osmosis, so aldosterone helps to maintain blood volume and pressure.

Cortisol (also known clinically as *hydrocortisone*) is the most potent glucocorticoid, but the adrenals also secrete a weaker one called *corticosterone.* Glucocorticoids are secreted by the zona fasciculata and zona reticularis in response to ACTH from the pituitary. They stimulate fat and protein catabolism, gluconeogenesis, and the release of fatty acids and glucose into the blood. This helps the body adapt to stress and repair damaged tissues. Glucocorticoids also have an anti-inflammatory effect; hydrocortisone is widely used in ointments to relieve swelling and other signs of inflammation. Excessive glucocorticoid secretion or medical use, however, suppresses the immune system for reasons we will see in the discussion of stress physiology later in this chapter.

Androgens are the primary adrenal sex steroids, but the adrenals also produce small amounts of estrogen. ACTH regulates both adrenal androgen and cortisol secretion. The sex steroids, too, come from both the zona fasciculata and zona reticularis. The major androgen is **dehydroepiandrosterone (DHEA)** (de-HY-dro-EP-ee-an-DROSS-tur-own). It has little biological activity in

---

[18]*zona* = zone; *glomerul* = little balls; *osa* = full of
[19]*zona* = zone; *fascicul* = little cords; *ata* = possessing
[20]*zona* = zone; *reticul* = little network; *aris* = like

itself, but many tissues convert it to the more potent forms, *testosterone* and *dihydrotestosterone*. DHEA is produced in tremendous quantities by the large adrenal glands of the male fetus and plays an important role in the prenatal development of the male reproductive tract. At puberty in both sexes, androgens induce the growth of pubic and axillary hair and their associated apocrine sweat glands, and they stimulate the libido (sex drive) throughout adolescent and adult life. In men, the large amount of androgen secreted by the testes overshadows that produced by the adrenals. In women, however, the adrenal glands meet about 50% of the androgen requirement.

Estradiol is the main adrenal estrogen. It is normally of minor importance to women of reproductive age because its quantity is small compared with estrogen from the ovaries. After menopause, however, the ovaries no longer function and only the adrenals secrete estrogen. However, several other tissues, such as fat, convert androgens into additional estrogen. Both androgens and estrogens promote adolescent skeletal growth and help to sustain adult bone mass.

The medulla and cortex are not as functionally independent as once thought; each of them stimulates the other. Without stimulation by cortisol, the adrenal medulla atrophies significantly. Conversely, some chromaffin cells from the medulla extend into the cortex. When stress activates the sympathetic nervous system, these cells stimulate the cortex to secrete corticosterone and perhaps other corticosteroids.

▶▶▶ **APPLY WHAT YOU KNOW**

The zona fasciculata thickens significantly in pregnant women. What do you think would be the benefit of this phenomenon?

17.3f The Pancreatic Islets

The **pancreas** is an elongated, spongy gland located below and behind the stomach; most of it is retroperitoneal **(fig. 17.12).** It is primarily an exocrine digestive gland, and its gross anatomy is described in section 25.4c. Scattered throughout the exocrine tissue, however, are 1 to 2 million endocrine cell clusters called **pancreatic islets (islets of Langerhans**[21]**).** Although they are less than 2% of the pancreatic tissue, the islets secrete hormones of vital importance, especially in the regulation of **glycemia,** the blood glucose concentration. A typical islet measures about 75×175 μm and contains from a few to 3,000 cells. Its main cell types are alpha cells (20%), beta cells (70%), delta cells (5%), and a small number of PP and other cells. Islet cells respond directly to blood nutrient levels associated with the cycle of eating and fasting. Their functions are as follows:

- **Alpha (α) cells,** or **glucagon cells,** secrete **glucagon** between meals when the blood glucose concentration falls below 100 mg/dL. Glucagon exerts two primary actions on the

[21]Paul Langerhans (1847–88), German anatomist

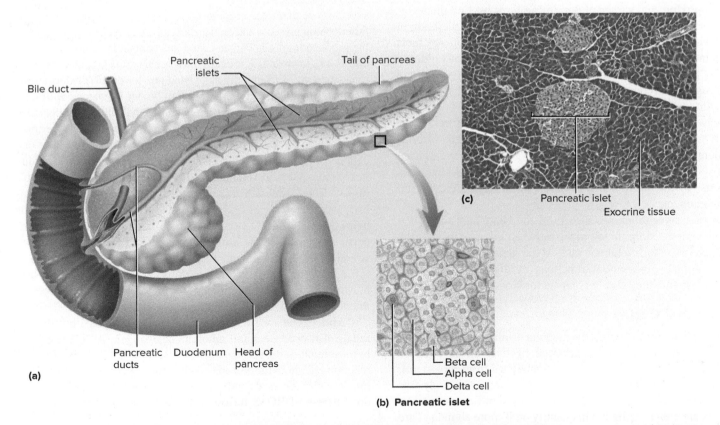

(a)

FIGURE 17.12 The Pancreas. (a) Gross anatomy and relationship to the duodenum. Pancreatic islets are most concentrated in the tail of the pancreas. (b) Cells of a pancreatic islet. (PP and G cells are not shown; they are few in number and cannot be distinguished with ordinary histological staining.) (c) Light micrograph of a pancreatic islet amid the darker exocrine acini, which produce digestive enzymes. **APR**

c: Al Telser/McGraw-Hill Education

liver: (1) glycogenolysis, the breakdown of glycogen into glucose; and (2) gluconeogenesis, the synthesis of glucose from fats and proteins (see fig. 17.23). These effects lead to the release of glucose into circulation, thus raising the blood glucose level. In adipose tissue, glucagon stimulates fat catabolism and the release of free fatty acids. Glucagon is also secreted in response to rising amino acid levels in the blood after a high-protein meal. It promotes amino acid absorption and thereby provides cells with the raw material for gluconeogenesis.

- **Beta (β) cells,** or **insulin cells,** secrete two hormones, *insulin* and *amylin.* **Insulin,** "the hormone of nutrient abundance," is secreted during and immediately following a meal when blood nutrient levels are rising; even the appetizing aroma of food stimulates insulin release in anticipation of eating. Osteocalcin and lipocalin 2, two hormones from the osteoblasts of bone, stimulate multiplication of beta cells, insulin secretion, and insulin sensitivity of other body tissues. The principal targets of insulin are the liver, skeletal muscles, and adipose tissue. In times of plenty, insulin stimulates cells to absorb glucose, fatty acids, and amino acids and to store or metabolize them; therefore, it lowers the level of blood glucose and other nutrients. It promotes the synthesis of glycogen, fat, and protein, thereby promoting the storage of excess nutrients for later use and enhancing cellular growth and differentiation. It also antagonizes glucagon, thus suppressing the use of already-stored fuels. The brain, liver, kidneys, and red blood cells absorb and use glucose without need of insulin, but insulin promotes glycogen synthesis in the liver. Insulin insufficiency or inaction is well known as the cause of diabetes mellitus, detailed later in this chapter. The beta cells also secrete another hormone, **amylin,** simultaneously with insulin. Amylin helps to reduce spikes in blood glucose by slowing the emptying of the stomach; modulating the secretion of gastric enzymes, acid, and bile; inhibiting glucagon secretion; and stimulating the sense of satiety (having had enough to eat).

- **Delta (δ) cells,** or **somatostatin cells,** secrete **somatostatin (growth hormone–inhibiting hormone)** concurrently with the release of insulin by the beta cells. Somatostatin helps to regulate the speed of digestion and nutrient absorption, and perhaps modulates the activity of other pancreatic islet cells.

- **PP cells** secrete **pancreatic polypeptide (PP)** for 4 or 5 hours after a meal. By acting on receptors in the brain, PP inhibits stimulation of the pancreas by the vagus nerve.

Any hormone that raises blood glucose concentration is called a *hyperglycemic hormone.* You may have noticed that glucagon is not the only hormone that does so; so do growth hormone, epinephrine, norepinephrine, cortisol, and corticosterone. Insulin is called a *hypoglycemic hormone* because it lowers blood glucose levels.

17.3g The Gonads

Like the pancreas, the **gonads** (ovaries and testes) function as both endocrine and exocrine glands. Their exocrine products are eggs and sperm, and their endocrine products are the *gonadal hormones,* most of which are steroids. Their gross anatomy is described in sections 27.2b and 28.1b. The gonads are hormonally inactive in childhood, but from puberty through adulthood they are regulated by the gonadotropic hormones of the anterior pituitary.

The ovaries secrete chiefly **estradiol, progesterone,** and **inhibin.** Each egg develops in its own follicle, which is lined by a wall of **granulosa cells** and surrounded by a capsule, the **theca (fig. 17.13a).** Theca cells synthesize the androgen *androstenedione,* and granulosa cells convert this to estradiol and lesser amounts of two other estrogens, *estriol* and *estrone.* In the middle of the monthly ovarian cycle, a mature follicle ovulates (ruptures and releases the egg). The remains of the follicle become the corpus luteum, which secretes progesterone for the next 12 days or so in a typical cycle (several weeks in the event of pregnancy).

The functions of estradiol and progesterone are detailed in section 28.3. In brief, they contribute to the development of the reproductive system and feminine physique, promote adolescent bone growth, regulate the menstrual cycle, sustain pregnancy, and prepare the mammary glands for lactation. Inhibin, which is also secreted by the follicle and corpus luteum, suppresses FSH secretion by means of negative feedback inhibition of the anterior pituitary.

The testis consists mainly of minute *seminiferous tubules* that produce sperm. Its endocrine secretions are **testosterone,** lesser amounts of weaker androgens and estrogens, and inhibin. Inhibin comes from **nurse cells** that form the walls of the seminiferous tubules. By limiting FSH secretion, it regulates the rate of sperm production. Nestled between the tubules are clusters of **interstitial endocrine cells,** the source of testosterone and the other sex steroids **(fig. 17.13b).** Testosterone stimulates development of the male reproductive system in the fetus and adolescent, the development of the masculine physique in adolescence, and the sex drive. It sustains sperm production and the sexual instinct throughout adult life.

17.3h Endocrine Functions of Other Tissues and Organs

Several other tissues and organs beyond the classical endocrine glands secrete hormones or hormone precursors:

- **The skin.** Keratinocytes of the epidermis convert a cholesterol-like steroid into **cholecalciferol** (COAL-eh-cal-SIF-er-ol), using energy from solar UV radiation. The liver and kidneys further convert cholecalciferol to a calcium-regulating hormone, **calcitriol** (see the following paragraphs).

- **The liver.** The liver is involved in the production of at least five hormones: (1) It converts the cholecalciferol from the skin into **calcidiol,** the next step in calcitriol synthesis. (2) It secretes a protein called **angiotensinogen,** which the kidneys, lungs, and other organs convert to a hormone called *angiotensin II,* a regulator of blood pressure (part of the renin–angiotensin–aldosterone system mentioned earlier). (3) It secretes about 15% of the body's **erythropoietin (EPO)** (er-RITH-ro-POY-eh-tin), a hormone that stimulates the red bone marrow to produce red blood cells (erythrocytes). The liver is therefore important in regulating the oxygen-carrying capacity of the blood. (4) It secretes **insulin-like growth factor I (IGF-I),** a hormone that mediates the action of growth hormone. (5) It secretes **hepcidin,** the principal hormonal mechanism of iron homeostasis. Hepcidin controls plasma iron level by inhibiting intestinal absorption of iron and

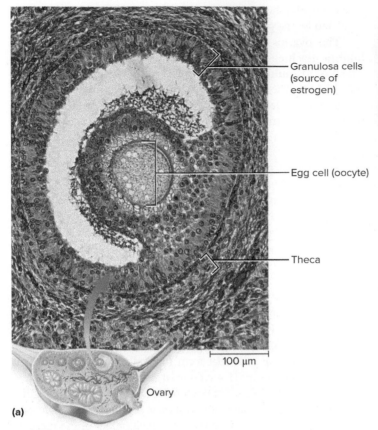

Granulosa cells (source of estrogen)

Egg cell (oocyte)

Theca

Ovary

(a)

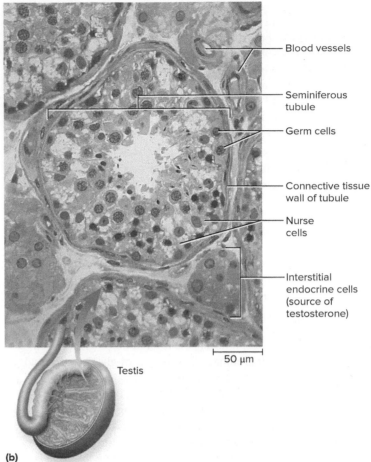

Blood vessels

Seminiferous tubule

Germ cells

Connective tissue wall of tubule

Nurse cells

Interstitial endocrine cells (source of testosterone)

Testis

(b)

FIGURE 17.13 The Gonads. (a) Histology of an ovarian follicle. (b) Histology of the testis. The granulosa cells of the ovary and interstitial cells of the testis are endocrine cells. **APR**

a: Ed Reschke/Getty Images; b: Ed Reschke

mobilization of iron by the liver; thus, it prevents iron overload. In anemia, hepcidin levels fall and more iron is mobilized to support hemoglobin synthesis. In infections, hepcidin levels rise, reducing the level of free iron available to infectious microorganisms that need it for their reproduction.

- **The kidneys.** The kidneys play endocrine roles in the production of three hormones—calcitriol, angiotensin II, and erythropoietin. (1) They convert calcidiol into **calcitriol (vitamin D₃),** thus completing the three-step process begun by the skin and liver. Calcitriol raises the blood concentration of calcium by promoting its intestinal absorption and slightly inhibiting its loss in the urine. This makes more calcium available for bone deposition and other uses. (2) They secrete an enzyme called **renin** (REE-nin), which converts angiotensinogen to angiotensin I. As angiotensin I circulates through various organs, especially the lungs, *angiotensin-converting enzyme (ACE)* on the linings of the blood capillaries converts it to **angiotensin II,** a small peptide. This is a very potent hormone that constricts blood vessels throughout the body and thereby raises blood pressure. (3) The kidneys secrete about 85% of the body's erythropoietin. For this reason, renal failure tends to cause anemia as the EPO output of the failing kidneys declines.

- **The heart.** Rising blood pressure stretches the heart wall and stimulates cardiac muscle in the atria to secrete two similar

natriuretic[22] **peptides.** These hormones increase sodium excretion and urine output and oppose the action of angiotensin II, just described. Together, these effects lower the blood pressure.

- **The stomach and intestines.** The largest endocrine network of all is in the stomach and intestines. These have more than 15 kinds of *enteroendocrine cells,*[23] constituting about 1% of all the epithelial cells of the GI tract. Their hormones are collectively called **enteric hormones.** They coordinate different regions and glands of the digestive system with each other and affect feeding, digestion, gastrointestinal motility and secretion, and maintenance of the mucosa. Some of them are called **gut–brain peptides** because they originate in the digestive tract but stimulate the brain. **Peptide YY (PYY),** secreted by the small and large intestines, signals satiety (fullness) and tends to terminate eating. **Cholecystokinin**[24] **(CCK)** (CO-leh-SIS-toe-KY-nin), secreted by the small intestine in response to fats, stimulates the gallbladder to release bile and has an appetite-suppressing effect on the brain. **Ghrelin,**[25] as noted in the earlier remarks on growth hormone, is secreted

---

[22]*natri* = sodium; *uretic* = pertaining to urine
[23]*entero* = intestine
[24]*chole* = bile; *cysto* = sac (gallbladder); *kin* = action, motion
[25]named partly from *ghre* = growth, and partly as an acronym derived from growth hormone–releasing hormone

when the stomach is empty; it stimulates the appetite and the secretion of growth hormone–releasing hormone and thus, indirectly, growth hormone itself. **Gastrin**[26] is secreted by the stomach upon the arrival of food and stimulates other cells of the stomach to secrete hydrochloric acid. Gut–brain peptides and the endocrine regulation of hunger are further discussed in section 26.1b.

- **Adipose tissue.** Fat cells secrete at least three hormones that regulate carbohydrate and fat metabolism. The best-known one is **leptin,** which has long-term effects on appetite-regulating centers of the hypothalamus. A low level of leptin, signifying a deficiency of body fat, increases appetite and food intake, whereas a high level of leptin tends to blunt the appetite. Leptin also serves as a signal for the onset of puberty, which is delayed in persons with abnormally low

body fat. Leptin is treated with other enteric hormones in the aforementioned discussion of appetite.

- **Osseous tissue.** Osteoblasts secrete the hormones **osteocalcin** and **lipocalin 2.** Both of these hormones stimulate pancreatic beta cells and promote insulin secretion and action. Osseous tissue thus plays an important role in glucose metabolism and the regulation of blood glucose levels.

- **The placenta.** This organ performs many functions in pregnancy, including fetal nutrition, oxygenation, and waste removal. But it also secretes estrogen, progesterone, and other hormones that regulate pregnancy and stimulate development of the fetus and the mother's mammary glands.

You can see that the endocrine system is extensive. It includes numerous discrete glands as well as individual cells in the tissues of other organs. The endocrine organs and tissues other than the hypothalamus and pituitary are surveyed in **table 17.5.**

---

[26]*gastr* = stomach

TABLE 17.5	Hormones from Sources Other Than the Hypothalamus and Pituitary		
Source	**Hormone**	**Target Organs and Tissues**	**Principal Effects**
Pineal gland	Melatonin	Brain	Uncertain; may influence mood and sexual maturation
Thymus	Thymopoietin, thymosin, thymulin	Immune cells (T lymphocytes)	Stimulate T lymphocyte development and activity
Thyroid gland	Thyroxine (T_4) and triiodothyronine (T_3)	Most tissues	Elevate metabolic rate and heat production; increase respiratory rate, heart rate, and strength of heartbeat; stimulate appetite and accelerate breakdown of nutrients; promote alertness and quicken reflexes; stimulate growth hormone secretion and growth of skin, hair, nails, teeth, and fetal nervous system
	Calcitonin	Bone	Stimulates bone deposition, mainly in children
Parathyroid glands	Parathyroid hormone (PTH)	Bone, kidneys, small intestine	Raises blood Ca^{2+} level by stimulating bone resorption and inhibiting deposition, reducing urinary Ca^{2+} excretion, and enhancing calcitriol synthesis
Adrenal medulla	Epinephrine, norepinephrine, dopamine	Most tissues	Promote alertness; mobilize organic fuels; raise metabolic rate; stimulate circulation and respiration; increase blood glucose level; inhibit insulin secretion and glucose uptake by insulin-dependent organs (sparing glucose for brain)
Adrenal cortex	Aldosterone	Kidney	Promotes Na^+ and water retention and K^+ excretion; maintains blood pressure and volume
	Cortisol and corticosterone	Most tissues	Stimulate fat and protein catabolism, gluconeogenesis, stress resistance, and tissue repair
	Dehydroepiandrosterone	Bone, muscle, integument, brain, many other tissues	Precursor of testosterone; indirectly promotes growth of bones, pubic and axillary hair, apocrine glands, and fetal male reproductive tract; stimulates libido
Pancreatic islets	Glucagon	Primarily liver	Stimulates amino acid absorption, gluconeogenesis, glycogen and fat breakdown; raises blood glucose and fatty acid levels
	Insulin	Most tissues	Stimulates glucose and amino acid uptake; lowers blood glucose level; promotes glycogen, fat, and protein synthesis
	Somatostatin	Stomach, intestines, pancreatic islet cells	Modulates digestion, nutrient absorption, and glucagon and insulin secretion
	Gastrin	Stomach	Stimulates acid secretion and gastric motility

(continued)

TABLE 17.5	Hormones from Sources Other Than the Hypothalamus and Pituitary *(continued)*		
Source	**Hormone**	**Target Organs and Tissues**	**Principal Effects**
Ovaries	Estradiol	Many tissues	Stimulates female reproductive development and adolescent growth; regulates menstrual cycle and pregnancy; prepares mammary glands for lactation
	Progesterone	Uterus, mammary glands	Regulates menstrual cycle and pregnancy; prepares mammary glands for lactation
	Inhibin	Anterior pituitary	Inhibits FSH secretion
Testes	Testosterone	Many tissues	Stimulates fetal and adolescent reproductive development, musculoskeletal growth, sperm production, and libido
	Inhibin	Anterior pituitary	Inhibits FSH secretion
Skin	Cholecalciferol	—	Precursor of calcitriol (see kidneys)
Liver	Calcidiol	—	Precursor of calcitriol (see kidneys)
	Angiotensinogen	—	Precursor of angiotensin II (see kidneys)
	Erythropoietin	Red bone marrow	Promotes red blood cell production, increases oxygen-carrying capacity of blood
	Hepcidin	Small intestine, liver	Regulates plasma iron level
	Insulin-like growth factor I	Many tissues	Prolongs and mediates action of growth hormone
Kidneys	Angiotensin I	—	Precursor of angiotensin II, a vasoconstrictor
	Calcitriol	Small intestine	Increases blood calcium level mainly by promoting intestinal absorption of Ca^{2+}
	Erythropoietin	Red bone marrow	Promotes red blood cell production, increases oxygen-carrying capacity of blood
Heart	Natriuretic peptides	Kidney	Lower blood volume and pressure by promoting Na^+ and water loss
Stomach and small intestine	Cholecystokinin	Gallbladder, brain	Bile release; appetite suppression
	Gastrin	Stomach	Stimulates acid secretion
	Ghrelin	Brain	Stimulates hunger, initiates feeding
	Peptide YY	Brain	Produces sense of satiety, terminates feeding
	Other enteric hormones	Stomach, intestines	Coordinate secretion and motility in different regions of digestive tract
Adipose tissue	Leptin	Brain	Limits appetite over long term
Osseous tissue	Osteocalcin	Pancreas, adipose tissue	Stimulates pancreatic beta cells to multiply, increases insulin secretion, enhances insulin sensitivity of various tissues, and reduces fat deposition
	Lipocalin 2	Pancreatic beta cells	Promotes insulin secretion and action
Placenta	Estrogen, progesterone	Many tissues of mother and fetus	Stimulate fetal development and maternal bodily adaptations to pregnancy; prepare mammary glands for lactation

Answer the following questions to test your understanding of the preceding section:

11. Identify three endocrine glands that are larger or more functional in infants or children than in adults. What is the term for the shrinkage of a gland with age?

12. Why does thyroid hormone elevate the body temperature?

13. Name a glucocorticoid, a mineralocorticoid, and a catecholamine secreted by the adrenal gland.

14. Does the action of glucocorticoids more closely resemble that of glucagon or insulin? Explain.

15. Define *hypoglycemic hormone* and *hyperglycemic hormone* and give an example of each.

16. What is the difference between a gonadal hormone and a gonadotropin?

17.4 Hormones and Their Actions

Expected Learning Outcomes

When you have completed this section, you should be able to

a. identify the chemical classes to which various hormones belong;

b. describe how hormones are synthesized and transported to their target organs;

c. describe how hormones stimulate their target cells;

d. explain how target cells regulate their sensitivity to circulating hormones;

e. describe how hormones affect each other when two or more of them stimulate the same target cells; and

f. discuss how hormones are removed from circulation after they have performed their roles.

Having surveyed the body's major hormones and their effects, we have established a cast of characters for the endocrine story, but we're left with some deeper questions: Exactly what is a hormone? How are hormones synthesized and transported to their destinations? How does a hormone produce its effects on a target organ? Thus, we now address endocrinology at the molecular and cellular levels.

17.4a Hormone Chemistry

Most hormones fall into three chemical classes: *steroids, monoamines,* and *peptides* (**table 17.6, fig. 17.14**).

1. **Steroid hormones** are derived from cholesterol. They include sex steroids produced by the testes and ovaries (such as estrogens, progesterone, and testosterone) and corticosteroids produced by the adrenal gland (such as cortisol, aldosterone, and DHEA). The gonads and adrenal cortex are

TABLE 17.6	Chemical Classification of Hormones
Steroids and Steroid Derivatives	**Monoamines**
Aldosterone	Dopamine
Androgens	Epinephrine
Calcitriol	Melatonin
Corticosterone	Norepinephrine
Cortisol	Thyroid hormone
Estrogens	
Progesterone	
Oligopeptides (3–10 Amino Acids)	
Angiotensin II	Gonadotropin-releasing hormone
Antidiuretic hormone	Oxytocin
Cholecystokinin	Thyrotropin-releasing hormone
Polypeptides (More Than 10 Amino Acids)	
Adrenocorticotropic hormone	Insulin
Calcitonin	Leptin
Corticotropin-releasing hormone	Natriuretic peptides
Gastrin	Pancreatic polypeptide
Ghrelin	Parathyroid hormone
Glucagon	Prolactin
Growth hormone	Somatostatin
Growth hormone–releasing hormone	Thymic hormones
Hepcidin	
Glycoproteins (Protein–Carbohydrate Complexes)	
Erythropoietin	Luteinizing hormone
Follicle-stimulating hormone	Thyroid-stimulating hormone
Inhibin	

the only sites of steroid hormone synthesis. Calcitriol, the calcium-regulating hormone, isn't a steroid but is derived from one and has the same hydrophobic character and mode of action as the steroids, so it is commonly grouped with them.

2. **Monoamines (biogenic amines)** were introduced in section 12.5c, since this class also includes several neurotransmitters (see fig. 12.22). The monoamine hormones include dopamine, epinephrine, norepinephrine, melatonin, and thyroid hormone. The first three of these are also called *catecholamines.* Monoamines are made from amino acids

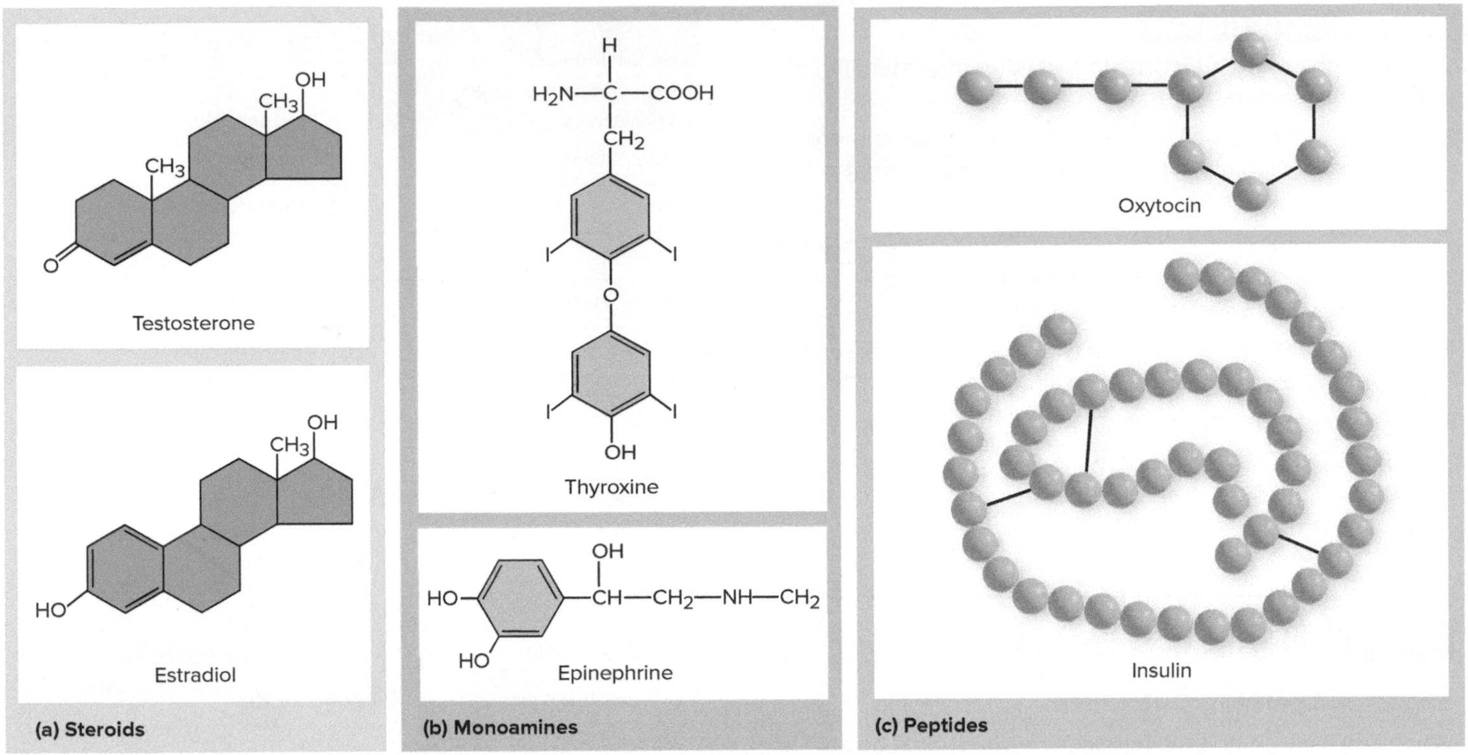

FIGURE 17.14 The Chemical Classes of Hormones. (a) Two steroid hormones, defined by their four-membered rings derived from cholesterol. (b) Two monoamines, derived from amino acids and defined by their —NH— or —NH$_2$ (amino) groups. (c) A small peptide hormone, oxytocin, and a protein hormone, insulin, defined by their chains of amino acids (the yellow circles).

and retain an amino group, from which this hormone class gets its name.

3. **Peptide hormones** are chains of 3 to 200 or more amino acids. The two posterior pituitary hormones, oxytocin and antidiuretic hormone, are very similar oligopeptides of just nine amino acids. Probably the best-known large peptide (protein) hormone is insulin. Except for dopamine, the releasing and inhibiting hormones produced by the hypothalamus are polypeptides. Most hormones of the anterior pituitary are polypeptides or glycoproteins—polypeptides conjugated with short carbohydrate chains. Glycoprotein hormones usually have an identical alpha chain of 92 amino acids and a variable beta chain that distinguishes them from each other.

17.4b Hormone Synthesis

All hormones are made from either cholesterol or amino acids, with carbohydrate added in the case of glycoproteins.

Steroids

Steroid hormones are synthesized from cholesterol and differ mainly in the functional groups attached to the four-ringed steroid backbone. **Figure 17.15** shows the synthetic pathway for several

steroid hormones. Notice that while estrogen and progesterone are typically thought of as "female" hormones and testosterone as a "male" hormone, these sex steroids are interrelated in their synthesis and have roles in both sexes.

Peptides

Peptide hormones are synthesized the same way as any other protein. The gene for the hormone is transcribed to form a molecule of mRNA, and ribosomes translate the mRNA and assemble amino acids in the right order to make the peptide. After the basic amino acid sequence is assembled, the rough endoplasmic reticulum and Golgi complex may further modify the peptide to form the mature hormone. Insulin, for example, begins as a single amino acid chain called *proinsulin*. A middle portion called the *connecting peptide* is removed to convert proinsulin to insulin, now composed of two polypeptide chains connected to each other by disulfide bridges **(fig. 17.16)**.

▶▶▶ APPLY WHAT YOU KNOW

During the synthesis of glycoprotein hormones, where in the cell would the carbohydrate be added? (Hint: Look within section 4.2.)

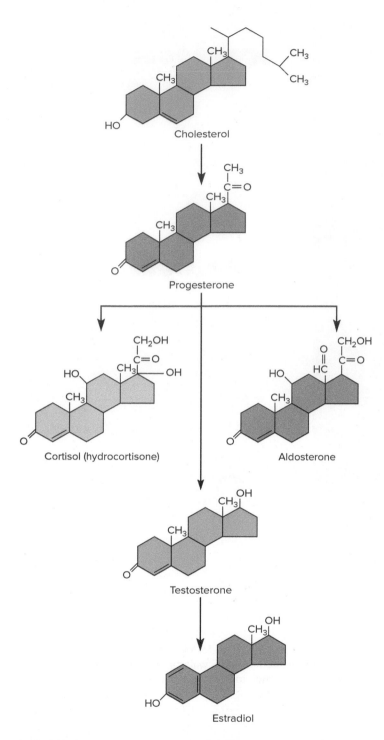

FIGURE 17.15 The Synthesis of Steroid Hormones from Cholesterol. The ovaries secrete progesterone and estradiol, the adrenal cortex secretes cortisol and aldosterone, and the testes secrete testosterone.

Monoamines

Melatonin is synthesized from the amino acid tryptophan and all the other monoamines from the amino acid tyrosine. Thyroid hormone (TH) is unusual in that it is made of *two* tyrosines, and is the only process in the human body that uses iodine; a lack

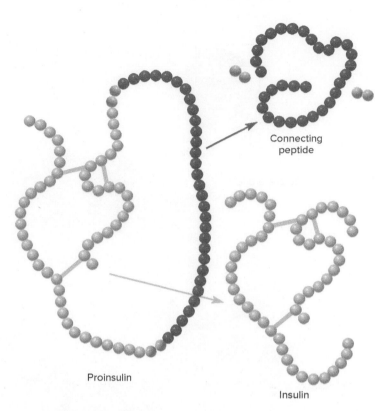

FIGURE 17.16 The Synthesis of Insulin, a Representative Polypeptide Hormone. Proinsulin has a connecting (C) peptide, 31 amino acids long, that is removed to leave insulin. Insulin has two polypeptide chains, 30 and 21 amino acids long, joined by two disulfide bridges (—S—S—) represented by the yellow bars. A third disulfide bridge creates a loop in the short chain.

of dietary iodine causes a thyroid disorder called *goiter* (see fig. 17.26). **Figure 17.17** shows the steps in TH synthesis.

(1) Cells of the thyroid follicule begin the process by absorbing iodide (I⁻) ions from the blood of nearby capillaries. At the apical surface of the cells, facing the lumen of the follicle, they oxidize I⁻ to a reactive form of iodine represented by I* in the figure.

(2) In the meantime, the follicle cells also synthesize a large protein called **thyroglobulin (Tg).** Each Tg has 123 tyrosines among its amino acids, but only 4 to 8 of them are used to make TH. The cells release thyroglobulin by exocytosis from their apical surfaces into the lumen.

(3) An enzyme at the cell surface adds iodine to a few of the tyrosines. Some tyrosines receive one iodine and become *monoiodotyrosine (MIT)* (MON-oh-eye-OH-do-TY-ro-seen); some receive two and become *diiodotyrosine (DIT)* (fig. 17.17b). Where Tg folds back on itself and two iodinated tyrosines meet, or where one tyrosine meets another on an adjacent Tg, the tyrosines link to each other through their side groups. If an MIT links up with a DIT, they form a complex with three iodines, destined to become the T_3 form of thyroid hormone; if two DITs unite, they form the forerunner of the T_4 form, with four iodines. One tyrosine then breaks away from

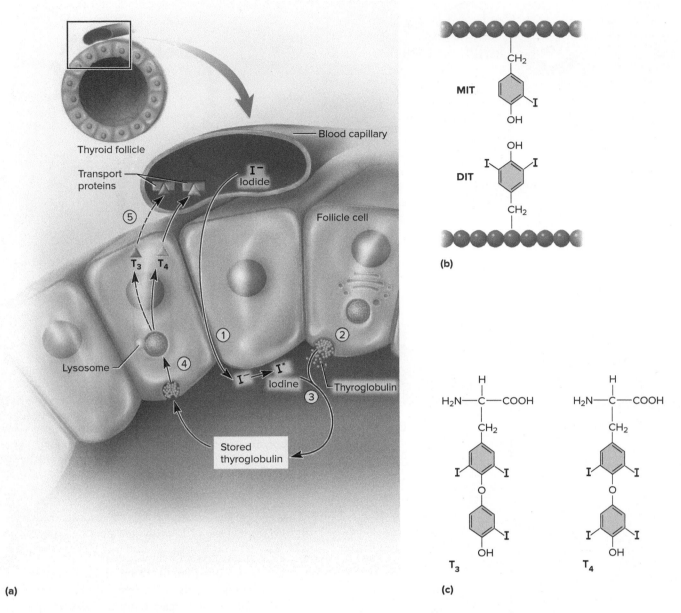

FIGURE 17.17 Thyroid Hormone Synthesis and Secretion. (a) TH synthesis in relation to the thyroid follicle. See text for explanation of numbered steps. (b) The meeting of an MIT and a DIT would produce the T_3 form of thyroid hormone, with three iodines. If both of these were DITs, it would produce the T_4 form with four iodines. (c) The two forms of mature thyroid hormone, triiodothyronine (T_3) and tetraiodothyronine (T_4).

its Tg, but for the time being, the hormone remains anchored to Tg through its other tyrosine. Tg is stored in the follicles until the thyroid gland receives a signal to release it. It is the pink-staining material in figure 17.9b.

④ When the follicle cells receive thyroid-stimulating hormone (TSH) from the anterior pituitary, they absorb droplets of Tg by pinocytosis. Within the cells, a lysosome contributes an enzyme that hydrolyzes the Tg chain, liberating thyroid hormone (TH).

⑤ TH is released from the basal side of the follicle cells into nearby blood capillaries. In the blood, it binds to various

transport proteins that carry it to its target cells. The released hormone is about 10% T_3 and 90% T_4 (fig. 17.17c); the respective roles of T_3 and T_4 are discussed shortly.

17.4c Hormone Secretion

Hormones aren't secreted at steady rates, nor do they have constant levels in the bloodstream throughout the day. Rather, they are secreted in some cases on a daily (circadian) rhythm, in other cases on a monthly rhythm (in a woman's ovarian cycle), or under the influence of stimuli that signify a need for them. These stimuli are of three kinds.

1. **Neural stimuli.** Nerve fibers supply some endocrine glands and elicit the release of their hormones. For example, the sympathetic nervous system stimulates the adrenal medulla to secrete epinephrine and norepinephrine in situations of stress. In childbirth, nerve signals originate from stretch receptors in the uterus, travel up the spinal cord and brainstem to the hypothalamus, and stimulate the release of oxytocin (see fig. 1.9).

2. **Hormonal stimuli.** Hormones from the hypothalamus regulate secretion by the anterior pituitary gland, and pituitary hormones stimulate other endocrine glands to release thyroid hormone, sex hormones, and cortisol.

3. **Humoral stimuli.** This refers to blood-borne stimuli. For example, rising blood glucose concentration stimulates the release of insulin, low blood osmolarity stimulates the secretion of aldosterone, and a low blood calcium level stimulates the secretion of parathyroid hormone.

Peptide hormones such as growth hormone and oxytocin, and catecholamines such as epinephrine and dopamine, are stored in secretory vesicles of the endocrine cell until needed and released by exocytosis when the cell receives a stimulus to do so. Steroid hormones such as estrogen and cortisol, however, are not stored in vesicles or released by exocytosis. They don't accumulate in the endocrine cell, but are released as fast as they're synthesized by diffusion through the cell surface. But this doesn't mean they're secreted at a constant rate, hour by hour and day by day. Stimuli such as FSH and ACTH can increase the synthesis and release of a steroid hormone by several-fold within hours. Thyroid hormone (TH) also diffuses freely through plasma membranes, but unlike steroids, it does accumulate in the gland awaiting a stimulus for secretion. It isn't stored in the endocrine cells, but in the extracellular spaces enclosed by the thyroid follicles. Until the stimulus (TSH) to secrete it arrives, it is bound to the protein thyroglobulin and cannot escape. The thyroid gland is thus able to store a large quantity of hormone, enough to meet the body's need for months even if TH synthesis ceases.

17.4d Hormone Transport

To get from an endocrine cell to a target cell, a hormone must travel in the blood, which is mostly water. Most of the monoamines and peptides are hydrophilic, so mixing with the blood plasma is no problem for them. Steroids and thyroid hormone, however, are hydrophobic. To travel in the watery bloodstream, they must bind to hydrophilic **transport proteins**—albumins and globulins synthesized by the liver. A hormone attached to a transport protein is called a **bound hormone,** and one that is not attached is an **unbound (free) hormone.** Only the unbound hormone can leave a blood capillary and get to a target cell.

Transport proteins not only carry the hydrophobic hormones, but also prolong their half-lives. They protect hormones from being broken down by enzymes in the blood plasma and liver and from being filtered out of the blood by the kidneys. Free hormone may be broken down or removed from the blood in a few minutes, whereas bound hormone may circulate for hours to weeks.

Thyroid hormone binds to three transport proteins in the blood plasma: *albumin;* an albumin-like protein called *thyretin;* and most of all, an alpha globulin named *thyroxine-binding globulin (TBG).* More than 99% of circulating TH is protein-bound. Bound TH serves as a long-lasting blood reservoir, so even if the thyroid is surgically removed (as for cancer), no signs of TH deficiency appear for about 2 weeks.

Steroid hormones bind to globulins such as *transcortin,* the transport protein for cortisol. Aldosterone is unusual. It has no specific transport protein but binds weakly to albumin and others. However, 85% of it remains unbound, and correspondingly, it has a half-life of only 20 minutes.

17.4e Hormone Receptors and Modes of Action

Hormones stimulate only those cells that have receptors for them—their *target cells.* The receptors are proteins or glycoproteins located on the plasma membrane, in the cytoplasm, or in the nucleus. They act like switches to turn certain metabolic pathways on or off when the hormones bind to them. A target cell usually has a few thousand receptors for a given hormone. Receptor defects lie at the heart of several endocrine diseases (see Deeper Insight 17.2).

Receptor–hormone interactions are similar to the enzyme–substrate interactions described in section 2.4f. Unlike enzymes, receptors do not chemically change their ligands, but they do exhibit enzymelike specificity and saturation. *Specificity* means that the receptor for one hormone will not bind other hormones. *Saturation* is the condition in which all the receptor molecules are occupied by hormone molecules. Adding more hormone cannot produce any greater effect.

Hormones fall into two broad classes according to where they act on their target cells—those that cannot enter the target cell but act through receptors at the cell surface, and those that can enter the target cell and act through receptors within it. The next two sections describe the mode of action of each of these classes.

 DEEPER INSIGHT 17.2

CLINICAL APPLICATION

Hormone Receptors and Therapy

In treating endocrine disorders, it is essential to understand the role of hormone receptors. For example, a defect or deficiency of insulin receptors causes type 2 diabetes mellitus. No amount of insulin replacement can correct this. And while growth hormone is now abundantly available thanks to genetic engineering, it is useless to children with *Laron dwarfism,* who have a hereditary defect in their GH receptors. *Androgen insensitivity syndrome* is due to an androgen receptor defect or deficiency; it causes genetic males to develop feminine genitalia and other features (see Deeper Insight 27.1). Estrogen stimulates the growth of some malignant tumors with estrogen receptors. For this reason, estrogen replacement therapy should not be used for women with estrogen-dependent cancer.

Peptides and Catecholamines

Peptides and catecholamines are hydrophilic and cannot penetrate a target cell's plasma membrane, so they must stimulate its physiology indirectly. They bind to cell surface receptors, which are linked to second-messenger systems on the other side of the membrane (**fig. 17.18a**). The best-known second messenger is cyclic adenosine monophosphate (cAMP) (**fig. 17.19**). When glucagon binds to the surface of a liver cell, for example, its receptor activates a G protein, which in turn activates adenylate cyclase, the membrane enzyme that produces cAMP. cAMP leads ultimately to the activation of enzymes that hydrolyze glycogen stored in the cell, leading to the release of free glucose into the blood and fulfillment of the function of glucagon. Somatostatin, by contrast, *inhibits* cAMP synthesis. Second messengers don't linger in the cell for long. cAMP, for example, is quickly broken down by an enzyme called **phosphodiesterase,** and the hormonal effect is therefore short-lived.

Two other second-messenger systems begin with one of the phospholipids in the plasma membrane. When activated by certain hormones (blue box in **fig. 17.20**), the receptor activates a G protein linked to a nearby enzyme, *phospholipase,* in the plasma membrane. Phospholipase splits a membrane phospholipid into two fragments—a small phosphate-containing piece called **inositol triphosphate (IP$_3$)** (eye-NOSS-ih-tol), and a larger piece, the triglyceride backbone with two fatty acids still attached, called **diacylglycerol (DAG)** (di-ACE-ul-GLISS-ur-ol). IP$_3$ and DAG are the second messengers that go on to activate a wide variety of metabolic changes in the target cells, depending on what cells are involved and what internal signaling pathways they use.

DAG activates a protein kinase (PK), much like cAMP does in figure 17.19. PK phosphorylates various other enzymes, turning them on or off and thereby activating or suppressing equally various metabolic processes in the target cell. For example, we saw earlier that thyroid-stimulating hormone (TSH) binds to thyroid follicle cells and stimulates them to release thyroid hormone into the bloodstream. TSH works through the DAG second-messenger system. In other cells, DAG stimulates mitosis and cell proliferation. Some cancer-causing agents (carcinogens) act by mimicking this *mitogenic* effect of DAG.

IP$_3$ works by increasing the calcium (Ca^{2+}) concentration in the target cell. It can open Ca^{2+} channels in the plasma membrane, letting Ca^{2+} into the cell from the extracellular fluid, or it can open channels in the endoplasmic reticulum, causing it to release a flood of Ca^{2+} into the cytosol. Calcium then acts through several means to alter cell physiology:

1. It binds to certain calcium-dependent cytoplasmic enzymes that alter cell metabolism.

2. It can bind to a cytoplasmic calcium receptor, **calmodulin.** Not only is calcium-bound calmodulin the key to smooth muscle contraction, but it can also activate protein kinases with downstream effects just like cAMP or DAG.

3. It binds to membrane channels and changes their permeability to other solutes, in some cases altering the membrane potential (voltage) of the cell.

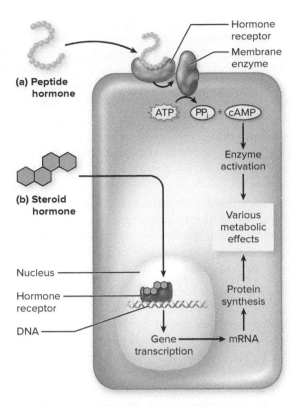

FIGURE 17.18 Hormone Actions on a Target Cell. Some process steps are omitted for simplicity. (a) Action of a peptide hormone through a surface receptor and second messenger. (b) Action of a steroid hormone by diffusing into the nucleus and binding to a nuclear receptor associated with a gene. Either process can lead to a great variety of effects on the target cell.

Childbirth affords one example of how an IP$_3$ second-messenger system works. Oxytocin (OT) from the pituitary gland binds to receptors on the smooth muscle cells of the uterus. It triggers the foregoing IP$_3$-releasing process, and IP$_3$, in turn, stimulates the sarcoplasmic reticulum to release Ca^{2+}. This initial burst of calcium then opens channels in the plasma membrane that admit still more calcium into the cell from the extracellular fluid. Calcium binds to calmodulin, and stimulates the labor contractions (see contraction of smooth muscle in section 11.7b).

The general point of all this is that hydrophilic hormones such as those listed in the blue box at the left side of figure 17.20 cannot enter the target cell. Yet by merely "knocking on the door" (binding to a surface receptor), they can initiate a flurry of metabolic activity within. The initial steps in this process are activation of a G protein and phospholipase. From there, divergent pathways are taken that involve DAG, IP$_3$, and Ca^{2+} as second messengers. Ultimately these pathways lead to metabolic pathways being switched on or off within the cell.

A given hormone doesn't always employ the same second messenger. ADH employs the IP$_3$–calcium system in smooth muscle but the cAMP system in kidney tubules. Insulin differs from all the foregoing mechanisms. Rather than using a second-messenger system, it binds to a plasma membrane enzyme, tyrosine kinase, which directly phosphorylates cytoplasmic proteins.

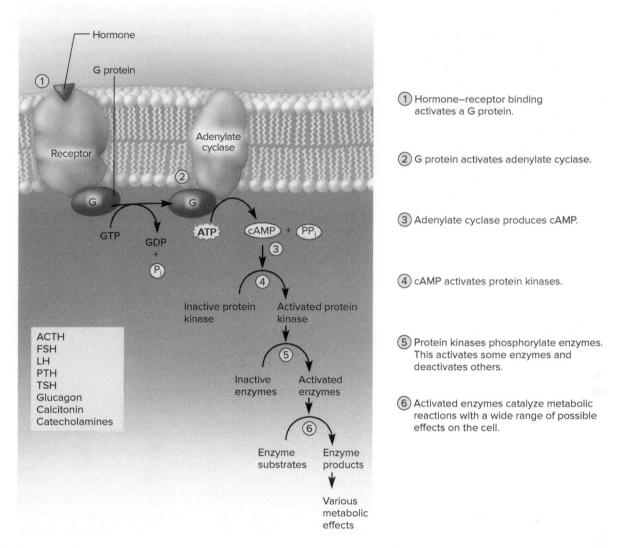

FIGURE 17.19 Cyclic AMP (cAMP) as a Second Messenger. The green box lists some hormones that act in this manner.

? *Why are no steroid hormones listed in this box?*

Hormonal effects mediated through surface receptors tend to be relatively quick, because they don't depend on the cell synthesizing new proteins before anything else can happen. The oxytocin-induced labor contractions are a good example.

Steroids and Thyroid Hormone

Steroid hormones and thyroid hormone act more simply and directly. They are hydrophobic and pass easily through the plasma membrane of a target cell **(fig. 17.18b).** Most steroids go directly into the nucleus and bind to a receptor there; glucocorticoids, however, bind to a receptor in the cytosol, and the hormone–receptor complex is then transported into the nucleus. In either case, the receptor associates with the target gene in the nucleus and either activates or inhibits transcription of a gene for a metabolic enzyme or other protein. For a good example of this, see the *permissive effect* of estrogen on progesterone action on the uterus in forthcoming section 17.4h.

Thyroid hormone also acts on nuclear receptors but is handled a little differently. It enters the target cell by means of an ATP-dependent transport protein. Surprisingly, although 90% of the TH secreted by the thyroid gland is thyroxine (T_4), T_4 has little metabolic effect. Within the target-cell cytoplasm, an enzyme removes one iodine and converts it to the active form, T_3. This T_3, as well as a smaller amount of T_3 produced directly by the thyroid and absorbed from the blood, enters the nucleus and binds to receptors in the chromatin. One of the genes activated by T_3 is for the enzyme Na^+–K^+ ATPase (the Na^+–K^+ pump). One effect of this is to liberate heat from ATP, thus accounting for the calorigenic effect of thyroid hormone. T_3 also activates the transcription of genes for a norepinephrine receptor and part of the muscle protein myosin, thus enhancing the responsiveness of cells such as cardiac muscle to sympathetic stimulation and increasing the strength of the heartbeat.

Steroid and thyroid hormones typically require several hours to days to show an effect. This lag is due to the time required for genetic transcription, translation, and accumulation of enough protein product to have a significant effect on target-cell metabolism.

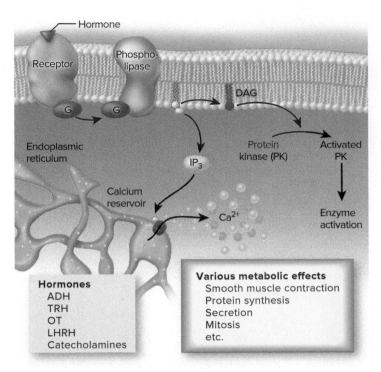

FIGURE 17.20 Diacylglycerol (DAG) and Inositol Triphosphate (IP$_3$) Second-Messenger System. These are employed by hormones listed in the blue box.

17.4f Signal Amplification

Hormones are extraordinarily potent chemicals. Through a mechanism called **signal amplification** (or the **cascade effect**), one hormone molecule triggers the synthesis of not just one enzyme molecule but an enormous number (**fig. 17.21**). To put it in a simplistic but illustrative way, suppose 1 glucagon molecule triggered the formation of 1,000 molecules of cAMP, cAMP activated a protein kinase, each protein kinase activated 1,000 other enzyme

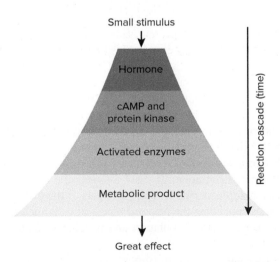

FIGURE 17.21 Signal Amplification. A single hormone molecule can trigger the production of many cAMP molecules and activation of many molecules of protein kinase. Amplification of the process at this and each succeeding step allows for a very small hormonal stimulus to cause a very large metabolic effect.

molecules, and each of those produced 1,000 molecules of a reaction product. These are modest numbers as chemical reactions go, yet even at this low estimate, each glucagon molecule would trigger the production of 1 billion molecules of reaction product. Whatever the actual numbers may be, you can see how signal amplification enables a very small stimulus to produce a very large effect. Hormones are therefore powerfully effective in tiny quantities. Their circulating concentrations are very low compared with other blood substances—on the order of nanograms per deciliter. Blood glucose, for example, is about 100 million times this concentrated. Because of signal amplification, target cells don't need a great number of hormone receptors.

17.4g Modulation of Target-Cell Sensitivity

Target cells can adjust their sensitivity to a hormone by changing the number of receptors for it. In **up-regulation,** a cell increases the number of receptors and becomes more sensitive to the hormone (**fig. 17.22a**). In late pregnancy, for example, the uterus produces oxytocin receptors, preparing itself for the surge of oxytocin that will occur during childbirth.

Down-regulation is the process in which a cell reduces its receptor population and thus becomes less sensitive to a hormone

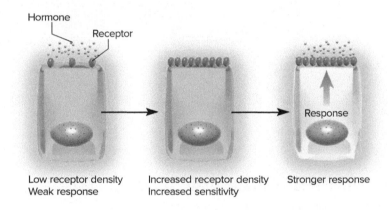

(a) Up-regulation

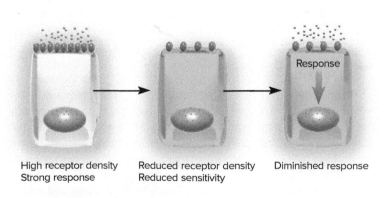

(b) Down-regulation

FIGURE 17.22 Modulation of Target-Cell Sensitivity. (a) Up-regulation, in which a cell produces more receptors and increases its own sensitivity to a hormone. (b) Down-regulation, in which a cell reduces the density of its receptors and lessens its sensitivity to a hormone.

(fig. 17.22b). This sometimes happens in response to long-term exposure to a high hormone concentration. For example, adipocytes down-regulate when exposed to high concentrations of insulin, and cells of the testis down-regulate in response to high concentrations of luteinizing hormone.

Hormone therapy often involves long-term use of abnormally high *pharmacological doses* of hormone, which may have undesirable side effects. Two ways in which adverse side effects can arise are: (1) Excess hormone may bind to receptor sites for other related hormones and mimic their effects; and (2) a target cell may convert one hormone into another, such as testosterone to estrogen. Thus, long-term high doses of testosterone can, paradoxically, have feminizing effects.

17.4h Hormone Interactions

No hormone travels in the bloodstream alone, and no cell is exposed to only one hormone. Rather, there are many hormones in the blood and tissue fluid at once. Cells ignore the majority of them because they have no receptors for them, but most cells are sensitive to more than one. In these cases, the hormones may have three kinds of interactive effects:

1. **Synergistic effects,** in which two or more hormones act together to produce an effect that is greater than the sum of their separate effects. For example, neither FSH nor testosterone alone stimulates much sperm production. When they act together, however, the testes produce some 300,000 sperm per minute.

2. **Permissive effects,** in which one hormone enhances the target organ's response to a second hormone to come later. For example, when estrogen from the ovaries enters cells of the uterine mucosa, it binds to its nuclear receptors and activates the gene for the progesterone receptor. The uterine cells then up-regulate their nuclear progesterone receptors. Progesterone comes later in the menstrual cycle, binds to these receptors, and stimulates transcription of the gene for a glycogen-synthesizing enzyme. The uterine cells then synthesize and accumulate glycogen for the nourishment of an embryo in the event of pregnancy. Progesterone has no effect on the uterine lining unless estrogen has been there earlier and prepared the way by inducing the synthesis of progesterone receptors. Estrogen thus has a permissive effect on progesterone action.

3. **Antagonistic effects,** in which one hormone opposes the action of another. For example, insulin lowers blood glucose level and glucagon raises it **(fig. 17.23).** During pregnancy, estrogen from the placenta inhibits the mammary glands from responding to prolactin; thus milk is not secreted until the placenta is shed at birth.

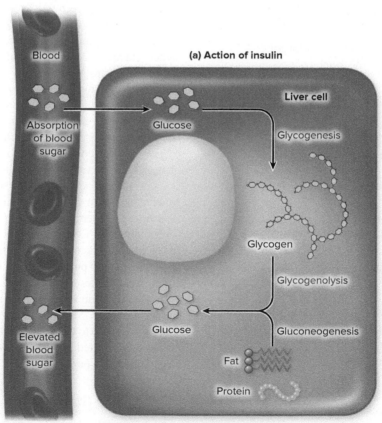

FIGURE 17.23 Antagonistic Effects of Insulin and Glucagon on the Liver. (a) Insulin action in promoting glucose uptake, glycogen storage, and lowering of blood glucose level. (b) Glucagon action in promoting glycogen breakdown, glucose synthesis, glucose release into the blood, and elevation of blood glucose level. Glycogenesis is the synthesis of glycogen; glycogenolysis is its hydrolysis (breakdown to glucose); and gluconeogenesis is the synthesis of glucose from noncarbohydrates, especially fats and proteins.

17.4i Hormone Clearance

Hormonal signals, like nervous signals, must be turned off when they have served their purpose. Most hormones are taken up and degraded by the liver and kidneys and then excreted in the bile or urine. Some are degraded by their target cells. As noted earlier, hormones that bind to transport proteins are removed from the blood much more slowly than hormones that don't employ transport proteins.

The rate of hormone removal is called the **metabolic clearance rate (MCR),** and the length of time required to clear 50% of the hormone from the blood is its **half-life.** The faster the MCR, the shorter is the half-life. Growth hormone, for example, uses no transport protein and has a half-life of only 6 to 20 minutes. Thyroxine, by contrast, is protected by transport proteins and maintains a physiologically effective level in the blood for up to 2 weeks after its secretion ceases.

> **BEFORE YOU GO ON**
>
> Answer the following questions to test your understanding of the preceding section:
>
> **17.** What are the three chemical classes of hormones? Name at least one hormone in each class.
>
> **18.** Why do corticosteroids and thyroid hormones require transport proteins to travel in the bloodstream?
>
> **19.** Explain how MIT, DIT, T_3, and T_4 relate to each other structurally.
>
> **20.** Where are hormone receptors located in target cells? Name one hormone that employs each receptor location.
>
> **21.** Explain how one hormone molecule can activate millions of enzyme molecules.

17.5   Stress and Adaptation

Expected Learning Outcomes

When you have completed this section, you should be able to

a. give a physiological definition of *stress;* and

b. discuss how the body adapts to stress through its endocrine and sympathetic nervous systems.

Stress is defined as any situation that upsets homeostasis and threatens one's physical or emotional well-being. It affects us all from time to time, and we react to it in ways that are mediated mainly by the endocrine and sympathetic nervous systems. Physical causes of stress *(stressors)* include injury, surgery, hemorrhage, infection, intense exercise, temperature extremes, pain, and malnutrition. Emotional causes include anger, grief, depression, anxiety, fear, and guilt.

Whatever the cause, the body reacts to stress in a fairly consistent way called the **stress response** or **general adaptation syndrome (GAS).** The response typically involves elevated levels of epinephrine and cortisol; some physiologists define *stress* as any

situation that raises the cortisol level. A pioneering researcher on stress physiology, Canadian biochemist Hans Selye, showed in 1936 that the GAS typically occurs in three stages, which he called the *alarm reaction,* the *stage of resistance,* and the *stage of exhaustion.*

17.5a The Alarm Reaction

The initial response to stress is the **alarm reaction,** mediated mainly by norepinephrine from the sympathetic nervous system and epinephrine from the adrenal medulla. In extreme cases, as in wild animals, these prepare the body to take action such as fighting or escaping danger. One of their effects, even in humans, is the consumption of stored glycogen, which is particularly important in the transition to the next stage of the stress response. Angiotensin and aldosterone levels also rise during the alarm reaction. Angiotensin helps to raise the blood pressure, and aldosterone promotes sodium and water conservation, which helps to offset possible losses by sweating and bleeding.

17.5b The Stage of Resistance

After a few hours, glycogen reserves are exhausted, yet the nervous system continues to demand glucose. If a stressful situation isn't resolved before the glycogen is gone, the body enters the **stage of resistance,** in which the first priority is to provide alternative fuels for metabolism. This stage is dominated by cortisol. The hypothalamus secretes corticotropin-releasing hormone (CRH); the pituitary responds by secreting adrenocorticotropic hormone (ACTH); and this, in turn, stimulates the adrenal cortex to secrete cortisol and other glucocorticoids. Cortisol promotes the breakdown of fat and protein into glycerol, fatty acids, and amino acids, providing the liver with raw material for gluconeogenesis. Like epinephrine, cortisol inhibits glucose uptake by most organs and thus has a glucose-sparing effect. It also inhibits protein synthesis, leaving the free amino acids available for gluconeogenesis.

Excessive cortisol secretion (or medical use of hydrocortisone) can, however, have some adverse effects. Cortisol suppresses the secretion of sex hormones such as estrogen, testosterone, and luteinizing hormone, causing disturbances of fertility and sexual function. Long-term elevation of cortisol secretion also compromises one's immunity (see Deeper Insight 21.4). It inhibits the synthesis of protective leukotrienes and prostaglandins (see section 17.6), suppresses antibody production, and kills immature T and B cells—two important families of immune cells. Wounds heal poorly, and a person under chronic stress is more susceptible to infections and some forms of cancer. Stress can aggravate peptic ulcers because of reduced resistance to the bacteria that cause them and because circulating epinephrine reduces secretion of the gastric mucus and pancreatic bicarbonate that normally protect the stomach lining.

17.5c The Stage of Exhaustion

The body's fat reserves can carry it through months of stress, but when fat is depleted, stress overwhelms homeostasis. The **stage of exhaustion** sets in, often marked by rapid decline and death. With its fat stores gone, the body now relies primarily on protein breakdown to meet its energy needs. Thus, there is a progressive wasting away of the muscles and weakening of the body. After prolonged stimulation, the adrenal cortex may stop producing glucocorticoids, making it all the more difficult to maintain glucose homeostasis. Aldosterone sometimes promotes so much water retention that it creates a state of hypertension, and while it conserves sodium, it hastens the elimination of potassium and hydrogen ions. This creates a state of hypokalemia (potassium deficiency in the blood) and alkalosis (excessively high blood pH), resulting in nervous and muscular system dysfunctions. Death frequently results from heart failure, kidney failure, or overwhelming infection.

> **BEFORE YOU GO ON**
>
> Answer the following questions to test your understanding of the preceding section:
>
> **22.** Define *stress* from the standpoint of endocrinology.
>
> **23.** Describe the stages of the general adaptation syndrome.
>
> **24.** List six hormones that show increased secretion in the stress response. Describe how each one contributes to recovery from stress.

17.6 Eicosanoids and Other Signaling Molecules

Expected Learning Outcomes

When you have completed this section, you should be able to

a. explain what eicosanoids are and how they are produced;

b. identify some classes and functions of eicosanoids; and

c. describe several physiological roles of prostaglandins.

Neurotransmitters and hormones are not the only chemical messengers in the body. Others are *paracrine* and *autocrine* messengers—chemical signals that don't travel in the blood but stay and exert their effects locally. **Paracrine** signals diffuse only to nearby cells in the same tissue. Histamine, for example, is released by *mast cells* that lie alongside blood vessels in the connective tissues. It diffuses to the smooth muscle of the blood vessel, relaxing it and allowing vasodilation. Catecholamines such as epinephrine diffuse from the adrenal medulla to the cortex to stimulate corticosterone secretion. **Autocrine** signals stimulate the same cell that secretes them. For example, liver cells secrete a signaling molecule called *hepcidin* that controls our blood iron level (detailed in section 25.6f). Acting as a hormone, it travels in the blood to the small intestine and regulates its absorption of dietary iron. Acting as an autocrine signal, it also stimulates the very liver cells that secrete it and regulates their release of stored iron into the blood. Thus, a single chemical can be considered a hormone, paracrine, autocrine, or neurotransmitter depending on location and circumstances.

The **eicosanoids**[27] (eye-CO-sah-noyds) are an important family of paracrine secretions. They have 20-carbon backbones derived

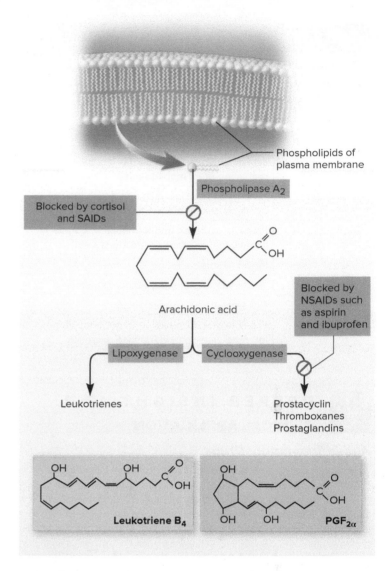

FIGURE 17.24 Eicosanoid Synthesis and Related Drug Actions. SAIDs are steroidal anti-inflammatory drugs such as hydrocortisone; NSAIDs are nonsteroidal anti-inflammatory drugs such as aspirin and ibuprofen. A representative leukotriene and a prostaglandin are shown at the bottom.

? *How would the body be affected by a drug that selectively inhibited lipoxygenase?*

from a fatty acid called **arachidonic acid** (ah-RACK-ih-DON-ic). Some peptide hormones and other stimuli liberate arachidonic acid from one of the phospholipids of the plasma membrane, and the following two enzymes then convert it to various eicosanoids **(fig. 17.24).**

Lipoxygenase helps to convert arachidonic acid to **leukotrienes**—eicosanoids that mediate allergic and inflammatory reactions. **Cyclooxygenase** converts arachidonic acid to three other eicosanoids:

1. **Prostacyclin** is produced by the walls of the blood vessels, where it inhibits blood clotting and vasoconstriction.

2. **Thromboxanes** are produced by blood platelets. In the event of injury, they override prostacyclin and stimulate

---

[27]*eicosa* (varination of *icosa*) = 20

TABLE 17.7	Some of the Roles of Prostaglandins
Prostaglandins	**Function**
Inflammatory	Promote fever and pain, two cardinal signs of inflammation
Endocrine	Mimic effects of TSH, ACTH, and other hormones; alter sensitivity of anterior pituitary to hypothalamic hormones; work with glucagon, catecholamines, and other hormones in regulation of fat mobilization
Nervous	Function as neuromodulators, altering the release or effects of neurotransmitters in the brain
Reproductive	Promote ovulation and formation of corpus luteum; induce labor contractions
Gastrointestinal	Inhibit gastric secretion
Vascular	Act as vasodilators and vasoconstrictors
Respiratory	Constrict or dilate bronchioles
Renal	Promote blood circulation through the kidney, increase water and electrolyte excretion

DEEPER INSIGHT 17.3
CLINICAL APPLICATION

Anti-Inflammatory Drugs

Cortisol and corticosterone are used as *steroidal anti-inflammatory drugs (SAIDs).* They inhibit inflammation by blocking the release of arachidonic acid from the plasma membrane, thus inhibiting the synthesis of all eicosanoids. Their main disadvantage is that prolonged use causes side effects that mimic Cushing syndrome (described in the next section). Aspirin, ibuprofen (Motrin), and celecoxib (Celebrex) are *nonsteroidal anti-inflammatory drugs (NSAIDs),* also called *COX inhibitors* because they block the action of cyclooxygenase (COX). Their advantage is that they do not affect lipoxygenase function or leukotriene production. One form of cyclooxygenase, COX-2, is specific to the cells of inflammation, so there has been a particular interest in developing safe COX-2 inhibitors that can treat inflammation without undesirable side effects such as gastrointestinal damage and cardiovascular events such as stroke and myocardial infarction.

COX inhibitors are also useful in the treatment of fever and thrombosis (undesirable blood clotting). Fever is thought to result from the action of prostaglandins on the hypothalamus. Aspirin exerts its antipyretic (fever-reducing) effect by inhibiting prostaglandin synthesis and its antithrombotic effect by inhibiting thromboxane synthesis.

vasoconstriction and clotting. Prostacyclin and thromboxanes are further discussed in chapter 18.

3. **Prostaglandins (PGs)** are the most diverse eicosanoids. They have a five-sided carbon ring in their backbone. They are named PG for *prostaglandin,* plus a third letter that indicates the type of ring structure (PGE, PGF, etc.) and a subscript that indicates the number of C=C double bonds in the side chain—such as the $PGF_{2\alpha}$ shown in figure 17.24. They were first found in bull semen and the prostate gland,

hence their name, but they are now thought to be produced in most organs of the body. The PGEs are usually antagonized by PGFs. For example, the PGE family relaxes smooth muscle in the bladder, intestines, bronchioles, and uterus and stimulates contraction of the smooth muscle of blood vessels. $PGF_{2\alpha}$ has precisely the opposite effects. Some other roles of prostaglandins are described in **table 17.7.**

Understanding the pathways of eicosanoid synthesis makes it possible to understand the action of some familiar drugs (see Deeper Insight 17.3). The roles of prostaglandins and other eicosanoids are further explored in later chapters on blood, immunity, and reproduction.

BEFORE YOU GO ON

Answer the following questions to test your understanding of the preceding section:

25. What are eicosanoids and how do they differ from neurotransmitters and hormones?

26. Distinguish between paracrine and endocrine effects.

27. State four functions of prostaglandins.

17.7 Endocrine Disorders

Expected Learning Outcomes

When you have completed this section, you should be able to

a. explain some general causes and examples of hormone hyposecretion and hypersecretion;

b. briefly describe some common disorders of pituitary, thyroid, parathyroid, and adrenal function; and

c. in more detail, describe the causes and pathology of diabetes mellitus.

As we saw in the discussion of signal amplification, a little hormone can have a great effect. Thus, it is necessary to tightly regulate hormone secretion and blood concentration. Variations in secretion and target-cell sensitivity often have very noticeable effects on the body. This section deals with some of the better-known dysfunctions of the endocrine system. The effects of aging on the endocrine system are described in section 29.4a.

17.7a Hyposecretion and Hypersecretion

Inadequate hormone release is called **hyposecretion.** It can result from tumors or lesions that destroy an endocrine gland or interfere with its ability to receive signals from another cell. For example, a fractured sphenoid bone can sever the hypothalamo–hypophysial tract and prevent the transport of oxytocin and antidiuretic hormone (ADH) to the posterior pituitary. The resulting ADH hyposecretion disables the water-conserving capability of the kidneys and leads to **diabetes insipidus,** an output of abundant but glucose-free urine. (*Insipidus* means "without taste" and refers to the lack of sweetness of the urine, in contrast to the sugary urine of diabetes mellitus.) Autoimmune diseases can also lead to hormone hyposecretion when endocrine cells are attacked by one's own antibodies or immune cells. This is one of the causes of diabetes mellitus. A congenital absence or underdevelopment of the pituitary gland causes *panhypopituitarism,* wide-spectrum hyposecretion of multiple hormones affected by the pituitary, requiring lifelong multihormone replacement therapy.

Excessive hormone release, called **hypersecretion,** has multiple causes. Some tumors involve the overgrowth of functional endocrine tissue. A **pheochromocytoma** (FEE-o-CRO-mo-sy-TOE-muh), for example, is a tumor of the adrenal medulla that secretes excessive amounts of epinephrine and norepinephrine. Some tumors in nonendocrine organs produce hormones. For example, certain lung tumors secrete ACTH and overstimulate cortisol secretion by the adrenal gland. Whereas some autoimmune disorders can cause endocrine hyposecretion, others cause hypersecretion. An example of this is **toxic goiter** (Graves[28] disease), in which autoantibodies mimic the effect of TSH on the thyroid, activating the TSH receptor and causing thyroid hypersecretion. Endocrine hypersecretion disorders can also be mimicked by excess or long-term clinical administration of hormones such as cortisol.

Following are brief descriptions of some of the better-known disorders of the major endocrine glands. **Table 17.8** provides further details on some of these and lists some additional endocrine disorders.

17.7b Pituitary Disorders

The hypersecretion of growth hormone (GH) in childhood or adolescence, before the epiphysial plates (growth zones) of the long bones are depleted, causes **gigantism,** whereas childhood hyposecretion causes **pituitary dwarfism.** Now that growth

[28]Robert James Graves (1796–1853), Irish physician

hormone is plentiful, made by genetically engineered bacteria containing the human GH gene, pituitary dwarfism has become rare. In adulthood, after the epiphysial plates have closed, GH hyposecretion causes little if any problem, but hypersecretion causes **acromegaly**—thickening of the bones and soft tissues, with especially noticeable effects on the hands, feet, and face **(fig. 17.25).**

17.7c Thyroid and Parathyroid Disorders

Congenital hypothyroidism is thyroid hyposecretion present from birth. Severe or prolonged adult hypothyroidism can cause **myxedema** (MIX-eh-DEE-muh). Both syndromes are described in table 17.8, and both can be treated with oral thyroid hormone.

A more conspicuous, often striking abnormality of the thyroid is **endemic goiter (fig. 17.26),** caused by a deficiency of dietary iodine. Without iodine, the gland cannot synthesize TH. Without TH, the pituitary gland receives no feedback and acts as if the thyroid were understimulated. As if trying to stimulate it more strongly, the pituitary secretes extra TSH, which makes the thyroid produce more and more colloid (thyroglobulin). However, the colloid cannot be iodinated to make TH, so it simply accumulates in the gland, often producing visible swelling in the neck. The word *endemic* refers to the occurrence of a disease in a defined geographic locality. Endemic goiter was once common in the midwestern United States (the "goiter belt") because of iodine-poor soil and little access to iodine-rich seafood. It has now become almost nonexistent in developed countries, however, because of the addition of iodine to table salt, animal feeds, and fertilizers. It now occurs most often in localities that have neither these benefits nor access to seafood—notably central Africa and mountainous regions of South America, central Asia, and Indonesia.

The parathyroids, because of their location and small size, are sometimes accidentally removed in thyroid surgery or degenerate when neck surgeries cut off their blood supply. Without hormone replacement therapy, the resulting **hypoparathyroidism** causes a rapid decline in blood calcium level; in as little as 2 or 3 days, this can lead to a fatal, suffocating spasm of the muscles of the larynx *(hypocalcemic tetany).* **Hyperparathyroidism,** excess PTH secretion, is usually caused by a parathyroid tumor. It causes the bones to become soft, deformed, and fragile; it raises the blood levels of calcium and phosphate ions; and it promotes the formation of *renal calculi* (kidney stones) composed of calcium phosphate. Section 7.4b further describes the relationship among parathyroid function, blood calcium, and bone tissue.

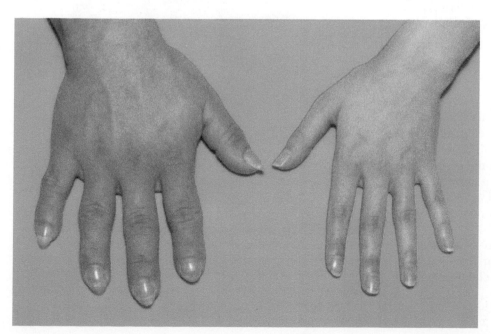

FIGURE 17.25 Acromegaly, a Condition Caused by Growth Hormone Hypersecretion in Adulthood. The hand on the left exemplifies characteristic thickening compared to the normal hand on the right.
Barts Medical Library/Phototake

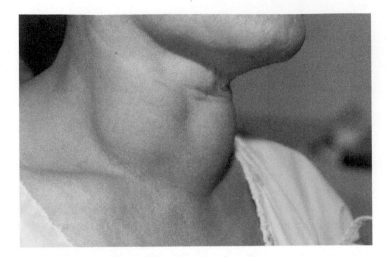

FIGURE 17.26 Endemic Goiter.

Karan Bunjean/Shutterstock

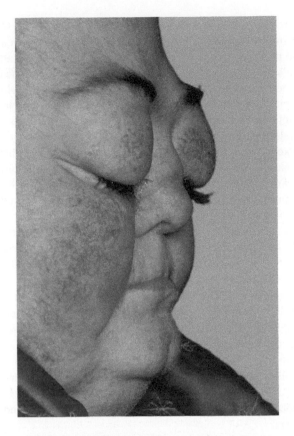

FIGURE 17.27 Cushing Syndrome. Note the "moon face" appearance characteristic of this syndrome.

Biophoto Associates/Science Source

17.7d Adrenal Disorders

Cushing[29] syndrome is excess cortisol secretion owing to any of several causes: ACTH hypersecretion by the pituitary, ACTH-secreting tumors, or hyperactivity of the adrenal cortex independently of ACTH. Cushing syndrome disrupts carbohydrate and protein metabolism, leading to hyperglycemia, hypertension, muscular weakness, and edema. Muscle and bone mass are lost rapidly as protein is catabolized. Some patients exhibit abnormal fat deposition between the shoulders ("buffalo hump") or in the face ("moon face") **(fig. 17.27).** Long-term hydrocortisone therapy can have similar effects.

Adrenogenital syndrome (AGS), the hypersecretion of adrenal androgens, commonly accompanies Cushing syndrome. In children, AGS often causes enlargement of the penis or clitoris and the premature onset of puberty **(fig. 17.28).** Prenatal AGS can result in newborn girls exhibiting masculinized genitalia and being misidentified as boys. In women, AGS produces such masculinizing effects as increased body hair, deepening of the voice, and beard growth.

17.7e Diabetes Mellitus

The world's most prevalent metabolic disease is diabetes mellitus, affecting about 7% of the U.S. population and even more in areas such as Scandinavia and the Pacific Islands. It is the leading cause of adult blindness, renal failure, gangrene, and the necessity for limb amputations, and warrants a more extended discussion than the less common endocrine diseases. The pathology of DM is described here, and the chapter ends with an essay on the history of insulin (see Deeper Insight 17.4).

Diabetes mellitus[30] (DM) can be defined as a disruption of carbohydrate, fat, and protein metabolism resulting from the hyposecretion or inaction of insulin. The classic signs and

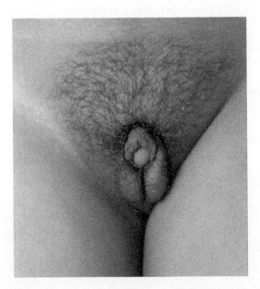

FIGURE 17.28 Adrenogenital Syndrome (AGS). These are the genitals of a female with AGS, masculinized by prenatal hypersecretion of adrenal androgens. Note the resemblance of the labia majora to a scrotum and enlargement of the clitoris to resemble a penis. Infants with AGS are easily mistaken for boys and raised as such.

Medicimage RM/Medical Images

[29]Harvey Cushing (1869–1939), American physician
[30]*diabet* = to flow through; *melli* = honey

symptoms with which patients often first present to a physician are "the three polys": **polyuria**[31] (excessive urine output), **polydipsia**[32] (intense thirst), and **polyphagia**[33] (ravenous hunger). Blood and urine tests can confirm a diagnosis of DM by revealing three further signs: **hyperglycemia**[34] (elevated blood glucose), **glycosuria**[35] (glucose in the urine), and **ketonuria** (ketones in the urine). DM was originally named for the sweetness of the urine stemming from glycosuria. Before the advent of chemical tests for glucose, physicians tasted their patients' urine as part of their diagnostic process.

A little knowledge of kidney physiology is necessary to understand why glycosuria and polyuria occur. The kidneys filter blood plasma and convert the filtrate to urine. In a healthy person, the kidney tubules remove all glucose from the filtrate and return it to the blood, so there is little or no glucose in the urine. Water follows the glucose and other solutes by osmosis, so the tubules also reclaim most of the water in the filtrate.

But like any other carrier-mediated transport system, there is a limit to how fast the glucose transporters of the kidney can work. The maximum rate of reabsorption is called the *transport maximum*, T_m (see fig. 3.16). Because of the high blood glucose level in diabetes mellitus, glucose enters the kidney tubules so rapidly that it exceeds the T_m and the tubules can't reabsorb it fast enough. The excess passes through into the urine. Glucose and ketones in the tubules also raise the osmolarity of the tubular fluid and cause **osmotic diuresis**—water remains in the tubules with these solutes, so large amounts of water are passed in the urine. This accounts for the polyuria, dehydration, and thirst of diabetes. A person with untreated DM may pass 10 to 15 L of urine per day, compared with 1 or 2 L in a healthy person.

Types and Treatment

There are two forms of diabetes mellitus: type 1 and type 2. These were formerly called juvenile-onset or insulin-dependent DM, and adult-onset or non-insulin-dependent DM, respectively. These terms have lately been abandoned because they are too misleading. Although insulin is always used to treat type 1, it is frequently used for type 2 diabetes as well, and either type can occur at any age. Indeed, with the burgeoning problem of childhood obesity, nearly half of all new cases of childhood diabetes are now type 2.

Type 1 diabetes mellitus accounts for 5% to 10% of cases in the United States. What causes it? It begins with heredity. Several genes have been identified that predispose a person to type 1 DM. Then, when a genetically susceptible individual is infected by certain viruses (rubella, cytomegalovirus, or a few others), certain immune cells (CD4 and CD8 T cells discussed in section 21.4) attack and destroy pancreatic beta cells. To a great extent, this destruction is tolerated and produces no disease, but when 80% to 90% of the beta cells are gone, insulin falls to such a critically low level that it can no longer regulate glycemia, the blood glucose level. Now comes the problematic hyperglycemia and all of its insidious complications. Type 1 diabetes is usually diagnosed before the age of 30, but may occur later. Its victims require insulin to survive—usually periodic injections or continual subcutaneous delivery by a small insulin pump worn on the body. A dry insulin inhaler is now available, but is not suitable for all patients. Meal planning, exercise, and self-monitoring of blood glucose levels are also important aspects of the treatment regimen.

Some 90% to 95% of diabetics, however, have **type 2 DM,** and a great many more are prediabetic. Here, the chief problem is not lack of insulin, but *insulin resistance*—unresponsiveness of the target cells to the hormone. The level of insulin may actually be very high in the early stage of the disease, although it later tends to fall to normal or subnormal levels. Again, heredity is one of the causes, although no one gene, or even a mere few, can be blamed for the disease; nearly 100 genes are known, so far, to elevate the risk of type 2 DM. There are great differences in prevalence from one ethnic group to another; it is relatively high, for example, among people of Native American, Hispanic, and Asian descent. It also has a tendency to run in families, and shows high concordance between genetically identical twins—if one twin develops type 2 DM, there is more than a 90% probability that the other will too. Other important risk factors are age, obesity, and a sedentary lifestyle. All of these are accompanied by the progressive replacement of muscular tissue with fat. Muscle plays a highly important role in absorbing blood glucose and buffering glycemia, so as muscle mass diminishes, a person becomes less and less able to regulate glycemia.

Type 2 DM develops slowly and is usually diagnosed after age 40, but it is becoming increasingly prevalent in young people because of early obesity. Aside from the loss of the glucose-buffering role of muscle, another apparent factor in type 2 DM is that adipose tissue secretes chemical signals that indirectly interfere with glucose transport into most cells—so the more body fat, the less efficient is glucose uptake. It is no surprise, then, that type 2 DM can often be successfully managed through a weight-loss program of diet and exercise, often supplemented with glycemia-lowering oral medications such as metformin and drugs to lower blood pressure and blood lipids. If these approaches prove inadequate, supplemental insulin therapy is also employed. About 12% of patients with type 2 DM are treated with insulin alone and another 14% with insulin combined with oral hypoglycemic agents (OHAs).

Pathogenesis

When cells cannot absorb glucose, they must get their energy someplace else; they metabolize fat and protein. In time, this leads to muscular atrophy, emaciation, and weakness. Before insulin therapy was introduced in 1922, the victims of type 1 DM wasted away to an astonishing extent (see Deeper Insight 17.4). Diabetes was described in the first century as "a melting down of the flesh and limbs into urine." Adult patients weighed as little as 27 to 34 kg (60–75 lb) and looked like victims of severe famine. Their breath had a disagreeable sweet ketone smell, like rotten apples. One typical patient was described by medical historian Michael Bliss as "barely able to lift his head from his pillow, crying most of the time from pain, hunger, and despair." In the terminal stage, patients became increasingly drowsy, gasped for air, became comatose,

---

[31]*poly* = much, excessive; *uri* = urine
[32]*poly* = much, excessive; *dipsia* = drinking
[33]*poly* = much, excessive; *phagia* = eating
[34]*hyper* = excess; *glyc* = sugar, glucose; *emia* = blood condition
[35]*glyco* = glucose, sugar; *uria* = urine condition

and died within a few hours. Most diabetic children lived less than 1 year after diagnosis—a year of utmost misery at that. Such was the natural course of the disease in the centuries before insulin therapy.

Rapid fat catabolism raises blood levels of free fatty acids and their breakdown products, the ketone bodies (acetoacetic acid, acetone, and β-hydroxybutyric acid). Ketonuria promotes polyuria, which flushes Na^+ and K^+ from the body. The resulting electrolyte deficiencies can cause abdominal pain, vomiting, irregular heartbeat, and neurological dysfunction. As acids, ketones lower the pH of the blood and produce a condition called **ketoacidosis.** This causes a deep, gasping breathing called *Kussmaul* [36] *respiration,* typical of terminal diabetes. It also depresses the nervous system and produces diabetic coma.

DM also leads to long-term degenerative cardiovascular and neurological diseases—signs that were seldom seen before insulin therapy, when patients died too quickly to show long-term effects. Through multiple, complex mechanisms, chronic hyperglycemia has devastating effects on small to medium blood vessels *(microvascular disease),* including *atherosclerosis,* the obstruction of vessels by plaques of lipid and overgrown smooth muscle. Both types of DM also thicken the basement membrane of the blood vessels, interfering with the delivery of nutrients and hormones to the tissues and with the removal of their wastes. This leads to irreversible tissue degeneration in many organs. Two of the common complications of long-term DM are blindness and renal failure, brought on by arterial degeneration in the retinas and kidneys. Death from kidney failure is much more common in type 1 DM than in type 2. In type 2, the most common cause of death is heart failure stemming from coronary artery disease.

Another complication is *diabetic neuropathy*—nerve damage resulting from impoverished blood flow. This can lead to erectile dysfunction, incontinence, and loss of sensation from affected areas of the body. Microvascular disease in the skin results in poor healing of skin wounds, so even a minor break easily becomes ulcerated, infected, and gangrenous. This is especially common in the feet, because people take less notice of foot injuries; circulation is poorer in the feet (farthest from the heart) than anywhere else; pressure on the feet makes them especially susceptible to tissue injury; and neuropathy may make a person unaware of skin lesions or reluctant to consent to amputation of toes, or more, from which they feel no pain. DM outweighs all other reasons for the amputation of gangrenous appendages.

Diabetes mellitus is not the only kind of diabetes. Diabetes insipidus, a disease with no relation to insulin, has already been mentioned in this chapter, and other forms are discussed with the urinary system in section 23.6b.

BEFORE YOU GO ON

Answer the following questions to test your understanding of the preceding section:

28. Explain some causes of hormone hyposecretion, and give examples. Do the same for hypersecretion.

29. Why does a lack of dietary iodine lead to TSH hypersecretion? Why does the thyroid gland enlarge in endemic goiter?

30. In diabetes mellitus, explain the chain of events that lead to (a) osmotic diuresis, (b) ketoacidosis and coma, and (c) gangrene of the lower limbs.

[36]Adolph Kussmaul (1822–1902), German physician

TABLE 17.8	Some Disorders of the Endocrine System
Addison[37] disease	Hyposecretion of adrenal glucocorticoids and mineralocorticoids, causing hypoglycemia, hypotension, weight loss, weakness, loss of stress resistance, darkening of the skin, dehydration, hyponatremia (sodium deficiency), and other electrolyte imbalances; death can follow quickly from mineralocorticoid and electrolyte deficiencies.
Congenital hypothyroidism	Thyroid hormone hyposecretion present from birth, resulting in stunted physical development, thickened facial features, low body temperature, lethargy, and irreversible brain damage in infancy
Hyperinsulinism	Insulin excess caused by islet hypersecretion or injection of excess insulin, causing hypoglycemia, weakness, hunger, and sometimes *insulin shock,* which is characterized by disorientation, convulsions, or unconsciousness
Myxedema	A syndrome occurring in severe or prolonged adult hypothyroidism, characterized by low metabolic rate, sluggishness and sleepiness, weight gain, constipation, dry skin and hair, abnormal sensitivity to cold, and tissue swelling
Pheochromocytoma	A tumor of the adrenal medulla that secretes excess epinephrine and norepinephrine. Causes hypertension, elevated metabolic rate, nervousness, indigestion, hyperglycemia, and glycosuria.
Toxic goiter (Graves disease)	Thyroid hypertrophy and hypersecretion, occurring when autoantibodies mimic the effect of TSH and overstimulate the thyroid. Results in elevated metabolic rate and heart rate, nervousness, sleeplessness, weight loss, abnormal heat sensitivity and sweating, and bulging of the eyes (exophthalmos) resulting from eyelid retraction and edema of the orbital tissues.

You can find other endocrine system disorders described in the following places:

Acromegaly, adrenogenital syndrome, Cushing syndrome, diabetes inspidus, diabetes mellitus, endemic goiter, pituitary gigantism and *dwarfism,* and *hyper-* and *hypoparathyroidism* in section 17.7c; *gestational diabetes* in section 23.6b; and *androgen insensitivity syndrome* in Deeper Insight 27.1.

[37]Thomas Addison (1793–1860), English physician

DEEPER INSIGHT 17.4

MEDICAL HISTORY

The Discovery of Insulin

At the start of the twentieth century, physicians felt nearly helpless in the face of diabetes mellitus. They put patients on useless diets—the so-called oatmeal cure, potato cure, and others—or on starvation diets as low as 750 kcal per day so as not to "stress the system." They were resigned to the fact that their patients were doomed to die, and simple starvation seemed to produce the least suffering.

After the cause of diabetes was traced to the pancreatic islets in 1901, European researchers tried treating patients and experimental animals with extracts of pancreas, but became discouraged by the severe side effects of impurities in the extracts. They lacked the resources to pursue the problem to completion, and by 1913, the scientific community showed signs of giving up on diabetes.

But in 1920, Frederick Banting (1891–1941), a young Canadian physician with a faltering medical practice, became intrigued with a possible method for isolating the islets from the pancreas and testing extracts of the islets alone. He returned to his alma mater, the University of Toronto, to present his idea to Professor J. J. R. Macleod (1876–1935), a leading authority on carbohydrate metabolism. Macleod was unimpressed with Banting, finding his knowledge of the diabetes literature and scientific method superficial. Nevertheless, he felt Banting's idea was worth pursuing and thought that with his military surgical training, Banting might be able to make some progress where others had failed. He offered Banting laboratory space for the summer, giving him a marginal chance to test his idea. Banting was uncertain whether to accept, but when his fiancée broke off their engagement and an alternative job offer fell through, he closed his medical office, moved to Toronto, and began work. Little did either man realize that in 2 years' time, they would share a Nobel Prize and yet so thoroughly detest each other they would scarcely be on speaking terms.

A Modest Beginning

Macleod advised Banting on an experimental plan of attack and gave him an assistant, Charles Best (1899–1978). Best had just received his B.A. in physiology and looked forward to an interesting summer job with Banting before starting graduate school. Over the summer of 1921, they removed the pancreases from dogs to render them diabetic and tied off the pancreatic ducts in other dogs to make most of the pancreas degenerate while leaving the islets intact. Their plan was to treat the diabetic dogs with extracts made from the degenerated pancreases of the others.

It was a difficult undertaking. For a laboratory, they were assigned a tiny, filthy, unbearably hot, rooftop animal quarters that reeked of dog excrement. The tiny pancreatic ducts were very difficult to tie off, and it was hard to tell if all pancreatic tissue had been removed from the dogs intended to become diabetic. Several dogs died of overanesthesia, infection, and bleeding from Banting's clumsy surgical technique. Banting was also careless in reading his data and interpreting the results and had little interest in reading the literature to see what other researchers were doing. In Banting and Best's first publication, in early 1922, the data in their discussion disagreed with the data in the tables, and both disagreed with the data in their laboratory notebooks. These were not signs of promising researchers.

In spite of themselves, Banting and Best achieved modest positive results over the summer. Crude extracts brought one dog back from a diabetic coma and reduced the hyperglycemia and glycosuria of others. Buoyed by these results, Banting demanded a salary, a better laboratory,

and another assistant. Macleod grudgingly obtained salaries for the pair, but Banting began to loathe him for their disagreement over his demands, and he and Macleod grew in mutual contempt as the project progressed.

Success and Conflict

Macleod brought biochemist J. B. Collip (1892–1965) into the project in the fall of 1921 in hopes that he could produce purer extracts. More competent in experimental science, Collip was the first to show that pancreatic extracts could eliminate ketosis and restore the liver's ability to store glycogen. He obtained better and better results in diabetic rabbits until, by January 1922, the group felt ready for human trials. Banting was happy to have Collip on the team initially, but grew intensely jealous of him as Collip not only achieved better results than he had, but also developed a closer relationship with Macleod. Banting, who had no qualifications to perform human experiments, feared he would be pushed aside as the project moved to its clinical phase. At one point, the tension between Banting and Collip erupted into a near-fistfight in the laboratory.

Banting insisted that the first human trial be done with an extract he and Best prepared, not with Collip's. The patient was a 14-year-old boy who weighed only 29 kg (65 lb) and was on the verge of death. He was injected on January 11 with the Banting and Best extract, described by one observer as "a thick brown muck." The trial was an embarrassing failure, with only a slight lowering of the boy's blood glucose and a severe reaction to the impurities in the extract. On January 23, the same boy was treated again, but with Collip's cleaner extract. This time, his ketonuria and glycosuria were almost completely eliminated and his blood sugar dropped 77%. This was the first successful clinical trial of insulin. Six more patients were treated in February 1922 and quickly became stronger, more alert, and in better spirits. In April, the Toronto group began calling the product *insulin,* and at a medical conference in May, they gave the first significant public report of their success.

Banting felt increasingly sidelined from the project. He quit coming to the laboratory, drank heavily, and day-dreamed of leaving diabetes research to work on cancer. He remained only because Best pleaded with him to stay. Banting briefly operated a private diabetes clinic, but fearful of embarrassment over alienating the discoverer of insulin, the university soon lured him back with a salaried appointment and hospital privileges.

Banting had a number of high-profile, successful cases in 1922, such as 14-year-old Elizabeth Hughes, who weighed only 20 kg (45 lb) before treatment. She began treatment in August and showed immediate, dramatic improvement. She was a spirited, optimistic, and articulate girl who kept enthusiastic diaries of being allowed to eat bread, potatoes, and macaroni and cheese for the first time since the onset of her illness. "Oh it is simply too wonderful for words this stuff," she exuberantly wrote to her mother—even though the still-impure extracts caused her considerable pain and swelling. The world quickly beat a path to Toronto begging for insulin. The pharmaceutical firm of Eli Lilly and Company entered into an agreement with the University of Toronto for the mass production of insulin, and by the fall of 1923, over 25,000 patients were being treated at more than 60 Canadian and U.S. clinics.

The Bitter Fruits of Success

Banting's self-confidence was restored. He had become a public hero, and the Canadian Parliament awarded him an endowment generous enough to ensure a life of comfort. Several distinguished physiologists nominated Banting and Macleod for the 1923 Nobel Prize, and they won. When the award was announced, Banting was furious about having to share it with Macleod. At first, he threatened to refuse it, but when he cooled down, he announced that he would split his share of the prize money with Best. Macleod quickly announced that half of his share would go to Collip.

Interestingly, Romanian physiologist Nicolae Paulescu (1869–1931) succeeded in isolating insulin (which he called pancreine) and treating diabetic dogs with it in 1916, years before Banting even conceived or began his work. Paulescu published four papers on it in April 1921, 8 months before Banting and Best published their first, and he patented his method of isolating insulin in April 1922. Paulescu's work never advanced to clinical trials on humans, however, and was overlooked by the Nobel Committee.

As a recipient of Canada's first Nobel Prize, Banting basked in his stature as a national hero. He made life at the university so unbearable for Macleod, however, that Macleod left in 1928 to accept a university post in Scotland. Banting stayed on at Toronto. Although now wealthy and surrounded by admiring students, he achieved nothing significant in science for the rest of his career. He was killed in a plane crash in 1941. Best replaced Macleod on the Toronto faculty, led a distinguished career, and developed the anticoagulant heparin. Collip went on to play a lead role in the isolation of PTH, ACTH, and other hormones.

Insulin made an industry giant of Eli Lilly and Company. It became the first protein whose amino acid sequence was determined, for which Frederick Sanger received a Nobel Prize in 1958. Diabetics today no longer depend on a limited supply of insulin extracted from beef and pork pancreas. Human insulin is now in plentiful supply, made by genetically engineered bacteria. Paradoxically, while insulin has dramatically reduced the suffering caused by diabetes mellitus, it has increased the number of people who have the disease—because thanks to insulin, diabetics are now able to live long enough to raise families and pass on the genes for diabetes susceptibility.

Effects of the **ENDOCRINE SYSTEM** on Other Organ Systems

ALL SYSTEMS
The development and metabolism of most tissues are affected by growth hormone, insulin, insulin-like growth factors, thyroid hormone, and glucocorticoids.

INTEGUMENTARY SYSTEM
Sex hormones affect skin pigmentation, development of body hair and apocrine glands, and subcutaneous fat deposition.

SKELETAL SYSTEM
Skeletal growth and maintenance are regulated by numerous hormones—calcitonin, calcitriol, parathyroid hormone, growth hormone, estrogen, testosterone, and others.

MUSCULAR SYSTEM
Growth hormone and testosterone stimulate muscular growth; insulin regulates glucose uptake by muscle; other hormones regulate the electrolyte balances that are important in muscular contraction.

NERVOUS SYSTEM
Hormones exert negative feedback inhibition on the hypothalamus; several hormones affect nervous system development, mood, and behavior; hormones regulate the electrolyte balances that are important in neuron function.

CIRCULATORY SYSTEM
Angiotensin II, aldosterone, antidiuretic hormone, natriuretic peptides, and other hormones regulate blood volume and pressure; erythropoietin stimulates RBC production; thymic hormones stimulate WBC production; thrombopoietin stimulates platelet production; epinephrine, thyroid hormone, and other hormones affect the rate and force of the heartbeat.

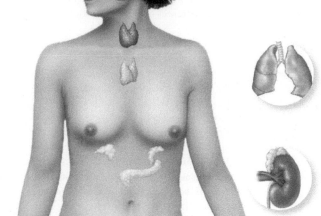

LYMPHATIC AND IMMUNE SYSTEMS
Thymic hormones activate immune cells; glucocorticoids suppress immunity and inflammation.

RESPIRATORY SYSTEM
Epinephrine and norepinephrine dilate the bronchioles and increase pulmonary airflow.

URINARY SYSTEM
Antidiuretic hormone regulates urine volume; calcitriol, parathyroid hormone, aldosterone, and natriuretic peptides regulate electrolyte absorption by the kidneys.

DIGESTIVE SYSTEM
Insulin and glucagon regulate nutrient storage and metabolism; enteric hormones control gastrointestinal secretion and motility; gut–brain peptides affect appetite and regulate food intake and body weight.

REPRODUCTIVE SYSTEM
Gonadotropins and sex steroids regulate sexual development, spermatogenesis and oogenesis, the ovarian and uterine cycles, sex drive, pregnancy, fetal development, and lactation.

STUDY GUIDE

▶ Assess Your Learning Outcomes

To test your knowledge, discuss the following topics with a study partner or in writing, ideally from memory.

17.1 Overview of the Endocrine System

1. The importance of intercellular communication for survival, and the body's four mechanisms of intercellular communication
2. The general term for the cells and glands that secrete hormones, and the name of that branch of science and medicine that specializes in hormones
3. How endocrine glands differ from exocrine glands
4. Similarities, differences, and interactions between the nervous and endocrine systems
5. The term for organs or cells that are influenced by a given hormone, and why they are the only ones to respond to it even though the hormone travels throughout the body

17.2 The Hypothalamus and Pituitary Gland

1. Why the hypothalamus should be considered part of the endocrine system
2. The anatomical relationship of the hypothalamus to the pituitary gland; the two major parts of the pituitary; and how the hypothalamus communicates with each
3. Six hormones that are secreted by the hypothalamus to regulate the anterior pituitary, and their effects
4. Two hormones synthesized in the hypothalamus and stored in the posterior pituitary; how they get to the pituitary; and how their later release into the bloodstream is controlled
5. Six hormones secreted by the anterior pituitary, their abbreviations, and their target organs and functions
6. Two hormones secreted by the posterior pituitary, their abbreviations, their target organs and effects, and the role of neuroendocrine reflexes in their release
7. Examples and mechanisms of positive and negative feedback control of the hypothalamus and pituitary
8. The actions of growth hormone (GH) and the role of insulin-like growth factors in its effects

17.3 Other Endocrine Glands

1. Anatomy of the pineal gland; its involution; and its hormone and function
2. Anatomy of the thymus; its involution; and its hormones and functions
3. Anatomy of the thyroid gland; its hormones and functions; and the cells that produce each hormone
4. Anatomy of the parathyroid glands; their hormone and function
5. Anatomy of the adrenal glands, and structural differences between the cortex and medulla
6. Hormones and functions of the adrenal medulla
7. Three tissue zones of the adrenal cortex, the hormones of each zone, and their functions
8. Pancreatic islets and their cell types, hormones, and functions
9. Endocrine components of the ovaries and testes, and their hormones and functions
10. Hormones produced by the following tissues and organs, and their effects: the skin, liver, kidneys, heart, digestive tract, adipose tissue, osseous tissue, and placenta

17.4 Hormones and Their Actions

1. Three main chemical classes of hormones and examples of each
2. The synthesis of steroid hormones
3. The synthesis of peptide hormones such as insulin
4. Two amino acids that serve as hormone precursors and which hormones are produced from each
5. The types of stimuli that elicit hormone secretion, and examples of each
6. Thyroid hormone synthesis and secretion
7. The problem that must be overcome to transport thyroid hormone (TH) and steroid hormones in the blood, and how the transport mechanism affects their half-life
8. Where hormone receptors are located in the target cells, and differences between receptor systems for hydrophilic and hydrophobic hormones
9. Which hormones require second messengers to activate a target cell; how second messengers work, especially cAMP, DAG, and IP$_3$
10. How signal amplification enables small amounts of hormone to produce great physiological effects
11. How target cells modulate their hormone sensitivity
12. Three kinds of interactions that can occur when two or more of them act simultaneously on a target cell
13. How hormones are inactivated and cleared from the blood after completing their task

17.5 Stress and Adaptation

1. The physiological or medical definition of *stress*
2. Definition of the *stress response (general adaptation syndrome)*
3. The three stages of the stress response; the dominant hormones and physiological effects of each stage; and what marks the transition from one stage to the next

17.6 Eicosanoids and Other Signaling Molecules

1. Paracrine and autocrine secretions, examples, and how they compare and contrast with hormones
2. The general structure and metabolic precursor of eicosanoids
3. Synthesis and effects of leukotrienes
4. Synthesis and effects of the three cyclooxygenase (COX) products: prostacyclin, thromboxanes, and prostaglandins
5. How prostaglandins are named

17.7 Endocrine Disorders

1. Effects of growth hormone hyposecretion and hypersecretion, and how the effects differ between adult versus childhood onset
2. Myxedema, endemic goiter, and toxic goiter
3. Effects of hypo- and hyperparathyroidism
4. Cushing syndrome and adrenogenital syndrome
5. The "three polys" of diabetes mellitus (DM), and three clinical findings that typically confirm DM
6. The mechanism of glycosuria and osmotic diuresis typical of DM; how this relates to the transport maximum (T$_m$) of carrier-mediated transport
7. Differences between the cause, pathology, and treatment of types 1 and 2 DM
8. Consequences of inadequately treated DM and why each of its many pathological effects occurs

STUDY GUIDE

▶ **Testing Your Recall**

Answers in Appendix A

1. CRH secretion would *not* raise the blood concentration of
   a. ACTH.
   b. thyroxine.
   c. cortisol.
   d. corticosterone.
   e. glucose.

2. Which of the following hormones has the least in common with the others?
   a. adrenocorticotropic hormone
   b. follicle-stimulating hormone
   c. thyrotropin
   d. thyroxine
   e. prolactin

3. Which hormone would no longer be secreted if the hypothalamo–hypophysial tract were destroyed?
   a. oxytocin
   b. follicle-stimulating hormone
   c. growth hormone
   d. adrenocorticotropic hormone
   e. corticosterone

4. Which of the following is *not* a hormone?
   a. prolactin
   b. prolactin-inhibiting hormone
   c. thyroxine-binding globulin
   d. atrial natriuretic peptide
   e. cortisol

5. Where are the receptors for insulin located?
   a. in the pancreatic beta cells
   b. in the blood plasma
   c. on the target-cell membrane
   d. in the target-cell cytoplasm
   e. in the target-cell nucleus

6. What would be the consequence of defective ADH receptors?
   a. diabetes mellitus
   b. adrenogenital syndrome
   c. dehydration
   d. seasonal affective disorder
   e. none of these

7. Which of these has more exocrine than endocrine tissue?
   a. the pineal gland
   b. the adenohypophysis
   c. the thyroid gland
   d. the pancreas
   e. the adrenal gland

8. Which of these cells stimulate bone deposition?
   a. alpha cells
   b. beta cells
   c. C cells
   d. G cells
   e. T cells

9. Which of these hormones relies on cAMP as a second messenger?
   a. ACTH
   b. progesterone
   c. thyroxine
   d. testosterone
   e. estrogen

10. Prostaglandins are derived from
    a. phospholipase.
    b. cyclooxygenase.
    c. leukotriene.
    d. lipoxygenase.
    e. arachidonic acid.

11. The _____ develops from a pouch in the pharynx of the embryo.

12. Thyroxine (T_4) is synthesized by combining two iodinated molecules of the amino acid _____.

13. Growth hormone hypersecretion in adulthood causes a disease called _____.

14. The dominant hormone in the stage of resistance of the stress response is _____.

15. Adrenal steroids that regulate glucose metabolism are collectively called _____.

16. Testosterone is secreted by the _____ cells of the testis.

17. Target cells can reduce pituitary secretion by a process called _____.

18. Hypothalamic releasing factors are delivered to the anterior pituitary by way of a network of blood vessels called the _____.

19. A hormone is said to have a/an _____ effect when it stimulates the target cell to develop receptors for other hormones to follow.

20. _____ is a process in which a cell increases its number of receptors for a hormone, thus increasing its hormone sensitivity and response.

STUDY GUIDE

▶ Building Your Medical Vocabulary

Answers in Appendix A

State a meaning of each word element, and give a medical term from this chapter that uses it or a slight variation of it.

1. adeno-

2. chole-

3. diabet-

4. eicosa-

5. luteo-

6. -oid

7. -osa

8. pro-

9. tropo-

10. uri-

▶ What's Wrong with These Statements?

Answers in Appendix A

Briefly explain why each of the following statements is false, or reword it to make it true.

1. Castration would lower a man's blood gonadotropin concentration.

2. The receptors for glycoprotein hormones are usually in the target cell's cytoplasm or nucleus.

3. Thyroglobulin cannot be synthesized without iodine.

4. A tumor in an endocrine gland always results in the hypersecretion of its hormones.

5. All hormones are secreted by endocrine glands.

6. The great majority of cases of diabetes mellitus are caused by insulin deficiency.

7. The pineal gland and thymus are larger in adults than in children.

8. A deficiency of dietary iodine would lead to negative feedback inhibition of TSH synthesis.

9. The tissue at the center of the adrenal gland is called the zona reticularis.

10. Of the endocrine organs covered in this chapter, only the adrenal glands are paired; the rest are single.

▶ Testing Your Comprehension

1. Propose a model of signal amplification for the effect of a steroid hormone and construct a diagram similar to figure 17.21 for your model. It may help to review protein synthesis in chapter 4.

2. Suppose you were browsing in a health-food store and saw a product advertised: "Put an end to heart disease. This herbal medicine will rid your body of cholesterol!" Would you buy it? Why or why not? If the product were as effective as claimed, what are some other effects it would produce?

3. A person with toxic goiter tends to sweat profusely. Explain this in terms of homeostasis.

4. How is the action of a peptide hormone similar to the action of the neurotransmitter norepinephrine?

5. A young man is involved in a motorcycle accident that fractures his sphenoid bone. Shortly thereafter, he begins to excrete enormous amounts of urine, up to 30 L/day, and suffers intense thirst. His neurologist diagnoses the problem as diabetes insipidus. Explain how his head injury resulted in these effects on urinary function and thirst. Why would a sphenoid fracture be more likely than an occipital bone fracture to cause diabetes insipidus? What hormone imbalance resulted from this accident? Would you expect to find elevated glucose in the urine of this diabetic patient? Why or why not?

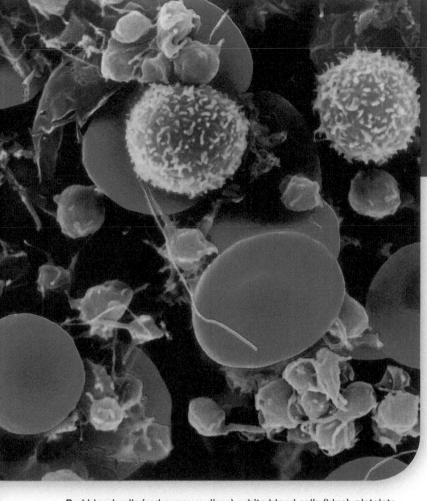

18

THE CIRCULATORY SYSTEM: BLOOD

Red blood cells (red concave discs), white blood cells (blue), platelets (green), and filaments of the clotting protein fibrin (gray) (SEM)

Science Photo Library/Alamy Stock Photo

Anatomy & Physiology Revealed 4.0

Module 9: Cardiovascular System

Blood has always had a special mystique. From time immemorial, people have seen blood flow from the body and, with it, the life of the individual. It is no wonder that blood was thought to carry a mysterious "vital force." Ancient Romans drank the blood of fallen gladiators in a belief that they could acquire a gladiator's vitality or that it could cure epilepsy. Even today, we become especially alarmed when we find ourselves bleeding, and the emotional impact of blood makes many people faint at the sight of it. From ancient Egypt to nineteenth-century America, physicians drained "bad blood" from their patients to treat everything from gout to headaches, from menstrual cramps to mental illness. It was long thought that hereditary traits were transmitted through the blood, and people still use such unfounded or metaphorical expressions as "I have one-quarter Cherokee blood."

Scarcely anything meaningful was known about blood until its cells were seen with the first microscopes. Even though blood is a uniquely accessible tissue, most of what we know about it dates only to the mid-twentieth century. Recent developments in this field have empowered us to save and improve the lives of countless people who would otherwise have suffered or died.

18.1   Introduction

Expected Learning Outcomes

When you have completed this section, you should be able to

a. describe the functions and major components of the circulatory system;

b. describe the components and physical properties of blood;

c. describe the composition of blood plasma;

d. explain the significance of blood viscosity and osmolarity; and

e. describe in general terms how blood is produced.

18.1a Functions of the Circulatory System

The **circulatory system** consists of the heart, blood vessels, and blood. The term **cardiovascular**[1] **system** refers only to the heart and vessels, which are the subject of the next two chapters. The study of blood, treated in this chapter, is called **hematology.**[2]

The fundamental purpose of the circulatory system is to transport substances from place to place in the body. Blood is the liquid medium in which these materials travel, blood vessels ensure the proper routing of blood to its destinations, and the heart is the pump that keeps the blood flowing.

More specifically, the functions of the circulatory system are as follows:

Transport

- Blood carries oxygen from the lungs to all of the body's tissues, while it picks up carbon dioxide from those tissues and carries it to the lungs to be removed from the body.

- It picks up nutrients from the digestive tract and delivers them to all of the body's tissues.

- It carries metabolic wastes to the kidneys for removal.

- It carries hormones from endocrine cells to their target organs.

- It transports a variety of stem cells from the bone marrow and other origins to the tissues where they lodge and mature.

Protection

- Blood plays several roles in inflammation, a mechanism for limiting the spread of infection.

- White blood cells destroy microorganisms and cancer cells and remove debris from the tissues.

- Antibodies and other blood proteins neutralize toxins and help to destroy pathogens.

- Platelets secrete factors that initiate blood clotting and other processes for minimizing blood loss, and contribute to tissue growth and blood vessel maintenance.

Regulation

- By absorbing or giving off fluid under different conditions, the blood capillaries stabilize fluid distribution in the body.

- By buffering acids and bases, blood proteins stabilize the pH of the extracellular fluids.

- Cutaneous blood flow is extremely important in dissipating metabolic heat from the body. Shifts in blood flow regulate body temperature by routing blood to the skin for heat loss or retaining it deeper in the body to conserve heat.

Considering the importance of efficiently transporting nutrients, wastes, hormones, and especially oxygen from place to place, it is easy to understand why an excessive loss of blood is quickly fatal, and why the circulatory system needs mechanisms for minimizing such losses.

---

[1] *cardio* = heart; *vas* = vessel
[2] *hem, hemato* = blood; *logy* = study of

18.1b Components and General Properties of Blood

Adults generally have about 4 to 6 liters of blood. It is a liquid connective tissue composed, like other connective tissues, of cells and an extracellular matrix. Its matrix is the blood **plasma,** a clear, light yellow fluid constituting a little over half of the blood volume. Suspended in the plasma are the **formed elements**— cells and cell fragments including the red blood cells, white blood cells, and platelets **(fig. 18.1).** The term *formed element* alludes to the fact that these are membrane-enclosed bodies with a definite structure visible with the microscope. Strictly speaking, they can't all be called *cells* because the platelets, as explained later, are merely fragments torn from certain bone marrow cells.

The formed elements are classified as follows:

    Erythrocytes[3] (red blood cells, RBCs)

    Platelets

    Leukocytes[4] (white blood cells, WBCs)

        Granulocytes

            Neutrophils

            Eosinophils

            Basophils

        Agranulocytes

            Lymphocytes

            Monocytes

Thus, there are seven kinds of formed elements: the erythrocytes, platelets, and five kinds of leukocytes. The five leukocyte types are divided into two categories, the *granulocytes* and *agranulocytes,* on grounds explained later.

Blood fractionation, the separation of blood into its basic components, is based on centrifugation and coagulation **(fig. 18.2).** First, a sample of blood in a tube is spun in a centrifuge for a few minutes. RBCs, the densest elements, settle to the bottom of the tube and typically constitute 37% to 52% of the total volume—a value called the **hematocrit** or **packed cell volume.** WBCs and platelets settle into a narrow cream- or buff-colored zone called the *buffy coat* just above the RBCs; they total 1% or less of the blood volume. At the top of the tube is the plasma, which is about 47% to 63% of the blood volume. If plasma is separated, allowed to coagulate (clot), and centrifuged again, the clotting proteins (mainly fibrin) settle to the bottom of the tube and the overlying fluid is then called **blood serum.** Serum is clinically valuable as a vehicle for vaccines, antivenins, and other therapies; for certain blood tests,

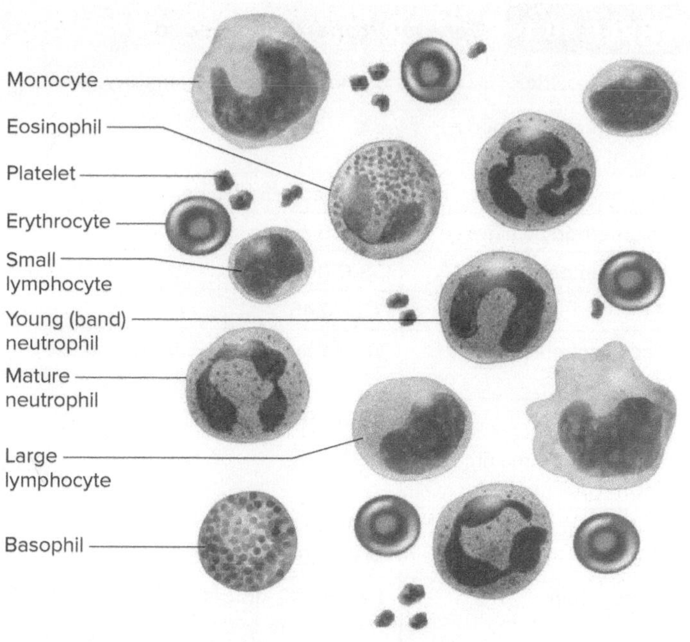

[3]*erythro* = red; *cyte* = cell
[4]*leuko* = white; *cyte* = cell

FIGURE 18.1 The Formed Elements of Blood.

❓ *Identify all the unlabeled formed elements by comparison to the labeled ones.*

Monocyte
Eosinophil
Platelet
Erythrocyte
Small lymphocyte
Young (band) neutrophil
Mature neutrophil
Large lymphocyte
Basophil

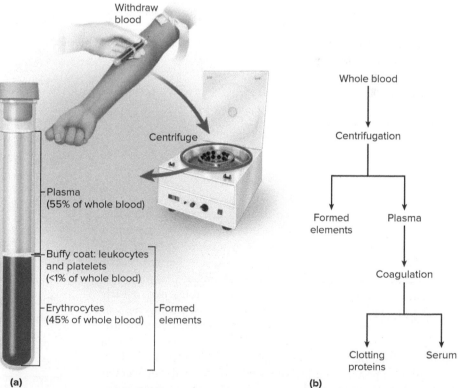

Withdraw blood

Centrifuge

Plasma (55% of whole blood)

Buffy coat: leukocytes and platelets (<1% of whole blood)

Erythrocytes (45% of whole blood) — Formed elements

(a)

Whole blood
↓
Centrifugation
↓
Formed elements   Plasma
↓
Coagulation
↓
Clotting proteins   Serum

(b)

FIGURE 18.2 The Components of Blood. (a) Centrifuging a sample of blood to separate formed elements from plasma and determine the hematocrit. (b) Fractionation of blood into formed elements, plasma, and serum.

TABLE 18.1	General Properties of Blood
Characteristic	**Typical Values for Healthy Adults***
Mean fraction of body weight	8%
Volume in adult body	Female: 4–5 L; male: 5–6 L
Volume/body weight	80–85 mL/kg
Mean temperature	38°C (100.4°F)
pH	7.35–7.45
Viscosity (relative to water)	Whole blood: 4.5–5.5; plasma: 2.0
Osmolarity	280–296 mOsm/L
Mean salinity (mainly NaCl)	0.9%
Hematocrit (packed cell volume)	Female: 37% to 48% Male: 45% to 52%
Hemoglobin	Female: 12–16 g/dL Male: 13–18 g/dL
Mean RBC count	Female: 4.2–5.4 million/µL Male: 4.6–6.2 million/µL
Platelet count	130,000–360,000/µL
Total WBC count	5,000–10,000/µL

*Values vary slightly depending on the testing methods used.

such as for hepatitis and prostate cancer; and for many clinical and research laboratory uses.

Table 18.1 lists several properties of blood. Some of the terms in that table are defined later in the chapter.

▶▶▶APPLY WHAT YOU KNOW

Based on your body weight, estimate the volume (in liters) and weight (in kilograms) of your own blood, using the data in table 18.1.

18.1c Blood Plasma

Even though blood plasma has no anatomy that we can study visually, we cannot ignore its importance as the matrix of this liquid connective tissue. Plasma is a complex mixture of water, proteins, nutrients, electrolytes, nitrogenous wastes, hormones, and gases **(table 18.2).** Protein is the most abundant plasma solute by weight, totaling 6 to 9 g/dL. Plasma proteins play a variety of roles including clotting, defense against pathogens, and transport of other solutes such as iron, copper, lipids, and hydrophobic hormones. There are three major categories of plasma proteins: albumin, globulins, and fibrinogen **(table 18.3).** Many other plasma proteins are indispensable to survival, but account for less than 1% of the total.

Albumin is the smallest and most abundant plasma protein. It serves to transport various solutes and buffer the pH of blood plasma. It also makes a major contribution to two physical

TABLE 18.2	Composition of Blood Plasma
Blood Component*	**Typical Values for Healthy Adults**
Water	92% by weight
Proteins	Total 6–9 g/dL
Albumin	60% of total protein, 3.2–5.5 g/dL
Globulins	36% of total protein, 2.3–3.5 g/dL
Fibrinogen	4% of total protein, 0.2–0.3 g/dL
Nutrients	
Glucose (dextrose)	70–110 mg/dL
Amino acids	33–51 mg/dL
Lactate	6–16 mg/dL
Total lipid	450–850 mg/dL
Cholesterol	120–220 mg/dL
Fatty acids	190–420 mg/dL
High-density lipoprotein (HDL)	30–80 mg/dL
Low-density lipoprotein (LDL)	62–185 mg/dL
Triglycerides (neutral fats)	40–150 mg/dL
Phospholipids	6–12 mg/dL
Iron	50–150 µg/dL
Trace elements	Traces
Vitamins	Traces
Electrolytes	
Sodium (Na^+)	135–145 mEq/L
Calcium (Ca^{2+})	9.2–10.4 mEq/L
Potassium (K^+)	3.5–5.0 mEq/L
Magnesium (Mg^{2+})	1.3–2.1 mEq/L
Chloride (Cl^-)	100–106 mEq/L
Bicarbonate (HCO_3^-)	23.1–26.7 mEq/L
Phosphate (HPO_4^{2-})	1.4–2.7 mEq/L
Sulfate (SO_4^{2-})	0.6–1.2 mEq/L
Nitrogenous Wastes	
Urea	10–20 mg/dL
Uric acid	1.5–8.0 mg/dL
Creatinine	0.6–1.5 mg/dL
Creatine	0.2–0.8 mg/dL
Ammonia	0.02–0.09 mg/dL
Bilirubin	0–1.0 mg/dL
Other Components	
Dissolved CO_2	2.62 mL/dL
Dissolved O_2	0.29 mL/dL
Dissolved N_2	0.98 mL/dL
Enzymes of diagnostic value	—
Hormones	—

*This table is limited to substances of greatest relevance to this and later chapters. Concentrations refer to plasma only, not to whole blood.

TABLE 18.3	Major Proteins of the Blood Plasma
Proteins	**Functions**
Albumin (60%)*	Responsible for colloid osmotic pressure; major contributor to blood viscosity; transports lipids, hormones, calcium, and other solutes; buffers blood pH
Globulins (36%)*	Transport and defense functions as itemized below
Alpha (α) Globulins	
Haptoglobulin	Transports hemoglobin released by dead erythrocytes
Ceruloplasmin	Transports copper
Prothrombin	Promotes blood clotting
Others	Transport lipids, fat-soluble vitamins, and hormones
Beta (β) Globulins	
Transferrin	Transports iron
Complement proteins	Aid in destruction of toxins and microorganisms
Others	Transport lipids
Gamma (γ) Globulins	Antibodies; combat pathogens
Fibrinogen (4%)*	Becomes fibrin, the major component of blood clots

*Mean percentage of the total plasma protein by weight

properties of blood: its *viscosity* and *osmolarity,* discussed shortly. Through its effects on these two variables, changes in albumin concentration can significantly affect blood volume, pressure, and flow. **Globulins** are divided into three subclasses; from smallest to largest in molecular weight, they are the alpha (α), beta (β), and gamma (γ) globulins. Globulins play various roles in solute transport, clotting, and immunity. **Fibrinogen** is a soluble precursor of *fibrin,* a sticky protein that forms the framework of a blood clot. Some of the other plasma proteins are enzymes involved in the clotting process.

The liver produces as much as 4 g of plasma protein per hour, contributing all of the major proteins except gamma globulins. The gamma globulins come from *plasma cells*—connective tissue cells that are descended from white blood cells called *B lymphocytes.*

▶▶▶**APPLY WHAT YOU KNOW**

How could a disease such as liver cancer or hepatitis result in impaired blood clotting?

In addition to protein, the blood plasma contains such nitrogen-containing compounds as free amino acids and nitrogenous wastes. **Nitrogenous wastes** are toxic end products of catabolism. The most abundant is *urea,* a product of amino acid

catabolism. These wastes are normally excreted by the kidneys at a rate that balances their production.

The plasma also transports nutrients absorbed by the digestive tract, including glucose, amino acids, fats, cholesterol, phospholipids, vitamins, and minerals. It transports dissolved oxygen, carbon dioxide, and nitrogen (see table 18.2). The dissolved nitrogen normally has no physiological role in the body (but see Deeper Insight 22.5).

Electrolytes are another important component of the blood plasma. Sodium ions constitute about 90% of the plasma cations. Sodium is more important than any other solute to the osmolarity of the blood. As such, it has a major influence on blood volume and pressure; people with high blood pressure are often advised to limit their sodium intake. Electrolyte concentrations are carefully regulated by the body and have rather stable concentrations in the plasma.

18.1d Blood Viscosity and Osmolarity

Two important properties of blood—viscosity and osmolarity—arise from the formed elements and plasma composition. **Viscosity** is the resistance of a fluid to flow, resulting from the cohesion of its particles. Loosely speaking, it is the thickness or stickiness of a fluid. At a given temperature, mineral oil is more viscous than water, for example, and honey is more viscous than mineral oil. Whole blood is 4.5 to 5.5 times as viscous as water, mainly because of the RBCs; plasma alone is 2.0 times as viscous as water, mainly because of its protein. Viscosity is important in circulatory function because it partially governs the flow of blood through the vessels. An RBC or protein deficiency reduces viscosity and causes blood to flow too easily, whereas an excess causes blood to flow too sluggishly. Either of these conditions puts a strain on the heart that may lead to serious cardiovascular problems if not corrected.

The **osmolarity** of blood, another important factor in cardiovascular function, is the total molarity of dissolved particles that cannot pass through the blood vessel wall. In order to nourish surrounding cells and remove their wastes, substances must pass between the bloodstream and tissue fluid through the capillary walls. This transfer of fluids depends on a balance between the filtration of fluid from the capillary and its reabsorption by osmosis (see section 20.3c). The rate of reabsorption is governed by the relative osmolarity of the blood versus the tissue fluid. If the blood osmolarity is too high, the bloodstream absorbs too much water. This raises the blood volume, resulting in high blood pressure and a potentially dangerous strain on the heart and arteries. If its osmolarity drops too low, too much water remains in the tissues. They become edematous (swollen) and the blood pressure may drop to dangerously low levels because of the water lost from the bloodstream.

It is therefore important that the blood maintain an optimal osmolarity. The osmolarity of the blood is a product mainly of its sodium ions, protein, and erythrocytes. The contribution of protein to blood osmotic pressure—called the **colloid osmotic pressure (COP)**—is especially important, as we see from the effects of extremely low-protein diets (see Deeper Insight 18.1).

DEEPER INSIGHT 18.1

CLINICAL APPLICATION

Starvation and Plasma Protein Deficiency

Several conditions can lead to *hypoproteinemia,* a deficiency of plasma protein: extreme starvation or dietary protein deficiency, liver diseases that interfere with protein synthesis, and protein loss through the urine or body surface in the cases of kidney disease and severe burns, respectively. As the protein content of the blood plasma drops, so does its osmolarity. The bloodstream loses more fluid to the tissues than it reabsorbs by osmosis. Thus, the tissues become edematous and a pool of fluid may accumulate in the abdominal cavity—a condition called *ascites* (ah-SY-teez) (see Deeper Insight 20.4).

Children who suffer severe dietary protein deficiencies often exhibit a condition called *kwashiorkor* (KWASH-ee-OR-cor) **(fig. 18.3).** The arms and legs are emaciated for lack of muscle, the skin is shiny and tight with edema, and the abdomen is swollen by ascites. *Kwashiorkor* is a Ghanian word for a "deposed" or "displaced" child who is no longer breast-fed. Symptoms appear when a child is weaned and placed on a diet consisting mainly of rice or other cereals. Children with kwashiorkor often die of diarrhea and dehydration.

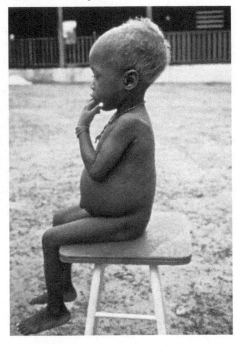

FIGURE 18.3 Child with Kwashiorkor. Note the thin limbs and fluid-distended abdomen.

IMTSSA/CNRI/Science Source

18.1e How Blood Is Produced APR

We lose blood continually, not only from bleeding but also as blood cells grow old and die and plasma components are consumed or excreted from the body. Therefore, we must continually replace it. Every day, an adult typically produces 400 billion platelets, 200 billion RBCs, and 10 billion WBCs. The production of blood, especially its formed elements, is called **hematopoiesis**[5] (he-MAT-oh-poy-EE-sis). A knowledge of this process provides an indispensable foundation for understanding leukemia, anemia, and other blood disorders.

The tissues that produce blood cells are called **hematopoietic tissues.** The first hematopoietic tissues of the human embryo form in the *yolk sac,* a membrane associated with all vertebrate embryos. In most vertebrates (fish, amphibians, reptiles, and birds), this sac encloses the egg yolk, transfers its nutrients to the growing embryo, and produces the forerunners of the first blood cells. Even animals that don't lay eggs, however, have a yolk sac that retains its hematopoietic function. (It is also the source of cells that later produce eggs and sperm.) Cell clusters called *blood islands* form here by the third week of human development. They produce primitive stem cells that migrate into the embryo proper and colonize the bone marrow, liver, spleen, and thymus. Here, the stem cells multiply and give rise to blood cells throughout fetal development. The liver stops producing blood cells around the time of birth. The spleen stops producing RBCs soon after, but it continues to produce lymphocytes for life.

From infancy onward, the red bone marrow produces all seven kinds of formed elements, while lymphocytes are also produced in the lymphatic tissues and organs—especially the thymus, tonsils, lymph nodes, spleen, and mucous membranes. Blood formation in the bone marrow and lymphatic organs is called, respectively, **myeloid**[6] and **lymphoid hematopoiesis.**

All formed elements trace their origins to a common type of **hematopoietic stem cell (HSC)** in the bone marrow. In the stem-cell terminology of section 5.6c, HSCs would be classified as multipotent stem cells, destined to develop into multiple mature cell types. Hematologists, however, often call them *pluripotent stem cells (PPSCs).* (Stem-cell biology is a young science and specialists in different fields sometimes use different terminology.) HSCs multiply to maintain a small but persistent population in the bone marrow, but some of them go on to become a variety of more specialized cells called **colony-forming units (CFUs).** Each CFU is destined to produce one or another class of formed elements. The specific processes leading from an HSC to RBCs, WBCs, and platelets are described at later points in this chapter.

Blood plasma also requires continual replacement. It is composed mainly of water, which it obtains primarily by absorption from the digestive tract. Its electrolytes and organic nutrients are also acquired there, and its gamma globulins come from connective tissue plasma cells and its other proteins mainly from the liver.

> **BEFORE YOU GO ON**

Answer the following questions to test your understanding of the preceding section:

1. Identify at least two each of the transport, protective, and regulatory functions of the circulatory system.

2. What are the two principal components of the blood?

3. List the three major classes of plasma proteins. Which one is absent from blood serum?

4. Define the *viscosity* and *osmolarity* of blood. Explain why each of these is important for human survival.

5. What does *hematopoiesis* mean? After birth, what one cell type is the starting point for all hematopoiesis?

---

[5]*hemato* = blood; *poiesis* = formation

[6]*myel* = bone marrow

18.2 Erythrocytes

Expected Learning Outcomes

When you have completed this section, you should be able to

a. discuss the structure and function of erythrocytes (RBCs);

b. describe the structure and function of hemoglobin;

c. state and define some clinical measurements of RBC and hemoglobin quantities;

d. describe the life history of erythrocytes; and

e. name and describe the types, causes, and effects of RBC excesses and deficiencies.

Erythrocytes, or **red blood cells (RBCs),** have two principal functions: (1) to pick up oxygen from the lungs and deliver it to tissues elsewhere, and (2) to pick up carbon dioxide from the tissues and unload it in the lungs. RBCs are the most abundant formed elements of the blood and therefore the most obvious things one sees upon its microscopic examination. They are also the most critical to survival; a severe deficiency of leukocytes or platelets can be fatal within a few days, but a severe deficiency of RBCs can be fatal within mere minutes. It is the lack of life-giving oxygen, carried by erythrocytes, that leads rapidly to death in cases of major trauma or hemorrhage.

18.2a Erythrocyte Form and Function

An erythrocyte is a discoidal cell with a biconcave shape—a thick rim and a thin sunken center. It is about 7.5 μm in diameter and 2.0 μm thick at the rim **(fig. 18.4).** Although most cells, including white blood cells, have an abundance of organelles, RBCs lose their nucleus and other organelles during maturation and are thus remarkably devoid of internal structure. When viewed with the transmission electron microscope, the interior of an RBC appears uniformly gray. Lacking mitochondria, RBCs rely exclusively on anaerobic fermentation to produce ATP. The lack of aerobic respiration prevents them from consuming the oxygen that they must transport to other tissues. If they were aerobic and consumed oxygen, they would be like a pizza delivery driver who ate a slice of your pizza on the way to your house. RBCs are made to deliver oxygen, not consume it. They are the only human cells that carry on anaerobic fermentation indefinitely.

The cytoplasm of an RBC consists mainly of a 33% solution of **hemoglobin** (about 280 million molecules per cell). This is the red pigment that gives an RBC its color and name. It is known especially for its role in oxygen transport, but it also aids in the transport of carbon dioxide and the buffering of blood pH. The cytoplasm also contains an enzyme, *carbonic anhydrase (CAH),* that catalyzes the reaction $CO_2 + H_2O \rightleftharpoons H_2CO_3$. The role of CAH in gas transport and pH balance is discussed in later chapters.

The plasma membrane of a mature RBC has glycolipids on the outer surface that determine a person's blood type. On its

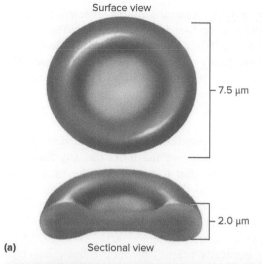

Surface view

7.5 μm

2.0 μm

(a) Sectional view

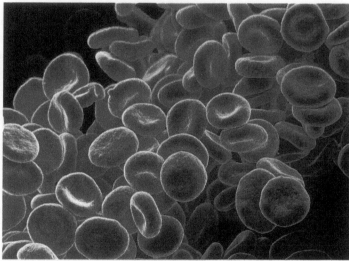

(b)

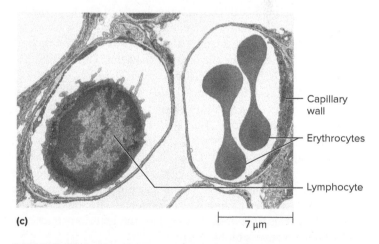

Capillary wall

Erythrocytes

Lymphocyte

(c) 7 μm

FIGURE 18.4 The Structure of Erythrocytes. (a) Dimensions and shape of an erythrocyte. (b) SEM photo showing the biconcave shape of RBCs. (c) TEM photo of a lymphocyte (left) and two erythrocytes (right) in blood capillaries of the lung. Note how thin the RBCs are at the center, and their lack of organelles or other internal structure. **APR**

b: Susumu Nishinaga/Getty Images; c: Thomas Deernick, NCMIR/Science Source

? *Why are erythrocytes caved in at the center?*

inner surface are two cytoskeletal proteins, *spectrin* and *actin,* that give the membrane resilience and durability. This is especially important when RBCs pass through small blood capillaries and sinusoids. Many of these passages are narrower than the diameter of an RBC, forcing the RBCs to stretch, bend, and fold as they squeeze through. When they enter larger vessels, RBCs spring back to their discoidal shape like an air-filled inner tube.

There has been appreciable, unresolved debate over whether the biconcave shape of the RBC has any functional advantage. Some suggest that it maximizes the ratio of cell surface area to volume and thereby promotes the quick diffusion of oxygen to all of the hemoglobin in the cell. This is hard to reconcile with the fact that the only place RBCs load oxygen is in the capillaries, and while squeezing through the tiny capillaries, they generally are not biconcave but compressed into ovoid or teardrop shapes. They spring back to the biconcave shape when reentering larger blood vessels, but no oxygen pickup occurs here. Another hypothesis is that the biconcave shape minimizes RBC spin (like a spinning ice-skater with her arms extended) and turbulence, enabling the dense slurry of RBCs to flow through the larger blood vessels with a smooth *laminar flow.* It has also been argued that it is simply the easiest, most stable shape for the cell and its cytoskeleton to relax into when the nucleus is removed, and it may have no physiological function at all.

18.2b Hemoglobin

Hemoglobin consists of four protein chains called **globins** (**fig. 18.5**). Two of these, the *alpha* (α) *chains,* are 141 amino acids long, and the other two, the *beta* (β) *chains,* are 146 amino acids long. Each chain is conjugated with a nonprotein moiety called the **heme** group, which binds oxygen to an iron atom (Fe) at its center. Each heme can carry one molecule of O_2; thus, the hemoglobin molecule as a whole can transport up to 4 O_2. About 5% of the CO_2 in the bloodstream is also transported by hemoglobin but is bound to the globin rather than to the heme. Gas transport by hemoglobin is discussed in detail in section 22.3c.

Hemoglobin exists in several forms with slight differences in the globin chains. The form just described is called *adult hemoglobin (HbA).* About 2.5% of an adult's hemoglobin, however, is of a form called HbA_2, which has two *delta* (δ) *chains* in place of the beta chains. The fetus produces a form called *fetal hemoglobin (HbF),* which has two *gamma* (γ) *chains* in place of the beta chains. The delta and gamma chains are the same length as the beta chains but differ in amino acid sequence. HbF binds oxygen more tightly than HbA does; this enables the fetus to extract oxygen from the mother's bloodstream.

18.2c Quantities of Erythrocytes and Hemoglobin

The RBC count and hemoglobin concentration are important clinical data because they determine the amount of oxygen the blood can carry. Three of the most common measurements are hematocrit, hemoglobin concentration, and RBC count. The

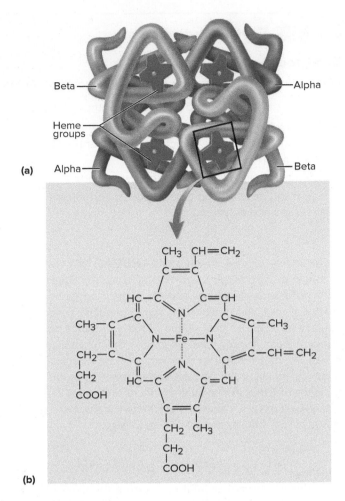

FIGURE 18.5 The Structure of Hemoglobin. (a) The hemoglobin molecule consists of two alpha proteins and two beta proteins, each conjugated to a nonprotein heme group. (b) Structure of the heme group. Oxygen binds to iron (Fe) at the center of the heme.

? *In what way does this exemplify a quaternary protein structure? What is the prosthetic group of hemoglobin? (Hint: See "Protein Structure" in section 2.4e.)*

hematocrit[7] **(packed cell volume, PCV)** is the percentage of whole blood volume composed of RBCs (see fig. 18.2). In men, it normally ranges between 42% and 52%; in women, between 37% and 48%. The **hemoglobin concentration** of whole blood is normally 13 to 18 g/dL in men and 12 to 16 g/dL in women. The RBC count is normally 4.6 to 6.2 million RBCs/μL in men and 4.2 to 5.4 million/μL in women. This is often expressed as cells per cubic millimeter (mm^3); 1 μL = 1 mm^3.

Notice that these values tend to be lower in women than in men. There are three physiological reasons for this: (1) Androgens stimulate RBC production, and men have higher androgen levels than women; (2) women of reproductive age have periodic menstrual losses; and (3) the hematocrit is inversely

---

[7]*hemato* = blood; *crit* = to separate

proportional to percentage body fat, which averages higher in women than in men. In men, the blood also clots faster and the skin has fewer blood vessels than in women. Such differences are not limited to humans. From the evolutionary standpoint, their adaptive value may lie in the fact that male animals fight more than females and suffer more injuries. These traits may serve to minimize or compensate for their blood loss.

▶▶▶ APPLY WHAT YOU KNOW

Explain why the hemoglobin concentration could appear deceptively high in a patient who is dehydrated, when in fact the patient does not have a hemoglobin or RBC excess.

18.2d The Erythrocyte Life History

An erythrocyte lives for an average of 120 days from the time it is produced in the red bone marrow until it dies and breaks up. In a state of balance and stable RBC count, the birth and death of RBCs amount to nearly 100 billion cells per day (1 million per second), or a packed cell volume of 20 mL/day.

Erythrocyte Production

Erythrocyte production is called **erythropoiesis** (eh-RITH-ro-poy-EE-sis). The process normally takes 3 to 5 days and involves four major developments: a reduction in cell size, an increase in cell number, the synthesis of hemoglobin, and the loss of the nucleus and other organelles.

Erythropoiesis begins when a hematopoietic stem cell (HSC) becomes an *erythrocyte colony-forming unit (ECFU)* **(fig. 18.6),** which has receptors for **erythropoietin (EPO),** a hormone secreted by the kidneys. EPO stimulates the ECFU to transform into an *erythroblast (normoblast).* Erythroblasts multiply, build up a large cell population, and synthesize hemoglobin. When this task is completed, the nucleus shrivels and is discharged from the cell. The cell is now called a *reticulocyte,* named for a temporary network (reticulum) of ribosome clusters transcribing the cell's remaining mRNA (polyribosomes; see the photo on the opening page of chapter 4).

Reticulocytes leave the bone marrow and enter the circulating blood. In a day or two, the last of the polyribosomes disintegrate and disappear, and the cell is a mature erythrocyte. Normally, about 0.5% to 1.5% of the circulating RBCs are reticulocytes, but this percentage rises under certain circumstances. Blood loss, for example, stimulates accelerated erythropoiesis and leads to an increasing number of reticulocytes in circulation—as if the bone marrow is in such a hurry to replenish the lost RBCs that it rushes many developing RBCs into circulation a little early.

Iron Metabolism

Iron is a critical part of the hemoglobin molecule and therefore one of the key nutritional requirements for erythropoiesis. Men lose about 0.9 mg of iron per day through the urine, feces, and bleeding, and women of reproductive age lose an average of 1.7 mg/day through these routes and the added factor of menstruation. Since we absorb only a fraction of the iron in our food, we must consume 5 to 20 mg/day to replace our losses. A pregnant woman needs 20 to 48 mg/day, especially in the last 3 months, to meet not only her own need but also that of the fetus.

Dietary iron exists in two forms: ferric (Fe^{3+}) and ferrous (Fe^{2+}) ions. Stomach acid converts most Fe^{3+} to Fe^{2+}, the only form that the small intestine can absorb **(fig. 18.7).** A protein called **gastroferritin,**[8] produced by the stomach, then binds Fe^{2+} and transports it to the small intestine. Here, it is absorbed into the blood, binds to a plasma protein called **transferrin,** and travels to the bone marrow, liver, and other tissues. Bone marrow uses iron for hemoglobin synthesis; muscle uses it to make the oxygen-binding protein myoglobin; and nearly all cells use iron to make electron-transport molecules called cytochromes in their mitochondria. The liver binds surplus iron to a protein called *apoferritin,*[9] forming an iron-storage complex called **ferritin.** It releases Fe^{2+} into circulation when needed.

Some other nutritional requirements for erythropoiesis are vitamin B_{12} and folic acid, required for the rapid cell division and DNA synthesis that occurs in erythropoiesis, and vitamin C and copper, which are cofactors for some of the enzymes that synthesize hemoglobin.

---

[8]*gastro* = stomach; *ferrit* = iron; *in* = protein
[9]*apo* = separated from; *ferrit* = iron; *in* = protein

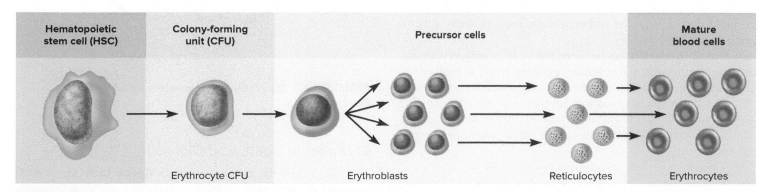

Hematopoietic stem cell (HSC)	Colony-forming unit (CFU)	Precursor cells	Mature blood cells
	Erythrocyte CFU	Erythroblasts	Reticulocytes	Erythrocytes

FIGURE 18.6 Erythropoiesis. Stages in the development of a red blood cell.

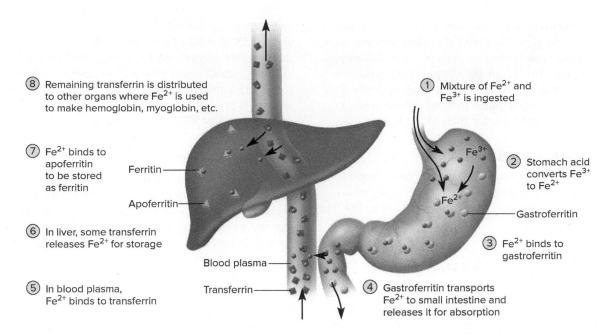

⑧ Remaining transferrin is distributed to other organs where Fe^{2+} is used to make hemoglobin, myoglobin, etc.

⑦ Fe^{2+} binds to apoferritin to be stored as ferritin

Ferritin

Apoferritin

⑥ In liver, some transferrin releases Fe^{2+} for storage

Blood plasma

⑤ In blood plasma, Fe^{2+} binds to transferrin

Transferrin

① Mixture of Fe^{2+} and Fe^{3+} is ingested

Fe^{3+}

② Stomach acid converts Fe^{3+} to Fe^{2+}

Fe^{2+}

Gastroferritin

③ Fe^{2+} binds to gastroferritin

④ Gastroferritin transports Fe^{2+} to small intestine and releases it for absorption

FIGURE 18.7 Iron Metabolism. Read clockwise from the upper right.

Erythrocyte Homeostasis

RBC count is maintained in a classic negative feedback manner (**fig. 18.8**). If the count should drop (for example, because of hemorrhaging), it may result in a state of **hypoxemia**[10] (oxygen deficiency in the blood). The kidneys detect this and increase their EPO output. Three or four days later, the RBC count begins to rise and reverses the hypoxemia that started the process.

Hypoxemia has many causes other than blood loss. Another is a low level of oxygen in the atmosphere. If you were to move from Miami to Denver, for example, the lower O_2 level at the high elevation of Denver would produce temporary hypoxemia and stimulate EPO secretion and erythropoiesis. The blood of an average adult has about 5 million RBCs/μL, but people who live at high elevations may have counts of 7 to 8 million RBCs/μL. Another cause of hypoxemia is an abrupt increase in the body's oxygen consumption. If a formerly lethargic person takes up tennis or aerobics, for example, the muscles consume oxygen more rapidly and create a state of hypoxemia that stimulates erythropoiesis. Endurance-trained athletes commonly have RBC counts as high as 6.5 million RBCs/μL. "Doping" with erythropoietin to build their RBC count and endurance has cost many athletes their careers and honors.

Not all hypoxemia can be corrected by increasing erythropoiesis. In emphysema, for example, less lung tissue is available to oxygenate the blood. Raising the RBC count cannot correct this, but the kidneys and bone marrow have no way of knowing it. The RBC count continues to rise in a futile attempt to restore homeostasis, resulting in a dangerous excess called *polycythemia*, discussed shortly.

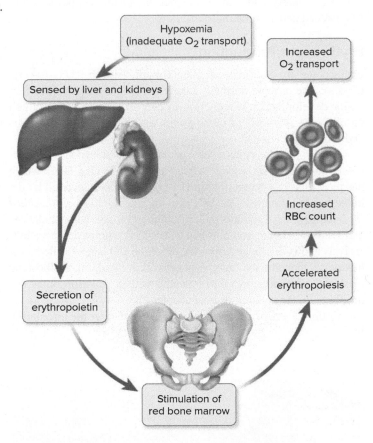

Hypoxemia (inadequate O_2 transport)

Sensed by liver and kidneys

Secretion of erythropoietin

Stimulation of red bone marrow

Accelerated erythropoiesis

Increased RBC count

Increased O_2 transport

FIGURE 18.8 Correction of Hypoxemia by a Negative Feedback Loop.

Erythrocyte Death and Disposal

The life of an RBC is summarized in **figure 18.9.** As an RBC ages and its membrane proteins (especially spectrin) deteriorate, the membrane grows increasingly fragile. Without a nucleus or

---

[10]*hyp* = below normal; *ox* = oxygen; *emia* = blood condition

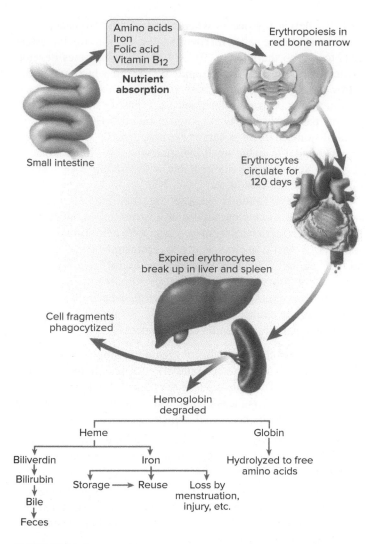

FIGURE 18.9 The Life and Death of Erythrocytes. Note especially the stages of hemoglobin breakdown and disposal.

ribosomes, an RBC cannot synthesize new spectrin. Many RBCs die in the spleen, which has been called the "erythrocyte graveyard." The spleen has channels as narrow as 3 μm that severely test the ability of old, fragile RBCs to squeeze through the organ. Old cells become trapped, broken up, and destroyed. An enlarged and tender spleen sometimes indicates diseases in which RBCs are rapidly breaking down.

Hemolysis[11] (he-MOLL-ih-sis), the rupture of RBCs, releases hemoglobin and leaves empty plasma membranes. The membrane fragments are easily digested by macrophages in the liver and spleen, but hemoglobin disposal is a bit more complicated. It must be disposed of efficiently, however, or it can block kidney tubules and cause renal failure. Macrophages begin the disposal process by separating the heme from the globin. They hydrolyze the globin into free amino acids, which can be used for energy-releasing catabolism or recycled for protein synthesis.

Disposing of the heme is another matter. First, the macrophage removes the iron and releases it into the blood, where it

combines with transferrin and is used or stored in the same way as dietary iron. The macrophage converts the rest of the heme into a greenish pigment called **biliverdin**[12] (BIL-ih-VUR-din), then further converts most of this to a yellow-green pigment called **bilirubin.**[13] Bilirubin is released by the macrophages and binds to albumin in the blood plasma. The liver removes it from the albumin and secretes it into the bile, to which it imparts a dark green color as the bile becomes concentrated in the gallbladder. Biliverdin and bilirubin are collectively known as **bile pigments.** The gallbladder discharges the bile into the small intestine, where bacteria convert bilirubin to *urobilinogen,* responsible for the brown color of the feces. Another hemoglobin breakdown pigment, *urochrome,* produces the yellow color of urine. A high level of bilirubin in the blood causes *jaundice,* a yellowish cast in the skin and whites of eyes. Jaundice may be a sign of rapid hemolysis or a liver disease or bile duct obstruction that interferes with bilirubin disposal.

18.2e Erythrocyte Disorders

Any imbalance between the rates of erythropoiesis and RBC destruction may produce an excess or deficiency of red cells. An RBC excess is called *polycythemia*[14] (POL-ee-sy-THEE-me-uh), and a deficiency of either RBCs or hemoglobin is called *anemia.*[15]

Polycythemia

Primary polycythemia (polycythemia vera) is due to cancer of the erythropoietic line of the red bone marrow. It can result in an RBC count as high as 11 million RBCs/μL and a hematocrit as high as 80%. Polycythemia from all other causes, called **secondary polycythemia,** is characterized by RBC counts as high as 6 to 8 million RBCs/μL. It can result from dehydration because water is lost from the bloodstream while erythrocytes remain and become abnormally concentrated. More often, it is caused by smoking, air pollution, emphysema, high altitude, excessive aerobic exercise, or other factors that create a state of hypoxemia and stimulate erythropoietin secretion.

The principal dangers of polycythemia are increased blood volume, pressure, and viscosity. Blood volume can double in primary polycythemia and cause the circulatory system to become tremendously engorged. Blood viscosity may rise to three times normal. Circulation is poor, the capillaries are congested with viscous blood, and the heart is dangerously strained. Chronic (long-term) polycythemia can lead to embolism, stroke, or heart failure. The deadly consequences of emphysema and some other lung diseases are due in part to polycythemia.

Anemia

The causes of **anemia** fall into three categories: (1) inadequate erythropoiesis or hemoglobin synthesis, (2) **hemorrhagic**

---

[11]*hemo* = blood; *lysis* = splitting, breakdown

[12]*bili* = bile; *verd* = green; *in* = substance
[13]*bili* = bile; *rub* = red; *in* = substance
[14]*poly* = many; *cyt* = cell; *hem* = blood; *ia* = condition
[15]*an* = without; *em* = blood; *ia* = condition

TABLE 18.4	Causes of Anemia
Categories of Anemia	**Causes or Examples**
Inadequate Erythropoiesis	
Iron-deficiency anemia	Dietary iron deficiency
Other nutritional anemias	Dietary folic acid, vitamin B_{12}, or vitamin C deficiency
Anemia due to renal insufficiency	Deficiency of EPO secretion
Pernicious anemia	Deficiency of intrinsic factor leading to inadequate vitamin B_{12} absorption
Hypoplastic and aplastic anemia	Destruction of myeloid tissue by radiation, viruses, some drugs and poisons (arsenic, benzene, mustard gas), or autoimmune disease
Anemia of old age	Declining erythropoiesis due to nutritional deficiencies, reduced physical activity, gastric atrophy (reduced intrinsic factor secretion), or renal atrophy (depressed EPO secretion)
Blood Loss (Hemorrhagic Anemia)	
From hereditary clotting deficiencies	Hemophilia
From nonhereditary causes	Trauma, aneurysm, menstruation, ulcer, etc.
RBC Destruction (Hemolytic Anemia)	
Drug reactions	Penicillin allergy
Poisoning	Mushroom toxins, snake and spider venoms
Parasitic infection	RBC destruction by malaria parasites
Hereditary hemoglobin defects	Sickle-cell disease, thalassemia
Blood type incompatabilities	Hemolytic disease of the newborn, transfusion reactions

anemia from bleeding, and (3) **hemolytic anemia** from RBC destruction. **Table 18.4** gives specific examples and causes for each category.

Anemia often results from kidney failure, because RBC production depends on erythropoietin, which is produced mainly by the kidneys. Erythropoiesis also declines with age, simply because the kidneys atrophy and produce less and less EPO as we get older. Compounding this problem, elderly people tend to get less exercise and eat less well, and both of these factors reduce erythropoiesis.

Nutritional anemia results from a dietary deficiency of any of the requirements for erythropoiesis discussed earlier. Its most common form is **iron-deficiency anemia,** characterized by small pale erythrocytes. Iron-deficiency anemia is usually caused by blood loss without getting enough dietary iron to compensate for it. A deficiency of vitamin B_{12} also causes anemia, but B_{12} is so abundant in meat that a deficiency is rare except in strict vegetarians. More

often, B_{12} deficiency occurs when glands of the stomach fail to produce a substance called **intrinsic factor** that the small intestine needs to absorb the vitamin. Elderly people sometimes develop **pernicious anemia,** an autoimmune disease in which antibodies destroy stomach tissue. Pernicious anemia can also be hereditary. Without proper postsurgical management, gastric-bypass and gastrectomy patients can develop a similar anemia because of the removal of stomach tissue or surgical rearrangement of the stomach, disconnecting it from the small intestine where the intrinsic factor is needed. Such anemias are treatable with vitamin B_{12} injections or oral B_{12} and intrinsic factor.

Hypoplastic[16] **anemia** is caused by a decline in erythropoiesis, whereas the complete failure or destruction of the myeloid tissue produces **aplastic anemia,** a complete cessation of erythropoiesis. Aplastic anemia leads to grotesque tissue necrosis and blackening of the skin. Barring successful treatment, most victims die within a year. About half of all cases of hypoplastic anemia are of unknown or hereditary cause, especially in adolescents and young adults.

Anemia has three potential consequences:

1. The tissues suffer **hypoxia** (oxygen deprivation). The individual is lethargic and becomes short of breath upon physical exertion. The skin is pallid because of the deficiency of hemoglobin. Severe anemic hypoxia can cause life-threatening necrosis of brain, heart, and kidney tissues.

2. Blood osmolarity is reduced. More fluid thus transfers from the bloodstream to the intercellular spaces, resulting in edema.

3. Blood viscosity is reduced. Because the blood puts up less resistance to flow, the heart beats faster than normal and cardiac failure may ensue. Blood pressure also drops because of the reduced volume and viscosity.

Sickle-Cell Disease

Sickle-cell disease and thalassemia (see table 18.8) are hereditary hemoglobin defects that occur mostly among people of African and Mediterranean descent, respectively. **Sickle-cell disease** afflicts about 1.3% of people of African-American heritage. It is caused by a recessive allele that modifies the hemoglobin. Sickle-cell hemoglobin (HbS) differs from normal HbA only in the sixth amino acid of the beta chain, where HbA has glutamic acid and HbS has valine. People who are homozygous for HbS exhibit sickle-cell disease. People who are heterozygous for it—about 7.7% of African-Americans—have *sickle-cell trait* but rarely have severe symptoms. However, if two carriers reproduce, each of their children has a 25% chance of being homozygous and having the disease.

HbS doesn't bind oxygen very well. At low oxygen concentrations, it becomes deoxygenated, polymerizes, and forms a gel that makes erythrocytes become elongated and pointed at the ends **(fig. 18.10),** hence the name of the disease. Sickled

[16]*hypo* = below normal; *plas* = formation; *tic* = pertaining to

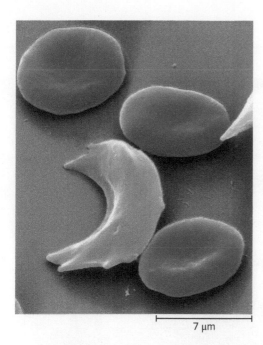

7 μm

FIGURE 18.10 Sickle-Cell Disease. Shows one deformed, pointed erythrocyte and three normal erythrocytes.

Eye of Science/Science Source

Answer the following questions to test your understanding of the preceding section:

6. Describe the size, shape, and contents of an erythrocyte, and explain how it acquires its unusual shape.

7. What is the function of hemoglobin? What are its protein and nonprotein moieties called?

8. Define *hematocrit, hemoglobin concentration,* and *RBC count* and give the units of measurement in which each is expressed.

9. List the stages in the production of an RBC and describe how each stage differs from the previous one.

10. What is the role of erythropoietin in the regulation of RBC count? What is the role of gastroferritin?

11. What happens to each component of an RBC and its hemoglobin when it dies and disintegrates?

12. What are the three primary causes or categories of anemia? What are its three primary consequences?

18.3 Blood Types

Expected Learning Outcomes

When you have completed this section, you should be able to

a. explain what determines a person's ABO and Rh blood types and how this relates to transfusion compatibility;

b. list some blood groups other than ABO and Rh and explain how they may be useful; and

c. describe the effects of a blood type incompatibility between mother and fetus.

erythrocytes are sticky; they **agglutinate**[17] (clump) and block small blood vessels, causing intense pain in oxygen-starved tissues. Blockage of the circulation can also lead to kidney or heart failure, stroke, severe joint pain, or paralysis. Hemolysis of the fragile cells causes anemia, which results in a hypoxemia that triggers further sickling in a deadly positive feedback loop. Chronic hypoxemia also causes fatigue, weakness, poor mental development, and deterioration of the heart and other organs. In a futile effort to counteract the hypoxemia, the hematopoietic tissues become so active that bones of the cranium and elsewhere become enlarged and misshapen. The spleen reverts to a hematopoietic role, while also disposing of dead RBCs, and becomes enlarged and fibrous. Sickle-cell disease is a prime example of *pleiotropy*—the occurrence of multiple phenotypic effects arising from a change in a single gene.

Without treatment, a child with sickle-cell disease has little chance of living to age 2. Advances in treatment, however, have steadily raised life expectancy to a little beyond age 50.

Why does sickle-cell disease exist? In Africa, where it originated, vast numbers of people die of malaria. Malaria is caused by a parasite that invades the RBCs and feeds on hemoglobin. Sickle-cell hemoglobin is detrimental to the parasites, and people heterozygous for sickle-cell disease are resistant to malaria. The lives saved by this gene far outnumber the deaths of homozygous individuals, so the gene persists in the population. The sickle-cell gene is less common in the United States and other essentially nonmalarious regions than it is in Africa.

Blood types and transfusion compatibility are a matter of interactions between the plasma and erythrocytes. Ancient Greek physicians attempted to transfuse blood from one person to another by squeezing it from a pig's bladder through a porcupine quill into the recipient's vein. Although some patients benefited from the procedure, it was fatal to others. The reason some people have compatible blood and some don't remained obscure until 1900, when Karl Landsteiner discovered blood types A, B, and O—a discovery that won him a Nobel Prize in 1930; type AB was discovered later. World War II stimulated great improvements in transfusions, blood banking, and blood substitutes (see Deeper Insight 18.2).

Blood types are based on large molecules called *antigens* and *antibodies.* Explained more fully in chapter 21, these will be introduced only briefly here. **Antigens** are complex molecules such as proteins, glycoproteins, and glycolipids that are genetically unique to each individual (except identical twins). They occur on the surfaces of all cells and enable the body to distinguish its own cells from foreign matter. When the body detects an antigen of foreign origin, it activates an immune response. This response consists partly of the *plasma cells,* mentioned earlier, secreting proteins called **antibodies.**

---

[17]*ag* = together; *glutin* = glue

DEEPER INSIGHT 18.2

MEDICAL HISTORY

Charles Drew—Blood-Banking Pioneer

Charles Drew (**fig. 18.11**) was a scientist remembered for his seminal contributions in hematology and civil rights, and for a sadly ironic end to his life. After receiving his M.D. from McGill University of Montreal in 1933, Drew became the first black person to pursue the advanced degree of Doctor of Science in Medicine, for which he studied transfusion and blood banking at Columbia University. He became the director of a new blood bank at Columbia Presbyterian Hospital in 1939 and organized numerous blood banks during World War II.

Drew saved countless lives by convincing physicians to use plasma rather than whole blood for battlefield and other emergency transfusions. Whole blood could be stored for only a week and given only to recipients with compatible blood types. Plasma could be stored longer and was less likely to cause transfusion reactions.

When the U.S. War Department issued a directive forbidding the storage of "Caucasian and Negro blood" in the same military blood banks, Drew denounced the order and resigned his position. He became a professor of surgery at Howard University in Washington, D.C., and later chief of staff at Freedmen's Hospital. He was a mentor for numerous young black physicians and campaigned to get them accepted into the medical community. The American Medical Association, however, refused to admit black members until the 1960s, excluding even Drew himself.

Late one night in 1950, Drew and three colleagues set out to volunteer their medical services to an annual free clinic in Tuskegee, Alabama. Drew fell asleep at the wheel and was critically injured in the resulting accident. Contrary to a myth that Drew was refused emergency treatment because of his race, doctors at the nearest hospital administered blood and attempted to revive him. Yet, for all the lives he saved through his pioneering work in transfusion, Drew himself bled to death at the age of 45.

FIGURE 18.11 Charles Drew (1904–50).

Alfred Eisenstaedt/The LIFE Picture Collection/Getty Images

Antibodies bind to antigens and mark them, or the cells bearing them, for destruction. One method of antibody action is **agglutination,** in which each antibody molecule binds to two or more foreign cells and sticks them together. Repetition of this process produces large clumps of cells that can cause the complications of the transfusion reaction discussed shortly. The RBC surface antigens that trigger agglutination are called **agglutinogens** (ah-glue-TIN-oh-jens) and the plasma antibodies that bind to them are called **agglutinins** (ah-GLUE-tih-nins).

18.3a The ABO Group

Blood types A, B, AB, and O form the **ABO blood group** (**table 18.5**). One's ABO blood type is determined by the hereditary presence or absence of antigens A and B on the RBCs. The genetic determination of blood types is explained in section 4.4c. The antigens are glycolipids—membrane phospholipids with short carbohydrate chains bonded to them. **Figure 18.12** shows how the carbohydrate moieties of RBC surface antigens determine the ABO blood types.

Antibodies of the ABO group begin to appear in the plasma 2 to 8 months after birth. They reach their maximum concentrations between 8 and 10 years of age and then slowly decline for the rest of one's life. They are produced mainly in response to bacteria that inhabit the intestines, but they cross-react with RBC antigens and are therefore best known for their significance in transfusions.

Antibodies of the ABO group react against any A or B antigen except one's own. The antibody that reacts against antigen A is called *alpha agglutinin,* or *anti-A;* it is present in the plasma of people with type O or type B blood—that is, anyone who does *not* possess antigen A. The antibody that reacts against antigen B is *beta agglutinin,* or *anti-B,* and is present in type O and type A individuals—those who do not possess antigen B. Each antibody molecule has 10 binding sites where it can attach to either an A or B antigen. An antibody can therefore attach to several RBCs at once and agglutinate them (**fig. 18.13**).

A person's ABO blood type can be determined by placing one drop of blood in a pool of anti-A serum and another drop in a pool of anti-B. Blood type AB exhibits conspicuous agglutination in

TABLE 18.5	The ABO Blood Group			
	ABO Blood Type			
Characteristics	**Type O**	**Type A**	**Type B**	**Type AB**
Possible genotypes*	*ii*	$I^A I^A$ or $I^A i$	$I^B I^B$ or $I^B i$	$I^A I^B$
RBC antigen	Neither A nor B	A	B	Both A and B
Plasma antibody	Anti-A, anti-B	Anti-B	Anti-A	Neither
May safely receive RBCs of	Type O	Type O or A	Type O or B	Type O, A, B, or AB
May safely donate RBCs to	Type O, A, B, or AB	Type A or AB	Type B or AB	Type AB
Frequency in U.S. Population				
White	45%	40%	11%	4%
Black	49%	27%	20%	4%
Hispanic	63%	14%	20%	3%
Japanese	31%	38%	22%	9%
Native American	79%	16%	4%	<1%

*I^A is the dominant allele for agglutinogen A; I^B is the dominant allele for agglutinogen B; and allele *i* is recessive to both of these.

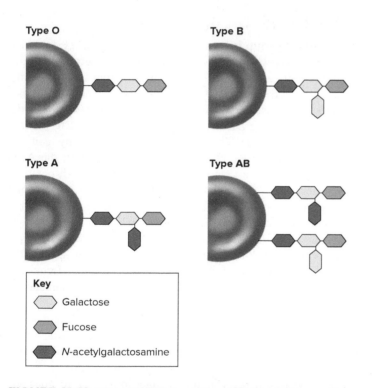

Key
- ⬡ Galactose
- ⬡ Fucose
- ⬡ *N*-acetylgalactosamine

FIGURE 18.12 Chemical Basis of the ABO Blood Types. The terminal carbohydrates of the antigenic glycolipids are shown. All of them end with galactose and fucose (not to be confused with fructose). In type A, the galactose also has *N*-acetylgalactosamine added to it; in type B, it has another galactose; and in type AB, both of these chain types are present.

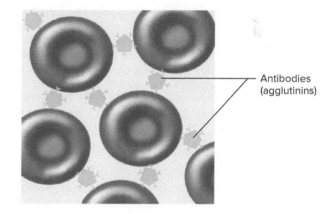

FIGURE 18.13 Agglutination of RBCs by an Antibody. Anti-A and anti-B have 10 binding sites, located at the 2 tips of each of the 5 Ys, and can therefore bind multiple RBCs to each other.

both antisera; type A or B agglutinates only in the corresponding antiserum; and type O doesn't agglutinate in either one **(fig. 18.14).**

Type O blood is the most common and AB is the rarest in the United States. Percentages differ from one region of the world to another and among ethnic groups. People tend to marry within their locality and ethnic group, thus perpetuating statistical variations particular to that group (table 18.5).

In giving transfusions, it is imperative that the donor's RBCs not agglutinate as they enter the recipient's bloodstream. For example, if type B blood were transfused into a type A recipient, the recipient's anti-B would immediately agglutinate the donor's RBCs **(fig. 18.15).** A mismatch causes a **transfusion reaction**—the agglutinated RBCs block small blood vessels, hemolyze, and release their hemoglobin over the next few hours to days. Free hemoglobin can block the kidney tubules and cause death from acute renal failure within a week or so.

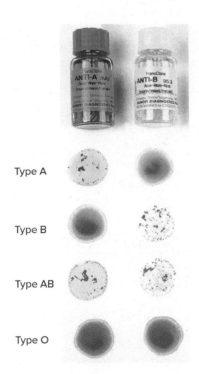

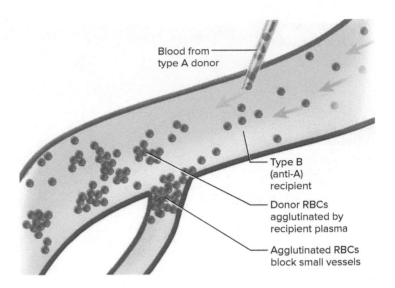

FIGURE 18.15 Effects of a Mismatched Transfusion. Donor RBCs become agglutinated in the recipient's blood plasma. The agglutinated RBCs lodge in smaller blood vessels downstream from this point and cut off the blood flow to vital tissues.

FIGURE 18.14 ABO Blood Typing. Each row shows the appearance of a drop of blood mixed with anti-A and anti-B antisera. Blood cells become clumped if they possess the antigens for the antiserum (top row left, second row right, third row both) but otherwise remain uniformly mixed. Thus, type A agglutinates only in anti-A; type B agglutinates only in anti-B; type AB agglutinates in both; and type O agglutinates in neither of them. The antisera in the vials at the top are artificially colored to make them more easily distinguishable.

Claude Revey/Phototake

For this reason, a person with type A (anti-B) blood must never be given a transfusion of type B or AB blood. A person with type B (anti-A) must never receive type A or AB blood. Type O (anti-A and anti-B) individuals cannot safely receive type A, B, or AB blood.

Type AB is sometimes called the *universal recipient* because this blood type lacks both anti-A and anti-B antibodies; thus, it will not agglutinate donor RBCs of any ABO type. However, this overlooks the fact that the *donor's* plasma can agglutinate the *recipient's* RBCs if it contains anti-A, anti-B, or both. For similar reasons, type O is sometimes called the *universal donor*. The plasma of a type O donor, however, can agglutinate the RBCs of a type A, B, or AB recipient. There are procedures for reducing the risk of a transfusion reaction in certain mismatches, however, such as giving packed RBCs with a minimum of plasma.

Contrary to some people's belief, blood type is not changed by transfusion. It is fixed at conception and remains the same for life.

▶▶▶**APPLY WHAT YOU KNOW**

Scientists have developed a method of enzymatically splitting N-acetylgalactosamine off the glycolipid of type A blood cells (see fig. 18.12). What clinical benefit do you think they saw as justifying their research effort?

18.3b The Rh Group

The **Rh blood group** is named for the rhesus monkey, in which the Rh antigens were discovered in 1940. This group includes numerous RBC antigens, of which the principal types are antigens C, D, and E. Antigen D is by far the most reactive of these, so a person is considered **Rh-positive (Rh+)** if he or she has the D antigen (genotype *DD* or *Dd*) and **Rh-negative (Rh−)** if it is lacking (genotype *dd*). The Rh blood type is tested by using an anti-D reagent. The Rh type is often combined with the ABO type in a single expression such as O+ for type O, Rh-positive; or AB− for type AB, Rh-negative. Rh frequencies vary among ethnic groups just as ABO frequencies do. About 85% of white Americans are Rh+ and 15% are Rh−, whereas about 99% of Asians are Rh+. ABO blood type has no influence on Rh type, or vice versa. If the frequency of type O whites in the United States is 45%, and 85% of these are also Rh+, then the frequency of O+ individuals is the product of these separate frequencies: $0.45 \times 0.85 = 0.38$, or 38%.

In contrast to the ABO group, anti-D antibodies are not normally present in the blood. They form only in Rh− individuals who are exposed to Rh+ blood. If an Rh− person receives an Rh+ transfusion, the recipient produces anti-D. Since anti-D doesn't appear instantaneously, this presents little danger in the first mismatched transfusion. But if that person should later receive another Rh+ transfusion, his or her anti-D could agglutinate the donor's RBCs.

18.3c Other Blood Groups

ABO and Rh are not the only known blood groups. There are 33 groups in all, with more than 300 RBC antigens in addition to A, B, and D. Other groups include the Duffy, Kell, Kidd, Lewis, and MNS groups. These rarely cause transfusion reactions, but they are useful for such legal purposes as paternity and criminal cases and for research in anthropology and population genetics.

Now that DNA sequencing is more economical, however, it has replaced blood typing in many such applications.

18.3d Maternal–Fetal Mismatches

A condition called **hemolytic disease of the newborn (HDN),** or **erythroblastosis fetalis,** can occur when a woman has a baby with a mismatched blood type—most famously, but by no means all cases, when she is Rh– and carries an Rh+ fetus. The first pregnancy is likely to be uneventful because the placenta normally prevents maternal and fetal blood from mixing. However, if there is placental leakage during pregnancy, or at the time of birth, or if a miscarriage occurs, the mother is exposed to Rh+ fetal blood. She then begins to produce anti-D antibodies **(fig. 18.16).** If she becomes pregnant again with an Rh+ fetus, her anti-D antibodies may pass through the placenta and agglutinate the fetal erythrocytes. Agglutinated RBCs hemolyze, and the baby is born with hemolytic anemia, HDN.

If an Rh– woman has had one or more previous Rh+ pregnancies, her subsequent Rh+ children have about a 17% probability of being born with HDN. Such infants are often severely anemic. As the fetal hematopoietic tissues respond to the need for more RBCs, erythroblasts (immature RBCs) enter the circulation prematurely— hence the name *erythroblastosis fetalis.* Hemolyzed RBCs release

hemoglobin, which is converted to bilirubin. High bilirubin levels can cause *kernicterus,* a syndrome of toxic brain damage that can be lethal or leave the child with motor, sensory, and mental deficiencies. HDN can be treated with *phototherapy*—exposing the infant to ultraviolet radiation, which degrades bilirubin as blood passes through capillaries of the skin. In more severe cases, an *exchange transfusion* may be given to completely replace the infant's Rh+ blood with Rh–. In time, the infant's hematopoietic tissues will replace the donor's RBCs with Rh+ cells, and by then the mother's antibody will have disappeared from the infant's blood.

Rh-based HDN, like so many other disorders, is easier to prevent than to treat. If an Rh– woman gives birth to (or miscarries) an Rh+ child, she can be given an *Rh immune globulin* (sold under such trade names as RhoGAM and Gamulin Rh). The immune globulin binds fetal RBC antigens so they cannot stimulate her immune system to produce anti-D. It is now common to give immune globulin at 28 to 32 weeks' gestation and at birth in any pregnancy in which the mother is Rh–.

Although an Rh mismatch produces the most severe HDN, it isn't the most common cause. Two out of three cases are due to ABO mismatches. In about 15% of U.S. pregnancies, the mother is type O and her fetus is type A, B, or AB. About 3% of these

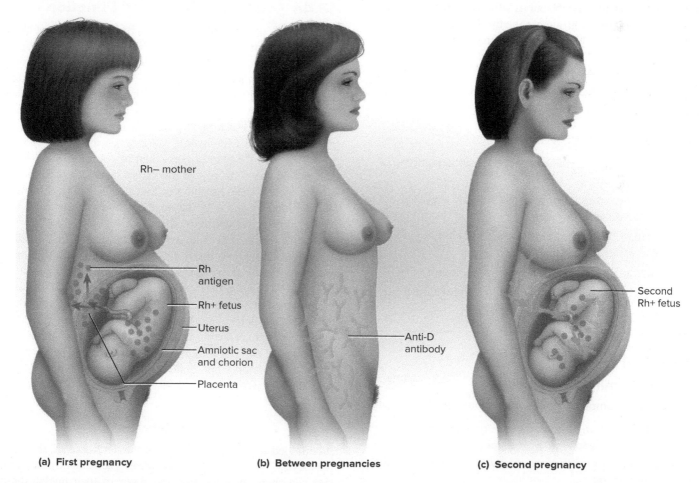

(a) **First pregnancy**

Rh– mother

Rh antigen

Rh+ fetus

Uterus

Amniotic sac and chorion

Placenta

(b) **Between pregnancies**

Anti-D antibody

(c) **Second pregnancy**

Second Rh+ fetus

FIGURE 18.16 Hemolytic Disease of the Newborn (HDN). (a) When an Rh– woman is pregnant with an Rh+ fetus, she is exposed to D (Rh) antigens, especially during childbirth. (b) Following that pregnancy, her immune system produces anti-D antibodies. (c) If she later becomes pregnant with another Rh+ fetus, her anti-D antibodies can cross the placenta and agglutinate the blood of that fetus, causing that child to be born with HDN.

DEEPER INSIGHT 18.3

CLINICAL APPLICATION

Bone Marrow and Cord Blood Transplants

A bone marrow transplant is one treatment option for leukemia, sickle-cell disease, and some other disorders. The principle is to eradicate the patient's original bone marrow with radiation or chemotherapy, including immune T cells that would attack transplanted marrow, and then replace with donor stem cells in hopes that they will rebuild a population of normal marrow and blood cells. Marrow is drawn from the donor's sternum or hip bone and injected into the recipient's circulation. Donor stem cells colonize the patient's marrow cavities and, ideally, build healthy marrow.

There are, however, drawbacks to this procedure. It is difficult to find compatible donors; surviving T cells in the patient may attack the donor marrow; and donor T cells may attack the patient's tissues (the graft-versus-host response). To inhibit graft rejection, the patient must take immunosuppressant drugs for life. These leave a person vulnerable to infection and have other adverse side effects. Infections are sometimes contracted from the donated marrow itself. In short, marrow transplant is

a high-risk procedure; up to one-third of patients die from complications of treatment (see the David Vetter case in fig 21.29).

An alternative is to use blood from placentas, which are normally discarded at every childbirth. Placental blood contains more stem cells than adult bone marrow, and is less likely to carry infectious microbes. With the parents' consent, it can be harvested from the umbilical cord with a syringe and stored almost indefinitely at cord blood banks. The immature immune cells in cord blood have less tendency to attack the recipient's tissues; thus, cord blood transplants have lower rejection rates and don't require as close a match between donor and recipient, meaning that more donors are available to a patient in need. Pioneered in the 1980s, cord blood transplants have successfully treated leukemia and a wide range of other blood diseases.

The use of cord blood may soon be overshadowed, however, by stem cell harvesting from peripheral blood (drawn from the blood vessels). Peripheral blood is more accessible than bone marrow, and with improvements in technique, it yields faster replacement of hematopoietic stem cells in the recipient.

---

pregnancies also result in HDN, but usually with mild effects. Mismatches in the Kell blood group are the third most common cause of HDN, followed by Kidd and Duffy mismatches.

▶▶▶**APPLY WHAT YOU KNOW**

A baby with HDN typically has jaundice and an enlarged spleen. Explain these effects.

BEFORE YOU GO ON

Answer the following questions to test your understanding of the preceding section:

13. What are antibodies and antigens? How do they interact to cause a transfusion reaction?

14. What antibodies and antigens are present in people with each of the four ABO blood types?

15. Describe the causes, prevention, and treatment of HDN.

16. Why might someone be interested in determining a person's blood type other than ABO/Rh?

18.4 Leukocytes

Expected Learning Outcomes

When you have completed this section, you should be able to

a. explain the function of leukocytes in general and the individual role of each leukocyte type;

b. describe the appearance and relative abundance of each type of leukocyte;

c. describe the formation and life history of leukocytes; and

d. discuss the types, causes, and effects of leukocyte excesses and deficiencies.

18.4a Leukocyte Form and Function

Leukocytes, or **white blood cells (WBCs),** are the least abundant formed elements, totaling only 5,000 to 10,000 WBCs/μL. Yet we cannot live long without them, because they afford protection against infection and other diseases. WBCs are easily recognized in stained blood films because they have conspicuous nuclei that stain from light violet to dark purple with the most common blood stains. They are much more abundant in the body than their low number in blood films would suggest, because they spend only a few hours in the bloodstream, then migrate into the connective tissues and spend the rest of their lives there. It's as if the bloodstream were merely the subway that the WBCs take to work; in blood films, we see only the ones on their way to work, not the WBCs already at work in the tissues.

Leukocytes differ from erythrocytes in that they retain their organelles throughout life; thus, when viewed with the transmission electron microscope, they show a complex internal structure **(fig. 18.17).** Among their organelles are the usual instruments of protein synthesis—the nucleus, rough endoplasmic reticulum, ribosomes, and Golgi complex—for leukocytes must synthesize proteins in order to carry out their functions. Some of these proteins are packaged into lysosomes and other organelles, which appear as conspicuous cytoplasmic granules that distinguish one WBC type from another.

18.4b Types of Leukocytes

As outlined at the beginning of this chapter, there are five kinds of leukocytes. They are distinguished from each other by their relative size and abundance, the size and shape of their nuclei, the presence or absence of certain cytoplasmic granules, the coarseness and staining properties of those granules, and most importantly by their functions. Individual WBC types rise or fall in number in various disease conditions and physiological states.

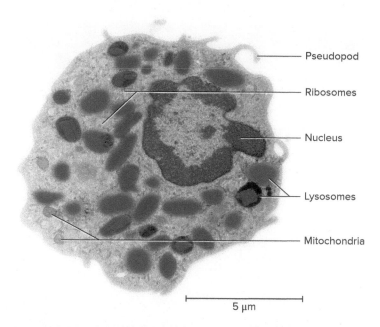

Pseudopod

Ribosomes

Nucleus

Lysosomes

Mitochondria

5 μm

FIGURE 18.17 The Structure of a Leukocyte (TEM). This example is an eosinophil. The lysosomes seen here in orange are the coarse pink granules seen in the eosinophil in table 18.6.

Scott Camazine/Alamy

All WBCs have lysosomes called **nonspecific granules** in the cytoplasm, also called *azurophilic*[18] *granules* because they absorb the blue or violet dyes of blood stains. Three of the five types—neutrophils, eosinophils, and basophils—are called **granulocytes** because they also have various kinds of **specific granules** that stain conspicuously and distinguish each cell type from the others. Basophils are named for the fact that their specific granules stain with methylene blue, a basic dye in a common blood-staining mixture called Wright's stain. Eosinophils are so named because they stain with eosin, an acidic dye in Wright's stain. The specific granules of neutrophils don't stain intensely with either basic or acidic stains. The colors in the following descriptions and table are those typically seen with Wright's stain, but may differ on slides you examine because of the use of other stains. Specific granules contain enzymes and other chemicals employed in defense against pathogens. The two remaining WBC types—monocytes and lymphocytes—are called **agranulocytes** because they lack specific granules. Nonspecific granules are inconspicuous to the light microscope, and these cells therefore have relatively clear-looking cytoplasm. **Table 18.6** shows the appearance and summarizes the characteristics and functions of each of the following WBC types.

Granulocytes

- **Neutrophils** (NEW-tro-fills) are the most abundant WBCs—generally about 4,150 cells/μL and constituting 60% to 70% of the circulating leukocytes. The nucleus is clearly visible and, in a mature neutrophil, typically consists of three to five lobes connected by slender nuclear strands. These strands are sometimes so delicate that they are scarcely visible, and

the neutrophil may seem as if it had multiple nuclei. Young neutrophils have an undivided band-shaped nucleus and are called *band cells*. Neutrophils are also called *polymorphonuclear leukocytes (PMNs)* because of their varied nuclear shapes. The cytoplasm contains fine reddish to violet specific granules, which contain lysozyme and other antimicrobial agents. The individual granules are barely visible with the light microscope, but their combined effect gives the cytoplasm a pale lilac color. Neutrophils are aggressively antibacterial cells. Their numbers rise—a condition called *neutrophilia*—in response to bacterial infections. They destroy bacteria in ways detailed in section 21.2b.

- **Eosinophils** (EE-oh-SIN-oh-fills) are harder to find in a blood film because they are only 2% to 4% of the WBC total, typically averaging about 170 cells/μL. Although relatively scanty in the blood, eosinophils are abundant in the mucous membranes of the respiratory, digestive, and lower urinary tracts. The eosinophil nucleus usually has two large lobes connected by a thin strand, and the cytoplasm has an abundance of coarse rosy to orange-colored specific granules. Eosinophils secrete chemicals that weaken or destroy relatively large parasites such as hookworms and tapeworms, too big for any one WBC to phagocytize. They also phagocytize and dispose of inflammatory chemicals, antigen–antibody complexes, and allergens (foreign antigens that trigger allergies). Allergies, parasitic infections, collagen diseases, and diseases of the spleen and central nervous system can cause an elevated eosinophil count called *eosinophilia*. The eosinophil count also fluctuates greatly from day to night, seasonally, and with the phase of the menstrual cycle.

- **Basophils** are the rarest of all formed elements. They average about 40 cells/μL and usually constitute less than 0.5% of the WBC count. They can be recognized mainly by an abundance of very coarse, dark violet specific granules. The nucleus is largely hidden from view by these granules, but is large, pale, and typically S- or U-shaped. Basophils secrete two chemicals that aid in the body's defense processes: (1) **histamine,** a vasodilator that widens the blood vessels, speeds the flow of blood to an injured tissue, and makes the blood vessels more permeable so that blood components such as neutrophils and clotting proteins can get into the connective tissues more quickly; and (2) **heparin,** an anticoagulant that inhibits blood clotting and thus promotes the mobility of other WBCs in the area. They also release chemical signals that attract eosinophils and neutrophils to a site of infection.

Agranulocytes

- **Lymphocytes** (LIM-fo-sites) are second to neutrophils in abundance and are thus quickly spotted when you examine a blood film. They average about 2,200 cells/μL and are 25% to 33% of the WBC count. They include the smallest WBCs; at 5 to 17 μm in diameter, they range from smaller than RBCs to two and a half times as large. They are sometimes classified into three size classes (table 18.6), but there are gradations between them. Medium and large lymphocytes are usually seen in fibrous connective tissues and only occasionally in the

[18]*azuro* = blue; *philic* = loving

TABLE 18.6	The White Blood Cells (Leukocytes)

Neutrophils

Differential count (% of WBCs)	60% to 70%
Mean absolute count	4,150 cells/μL
Diameter	9–12 μm

Appearance

Nucleus usually with 3–5 lobes in S- or C-shaped array

Fine reddish to violet specific granules in cytoplasm

Variations in Number

Increase in bacterial infections

Functions

Phagocytize bacteria

Release antimicrobial chemicals

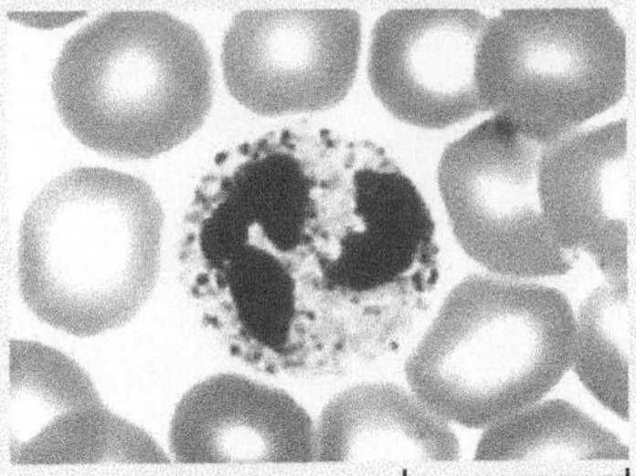

Neutrophil 10 μm

Eosinophils

Differential count (% of WBCs)	2% to 4%
Mean absolute count	165 cells/μL
Diameter	10–14 μm

Appearance

Nucleus usually has two large lobes connected by thin strand

Large orange-pink specific granules in cytoplasm

Variations in Number

Fluctuate greatly from day to night, seasonally, and with phase of menstrual cycle

Increases in parasitic infections, allergies, collagen diseases, and diseases of spleen and central nervous system

Functions

Phagocytize antigen–antibody complexes, allergens, and inflammatory chemicals

Release enzymes that weaken or destroy parasites such as worms

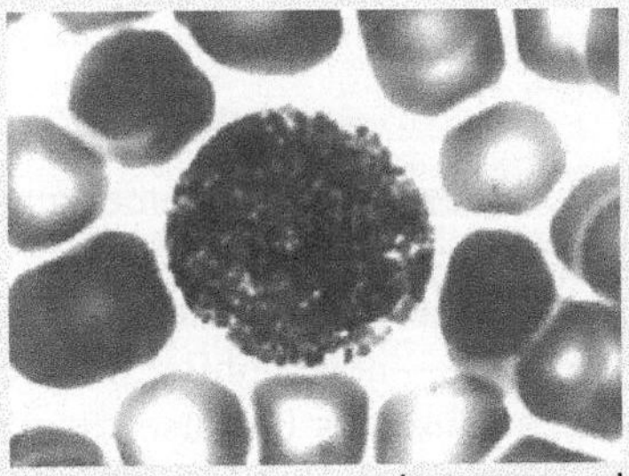

Eosinophil 10 μm

Basophils

Differential count (% of WBCs)	< 0.5%
Mean absolute count	44 cells/μL
Diameter	8–10 μm

Appearance

Nucleus large and U- to S-shaped, but typically pale and obscured from view

Coarse, abundant, dark violet specific granules in cytoplasm

Variations in Number

Relatively stable

Increase in chickenpox, sinusitis, diabetes mellitus, myxedema, and polycythemia

Functions

Secrete histamine (a vasodilator), which increases blood flow to a tissue

Secrete heparin (an anticoagulant), which promotes mobility of other WBCs by preventing clotting

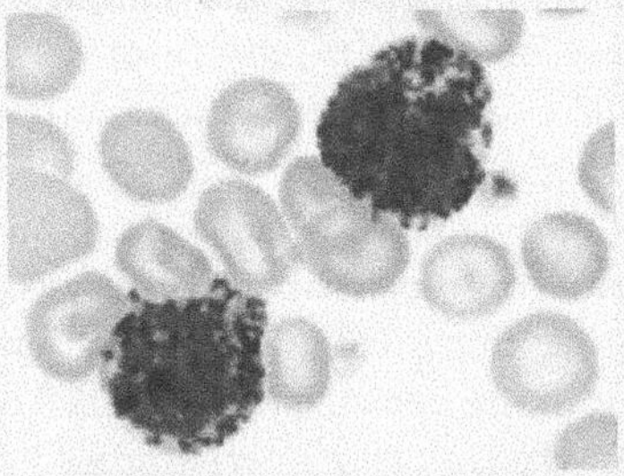

Basophils 10 μm

circulating blood (see fig. 18.1). The lymphocytes seen in blood films are mostly in the small size class. These are sometimes difficult to distinguish from basophils, but most basophils are conspicuously grainy, whereas the lymphocyte nucleus is uniform or merely mottled. Basophils also lack the rim of clear cytoplasm seen in most lymphocytes. Large lymphocytes are sometimes difficult to distinguish from monocytes. The lymphocyte

TABLE 18.6	The White Blood Cells (Leukocytes) *(continued)*

Lymphocytes

Differential count (% of WBCs)	25% to 33%
Mean absolute count	2,185 cells/µL
Diameter	
Small class	5–8 µm
Medium class	10–12 µm
Large class	14–17 µm

Appearance

Nucleus round, ovoid, or slightly dimpled on one side, of uniform or mottled dark violet color

In small lymphocytes, nucleus fills nearly all of the cell and leaves only a scanty rim of clear, light blue cytoplasm.

In larger lymphocytes, cytoplasm is more abundant; large lymphocytes may be hard to differentiate from monocytes.

Variations in Number

Increase in diverse infections and immune responses

Functions

Several functional classes usually indistinguishable by light microscopy

Destroy cancer cells, cells infected with viruses, and foreign cells

Present antigens to activate other cells of immune system

Coordinate actions of other immune cells

Secrete antibodies

Serve in immune memory

Lymphocyte 10 µm

Monocytes

Differential count (% of WBCs)	3% to 8%
Mean absolute count	456 cells/µL
Diameter	12–15 µm

Appearance

Nucleus ovoid, kidney-shaped, or horseshoe-shaped; violet

Abundant cytoplasm with sparse, fine nonspecific granules

Sometimes very large with stellate or polygonal shapes

Variations in Number

Increase in viral infections and inflammation

Functions

Differentiate into macrophages (large phagocytic cells of the tissues)

Phagocytize pathogens, dead neutrophils, and debris of dead cells

Present antigens to activate other cells of immune system

Monocyte 10 µm

Photos: **(Neutrophil, Eosinophil, Lymphocyte):** Alvin Telser/McGraw-Hill Education; **(Basophils):** LindseyRN/Shutterstock; **(Monocyte):** Victor P. Eroschenko

nucleus is round, ovoid, or slightly dimpled on one side, and usually stains dark violet. In small lymphocytes, it fills nearly the entire cell and leaves only a narrow rim of light blue cytoplasm, often barely detectable, around the cell perimeter. The cytoplasm is more abundant in medium and large lymphocytes. There are several subclasses of lympho-cytes with different immune functions (see section 21.1b), but they cannot be distinguished by microscopic examination of blood films. Collectively, they destroy cells that have been infected with viruses or turned malignant, and foreign cells (including parasites) that have been introduced into the body; they secrete chemicals that communicate with other

WBCs and coordinate their actions; they present antigens to activate immune responses; they give rise to the cells that secrete antibodies; and they provide long-term immunity to pathogens.

- **Monocytes** (MON-oh-sites) are usually the largest WBCs seen on a blood slide, often two or three times the diameter of an RBC. They average about 460 cells/μL and about 3% to 8% of the WBC count. The nucleus is large and clearly visible, often a relatively light violet, and typically ovoid, kidney-shaped, or horseshoe-shaped. The cytoplasm is abundant and contains sparse, fine granules. In prepared blood films, monocytes often assume sharply angular to spiky shapes (see fig. 18.1). The monocyte count rises in inflammation and viral infections. Monocytes go to work only after leaving the bloodstream and transforming into large tissue cells called **macrophages** (MAC-ro-fay-jez). Macrophages are highly phagocytic cells that consume dead or dying host and foreign cells, pathogenic chemicals and microorganisms, and other foreign matter equivalent to as much as 25% of their own volume per hour. They also chop up or process foreign antigens and display fragments of them on the cell surface to alert the immune system to the presence of a pathogen. Thus, they and a few other cells are called *antigen-presenting cells (APCs)*. The functions of macrophages are further detailed in chapter 21.

18.4c The Leukocyte Life History

Leukopoiesis (LOO-co-poy-EE-sis), the production of white blood cells, begins with the same hematopoietic stem cells (HSCs) as erythropoiesis. Some HSCs differentiate into distinct types of colony-forming units (CFUs) and then go on to produce the following cell lines (yellow zone in **fig. 18.18**), each of them now irreversibly committed to a certain outcome.

1. *Myeloblasts,* which ultimately differentiate into the three types of granulocytes (neutrophils, eosinophils, and basophils)
2. *Monoblasts,* which look identical to myeloblasts but lead ultimately to monocytes
3. *Lymphoblasts,* which produce all lymphocyte types

CFUs have receptors for *colony-stimulating factors (CSFs)*. Mature lymphocytes and macrophages secrete several types of CSFs in response to infections and other immune challenges. Each CSF stimulates a different WBC type to develop in response to specific needs. Thus, a bacterial infection may trigger the production of neutrophils, whereas an allergy stimulates eosinophil production, each process working through its own CSF.

The red bone marrow stores granulocytes and monocytes until they are needed and contains 10 to 20 times more of these cells than the circulating blood does. Lymphocytes begin developing in the bone marrow but don't stay there. Some types mature there and others migrate to the thymus to complete their development. Mature lymphocytes from both locations then colonize the spleen, lymph nodes, and other lymphatic organs and tissues.

Circulating leukocytes don't stay in the blood for very long. Granulocytes circulate for 4 to 8 hours and then migrate into the tissues, where they live another 4 or 5 days. Monocytes travel in the blood for 10 to 20 hours, then migrate into the tissues and transform into a variety of macrophages, which can live as long as a few years. Lymphocytes, responsible for long-term immunity, survive from a few weeks to decades; they leave the bloodstream for the tissues and eventually enter the lymphatic system, which empties them back into the bloodstream. Thus, they are continually recycled from blood to tissue fluid to lymph and back to the blood.

When leukocytes die, they are generally phagocytized and digested by macrophages. Dead neutrophils, however, are responsible for the creamy color of pus, and are sometimes disposed of by the rupture of a blister onto the skin surface.

▶▶▶APPLY WHAT YOU KNOW

It is sometimes written that RBCs do not live as long as WBCs because RBCs do not have a nucleus and therefore cannot repair and maintain themselves. Explain the flaw in this argument.

18.4d Leukocyte Disorders

The total WBC count is normally 5,000 to 10,000 WBCs/μL. A count below this range, called **leukopenia**[19] (LOO-co-PEE-nee-uh), is seen in lead, arsenic, and mercury poisoning; radiation sickness; and such infectious diseases as measles, mumps, chickenpox, polio, influenza, typhoid fever, and AIDS. It can also be produced by glucocorticoids, anticancer drugs, and immunosuppressant drugs given to organ-transplant patients. Since WBCs are protective cells, leukopenia presents an elevated risk of infection and cancer. A count above 10,000 WBCs/μL, called **leukocytosis**,[20] usually indicates infection, allergy, or other diseases but can also occur in response to dehydration or emotional disturbances. More useful than a total WBC count is a *differential WBC count*, which identifies what percentage of the total WBC count consists of each type of leukocyte (see Deeper Insight 18.4).

Leukemia is a cancer of the hematopoietic tissues that usually produces an extraordinarily high number of circulating leukocytes and their precursors **(fig. 18.19)**. Leukemia is classified as myeloid or lymphoid, acute or chronic. **Myeloid leukemia** is marked by uncontrolled granulocyte production, whereas **lymphoid leukemia** involves uncontrolled lymphocyte or monocyte production. **Acute leukemia** appears suddenly, progresses rapidly, and causes death within a few months if it is not treated. **Chronic leukemia** develops more slowly and may go undetected for many months; if untreated, the typical survival time is about 3 years. Both myeloid and lymphoid leukemia occur in acute and chronic forms. The greatest success in treatment and cure has been with acute lymphoblastic leukemia, the most common type of childhood cancer. Treatment employs chemotherapy and marrow transplants along with the control of side effects such as anemia, hemorrhaging, and infection.

As leukemic cells proliferate, they replace normal bone marrow and a person suffers from a deficiency of normal granulocytes,

---

[19]*leuko* = white; *penia* = deficiency
[20]*leuko* = white; *cyt* = cell; *osis* = condition

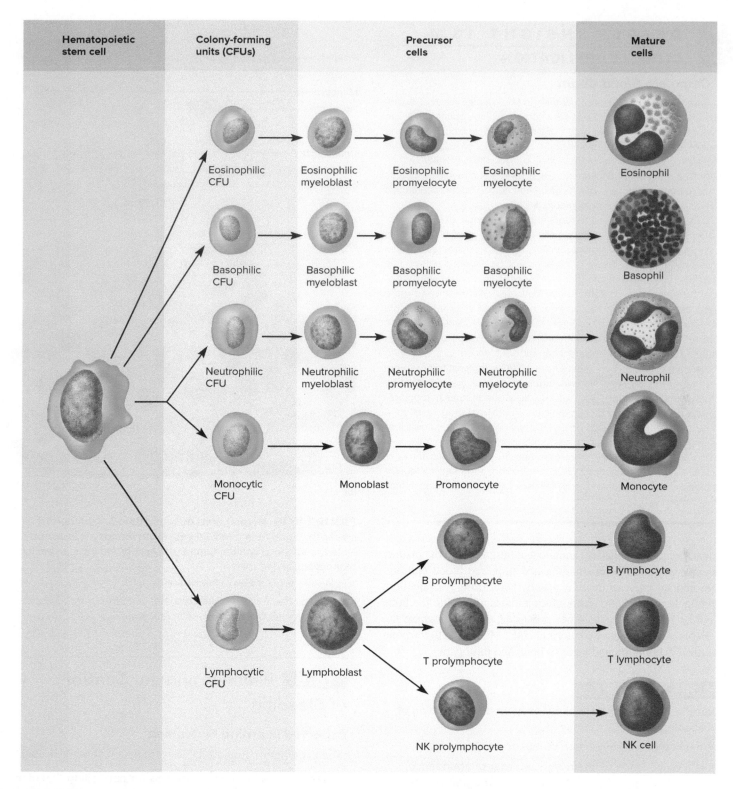

Hematopoietic stem cell	Colony-forming units (CFUs)	Precursor cells			Mature cells

Eosinophilic CFU → Eosinophilic myeloblast → Eosinophilic promyelocyte → Eosinophilic myelocyte → Eosinophil

Basophilic CFU → Basophilic myeloblast → Basophilic promyelocyte → Basophilic myelocyte → Basophil

Neutrophilic CFU → Neutrophilic myeloblast → Neutrophilic promyelocyte → Neutrophilic myelocyte → Neutrophil

Monocytic CFU → Monoblast → Promonocyte → Monocyte

Lymphocytic CFU → Lymphoblast → B prolymphocyte → B lymphocyte

Lymphoblast → T prolymphocyte → T lymphocyte

Lymphoblast → NK prolymphocyte → NK cell

FIGURE 18.18 Leukopoiesis. Stages in the development of white blood cells. The hematopoietic stem cell at the left also is the ultimate source of red blood cells (see fig. 18.6) and platelet-producing cells.

❓ *Explain the meaning and relevance of the combining form* myelo- *seen in so many of these cell names.*

erythrocytes, and platelets. Although enormous numbers of leukocytes are produced and spill over into the bloodstream, they don't provide the usual protective functions of WBCs. They are like an army of children, present in vast numbers but too immature to perform a useful defensive role. The deficiency of competent WBCs leaves the patient vulnerable to **opportunistic infection**—the establishment of pathogenic organisms that usually cannot get a foothold in people with healthy immune systems. The RBC

DEEPER INSIGHT 18.4

CLINICAL APPLICATION

The Complete Blood Count

One of the most common laboratory tests in both routine medical examinations and the diagnosis of disease is a *complete blood count (CBC)*. The CBC yields a highly informative profile of data on multiple blood values: the number of RBCs, WBCs, and platelets per microliter of blood; the relative numbers (percentages) of each WBC type, called a *differential WBC count;* hematocrit; hemoglobin concentration; and various *RBC indices* such as RBC size *(mean corpuscular volume, MCV)* and hemoglobin concentration per RBC *(mean corpuscular hemoglobin, MCH).*

RBC and WBC counts used to require the microscopic examination of films of diluted blood on a calibrated slide, and a differential WBC count required examination of stained blood films. Today, most laboratories use *electronic cell counters*. These devices draw a blood sample through a very narrow tube with sensors that identify cell types and measure cell sizes and hemoglobin content. These counters give faster and more accurate results based on much larger numbers of cells than the old visual methods. However, cell counters still misidentify some cells, and a medical technologist must review the results for suspicious abnormalities and identify cells that the instrument cannot.

The wealth of information gained from a CBC is too vast to give more than a few examples here. Various forms of anemia are indicated by low RBC counts or abnormalities of RBC size, shape, and hemoglobin content. A platelet deficiency can indicate an adverse drug reaction. A high neutrophil count suggests bacterial infection, and a high eosinophil count suggests an allergy or parasitic infection. Elevated numbers of specific WBC types or WBC stem cells can indicate various forms of leukemia. If a CBC does not provide enough information or if it suggests other disorders, additional tests may be done, such as coagulation time and bone marrow biopsy.

deficiency renders the patient anemic and fatigued, and the platelet deficiency results in hemorrhaging and impaired blood clotting. The immediate cause of death is usually hemorrhage or infection. Cancerous hematopoietic tissue often metastasizes from the bone marrow or lymph nodes to other organs of the body, where the cells displace or compete with normal cells. Metastasis to the bone tissue itself is common and leads to bone and joint pain.

BEFORE YOU GO ON

Answer the following questions to test your understanding of the preceding section:

17. What is the overall function of leukocytes?

18. List the five kinds of leukocytes in order of abundance, identify whether each is a granulocyte or agranulocyte, and describe the functions of each one.

19. What does leukopoiesis have in common with erythropoiesis? How does it differ?

20. What can cause an abnormally high or low WBC count?

21. Suppose myeloblasts began multiplying out of control, but their subsequent development remained normal. What types of mature WBCs would be produced in excess? What types would not?

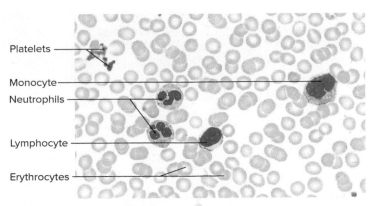

Platelets
Monocyte
Neutrophils
Lymphocyte
Erythrocytes

(a)

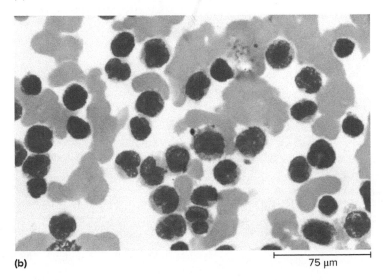

(b)   75 μm

FIGURE 18.19 Normal and Leukemic Blood. (a) A normal blood smear. (b) Blood from a patient with acute monocytic leukemia. Note the abnormally high number of white blood cells, especially monocytes, in part (b).

a: Ed Reschke; b: Leonard Lessin/Science Source

With all these extra white cells, why isn't the body's infection-fighting capability increased in leukemia?

18.5 Platelets and the Control of Bleeding

Expected Learning Outcomes

When you have completed this section, you should be able to

a. describe the body's mechanisms for controlling bleeding;

b. list the functions of platelets;

c. describe two reaction pathways that produce blood clots;

d. explain what happens to blood clots when they are no longer needed;

e. explain what keeps blood from clotting in the absence of injury; and

f. describe some disorders of blood clotting.

Circulatory systems developed very early in animal evolution, and with them evolved mechanisms for stopping leaks, which are potentially fatal. **Hemostasis**[21] is the cessation of bleeding. Although hemostatic mechanisms may not stop a hemorrhage from a large blood vessel, they are quite effective at closing breaks in small ones. Platelets play multiple roles in hemostasis, so we begin with a consideration of their form and function.

18.5a Platelet Form and Function

Platelets are not cells but small fragments of marrow cells called *megakaryocytes.* They are the second most abundant formed elements, after erythrocytes; a normal platelet count in blood from a fingerstick ranges from 130,000 to 400,000 platelets/μL (averaging about 250,000). The platelet count can vary greatly, however, under different physiological conditions and in blood samples taken from various places in the body. In spite of their numbers, platelets are so small (2 to 4 μm in diameter) that they contribute even less than WBCs to the blood volume.

Platelets have a complex internal structure that includes lysosomes, mitochondria, microtubules, and microfilaments; **granules** filled with platelet secretions; and a system of channels called the **open canalicular system,** which opens onto the platelet surface **(fig. 18.20a).** They have no nucleus. When activated, they form pseudopods and are capable of ameboid movement.

Despite their small size, platelets have a greater variety of functions than any of the true blood cells:

- They secrete *vasoconstrictors,* chemicals that stimulate spasmodic constriction of broken vessels and thereby help to reduce blood loss.
- They stick together to form temporary *platelet plugs* that seal small breaks in injured blood vessels.
- They secrete *procoagulants,* or clotting factors, which promote blood clotting.
- They initiate the formation of a clot-dissolving enzyme that dissolves blood clots that have outlasted their usefulness.
- They secrete chemicals that attract neutrophils and monocytes to sites of inflammation.
- They internalize and destroy bacteria.
- They secrete *growth factors* that stimulate mitosis in fibroblasts and smooth muscle and thereby help to maintain and repair blood vessels.

18.5b Platelet Production

The production of platelets is a division of hematopoiesis called **thrombopoiesis** (THROM-bo-poy-EE-sis). (Platelets are occasionally called *thrombocytes.*[22]) Thrombopoiesis is stimulated by a hormone from the liver and kidneys called *thrombopoietin* (THROM-bo-POY-eh-tin). Some hematopoietic stem cells develop receptors for thrombopoietin and, under its influence, become *megakaryoblasts*—cells committed to the platelet-producing line.

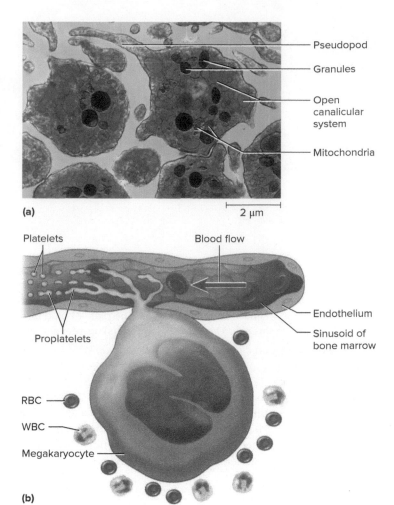

(a)

(b)

FIGURE 18.20 Platelets. (a) Structure of blood platelets (TEM). (b) Platelets being produced by the shearing of proplatelets from a megakaryocyte. Note the sizes of the megakaryocyte and platelets relative to RBCs and WBCs. **APR**

a: NIBSC/Science Photo Library/Science Source

The megakaryoblast duplicates its DNA repeatedly without undergoing nuclear or cytoplasmic division. The result is a **megakaryocyte**[23] (MEG-ah-CAR-ee-oh-site), a gigantic cell up to 150 μm in diameter, visible to the naked eye, with a huge multilobed nucleus and multiple sets of chromosomes **(fig. 18.20b).** Most megakaryocytes live in the red bone marrow adjacent to blood-filled spaces called *sinusoids,* lined with a thin simple squamous epithelium called the *endothelium* (see fig. 21.8). Recent animal research has discovered, however, that megakaryocytes migrate freely between the lungs and bone marrow and produce most platelets while in the lungs. Whether this is also true in humans awaits confirmation.

A megakaryocyte sprouts long tendrils called *proplatelets* that protrude through the endothelium into the blood of the sinusoid. The blood flow shears off the proplatelets, which break up into platelets as they travel in the bloodstream. Much of this breakup is thought to occur when they pass through the small vessels of the lungs, because blood counts show more proplatelets entering the

---

[21]*hemo* = blood; *stasis* = stability
[22]*thrombo* = clotting; *cyte* = cell

[23]*mega* = giant; *karyo* = nucleus; *cyte* = cell

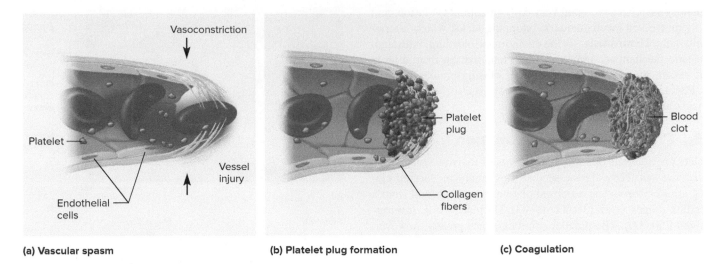

(a) Vascular spasm   **(b) Platelet plug formation**   **(c) Coagulation**

FIGURE 18.21 Hemostasis. (a) Vasoconstriction of a broken vessel reduces bleeding. (b) A platelet plug forms as platelets adhere to exposed collagen fibers of the vessel wall. The platelet plug temporarily seals the break. (c) A blood clot forms as platelets become enmeshed in fibrin threads. This forms a longer-lasting seal and gives the vessel a chance to repair itself.

❓ *How does a blood clot differ from a platelet plug?*

lungs than leaving and more platelets exiting. About 25% to 40% of the platelets are stored in the spleen and released as needed. The remainder circulate freely in the blood and live for about 5 to 6 days. Anything that interferes with platelet production can produce a dangerous platelet deficiency called **thrombocytopenia**[24] (see table 18.8).

18.5c Hemostasis

There are three hemostatic mechanisms—*vascular spasm, platelet plug formation,* and *blood clotting (coagulation)* **(fig. 18.21).** Platelets play an important role in all three.

Vascular Spasm

The most immediate protection against blood loss is **vascular spasm,** a prompt constriction of the broken vessel. Several things trigger this reaction. An injury stimulates pain receptors, some of which directly innervate nearby blood vessels and cause them to constrict. This effect lasts only a few minutes, but other mechanisms take over by the time it subsides. Injury to the smooth muscle of the blood vessel itself causes a longer-lasting vasoconstriction, and platelets release serotonin, a chemical vasoconstrictor. Thus, the vascular spasm is maintained long enough for the other two hemostatic mechanisms to come into play.

Platelet Plug Formation

Platelets don't adhere to the endothelium that lines healthy blood vessels and the heart. The endothelium is normally very smooth and coated with **prostacyclin,** a platelet repellent. When a vessel is broken, however, collagen fibers of its wall are exposed to

the blood. Upon contact with collagen or other rough surfaces, platelets grow long spiny pseudopods that adhere to the vessel and to other platelets; the pseudopods then contract and draw the walls of the vessel together. The mass of platelets thus formed, called a **platelet plug,** may reduce or stop minor bleeding. The platelet plug is looser and more delicate than the blood clot to follow; for this reason, a bleeding injury should be blotted with absorbent paper rather than wiped.

As platelets aggregate, they undergo **degranulation**—the exocytosis of their cytoplasmic granules and release of factors that promote hemostasis. Among these are serotonin, a vasoconstrictor; adenosine diphosphate (ADP), which attracts more platelets to the area and stimulates their degranulation; and **thromboxane A$_2$,** an eicosanoid that promotes platelet aggregation, degranulation, and vasoconstriction. Thus, a positive feedback cycle is activated that can quickly seal a small break in a blood vessel.

Coagulation

Coagulation (clotting) of the blood is the last but most effective defense against bleeding. It is important for the blood to clot quickly when a vessel has broken, but equally important for it not to clot in the absence of vessel damage. Because of this delicate balance, coagulation is one of the most complex processes in the body, involving over 30 chemical reactions. It is presented here in a very simplified form.

Perhaps clotting is best understood if we first consider its goal. The objective is to convert the plasma protein fibrinogen into **fibrin,** a sticky protein that adheres to the walls of a vessel. As blood cells and platelets arrive, they stick to the fibrin like insects in a spider web **(fig. 18.22,** inset). The resulting mass of fibrin, blood cells, and platelets ideally seals the break in the blood vessel. The complexity of clotting lies in how the fibrin is formed.

---

[24]*thrombo* = clotting; *cyto* = cell; *penia* = deficiency

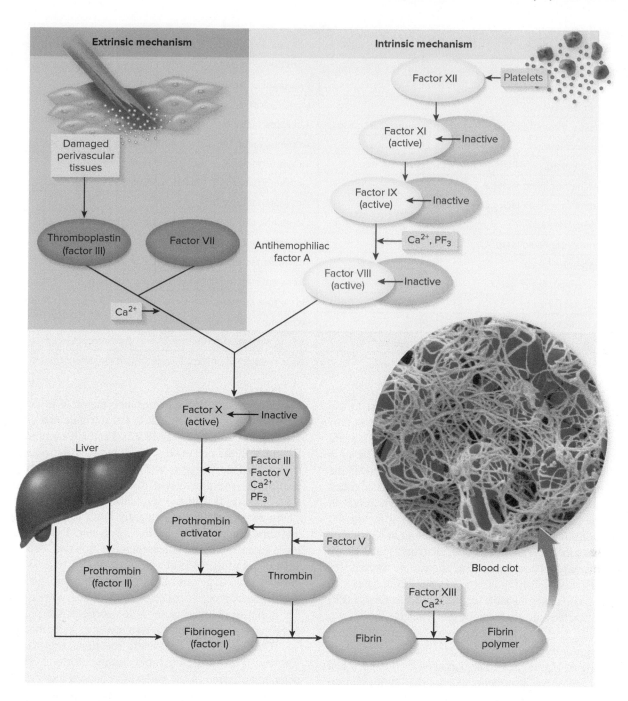

FIGURE 18.22 The Pathways of Coagulation. Most clotting factors act as enzymes that convert the next factor from an inactive form to an active form. One enzyme molecule at any given level activates many enzyme molecules at the next level down, so the overall effect becomes amplified at each step. Inset: Erythrocytes trapped in a mesh of sticky fibrin polymer.

(inset): Steve Gschmeissner/Science Photo Library/Getty Images

❓ *After you read about hemophilia C later in section 18.5f, explain whether it would affect the extrinsic mechanism, the intrinsic mechanism, or both.*

There are two reaction pathways to coagulation. One of them, the **extrinsic mechanism** (left side of fig. 18.22), is initiated by clotting factors released by the damaged blood vessel and perivascular[25] tissues. The word *extrinsic* refers to the fact that these factors come from sources external to the blood itself. Blood may also clot, however, without these tissue factors—for example, when platelets adhere to a fatty plaque of atherosclerosis or to a test tube. The reaction pathway in this case is called the **intrinsic mechanism** (right side of the figure) because it uses only clotting factors found in the blood itself. In most cases of bleeding, both the extrinsic and intrinsic mechanisms work simultaneously and interact with each other to achieve hemostasis.

[25]*peri* = around; *vas* = vessel; *cular* = pertaining to

TABLE 18.7	Clotting Factors (Procoagulants)		
Number	Name	Origin	Function
I	Fibrinogen	Liver	Precursor of fibrin
II	Prothrombin	Liver	Precursor of thrombin
III	Tissue thromboplastin	Perivascular tissue	Activates factor VII
V	Proaccelerin	Liver	Activates factor VII; combines with factor X to form prothrombin activator
VII	Proconvertin	Liver	Activates factor X in extrinsic pathway
VIII	Antihemophiliac factor A	Liver	Activates factor X in intrinsic pathway
IX	Antihemophiliac factor B	Liver	Activates factor VIII
X	Thrombokinase	Liver	Combines with factor V to form prothrombin activator
XI	Antihemophiliac factor C	Liver	Activates factor IX
XII	Hageman factor	Liver, platelets	Activates factor XI and plasmin; converts prekallikrein to kallikrein
XIII	Fibrin-stabilizing factor	Platelets, plasma	Cross-links fibrin filaments to make fibrin polymer and stabilize clot
PF_1	Platelet factor 1	Platelets	Same role as factor V; also accelerates platelet activation
PF_2	Platelet factor 2	Platelets	Accelerates thrombin formation
PF_3	Platelet factor 3	Platelets	Aids in activation of factor VIII and prothrombin activator
PF_4	Platelet factor 4	Platelets	Binds heparin during clotting to inhibit its anticoagulant effect

Clotting factors are called **procoagulants,** in contrast to the **anticoagulants** discussed later (see Deeper Insight 18.6). Most procoagulants are proteins produced by the liver **(table 18.7).** They are always present in the plasma in inactive form, but when one factor is activated, it functions as an enzyme that activates the next one in the pathway. That factor activates the next, and so on, in a sequence called a **reaction cascade**—a series of reactions, each of which depends on the product of the preceding one. Many of the clotting factors are identified by roman numerals, which indicate the order in which they were discovered, not the order of the reactions. Factors IV and VI are not included in this table. These terms were abandoned when it was found that factor IV was calcium and factor VI was activated factor V. The last four procoagulants in the table are called *platelet factors* (PF_1 through PF_4) because they are produced by the platelets.

Initiation of Coagulation The extrinsic mechanism is diagrammed on the top left side of figure 18.22. The damaged blood vessel and perivascular tissues release a lipoprotein mixture called **tissue thromboplastin**[26] **(factor III).** Factor III combines with factor VII to form a complex that, in the presence of Ca^{2+}, activates factor X. The extrinsic and intrinsic pathways differ only in how they arrive at active factor X. Therefore, before examining their common pathway from factor X to the end, let's consider how the intrinsic pathway reaches this step.

The intrinsic mechanism is diagrammed on the top right side of figure 18.22. Everything needed to initiate it is present in the plasma or platelets. When platelets degranulate, they release factor XII (Hageman factor, named for the patient in whom it was discovered). Through a cascade of reactions, this leads to activated factors XI, IX, and VIII, in that order—each serving as an enzyme that catalyzes the next step—and finally to factor X. This pathway also requires Ca^{2+} and PF_3.

Completion of Coagulation Once factor X is activated, the remaining events are identical in the intrinsic and extrinsic mechanisms (bottom half of fig. 18.22). Factor X combines with factors III and V in the presence of Ca^{2+} and PF_3 to produce *prothrombin activator.* This enzyme acts on a globulin called **prothrombin (factor II)** and converts it to the enzyme **thrombin.** Thrombin then converts fibrinogen into shorter strands of *fibrin monomer.* These monomers then covalently bond to each other end to end and form longer fibers of *fibrin polymer.* Factor XIII cross-links these strands to create a dense aggregation that forms the structural framework of the blood clot.

Once a clot begins to form, it launches a self-accelerating positive feedback process that seals off the damaged vessel more quickly. Thrombin works with factor V to accelerate the production of prothrombin activator, which in turn produces more thrombin.

The cascade of enzymatic reactions acts as an amplifying mechanism to ensure the rapid clotting of blood **(fig. 18.23).** Each activated enzyme in the pathway produces a larger number of enzyme molecules at the following step. One activated molecule of factor XII at the start of the intrinsic pathway, for example, very quickly produces thousands if not millions of fibrin molecules. Note the similarity of this process to the *signal amplification* that occurs in hormone action (see fig. 17.21).

Notice that the extrinsic mechanism requires fewer steps to activate factor X than the intrinsic mechanism does; it is a "shortcut" to coagulation. It takes 3 to 6 minutes for a clot to form by the intrinsic pathway but only 15 seconds or so by the extrinsic pathway. For this reason, when a small wound bleeds, you can stop the bleeding sooner by massaging the site. This releases thromboplastin from the perivascular tissues and activates or speeds up the extrinsic pathway.

After a clot has formed, spinous pseudopods of the platelets adhere to strands of fibrin and contract. This pulls on the fibrin

---

[26]*thrombo* = clot; *plast* = forming; *in* = substance

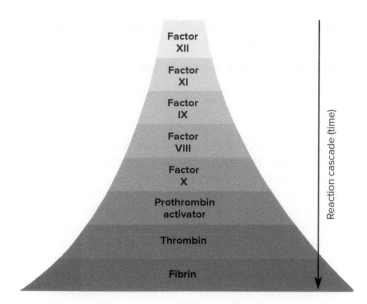

FIGURE 18.23 The Reaction Cascade in Blood Clotting. Each clotting factor produces many molecules of the next one, so the number of active clotting factors increases rapidly and a large amount of fibrin is quickly formed. The example shown here is for the intrinsic mechanism.

? *How does this compare with signal amplification in hormone action (compare fig. 17.21)?*

threads and draws the edges of the broken vessel together, like a drawstring closing a purse. Through this process of **clot retraction,** the clot becomes more compact within about 30 minutes.

A number of laboratory tests are used to evaluate the efficiency of coagulation. Normally, the bleeding of a fingerstick should stop within 2 to 3 minutes, and a sample of blood in a clean test tube should clot within 15 minutes. **Bleeding time** is most precisely measured by the *Ivy method*—inflating a blood pressure cuff on the arm to 40 mm Hg, making a 1 mm deep incision in the forearm, and measuring the time for it to stop bleeding. Normally it should stop in 1 to 9 minutes. Other techniques are available that can separately assess the effectiveness of the intrinsic and extrinsic mechanisms.

18.5d The Fate of Blood Clots

Once a clot has formed, a process of local tissue repair begins. Platelets and endothelial cells secrete a mitotic stimulant named **platelet-derived growth factor (PDGF).** PDGF stimulates fibroblasts and smooth muscle cells to multiply and repair the damaged blood vessel. Fibroblasts also invade the clot and produce fibrous connective tissue, which helps to strengthen and seal the vessel while the repairs take place.

Eventually, tissue repair is completed and the clot must be disposed of. **Fibrinolysis,** the dissolution of a clot, is achieved by a small cascade of reactions with a positive feedback component **(fig. 18.24).** In addition to promoting clotting, factor XII catalyzes the formation of a plasma enzyme called **kallikrein** (KAL-ih-KREE-in). Kallikrein, in turn, converts the inactive protein *plasminogen* into **plasmin,** a fibrin-dissolving enzyme that breaks up the clot. Thrombin also activates plasmin, and plasmin indirectly promotes the formation of more kallikrein, thus completing a positive feedback loop.

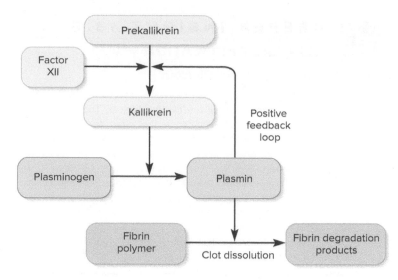

FIGURE 18.24 The Mechanism for Dissolving Blood Clots. Prekallikrein is converted to kallikrein. Kallikrein is an enzyme that catalyzes the formation of plasmin. Plasmin is an enzyme that dissolves the blood clot.

18.5e Prevention of Inappropriate Clotting

Precise controls are required to prevent coagulation when it isn't needed. These include the following:

- **Platelet repulsion.** As noted earlier, platelets don't adhere to the smooth prostacyclin-coated endothelium of healthy blood vessels.

- **Dilution.** Small amounts of thrombin form spontaneously in the plasma, but at normal rates of blood flow, the thrombin is diluted so quickly that a clot has little chance to form. If flow decreases, however, enough thrombin can accumulate to cause clotting. This can happen in circulatory shock, for example. When output from the heart is diminished and circulation slows down, widespread clotting throughout the circulatory system may occur.

- **Anticoagulants.** Thrombin formation is suppressed by anticoagulants in the plasma. **Antithrombin,** secreted by the liver, deactivates thrombin before it can act on fibrinogen. **Heparin,** secreted by basophils and mast cells, interferes with the formation of prothrombin activator, blocks the action of thrombin on fibrinogen, and promotes the action of antithrombin. Heparin is given by injection to patients with abnormal clotting tendencies.

18.5f Clotting Disorders

In a process as complex as coagulation, it's not surprising that things can go wrong. Clotting deficiencies can result from causes as diverse as malnutrition, leukemia, and gallstones (see Deeper Insight 18.5).

A deficiency of any clotting factor can shut down the coagulation cascade. This happens in **hemophilia,** a family of hereditary diseases characterized by deficiencies of one factor or another. Because of the sex-linked recessive mechanism of heredity, hemophilia occurs predominantly in males. They can inherit it only from their mothers, however, as happened with the descendants of Queen Victoria.

DEEPER INSIGHT 18.5

CLINICAL APPLICATION

Liver Disease and Blood Clotting

Proper blood clotting depends on normal liver function for two reasons. First, the liver synthesizes most of the clotting factors. Therefore, diseases such as hepatitis, cirrhosis, and cancer that degrade liver function result in a deficiency of clotting factors. Second, the synthesis of clotting factors II, VII, IX, and X require vitamin K. The absorption of vitamin K from the diet requires bile, a liver secretion. Gallstones can lead to a clotting deficiency by obstructing the bile duct and thus interfering with bile secretion and vitamin K absorption. Efficient blood clotting is especially important in childbirth, since both the mother and infant bleed from the trauma of birth. Therefore, pregnant women may be advised to take vitamin K supplements to ensure fast clotting, and newborn infants may be given vitamin K injections.

The lack of factor VIII causes *classical hemophilia (hemophilia A),* which accounts for about 83% of cases and afflicts 1 in 5,000 males worldwide. Lack of factor IX causes *hemophilia B,* which accounts for 15% of cases and occurs in about 1 out of 30,000 males. Factors VIII and IX are therefore known as *antihemophilic factors A and B.* A rarer form called *hemophilia C* (factor XI deficiency) is autosomal and not sex-linked, so it occurs equally in both sexes.

Before purified factor VIII became available in the 1960s, more than half of those with hemophilia died before age 5 and only 10% lived to age 21. Physical exertion causes bleeding into the muscles and joints. Excruciating pain and eventual joint immobility can result from intramuscular and joint **hematomas**[27] (masses of clotted blood in the tissues). Hemophilia varies in severity, however. Half of the normal level of clotting factor is enough to prevent the symptoms, and the symptoms are mild even in individuals with as little as 30% of the normal amount. Such cases may go undetected even into

adulthood. Bleeding can be relieved for a few days by transfusion of plasma or purified clotting factors.

▶▶▶APPLY WHAT YOU KNOW

Why is it important for people with hemophilia not to use aspirin? (Hint: See fig. 17.24, and do not say that aspirin "thins the blood," a figure of speech that is not literally true.)

Failure of the blood to clot takes far fewer lives, however, than unwanted clotting. **Thrombosis,** the abnormal clotting of blood in an unbroken blood vessel, becomes increasingly problematic in old age. About 25% of people over age 50 experience venous blockage by thrombosis, especially people who don't exercise regularly or who are confined to a bed or wheelchair. The blood clots especially easily in the veins, where blood flow is slowest. A **thrombus** (clot) may grow large enough to obstruct a small vessel, or a piece of it may break loose and begin to travel in the bloodstream as an **embolus.**[28] An embolus can lodge in a small artery and block blood flow from that point on. If that vessel supplies vital tissue of the heart, brain, lung, or kidney, *infarction* (tissue death) may result. About 650,000 Americans die annually of *thromboembolism* (traveling blood clots) in the cerebral, coronary, and pulmonary arteries. Most strokes and heart attacks are due to thrombosis, and pulmonary failure often results from thromboembolism.

Thrombosis is more likely to occur in veins than in arteries because blood flows more slowly in the veins and doesn't dilute thrombin and fibrin as rapidly. Most venous blood flows directly to the heart and then to the lungs. Therefore, blood clots arising in the limbs commonly lodge in the lungs and cause *pulmonary embolism.* When blood cannot circulate freely through the lungs, it cannot receive oxygen and a person may die of hypoxia.

Table 18.8 describes some additional disorders of the blood. The effects of aging on the blood are described in section 29.4a.

---

[27]*hemato* = blood; *oma* = mass

[28]*em* = in, within; *bolus* = ball, mass

TABLE 18.8	Some Disorders of the Blood
Disseminated intravascular coagulation (DIC)	Widespread clotting within unbroken vessels, limited to one organ or occurring throughout the body. Usually triggered by septicemia but also occurs when blood circulation slows markedly (as in cardiac arrest). Marked by widespread hemorrhaging, congestion of the vessels with clotted blood, and tissue necrosis in blood-deprived organs.
Infectious mononucleosis	Infection of B lymphocytes with Epstein–Barr virus, most commonly in adolescents and young adults. Usually transmitted by exchange of saliva, as in kissing. Causes fever, fatigue, sore throat, inflamed lymph nodes, and leukocytosis. Usually self-limiting and resolves within a few weeks.
Septicemia	Bacteremia (bacteria in the bloodstream) accompanying infection elsewhere in the body. Often causes fever, chills, and nausea, and may cause DIC or septic shock.
Thalassemia	A group of hereditary anemias most common in Greeks, Italians, and others of Mediterranean descent; shows a deficiency or absence of alpha or beta hemoglobin and RBC counts that may be less than 2 million/μL.
Thrombocytopenia	A platelet count below 100,000/mL. Causes include bone marrow destruction by radiation, drugs, poisons, or leukemia. Signs include small hemorrhagic spots in the skin or hematomas in response to minor trauma.

You can find other hematologic disorders described in the following places:

Hypoproteinemia in Deeper Insight 18.1; *anemia, polycythemia, hypoxemia,* and *sickle-cell disease* in section 18.2e; *transfusion reactions* and *hemolytic disease of the newborn* in sections 18.3b and 18.3d; *leukemia, leukocytosis,* and *leukopenia* in section 18.4d; and *hematoma, hemophilia, thrombosis,* and *thromboembolism* in section 18.5f.

BEFORE YOU GO ON

Answer the following questions to test your understanding of the preceding section:

22. What are the three basic mechanisms of hemostasis?

23. How do the extrinsic and intrinsic mechanisms of coagulation differ? What do they have in common?

24. In what respect does blood clotting represent a negative feedback loop? What part of it is a positive feedback loop?

25. Describe some of the mechanisms that prevent clotting in undamaged vessels.

26. Describe a common source and effect of pulmonary embolism.

DEEPER INSIGHT 18.6

CLINICAL APPLICATION

Clinical Management of Blood Clotting

For many cardiovascular patients, the goal of treatment is to prevent clotting or to dissolve clots that have already formed. Several strategies employ inorganic salts and products of bacteria, plants, and animals with anticoagulant and clot-dissolving effects.

Preventing Clots from Forming

Since calcium is an essential requirement for blood clotting, blood samples can be kept from clotting by adding a few crystals of sodium oxalate, sodium citrate, or EDTA[29]—salts that bind calcium ions and prevent them from participating in the coagulation reactions. Blood-collection equipment such as hematocrit tubes may also be coated with heparin, a natural anticoagulant whose action was explained earlier.

Since vitamin K is required for the synthesis of clotting factors, anything that antagonizes vitamin K usage makes the blood clot less readily. One vitamin K antagonist is *coumarin*[30] (COO-muh-rin), a sweet-smelling extract of tonka beans, sweet clover, and other plants, used in perfume. Taken orally by patients at risk for thrombosis, coumarin takes up to 2 days to act, but it has longer-lasting effects than heparin. A similar vitamin K antagonist is the pharmaceutical preparation *warfarin*[31] *(Coumadin),* which was originally developed as a pesticide—it makes rats bleed to death. Obviously, such anticoagulants must be used in humans with great care.

Many parasites feed on the blood of vertebrates and secrete anticoagulants to keep the blood flowing. Among these are aquatic worms known as leeches. Leeches secrete a local anesthetic that makes their bites painless; therefore, as early as 1567 BCE, physicians used them for bloodletting. This method was less painful and repugnant to their patients than *phlebotomy*[32]—cutting a vein—and indeed, leeching became very popular. In seventeenth-century France, it was quite the rage; tremendous numbers of leeches were used in ill-informed attempts to treat headaches, insomnia, whooping cough, obesity, tumors, menstrual cramps, mental illness, and almost anything else doctors or their patients imagined to be caused by "bad blood."

The first known anticoagulant was discovered in the saliva of the medicinal leech, *Hirudo medicinalis,* in 1884. Named *hirudin,* it is a polypeptide that prevents clotting by inhibiting thrombin. It causes the blood to flow freely while the leech feeds and for as long as an hour thereafter. While the doctrine of bad blood is now long discredited, leeches have lately reentered medical usage for other reasons **(fig. 18.25).** A major problem in reattaching a severed body part such as a finger or ear is that the tiny veins draining these organs are too small to reattach surgically. Since arterial blood flows into the reattached organ and can't flow out as easily, it pools and clots there. This inhibits the regrowth of veins and the flow of fresh blood through the organ, and often leads to necrosis. Some vascular

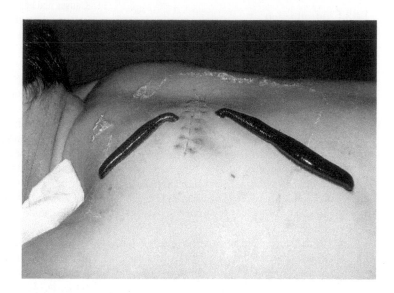

FIGURE 18.25 A Modern Use of Leeching. Two medicinal leeches are being used to remove clotted blood from a postsurgical hematoma. Despite their formidable size, the leeches secrete a natural anesthetic and produce a painless bite.
SPL/Science Source

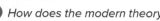 *How does the modern theory behind leeching differ from the theory of leeching that was popular a few centuries ago?*

surgeons now place leeches on the reattached part. Their anticoagulant keeps the blood flowing freely and allows new veins to grow. After 5 to 7 days, venous drainage is restored and leeching can be stopped.

Dissolving Clots That Have Already Formed

When a clot has already formed, it can be treated with clot-dissolving drugs such as *streptokinase,* an enzyme made by certain bacteria (streptococci). Intravenous streptokinase is used to dissolve blood clots in coronary vessels, for example. It is nonspecific, however, and digests almost any protein. *Tissue plasminogen activator (TPA)* works faster, is more specific, and is now made by transgenic bacteria. TPA converts plasminogen into the clot-dissolving enzyme plasmin. Some anticoagulants of animal origin also work by dissolving fibrin. A giant Amazon leech, *Haementeria,* produces one such anticoagulant named *hementin.* This, too, has been successfully produced by genetically engineered bacteria and used in cardiac patients to dissolve blood clots that do not yield to streptokinase or other drugs.

---

[29]ethylenediaminetetraacetic acid
[30]*coumaru* = tonka bean tree

[31]acronym from Wisconsin Alumni Research Foundation
[32]*phlebo* = vein; *tomy* = cutting

STUDY GUIDE

▶ Assess Your Learning Outcomes

To test your knowledge, discuss the following topics with a study partner or in writing, ideally from memory.

18.1 Introduction

1. Components of the circulatory system; the difference between the terms *circulatory system* and *cardiovascular system*
2. The diverse functions of blood; contributions of the blood to homeostasis
3. The two main components of whole blood; relative amounts of plasma and formed elements in the blood; and the three main categories of formed elements
4. The composition of blood plasma and serum
5. Importance of the viscosity and osmolarity of blood, what accounts for each, and the pathological effects of abnormal viscosity or osmolarity
6. The definition of *colloid osmotic pressure*
7. General aspects of hematopoiesis; where it occurs in the embryo, in the fetus, and after birth; and the stem cell with which all hematopoietic pathways begin

18.2 Erythrocytes

1. Erythrocyte (RBC) structure and function
2. The functions of hemoglobin and carbonic anhydrase
3. Hemoglobin structure and what parts of it bind O_2 and CO_2
4. Three ways of quantifying the RBCs and hemoglobin level of the blood; the definition and units of measurement of each; and reasons for the differences between male and female values
5. Stages of erythropoiesis and major transformations in each
6. Why iron is essential; how the stomach converts dietary iron to a usable form; and the roles of gastroferritin, transferrin, and ferritin in iron metabolism
7. Homeostatic regulation of erythropoiesis, including the origins and role of erythropoietin (EPO)
8. The life span of an RBC and how the body disposes of old RBCs
9. How the body disposes of the hemoglobin from expired RBCs and how this relates to the pigments of bile, feces, and urine

10. Excesses and deficiencies in RBC count and the forms, causes, and pathological consequences of each
11. Causes and effects of hemoglobin deficiencies and the pathology of sickle-cell disease and thalassemia

18.3 Blood Types

1. What determines a person's blood type; blood types of the ABO group and how they differ in genetics and RBC antigens
2. Why an individual does not have plasma antibodies against the ABO types at birth, but develops them during infancy; how these antibodies limit transfusion compatibility
3. The cause and mechanism of a transfusion reaction and why it can lead to renal failure and death; the meanings of *agglutination* and *hemolysis*
4. Blood types of the Rh group and how they differ in their genetics and RBC antigens
5. What can cause a person to develop antibodies against Rh-positive RBCs
6. Blood groups other than ABO and Rh, and their usefulness for certain purposes
7. Hemolytic disease of the newborn; why it seldom occurs in a woman's first susceptible child, but is more common in later pregnancies; and how it is treated and prevented

18.4 Leukocytes

1. The general function of all leukocytes (WBCs)
2. Three kinds of granulocytes, two kinds of agranulocytes, and what distinguishes granulocytes from agranulocytes as a class
3. The appearance, relative size and number, and functions of each WBC type, and the conditions under which each type increases in a differential WBC count
4. Three principal cell lines, the stages, and the anatomical sites of leukopoiesis
5. The relative length of time that WBCs travel in the bloodstream and spend in other tissues; which type recirculates into the blood and which types do not; and the relative life spans of WBCs
6. Causes and effects of leukopenia and leukocytosis

7. The naming and classification of various kinds of leukemia; why leukemia is typically accompanied by RBC and platelet deficiencies and elevated risk of opportunistic infection

18.5 Platelets and the Control of Bleeding

1. Platelet structure and functions, a typical platelet count, and why platelets are not considered to be cells
2. The sites and process of platelet production, and the hormone that stimulates it
3. Three mechanisms of hemostasis and their relative quickness and effectiveness
4. The general objective of coagulation; the end product of the coagulation reactions, and basic differences between the extrinsic and intrinsic mechanisms
5. Essentials of the extrinsic mechanism including the chemical that initiates it, other procoagulants involved, and the point at which it converges with the intrinsic mechanism at a common intermediate
6. Essentials of the intrinsic mechanism including the chemical that initiates it, other procoagulants involved, and the aforesaid point of convergence with the extrinsic mechanism
7. Steps in the continuation of coagulation from factor X to fibrin, including the procoagulants involved
8. The roles of positive feedback and enzyme amplification in coagulation
9. The processes of clot retraction, vessel repair, and fibrinolysis
10. Three mechanisms of preventing inappropriate coagulation in undamaged vessels
11. Causes of clotting deficiencies including the types, genetics, and pathology of hemophilia
12. Terms for unwanted or inappropriate clotting in a vessel, the clot itself, and a clot that breaks free and travels in the bloodstream
13. Why spontaneous clotting more often occurs in the veins than in the arteries; the danger presented by traveling blood clots; and why traveling clots so often lodge in the lungs even if they originate as far away as the lower limbs

STUDY GUIDE

▶ Testing Your Recall

Answers in Appendix A

1. Antibodies belong to a class of plasma proteins called
   a. albumins.
   b. gamma globulins.
   c. alpha globulins.
   d. procoagulants.
   e. agglutinins.

2. Serum is blood plasma minus its
   a. sodium ions.
   b. calcium ions.
   c. clotting proteins.
   d. globulins.
   e. albumin.

3. Which of the following conditions is most likely to cause hemolytic anemia?
   a. folic acid deficiency
   b. iron deficiency
   c. mushroom poisoning
   d. alcoholism
   e. hypoxemia

4. It is impossible for a type O+ baby to have a type _____ mother.
   a. AB–
   b. O–
   c. O+
   d. A+
   e. B+

5. Which of the following is *not* a component of hemostasis?
   a. platelet plug formation
   b. agglutination
   c. clot retraction
   d. vascular spasm
   e. degranulation

6. Which of the following contributes most to the viscosity of blood?
   a. albumin
   b. sodium
   c. globulins
   d. erythrocytes
   e. fibrin

7. Which of these is a granulocyte?
   a. a monocyte
   b. a lymphocyte
   c. a macrophage
   d. an eosinophil
   e. an erythrocyte

8. Excess iron is stored in the liver as a complex called
   a. gastroferritin.
   b. transferrin.
   c. ferritin.
   d. hepatoferritin.
   e. erythropoietin.

9. Pernicious anemia is a result of
   a. hypoxemia.
   b. iron deficiency.
   c. malaria.
   d. lack of intrinsic factor.
   e. Rh incompatibility.

10. The first clotting factor that the intrinsic and extrinsic pathways have in common is
    a. thromboplastin.
    b. Hageman factor.
    c. factor X.
    d. prothrombin activator.
    e. factor VIII.

11. Production of all the formed elements of blood is called _____.

12. The percentage of blood volume composed of RBCs is called the _____.

13. The extrinsic pathway of coagulation is activated by _____ from damaged perivascular tissues.

14. The RBC antigens that determine transfusion compatibility are called _____.

15. The hereditary lack of factor VIII causes a disease called _____.

16. The overall cessation of bleeding, involving several mechanisms, is called _____.

17. _____ results from a mutation that changes one amino acid in the hemoglobin molecule.

18. An excessively high RBC count is called _____.

19. Intrinsic factor enables the small intestine to absorb _____.

20. The kidney hormone _____ stimulates RBC production.

▶ Building Your Medical Vocabulary

Answers in Appendix A

State a meaning of each word element, and give a medical term from this chapter that uses it or a slight variation of it.

1. an-
2. -blast
3. erythro-
4. glutino-
5. hemo-
6. leuko-
7. -penia
8. phlebo-
9. -poiesis
10. thrombo-

STUDY GUIDE

▶ What's Wrong with These Statements?

Answers in Appendix A

Briefly explain why each of the following statements is false, or reword it to make it true.

1. Erythrocytes normally constitute most of the volume of the blood.

2. An abnormal increase in blood albumin concentration causes the blood to flow more sluggishly and therefore reduces blood pressure.

3. Anemia is caused by a low oxygen concentration in the blood.

4. *Hemostasis, coagulation,* and *clotting* are three terms for the same process.

5. If a type B+ woman has a baby with type O– blood, then her husband, who is type A+, cannot be the biological father.

6. Lymphocytes are the most abundant WBCs in the blood.

7. Potassium ions are a necessary cofactor at several steps in the blood-clotting process.

8. All formed elements of the blood except platelets come ultimately from the same pluripotent stem cells.

9. When RBCs die and break down, the globin moiety of hemoglobin is excreted and the heme is recycled to new RBCs.

10. Leukemia is a severe deficiency of white blood cells.

▶ Testing Your Comprehension

1. Why would erythropoiesis not correct the hypoxemia resulting from lung cancer?

2. People with chronic kidney disease often have hematocrits of less than half the normal value. Explain why.

3. An elderly white woman is hit by a bus and severely injured. Accident investigators are informed that she lives in an abandoned warehouse, where her few personal effects include several empty wine bottles and an expired driver's license indicating she is 72 years old. At the hospital, she is found to be severely anemic. List all the factors you can think of that may contribute to her anemia.

4. How is coagulation different from agglutination?

5. Although fibrinogen and prothrombin are equally necessary for blood clotting, fibrinogen is about 4% of the plasma protein whereas prothrombin is present only in small traces. In light of the roles of these clotting factors and your knowledge of enzymes, explain this difference in abundance.

THE CIRCULATORY SYSTEM: HEART

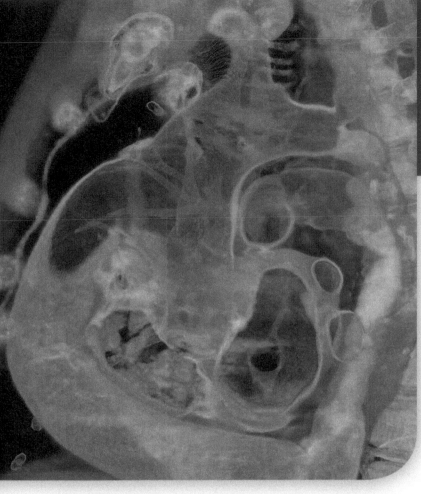

A three-dimensional CT scan of the heart; lateral view of a person facing left

Gondelon/Science Source

Anatomy & Physiology Revealed® 4.0

Module 9: Cardiovascular System

BRUSHING UP

- For the best understanding of cardiac muscle, be sure you are familiar with desmosomes and gap junctions (see section 5.5a) and with the structure of striated muscle cells (see section 11.2, which describes skeletal muscle fibers but also applies to cardiac muscle).

- You must be familiar with membrane resting potentials and action potentials (see sections 12.4b–12.4c) to understand cardiac pacemaker physiology and the excitation of cardiac muscle.

- Review excitation–contraction coupling in skeletal muscle (see fig. 11.9 and the associated text) for comparison with the process in cardiac muscle.

- The length–tension relationship of striated muscle (see fig. 11.12 and the associated text) helps to explain variation in the ejection of blood by the heart.

- Adjustment of cardiac output to states of rest and physical exertion hinges on understanding the anatomy and action of the sympathetic and parasympathetic nervous systems (see section 15.3a).

We are more conscious of our heart than we are of most organs, and more wary of its failure. Speculation about the heart is at least as old as written history. Some ancient Chinese, Egyptian, Greek, and Roman scholars correctly surmised that the heart is a pump for filling the vessels with blood. Aristotle's views, however, were a step backward. Perhaps because the heart quickens its pace when we're emotionally aroused, and because grief causes "heartache," he regarded it primarily as the seat of emotion, as well as a source of heat to aid digestion. During the Middle Ages, Western medical schools clung dogmatically to the ideas of Aristotle. Perhaps the only significant advance came from Arabic medicine, when thirteenth-century physician Ibn an-Nafis described the role of the coronary blood vessels in nourishing the heart. The sixteenth-century dissections and anatomical charts of Vesalius, however, greatly improved knowledge of cardiovascular anatomy and set the stage for a more scientific study of the heart and treatment of its disorders—the science we now call **cardiology.**[1]

In the early decades of the twentieth century, little could be recommended for heart disease other than bed rest. Then nitroglycerin was found to improve coronary circulation and relieve the pain resulting from physical exertion, digitalis proved helpful for treating abnormal heart rhythms, and diuretics were first used to reduce hypertension. Coronary bypass surgery; replacement of diseased valves; clot-dissolving enzymes; heart transplants; and artificial pacemakers, valves, and hearts have made cardiology one of today's most dramatic and attention-getting fields of medicine.

19.1 Overview of the Cardiovascular System

Expected Learning Outcomes

When you have completed this section, you should be able to

a. define and distinguish between the *pulmonary circuit* and *systemic circuit;*

b. describe the general location, size, and shape of the heart; and

c. describe the pericardium that encloses the heart.

The **cardiovascular**[2] **system** consists of the heart and blood vessels. The heart is a muscular pump that keeps blood flowing through the vessels. The vessels deliver the blood to all the body's organs and then return it to the heart. The broader term *circulatory system* also includes the blood, and some authorities use it to include the lymphatic system as well (described in section 21.1).

19.1a The Pulmonary and Systemic Circuits

The cardiovascular system has two major divisions: a **pulmonary circuit,** which carries blood to the lungs for gas exchange and returns it to the heart, and a **systemic circuit,** which supplies blood to every organ of the body, including other parts of the lungs and the wall of the heart itself **(fig. 19.1).**

The right half of the heart supplies the pulmonary circuit. It receives blood that has circulated through the body, unloaded its oxygen and nutrients, and picked up a load of carbon dioxide and other wastes. It pumps this oxygen-poor blood into a large artery, the *pulmonary trunk,* which immediately divides into right and left *pulmonary arteries.* These transport blood to the air sacs *(alveoli)* of the lungs, where carbon dioxide is unloaded and oxygen is picked up. The oxygen-rich blood then flows by way of the *pulmonary veins* to the left side of the heart.

The left side supplies the systemic circuit. Blood leaves it by way of another large artery, the *aorta.* The aorta turns like an inverted U, the *aortic arch,* and passes downward posterior to the heart. The arch gives off arteries that supply the head, neck, and upper limbs. The aorta then travels through the thoracic and abdominal cavities and issues smaller arteries to the other organs before branching into the lower limbs. After circulating through the body, the now deoxygenated systemic blood returns to the right side of the heart mainly by way of two large veins: the *superior vena cava* (draining the upper body) and *inferior vena cava* (draining everything below the diaphragm). The major arteries and veins entering and leaving the heart are called the *great vessels (great arteries* and *veins)* because of their relatively large diameters. These circulatory routes are detailed in the next chapter.

---

[1] *cardio* = heart; *logy* = study

[2] *cardio* = heart; *vas* = vessel

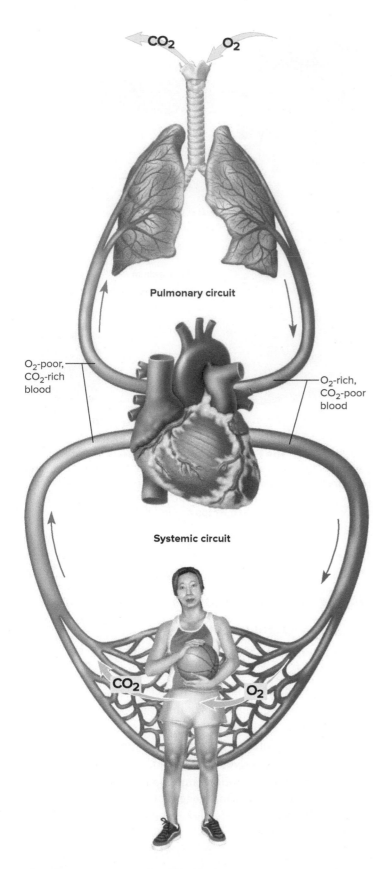

FIGURE 19.1 General Schematic of the Cardiovascular System.

❓ *Are the lungs supplied by the pulmonary circuit, the systemic circuit, or both? Explain.* **A&PR**

19.1b Position, Size, and Shape of the Heart

The heart lies within a thick partition called the **mediastinum** between the two lungs. It extends from a broad **base** at its uppermost end, where the great vessels are attached, to a bluntly pointed **apex** at the lower end, just above the diaphragm. It tilts toward the left from base to apex, so somewhat more than half the heart is to the left of the body's median plane. We can see this especially in a cross (horizontal) section through the thorax (**fig. 19.2;** see also figs. B.10, B.11 in atlas B).

The adult heart is about 9 cm (3.5 in.) wide at the base, 13 cm (5 in.) from base to apex, and 6 cm (2.5 in.) from anterior to posterior at its thickest point. Whatever one's body size, from child to adult, the heart is roughly the same size as the fist. It weighs about 300 g (10 ounces) in adults.

19.1c The Pericardium

The heart is enclosed in a double-walled sac called the **pericardium.**[3] The outer wall of the pericardium is a tough fibrous sac called the **fibrous pericardium.** It surrounds the heart but isn't attached to it. Deep to this is a thin membrane called the **serous pericardium.** This has two layers—a *parietal layer* that lines the inside of the fibrous pericardium, and a *visceral layer* that adheres to the heart surface and forms the outermost layer of the heart itself, the *epicardium* (**fig. 19.3**). The fibrous pericardium is anchored by ligaments to the diaphragm below and the sternum anterior to it, and more loosely anchored by fibrous connective tissue to mediastinal tissue posterior to the heart.

The space between the parietal and visceral layers of the serous pericardium is called the **pericardial cavity** (figs. 19.2b, 19.3). The heart isn't inside the pericardial cavity but enfolded by it. The relationship of the heart to the pericardium is often described by comparison to a fist pushed into an underinflated balloon (fig. 19.3c). The balloon surface in contact with the fist is like the epicardium; the outer balloon surface is like the parietal layer, and the air space between them is like the pericardial cavity.

The pericardial cavity contains 5 to 30 mL of **pericardial fluid,** exuded by the serous pericardium. The fluid lubricates the membranes and allows the heart to beat with minimal friction. In *pericarditis*—inflammation of the pericardium—the membranes may become roughened and produce a painful *friction rub* with each heartbeat. In addition to reducing friction, the pericardium isolates the heart from other thoracic organs and anchors it within the thorax. It allows the heart room to expand, yet resists excessive expansion (see *cardiac tamponade* in Deeper Insight A.1 in atlas A).

BEFORE YOU GO ON

Answer the following questions to test your understanding of the preceding section:

1. Distinguish between the pulmonary and systemic circuits and state which part of the heart supplies each one.

2. Predict the effect of a fibrous pericardium that fits too tightly around the heart. Predict the effect of a failure of the serous pericardium to secrete pericardial fluid.

---

[3]*peri* = around; *cardi* = heart

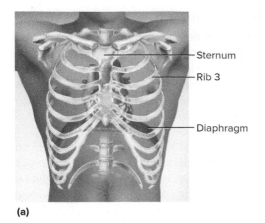

(a)

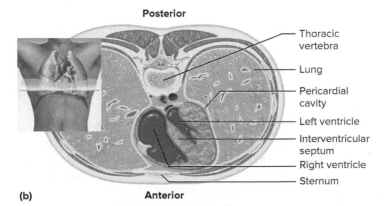

(b)

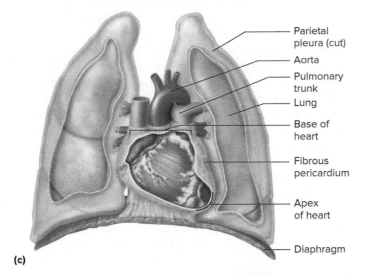

(c)

FIGURE 19.2 Position of the Heart in the Thoracic Cavity.
(a) Relationship to the thoracic cage. (b) Cross section of the thorax at the level of the heart. (c) Frontal view with the lungs slightly retracted and the fibrous pericardium opened. **APR**

❓ *Does most of the heart lie to the right or left of the median plane?*

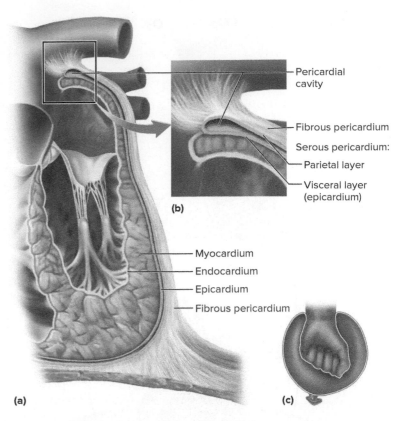

(a)   (b)   (c)

FIGURE 19.3 The Pericardium and Heart Wall. (a) Frontal section of the heart showing the three layers of the heart wall and relationship to the pericardium. (b) Detail of the pericardium and pericardial cavity. (c) A fist in a balloon shows, by analogy, how the double-walled pericardium wraps around the heart.

19.2   Gross Anatomy of the Heart

Expected Learning Outcomes

When you have completed this section, you should be able to

a. describe the three layers of the heart wall;

b. identify the four chambers of the heart;

c. identify the surface features of the heart and correlate them with its internal four-chambered anatomy;

d. identify the four valves of the heart;

e. trace the flow of blood through the four chambers and valves of the heart and adjacent blood vessels; and

f. describe the arteries that nourish the myocardium and the veins that drain it.

19.2a The Heart Wall

The heart wall consists of three layers: *epicardium, myocardium,* and *endocardium.*

The **epicardium**[4] (visceral layer of the serous pericardium) is a serous membrane of the external heart surface. It consists mainly of a simple squamous epithelium overlying a thin layer of areolar tissue. In some places, it also includes a thick layer of adipose tissue, whereas in other areas it is fat-free and translucent, so the muscle of the underlying myocardium shows through (**figs. 19.4a, 19.5**). The largest branches of the coronary blood vessels travel through the epicardium.

The **endocardium,**[5] a similar layer, lines the interior of the heart chambers (figs. 19.3, **19.4b**). Like the epicardium, this is a simple squamous epithelium overlying a thin areolar tissue layer; however, it has no adipose tissue. The endocardium covers the valve surfaces and is continuous with the endothelium of the blood vessels.

The **myocardium**[6] between these two is composed of cardiac muscle. This is by far the thickest layer and performs the work of the heart. Its thickness is proportional to the workload on the individual chambers. Its muscle is organized into bundles that spiral around the heart, forming the **vortex of the heart** (**fig. 19.6**). Consequently, when the ventricles contract, they exhibit a twisting or wringing motion that enhances the ejection of blood. Later we will examine the microscopic structure of the cardiac muscle cells, or *cardiomyocytes,* more closely.

The heart also has a framework of collagenous and elastic fibers that make up the **fibrous skeleton.** This tissue is especially concentrated in the walls between the heart chambers, in *fibrous rings (anuli fibrosi)* around the valves, and in sheets of tissue that interconnect these rings (fig. 19.8). The fibrous skeleton

---

[4]*epi* = upon; *cardi* = heart

[5]*endo* = internal, within; *cardi* = heart
[6]*myo* = muscle; *cardi* = heart

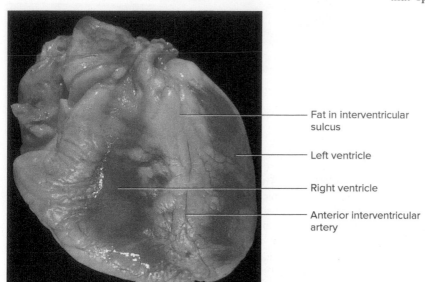

Fat in interventricular sulcus

Left ventricle

Right ventricle

Anterior interventricular artery

(a) Anterior view, external anatomy

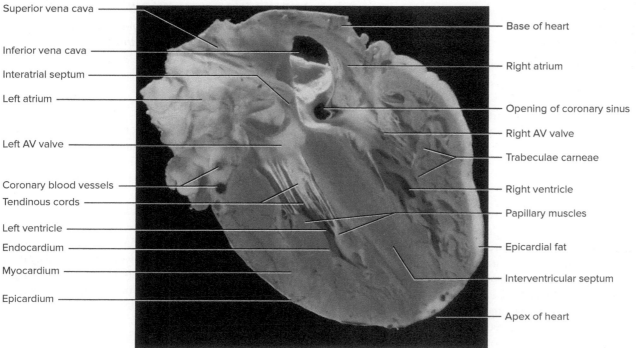

Superior vena cava

Inferior vena cava

Interatrial septum

Left atrium

Left AV valve

Coronary blood vessels

Tendinous cords

Left ventricle

Endocardium

Myocardium

Epicardium

Base of heart

Right atrium

Opening of coronary sinus

Right AV valve

Trabeculae carneae

Right ventricle

Papillary muscles

Epicardial fat

Interventricular septum

Apex of heart

(b) Posterior view, internal anatomy

FIGURE 19.4 The Heart of a Human Cadaver. (a) Anterior view, external anatomy. (b) Posterior view, internal anatomy.

a, b: McGraw-Hill Education

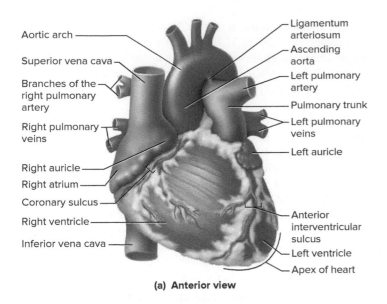

(a) Anterior view

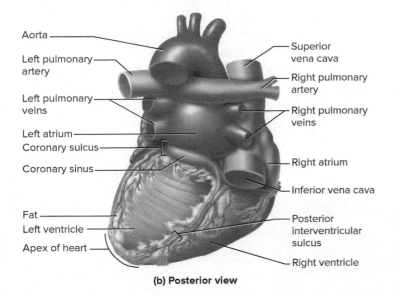

(b) Posterior view

FIGURE 19.5 Surface Anatomy of the Heart. (a) Anterior view. (b) Posterior view. The coronary blood vessels on the heart surface are identified in figure 19.10. **APR**

has multiple functions: (1) It provides structural support for the heart, especially around the valves and the openings of the great vessels; it holds these orifices open and prevents them from excessively stretching when blood surges through them. (2) It anchors the cardiomyocytes and gives them something to pull against. (3) As a nonconductor of electricity, it serves as electrical insulation between the atria and the ventricles, so the atria cannot stimulate the ventricles directly. This insulation is important to the timing and coordination of electrical and contractile activity. (4) Some authorities think (though others disagree) that elastic recoil of the fibrous skeleton may aid in refilling the heart with blood after each beat in a manner described later.

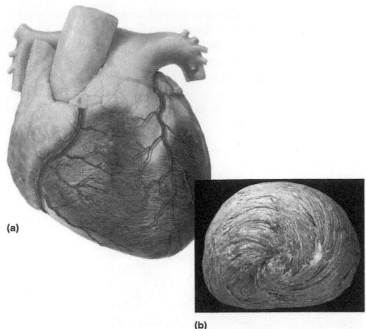

(a)

(b)

FIGURE 19.6 The Vortex of the Heart. (a) Anterior view of the heart with the epicardium rendered transparent to expose the bundles of myocardial muscle. (b) View from the apex to show the way the muscle coils around the heart. This results in a twisting motion when the ventricles contract.

a, b: Photo and illustration by Roy Schneider, University of Toledo. Plastinated heart model for illustration courtesy of Dr. Carlos Baptista, University of Toledo

▶▶▶**APPLY WHAT YOU KNOW**

Parts of the fibrous skeleton sometimes become calcified in old age. How would you expect this to affect cardiac function?

19.2b The Chambers

The heart has four chambers, best seen in a frontal section (**fig. 19.7;** also see fig. 19.4b). The two superior chambers are the **right** and **left atria** (AY-tree-uh; singular, *atrium*[7]). They are receiving chambers for blood returning to the heart by way of the great veins. Most of the mass of each atrium is on the posterior side of the heart, so only a small portion is visible from an anterior view. Here, each atrium has an earlike flap called an **auricle**[8] that slightly increases its volume (fig. 19.5a). The atria exhibit thin flaccid walls corresponding to their light workload—all they do is pump blood into the ventricles immediately below. They are separated from each other by a wall called the **interatrial septum.** The right atrium and both auricles exhibit internal ridges of myocardium called **pectinate**[9] **muscles.**

---

[7]*atrium* = entryway
[8]*auricle* = little ear
[9]*pectin* = comb; *ate* = like

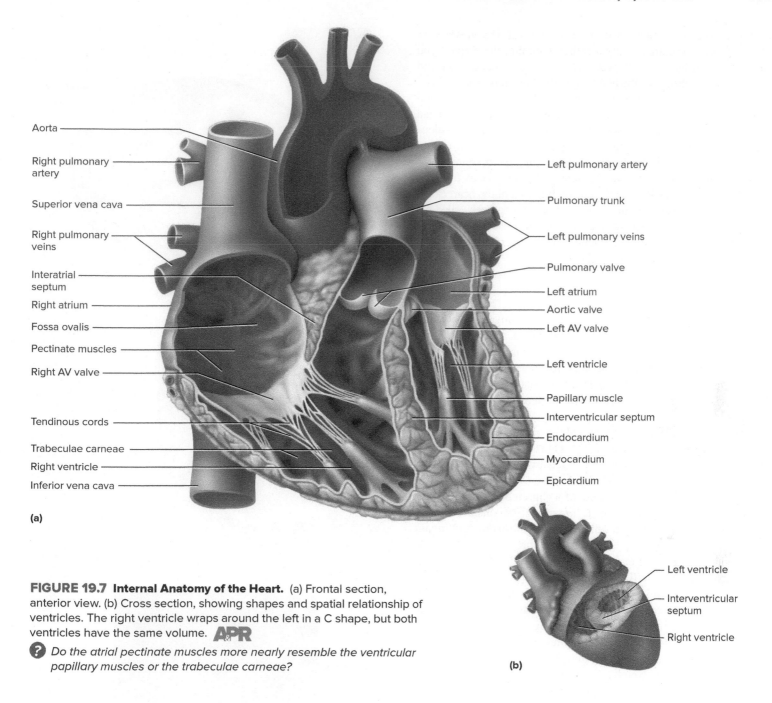

Aorta

Right pulmonary artery

Superior vena cava

Right pulmonary veins

Interatrial septum

Right atrium

Fossa ovalis

Pectinate muscles

Right AV valve

Tendinous cords

Trabeculae carneae

Right ventricle

Inferior vena cava

Left pulmonary artery

Pulmonary trunk

Left pulmonary veins

Pulmonary valve

Left atrium

Aortic valve

Left AV valve

Left ventricle

Papillary muscle

Interventricular septum

Endocardium

Myocardium

Epicardium

(a)

Left ventricle

Interventricular septum

Right ventricle

(b)

FIGURE 19.7 Internal Anatomy of the Heart. (a) Frontal section, anterior view. (b) Cross section, showing shapes and spatial relationship of ventricles. The right ventricle wraps around the left in a C shape, but both ventricles have the same volume. **A&PR**

❓ *Do the atrial pectinate muscles more nearly resemble the ventricular papillary muscles or the trabeculae carneae?*

The two inferior chambers, the **right** and **left ventricles,**[10] are the pumps that eject blood into the arteries and keep it flowing around the body. The right ventricle constitutes most of the anterior aspect of the heart, whereas the left ventricle forms the apex and inferoposterior aspect. Internally, the ventricles are separated by a thick muscular wall, the **interventricular septum.** The right ventricle pumps blood only to the lungs and back to the left atrium, so its wall is only moderately muscular. The wall of the left ventricle, including the septum, is two to four times as thick because it bears the greatest workload of all four chambers, pumping blood

through the entire body. The left ventricle is roughly circular in cross section, whereas the right ventricle wraps around the left and has a C shape (fig. 19.7b). To help visualize this, make a fist of your left hand and enfold it in your right hand; your left and right hands then approximate the shapes and spatial relationship of the left and right ventricles.

Both ventricles exhibit internal ridges called **trabeculae carneae**[11] (trah-BEC-you-lee CAR-nee-ee). It is thought that these ridges may serve to keep the ventricular walls from clinging to each other like suction cups when the heart contracts, and thus allow the

---

[10]*ventr* = belly, lower part; *icle* = little

[11]*trabecula* = little beam; *carne* = flesh, meat

chambers to expand more easily when they refill. If you wet your hands, press your palms firmly together, then pull them apart, you can appreciate how smooth wet surfaces cling to each other and how, without trabeculae, the heart walls might also do so.

On the surface, the boundaries of the four chambers are marked by three sulci (grooves), which are largely filled by fat and the coronary blood vessels (see fig. 19.5a). The **coronary**[12] **sulcus** encircles the heart near the base and separates the atria above from the ventricles below. It can be exposed by lifting the margins of the atria. The other two sulci extend obliquely down the heart from the coronary sulcus toward the apex—one on the front of the heart called the **anterior interventricular sulcus** and one on the back called the **posterior interventricular sulcus.** These sulci overlie the interventricular septum. The coronary sulcus and two interventricular sulci harbor the largest of the coronary blood vessels.

19.2c The Valves

To pump blood effectively, the heart needs valves that ensure a one-way flow. There is a valve between each atrium and its ventricle and another at the exit from each ventricle into its great artery (fig. 19.7), but the heart has no valves where the great veins empty into the atria. Each valve consists of two or three fibrous flaps of tissue called **cusps** or **leaflets,** covered with endocardium.

The **atrioventricular (AV) valves** regulate the openings between the atria and ventricles. The **right AV (tricuspid) valve** has three cusps and the **left AV valve** has two **(fig. 19.8).** The left AV valve is also known as the **mitral valve** (MY-trul) after its resemblance to a miter, the headdress of a church bishop; it has also formerly gone by the name of *bicuspid valve,* now considered inaccurate and obsolete. Stringy **tendinous cords (chordae tendineae)** (COR-dee ten-DIN-ee-ee), resembling the shroud lines of a parachute, connect the valve cusps to conical **papillary**[13] **muscles** on the floor of the ventricle. They prevent the AV valves from flipping inside out or bulging into the atria when the ventricles contract. Each papillary muscle has two or three basal attachments to the trabeculae carneae of the heart wall. Among other functions, these multiple attachments may govern the timing of electrical excitation of the papillary muscles, and they may distribute mechanical stress in a way similar to the weight of the Eiffel Tower supported on its four legs. The multiple attachments also provide some redundancy that protects an AV valve from complete mechanical failure should one attachment fail.

The **semilunar**[14] **valves** (pulmonary and aortic valves) regulate the flow of blood from the ventricles into the great arteries. The **pulmonary valve** controls the opening from the right ventricle into the pulmonary trunk, and the **aortic valve** controls the opening from the left ventricle into the aorta. Each has three cusps shaped like shirt pockets (fig. 19.8b). When blood is ejected from the ventricles, it pushes through these valves from below and

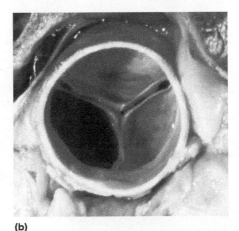

Right AV (tricuspid) valve —
Fibrous skeleton —
Aortic valve —
Coronary arteries —
Pulmonary valve —
Left AV (mitral) valve

(a)

(b)

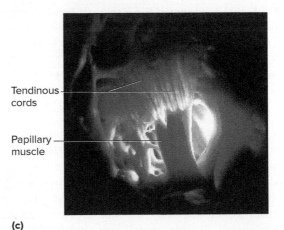

Tendinous cords —
Papillary muscle

(c)

FIGURE 19.8 The Heart Valves. (a) Superior view of the heart with the atria removed. (b) The aortic valve, superior view, showing the three cusps meeting like a Y. One cusp is darkened by a blood clot. (c) Papillary muscle and tendinous cords seen from within the right ventricle. The upper ends of the cords are attached to the cusps of the right AV valve.

b: Biophoto Associates/Science Source; c: McGraw-Hill Education

---

[12]*coron* = crown; *ary* = pertaining to
[13]*papill* = nipple; *ary* = like, shaped
[14]*semi* = half; *lun* = moon

presses their cusps against the arterial walls. When the ventricles relax, arterial blood flows backward toward the ventricles, but quickly fills the cusps. The inflated pockets meet at the center and quickly seal the opening, so little blood flows back into the ventricles. Because of the way these valves are attached to the arterial wall, they cannot prolapse any more than a shirt pocket turns inside out if you jam your hand into it. Thus, they don't require or possess tendinous cords.

The valves don't open and close by any muscular effort of their own. The cusps are simply pushed open and closed by changes in blood pressure that occur as the heart chambers contract and relax. Later in this chapter, we will take a closer look at these pressure changes and their effect on the valves.

19.2d Blood Flow Through the Chambers

Until the sixteenth century, blood was thought to flow directly from the right ventricle into the left through invisible pores in the septum. This of course is not true. Blood is kept entirely separate on the right and left sides of the heart. **Figure 19.9** shows the pathway of the blood as it travels from the right atrium through the body and back to the starting point.

Blood that has been through the systemic circuit returns by way of the superior and inferior venae cavae to the right atrium. It flows directly from the right atrium, through the right AV (tricuspid) valve, into the right ventricle. When the right ventricle contracts, it ejects blood through the pulmonary valve into the pulmonary trunk, on its way to the lungs to exchange carbon dioxide for oxygen.

Blood returns from the lungs by way of two pulmonary veins on the left and two on the right; all four of these empty into the left atrium. Blood flows through the left AV (mitral) valve into the left ventricle. Contraction of the left ventricle ejects this blood through the aortic valve into the ascending aorta, on its way to another trip around the systemic circuit.

19.2e The Coronary Circulation

If your heart lasts for 80 years and beats an average of 75 times a minute, it will beat more than 3 billion times and each ventricle will pump more than 200 million liters of blood. It is, in short, a remarkably hardworking organ, and understandably, it needs an abundant supply of oxygen and nutrients. These needs aren't met to any appreciable extent by the blood in the heart chambers, because the diffusion of substances from there through the myocardium

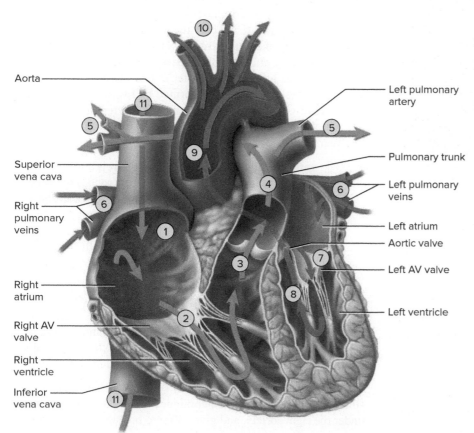

① Blood enters right atrium from superior and inferior venae cavae.

② Blood in right atrium flows through right AV valve into right ventricle.

③ Contraction of right ventricle forces pulmonary valve open.

④ Blood flows through pulmonary valve into pulmonary trunk.

⑤ Blood is distributed by right and left pulmonary arteries to the lungs, where it unloads CO_2 and loads O_2.

⑥ Blood returns from lungs via pulmonary veins to left atrium.

⑦ Blood in left atrium flows through left AV valve into left ventricle.

⑧ Contraction of left ventricle (simultaneous with step 3) forces aortic valve open.

⑨ Blood flows through aortic valve into ascending aorta.

⑩ Blood in aorta is distributed to every organ in the body, where it unloads O_2 and loads CO_2.

⑪ Blood returns to right atrium via venae cavae.

FIGURE 19.9 The Pathway of Blood Flow Through the Heart. The pathway from 4 through 6 is the pulmonary circuit, and the pathway from 9 through 11 is the systemic circuit. Violet arrows indicate oxygen-poor blood; orange arrows indicate oxygen-rich blood. **APR**

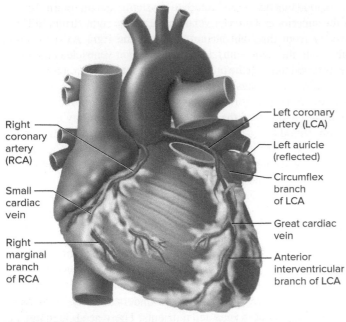

Right coronary artery (RCA)

Small cardiac vein

Right marginal branch of RCA

Left coronary artery (LCA)

Left auricle (reflected)

Circumflex branch of LCA

Great cardiac vein

Anterior interventricular branch of LCA

(a) Anterior view

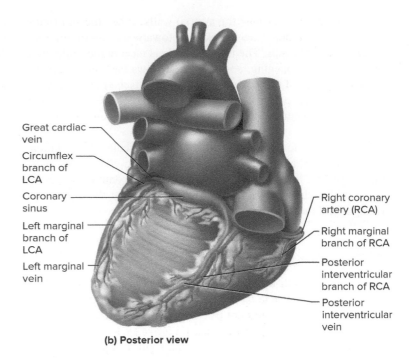

Great cardiac vein

Circumflex branch of LCA

Coronary sinus

Left marginal branch of LCA

Left marginal vein

Right coronary artery (RCA)

Right marginal branch of RCA

Posterior interventricular branch of RCA

Posterior interventricular vein

(b) Posterior view

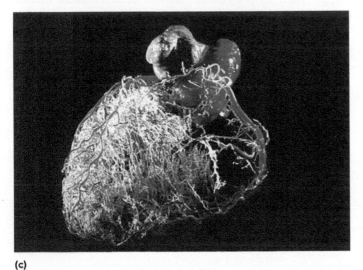

(c)

FIGURE 19.10 The Principal Coronary Blood Vessels.
(a) Anterior view. (b) Posterior view. (c) A vascular corrosion cast of the coronary circulation. Note the great density of small vessels that service the hardworking myocardium. **A&PR**

c: Science Photo Library/Science Source

would be too slow. Instead, the myocardium has its own supply of arteries and capillaries that deliver blood to every muscle cell. The blood vessels of the heart wall constitute the **coronary circulation (fig. 19.10).**

At rest, the coronary blood vessels supply the myocardium with about 250 mL of blood per minute. This constitutes about 5% of the circulating blood going to meet the metabolic needs of the heart, even though the heart is only 0.5% of the body's weight. It receives 10 times its "fair share" to sustain its strenuous workload.

Arterial Supply

The coronary circulation is the most variable aspect of cardiac anatomy. The following description covers only the pattern seen in about 70% to 85% of persons, and only the few largest vessels. (Compare the great density of coronary blood vessels seen in fig. 19.10c.)

Immediately after the aorta leaves the left ventricle, it gives off a right and left coronary artery. The orifices of these two arteries lie deep in the pockets formed by two of the aortic valve cusps (see fig. 19.8a). The **left coronary artery (LCA)** travels through the coronary sulcus under the left auricle and divides into two branches:

1. The **anterior interventricular branch** travels down the anterior interventricular sulcus to the apex, rounds the bend, and travels a short distance up the posterior side of the heart. There it joins the posterior interventricular branch described shortly. Clinically, it is also called the *left anterior descending (LAD) branch.* This artery supplies blood to both ventricles and the anterior two-thirds of the interventricular septum.

2. The **circumflex branch** continues around the left side of the heart in the coronary sulcus. It gives off a **left marginal branch** that passes down the left margin of the heart and furnishes blood to the left ventricle. The circumflex branch then ends on the posterior side of the heart. It supplies blood to the left atrium and posterior wall of the left ventricle.

The **right coronary artery (RCA)** supplies the right atrium and sinuatrial node (pacemaker), continues along the coronary sulcus under the right auricle, and gives off two branches of its own:

1. The **right marginal branch** runs toward the apex of the heart and supplies the lateral aspect of the right atrium and ventricle.

2. The RCA continues around the right margin of the heart to the posterior side, sends a small branch to the atrioventricular node, then gives off a large **posterior interventricular branch.** This branch travels down the corresponding sulcus and supplies the posterior walls of both ventricles as well as the posterior portion of the interventricular septum. It ends by joining the anterior interventricular branch of the LCA.

The energy demand of the cardiac muscle is so critical that an interruption of the blood supply to any part of the myocardium can cause necrosis within minutes. A fatty deposit or blood clot in a coronary artery can cause a **myocardial infarction**[15] **(MI),** or heart attack (see Deeper Insight 19.1). To protect against this, some coronary arteries converge at various points and combine their blood flow to points farther downstream. Points where two arteries come together are called *arterial anastomoses* (ah-NASS-tih-MO-seez). They provide alternative routes of blood flow *(collateral circulation)* that can supply the heart tissue with blood if the primary route becomes obstructed.

In organs other than the heart, blood flow usually peaks when the heart contracts and ejects blood into the systemic arteries, and diminishes when the ventricles relax and refill. The opposite is true in the coronary arteries: Flow peaks when the heart relaxes. There are three reasons for this. (1) Contraction of the myocardium squeezes the coronary arteries and obstructs blood flow. (2) When the ventricles contract, the aortic valve is forced open and its cusps

cover the openings to the coronary arteries, blocking blood from flowing into them. (3) When they relax, blood in the aorta briefly surges back toward the heart. It fills the aortic valve cusps and some of it flows into the coronary arteries, like water pouring into a bucket and flowing out through a hole in the bottom. In the coronary blood vessels, therefore, blood flow increases during ventricular relaxation.

19.2f Venous Drainage

Venous drainage refers to the route by which blood leaves an organ. After flowing through capillaries of the heart wall, about 5% to 10% of the coronary blood empties from multiple tiny vessels called *small cardiac veins* directly into the heart chambers, especially the right ventricle. The rest returns to the right atrium by the following route:

- The **great cardiac vein** collects blood from the anterior aspect of the heart and travels alongside the anterior interventricular artery. It carries blood from the apex toward the coronary sulcus, then arcs around the left side of the heart and empties into the coronary sinus.

- The **posterior interventricular (middle cardiac) vein,** found in the posterior interventricular sulcus, collects blood from the posterior aspect of the heart. It, too, carries blood from the apex upward and drains into the same sinus.

- The **left marginal vein** travels from a point near the apex up the left margin, and also empties into the coronary sinus.

- The **coronary sinus,** a large transverse vein in the coronary sulcus on the posterior side of the heart, collects blood from all three of the aforementioned veins as well as some smaller ones. It empties blood into the right atrium.

DEEPER INSIGHT 19.1

CLINICAL APPLICATION

Angina and Heart Attack

An obstruction of coronary blood flow can cause a chest pain known as *angina pectoris*[16] (an-JY-na PEC-toe-riss) or, more seriously, *myocardial infarction* (heart attack). Angina is a sense of heaviness or pain in the chest resulting from temporary and reversible *ischemia*[17] (iss-KEE-me-ah), or deficiency of blood flow to the cardiac muscle. It typically occurs when a partially blocked coronary artery constricts. The oxygen-deprived myocardium shifts to anaerobic fermentation, producing lactate, which stimulates pain receptors in the heart. The pain abates when the artery relaxes and normal blood flow resumes.

Myocardial infarction (MI), on the other hand, is the sudden death of a patch of myocardium resulting from long-term obstruction of the coronary circulation. Coronary arteries often become obstructed by a blood clot or fatty deposit called an *atheroma* (see Deeper Insight 19.4). As cardiac muscle downstream from the obstruction dies, the individual commonly feels a sense of heavy pressure or squeezing pain in the chest, often "radiating" to the shoulder and left arm. Some MIs are painless, "silent" heart attacks, especially in elderly or diabetic individuals. Infarctions weaken the heart wall and disrupt electrical conduction pathways, potentially leading to fibrillation and cardiac arrest. MI causes about 27% of deaths in the United States.

BEFORE YOU GO ON

Answer the following questions to test your understanding of the preceding section:

3. Name the three layers of the heart and describe their structural differences.

4. What are the functions of the fibrous skeleton?

5. Trace the flow of blood through the heart, naming each chamber and valve in order.

6. What are the three principal branches of the left coronary artery? Where are they located on the heart surface? What are the branches of the right coronary artery, and where are they located?

7. What is the medical significance of anastomoses in the coronary arterial system?

8. Why do the coronary arteries carry a greater blood flow during ventricular relaxation than they do during ventricular contraction?

9. What are the three major veins that empty into the coronary sinus?

---

[15]*infarct* = to stuff
[16]*angina* = to choke, strangle; *pectoris* = of the chest
[17]*isch* = holding back; *em* = blood; *ia* = condition

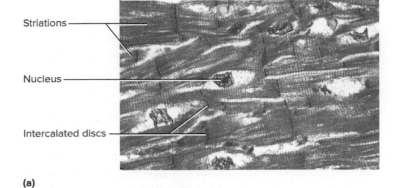

(a)

19.3 Cardiac Muscle and the Cardiac Conduction System

Expected Learning Outcomes

When you have completed this section, you should be able to

a. describe the unique structural and metabolic characteristics of cardiac muscle;

b. explain the nature and functional significance of the intercellular junctions between cardiac muscle cells; and

c. describe the heart's pacemaker and internal electrical conduction system.

The most obvious physiological fact about the heart is its rhythmicity. It contracts at regular intervals, typically about 75 beats per minute (bpm) in a resting adult. Among invertebrates such as clams, crabs, and insects, each heartbeat is triggered by a pacemaker in the nervous system. But in vertebrates from fish to humans, the heartbeat is said to be *myogenic*[18] because the signal originates within the heart itself. The heart is described as **autorhythmic**[19] because it doesn't depend on the nervous system for its rhythm. It has its own built-in pacemaker and electrical system. We now turn our attention to the cardiac muscle, pacemaker, and internal electrical system—the foundations for its electrical activity and rhythmic beat.

19.3a Structure of Cardiac Muscle

The heart is mostly muscle. Cardiac muscle is striated like skeletal muscle, but quite different from it in other structural and functional respects—and it has to be if we want it to pump infallibly, more than once every second, for at least eight or nine decades.

Cardiomyocytes, the muscle cells of the heart, are relatively short, thick, branched cells, typically 50 to 100 μm long and 10 to 20 μm wide **(fig. 19.11).** The ends of the cell are slightly branched, like a log with deep notches in the end. Through these branches, each cardiomyocyte contacts several others, so collectively they form a network throughout each pair of heart chambers—one network in the atria and one in the ventricles.

Most cardiomyocytes have a single, centrally placed nucleus, but up to one-third of them have two or more nuclei. The nucleus is often surrounded by a light-staining mass of glycogen. The sarcoplasmic reticulum is less developed than in skeletal muscle; it lacks terminal cisterns, although it does have footlike sacs associated with the T tubules. The T tubules are much larger than in skeletal muscle. During excitation of the cell, they admit calcium ions from the extracellular fluid to activate muscle contraction.

Cardiomyocytes are joined end to end by thick connections called **intercalated discs** (in-TUR-ka-LAY-ted). With the right histological stain, these appear as dark lines thicker than the

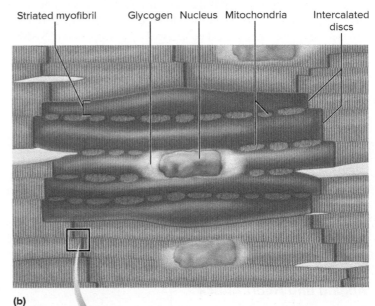

(b)

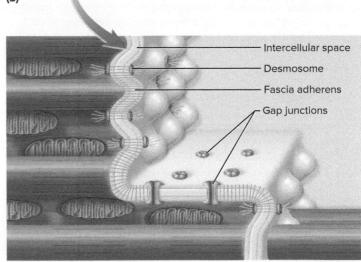

(c)

FIGURE 19.11 Cardiac Muscle. (a) Light micrograph. (b) Structure of a cardiomyocyte and its relationship to adjacent cardiomyocytes. All of the colored area is a single cell. Note that it is notched at the ends and typically linked to two or more neighboring cardiomyocytes by the mechanical and electrical junctions of the intercalated discs. (c) Structure of an intercalated disc.

a: Ed Reschke

---

[18]*myo* = muscle; *genic* = arising from
[19]*auto* = self

striations. An intercalated disc is a complex steplike structure with three distinctive features not found in skeletal muscle:

1. **Interdigitating folds.** The plasma membrane at the end of the cell is folded somewhat like the bottom of an egg carton. The folds of adjoining cells interlock with each other and increase the surface area of intercellular contact.

2. **Mechanical junctions.** The cells are tightly joined by two types of mechanical junctions: the fascia adherens and desmosomes. The *fascia adherens*[20] (FASH-ee-ah ad-HEER-enz) is the most extensive. It is a broad band, analogous to a strip of Velcro, in which the actin of the thin myofilaments is anchored to the plasma membrane and each cell is linked to the next via transmembrane proteins. The fascia adherens is interrupted here and there by *desmosomes*—patches of mechanical linkage that prevent the contracting cardiomyocytes from pulling apart. Both desmosomes and gap junctions (next) are described in greater detail in section 5.5a.

3. **Electrical junctions.** The intercalated discs also contain *gap junctions,* which form channels that allow ions to flow from the cytoplasm of one cardiomyocyte directly into the next. They enable each cardiomyocyte to electrically stimulate its neighbors. Thus, the entire myocardium of the two atria behaves almost like a single cell, as does the entire myocardium of the two ventricles. This unified action is essential for the effective pumping of a heart chamber.

Skeletal muscle contains satellite cells that can divide and replace dead muscle fibers to some extent. Cardiac muscle lacks these, however, so the repair of damaged cardiac muscle is almost

[20]*fascia* = band; *adherens* = adhering

entirely by fibrosis (scarring). Cardiac muscle has very limited capacity for mitosis and regeneration.

19.3b Metabolism of Cardiac Muscle

Cardiac muscle depends almost exclusively on aerobic respiration to make ATP. It is very rich in myoglobin (a short-term source of oxygen for aerobic respiration) and glycogen (for stored energy). Its huge mitochondria fill about 25% of the cell; skeletal muscle fibers, by comparison, have much smaller mitochondria that occupy only 2% of the fiber. Cardiac muscle is relatively adaptable with respect to the organic fuels used. At rest, the heart gets about 60% of its energy from fatty acids, 35% from glucose, and 5% from other fuels such as ketones, lactate, and amino acids. Cardiac muscle is more vulnerable to an oxygen deficiency than it is to the lack of any specific fuel. Because it makes little use of anaerobic fermentation or the oxygen debt mechanism, it is not prone to fatigue. You can easily appreciate this fact by squeezing a rubber ball in your fist once every second for a minute or two. You will soon feel weakness and fatigue in your hand muscles and perhaps feel all the more grateful that cardiac muscle can maintain a rhythm like this, without fatigue, for a lifetime.

19.3c The Conduction System

The heartbeat is coordinated by a **cardiac conduction system** composed of an internal pacemaker and nervelike conduction pathways through the myocardium. It generates and conducts rhythmic electrical signals in the following order **(fig. 19.12):**

① The **sinuatrial (SA) node** is a patch of modified cardiomyocytes in the right atrium, just under the epicardium near the superior vena cava. This is the **pacemaker** that initiates each heartbeat and determines the heart rate.

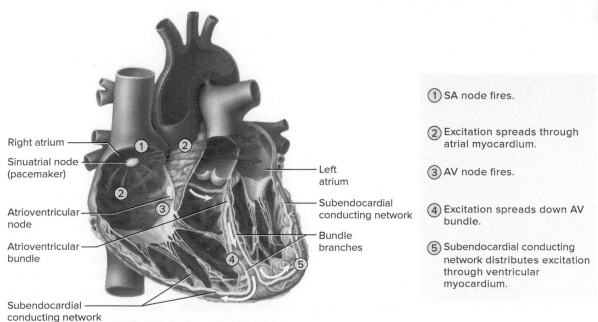

Right atrium
Sinuatrial node (pacemaker)
Atrioventricular node
Atrioventricular bundle
Subendocardial conducting network

Left atrium
Subendocardial conducting network
Bundle branches

① SA node fires.

② Excitation spreads through atrial myocardium.

③ AV node fires.

④ Excitation spreads down AV bundle.

⑤ Subendocardial conducting network distributes excitation through ventricular myocardium.

FIGURE 19.12 The Cardiac Conduction System. Electrical signals travel along the pathways indicated by the arrows.

❓ *Which atrium is first to receive the signal that induces atrial contraction?*

(2) Signals from the SA node spread throughout the atria, as shown by the red arrows in the figure.

(3) The **atrioventricular (AV) node** is located at the lower end of the interatrial septum near the right AV valve. This node acts as an electrical gateway to the ventricles; the fibrous skeleton acts as an insulator to prevent currents from getting to the ventricles by any other route.

(4) The **atrioventricular (AV) bundle** is the pathway by which signals leave the AV node. The bundle soon forks into **right** and **left bundle branches,** which enter the interventricular septum and descend toward the apex.

(5) The **subendocardial conducting network** (formerly called *Purkinje fibers*) consists of processes that arise from the lower end of the bundle branches. Although nervelike in their action, they are composed of modified cardiomyocytes specialized for electrical conduction rather than contraction. At the apex of the heart, they turn upward and ramify throughout the ventricular myocardium, distributing electrical excitation to the cardiomyocytes of the ventricles. They form a more elaborate network in the left ventricle than in the right. Once they have delivered the electrical signal to their limits, the cardiomyocytes themselves perpetuate it by passing ions from cell to cell through their gap junctions.

BEFORE YOU GO ON

Answer the following questions to test your understanding of the preceding section:

10. What organelle(s) is/are less developed in cardiac muscle than in skeletal muscle? What one(s) is/are more developed? What is the functional significance of these differences between muscle types?

11. What exactly is an intercalated disc, and what function is served by each of its components?

12. Cardiac muscle rarely uses anaerobic fermentation to generate ATP. What benefit do we gain from this fact?

13. Where is the pacemaker of the heart located? What is it called? Trace the path of electrical excitation from there to a cardiomyocyte of the left ventricle, naming each component of the conduction system along the way.

19.4 Electrical and Contractile Activity of the Heart

Expected Learning Outcomes

When you have completed this section, you should be able to

a. explain why the SA node fires spontaneously and rhythmically;

b. explain how the SA node excites the myocardium;

c. describe the unusual action potentials of cardiac muscle and relate them to the contractile behavior of the heart; and

d. interpret a normal electrocardiogram.

In this section, we examine how the electrical events in the heart produce its cycle of contraction and relaxation. Contraction is called **systole** (SIS-toe-lee) and relaxation is **diastole** (dy-ASS-toe-lee). These terms can refer to a specific part of the heart (for example, atrial systole), but if no particular chamber is specified, they usually refer to the more conspicuous and important ventricular action, which ejects blood from the heart.

19.4a The Cardiac Rhythm

The normal heartbeat triggered by the SA node is called the **sinus rhythm.** At rest, the adult heart typically beats about 70 to 80 times per minute, although heart rates from 60 to 100 bpm are not unusual.

Any region of spontaneous firing other than the SA node is called an **ectopic**[21] **focus.** If the SA node is damaged, an ectopic focus may take over the governance of the heart rhythm. The most common ectopic focus is the AV node, which produces a slower heartbeat of 40 to 50 bpm called a **nodal (junctional) rhythm.** If neither the SA nor AV node is functioning, other ectopic foci fire at rates of 20 to 40 bpm. The nodal rhythm is sufficient to sustain life, but a rate of 20 to 40 bpm provides too little flow to the brain to be survivable. This is one of the conditions that can call for an artificial pacemaker.

19.4b Pacemaker Physiology

Why does the SA node spontaneously fire at regular intervals? Unlike skeletal muscle or neurons, cells of the SA node don't have a stable resting membrane potential. Their membrane potential starts at about –60 mV and drifts upward, showing a gradual depolarization called the **pacemaker potential (prepotential) (fig. 19.13).** This results primarily from a slow inflow of Na^+ without a compensating outflow of K^+.

When the pacemaker potential reaches a threshold of –40 mV, voltage-gated calcium channels open and Ca^{2+} flows in from the extracellular fluid. This produces the rising (depolarizing) phase of the action potential, which peaks slightly above 0 mV. At that point, K^+ channels open and K^+ leaves the cell. This makes the cytosol increasingly negative and creates the falling (repolarizing) phase of the action potential. When repolarization is complete, the K^+ channels close and the pacemaker potential starts over, on its way to producing the next heartbeat. Each depolarization of the SA node sets off one heartbeat. When the SA node fires, it excites the other components in the conduction system; thus, the SA node serves as the system's pacemaker. At rest, it typically fires every 0.8 second or so, creating a heart rate of about 75 bpm.

---

[21]*ec* = out of; *top* = place

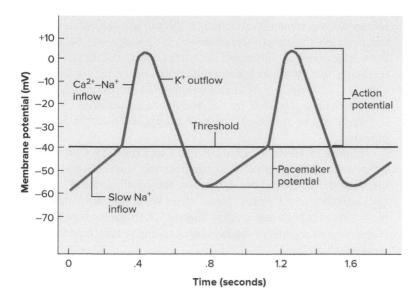

FIGURE 19.13 Pacemaker Potentials and Action Potentials of the SA Node.

19.4c Impulse Conduction to the Myocardium

Firing of the SA node excites atrial cardiomyocytes and stimulates the two atria to contract almost simultaneously. The signal travels at a speed of about 1 m/s through the atrial myocardium and reaches the AV node in about 50 ms. In the AV node, the signal slows down to about 0.05 m/s, partly because the cardiomyocytes here are thinner, but more importantly because they have fewer gap junctions over which the signal can be transmitted. This delays the signal at the AV node for about 100 ms—like

highway traffic slowing down at a small town. This delay is essential because it gives the ventricles time to fill with blood before they begin to contract.

The ventricular myocardium has a conduction speed of only 0.3 to 0.5 m/s. If this were the only route of travel for the excitatory signal, some cardiomyocytes would be stimulated much sooner than others. Ventricular contraction wouldn't be synchronized and the pumping effectiveness of the ventricles would be severely compromised. But signals travel through the AV bundle and subendocardial conducting network at a speed of 4 m/s, the fastest in the conduction system, owing to their very high density of gap junctions. Consequently, the entire ventricular myocardium depolarizes within 200 ms after the SA node fires, causing the ventricles to contract in near unison.

Ventricular systole begins at the apex of the heart, which is first to be stimulated, and progresses upward—pushing the blood upward toward the semilunar valves. Because of the spiral arrangement of the vortex of the heart, the ventricles twist slightly as they contract, like someone wringing out a towel.

▶▶▶APPLY WHAT YOU KNOW

Some people have abnormal cords or bridges of myocardium that extend from atrium to ventricle, bypassing the AV node and other parts of the conduction system. How would you expect this to affect the cardiac rhythm?

19.4d Electrical Behavior of the Myocardium

The action potentials of cardiomyocytes are significantly different from those of neurons and skeletal muscle fibers **(fig. 19.14).**

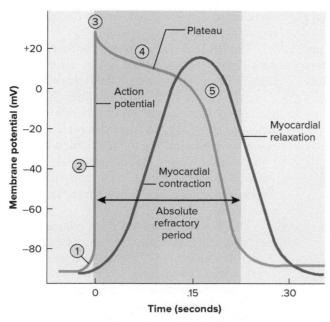

① Voltage-gated Na⁺ channels open.

② Na⁺ inflow depolarizes the membrane and triggers the opening of still more Na⁺ channels, creating a positive feedback cycle and a rapidly rising membrane voltage.

③ Na⁺ channels close when the cell depolarizes, and the voltage peaks at nearly +30 mV.

④ Ca²⁺ entering through slow Ca²⁺ channels prolongs depolarization of membrane, creating a plateau. Plateau falls slightly because of some K⁺ leakage, but most K⁺ channels remain closed until end of plateau.

⑤ Ca²⁺ channels close and Ca²⁺ is transported out of cell. K⁺ channels open, and rapid K⁺ outflow returns membrane to its resting potential.

FIGURE 19.14 Action Potential of a Ventricular Cardiomyocyte. The green curve is the action potential. The red curve represents rising and falling muscle tension as the myocardium contracts and relaxes.

❓ *What is the benefit of having such a long absolute refractory period in cardiac muscle?*

Cardiomyocytes have a stable resting potential of –90 mV and normally depolarize only when stimulated, unlike cells of the SA node. A stimulus opens voltage-gated sodium channels, causing a Na^+ inflow and depolarizing the cell to its threshold. The threshold voltage rapidly opens additional Na^+ channels and triggers a positive feedback cycle like the one seen in the firing of a neuron. The action potential peaks at nearly +30 mV. The Na^+ channels close quickly, and the rising phase of the action potential is very brief.

As action potentials spread over the plasma membrane, they open voltage-gated **slow calcium channels,** which admit a small amount of Ca^{2+} from the extracellular fluid into the cell. This Ca^{2+} binds to ligand-gated Ca^{2+} channels on the sarcoplasmic reticulum (SR), opening them and releasing a greater quantity of Ca^{2+} from the SR into the cytosol. This second wave of Ca^{2+} binds to troponin and triggers contraction in the same way as it does in skeletal muscle. The SR provides 90% to 98% of the Ca^{2+} needed for myocardial contraction.

In skeletal muscle and neurons, an action potential falls back to the resting potential within 2 ms. In cardiac muscle, however, the depolarization is prolonged for 200 to 250 ms (at a heart rate of 70–80 bpm), producing a long plateau in the action potential—perhaps because the Ca^{2+} channels of the SR are slow to close or because the SR is slow to remove Ca^{2+} from the cytosol. Cardiomyocytes remain contracted for as long as the action potential is in its plateau. Thus, in the figure, you can see the development of muscle tension (myocardial contraction) following closely behind the depolarization and plateau. Rather than showing a brief twitch like skeletal muscle, cardiac muscle has a more sustained contraction necessary to expel blood from the heart chambers. Both atrial and ventricular cardiomyocytes exhibit these plateaus, but they are more pronounced in the ventricles.

At the end of the plateau, Ca^{2+} channels close and K^+ channels open. Potassium diffuses rapidly out of the cell and Ca^{2+} is transported back into the extracellular fluid and SR. Membrane voltage drops rapidly, and muscle tension declines soon afterward.

Cardiac muscle has an *absolute refractory period* of 250 ms, compared with 1 to 2 ms in skeletal muscle. This long refractory period prevents wave summation and tetanus (in contrast to skeletal muscle, fig. 11.15), which would stop the pumping action of the heart if they occurred.

▶▶▶ APPLY WHAT YOU KNOW

With regard to the ions involved, how does the falling (repolarization) phase of a myocardial action potential differ from that of a neuron's action potential? (See fig. 12.14.)

19.4e The Electrocardiogram

We can detect electrical currents in the heart by means of electrodes *(leads)* applied to the skin. An instrument called the *electrocardiograph* amplifies these signals and produces a record, usually on a moving paper chart, called an **electrocardiogram**[22] **(ECG** or **EKG).** To record an ECG,

electrodes are typically attached to the wrists, ankles, and six locations on the chest. Simultaneous recordings can be made from electrodes at different distances from the heart; collectively, they provide a comprehensive image of the heart's electrical activity. An ECG is a composite recording of all action potentials produced by the nodal and myocardial cells—it should not be misconstrued as a tracing of a single action potential.

Figure 19.15 shows a typical ECG, and **table 19.1** provides a functional interpretation of its components. The ECG has three principal deflections above and below the baseline: the *P wave, QRS complex,* and *T wave.* (These letters were arbitrarily chosen; they don't stand for any words.) **Figure 19.16** shows how these correspond to regions of the heart undergoing depolarization and repolarization.

The **P wave** is produced when a signal from the SA node spreads through the atria and depolarizes them. Atrial systole begins about 100 ms after the P wave begins, during the *PQ segment.* This segment is about 160 ms long and represents the time required for impulses to travel from the SA node to the AV node.

The **QRS complex** consists of a small downward deflection (Q), a tall sharp peak (R), and a final downward deflection (S). It is produced when the signal from the AV node spreads through the ventricular myocardium and depolarizes the muscle. This is the most conspicuous part of the ECG because it is produced mainly by depolarization of the ventricles, which constitute the largest muscle mass of the heart and generate the greatest electrical current. Its complex shape is due to the different sizes of the two ventricles and the different times required for them to depolarize. Ventricular systole begins shortly after the QRS complex, in the *ST segment.* The QRS interval is also a time of atrial repolarization and diastole, but atrial repolarization sends a relatively weak signal that is obscured by the electrical activity of the more muscular ventricles.

The PR interval represents the time it takes for a signal to pass through the AV node before activating the ventricles. It doesn't extend all the way to the R wave because the ventricular response begins at Q. Abnormalities in this interval can thus indicate defects that affect conduction time. The QT interval indicates how long the ventricles remain depolarized, and corresponds approximately to the duration of a cardiomyocyte action potential. It gets shorter during exercise. The ST segment corresponds to the plateau in the myocardial action potential and thus represents the time during which the ventricles contract and eject blood.

The **T wave** is generated by ventricular repolarization immediately before diastole. The ventricles take longer to repolarize than to depolarize; the T wave is therefore smaller and more spread out than the QRS complex, and it has a rounder peak. Even when the T wave is taller than the QRS complex, it can be recognized by its relatively rounded peak.

The ECG affords a wealth of information about the normal electrical activity of the heart. Deviations from normal—such as enlarged, inverted, or misshapen waves and abnormal time intervals between waves—are invaluable for diagnosing abnormalities

---

[22]*electro* = electricity; *cardio* = heart; *gram* = record of; the common abbreviation *EKG* comes from the German spelling, *elektrokardiogramm*

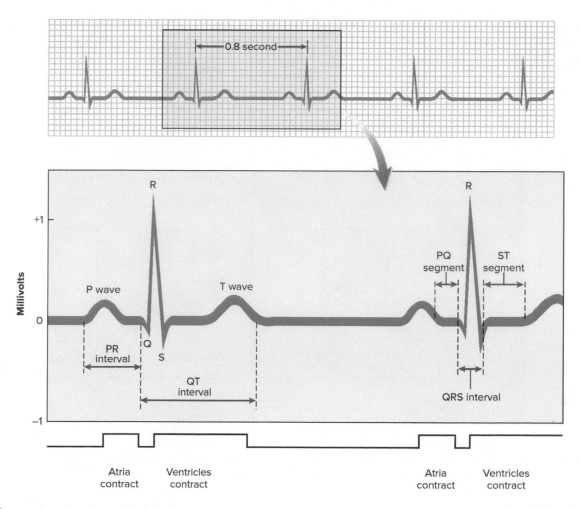

FIGURE 19.15 The Normal Electrocardiogram.

in the conduction pathways, myocardial infarction, enlargement of the heart, and electrolyte and hormone imbalances, among other disorders (see Deeper Insight 19.2).

TABLE 19.1	Interpretation of the Electrocardiogram
P wave	Atrial depolarization
QRS complex	Ventricular depolarization
T wave	Ventricular repolarization
PR interval	Signal conduction through AV node, before activating ventricles
QT interval	Duration of ventricular depolarization; shorter during exercise.
QRS interval	Atrial repolarization and diastole; repolarization concealed by QRS wave.
PQ segment	Signal conduction from SA node to AV node; atrial systole begins.
ST segment	Ventricular systole and ejection of blood; corresponds to plateau of cardiomyocyte action potential.

Any deviation from the regular, SA node–driven sinus rhythm of the heartbeat is called an **arrhythmia.** The most familiar and feared of these is **ventricular fibrillation (VF, VFib),**[23] the hallmark of a heart attack (myocardial infarction). Most cases occur in patients with a history of coronary artery disease. In striking contrast to the steady sinus rhythm, the ECG shows weak, chaotic ventricular depolarizations (compare **fig. 19.17a, b**) as electrical signals travel randomly about the myocardium and return to repeatedly restimulate the same area instead of dying out like a normal ventricular depolarization. To the surgeon's eye and hand, a fibrillating ventricle exhibits squirming, uncoordinated contractions often described as feeling "like a bag of worms." A fibrillating ventricle pumps no blood, so there is no coronary blood flow and myocardial tissue rapidly dies of ischemia, as does cerebral tissue. *Cardiac arrest* is the cessation of cardiac output, with the ventricles either motionless or in fibrillation.

Fibrillation kills quickly if it isn't stopped. *Defibrillation* is an emergency procedure in which the heart is given a strong electrical

---

[23]*fibril* = small fiber; *ation* = action, process

Key

■ Wave of depolarization
■ Wave of repolarization

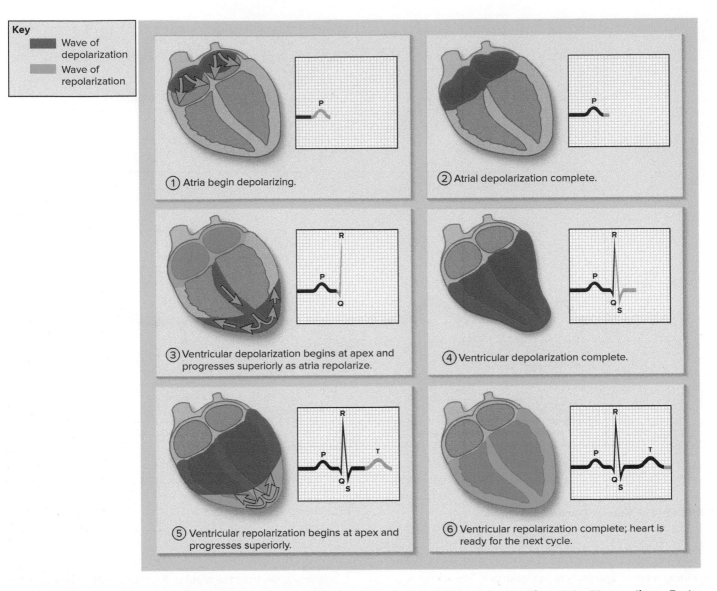

① Atria begin depolarizing.

② Atrial depolarization complete.

③ Ventricular depolarization begins at apex and progresses superiorly as atria repolarize.

④ Ventricular depolarization complete.

⑤ Ventricular repolarization begins at apex and progresses superiorly.

⑥ Ventricular repolarization complete; heart is ready for the next cycle.

FIGURE 19.16 Relationship of the Electrocardiogram (ECG) to Electrical Activity and Contraction of the Myocardium. Each heart diagram indicates the events occurring at the time of the colored segment of the ECG. Red indicates depolarizing or depolarized myocardium, and green indicates repolarizing or repolarized myocardium. Arrows indicate the direction in which a wave of depolarization or repolarization is traveling. **APR**

shock with a pair of paddle electrodes. The purpose is to depolarize the entire myocardium and stop the fibrillation, with the hope that the SA node will resume its sinus rhythm. This doesn't correct the underlying cause of the fibrillation, but it may sustain a patient's life long enough to allow for other corrective action.

BEFORE YOU GO ON

Answer the following questions to test your understanding of the preceding section:

14. Define *systole* and *diastole*.

15. How does the pacemaker potential of the SA node differ from the resting membrane potential of a neuron? Why is this important in creating the heart rhythm?

16. Why is it important that the AV node slow down signal conduction to the ventricles?

17. How does excitation–contraction coupling in cardiac muscle resemble that of skeletal muscle? How is it different?

18. What produces the plateau in the action potentials of cardiomyocytes? Why is this important to the pumping ability of the heart?

19. Identify the portion of the ECG that coincides with each of the following events: atrial depolarization, atrial systole, atrial repolarization, ventricular depolarization, ventricular systole, ventricular repolarization, ventricular diastole.

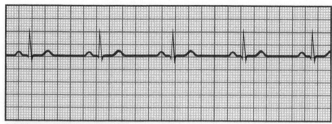

(a) Sinus rhythm (normal)

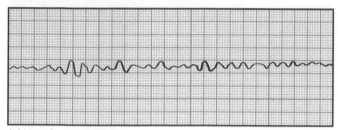

(b) Ventricular fibrillation

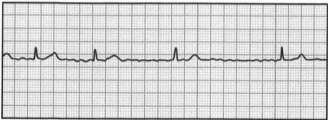

(c) Atrial fibrillation

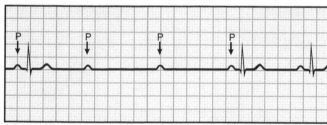

(d) Heart block

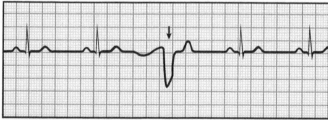

(e) Premature ventricular contraction

FIGURE 19.17 Normal and Pathological Electrocardiograms. (a) Normal sinus rhythm. (b) Ventricular fibrillation, with grossly irregular waves of depolarization, as seen in a heart attack (myocardial infarction). (c) Atrial fibrillation; between heartbeats, the atria exhibit weak, chaotic, high-frequency depolarizations instead of normal P waves. (d) Heart block, in which some atrial depolarizations (P waves) are not conducted to the ventricles and not followed by ventricular QRS waves. (e) Premature ventricular contraction, or extrasystole (at arrow); note the absence of a P wave, the inverted QRS complex, and the misshapen QRS and elevated T.

DEEPER INSIGHT 19.2

CLINICAL APPLICATION

Cardiac Arrhythmias

Ventricular fibrillation **(fig. 19.17b)** is the most widely known arrhythmia, but others are not uncommon. *Atrial fibrillation (AF, AFib)* **(fig. 19.17c)** is a weak rippling contraction in the atria, manifested in the ECG by chaotic, high-frequency depolarizations (400–650/min.). Fibrillating atria fail to stimulate the ventricles, so we see a dissociation between the random atrial depolarizations and the ventricular QRS and T waves of the ECG. This is the most common atrial arrhythmia in the elderly. It can result from such causes as valvular disease, thyroid hormone excess, or myocardial inflammation, and is often seen in alcoholism. Blood continues to flow through the atria into the ventricles even during AF, so AF isn't immediately life-threatening. Blood flow is more sluggish, however, and there is a higher risk of blood clots causing pulmonary embolism or stroke.

Heart block is a failure of any part of the cardiac conduction system to conduct signals, usually as the result of disease and degeneration of conduction system fibers. In the ECG, one sees rhythmic atrial P waves, but the ventricles fail to receive the signal and no QRS wave follows the P (as in the second and third P waves of **fig. 19.17d**). A *bundle branch block* is a heart block resulting from damage to one or both branches of the AV bundle. Damage to the AV node causes *total heart block,* in which signals from the atria fail to reach the ventricles at all, and the ventricles beat at their own intrinsic rhythm of 20 to 40 bpm.

Premature ventricular contraction (PVC) is the result of a ventricular ectopic focus firing and setting off an extra beat *(extrasystole)* before the normal signal from the SA node arrives. The P wave is missing and the QRS wave is inverted and misshapen (see arrow in **fig. 19.17e**). PVCs can occur singly or in bursts. An occasional extra beat isn't serious, and may result from emotional stress, lack of sleep, or irritation of the heart by stimulants (nicotine, caffeine). Persistent PVCs, however, can indicate more serious pathology and sometimes lead to ventricular fibrillation and sudden death.

19.5 Blood Flow, Heart Sounds, and the Cardiac Cycle

Expected Learning Outcomes

When you have completed this section, you should be able to

a. explain why blood pressure is expressed in millimeters of mercury;

b. describe how changes in blood pressure operate the heart valves;

c. explain what causes the sounds of the heartbeat;

d. describe in detail one complete cycle of heart contraction and relaxation; and

e. relate the events of the cardiac cycle to the volume of blood entering and leaving the heart.

A **cardiac cycle** consists of one complete contraction and relaxation of all four heart chambers. We will examine these events in detail to see how they relate to the entry and expulsion of blood, but first we consider two related issues: (1) some general principles of pressure changes and how they affect the flow of blood, and (2) the heart sounds produced during the cardiac cycle, which we can then relate to the stages of the cycle.

19.5a Principles of Pressure and Flow

A fluid is a state of matter that can flow in bulk from place to place. In the body, this includes both liquids and gases—blood, lymph, air, and urine, among others. Certain basic principles of fluid movement *(fluid dynamics)* apply to all of these. In particular, flow is governed by two main variables: **pressure,** which impels a fluid to move, and **resistance,** which opposes flow. In this chapter, we will focus on how pressure changes govern the operation of the heart valves, the entry of blood into the heart chambers, and its expulsion into the arteries. In the next chapter, we will examine the roles of pressure and resistance in the flow of blood through the blood vessels, and later in the book, we apply the same principles to respiratory airflow. The flow of blood and of air down their pressure gradients are two applications of the general principle of gradients and flow described in section 1.6e.

Measurement of Pressure

Pressure is commonly measured by a device called a *manometer.* In simplest form, this is typically a J-shaped glass tube partially filled with mercury. The sealed upper end, above the mercury, contains a vacuum, whereas the lower end is open. Pressure applied at the lower end is measured in terms of how high it can push the mercury column up the evacuated end of the tube. In principle, any liquid would do, but mercury is used because it's so dense; it enables us to measure pressure with shorter columns than we would need with a less dense liquid such as water. Pressures are therefore commonly expressed in millimeters of mercury (mm Hg). Blood pressure, specifically, has been traditionally measured with a **sphygmomanometer**[24] (SFIG-mo-ma-NOM-eh-tur)—a calibrated mercury manometer with its open lower end attached to an inflatable pressure cuff wrapped around the arm (although mercury sphygmomanometers have been increasingly replaced by dial and digital devices). Blood pressure and the method of measuring it are discussed in greater detail in section 20.2a.

Pressure Gradients and Flow

A fluid flows only if it is subjected to more pressure at one point than at another. The difference creates a **pressure gradient,** and fluids always flow down their pressure gradients, from the high-pressure point to the low-pressure point. Before we relate this to blood flow, it may be easier to begin with an analogy—an air-filled syringe **(fig. 19.18).**

At rest, the air pressures within the syringe barrel and in the atmosphere surrounding it are equal. But for a given quantity (mass) of air, and assuming a constant temperature, pressure is inversely proportional to the volume of the container—the greater

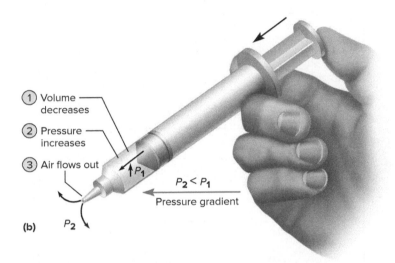

FIGURE 19.18 Principles of Volume, Pressure, and Flow Illustrated with a Syringe. (a) As the plunger is pulled back, the volume of the enclosed space increases, its pressure falls, and pressure inside the syringe (P_1) is lower than the pressure outside (P_2). The pressure gradient causes air to flow inward until the pressures are equal. This is analogous to the filling of an expanding heart chamber. (b) As the plunger is depressed, the volume of the enclosed space decreases, P_1 rises above P_2, and air flows out until the pressures are equal. This is analogous to the ejection of blood from a contracting heart chamber. In both cases, fluids flow down their pressure gradients.

the volume, the lower the pressure, and vice versa. Suppose you pull back the plunger of the syringe (fig. 19.18a). This increases the volume and thus lowers the air pressure within the barrel. Now you have a pressure gradient, with pressure outside the syringe being greater than the pressure inside. Air will flow down its gradient into the syringe until the two pressures are equal. If you then push the plunger in (fig. 19.18b), pressure inside the barrel will rise above the pressure outside, and air will flow out—again going down its pressure gradient but in the reverse direction.

---

[24]*sphygmo* = pulse; *mano* = rare, sparse, roomy

The syringe barrel is analogous to a heart chamber such as the left ventricle. When the ventricle expands, its internal pressure falls. If the AV valve is open, blood flows into the ventricle from the atrium above. When the ventricle contracts, its internal pressure rises. When the aortic valve opens, blood is ejected from the ventricle into the aorta.

The opening and closing of the heart valves are governed by these pressure changes. Remember that the valves are just soft flaps of connective tissue with no muscle. They don't exert any effort of their own, but are passively pushed open and closed by the changes in blood pressure on the upstream and downstream sides of the valve.

When the ventricles are relaxed and their pressure is low, the AV valve cusps hang down limply and both valves are open

(fig. 19.19a). Blood flows freely from the atria into the ventricles even before the atria contract. As the ventricles fill with blood, the cusps float upward toward the closed position. When the ventricles contract, their internal pressure rises sharply and blood surges against the AV valves from below. This pushes the cusps together, seals the openings, and prevents blood from flowing back into the atria. The papillary muscles contract slightly before the rest of the ventricular myocardium and tug on the tendinous cords, preventing the valves from bulging excessively (prolapsing) into the atria or turning inside out like windblown umbrellas. (See *mitral valve prolapse* in Deeper Insight 19.3.)

The rising pressure in the ventricles also acts on the aortic and pulmonary valves. Up to a point, pressure in the aorta and pulmonary trunk opposes their opening, but when the ventricular

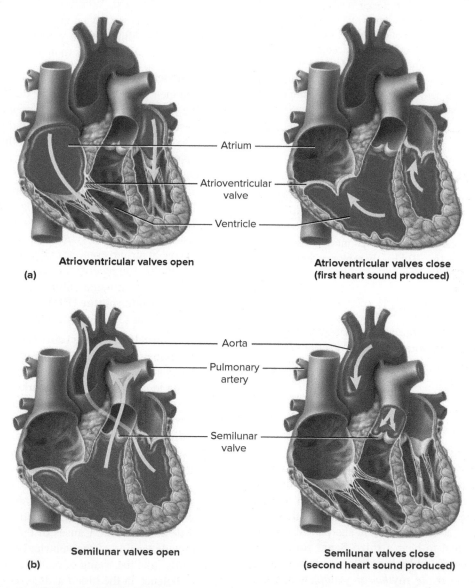

FIGURE 19.19 Operation of the Heart Valves. These are correlated with the heart sounds described in section 19.5b. (a) The atrioventricular valves. When atrial pressure is greater than ventricular pressure, the valve opens and blood flows through (green arrows). When ventricular pressure rises above atrial pressure, the blood in the ventricle pushes the valve cusps closed. (b) The semilunar valves. When the pressure in the ventricles is greater than the pressure in the great arteries, the semilunar valves are forced open and blood is ejected. When ventricular pressure is lower than arterial pressure, arterial blood holds these valves closed.

? *What role do the tendinous cords play?*

DEEPER INSIGHT 19.3

CLINICAL APPLICATION

Valvular Insufficiency

Valvular insufficiency (incompetence) refers to any failure of a valve to prevent *reflux* (regurgitation)—the backward flow of blood. *Valvular stenosis*[25] is a form of insufficiency in which the cusps are stiffened and the opening is constricted by scar tissue. It frequently results from rheumatic fever, an autoimmune disease in which antibodies produced to fight a bacterial infection also attack the mitral and aortic valves. As the valves become scarred and constricted, the heart is overworked by the effort to force blood through the openings and may become enlarged. Regurgitation of blood through the incompetent valves creates turbulence that can be heard with a stethoscope as a *heart murmur.*

Mitral valve prolapse (MVP) is an insufficiency in which one or both mitral valve cusps bulge into the atrium during ventricular contraction. It is often hereditary and affects about 1 out of 40 people, especially young women. In many cases, it causes no serious dysfunction, but in some people it causes chest pain, fatigue, and shortness of breath.

In some cases, an incompetent valve can eventually lead to heart failure. A defective valve can be surgically repaired or replaced with an artificial valve or a valve transplanted from a pig heart.

---

pressure rises above the arterial pressure, it forces the valves open and blood is ejected from the heart **(fig. 19.19b).** Then as the ventricles relax again and their pressure falls below that in the arteries, arterial blood briefly flows backward and fills the pocketlike cusps of the semilunar valves. The three cusps meet in the middle of the orifice and seal it (see fig. 19.8b), thereby preventing arterial blood from reentering the heart.

▶▶▶APPLY WHAT YOU KNOW

How would aortic valvular stenosis (see Deeper Insight 19.3) affect the amount of blood pumped into the aorta? How might this affect a person's physical stamina? Explain your reasoning.

19.5b Heart Sounds

As we follow events through the cardiac cycle, we will note the occurrence of two or three *heart sounds* audible with a stethoscope. Listening to sounds made by the body is called **auscultation** (AWS-cul-TAY-shun). The **first** and **second heart sounds,** symbolized S_1 and S_2, are often described as a "lubb-dupp"—S_1 is louder and longer and S_2 a little softer and sharper. In children and adolescents, it is normal to hear a **third heart sound** (S_3). This is rarely audible in people older than 30, but when it is, the heartbeat is said to show a *triple rhythm* or *gallop,* which may indicate an enlarged and failing heart. If the normal sounds are roughly simulated by drumming two fingers on a table, a triple rhythm sounds a little like drumming with three fingers. The heart

valves themselves operate silently, but S_1 and S_2 occur in conjunction with the closing of the valves as a result of turbulence in the bloodstream and movements of the heart wall.

19.5c Phases of the Cardiac Cycle

We now examine the phases of the cardiac cycle, the pressure changes that occur, and how the pressure changes and valves govern the flow of blood. Cardiovascular physiologist Carl J. Wiggers (1883–1963) devised an enormously informative chart, now known as the *Wiggers diagram* **(fig. 19.20),** for showing the major events that occur simultaneously at each moment throughout the cardiac cycle. Here, it is divided into colored and numbered bars to correspond to the following phases. Closely follow the figure as you study the text. Where to begin when describing a circular chain of events is somewhat arbitrary, but in this presentation, we begin with the filling of the ventricles. Remember that all these events are completed in less than 1 second.

1. **Ventricular filling.** During diastole, the ventricles expand and their pressure drops below that of the atria. As a result, the AV valves open and blood pours into the ventricles, raising the ventricular pressure and lowering atrial pressure. Ventricular filling occurs in three phases: **(1a)** The first one-third is *rapid ventricular filling,* when blood enters especially quickly. **(1b)** The second one-third, called *diastasis* (di-ASS-tuh-sis), is marked by slower filling. The P wave of the electrocardiogram occurs at the end of diastasis, marking the depolarization of the atria. **(1c)** In the last one-third, *atrial systole* completes the filling process. The right atrium contracts slightly before the left because it is the first to receive the signal from the SA node. At the end of ventricular filling, each ventricle contains an **end-diastolic volume (EDV)** of about 130 mL of blood. Only 40 mL (31%) of this is contributed by atrial systole.

2. **Isovolumetric contraction.** The atria repolarize, relax, and remain in diastole for the rest of the cardiac cycle. The ventricles depolarize, generate the QRS complex, and begin to contract. Wave Q marks the end of ventricular filling; R marks the transition from atrial systole to isovolumetric contraction of the ventricles; and S occurs during isovolumetric contraction. Pressure in the ventricles rises sharply and reverses the pressure gradient between atria and ventricles. The AV valves close as ventricular blood surges back against the cusps. Heart sound S_1 occurs at the beginning of this phase and is produced mainly by the left ventricle; the right ventricle is thought to make little contribution. Causes of the sound are thought to include tensing of the ventricular tissues and tendinous cords (like the twang of a suddenly stretched rubber band), turbulence in the blood as it surges against the closed AV valves, and impact of the heart against the chest wall.

    This phase is called *isovolumetric*[26] because even though the ventricles contract, they don't eject blood yet and

---

[25]*steno* = narrow; *osis* = condition

[26]*iso* = same; *volum* =volume; *metr* = measure

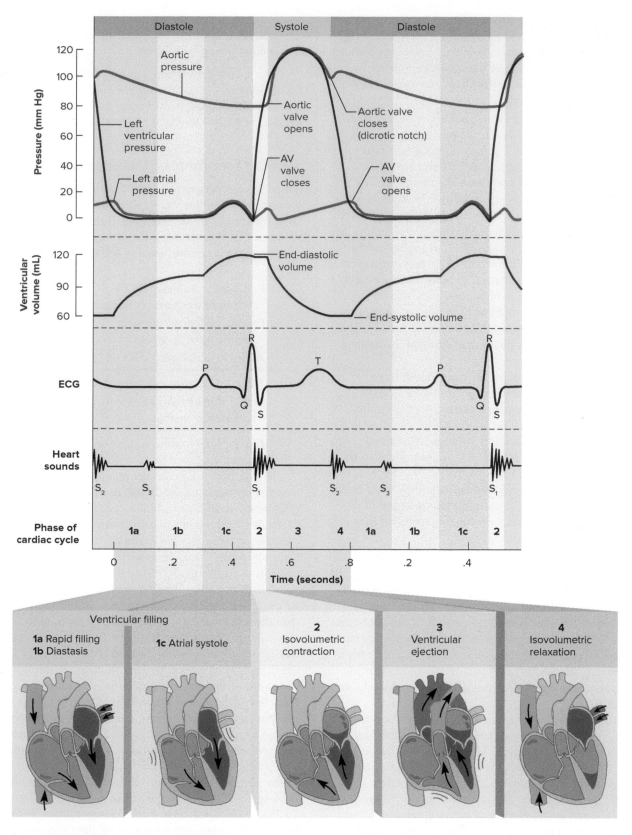

FIGURE 19.20 Modified Wiggers Diagram, Illustrating Events of the Cardiac Cycle. Two cycles are shown. The phases are numbered across the bottom to correspond to the text description.

❓ *Explain why the aortic pressure curve begins to rise abruptly at about 0.5 second.*

there is no change in their volume. This is because pressures in the aorta (80 mm Hg) and pulmonary trunk (10 mm Hg) are still greater than the pressures in the respective ventricles and thus oppose the opening of the semilunar valves. The cardiomyocytes exert force, but with all four valves closed, the blood can't go anywhere.

3. **Ventricular ejection.** The ejection of blood begins when ventricular pressure exceeds arterial pressure and forces the semilunar valves open. The pressure peaks at typically 120 mm Hg in the left ventricle and 25 mm Hg in the right. Blood spurts out of each ventricle rapidly at first (*rapid ejection*), then flows out more slowly under less pressure (*reduced ejection*). By analogy, suppose you were to shake up a bottle of carbonated beverage and remove the cap. The liquid would spurt out rapidly at high pressure and then more would dribble out at lower pressure, much like the blood leaving the ventricles. Ventricular ejection lasts about 200 to 250 ms, which corresponds to the plateau of the myocardial action potential but lags somewhat behind it (review the red tension curve in fig. 19.14). The T wave occurs late in this phase, beginning at the moment of peak ventricular pressure.

The ventricles don't expel all their blood. In an average resting heart, each ventricle contains an EDV of 130 mL. The amount ejected, about 70 mL, is called the **stroke volume (SV).** This is about 54% of the EDV, a percentage called the **ejection fraction.** The blood remaining behind, about 60 mL in this case, is called the **end-systolic volume (ESV).** Note that EDV − SV = ESV. In vigorous exercise, the ejection fraction may be as high as 90%. Ejection fraction is an important measure of cardiac health. A diseased heart may eject much less than 50% of the blood it contains.

4. **Isovolumetric relaxation.** This is early ventricular diastole, when the T wave ends and the ventricles begin to expand. There are competing hypotheses as to how they expand. One is that the blood flowing into the ventricles inflates them. Another is that contraction of the ventricles deforms the fibrous skeleton, which subsequently springs back like the rubber bulb of a turkey baster that has been squeezed and released. This elastic recoil and expansion would cause pressure to drop rapidly and suck blood into the ventricles.

At the beginning of ventricular diastole, blood from the aorta and pulmonary trunk briefly flows backward through the semilunar valves. The backflow, however, quickly fills the cusps and closes them, creating a slight pressure rebound that appears as the *dicrotic notch* of the aortic pressure curve (the top curve in the Wiggers diagram). Heart sound S_2 occurs as blood rebounds from the closed semilunar valves and the ventricles expand. This phase is called *isovolumetric* because the semilunar valves are closed, the AV valves haven't yet opened, and the ventricles are therefore taking in no blood. When the AV valves open, ventricular filling (phase 1) begins again.

Heart sound S_3, if it occurs, is thought to result from the transition from expansion of the empty ventricles to their sudden filling with blood.

In a resting person, atrial systole lasts about 0.1 second; ventricular systole, 0.3 second; and the *quiescent period* (when all four chambers are in diastole), 0.4 second. Total duration of the cardiac cycle is therefore 0.8 second (800 ms) in a heart beating at 75 bpm.

19.5d Overview of Volume Changes

An additional perspective on the cardiac cycle can be gained if we review the volume changes that occur. This "balance sheet" is from the standpoint of one ventricle; both ventricles have equal volumes. The volumes vary somewhat from one person to another and depend on a person's state of activity.

End-systolic volume (ESV) left from the previous heartbeat	60 mL
Passively added to the ventricle during atrial diastole	+ 30 mL
Added by atrial systole	+ 40 mL
Total: End-diastolic volume (EDV)	130 mL
Stroke volume (SV) ejected by ventricular systole	− 70 mL
Leaves: End-systolic volume (ESV)	60 mL

Notice that the ventricle pumps out as much blood as it received during diastole: 70 mL in this example. Both ventricles eject the same amount of blood even though pressure in the right ventricle is only about one-fifth the pressure in the left. Blood pressure in the pulmonary trunk is relatively low, so the right ventricle doesn't need to generate very much pressure to overcome it.

Equal output by the two ventricles is essential for homeostasis. If the right ventricle pumps more blood into the lungs than the left ventricle can handle on return, blood accumulates in the lungs, causing pulmonary hypertension, edema, and a risk of drowning in one's own body fluid **(fig. 19.21a).** One of the first signs of left ventricular failure is respiratory distress—shortness of breath and a sense of suffocation. Conversely, if the left ventricle pumps more blood than the right, blood accumulates in the systemic circuit, causing hypertension and widespread systemic edema **(fig. 19.21b).** Such systemic edema, once colloquially called *dropsy,* is marked by enlargement of the liver; distension of the jugular veins in the neck; swelling of the fingers, ankles, and feet; and **ascites** (ah-SITE-eez), a pooling of fluid in the abdominal cavity (see figures 18.3 and 20.38). It can lead to stroke or kidney failure. A failure of one ventricle increases the workload on the other, which stresses it and often leads to its eventual failure as well. In principle, if the output of the left ventricle were just 1% greater than output of the right, it would completely drain the lungs of blood in less than 10 minutes (although death would occur much sooner).

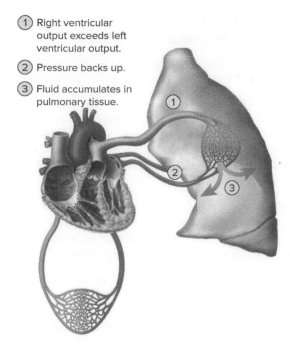

① Right ventricular output exceeds left ventricular output.

② Pressure backs up.

③ Fluid accumulates in pulmonary tissue.

(a) Pulmonary edema

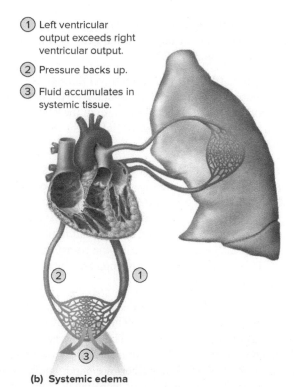

① Left ventricular output exceeds right ventricular output.

② Pressure backs up.

③ Fluid accumulates in systemic tissue.

(b) Systemic edema

FIGURE 19.21 The Necessity of Balanced Ventricular Output. (a) If the left ventricle pumps less blood than the right, blood pressure backs up into the lungs and causes pulmonary edema. (b) If the right ventricle pumps less blood than the left, pressure backs up in the systemic circulation and causes systemic edema. To maintain homeostasis, both ventricles must pump the same average amount of blood.

Fluid accumulation in either circuit due to insufficiency of ventricular pumping is called **congestive heart failure (CHF).** Common causes of CHF are myocardial infarction, chronic hypertension, valvular defects, and congenital (birth) defects in cardiac anatomy.

> **BEFORE YOU GO ON**
>
> Answer the following questions to test your understanding of the preceding section:
>
> 20. Explain how a pressure gradient across a heart valve determines whether a ventricle ejects blood.
>
> 21. What factors are thought to cause the first and second heart sounds? When do these sounds occur?
>
> 22. What phases of the cardiac cycle are isovolumetric? Explain what this means.
>
> 23. Define *end-diastolic volume* and *end-systolic volume;* explain verbally why stroke volume is the difference between these two.
>
> 24. Why is it so important that neither the right nor left ventricle pump more blood than the other one for any prolonged time?

19.6 Regulation of Cardiac Output

Expected Learning Outcomes

When you have completed this section, you should be able to

a. trace the routes of sympathetic and parasympathetic nerves to their target cells in the heart;

b. define *cardiac output* and explain its importance;

c. identify the factors that govern cardiac output;

d. discuss some of the nervous and chemical factors that alter heart rate, stroke volume, and cardiac output;

e. explain how the right and left ventricles achieve balanced output; and

f. describe some effects of exercise on cardiac output.

The heart doesn't pump the same amount of blood every minute of every day, but varies its output according to states of rest, exercise, emotion, and other factors. We all know of circumstances that make our hearts beat faster or harder. In this section, we explore how the sympathetic and parasympathetic nervous systems, hormones and drugs, and other factors regulate the heart.

19.6a Autonomic Innervation of the Heart

Even though the heart has its own pacemaker, its rhythm and contraction strength are moderated by signals arising from two **cardiac centers** in the medulla oblongata of the brainstem. One of these, the **cardioacceleratory center,** communicates with the heart by way of right and left **cardiac nerves** carrying sympathetic postganglionic nerve fibers. The other is the nearby **cardioinhibitory center,** which communicates with the heart by way of the right and left **vagus nerves** carrying parasympathetic preganglionic nerve fibers.

The sympathetic pathway to the heart is shown on the left side of **figure 19.22,** numbered as follows:

① Stimulatory signals from the cardioaccelerator center descend to the upper thoracic segments (T1–T4) of the spinal cord, ending on the sympathetic preganglionic neurons

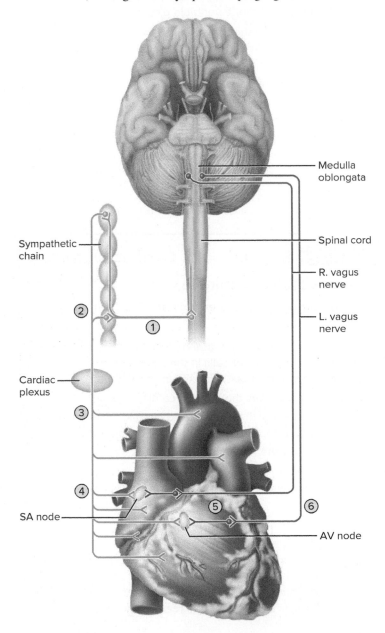

FIGURE 19.22 Autonomic Innervation of the Heart.
For schematic purposes, the cardiac plexus is shown offset from the heart, not in its natural location. The sympathetic and parasympathetic pathways both occur on the right and left, even though the sympathetic chain and nerves are illustrated only on the left and both vagus nerves are illustrated on the right.

in the lateral horn. Preganglionic fibers arise here and travel to the adjacent sympathetic chain ganglia.

② Some of these fibers synapse with postganglionic neurons at the level of entry into the chain, and others ascend to the cervical ganglia and meet the postganglionic neurons there.

③ Postganglionic fibers emerging from the sympathetic chain form the cardiac nerves. These lead to the **cardiac plexus,** a web of mixed sympathetic and parasympathetic fibers tucked in between the aortic arch, pulmonary trunk, and lower trachea.

④ Postganglionic fibers continue through the plexus without synapsing and end on several targets in and near the heart: the SA node, AV node, atrial and ventricular myocardium, aorta, pulmonary trunk, and coronary arteries.

Sympathetic stimulation increases the heart rate and contraction strength and dilates the coronary arteries to increase blood supply to the exercising myocardium.

The parasympathetic pathway is shown on the right side of the same figure. Parasympathetic signals from the cardioinhibitory center exit the medulla oblongata through the two vagus nerves. These nerves travel down the right and left sides of the mediastinum, but both are shown on the right side of the figure just for diagrammatic convenience. For a photo of the sympathetic chain and right vagus nerve in relation to the heart, see figure 15.3. The vagus nerves travel to their targets in the heart by the route numbered as follows in figure 19.22:

⑤ Preganglionic fibers of the vagus travel through the cardiac plexus, mingling with the sympathetic fibers. They synapse with short postganglionic fibers here in the plexus or in the epicardium of the atria, especially near the SA and AV nodes.

⑥ Short postganglionic fibers of the right vagus nerve lead mainly to the SA node and those of the left vagus lead mainly to the AV node, but each has some fibers that cross over to the other target cells. Furthermore, some parasympathetic fibers terminate on sympathetic fibers and inhibit them from stimulating the heart and opposing the parasympathetic effect. There is little or no parasympathetic innervation of the myocardium or ventricles.

In general, the sympathetic nerves dominate the control of contraction strength. Heart rate is strongly influenced by both divisions, but dominated by the vagus nerves. The cardiac nerves carry not only sympathetic efferent fibers, but also sensory (afferent) fibers from the heart to the CNS. These fibers are important in cardiovascular reflexes and the transmission of pain signals from the heart.

19.6b Cardiac Output

The entire point of all the cardiac physiology we have considered is to eject blood from the heart. The amount ejected by each ventricle in 1 minute is called the **cardiac output (CO).** If HR is heart rate (beats/min.) and SV is stroke volume (mL/beat),

$$CO = HR \times SV$$

At typical resting values,

CO = 75 beats/min. × 70 mL/beat = 5,250 mL/min.

Thus, the body's total volume of blood (4–6 L) passes through the heart every minute; or to look at it another way, an RBC leaving the left ventricle will, on average, arrive back at the left ventricle in about 1 minute.

Cardiac output varies with the body's state of activity. Vigorous exercise increases CO to as much as 21 L/min. in a person in good condition, and more than 40 L/min. in world-class athletes. The difference between the maximum and resting cardiac output is called **cardiac reserve.** People with severe heart disease may have little or no cardiac reserve and little tolerance of physical exertion.

Given that cardiac output equals HR × SV, you can see that there are only two ways to change it: Change the heart rate or change the stroke volume. We will consider factors that influence each of these variables, but bear in mind that heart rate and stroke volume are somewhat interdependent. They usually change together and in opposite directions. As heart rate goes up, stroke volume goes down, and vice versa.

19.6c Heart Rate and Chronotropic Agents

Heart rate is most easily measured by taking a person's **pulse** at some point where an artery runs close to the body surface, such as the *radial artery* in the wrist or *common carotid artery* in the neck. Each beat of the heart produces a surge of pressure that can be felt by palpating a superficial artery with the fingertips. Heart rate can be obtained by counting the number of pulses in 15 seconds and multiplying by 4 to get beats per minute. In newborn infants, the resting heart rate is commonly 120 bpm or greater. It declines steadily with age, averaging 72 to 80 bpm in young adult females and 64 to 72 bpm in young adult males. It rises again in the elderly.

Tachycardia[27] is a persistent, resting adult heart rate above 100 bpm. It can be caused by stress, anxiety, stimulants, heart disease, or fever. Heart rate also rises to compensate to some extent for a drop in stroke volume. Thus, the heart races when the body has lost a significant quantity of blood or when there is damage to the myocardium.

Bradycardia[28] is a persistent, resting adult heart rate below 60 bpm. It is common during sleep and in endurance-trained athletes. Endurance training enlarges the heart and increases its stroke volume, enabling it to maintain the same output with fewer beats. Hypothermia (low body temperature) also slows the heart and may be deliberately induced in preparation for cardiac surgery. Diving mammals such as whales and seals exhibit bradycardia during the dive, as do humans to some extent when the face is immersed in cool water.

Factors outside of the heart itself that raise the heart rate are called **positive chronotropic**[29] **agents,** and factors that lower it are **negative chronotropic agents.** We next consider some

chronotropic effects of the autonomic nervous system, hormones, electrolytes, and blood gases.

The Autonomic Nervous System

Although the nervous system doesn't initiate the heartbeat, it does modulate its rhythm and force through the aforementioned autonomic nerves. The sympathetic nervous system exerts its effects directly through the cardiac nerves and indirectly by stimulating the adrenal medulla. The nerve fibers secrete norepinephrine (NE) and the adrenal medulla secretes a mixture of about 85% epinephrine (Epi) and 15% NE—known collectively as *catecholamines.* Both of these have positive chronotropic *and* inotropic effects on the heart, but for the moment, we will focus on the chronotropic effect.

Epi and NE bind to β-adrenergic receptors in the heart and activate the cyclic adenosine monophosphate (cAMP) second-messenger system (see fig. 3.8). Cyclic AMP activates an enzyme that opens Ca^{2+} channels in the plasma membrane, admitting calcium from the extracellular fluid into the SA node and cardiomyocytes. This accelerates depolarization of the SA node and speeds up signal conduction through the AV node. Both of these quicken the contractions of the ventricular myocardium and speed up the heartbeat. In addition, cAMP accelerates the reuptake of Ca^{2+} by the sarcoplasmic reticulum of the cardiomyocytes. Quick Ca^{2+} reuptake shortens ventricular systole and the QT interval (see table 19.1), enabling the ventricles to relax and refill sooner than they do at rest. By accelerating *both* the contraction and relaxation of the heart, cAMP increases the heart rate.

Adrenergic stimulation can, in fact, raise the heart rate to as high as 230 bpm. This limit is set mainly by the refractory period of the SA node, which prevents it from firing any more frequently. Cardiac output peaks, however, at a rate of 160 to 180 bpm. At rates any higher than this, the ventricles have too little time to fill between beats. At a resting rate of 65 bpm, ventricular diastole lasts about 0.62 second, but at 200 bpm, it lasts only 0.14 second. Thus you can see that at excessively high heart rates, diastole is too brief to allow complete filling of the ventricles, and therefore stroke volume and cardiac output are reduced.

The parasympathetic vagus nerves, by contrast, have a negative chronotropic effect. Left to itself, the SA node and the heart as a whole have a resting rhythm of about 100 bpm; this is seen if all nerves to the heart are severed or if all sympathetic and parasympathetic action is pharmacologically blocked. But with intact, functional innervation, the vagus nerves have a steady background firing rate called **vagal tone** that holds the heart rate down to its usual 70 to 80 bpm at rest. The heart can be accelerated not only by sympathetic stimulation but also by reducing vagal tone and allowing the heart to "do its own thing." Extreme vagal stimulation can reduce the heart rate to as low as 20 bpm or even stop the heart briefly.

The postganglionic neurons of the vagus are cholinergic—they secrete acetylcholine (ACh) at the SA and AV nodes. ACh binds to muscarinic receptors and opens K^+ gates in the nodal cells. The resulting outflow of K^+ hyperpolarizes the cells, so the SA node fires less frequently and the heart slows down. ACh acts primarily on the SA node but also slows signal conduction through the AV

---

[27]*tachy* = speed, fast; *card* = heart; *ia* = condition
[28]*brady* = slow; *card* = heart; *ia* = condition
[29]*chrono* = time; *trop* = to change, to influence

node, thus delaying excitation of the ventricles. The vagus nerves have a faster-acting effect on the heart than the sympathetic nerves because ACh acts directly on membrane ion channels; sympathetic effects are slower because of the time taken for the cAMP system to open ion channels.

▶▶▶**APPLY WHAT YOU KNOW**

Which of the intervals or segments of the electrocardiogram do you think is or are most affected by ACh? Explain your answer.

The Central Nervous System

There is a benefit to placing heart rate under the influence of cardiac centers in the medulla—these centers can receive input from many other sources and integrate it into a decision as to whether the heart should beat more quickly or slowly. Sensory and emotional stimuli can act on the cardiac centers by way of the cerebral cortex, limbic system, and hypothalamus; therefore, heart rate can climb even as you anticipate taking the first plunge on a roller coaster or competing in an athletic event, and it is influenced by emotions such as love and anger. The medulla also receives input from the following receptors in the muscles, joints, arteries, and brainstem:

- **Proprioceptors** in the muscles and joints provide information on changes in physical activity. Thus, the heart can increase its output even before the metabolic demands of the muscles rise.

- **Baroreceptors (pressoreceptors)** are pressure sensors in the aorta and internal carotid arteries (see figs. 15.1, 20.4). They send a continual stream of signals to the medulla. When the heart rate rises, cardiac output increases and raises the blood pressure at the baroreceptors. The baroreceptors increase their signaling to the medulla and, depending on circumstances, the medulla may issue vagal output to lower the heart rate. Conversely, the baroreceptors also inform the medulla of drops in blood pressure. The medulla can then issue sympathetic output to increase the heart rate, bringing cardiac output and blood pressure back up to normal (see fig. 1.8). Either way, a negative feedback loop usually prevents the blood pressure from deviating too far from normal.

- **Chemoreceptors** occur in the aortic arch, carotid arteries, and the medulla oblongata itself, and are sensitive to blood pH, CO_2, and O_2 levels. They are more important in respiratory control than in cardiovascular control, but they do influence the heart rate. If circulation to the tissues is too slow to remove CO_2 as fast as the tissues produce it, then CO_2 accumulates in the blood and cerebrospinal fluid (CSF) and produces a state of *hypercapnia* (CO_2 excess). Furthermore, CO_2 generates hydrogen ions by reacting with water: $CO_2 + H_2O \longrightarrow HCO_3^- + H^+$. The hydrogen ions lower the pH of the blood and CSF and may create a state of *acidosis* (pH < 7.35). Hypercapnia and acidosis stimulate the cardiac centers to increase the heart rate,

thus improving perfusion of the tissues and restoring homeostasis. The chemoreceptors also respond to extreme *hypoxemia* (oxygen deficiency), as in suffocation, but the effect is usually to slow down the heart, perhaps so the heart doesn't compete with the brain for the limited oxygen supply.

Such responses to fluctuations in blood chemistry and blood pressure, called **chemoreflexes** and **baroreflexes,** are good examples of negative feedback loops. They are discussed more fully in the next chapter.

Hormones, Drugs, and Other Chronotropic Chemicals

Heart rate is influenced by many other factors besides the autonomic nervous system. Thyroid hormone accelerates it by stimulating the up-regulation of β-adrenergic receptors, making the heart more sensitive to sympathetic stimulation; this is why tachycardia is one of the signs of hyperthyroidism. Glucagon, secreted by the alpha cells of the pancreatic islets, accelerates the heart by promoting cAMP production. Glucagon is sometimes given in cardiac emergencies to stimulate the heartbeat, and epinephrine is frequently given to support cardiac output and blood pressure in life-threatening allergic reactions.

Food-borne drugs and medications also have well-known chronotropic effects related to the catecholamine–cAMP mechanism. Nicotine accelerates the heart by stimulating catecholamine secretion. Caffeine and the related stimulants in tea and chocolate accelerate it by inhibiting cAMP breakdown, prolonging its adrenergic effect. Hypertension is often treated with drugs called *beta blockers,* which inhibit the binding of catecholamines to the β-adrenergic receptors and slow down the heart.

Electrolyte concentrations also strongly influence heart rate and contraction strength. The most powerful chronotropic effects are from potassium ions (K^+). In *hyperkalemia,*[30] a potassium excess, K^+ diffuses into the cardiomyocytes and keeps the membrane voltage elevated, inhibiting cardiomyocyte repolarization. The myocardium becomes less excitable, the heart rate becomes slow and irregular, and the heart may arrest in diastole. In *hypokalemia,* a potassium deficiency, K^+ diffuses out of the cardiomyocytes and they become hyperpolarized—the membrane potential is more negative than normal. This makes them harder to stimulate. These potassium imbalances are very dangerous and require emergency medical treatment.

Calcium also affects heart rate. A calcium excess *(hypercalcemia)* causes a slow heartbeat, whereas a calcium deficiency *(hypocalcemia)* elevates the heart rate. Such calcium imbalances are relatively rare, however, and when they do occur, their primary effect is on contraction strength, which is considered in the coming section on contractility. Section 24.2 further explores the causes and effects of imbalances in potassium, calcium, and other electrolytes.

---

[30]*hyper* = excess; *kal* = potassium (Latin, *kalium*); *emia* = blood condition

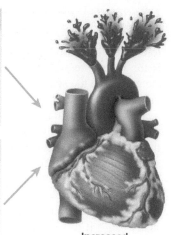

Increased heart rate (HR)

Positive chronotropic agents
  Sympathetic nervous system
  Epinephrine, norepinephrine
  Thyroid hormone
  Glucagon
  Nicotine, caffeine
  Hypocalcemia

Increased stroke volume (SV)

Increased preload (myocardial stretch)
Positive inotropic agents
  Sympathetic nervous system
  Epinephrine, norepinephrine
  Glucagon
  Digitalis
  Nicotine, caffeine
  Hypercalcemia

Reduced heart rate (HR)

Negative chronotropic agents
  Parasympathetic nervous system
  Acetylcholine
  Hypercalcemia
  Hypokalemia
  Beta blockers

Reduced stroke volume (SV)

Reduced preload
Reduced contractility
Increased afterload
Negative inotropic agents
  Hypocalcemia
  Hyperkalemia

Increased   **Reduced**

Cardiac Output
(CO = HR × SV)

FIGURE 19.23 Summary of Factors Affecting Cardiac Output. Factors on the left (green boxes) increase cardiac output, whereas factors on the right (red boxes) reduce it. These include the intrinsic state of the heart and adjacent arteries at a given time (preload, contractility, and afterload), and extrinsic agents that act on the heart (chronotropic and inotropic agents).

Several positive and negative chronotropic agents are shown in the top half of **figure 19.23,** summarizing how they affect cardiac output by altering heart rate. We move on now to the bottom half of the figure and inotropic agents, which act on cardiac output through their effects on contraction strength and stroke volume.

19.6d Stroke Volume and Inotropic Agents

The other factor in cardiac output is stroke volume. This is governed by three variables called *preload, contractility,* and *afterload.* Increased preload or contractility increases stroke volume, whereas increased afterload opposes the emptying of the ventricles and reduces stroke volume.

Preload

Preload is the amount of tension (stretch) in the ventricular myocardium immediately before it begins to contract. To understand how this influences stroke volume, imagine yourself engaged in heavy exercise. As active muscles massage your veins, they drive more blood back to the heart, increasing *venous return.* As more blood enters the heart, it stretches the myocardium. Because of the length–tension relationship of striated muscle (see fig. 11.12), moderate stretch enables the cardiomyocytes to generate more tension when they contract—that is, stretch increases preload. When the ventricles contract more forcefully, they expel more blood, thus adjusting cardiac output to the increase in venous return.

This principle is summarized by the **Frank–Starling law of the heart.**[31] In a concise, symbolic way, it states that SV ∝ EDV;

that is, stroke volume is proportional to the end-diastolic volume. In other words, the ventricles tend to eject as much blood as they receive. Within limits, the more they are stretched, the harder they contract on the next beat.

Although relaxed skeletal muscle is normally at an optimum length for the most forceful contraction, relaxed cardiac muscle is at less than optimum length. Additional stretch therefore produces a significant increase in contraction force on the next beat. This helps balance the output of the two ventricles. For example, if the right ventricle begins to pump an increased amount of blood, this soon arrives at the left ventricle, stretches it more than before, and causes it to increase its stroke volume and match that of the right.

Contractility

Contractility refers to how hard the myocardium contracts *for a given preload.* It doesn't describe the increase in tension produced by stretching the muscle, but rather an increase caused by factors that make the cardiomyocytes more responsive to stimulation. Factors that increase contractility are called **positive inotropic**[32] **agents,** and those that reduce it are **negative inotropic agents.**

Calcium has a strong, positive inotropic effect—it increases the strength of each contraction of the heart. This is not surprising, because Ca^{2+} not only is essential to the excitation–contraction coupling of muscle, but also prolongs the plateau of the myocardial action potential. Calcium imbalances therefore affect not only heart rate, as we have already seen, but also contraction strength. In hypercalcemia, extra Ca^{2+} diffuses into the cardiomyocytes and produces strong, prolonged contractions.

[31]Otto Frank (1865–1944), German physiologist; Ernest Henry Starling (1866–1927), English physiologist

[32]*ino* = fiber; *trop* = to change, to influence

In extreme cases, it can cause cardiac arrest in systole. In hypocalcemia, the cardiomyocytes lose Ca^{2+} to the extracellular fluid, leading to a weak, irregular heartbeat and potentially to cardiac arrest in diastole. However, severe hypocalcemia is likely to kill through skeletal muscle paralysis and suffocation before the cardiac effects are felt (see section 7.4b).

Agents that affect calcium availability have not only the chronotropic effects already examined, but also inotropic effects. We have already seen that norepinephrine increases calcium levels in the sarcoplasm; consequently, it increases not only heart rate but also contraction strength (as does epinephrine, for the same reason). The pancreatic hormone glucagon exerts an inotropic effect by stimulating cAMP production; a solution of glucagon and calcium chloride is sometimes used for the emergency treatment of heart attacks. Digitalis, a cardiac stimulant from the foxglove plant, also raises the intracellular calcium level and contraction strength; it is used to treat congestive heart failure.

Hyperkalemia has a negative inotropic effect because it reduces the strength of myocardial action potentials and thus reduces the release of Ca^{2+} into the sarcoplasm. The heart becomes dilated and flaccid. Hypokalemia, however, has little effect on contractility.

The vagus nerves have a negative inotropic effect on the atria, but they provide so little innervation to the ventricles that they have no significant effect on them.

▶▶▶**APPLY WHAT YOU KNOW**

Suppose a person has a heart rate of 70 bpm and a stroke volume of 70 mL. A negative inotropic agent then reduces the stroke volume to 50 mL. What would the new heart rate have to be to maintain the same cardiac output?

Afterload

Afterload is the sum of all forces a ventricle must overcome before it can eject blood. The most significant contribution to afterload is the blood pressure in the aorta and pulmonary trunk immediately distal to the semilunar valves; it opposes the opening of these valves and thus limits stroke volume. For this reason, hypertension increases the afterload and opposes ventricular ejection. Anything that impedes arterial circulation, such as atherosclerotic plaque in the arteries, can also increase the afterload. In some lung diseases, scar tissue forms in the lungs and restricts pulmonary circulation. This increases the afterload in the pulmonary trunk. As the right ventricle works harder to overcome this resistance, it gets larger like any other muscle. Stress and hypertrophy of a ventricle can eventually cause it to weaken and fail. Right ventricular failure due to obstructed pulmonary circulation is called *cor pulmonale*[33] (CORE PUL-mo-NAY-lee). It is a common complication of emphysema, chronic bronchitis, and black lung disease (see section 22.4b).

19.6e Exercise and Cardiac Output

It is no secret that exercise makes the heart work harder, and it should come as no surprise that this increases cardiac output. The main reason the heart rate increases at the beginning of exercise is that proprioceptors in the muscles and joints transmit signals to the cardiac centers, signifying that the muscles are active and will quickly need an increased blood flow. Sympathetic output from the cardiac centers then increases cardiac output to meet the expected demand. As the exercise progresses, muscular activity increases venous return. This increases the preload on the right ventricle and is soon reflected in the left ventricle as more blood

---

[33]*cor* = heart; *pulmo* = lung

TABLE 19.2	Some Disorders of the Heart
Acute pericarditis	Inflammation of the pericardium, sometimes due to infection, radiation therapy, or connective tissue disease, causing pain and friction rub
Cardiomyopathy	Any disease of the myocardium not resulting from coronary artery disease, valvular dysfunction, or other cardiovascular disorders; can cause dilation and failure of the heart, thinning of the heart wall, or thickening of the interventricular septum
Infective endocarditis	Inflammation of the endocardium, usually due to bacterial infection, especially *Streptococcus* and *Staphylococcus*
Myocardial ischemia	Inadequate blood flow to the myocardium, usually because of coronary atherosclerosis; can lead to myocardial infarction
Pericardial effusion	Seepage of fluid from the pericardium into the pericardial cavity, often resulting from pericarditis and sometimes causing cardiac tamponade
Septal defects	Abnormal openings in the interatrial or interventricular septum, resulting in blood from the right atrium flowing directly into the left atrium, or blood from the left ventricle returning to the right ventricle; results in pulmonary hypertension, difficulty breathing, and fatigue; often fatal in childhood if uncorrected

You can find other cardiac disorders described in the following places:

Cardiac tamponade in Deeper Insight A.1; *friction rub* in section 19.1c; *angina pectoris* and *myocardial infarction* in Deeper Insight 19.1; *ventricular fibrillation, atrial fibrillation, premature ventricular contraction, bundle branch block, total heart block,* and *cardiac arrest* in Deeper Insight 19.2; *valvular stenosis, mitral valve prolapse,* and *heart murmur* in Deeper Insight 19.3; *congestive heart failure* in section 19.5d; *bradycardia and tachycardia* in section 19.6c; *cor pulmonale* in section 19.6d; and *atherosclerosis, arteriosclerosis,* and *coronary artery disease* in Deeper Insight 19.4.

flows through the pulmonary circuit and reaches the left heart. As the heart rate and stroke volume rise, cardiac output rises, which compensates for the increased venous return.

A sustained program of exercise causes hypertrophy of the ventricles, which increases their stroke volume. As explained earlier, this allows the heart to beat more slowly and still maintain a normal resting cardiac output. Some world-class, endurance-trained athletes have resting heart rates as low as 30 to 40 bpm, but because of the higher stroke volume, their resting cardiac output is about the same as that of an untrained person. Such athletes have greater cardiac reserve, so they can tolerate more exertion than a sedentary person can.

The effects of aging on the heart are discussed in section 29.4a, and some common heart diseases are listed in **table 19.2**. Disorders of the blood and blood vessels are described in chapters 18 and 20.

BEFORE YOU GO ON

Answer the following questions to test your understanding of the preceding section:

25. Explain why the vagus nerves have no significant inotropic effect on the ventricular myocardium.

26. Define *cardiac output* in words and with a simple mathematical formula.

27. Describe the cardiac center and innervation of the heart.

28. Explain what is meant by positive and negative chronotropic and inotropic agents. Give two examples of each.

29. How do preload, contractility, and afterload influence stroke volume and cardiac output?

30. Explain the principle behind the Frank–Starling law of the heart. How does this mechanism normally prevent pulmonary or systemic congestion?

DEEPER INSIGHT 19.4

CLINICAL APPLICATION

Coronary Artery Disease

Coronary artery disease (CAD) is a constriction of the coronary arteries usually resulting from *atherosclerosis*[34]—an accumulation of lipid deposits that degrade the arterial wall and obstruct the lumen. The most dangerous consequence of CAD is myocardial infarction (heart attack).

Pathogenesis
CAD begins when hypertension, diabetes, or other factors damage the arterial lining. Monocytes adhere to the lining, penetrate into the tissue, and become macrophages. Macrophages and smooth muscle cells absorb cholesterol and fat from the blood, which gives them a frothy appearance. They are then called *foam cells* and form visible *fatty streaks* on the arterial wall. Seen even in infants and children, these are harmless in themselves but have the potential to grow into atherosclerotic *plaques (atheromas*[35]*)*.

Platelets adhere to these plaques and secrete a growth factor that stimulates local proliferation of smooth muscle and fibroblasts and deposition of collagen. The plaque grows into a bulging mass of lipid, fiber, and smooth muscle and other cells. When it obstructs 75% or more of the arterial lumen, it begins to cause symptoms such as angina pectoris. More seriously, inflammation of the plaque roughens its surface and creates a focal point for thrombosis. A blood clot can block what remains of the lumen, or break free and lodge in a smaller artery downstream. Sometimes a piece of plaque breaks free and travels as a *fatty embolus.* Furthermore, the plaque can contribute to spasms of the coronary artery, cutting off blood flow to the myocardium. If the lumen is already partially obstructed by a plaque and perhaps a blood clot, such a spasm can temporarily shut off the remaining flow and precipitate an attack of angina.

Over time, the resilient muscular and elastic tissue of an inflamed artery becomes increasingly replaced with scar tissue and calcium deposits, transforming an atheroma into a hard *complicated plaque* **(fig. 19.24)**. Hardening of the arteries by calcified plaques is one cause of *arteriosclerosis.*[36] For reasons explained in the next chapter, this results in excessive surges of blood pressure that may weaken and rupture smaller arteries, leading to stroke and kidney failure.

Risk, Prevention, and Treatment
A paramount risk factor for CAD is excess *low-density lipoproteins (LDLs)* in the blood combined with defective LDL receptors in the arterial walls. LDLs are protein-coated droplets of cholesterol, fats, free fatty acids, and phospholipids (see "Cholesterol and Serum Lipoproteins" in section 26.1g). Most cells have LDL receptors that enable them to absorb these droplets from the blood so they can metabolize the cholesterol and other lipids. CAD can occur when the arterial cells have dysfunctional LDL receptors that "don't know when to quit," so the cells absorb and accumulate excess cholesterol.

Some risk factors for CAD are unavoidable—for example, heredity and aging. Most risk factors, however, are preventable—obesity, smoking, lack of exercise, and a personality fraught with anxiety, stress, and aggression, all conducive to the hypertension that initiates arterial damage. Diet, of course, is very significant. Eating animal fat raises one's LDL level and reduces the number of LDL receptors. Foods high in soluble fiber (such as beans, apples, and oat bran) lower blood cholesterol by an interesting mechanism: The liver normally converts cholesterol to bile acids and secretes them into the small intestine to aid fat digestion. The bile acids are reabsorbed farther down the intestine and recycled to the liver for reuse. Soluble fiber, however, binds bile acids and carries them out in the feces. To replace them, the liver synthesizes more, thus consuming more cholesterol.

CAD is often treated with a *coronary artery bypass graft (CABG)*. Sections of the great saphenous vein of the leg or small thoracic arteries are used to construct a detour around the obstruction in the coronary artery. In *balloon angioplasty,*[37] a slender catheter is threaded into the coronary artery and then a balloon at its tip is inflated to press the atheroma against the arterial wall, widening the lumen. In *laser angioplasty,* the surgeon views the interior of the diseased artery with an illuminated catheter and vaporizes the atheroma with a laser. Angioplasty is less risky and expensive than bypass surgery, but is often followed by *restenosis*—atheromas grow back and reobstruct the artery months later. Insertion of a tube called a *stent* into the artery can prevent restenosis.

---

[34] *athero* = fat, fatty; *sclerosis* = hardening
[35] *athero* = fat, fatty; *oma* = mass, tumor
[36] *arterio* = artery; *sclerosis* = hardening

[37] *angio* = vessel; *plasty* = surgical repair

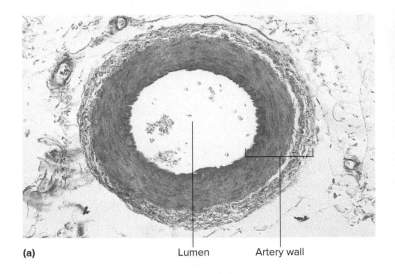

(a)
Lumen   Artery wall

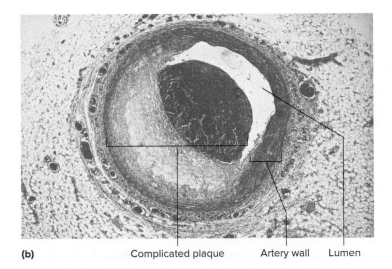

(b)
Complicated plaque   Artery wall   Lumen

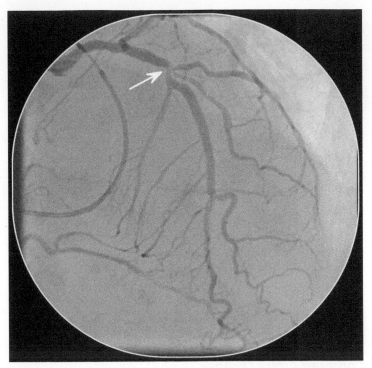

(c)

FIGURE 19.24 Coronary Artery Disease. (a) Cross section of a healthy coronary artery. (b) Cross section of an artery with advanced coronary atherosclerosis. Most of the original lumen is obstructed by a *complicated plaque* composed of calcified scar tissue. The lumen is reduced to a small space that can easily be blocked by a stationary or traveling blood clot (thrombosis or thromboembolism, respectively) or by vasoconstriction. (c) Coronary angiogram showing 60% obstruction, at arrow, of the anterior interventricular (left anterior descending, LAD) artery.

a: Ed Reschke/Getty Images; b: Image Source/Getty Images; c: kalewa/Shutterstock

STUDY GUIDE

▶ Assess Your Learning Outcomes

To test your knowledge, discuss the following topics with a study partner or in writing, ideally from memory.

19.1 Overview of the Cardiovascular System

1. Two subdivisions of the cardiovascular system and their respective functions
2. Names of the great vessels directly connected to the heart, and their relations to the heart chambers
3. The exact location of the heart, its size, and its base and apex
4. Anatomy and function of the pericardium and pericardial fluid

19.2 Gross Anatomy of the Heart

1. Three layers of the heart wall and their histological differences
2. Relative thickness of the myocardium in different chambers; the functional significance of those differences; and significance of the vortex of the heart
3. Structure and function of the fibrous skeleton of the heart
4. Anatomy and functions of the atria and ventricles; the internal septa that separate the four chambers and the external sulci that mark the chamber boundaries
5. Names and synonyms for all four valves of the heart
6. Structural differences between the valves; anatomy and function of the papillary muscles and tendinous cords
7. The path of blood flow through the heart chambers and valves
8. Anatomy of the coronary arteries and their main branches
9. Causes of myocardial infarction (MI) and how the collateral circulation in the coronary arteries reduces the risk of MI
10. Why coronary artery blood flow is greater when the heart relaxes than when it contracts, in contrast to the arterial system almost everywhere else in the body
11. Anatomy of the major veins that drain the myocardium, where this blood goes, and how the major veins are supplemented by the small cardiac veins

19.3 Cardiac Muscle and the Cardiac Conduction System

1. Structural properties of cardiomyocytes, how they differ from skeletal muscle, and how they relate to the unique function of cardiac muscle
2. Properties of cardiac muscle related to its nearly exclusive reliance on aerobic respiration
3. Components of the cardiac conduction system and the path traveled by electrical signals through the heart

19.4 Electrical and Contractile Activity of the Heart

1. The meanings of *systole* and *diastole*
2. Characteristics of the sinus rhythm of the heart; some causes of premature ventricular contraction; why an ectopic focus may take over control of the rhythm; how a nodal rhythm differs from the sinus rhythm; and the general term for any abnormal cardiac rhythm
3. The mechanism that causes cells of the SA node to depolarize rhythmically; a graph of the time course and voltages of the pacemaker potentials; how often this repeats itself in a normal resting heart; and the role of gated ion channels and specific ion inflows and outflows in creating the nodal rhythm
4. The spread of excitation through the atria, AV node, AV bundle and bundle branches, and subendocardial conducting network; changing conduction speeds at different points along this path, and why these changes are important; and the correlation of atrial and ventricular systole with the traveling wave of excitation
5. The twisting mode of ventricular contraction and the importance of the tendinous cords in preventing valvular prolapse
6. The cardiomyocyte resting potential; the actions of gated sodium, calcium, and potassium channels, and movements of these ions, in producing myocardial action potentials; how and why the shape of a myocardial action potential differs from that of a neuron; and how the plateau and unusually long refractory period of myocardial action potentials support the pumping effectiveness of the heart

7. Electrocardiograms and what happens in the heart during each ECG wave

19.5 Blood Flow, Heart Sounds, and the Cardiac Cycle

1. The principle on which a sphygmomanometer works, and why BP is expressed in millimeters of mercury (mm Hg)
2. The relationship of fluid volume, pressure, and flow, and how this relates to blood flow during the expansion and contraction of the heart chambers
3. Mechanisms that open and close the heart valves
4. The definition of *cardiac cycle,* and the names of its four phases
5. In each phase of the cardiac cycle, which chambers depolarize or repolarize, contract or relax; what each pair of valves does; what appears in the ECG; what accounts for the heart sounds; whether blood moves into or out of the atria or ventricles and where it is going when ejected; and blood volume and pressure changes in the left atrium, left ventricle, and aorta
6. The typical duration, in seconds, of atrial systole, ventricular systole, and the quiescent period, and how heart rate can be calculated from these values
7. The volume of blood typically found in each ventricle when it has finished filling; the volume ejected when a ventricle contracts; the percentage of ventricular blood that is ejected; the amount that remains behind when contraction is finished; and names of these four variables
8. Why it is necessary that each ventricle eject the same average amount of blood; what happens if either ventricle ejects more than the other over an extended period of time

19.6 Regulation of Cardiac Output

1. Pathways of sympathetic and parasympathetic innervation of the heart
2. The meaning of *cardiac output* and how to calculate it from heart rate and stroke volume
3. The typical resting heart rate and how it changes with age

STUDY GUIDE

4. Causes and terms for abnormally fast and slow resting heart rates
5. The definitions and cardiac effects of *positive* and *negative chronotropic agents*
6. Effects of the sympathetic and parasympathetic nervous systems on heart rate
7. The heart rate range associated with maximum cardiac output, and why cardiac output doesn't rise any farther at still faster heart rates
8. The intrinsic firing rate of the SA node and how vagal tone normally holds the resting heart rate below this

9. Control centers of the brainstem that regulate heart rate, and their mode of action
10. How proprioceptors, baroreceptors, and chemoreceptors influence heart rate
11. Effects of norepinephrine and acetylcholine on heart rate, and their mechanisms of action
12. Hormones and drugs that affect heart rate, and their mechanisms of action
13. Effects of potassium and calcium levels on heart rate, and their mechanisms of action
14. The meanings of *preload, contractility,* and *afterload,* and how each one affects stroke volume

15. How the Frank–Starling law of the heart matches stroke volume to venous return
16. The definitions and cardiac effects of *positive* and *negative inotropic agents*
17. How calcium and potassium affect myocardial contractility
18. How norepinephrine, glucagon, and digitalis affect contractility
19. How certain diseases reduce cardiac output by increasing afterload
20. The mechanisms by which exercise increases cardiac output
21. Why well-conditioned athletes may have unusually low resting heart rates

▶ Testing Your Recall

Answers in Appendix A

1. The cardiac conduction system includes all of the following *except*
   a. the SA node.
   b. the AV node.
   c. the bundle branches.
   d. the tendinous cords.
   e. the subendocardial conducting network.

2. To get from the right atrium to the right ventricle, blood flows through
   a. the pulmonary valve.
   b. the tricuspid valve.
   c. the bicuspid valve.
   d. the aortic valve.
   e. the mitral valve.

3. Assume that one ventricle of a child's heart has an EDV of 90 mL, an ESV of 60 mL, and a cardiac output of 2.55 L/min. What are the child's stroke volume (SV), ejection fraction (EF), and heart rate (HR)?
   a. SV = 60 mL; EF = 33%; HR = 85 bpm
   b. SV = 30 mL; EF = 60%; HR = 75 bpm
   c. SV = 150 mL; EF = 67%; HR = 42 bpm
   d. SV = 30 mL; EF = 33%; HR = 85 bpm
   e. Not enough information is given to calculate these.

4. A heart rate of 45 bpm and an absence of P waves suggest
   a. damage to the SA node.
   b. ventricular fibrillation.
   c. cor pulmonale.
   d. extrasystole.
   e. heart block.

5. There is/are _____ pulmonary vein(s) emptying into the right atrium of the heart.
   a. no
   b. one
   c. two
   d. four
   e. more than four

6. All of the following are positive chronotropic agents *except*
   a. caffeine.
   b. thyroid hormone.
   c. norepinephrine.
   d. acetylcholine.
   e. hypocalcemia.

7. The atria contract during
   a. the first heart sound.
   b. the second heart sound.
   c. the QRS complex.
   d. the PQ segment.
   e. the ST segment.

8. Cardiac muscle does not exhibit tetanus because it has
   a. fast Ca^{2+} channels.
   b. scanty sarcoplasmic reticulum.
   c. a long absolute refractory period.
   d. electrical synapses.
   e. exclusively aerobic respiration.

9. The blood contained in a ventricle during isovolumetric relaxation is
   a. the end-systolic volume.
   b. the end-diastolic volume.
   c. the stroke volume.
   d. the ejection fraction.
   e. none of these; the ventricle is empty then.

10. Drugs that increase myocardial contractility have a _____ effect.
    a. myogenic
    b. negative inotropic
    c. positive inotropic
    d. negative chronotropic
    e. positive chronotropic

11. The contraction of any heart chamber is called _____ and its relaxation is called _____.

12. The circulatory route from aorta to the venae cavae is the _____ circuit.

13. The circumflex artery travels in a groove called the _____.

14. The pacemaker potential of the SA node cells results from the slow inflow of _____.

15. Electrical signals pass quickly from one cardiomyocyte to another through the _____ of the intercalated discs.

16. Repolarization of the ventricles produces the _____ of the electrocardiogram.

17. The _____ nerves innervate the heart and tend to reduce the heart rate.

18. The death of cardiac tissue from lack of blood flow is commonly known as a heart attack, but clinically called _____.

19. Blood in the heart chambers is separated from the myocardium by a thin membrane called the _____.

20. The Frank–Starling law of the heart explains why the _____ of the left ventricle is the same as that of the right ventricle.

STUDY GUIDE

▶ Building Your Medical Vocabulary

Answers in Appendix A

State a meaning of each word element, and give a medical term from this chapter that uses it or a slight variation of it.

1. atrio-

2. brady-

3. cardio-

4. corono-

5. lun-

6. papillo-

7. semi-

8. tachy-

9. vaso-

10. ventro-

▶ What's Wrong with These Statements?

Answers in Appendix A

Briefly explain why each of the following statements is false, or reword it to make it true.

1. The blood supply to the myocardium is the coronary circulation; everything else is called the systemic circuit.

2. One-way valves prevent atrial systole from driving blood back into the venae cavae and pulmonary veins.

3. No blood can enter the ventricles until the atria contract.

4. The vagus nerves reduce the heart rate and the strength of ventricular contraction.

5. A high blood CO_2 level and low pH slow the heart rate.

6. The first heart sound occurs at the time of the P wave of the electrocardiogram.

7. If all nerves to the heart were severed, the heart would instantly stop beating.

8. If the two pulmonary arteries were clamped shut, pulmonary edema would soon follow.

9. Unlike skeletal muscle, cardiac muscle cells do not have a stable resting membrane potential.

10. An electrocardiogram is a tracing of the action potential of a cardiomyocyte.

▶ Testing Your Comprehension

1. Verapamil is a calcium channel blocker used to treat hypertension. It selectively blocks slow calcium channels. Would you expect it to have a positive or negative inotropic effect? Explain. (See Deeper Insight 3.1 to review calcium channel blockers.)

2. To temporarily treat tachycardia and restore the normal resting sinus rhythm, a physician may massage a patient's carotid artery near the angle of the mandible. Propose a mechanism by which this treatment would have the desired effect.

3. Becky, age 2, was born with a hole in her interventricular septum *(ventricular septal defect, or VSD)*. Considering that the blood pressure in the left ventricle is significantly higher than blood pressure in the right ventricle, predict the effect of the VSD on Becky's pulmonary blood pressure, systemic blood pressure, and long-term changes in the ventricular walls.

4. In ventricular systole, the left ventricle is the first to begin contracting, but the right ventricle is the first to expel blood. Aside from the obvious fact that the pulmonary valve opens before the aortic valve, how can you explain this difference?

5. In dilated cardiomyopathy of the left ventricle, the ventricle can become enormously enlarged. Explain why this might lead to regurgitation of blood through the mitral valve (blood flowing from the ventricle back into the left atrium) during ventricular systole.

THE CIRCULATORY SYSTEM: BLOOD VESSELS AND CIRCULATION

Blood capillary beds
Biophoto Associates/Science Source

Anatomy & Physiology *Revealed* 4.0

Module 9: Cardiovascular System

BRUSHING UP

- The concepts of homeostatic set point and dynamic equilibrium should be reviewed (see section 1.6c) as background for understanding the control of blood pressure.

- Blood circulation is governed by the principle of flow down pressure gradients (see section 1.6e).

- The principles of blood volume, pressure, and flow discussed in this chapter hinge on the reasons explained in section 18.1d for the osmolarity and viscosity of blood.

- Familiarity with cardiac systole and diastole (see section 19.4) is necessary for understanding blood pressure in this chapter.

- The exchange of materials between the blood capillaries and surrounding tissues is based on the principles of filtration, osmosis and osmotic pressure, diffusion, and transcytosis introduced in section 3.3.

- Blood vessels of the limbs are described in this chapter with reference to muscle compartments (see section 10.1b, fig. 10.3) and interosseous membranes (see sections 8.4b, 8.5b; figs. 8.34, 8.40).

The route taken by the blood after it leaves the heart was a point of much confusion for many centuries. In Chinese medicine as early as 2650 BCE, blood was believed to flow in a complete circuit around the body and back to the heart, just as we know today. The Roman physician Claudius Galen (129–c. 199), however, argued that it flowed back and forth in the veins, like air in the bronchial tubes. He believed that the liver received food directly from the esophagus and converted it to blood, the heart pumped the blood through the veins to all other organs, and those organs consumed it. The arteries were thought to contain only a mysterious "vital spirit."

The Chinese view was right, but the first experimental demonstration of this didn't come for another 4,000 years. English physician William Harvey (1578–1657) studied the filling and emptying of the heart in snakes, tied off the vessels above and below the heart to observe the effects on cardiac filling and output, and measured cardiac output in a variety of living animals and estimated it in humans. He concluded that (1) the heart pumps more blood in half an hour than there is in the entire body, (2) not enough food is consumed to account for the continual production of so much blood, and therefore (3) the blood returns to the heart rather than being consumed by the peripheral organs. He couldn't explain how, since the microscope had yet to be developed to the point that enabled Antony van Leeuwenhoek (1632–1723) and Marcello Malpighi (1628–94) to discover the blood capillaries.

Harvey's work was the first experimental study of animal physiology and a milestone in the history of biology and medicine. But so entrenched were the ideas of Aristotle and Galen in the medical community, and so strange was the idea of doing experiments on living animals, that Harvey's contemporaries rejected his ideas. Indeed, some of them regarded him as a crackpot because his conclusion flew in the face of common sense—if the blood was continually recirculated and not consumed by the

tissues, they reasoned, then what purpose could it serve? We now know, of course, that he was right. Harvey's case is one of the most interesting in biomedical history, for it shows how empirical science overthrows old theories and spawns better ones, and how common sense and blind allegiance to authority can interfere with the acceptance of truth. But most importantly, Harvey's contributions represent the birth of experimental physiology.

20.1 General Anatomy of the Blood Vessels

Expected Learning Outcomes

When you have completed this section, you should be able to

a. describe the structure of a blood vessel;

b. describe the types of arteries, capillaries, and veins;

c. trace the general route usually taken by the blood from the heart and back again; and

d. describe some variations on this route.

There are three principal categories of blood vessels: arteries, veins, and capillaries (**fig. 20.1**). **Arteries** are defined as the efferent vessels of the cardiovascular system—that is, vessels that carry blood away from the heart. **Veins** are defined as the afferent vessels that carry blood back to the heart. (They are not defined by whether the blood in them is high or low in oxygen; see later discussion.) **Capillaries** are microscopic, thin-walled vessels that connect the smallest arteries to the smallest veins.

20.1a The Vessel Wall

Aside from their general location and direction of blood flow, the three categories of blood vessels also differ in the histological structure of their walls. The walls of arteries and veins are composed of three layers called *tunics* (**fig. 20.2**):

1. The **tunica interna (tunica intima)** lines the inside of the vessel and is exposed to the blood. It consists of a simple squamous epithelium called the **endothelium** overlying a basement membrane and a sparse layer of loose connective tissue; it is continuous with the endocardium of the heart. The endothelium acts as a selectively permeable barrier to materials entering or leaving the bloodstream; it secretes chemicals that stimulate dilation or constriction of the vessel; and it normally repels blood cells and platelets so that they flow freely without sticking to the vessel wall. When the endothelium is damaged, however, platelets may adhere to it and form a blood clot; and when the tissue around a vessel is inflamed, the endothelial cells produce *cell-adhesion molecules* that induce leukocytes to adhere to the surface. This causes leukocytes to congregate in tissues where their defensive actions are needed.

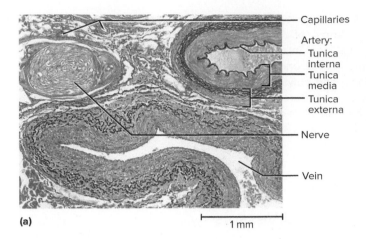

(a)

1 mm

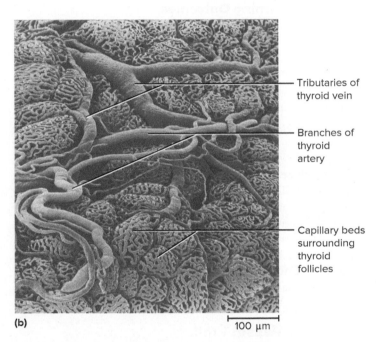

- Capillaries
- Artery:
- Tunica interna
- Tunica media
- Tunica externa
- Nerve
- Vein

- Tributaries of thyroid vein
- Branches of thyroid artery
- Capillary beds surrounding thyroid follicles

(b)

100 μm

FIGURE 20.1 Micrographs of Blood Vessels. (a) A neurovascular bundle, composed of a small artery, vein, and nerve traveling together in a common sheath of connective tissue (LM). (b) A vascular cast of blood vessels of the thyroid gland (SEM). Each round mass of capillaries corresponds to one of the thyroid follicles seen in figure 17.9. These vessels pick up thyroid hormone for distribution throughout the body. a: Dennis Strete/McGraw-Hill Education; b: Susumu Nishinaga/Science Source

2. The **tunica media,** the middle layer, is usually the thickest. It consists of smooth muscle, collagen, and in some cases, elastic tissue. The relative amounts of smooth muscle and elastic tissue vary greatly from one vessel to another and form a basis for classifying vessels as described in the next section. The tunica media strengthens the vessels and prevents blood pressure from rupturing them, and it regulates the diameter of a blood vessel.

3. The **tunica externa (tunica adventitia**[1]**)** is the outermost layer. It consists of loose connective tissue that often merges with that of neighboring blood vessels, nerves, or other organs (fig. 20.1a). It anchors the vessel to adjacent tissues and provides passage for small nerves, lymphatic vessels, and smaller blood vessels that supply the tissues of the larger ones.

All blood vessels require nutrition, oxygenation, and waste-removal services for their own tissues, and the medium to large arteries and veins cannot have these needs fully met by the blood flowing through them. That blood flows too rapidly and the vessel wall is too thick for adequate exchange of chemicals between the blood and tissue fluid. Therefore, smaller vessels penetrate into the external surface of the large ones, gaining access through the tunica externa, and branch into capillaries that supply the deeper tissues of the larger vessel. The network of smaller vessels serving the larger one is called the **vasa vasorum**[2] (VAY-za vay-SO-rum). They are most conspicuous in the tunica externa because the loose organization of the tissue here doesn't hide them from view as much as tissue of the tunica media does. They supply blood to at least the outer half of the vessel wall. Tissues of the inner half are thought to be nourished by diffusion from blood in the lumen.

20.1b Arteries

Arteries are sometimes called the *resistance vessels* of the cardiovascular system because they have a relatively strong, resilient tissue structure. Each beat of the heart creates a surge of pressure in the arteries as blood is ejected into them, and arteries are built to withstand this. Being more muscular than veins, they retain their round shape even when empty, so they appear relatively circular or elliptical in tissue sections. They are divided into three classes by size, but of course there is a gradual transition from one class to the next.

1. **Conducting (elastic** or **large) arteries** are the biggest. Examples include the aorta, common carotid and subclavian arteries, pulmonary trunk, and common iliac arteries. They have a layer of elastic tissue called the *internal elastic lamina* at the border between the tunica interna and media, but microscopically, it is incomplete and difficult to distinguish from the elastic tissue of the media. The tunica media consists of 40 to 70 layers of elastic sheets, perforated like slices of Swiss cheese rolled into a tube, alternating with thin layers of smooth muscle, collagen, and elastic fibers. In histological sections, the view is dominated by this elastic tissue. The perforations allow for vasa vasorum and nerves to penetrate through all layers of the vessel and for smooth muscle cells to communicate with each other through gap junctions. There is an *external elastic lamina* at the border between the media and externa, but it, too, is difficult to distinguish from the elastic sheets of the tunica media. The tunica externa is quite

---

[1]*advent* = added to
[2]*vasa* = vessels; *vasorum* = of the vessels

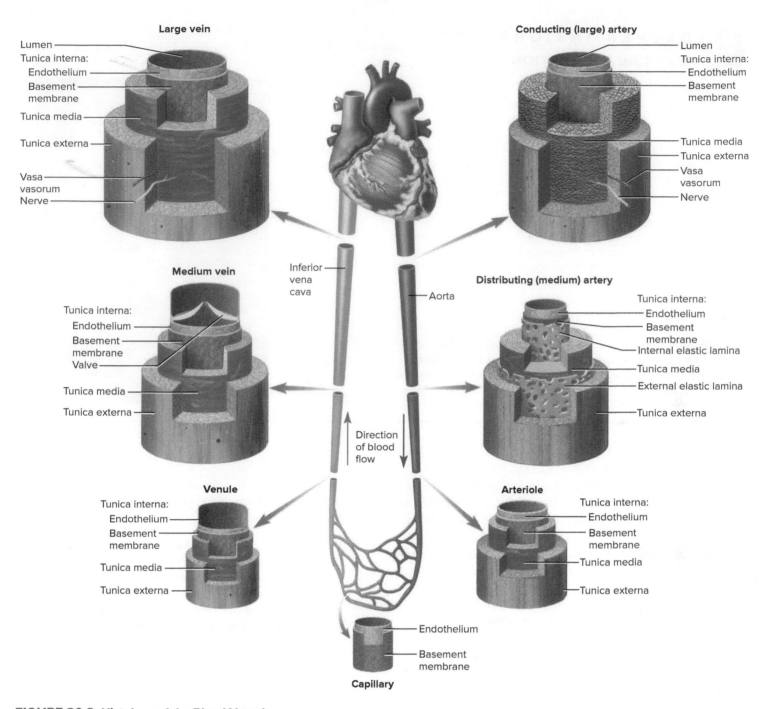

FIGURE 20.2 Histology of the Blood Vessels.

Why do the arteries have so much more elastic tissue than the veins do?

sparse in the largest arteries but is well supplied with vasa vasorum. Conducting arteries expand as they receive blood during ventricular systole, and recoil during diastole. As explained in the next section, this relieves smaller arteries downstream of excessive and harmful pressure surges. As arteries stiffen with age *(arteriosclerosis)*, this protective effect declines, downstream vessels are subjected to greater stress, and the risks of aneurysm and hemorrhage rise (see Deeper Insight 20.1).

2. **Distributing (muscular** or **medium) arteries** are smaller branches that distribute blood to specific organs. You could compare a conducting artery to an interstate highway and distributing arteries to the exit ramps and state highways that serve individual towns. Most arteries that have specific anatomical names are in these first two size classes. Distributing arteries include the brachial, femoral, renal, and splenic arteries. Distributing arteries typically have up to 40 layers of smooth muscle constituting about three-quarters of the

DEEPER INSIGHT 20.1

CLINICAL APPLICATION

Aneurysm

An *aneurysm*[3] is a weak point in an artery or the heart wall. It forms a thin-walled, bulging sac that pulsates with each beat of the heart and may eventually rupture. In a *dissecting aneurysm,* blood accumulates between the tunics of an artery and separates them, usually because of degeneration of the tunica media. The most common sites of aneurysms are the abdominal aorta **(fig. 20.3)**, renal arteries, and the arterial circle at the base of the brain. Even without hemorrhaging, aneurysms can cause pain or death by putting pressure on brain tissue, nerves, adjacent veins, pulmonary air passages, or the esophagus. Other consequences include neurological disorders, difficulty in breathing or swallowing, chronic cough, or congestion of the tissues with blood. Aneurysms sometimes result from congenital weakness of the blood vessels and sometimes from trauma or bacterial infections such as syphilis. The most common cause, however, is the combination of arteriosclerosis and hypertension.

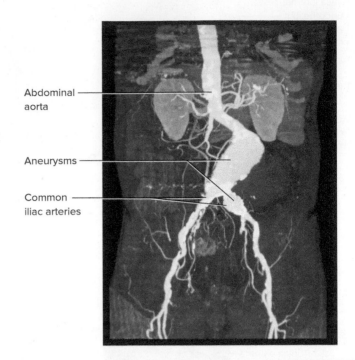

FIGURE 20.3 Aneurysms. A magnetic resonance angiogram (MRA) of the abdominopelvic region of a patient with hypertension, showing prominent bulges (aneurysms) of the inferior aorta and left common iliac artery.
Suttha Burawonk/Shutterstock

---

wall thickness. In histological sections, this smooth muscle is more conspicuous than the elastic tissue. Both the internal and external elastic laminae, however, are thick and often conspicuous.

3. **Resistance (small) arteries** are usually too variable in number and location to have individual names. They exhibit up to 25 layers of smooth muscle and relatively little elastic tissue. Compared to large arteries, they have a thicker tunica media in proportion to the lumen. The smallest of these arteries, up to 200 μm in diameter and with only one to three layers of smooth muscle, are called **arterioles.** Arterioles have very little tunica externa. They are the major point of control over how much blood an organ or tissue receives, as we shall see later.

In some places, such as the mesenteries, short vessels called **metarterioles**[4] **(thoroughfare channels)** link arterioles directly to venules and provide shortcuts through which blood can bypass the capillaries. They will be further discussed with capillary beds.

Arterial Sense Organs

Certain major arteries above the heart have sensory structures in their walls that monitor blood pressure and composition **(fig. 20.4).**

These receptors transmit information to the brainstem that serves to regulate the heartbeat, blood vessel diameters, and respiration. They are of three kinds:

1. **Carotid sinuses.** These are **baroreceptors**—sensors that monitor blood pressure. Ascending the neck on each side is a *common carotid artery,* which branches near the angle of the mandible, forming the *internal carotid artery* to the brain and *external carotid artery* to the face. The carotid sinuses are located in the wall of the internal carotid artery just above the branch point. The carotid sinus has a relatively thin tunica media and an abundance of glossopharyngeal nerve fibers in the tunica externa. The role of the baroreceptors in adjusting blood pressure, called the *baroreflex,* is described later in this chapter.

2. **Carotid bodies.** Also located near the branch of the common carotid arteries, these are oval receptors about 3×5 mm in size, innervated by sensory fibers of the glossopharyngeal nerves. They are **chemoreceptors**—sensors that monitor changes in blood composition. They primarily transmit signals to the brainstem respiratory centers, which adjust breathing to stabilize the blood pH and its CO_2 and O_2 levels.

3. **Aortic bodies.** These are one to three chemoreceptors located in the aortic arch near the arteries to the head and arms. They are structurally similar to the carotid bodies and have the same function, but transmit their signals to the brainstem via the vagus nerves.

---

[3]*aneurysm* = widening
[4]*meta* = beyond, next in a series

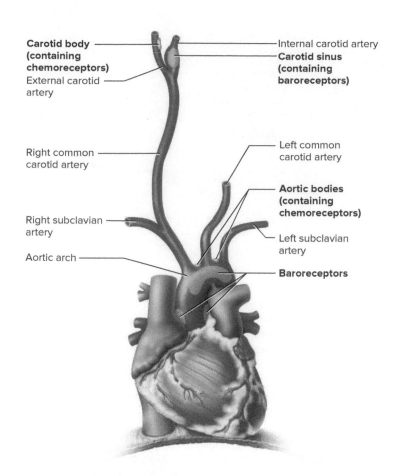

FIGURE 20.4 Baroreceptors and Chemoreceptors in the Arteries Superior to the Heart. The structures shown here in the right carotid arteries are repeated in the left carotids. **APR**

20.1c Capillaries

For the blood to serve any purpose, materials such as nutrients, wastes, hormones, and leukocytes must pass between the blood and tissue fluids, through the walls of the vessels. There are only two places in the circulation where this occurs—the capillaries and some venules. We can think of these as the "business end" of the cardiovascular system, because all the rest of the system exists to serve the exchange processes that occur here. Since capillaries greatly outnumber venules, they are the more important of the two. Capillaries are sometimes called the *exchange vessels* of the cardiovascular system; the arterioles, capillaries, and venules are also called the **microvasculature (microcirculation).**

Capillaries (see figs. 20.1, 20.2) consist of only an endothelium and basal lamina. Their walls are as thin as 0.2 μm. They average about 5 μm in diameter at the proximal end (where they receive arterial blood), widen to about 9 μm at the distal end (where they empty into a small vein), and often branch along the way. Since erythrocytes are about 7.5 μm in diameter, they have

to stretch into elongated shapes to squeeze through the smallest capillaries.

Scarcely any cell in the body is more than 60 to 80 μm (about four to six cell widths) away from the nearest capillary. There are a few exceptions: Capillaries are scarce in tendons and ligaments and absent from epithelia, cartilage, and the cornea and lens of the eye.

Types of Capillaries

There are three types of capillaries, distinguished by the ease with which they allow substances to pass through their walls and by structural differences that account for their greater or lesser permeability.

1. **Continuous capillaries** **(fig. 20.5a)** occur in most tissues and organs, such as the skeletal muscles, lungs, and brain. Their endothelial cells, held together by tight junctions, form a continuous tube. A thin protein–carbohydrate layer, the **basal lamina,** surrounds the endothelium and separates it from the adjacent connective tissues. The endothelial cells are separated by narrow **intercellular clefts** about 4 nm wide. Small solutes such as glucose can pass through these clefts, but most plasma protein, other large molecules, and platelets and blood cells are held back. The continuous capillaries of the brain lack intercellular clefts and have more complete tight junctions that form the blood–brain barrier discussed in section 14.2c.

   Some continuous capillaries exhibit cells called **pericytes** that lie external to the endothelium. Pericytes have elongated tendrils that wrap around the capillary. They contain the same contractile proteins as muscle, and it is thought that they can contract and regulate blood flow through the capillaries. They also can differentiate into endothelial and smooth muscle cells and thus contribute to vessel growth and repair.

2. **Fenestrated capillaries** have endothelial cells riddled with patches of **filtration pores (fenestrations[5]) (fig. 20.5b, c).** These pores are about 20 to 100 nm in diameter, and are often spanned by a glycoprotein membrane that is much thinner than the cell's plasma membrane. They allow for the rapid passage of small molecules, but still retain most proteins and larger particles in the bloodstream. Fenestrated capillaries are important in organs that engage in rapid absorption or filtration—the kidneys, endocrine glands, small intestine, and choroid plexuses of the brain, for example.

3. **Sinusoids** are irregular blood-filled spaces in the liver, bone marrow, spleen, and some other organs **(fig. 20.6).** They are twisted, tortuous passageways, typically 30 to 40 μm wide, that conform to the shape of the surrounding tissue. The endothelial cells are separated by wide gaps

[5]*fenestra* = window

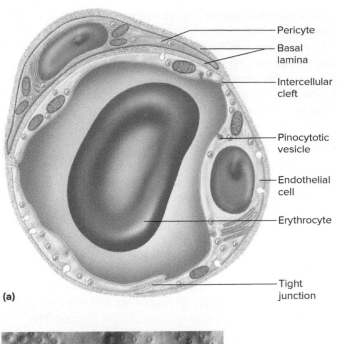

(a)

- Pericyte
- Basal lamina
- Intercellular cleft
- Pinocytotic vesicle
- Endothelial cell
- Erythrocyte
- Tight junction

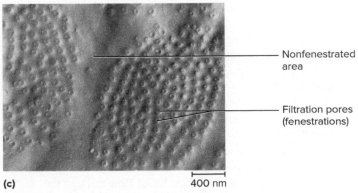

(c)

- Nonfenestrated area
- Filtration pores (fenestrations)

400 nm

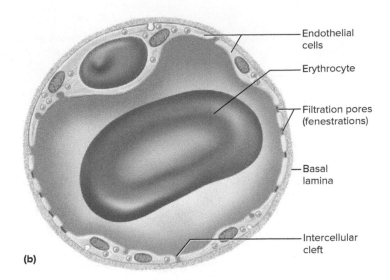

(b)

- Endothelial cells
- Erythrocyte
- Filtration pores (fenestrations)
- Basal lamina
- Intercellular cleft

FIGURE 20.5 Types of Blood Capillaries. (a) Continuous capillary, cross section. (b) Fenestrated capillary, cross section. (c) Surface of a fenestrated endothelial cell showing patches of filtration pores (fenestrations) separated by nonfenestrated areas (SEM).

c: Courtesy of S. McNutt

 Identify some organs that have fenestrated rather than continuous capillaries.

with no basal lamina, and the cells also frequently have especially large fenestrations through them. Even proteins and blood cells can pass through these pores; this is how albumin, clotting factors, and other proteins synthesized by the liver enter the blood, and how newly formed blood cells enter the circulation from the bone marrow and lymphatic organs. Some sinusoids contain macrophages or other specialized cells.

Capillary Beds

Capillaries are organized into webs called **capillary beds**—typically 10 to 100 capillaries supplied by a single arteriole or metarteriole (**fig. 20.7;** see also this chapter's opening photo). At their

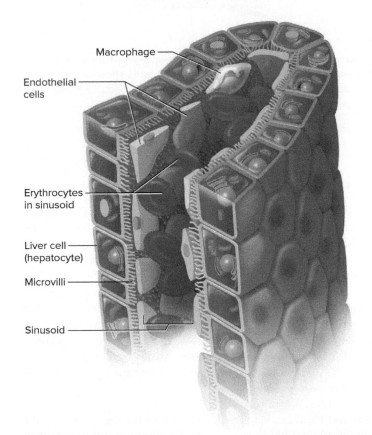

- Macrophage
- Endothelial cells
- Erythrocytes in sinusoid
- Liver cell (hepatocyte)
- Microvilli
- Sinusoid

FIGURE 20.6 A Sinusoid of the Liver. Large gaps between the endothelial cells allow blood plasma to directly contact the liver cells but retain blood cells in the lumen of the sinusoid.

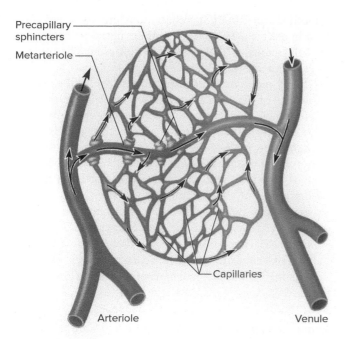

(a) Sphincters open

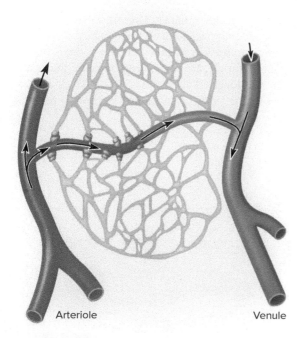

(b) Sphincters closed

FIGURE 20.7 Perfusion of a Capillary Bed. (a) Precapillary sphincters dilated and capillaries well perfused. (b) Precapillary sphincters closed, with most blood bypassing the capillaries.

distal end, capillaries transition to venules, gradually adding a thin tunica media. They may also drain into the distal end of a metarteriole, which then leads to a venule.

At any given time, about three-quarters of the body's capillaries are shut down because there isn't enough blood to supply all of them at once. In the skeletal muscles, for example, about 90% of the capillaries have little or no blood flow during periods of rest. During exercise, they receive an abundant flow while capillaries elsewhere—for example, in the skin and intestines—shut down to compensate. Capillary flow (perfusion) is usually regulated by the dilation or constriction of arterioles upstream from the capillary beds. In capillary beds supplied with metarterioles, there is often a single smooth muscle cell that wraps like a cuff around the opening to each capillary; it acts as a **precapillary sphincter** regulating blood flow. If the sphincters are relaxed, the capillaries are well perfused (fig. 20.7a). If many of the sphincters constrict, blood bypasses the capillaries, leaving them less perfused or even bloodless, and the blood takes a shortcut through the metarteriole directly to a nearby venule (fig. 20.7b).

20.1d Veins

Veins are regarded as the *capacitance vessels* of the cardiovascular system because they are relatively thin-walled and flaccid, and expand easily to accommodate an increased volume of blood; that is, they have a greater *capacity* for blood containment than arteries do. At rest, about 64% of the blood is found in the systemic veins as compared with only 13% in the systemic arteries **(fig. 20.8).** The reason veins are so thin-walled and accommodating is that, being distant from the ventricles of the heart, they are subjected to relatively low blood pressure. In large arteries, blood pressure averages 90 to 100 mm Hg and surges to 120 mm Hg during systole, whereas in veins it averages about 10 mm Hg. Furthermore, the blood flow in the veins is steady, rather than pulsating with the heartbeat like the flow in the arteries. Veins therefore don't require thick, pressure-resistant walls. They collapse when empty and thus have relatively flattened, irregular shapes in histological sections (see fig. 20.1a).

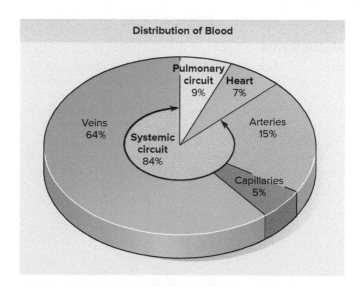

FIGURE 20.8 Typical Blood Distribution in a Resting Adult.

❓ *What anatomical fact allows the veins to contain so much more blood than the arteries do?*

As we trace blood flow in the arteries, we find it splitting off repeatedly into smaller and smaller *branches* of the arterial system. In the venous system, conversely, we find small veins merging to form larger and larger ones as they approach the heart. We refer to the smaller veins as *tributaries,* by analogy to the streams that converge and act as tributaries to rivers. In examining the types of veins, we will follow the direction of blood flow, working up from the smallest to the largest vessels.

1. **Postcapillary venules** are the smallest of the veins, beginning with diameters of about 10 to 20 μm. They receive blood from capillaries directly or by way of the distal ends of the metarterioles. They have a tunica interna with only a few fibroblasts around it and no muscle. Like capillaries, they are often surrounded by pericytes. Postcapillary venules are even more porous than capillaries; therefore, venules also exchange fluid with the surrounding tissues. Most leukocytes emigrate from the bloodstream through the venule walls.

2. **Muscular venules** receive blood from the postcapillary venules. They are up to 1 mm in diameter. They have a tunica media of one or two layers of smooth muscle, and a thin tunica externa.

3. **Medium veins** range up to 10 mm in diameter. Most veins with individual names are in this category, such as the radial and ulnar veins of the forearm and the small and great saphenous veins of the leg. Medium veins have a tunica interna with an endothelium, basement membrane, loose connective tissue, and sometimes a thin internal elastic lamina. The tunica media is much thinner than it is in medium arteries; it exhibits bundles of smooth muscle, but not a continuous muscular layer as seen in arteries. The muscle is interrupted by regions of collagenous, reticular, and elastic tissue. The tunica externa is relatively thick.

   Many medium veins, especially in the limbs, exhibit infoldings of the tunica interna that meet in the middle of the lumen, forming **venous valves** directed toward the heart (see fig. 20.21). The pressure in the veins isn't high enough to push all of the blood upward against the pull of gravity in a standing or sitting person. The upward flow of blood in these vessels depends partly on the massaging action of skeletal muscles and the ability of these valves to keep the blood from dropping down again when the muscles relax. When the muscles surrounding a vein contract, they force blood through these valves. The propulsion of venous blood by muscular massaging, aided by the venous valves, is a mechanism of blood flow called the *skeletal muscle pump.* Varicose veins result in part from the failure of the valves (see Deeper Insight 20.2).

4. **Venous sinuses** are veins with especially thin walls, large lumens, and no smooth muscle. Examples include the coronary sinus of the heart and the dural sinuses of the brain. Unlike other veins, they are not capable of vasoconstriction.

5. **Large veins** have diameters greater than 10 mm. They have some smooth muscle in all three tunics. They have a relatively thin tunica media with only a moderate amount of smooth muscle; the tunica externa is the thickest layer and contains longitudinal bundles of smooth muscle. Large veins include the venae cavae, pulmonary veins, internal jugular veins, and renal veins.

DEEPER INSIGHT 20.2

CLINICAL APPLICATION

Varicose Veins

In people who stand for long periods, such as barbers and cashiers, blood tends to pool in the lower limbs and stretch the veins. This is especially true of superficial veins, which are not surrounded by supportive tissue. Stretching pulls the cusps of the venous valves farther apart until the valves become incapable of sealing the vessel and preventing the backflow of blood. As the veins become further distended, their walls weaken and they develop into *varicose veins* with irregular dilations and twisted pathways **(fig. 20.9).** Obesity and pregnancy also promote development of varicose veins by putting pressure on large veins of the pelvic region and obstructing drainage from the lower limbs. Varicose veins sometimes develop because of hereditary weakness of the valves. With less drainage of blood, tissues of the leg and foot may become edematous and painful. *Hemorrhoids* are varicose veins of the anal canal.

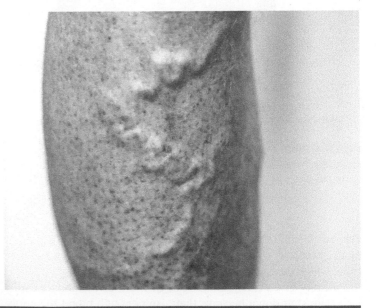

FIGURE 20.9 Varicose Veins.

20.1e Circulatory Routes

The simplest and most common route of blood flow is heart → arteries → capillaries → veins → heart. Blood usually passes through only one network of capillaries from the time it leaves the heart until the time it returns **(fig. 20.10a),** but there are exceptions, notably portal systems and anastomoses.

In a **portal system (fig. 20.10b),** blood flows through two consecutive capillary networks before returning to the heart. Portal systems occur in the kidneys, connect the hypothalamus to the anterior pituitary gland, and connect the intestines to the liver (see section 20.7g).

An **anastomosis** is a point of convergence between two blood vessels other than capillaries. In an **arteriovenous anastomosis (shunt),** blood flows from an artery directly into a vein and bypasses the capillaries **(fig. 20.10c).** Shunts occur in the fingers, palms, toes, and ears, where they reduce heat loss in cold weather by allowing warm blood to bypass these exposed surfaces. Unfortunately, this makes these poorly perfused areas more susceptible to frostbite. The most common anastomoses are **venous anastomoses,** in which one vein empties directly into another **(fig. 20.10d).** These provide several alternative routes of drainage from an organ, so blockage of a vein is rarely as life-threatening as blockage of an artery. **Arterial anastomoses,** in which two arteries merge **(fig. 20.10e),** provide *collateral* (alternative) routes of blood supply to a tissue. Those of the coronary circulation were mentioned in section 19.2e. They are also common around joints where limb movement may temporarily compress an artery and obstruct one pathway. Several arterial and venous anastomoses are described later in this chapter.

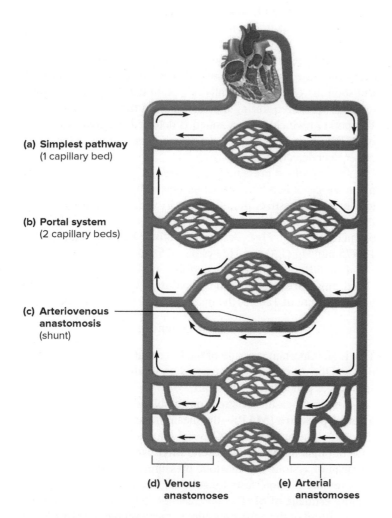

(a) Simplest pathway
(1 capillary bed)

(b) Portal system
(2 capillary beds)

(c) Arteriovenous anastomosis
(shunt)

(d) Venous anastomoses

(e) Arterial anastomoses

FIGURE 20.10 Variations in Circulatory Pathways. (a) The simplest and most common pathway, with one capillary bed. (b) Portal systems, with two capillary beds in series. (c) Arteriovenous anastomoses, bypassing capillaries. (d) Venous anastomoses, with one vein feeding into another. (e) Arterial anastomoses, with one artery feeding into another.

❓ *After studying the blood vessels in sections 20.7 and 20.8, identify specific sites in the body where one can find arterial anastomoses, venous anastomoses, and portal systems.*

BEFORE YOU GO ON

Answer the following questions to test your understanding of the preceding section:

1. Name the three tunics of a typical blood vessel and explain how they differ from each other.

2. Contrast the tunica media of a conducting artery, arteriole, and venule and explain how the histological differences are related to the functional differences between these vessels.

3. Describe the differences between a continuous capillary, a fenestrated capillary, and a sinusoid.

4. Describe two routes by which substances can escape the bloodstream and pass through a capillary wall into the tissue fluid.

5. Describe the differences between a medium vein and a medium (muscular) artery. State the functional reasons for these differences.

6. Contrast an anastomosis and a portal system with the more typical pathway of blood flow.

20.2 Blood Pressure, Resistance, and Flow

Expected Learning Outcomes

When you have completed this section, you should be able to

a. explain the relationship between blood pressure, resistance, and flow;

b. describe how blood pressure is measured and expressed;

c. show how pulse pressure and mean arterial pressure are calculated;

d. describe three factors that determine resistance to blood flow;

e. explain how vessel diameter influences blood pressure and flow; and

f. describe some local, neural, and hormonal influences on vessel diameter.

To sustain life, the circulatory system must deliver oxygen and nutrients to the tissues, and remove their wastes, at a rate that keeps pace with tissue metabolism. Inadequate circulatory services to a tissue can lead within minutes to tissue necrosis and possibly death of the individual. Thus, it is crucial for the cardiovascular system to respond promptly to local needs and ensure that the tissues have an adequate blood supply at all times. This section of the chapter explores the mechanisms for achieving this.

The blood supply to a tissue can be expressed in terms of *flow* and *perfusion*. **Flow** is the amount of blood flowing through an organ, tissue, or blood vessel in a given time (such as mL/min.). **Perfusion** is the flow per given volume or mass of tissue, usually expressed in milliliters of blood per 100 grams of tissue per minute. Thus, a large organ such as the femur could have a *greater flow* but *less perfusion* than a small organ such as the ovary, because the ovary receives much more blood per gram of tissue.

In a resting individual, *total* flow is quite constant and is equal to cardiac output (typically 5.25 L/min.). Flow through individual organs, however, varies from minute to minute as blood is redirected from one organ to another. Digestion, for example, requires abundant flow to the intestines, and the cardiovascular system makes this available by reducing flow through other organs such as the kidneys. When digestion and nutrient absorption are over, blood flow to the intestines declines and a higher priority is given to the kidneys and other organs. Great variations in regional flow can occur with little or no change in total flow.

Hemodynamics, the physical principles of blood flow, are based mainly on pressure and resistance. These relationships can be concisely summarized by the formula

$$F \propto \Delta P/R.$$

In other words, the greater the pressure difference (ΔP) between two points, the greater the flow (F); the greater the resistance (R), the less the flow. Therefore, to understand the flow of blood, we must consider the factors that affect pressure and resistance.

20.2a Blood Pressure

Blood pressure (BP) is the force exerted by blood on a vessel wall. Contraction of the heart initiates a wave of pressure that sharply decreases as the blood flows farther and farther away from the ventricle of origin. Blood pressure measurement is a familiar part of a routine physical examination. It is typically measured at the **brachial artery** of the arm with a **sphygmomanometer** (SFIG-mo-meh-NOM-eh-tur). This device consists of an inflatable cuff connected to a rubber bulb for pumping air into it, and an aneroid dial gauge, digital sensor, or calibrated mercury column for measuring air pressure in the cuff. Mercury sphygmomanometers are

the "gold standard" for accuracy, but other devices have advantages for convenience and home use.

To take a patient's blood pressure with a mercury sphygmomanometer, the examiner wraps the cuff snugly around the patient's arm and inflates it with the bulb until it exceeds the systolic blood pressure. By squeezing the brachial muscles, this procedure collapses the brachial artery deep within. Even during systole, the heart can't force blood through the artery, and there is no blood flow distal to that point. The examiner now listens with a stethoscope at the bend of the elbow (cubital fossa) while slowly releasing air from the cuff.

At first there is no sound, but as soon as the systolic BP slightly exceeds the cuff pressure, each heartbeat forces the brachial artery open and allows a brief jet of blood to pass through. The vessel collapses again at diastole. This jet of blood and the subsequent surge of blood against the recollapsed artery cause turbulence that the examiner hears as a faint "bump" sound. The cuff pressure at the instant of the first bump is noted as the systolic BP. As the cuff pressure continues to decline, a bump can be heard every time the artery collapses—that is, once in each heartbeat. But soon the cuff pressure falls to a point that the brachial artery remains open even during diastole, and no further sounds occur. The point at which the last sound is detected is noted as the diastolic BP. Digital devices rely on detecting pulsations in the artery rather than detecting sounds from it.

Arterial blood pressure is expressed as a ratio of the **systolic pressure** generated by contraction (systole) of the left ventricle, to **diastolic pressure,** the minimum to which the BP falls when the ventricle is in diastole. Both are expressed in millimeters of mercury (mm Hg). A representative, healthy adult BP is 120/75 mm Hg (120 mm Hg systolic, 75 mm Hg diastolic).

The difference between systolic and diastolic pressure is called **pulse pressure** (not to be confused with pulse *rate*). For a blood pressure of 120/75, the pulse pressure (PP) would be

$$120 - 75 = 45 \text{ mm Hg.}$$

This is an important measure of the force that drives blood circulation and the maximum stress exerted on small arteries by the pressure surges generated by the heart.

Another measure of stress on the blood vessels is the **mean arterial pressure (MAP)**—the mean pressure you would obtain if you took measurements at several intervals (say every 0.1 second) throughout the cardiac cycle. MAP isn't simply an arithmetic mean of systolic and diastolic pressures, however, because the low-pressure diastole lasts longer than the high-pressure systole. A close estimate of MAP is obtained by adding diastolic pressure and one-third of the pulse pressure. For a blood pressure of 120/75,

$$\text{MAP} \approx 75 + 45/3 = 90 \text{ mm Hg.}$$

This is typical for vessels at the level of the heart, but *MAP* varies with the influence of gravity. In a standing adult, it is about 62 mm Hg in the major arteries of the head and 180 mm Hg in major arteries of the ankle.

It is the mean arterial pressure that most influences the risk of disorders such as **syncope** (SIN-co-pee) (fainting), atherosclerosis, kidney failure, edema, and aneurysm. The importance of preventing excessive blood pressure is therefore clear. One of the body's chief means of doing so is the ability of the arteries to stretch and recoil during the cardiac cycle. If the arteries were rigid tubes, pressure would rise much higher in systole and drop to nearly zero in diastole. Blood throughout the circulatory system would flow and stop, flow and stop, and put great stress on the small vessels. But healthy conducting (elastic) arteries expand with each systole, absorb some of the force of the ejected blood, and store potential energy. Then, when the heart is in diastole, their elastic recoil releases that as kinetic energy, exerts pressure on the blood, and maintains blood flow throughout the cardiac cycle. The elastic arteries thus smooth out pressure fluctuations and reduce stress on the smaller arteries.

▶▶▶ APPLY WHAT YOU KNOW

Explain how the histological structure of large arteries relates to their ability to stretch during systole and recoil during diastole.

Nevertheless, blood flow in the arteries is *pulsatile*. In the aorta, blood rushes forward at 120 cm/s during systole and has an average speed of 40 cm/s over the cardiac cycle. When measured farther away from the heart, systolic and diastolic pressures are lower and there is less difference between them **(fig. 20.11)**. In capillaries and veins, the blood flows at a steady speed with little if any pulsation because the pressure surges have been damped out by the distance traveled and the elasticity of the arteries. This

is why an injured vein exhibits relatively slow, steady bleeding, whereas blood jets intermittently from a severed artery. In the inferior vena cava near the heart, however, venous flow fluctuates with the respiratory cycle for reasons explained later, and there is some fluctuation in the jugular veins of the neck.

As we get older, our arteries become less distensible and absorb less systolic force. This increasing stiffness of the arteries is called **arteriosclerosis**[6] ("hardening of the arteries"). The primary cause of it is cumulative damage by free radicals, which cause gradual deterioration of the elastic and other tissues of the arterial walls—much like old rubber bands that become less stretchy. Another contributing factor is **atherosclerosis,** the growth of lipid deposits in the arterial walls (see Deeper Insight 19.4). These deposits can become calcified *complicated plaques,* giving the arteries a hard, crunchy or bonelike consistency. As a result of these degenerative changes, blood pressure rises with age. Common blood pressures at the age of 20 are about 123/76 for males and 116/72 for females. For healthy persons at age 70, typical blood pressures are around 145/82 and 159/85 for the two sexes, respectively.

Hypertension (high BP) is commonly considered to be a chronic resting blood pressure higher than 140/90. (*Temporary* high BP resulting from emotion or exercise is not hypertension.) Among other effects, hypertension can weaken arteries and cause aneurysms, and it promotes the development of atherosclerosis (see Deeper Insight 20.6). **Hypotension** is chronic low resting BP. It may be a consequence of blood loss, dehydration, anemia, or other factors and is normal in people approaching death. There is no particular numerical criterion for hypotension.

Blood pressure is physiologically determined by three principal variables: cardiac output, blood volume, and resistance to flow. Cardiac output was discussed in section 19.6. Blood volume is regulated mainly by the kidneys, which have a greater influence than any other organ on blood pressure (assuming there is a beating heart). Their influence on blood pressure is discussed in chapters 23 and 24. Resistance to flow is our next topic of consideration.

20.2b Peripheral Resistance

Peripheral resistance is the opposition to flow that the blood encounters in vessels away from the heart. Moving blood would exert no pressure against a vessel wall unless it encountered at least some downstream resistance. Thus, pressure and resistance are not independent variables in blood flow—rather, pressure is affected by resistance, and flow is affected by both. Resistance, in turn, hinges on three variables that we consider now: blood viscosity, vessel length, and vessel radius.

Blood Viscosity

The viscosity of blood stems mainly from its plasma proteins (albumin) and erythrocytes (see section 18.1d). A deficiency of erythrocytes (anemia) or albumin (hypoproteinemia) reduces viscosity and speeds up blood flow. On the other hand, viscosity increases and flow declines in such conditions as polycythemia and dehydration.

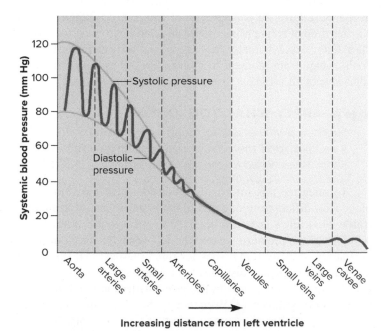

FIGURE 20.11 Changes in Blood Pressure Relative to Distance from the Heart. Because of arterial elasticity and the effect of friction against the vessel wall, all measures of blood pressure decline with distance—systolic pressure, diastolic pressure, pulse pressure, and mean arterial pressure. There is no pulse pressure beyond the arterioles, but there are slight pressure oscillations in the venae cavae caused by the respiratory pump described later in this chapter.

---

[6]*arterio* = artery; *sclerosis* = hardening

Vessel Length

The farther a liquid travels through a tube, the more cumulative friction it encounters; pressure and flow therefore decline with distance. Partly for this reason, if you were to measure mean arterial pressure in a reclining person, you would obtain a higher value in the arm, for example, than in the ankle. In a reclining person, a strong pulse in the dorsal artery of the foot is a good sign of adequate cardiac output. If perfusion is good at that distance from the heart, it is likely to be good elsewhere in the systemic circulation.

Vessel Radius

Blood viscosity and vessel lengths don't change in the short term, of course. In a healthy individual, the only significant ways of controlling peripheral resistance from moment to moment are **vasoconstriction,** the narrowing of a vessel, and **vasodilation,** the widening of a vessel. Vasoconstriction occurs when the smooth muscle of the tunica media contracts. Vasodilation, however, is brought about not by any muscular effort to widen a vessel, but rather by muscular passivity—relaxation of the smooth muscle, allowing blood pressure to expand the vessel. Vasoconstriction and vasodilation are collectively called **vasomotion.** Vasomotion is controlled in part by a nucleus in the medulla oblongata of the brain called the **vasomotor center.**

The effect of vessel radius on blood flow stems from the friction of the moving blood against the vessel walls. Blood normally exhibits smooth, silent **laminar**[7] **flow.** That is, it flows in layers—faster near the center of a vessel, where it encounters less friction, and slower near the walls, where it drags against the vessel. You can observe a similar effect from the vantage point of a riverbank. The current may be very swift in the middle of a river but quite sluggish near shore, where the water encounters more friction against the riverbank and bottom. When a blood vessel dilates, a greater portion of the blood is in the middle of the stream and the average flow may be quite swift. When the vessel constricts, more of the blood is close to the wall and the average flow is slower **(fig. 20.12).**

Thus, the radius of a vessel markedly affects blood flow. Indeed, flow (F) is proportional not merely to vessel radius (r) but to the *fourth power* of radius—that is, $F \propto r^4$. This makes radius a very potent factor in the control of flow. For the sake of simplicity, consider a hypothetical blood vessel with a 1 mm radius when maximally constricted and a 3 mm radius when completely dilated. At a 1 mm radius, suppose the flow rate is 1 mL/min. By the formula $F \propto r^4$, consider how the flow would change as radius changed:

if $r = 1$ mm, then $r^4 = 1^4 = 1$, and $F = 1$ mL/min. (given);

if $r = 2$ mm, then $r^4 = 2^4 = 16$, and $F = 16$ mL/min.; and

if $r = 3$ mm, then $r^4 = 3^4 = 81$, and $F = 81$ mL/min.

These actual numbers don't matter; what matters is that a mere 3-fold increase in radius has produced an 81-fold increase in flow—a demonstration that vessel radius exerts a very powerful influence

[7]*lamina* = layer

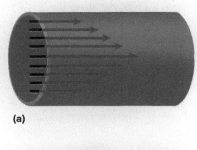

FIGURE 20.12 Laminar Flow and the Effect of Vessel Radius. Blood flows more slowly near the vessel wall, as indicated by shorter arrows, than it does near the center of the vessel. Each arrow can be construed as the distance that a hypothetical blood cell would travel in a given amount of time, varying with its distance from the vessel wall. (a) When the vessel radius is large, the average velocity of flow is high. (b) When the radius is less, the average velocity is lower because a larger portion of the blood is slowed down by friction against the vessel wall.

over flow. Blood vessels are, indeed, capable of substantial changes in radius. **Figure 20.13,** for example, depicts an experiment in which a drop of epinephrine caused an arteriole to constrict to one-third of its relaxed diameter. Since blood viscosity and vessel length don't change from moment to moment, vessel radius is the most adjustable of all variables that govern peripheral resistance.

▶▶▶ APPLY WHAT YOU KNOW

Suppose a vessel with a radius of 1 mm had a flow of 3 mL/min., and then the vessel dilated to a radius of 5 mm. What would be the new flow rate?

To integrate this information, consider how the velocity of blood flow differs from one part of the systemic circuit to another **(table 20.1).** Flow is fastest in the aorta because it is a large vessel close to the pressure source, the left ventricle. From aorta to capillaries, velocity diminishes for three reasons: (1) The blood has traveled a greater distance, so friction has slowed it down. (2) The arterioles and capillaries have smaller radii and therefore put up more resistance. (3) Even though the radii of individual vessels become smaller as we progress farther from the heart, the number of vessels and their *total* cross-sectional area become greater and greater. The aorta has a cross-sectional area of 3 to 5 cm^2, whereas the total cross-sectional area of all the capillaries is about 4,500 to 6,000 cm^2. Thus, a given volume of aortic blood is distributed over a greater total area in the capillaries, which *collectively* form a wider path in the bloodstream. Just as water slows down when a narrow mountain stream flows into a lake, blood slows down as it enters pathways with a greater total area or volume.

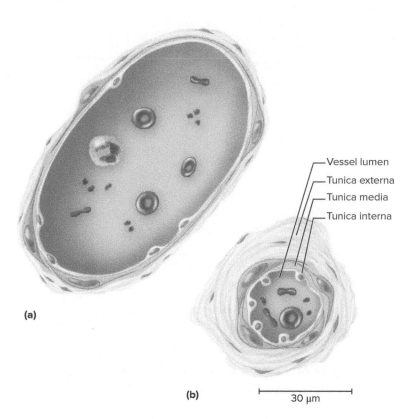

(a)

—Vessel lumen
—Tunica externa
—Tunica media
—Tunica interna

(b)

30 µm

FIGURE 20.13 The Capacity for Vasoconstriction in an Arteriole. (a) A dilated arteriole (cross section). (b) The same arteriole, at a point just 1 mm from the area shown in part (a). A single drop of epinephrine applied here caused the arteriole to constrict to about one-third of its dilated diameter. Drawn to scale from transmission electron micrographs.

TABLE 20.1	Blood Velocity in the Systemic Circuit	
Vessel	**Typical Lumen Diameter**	**Velocity***
Aorta	2.5 cm	1,200 mm/s
Arterioles	20–50 µm	15 mm/s
Capillaries	5–9 µm	0.4 mm/s
Venules	20 µm	5 mm/s
Inferior vena cava	3 cm	80 mm/s

*Peak systolic velocity in the aorta; mean or steady velocity in other vessels, assuming no upstream vasoconstriction adding to resistance

From capillaries to vena cava, velocity rises again. One reason for this is that the veins are larger than the capillaries, so they create less resistance. Furthermore, since many capillaries converge on one venule, and many venules on a larger vein, a large amount of blood is being forced into a progressively smaller channel—like water flowing from a lake into an outlet stream and thus flowing

faster again. Note, however, that blood in the veins never regains the velocity it had in the large arteries. This is because the veins are farther from the pressure head (the heart) and because they are more compliant than arteries—they stretch to accommodate more blood, and this reduces pressure and flow.

Arterioles are the most significant point of control over peripheral resistance and blood flow because (1) they are on the proximal sides of the capillary beds, so they are best positioned to regulate flow into the capillaries and thus regulate perfusion of the organs; (2) they greatly outnumber any other class of arteries and thus provide the most numerous control points; and (3) they are more muscular in proportion to their diameters than any other class of blood vessels and are highly capable of changing radius. Arterioles alone account for about half of the total peripheral resistance of the circulatory system. However, larger arteries and veins also influence peripheral resistance through their own constriction and dilation.

20.2c Regulation of Blood Pressure and Flow

Vasoreflexes, we have seen, are quick and powerful means of altering blood pressure and flow. There are three ways of controlling vasomotor activity: local, neural, and hormonal mechanisms. We now consider each of these influences in turn.

Local Control

Autoregulation is the ability of tissues to regulate their own blood supply. According to the *metabolic theory of autoregulation,* if a tissue is inadequately perfused, it becomes hypoxic and its metabolites (waste products) accumulate—CO_2, H^+, K^+, lactate, and adenosine, for example. These factors stimulate vasodilation, which increases blood flow. As the bloodstream delivers oxygen and carries away the metabolites, the vessels reconstrict. Thus, a homeostatic dynamic equilibrium is established that adjusts perfusion to the tissue's metabolic needs.

In addition, platelets, endothelial cells, and the perivascular tissues secrete a variety of **vasoactive chemicals** that stimulate vasodilation under such conditions as trauma, inflammation, and exercise. These include histamine, bradykinin, and prostaglandins. The drag of blood flowing against the endothelial cells creates a *shear stress* (like rubbing your palms together) that stimulates them to secrete prostacyclin and nitric oxide, which are vasodilators.

If a tissue's blood supply is cut off for a time and then restored, it often exhibits **reactive hyperemia**—an increase above the normal level of flow. This may be due to the accumulation of metabolites during the period of ischemia. Reactive hyperemia is seen when the skin flushes (reddens) after a person comes in from the cold. It also occurs in the forearm if a blood pressure cuff is inflated for too long and then loosened.

Over a longer time, a hypoxic tissue can increase its own perfusion by **angiogenesis**[8]—the growth of new blood vessels. (This

[8]*angio* = vessels; *genesis* = production of

term also refers to embryonic development of blood vessels.) Three situations in which this is important are the regrowth of the uterine lining after each menstrual period, the development of a higher density of blood capillaries in the muscles of well-conditioned athletes, and the growth of arterial bypasses around obstructions in the coronary circulation. There is great clinical importance in determining how growth factors and inhibitors control angiogenesis. Malignant tumors secrete growth factors that stimulate a dense network of vessels to grow into them and provide nourishment to the cancer cells. Oncologists are interested in finding a way to block *tumor angiogenesis,* thus to choke off a tumor's blood supply and perhaps shrink or kill it.

Neural Control

In addition to local control, the blood vessels are under remote control by the central and autonomic nervous systems. The vasomotor center of the medulla oblongata exerts sympathetic control over blood vessels throughout the body. (Precapillary sphincters have no innervation, however, and respond only to local and hormonal stimuli.) Sympathetic nerve fibers stimulate most blood vessels to constrict, and allow for vasodilation by reducing the nerve firing rate *(sympathetic tone).* The role of sympathetic and vasomotor tone in controlling vessel diameter is explained in section 15.3c.

The vasomotor center is an integrating center for three autonomic reflexes—*baroreflexes, chemoreflexes,* and the *medullary ischemic reflex.* A **baroreflex**[9] is a negative feedback response to changes in blood pressure (see fig. 15.1). The changes are detected by baroreceptors of the carotid sinuses (see fig. 20.4). Glossopharyngeal nerve fibers from these sinuses transmit signals continually to the brainstem. When blood pressure rises, their signaling rate rises. This *inhibits* the sympathetic cardiac and vasomotor neurons and reduces sympathetic tone, and it *excites* the vagal fibers to the heart. Thus, it reduces the heart rate and cardiac output, dilates the arteries and veins, and reduces blood pressure **(fig. 20.14).** When blood pressure drops below normal, on the other hand, the opposite reactions occur and BP rises back to normal.

Baroreflexes are important chiefly in short-term regulation of BP, for example in adapting to changes in posture. Perhaps you have jumped quickly out of bed and felt a little dizzy for a moment. This occurs because gravity draws the blood into the large veins of the abdomen and lower limbs when you stand, which reduces venous return to the heart and cardiac output to the brain. Normally, the baroreceptors respond quickly to this drop in pressure and restore cerebral perfusion (see fig. 1.8). Baroreflexes are not effective in correcting chronic hypertension, however. Within 2 days or less, they adjust their set point to the higher BP and maintain dynamic equilibrium at this new level.

A **chemoreflex** is an autonomic response to changes in blood chemistry, especially its pH and concentrations of O_2 and CO_2. It is initiated by the chemoreceptors called *aortic bodies* and *carotid bodies* described earlier. The primary role of chemoreflexes is to adjust respiration to changes in blood chemistry, but they have a secondary role in vasoreflexes. Hypoxemia (blood O_2 deficiency), hypercapnia

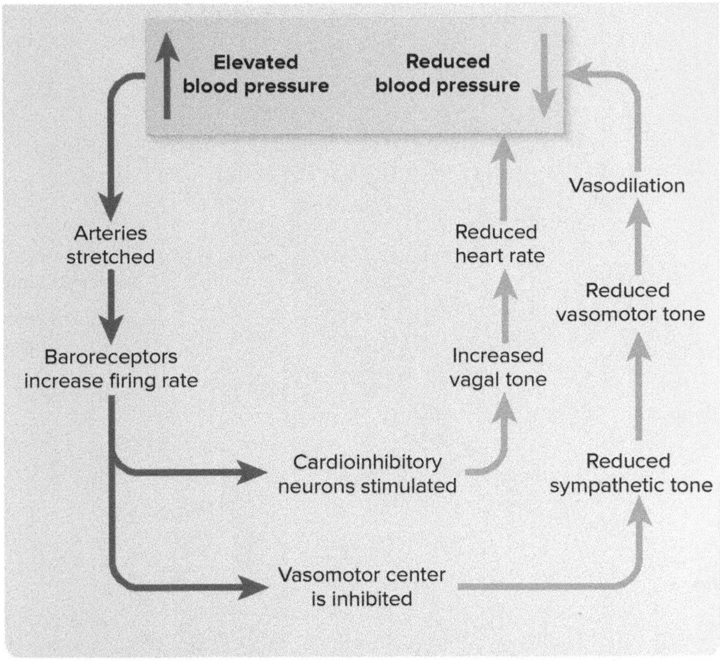

FIGURE 20.14 Negative Feedback Control of Blood Pressure. High blood pressure activates this cycle of reactions that ideally return blood pressure to normal.

(CO_2 excess), and acidosis (low blood pH) stimulate the chemoreceptors and act through the vasomotor center to induce widespread vasoconstriction. This increases overall BP, thus increasing perfusion of the lungs and the rate of gas exchange. Chemoreceptors also stimulate breathing, so increased ventilation of the lungs matches their increased perfusion. Increasing one without the other (airflow without blood flow, or vice versa) would be of little use.

The **medullary ischemic reflex** (iss-KEE-mic) is an autonomic response to reduced perfusion of the brain. The medulla oblongata monitors its own blood supply and activates corrective reflexes when it senses a state of ischemia (insufficient perfusion). Within seconds of a drop in perfusion, the cardiac and vasomotor centers of the medulla send sympathetic signals to the heart and blood vessels that accelerate the heart and constrict the vessels. These actions raise the blood pressure and ideally restore normal cerebral perfusion. The cardiac and vasomotor centers also receive input from other brain centers, so stress, anger, and arousal can raise the blood pressure. The hypothalamus acts through the vasomotor center to redirect blood flow in response to exercise or changes in body temperature.

Hormonal Control

Hormones are another means of remote control over perfusion. All of the following hormones influence blood pressure, some through their vasoactive effects and some through means such as regulating water balance:

- **Angiotensin II.** This is a potent vasoconstrictor that raises the blood pressure. Its synthesis and action are depicted in figure 23.15. Its synthesis requires *angiotensin-converting*

---

[9]*baro* = pressure

enzyme (ACE). Hypertension is often treated with drugs called *ACE inhibitors,* which block the action of this enzyme, thus lowering angiotensin II levels and blood pressure.

- **Aldosterone.** This "salt-retaining hormone" primarily promotes Na^+ retention by the kidneys. Since water follows sodium osmotically, Na^+ retention promotes water retention, thereby supporting blood pressure.

- **Natriuretic peptides.** These hormones, secreted by the heart, antagonize aldosterone. They increase Na^+ excretion by the kidneys, thus reducing blood volume and pressure. They also have a generalized vasodilator effect that helps to lower blood pressure.

- **Antidiuretic hormone.** ADH primarily promotes water retention, but at pathologically high concentrations it is also a vasoconstrictor—hence its alternate name, *arginine vasopressin.* Both of these effects raise blood pressure.

- **Epinephrine and norepinephrine.** These adrenal and sympathetic catecholamines bind to α-adrenergic receptors on the smooth muscle of most blood vessels. This stimulates vasoconstriction and raises the blood pressure.

▶▶▶ APPLY WHAT YOU KNOW

Renin inhibitors are drugs used to treat hypertension. Explain how you think they would produce the desired effect.

20.2d Two Purposes of Vasomotion

Vasomotion (vasoconstriction and vasodilation) serves two physiological purposes: a generalized raising or lowering of blood pressure throughout the body, and selectively modifying the perfusion of a particular organ and rerouting blood from one region of the body to another.

A generalized increase in blood pressure requires centralized control—an action on the part of the medullary vasomotor center or by hormones that circulate throughout the system, such as angiotensin II or epinephrine. Widespread vasoconstriction raises the overall blood pressure because the whole "container" (the blood vessels) squeezes on a fixed amount of blood, like water pressure rising if you squeeze a plastic water bottle. This can be important in supporting cerebral perfusion in situations such as hemorrhaging or dehydration, in which blood volume has significantly fallen. Conversely, generalized vasodilation lowers BP throughout the system.

The rerouting of blood and changes in the perfusion of individual organs can be achieved by either central or local control. For example, during periods of exercise, the sympathetic nervous system can selectively reduce flow to the kidneys and digestive tract. Yet as we saw earlier, metabolite accumulation in a tissue can stimulate local vasodilation and increase perfusion of that tissue without affecting circulation elsewhere in the body.

If a specific artery constricts, pressure downstream from the constriction drops and pressure upstream from it rises. If blood can travel by either of two routes and one route puts up more resistance than the other, most blood follows the path of least resistance. This mechanism enables the body to redirect blood from one organ to another.

For example, if you are dozing in an armchair after a big meal **(fig. 20.15a),** vasoconstriction shuts down blood flow to 90% or more of the capillaries in the muscles of your lower limbs (and muscles elsewhere). This raises the BP above the limbs, where the aorta gives off a branch, the superior mesenteric artery, supplying the small intestine. High resistance in the circulation of the limbs and low resistance in the superior mesenteric artery route blood to the small intestine, where it is needed to absorb the nutrients you are digesting.

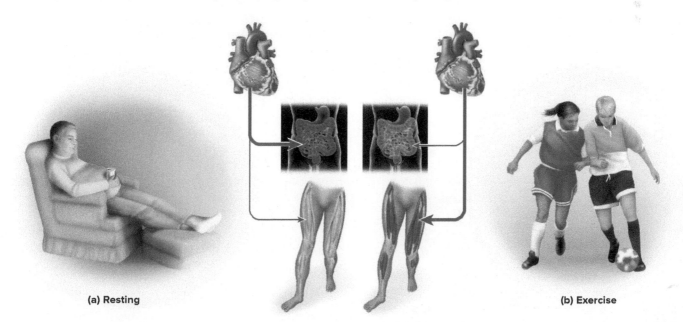

(a) Resting   **(b) Exercise**

FIGURE 20.15 Redirection of Blood Flow in Response to Changing Metabolic Needs. (a) After a meal, the intestines receive priority and the skeletal muscles receive relatively little flow. (b) During exercise, the muscles receive higher priority. The vasomotion that redirects such blood flow occurs mainly at the level of the arterioles in the respective organs.

On the other hand, during vigorous exercise, the arteries in your lungs, coronary circulation, and muscles dilate. To increase the circulation in these routes, vasoconstriction must occur elsewhere, such as the kidneys and digestive tract (**figs. 20.15b, 20.16**). That reduces their perfusion for the time being, making more blood available to the organs important in sustaining exercise. Thus, local changes in peripheral resistance can shift blood flow from one organ system to another to meet the changing metabolic priorities of the body.

BEFORE YOU GO ON

Answer the following questions to test your understanding of the preceding section:

7. Explain why a drop in diastolic pressure would raise one's pulse pressure even if systolic pressure remained unchanged. How could this rise in pulse pressure adversely affect the blood vessels?

8. Explain why arterial blood flow is pulsatile and venous flow is not.

9. What three variables affect peripheral resistance to blood flow? Which of these is most able to change from one minute to the next?

10. What are the three primary mechanisms for controlling vessel radius? Briefly explain each.

11. Explain how the baroreflex serves as an example of homeostasis and negative feedback.

12. Explain how the body can shift the flow of blood from one organ system to another.

20.3 Capillaries and Fluid Exchange

Expected Learning Outcomes

When you have completed this section, you should be able to

a. describe how materials get from the blood into the surrounding tissues;

b. describe and calculate the forces that enable capillaries to give off and reabsorb fluid; and

c. describe the causes and effects of edema.

Only 250 to 300 mL (5%) of the blood is in the capillaries at any given time. This, however, is the most important blood in the body, for it is mainly across capillary walls that exchanges occur between the blood and surrounding tissues. **Capillary exchange** refers to this two-way movement of fluid.

Chemicals given off by the capillary blood to the perivascular tissues include oxygen, glucose and other nutrients, antibodies, and hormones. Chemicals taken up by the capillaries include carbon dioxide and other wastes, and many of the same substances as they give off: glucose and fatty acids released from storage in the liver and adipose tissue; calcium and other minerals released from bone; antibodies secreted by immune cells; and hormones secreted by the endocrine glands. Thus, many chemicals have a two-way traffic between the blood and connective tissue, leaving the capillaries at one point and entering at another. Along with all these solutes, there is substantial movement of water into and out of the bloodstream across the capillary walls. Significant exchange also occurs across

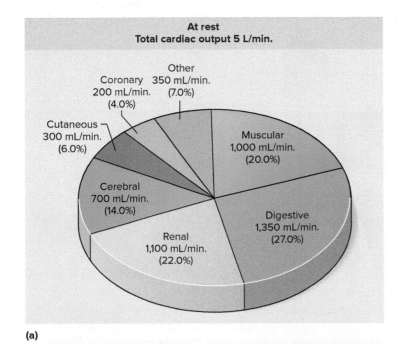

(a)

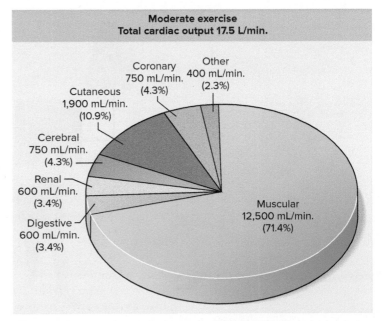

(b)

FIGURE 20.16 Differences in Systemic Blood Flow According to States of Physical Activity. (a) Relative blood flow at rest. (b) Relative blood flow during exercise.

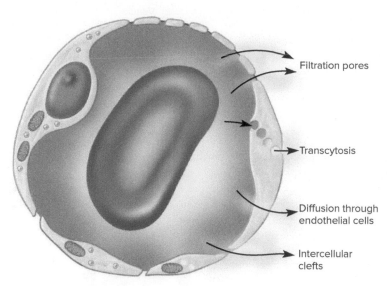

Filtration pores

Transcytosis

Diffusion through endothelial cells

Intercellular clefts

FIGURE 20.17 Routes of Fluid Exchange Across the Capillary Wall. Materials move through the capillary wall via filtration pores (in fenestrated capillaries only), by transcytosis, by diffusion through the endothelial cells, and via intercellular clefts.

the walls of the venules, but capillaries are the more important exchange site because they so greatly outnumber the venules.

The mechanisms of capillary exchange are difficult to study quantitatively because it is hard to measure pressure and flow in such small vessels. For some representative cutaneous capillaries, however, BP has been measured at 32 mm Hg at the arterial end and 15 mm Hg at the venous end, 1 mm away. Capillary BP drops rapidly because of the substantial friction the blood encounters in such narrow vessels. It takes 1 to 2 seconds for an RBC to pass through a typical capillary, traveling about 0.7 mm/s.

Chemicals pass through the capillary wall by three routes (**fig. 20.17**):

1. the endothelial cell cytoplasm;
2. intercellular clefts between the endothelial cells; and
3. filtration pores of the fenestrated capillaries.

The mechanisms of movement through the capillary wall are *diffusion, transcytosis, filtration,* and *reabsorption.*

20.3a Diffusion

The most important mechanism of exchange is diffusion. Glucose and oxygen, being more concentrated in the systemic blood than in the tissue fluid, diffuse out of the blood. Carbon dioxide and other wastes, being more concentrated in the tissue fluid, diffuse into the blood. (O_2 and CO_2 diffuse in the opposite directions in the lungs.) Such diffusion is possible only if the solute can either permeate the plasma membranes of the endothelial cells or find passages large enough to pass through—namely, the filtration pores and intercellular clefts. Such lipid-soluble substances as steroid hormones, O_2, and CO_2 diffuse easily through the plasma membranes. Substances insoluble in lipids, such as glucose and electrolytes, must

pass through membrane channels, filtration pores, or intercellular clefts. Large molecules such as proteins are usually held back.

20.3b Transcytosis

Transcytosis is a process in which endothelial cells pick up material on one side of the plasma membrane by pinocytosis or receptor-mediated endocytosis, transport the vesicles across the cell, and discharge the material on the other side by exocytosis (see fig. 3.22). This probably accounts for only a small fraction of solute exchange across the capillary wall, but fatty acids, albumin, and some hormones such as insulin move across the endothelium by this mechanism.

20.3c Filtration and Reabsorption

Capillary fluid exchange is driven in large part by the equilibrium between filtration and osmosis discussed in section 3.3. Typically, fluid filters out of the arterial end of a capillary and osmotically reenters it at the venous end. This fluid delivers materials to the cells and rinses away their metabolic wastes. It may seem odd that a capillary could give off fluid at one point and reabsorb it at another. This comes about as the result of a shifting balance between osmosis and hydrostatic pressure (**fig. 20.18**). **Hydrostatic pressure** is the physical force exerted by a liquid against a surface such as a capillary wall. Blood pressure is one example.

A typical capillary has a blood pressure of about 30 mm Hg at the arterial end. The hydrostatic pressure of the interstitial space has been difficult to measure, but a typical value accepted by many authorities is −3 mm Hg. The negative value indicates that this is a slight suction, which helps draw fluid out of the capillary. (This force will be represented hereafter as 3_{out}.) In this case, the positive hydrostatic pressure within the capillary and the negative interstitial pressure work in the same direction, creating a total outward force of about 33 mm Hg.

These forces are opposed by **colloid osmotic pressure (COP),** the portion of the osmotic pressure due to protein. The blood has a COP of about 28 mm Hg, due mainly to albumin. Tissue fluid has less than one-third the protein concentration of blood plasma and has a COP of about 8 mm Hg. The difference between the COP of blood and tissue fluid is called **oncotic pressure:** $28_{in} - 8_{out} = 20_{in}$. Oncotic pressure tends to draw water into the capillary by osmosis, opposing hydrostatic pressure.

These opposing forces produce a **net filtration pressure (NFP)** of 13 mm Hg out, as follows:

Hydrostatic pressure

Blood pressure		30_{out}
Interstitial pressure	+	3_{out}
Net hydrostatic pressure		33_{out}

Colloid osmotic pressure (COP)

Blood COP		28_{in}
Tissue fluid COP	−	8_{out}
Net COP (oncotic pressure)		20_{in}

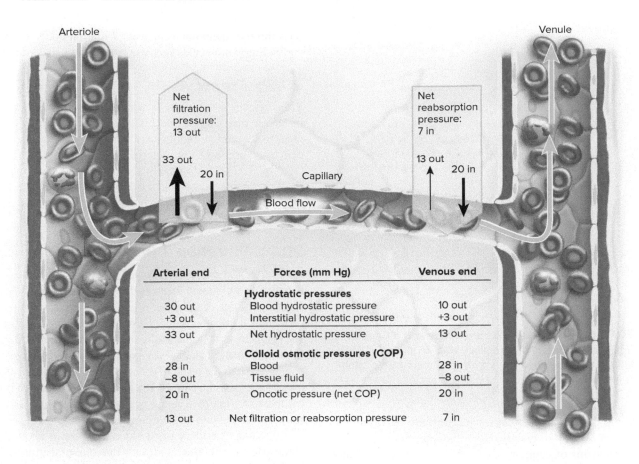

FIGURE 20.18 The Forces of Capillary Filtration and Reabsorption. Note the shift from net filtration at the arterial end (left) to net reabsorption at the venous end (right). **A&PR**

Net filtration pressure (NFP)

Net hydrostatic pressure		33_{out}
Oncotic pressure	−	20_{in}
Net filtration pressure		13_{out}

The NFP of 13 mm Hg causes about 0.5% of the blood plasma to leave the capillaries at the arterial end.

At the venous end, however, capillary blood pressure is lower—about 10 mm Hg. All the other pressures are essentially unchanged. Thus, we get the following:

Hydrostatic pressure

Blood pressure		10_{out}
Interstitial pressure	+	3_{out}
Net hydrostatic pressure		13_{out}

Net reabsorption pressure

Oncotic pressure		20_{in}
Net hydrostatic pressure	−	13_{out}
Net reabsorption pressure		7_{in}

The prevailing force is inward at the venous end because osmotic pressure overrides filtration pressure. The **net reabsorption pressure** of 7 mm Hg inward causes the capillary to reabsorb fluid at this end.

Now you can see why a capillary gives off fluid at one end and reabsorbs it at the other. The only pressure that changes significantly from the arterial end to the venous end is the capillary blood pressure, and this change is responsible for the shift from filtration to reabsorption. With a reabsorption pressure of 7 mm Hg and a net filtration pressure of 13 mm Hg, it might appear that far more fluid would leave the capillaries than reenter them. However, since capillaries branch along their length, there are more of them at the venous end than at the arterial end, which partially compensates for the difference between filtration and reabsorption pressures. They also typically have nearly twice the diameter at the venous end than they have at the arterial end, so there is more capillary surface area available to reabsorb fluid than to give it off. Consequently, capillaries in most places reabsorb about 85% of the fluid they filter. The rest is absorbed and returned to the blood by way of the lymphatic system, as described in the next chapter.

Of course, water is not the only substance that crosses the capillary wall by filtration and reabsorption. Chemicals dissolved in the water are "dragged" along with it and pass through the capillary wall if they are not too large. This process, called **solvent drag,** will be important in our discussions of kidney function in chapter 23.

Variations in Capillary Filtration and Reabsorption

The figures in the preceding discussion are only examples; circumstances differ from place to place in the body and from time to time in the same capillaries. Capillaries usually reabsorb most of the fluid they filter, but not always. The kidneys have capillary networks called *glomeruli* in which there is little or no reabsorption; they are entirely devoted to filtration. Alveolar capillaries of the lungs, by contrast, are almost entirely dedicated to absorption so fluid doesn't fill the air spaces.

Capillary activity also varies from moment to moment. In a resting tissue, most precapillary sphincters are constricted and the capillaries are collapsed. Capillary BP is very low (if there is any flow at all), and reabsorption predominates. When a tissue becomes more metabolically active, its capillary flow increases. In active muscles, capillary pressure rises to the point that filtration overrides reabsorption along the entire length of the capillary. Fluid accumulates in the muscle and increases muscular bulk by as much as 25%. Capillary permeability is also subject to chemical influences. Traumatized tissue releases such chemicals as substance P, bradykinin, and histamine, which increase permeability and filtration.

20.3d Edema

Edema is the accumulation of excess fluid in a tissue. It often shows as swelling of the face, fingers, abdomen, or ankles **(fig. 20.19),** but also occurs in internal organs where its effects are hidden from view. Edema occurs when fluid filters into a tissue faster than it is reabsorbed. It has three fundamental causes:

1. **Increased capillary filtration.** Numerous conditions can increase the rate of capillary filtration and accumulation of fluid in the tissues. Kidney failure, for example, leads to water retention and hypertension, raising capillary blood pressure and filtration rate. Histamine dilates arterioles and raises

capillary pressure and makes the capillary wall more permeable. Capillaries generally become more permeable in old age as well, putting elderly people at increased risk of edema. Capillary blood pressure also rises in cases of poor venous return—the flow of blood from the capillaries back to the heart. As we will see in the next section, good venous return depends on muscular activity. Therefore, edema is a common problem among people confined to bed or a wheelchair.

Failure of the right ventricle of the heart tends to cause pressure to back up in the systemic veins and capillaries, thus resulting in systemic edema. Failure of the left ventricle causes pressure to back up in the lungs, causing pulmonary edema.

2. **Reduced capillary reabsorption.** Capillary reabsorption depends on oncotic pressure, which is proportional to the concentration of blood albumin. Therefore, a deficiency of albumin (hypoproteinemia) produces edema by reducing the reabsorption of tissue fluid. Since albumin is produced by the liver, liver diseases such as cirrhosis tend to lead to hypoproteinemia and edema. Edema is commonly seen in regions of famine due to dietary protein deficiency (see Deeper Insight 18.1). Hypoproteinemia and edema also commonly result from severe burns, owing to the loss of protein from body surfaces no longer covered with skin, and from kidney diseases that allow protein to escape in the urine.

3. **Obstructed lymphatic drainage.** The lymphatic system, described in detail in the next chapter, is a network of one-way vessels that collect fluid from the tissues and return it to the bloodstream. Obstruction of these vessels or the surgical removal of lymph nodes can interfere with fluid drainage and lead to the accumulation of tissue fluid distal to the obstruction.

Edema has multiple pathological consequences. As the tissues become congested with fluid, oxygen delivery and waste removal are impaired and the tissues may begin to die. Pulmonary edema presents a threat of suffocation as fluid replaces air in the lungs,

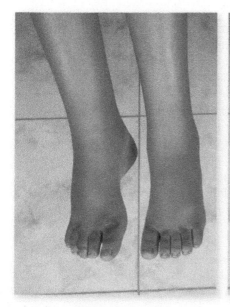
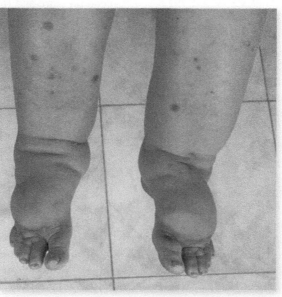

FIGURE 20.19 Lymphedema. On the right is a 52-year-old woman with severe lymphedema of the legs and feet; on the left, for comparison, is a 21-year-old woman without edema. Blockage of lymphatic vessels is one of several causes of edema.
MedicImage/Alamy

and cerebral edema can produce headaches, nausea, and sometimes delirium, seizures, and coma. In severe edema, so much fluid can transfer from the blood vessels to the tissue spaces that blood volume and pressure drop low enough to cause circulatory shock (described in the next section).

Answer the following questions to test your understanding of the preceding section:

13. List the three mechanisms of capillary exchange and relate each one to the structure of capillary walls.

14. What forces favor capillary filtration? What forces favor reabsorption?

15. How can a capillary shift from a predominantly filtering role at one time to a predominantly reabsorbing role at another?

16. State the three fundamental causes of edema and explain why edema can be dangerous.

20.4 Venous Return and Circulatory Shock

Expected Learning Outcomes

When you have completed this section, you should be able to

a. explain how blood in the veins is returned to the heart;

b. discuss the importance of physical activity in venous return;

c. discuss several causes of circulatory shock; and

d. name and describe the stages of shock.

Hieronymus Fabricius (1537–1619) discovered the valves of the veins but did not understand their function. That was left to his student, William Harvey, who performed simple experiments on the valves that you can easily reproduce. In **figure 20.20,** by Harvey, the experimenter has pressed on a vein at point H to block flow from the wrist toward the elbow. With another finger, he has milked the blood out of it up to point O, the first valve proximal to H. When he tries to force blood downward, it stops at that valve. It can go no farther, and it causes the vein to swell at that point. Blood can flow from right to left through that valve but not from left to right. So as Harvey correctly surmised, the valves serve to ensure a one-way flow of blood toward the heart.

You can easily demonstrate the action of these valves in your own hand. Hold your hand still, below waist level, until veins stand up on the back of it. (Do not apply a tourniquet!) Press on a vein close to your knuckles, and while holding it down, use another finger to milk that vein toward the wrist. It collapses as you force the blood out of it, and if you remove the second finger, it will not refill. The valves prevent blood from flowing back into it from

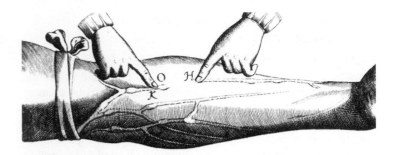

FIGURE 20.20 An Illustration from William Harvey's *De Motu Cordis* (1628). Such experiments demonstrated the existence of one-way valves in veins of the arms. See text for explanation.
UniversalImagesGroup/Getty Images

❓ *In the space between O and H, what (if anything) would happen if the experimenter lifted his finger from point O? What if he lifted his finger from point H? Why?*

above. When you remove the first finger, however, the vein fills from below.

20.4a Mechanisms of Venous Return

The flow of blood back to the heart, called **venous return,** is achieved by five mechanisms:

1. **The pressure gradient.** Pressure generated by the heart is the most important force in venous flow, even though it is substantially weaker in the veins than in the arteries. Pressure in the venules ranges from 12 to 18 mm Hg, and pressure at the point where the venae cavae enter the heart, called **central venous pressure,** averages 4.6 mm Hg. Thus, there is a venous pressure gradient (ΔP) of about 7 to 13 mm Hg favoring the flow of blood toward the heart. The pressure gradient and venous return increase when blood volume increases. Venous return also increases in the event of generalized, widespread vasoconstriction because this reduces the volume of the circulatory system and raises blood pressure and flow.

2. **Gravity.** When you are sitting or standing, blood from your head and neck returns to the heart simply by flowing downward through the large veins above the heart. Thus, the large veins of the neck are normally collapsed or nearly so, and their venous pressure is close to zero. The dural sinuses of the brain, however, have more rigid walls and cannot collapse. Their pressure is as low as −10 mm Hg, creating a risk of *air embolism* if they are punctured (see Deeper Insight 20.3).

3. **The skeletal muscle pump.** In the limbs, the veins are surrounded and massaged by the muscles. Contracting muscles squeeze the blood out of the compressed part of a vein, and the valves ensure that this blood can go only toward the heart **(fig. 20.21).**

4. **The thoracic (respiratory) pump.** This mechanism aids the flow of venous blood from the abdominal to the thoracic cavity. When you inhale, your thoracic cavity

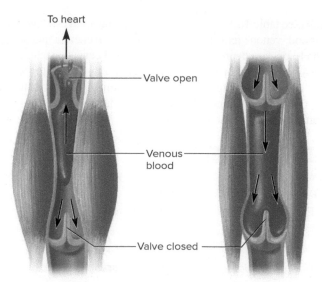

To heart

Valve open

Venous blood

Valve closed

(a) Contracted skeletal muscles   **(b) Relaxed skeletal muscles**

FIGURE 20.21 The Skeletal Muscle Pump. (a) Muscle contraction squeezes the deep veins and forces blood through the next valve in the direction of the heart. Valves below the point of compression prevent backflow. (b) When the muscles relax, blood flows back downward under the pull of gravity but can flow only as far as the nearest valve.

expands and its internal pressure drops, while downward movement of the diaphragm raises the pressure in your abdominal cavity. The *inferior vena cava (IVC),* your largest vein, is a flexible tube passing through both of these cavities. If abdominal pressure on the IVC rises while thoracic pressure on it drops, then blood is squeezed upward toward the heart. It isn't forced back into the lower limbs because the valves there prevent this. Because of the thoracic pump, central venous pressure fluctuates from 2 mm Hg when you inhale to 6 mm Hg when you exhale, and blood flows faster when you inhale. This is what produces the slight fluctuations in blood pressure at the right end of the graph in figure 20.11.

5. **Cardiac suction.** During ventricular systole, the tendinous cords pull the AV valve cusps downward, slightly expanding the atrial space. This creates a slight suction that draws blood into the atria from the venae cavae and pulmonary veins.

20.4b Venous Return and Physical Activity

Exercise increases venous return for multiple reasons. The heart beats faster and harder, increasing cardiac output and blood pressure. Blood vessels of the skeletal muscles, lungs, and coronary circulation dilate, increasing flow. The increase in respiratory rate and depth enhances the action of the thoracic pump. Muscle contractions increase venous return by means of the skeletal muscle pump. Increased venous return then increases cardiac output, which is important in perfusion of the muscles just when they need it most.

Conversely, when a person is still, blood accumulates in the limbs because venous pressure isn't high enough to override the weight of the blood and drive it upward. Such accumulation of blood is called **venous pooling.** To demonstrate this effect, hold one hand below your waist and hold the other hand over your head. After about 1 minute, quickly bring your two hands together and compare the palms. The hand held overhead will likely appear pale because its blood has drained out of it; the hand held below the waist will likely be redder than normal because of venous pooling in its veins and capillaries. Venous pooling can be troublesome to people who must stand for prolonged periods—such as cashiers, barbers and hairdressers, members of a choir, and people in military service—and when sitting still for too long, as in a cramped seat on a long airline flight. If enough blood accumulates in the limbs, cardiac output may fall so low that the brain is inadequately perfused and a person may experience dizziness or syncope. This can usually be prevented by periodically tensing the calf and other muscles to keep the skeletal muscle pump active. Military jet pilots often perform maneuvers that could cause the blood to pool in the abdomen and lower limbs, causing loss of vision or consciousness. To prevent this, they wear pressurized *G suits* that inflate and tighten on the lower limbs during these maneuvers; in addition, they can tense their abdominal muscles to prevent venous pooling and blackout.

▶▶▶ APPLY WHAT YOU KNOW

Why is venous pooling not a problem when you are sleeping and the skeletal muscle pump is inactive?

20.4c Circulatory Shock

Circulatory shock (not to be confused with electrical or spinal shock) is any state in which cardiac output is insufficient to meet the body's metabolic needs. All forms of circulatory shock fall into two categories: (1) **cardiogenic shock,** caused by inadequate pumping by the heart, usually as a result of myocardial infarction; and (2) **low venous return (LVR) shock,** in which cardiac output is low because too little blood is returning to the heart.

There are three principal forms of LVR shock:

1. **Hypovolemic shock,** the most common form, is produced by a loss of blood volume as a result of hemorrhage, trauma, bleeding ulcers, burns, or dehydration. Dehydration is a major cause of death from heat exposure. In hot weather, the body excretes as much as 1.5 L of sweat per hour. Water transfers from the bloodstream to replace tissue fluid lost in the sweat, and blood volume may drop too low to maintain adequate circulation.

2. **Obstructed venous return shock** occurs when any object, such as a growing tumor or aneurysm, compresses a vein and impedes its blood flow.

3. **Venous pooling shock** occurs when the body has a normal total blood volume, but too much of it accumulates in the lower body. This can result from long periods of standing

FIGURE 20.22 Venous Pooling Shock. This is a common consequence of prolonged, rigid standing in ceremonial attention.
Carlo Allegri/AFP/Getty Images

or sitting (**fig. 20.22**) or from widespread vasodilation. **Neurogenic shock** is a form of venous pooling shock that results from a sudden loss of vasomotor tone, allowing the vessels to dilate. This can result from causes as severe as brainstem trauma or as slight as an emotional shock.

Elements of both venous pooling and hypovolemic shock are present in certain cases, such as septic shock and anaphylactic shock, which involve both vasodilation and a loss of fluid through abnormally permeable capillaries. **Septic shock** occurs when bacterial toxins trigger vasodilation and increased capillary permeability. **Anaphylactic shock,** discussed more fully in section 21.6, results from exposure to an antigen to which a person is allergic, such as bee venom. Antigen–antibody complexes trigger the release of histamine, which causes generalized vasodilation and increased capillary permeability.

Responses to Circulatory Shock

Shock is clinically described according to severity as compensated or decompensated. In **compensated shock,** several homeostatic mechanisms bring about spontaneous recovery. The hypotension resulting from low cardiac output triggers the sympathetic barorreflex and the production of angiotensin II, both of which counteract shock by stimulating vasoconstriction. Furthermore, if a person faints and falls to a horizontal position, gravity restores blood flow to the brain. Even quicker recovery is achieved if the person's feet are elevated to promote drainage of blood from the legs.

If these mechanisms prove inadequate, **decompensated shock** ensues and several life-threatening positive feedback loops occur. Poor cardiac output results in myocardial ischemia and infarction, which further weaken the heart and reduce output. Slow circulation of the blood can lead to disseminated intravascular coagulation

(DIC) (see table 18.8). As the vessels become congested with clotted blood, venous return grows even worse. Ischemia and acidosis of the brainstem depress the vasomotor and cardiac centers, causing loss of vasomotor tone, further vasodilation, and further drop in BP and cardiac output. Before long, damage to the cardiac and brain tissues may be unsurvivable. About half of those who go into decompensated shock die from it.

> **BEFORE YOU GO ON**
>
> Answer the following questions to test your understanding of the preceding section:
>
> 17. Explain how respiration aids venous return.
> 18. Explain how muscular activity and venous valves aid venous return.
> 19. Define *circulatory shock.* What are some of the causes of low venous return shock?

20.5 Special Circulatory Routes

Expected Learning Outcomes
When you have completed this section, you should be able to

a. explain how the brain maintains stable perfusion;

b. discuss the causes and effects of strokes and transient ischemic attacks;

c. explain the mechanisms that increase muscular perfusion during exercise; and

d. contrast the blood pressure of the pulmonary circuit with that of the systemic circuit, and explain why the difference is important in pulmonary function.

Certain circulatory pathways have special physiological properties adapted to the functions of their organs. Two of these are described in other chapters: the coronary circulation (see fig. 19.10) and fetal and placental circulation (see fig. 29.10). Here we take a closer look at the circulation to the brain, skeletal muscles, and lungs.

20.5a Brain

Total blood flow to the brain fluctuates less than that of any other organ (about 700 mL/min. at rest). Such constancy is important because even a few seconds of oxygen deprivation causes loss of consciousness, and 4 or 5 minutes of anoxia is time enough to cause irreversible damage. Although total cerebral perfusion is fairly stable, blood flow can be shifted from one part of the brain to another in a matter of seconds as different parts engage in motor, sensory, or cognitive functions (see fig. 14.41).

The brain regulates its own blood flow in response to changes in BP and chemistry. The cerebral arteries dilate when the systemic BP drops and constrict when it rises, thus minimizing fluctuations in cerebral BP. Cerebral blood flow therefore remains quite stable even when mean arterial pressure (MAP) fluctuates from 60 to 140 mm Hg. However, an MAP below 60 mm Hg produces syncope and an MAP above 160 mm Hg causes cerebral edema.

The main chemical stimulus for cerebral autoregulation is pH. Poor perfusion allows CO_2 to accumulate in the brain. This lowers the pH of the tissue fluid and triggers local vasodilation, which improves perfusion. Extreme hypercapnia, however, depresses neural activity. The opposite condition, hypocapnia, raises the pH and stimulates vasoconstriction, thus reducing perfusion and giving CO_2 a chance to rise to a normal level. Hyperventilation (exhaling CO_2 faster than the body produces it) induces hypocapnia, which leads to cerebral vasoconstriction, ischemia, dizziness, and sometimes syncope.

Brief episodes of cerebral ischemia produce **transient ischemic attacks (TIAs),** characterized by temporary dizziness, loss of vision or other senses, weakness, paralysis, headache, or aphasia. A TIA may result from spasms of diseased cerebral arteries. It lasts from just a moment to a few hours and is often an early warning of an impending stroke. People with TIAs should receive prompt medical attention to identify the cause using brain imaging and other diagnostic means. Immediate treatment should be initiated to prevent a stroke. **Stroke, or cerebrovascular accident (CVA),** is far more serious, entailing death (infarction) of brain tissue and often irreversible loss of bodily functions. Stroke is discussed more extensively in Deeper Insight 14.2.

20.5b Skeletal Muscles

In contrast to the brain, the skeletal muscles receive a highly variable blood flow depending on their state of exertion. At rest, the arterioles are constricted, most of the capillary beds are shut down, and total flow through the muscular system is about 1 L/min. During exercise, the arterioles dilate in response to muscle metabolites such as lactate, nitric oxide (NO), adenosine, CO_2, and H^+. Blood flow through the muscles can increase more than 20-fold during strenuous exercise, which requires that blood be diverted from other organs such as the digestive tract and kidneys to meet the needs of the working muscles.

Muscular contraction compresses the blood vessels and impedes flow. For this reason, isometric contraction causes fatigue more quickly than intermittent isotonic contraction. If you squeeze a rubber ball as hard as you can without relaxing your grip, you feel the muscles fatigue more quickly than if you intermittently squeeze and relax.

20.5c Lungs

After birth, the pulmonary circuit is the only route in which the arteries carry oxygen-poor blood and the veins carry oxygen-rich blood; the opposite situation prevails in the systemic circuit. The pulmonary arteries have thin distensible walls with less elastic tissue than the systemic arteries. Thus, they have a BP of only 25/10 mm Hg. Capillary hydrostatic pressure is about 10 mm Hg in the pulmonary circuit as compared with an average of 17 mm Hg in systemic capillaries. This lower pressure has two implications for pulmonary circulation: (1) Blood flows more slowly through the pulmonary capillaries, and therefore it has more time for gas exchange; and (2) oncotic pressure overrides hydrostatic pressure, so these capillaries are engaged almost entirely in absorption. This prevents fluid accumulation in the alveolar walls and lumens, which would compromise gas exchange. In a condition such as

mitral valve stenosis, however, blood may back up in the pulmonary circuit, raising the capillary hydrostatic pressure and causing pulmonary edema, congestion, and hypoxemia.

Another unique characteristic of the pulmonary arteries is their response to hypoxia. Systemic arteries dilate in response to local hypoxia and improve tissue perfusion. By contrast, pulmonary arteries constrict. Pulmonary hypoxia indicates that part of the lung is not being ventilated well, perhaps because of mucous congestion of the airway or a degenerative lung disease. Vasoconstriction in poorly ventilated regions of the lung redirects blood flow to better ventilated regions.

▶▶▶ APPLY WHAT YOU KNOW

What abnormal skin coloration would result from pulmonary edema?

BEFORE YOU GO ON

Answer the following questions to test your understanding of the preceding section:

20. In what conspicuous way does perfusion of the brain differ from perfusion of the skeletal muscles?

21. How does a stroke differ from a transient ischemic attack? Which of these bears closer resemblance to a myocardial infarction?

22. How does the low hydrostatic blood pressure in the pulmonary circuit affect the fluid dynamics of the capillaries there?

23. Contrast the vasomotor response of the lungs with that of skeletal muscles to hypoxia.

20.6 Anatomy of the Pulmonary Circuit

Expected Learning Outcome

When you have completed this section, you should be able to

a. trace the route of blood through the pulmonary circuit.

The next three sections of this chapter center on the names and pathways of the principal arteries and veins. The pulmonary circuit is described here, and the systemic arteries and veins are described in the two sections that follow.

The pulmonary circuit **(fig. 20.23)** begins with the **pulmonary trunk,** a large vessel that ascends diagonally from the right ventricle and branches into the right and left **pulmonary arteries.** As it approaches the lung, the right pulmonary artery branches in two, and both branches enter the lung at a medial indentation called the *hilum* (see fig. 22.9). The upper branch is the **superior lobar artery,** serving the superior lobe of the lung. The lower branch divides again within the lung to form the **middle lobar** and **inferior lobar arteries,** supplying the lower two lobes of that lung. The left pulmonary artery is much more variable. It gives off several superior lobar arteries to the superior lobe before entering

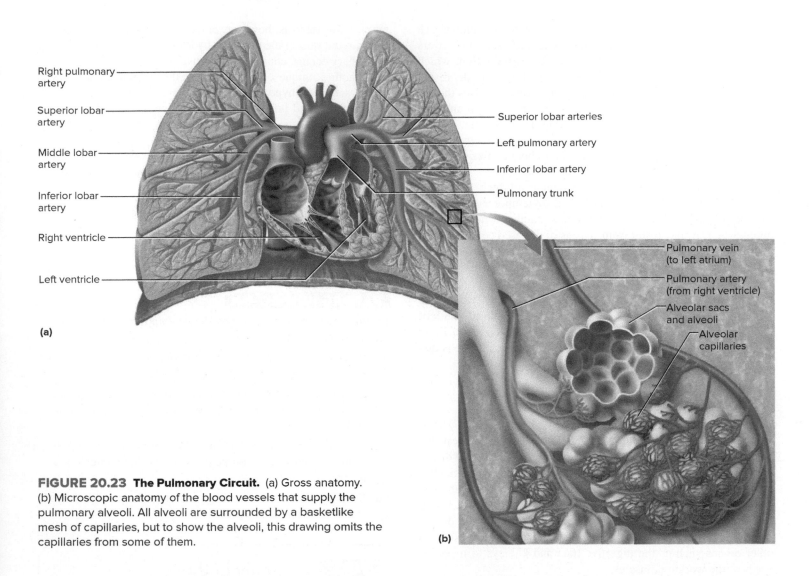

Right pulmonary artery

Superior lobar artery

Middle lobar artery

Inferior lobar artery

Right ventricle

Left ventricle

Superior lobar arteries

Left pulmonary artery

Inferior lobar artery

Pulmonary trunk

Pulmonary vein (to left atrium)

Pulmonary artery (from right ventricle)

Alveolar sacs and alveoli

Alveolar capillaries

(a)

(b)

FIGURE 20.23 The Pulmonary Circuit. (a) Gross anatomy. (b) Microscopic anatomy of the blood vessels that supply the pulmonary alveoli. All alveoli are surrounded by a basketlike mesh of capillaries, but to show the alveoli, this drawing omits the capillaries from some of them.

the hilum, then enters the lung and gives off a variable number of inferior lobar arteries to the inferior lobe.

In both lungs, these arteries lead ultimately to small basketlike capillary beds that surround the pulmonary alveoli (air sacs). This is where the blood unloads CO_2 and picks up O_2. After leaving the alveolar capillaries, the pulmonary blood flows into venules and veins, ultimately leading to the main **pulmonary veins** that exit the lung at the hilum. The left atrium of the heart receives two pulmonary veins on each side (see fig. 19.5b).

The purpose of the pulmonary circuit is primarily to exchange CO_2 for O_2. The lungs also receive a separate systemic blood supply by way of the *bronchial arteries* (see section 20.7d).

BEFORE YOU GO ON

Answer the following questions to test your understanding of the preceding section:

24. Trace the flow of an RBC from right ventricle to left atrium and name the vessels along the way.

25. The lungs have two separate arterial supplies. Explain their functions.

20.7 Systemic Vessels of the Axial Region

Expected Learning Outcomes

When you have completed this section, you should be able to

a. identify the principal systemic arteries and veins of the axial region; and

b. trace the flow of blood from the heart to any major organ of the axial region and back to the heart.

The systemic circuit (**figs. 20.24, 20.25**) supplies oxygen and nutrients to all organs and removes their metabolic wastes. The coronary circulation, already described, is part of this. This section surveys the remaining arteries and veins of the axial region—the head, neck, and trunk. The following sections, 20.7a through 20.7g, trace arterial outflow and venous return, region by region. They outline only the most common circulatory pathways; there is

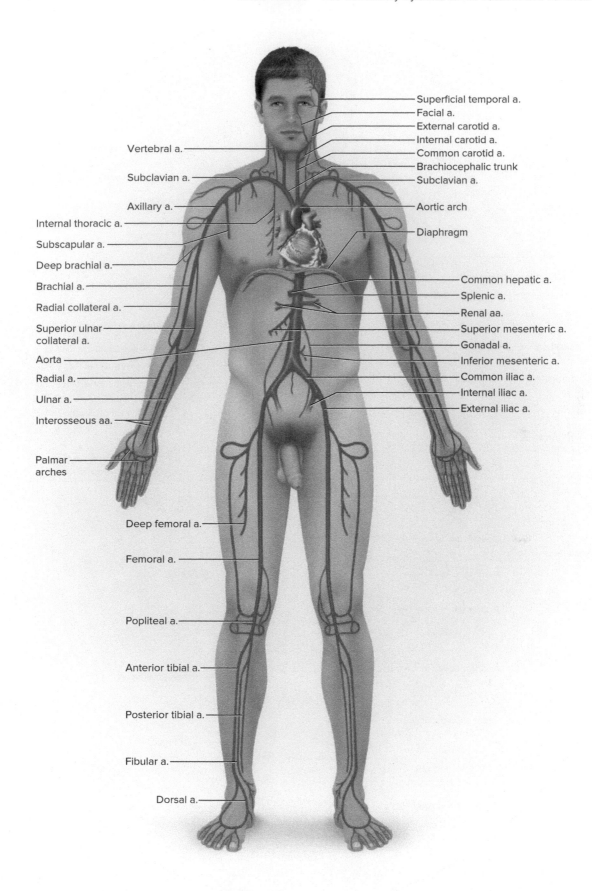

FIGURE 20.24 The Major Systemic Arteries. Different arteries are illustrated on the left than on the right for clarity, but nearly all of those shown occur on both sides.

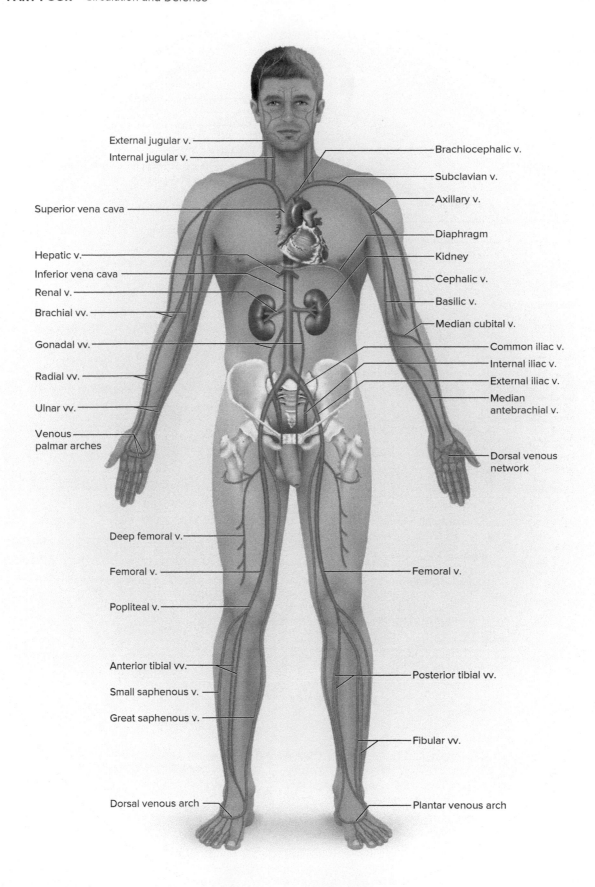

External jugular v.
Internal jugular v.
Superior vena cava
Hepatic v.
Inferior vena cava
Renal v.
Brachial vv.
Gonadal vv.
Radial vv.
Ulnar vv.
Venous palmar arches
Deep femoral v.
Femoral v.
Popliteal v.
Anterior tibial vv.
Small saphenous v.
Great saphenous v.
Dorsal venous arch

Brachiocephalic v.
Subclavian v.
Axillary v.
Diaphragm
Kidney
Cephalic v.
Basilic v.
Median cubital v.
Common iliac v.
Internal iliac v.
External iliac v.
Median antebrachial v.
Dorsal venous network
Femoral v.
Posterior tibial vv.
Fibular vv.
Plantar venous arch

FIGURE 20.25 The Major Systemic Veins. Different veins are illustrated on the left than on the right for clarity, but nearly all of those shown occur on both sides.

a great deal of anatomical variation in the circulatory system from one person to another.

The names of the blood vessels often describe their location by indicating the body region traversed (as in the *axillary artery* and *brachial veins*), an adjacent bone (as in *temporal artery* and *ulnar vein*), or the organ supplied or drained by the vessel (as in *hepatic artery* and *renal vein*). In many cases, an artery and adjacent vein have similar names (*femoral artery* and *femoral vein,* for example).

As you trace blood flow in these sections, it is important to refer frequently to the illustrations. Verbal descriptions alone are likely to seem obscure if you don't make full use of the explanatory illustrations. Throughout the remaining figures, the abbreviations *a.* and *aa.* mean *artery* and *arteries,* and *v.* and *vv.* mean *vein* and *veins.*

20.7a The Aorta and Its Major Branches

All systemic arteries arise from the aorta, which has three principal regions, often compared to the shape of an umbrella handle (**fig. 20.26**).

1. The **ascending aorta** rises for about 5 cm above the left ventricle. Its only branches are the coronary arteries, which arise behind two cusps of the aortic valve. They are the origins of the coronary circulation (see section 19.2e).

2. The **aortic arch** curves to the left like an inverted U superior to the heart. It gives off three major arteries in this order: the **brachiocephalic**[10] **trunk** (BRAY-kee-oh-seh-FAL-ic), **left common carotid artery** (cah-ROT-id), and **left subclavian**[11] **artery** (sub-CLAY-vee-un). These are further traced in sections 20.7b and 20.8a.

3. The **descending aorta** passes downward posterior to the heart, at first to the left of the vertebral column and then anterior to it, through the thoracic and abdominal cavities. It is called the **thoracic aorta** above the diaphragm and the **abdominal aorta** below it. It ends in the lower abdominal cavity by forking into the right and left *common iliac arteries.*

20.7b Arteries of the Head and Neck

All blood supply to the head, neck, and upper limbs comes from the aortic arch by way of the following arteries.

Origins of the Head–Neck Arteries

The head and neck (including the brain) receive blood from four pairs of arteries (**fig. 20.27**):

1. The **common carotid arteries,** probably the best-known avenues to the head, ascend the anterolateral region of the neck alongside the trachea. Shortly after leaving the aortic arch, the brachiocephalic trunk divides into the **right common carotid artery** to the head and the *right subclavian artery* leading to the right arm (further traced in section 20.7d). The **left common carotid artery** arises independently from the aortic arch a little distal to the brachiocephalic trunk.

2. The **vertebral arteries** arise from the right and left subclavian arteries, travel up the neck through the transverse foramina of vertebrae C1 through C6, and enter the cranial cavity through the foramen magnum.

3. The **thyrocervical**[12] **trunks** are tiny arteries arising from the subclavians lateral to the vertebral arteries. They supply the thyroid gland and some scapular muscles.

4. The **costocervical**[13] **trunks** arise from the subclavian arteries a little farther laterally. They supply the deep neck muscles and some of the intercostal muscles of the superior rib cage.

Continuation of the Common Carotid Arteries

The common carotid arteries have the most extensive distribution of all head–neck arteries. Near the laryngeal prominence ("Adam's apple"), each common carotid branches into an *external* and *internal carotid artery,* with further branches as follows:

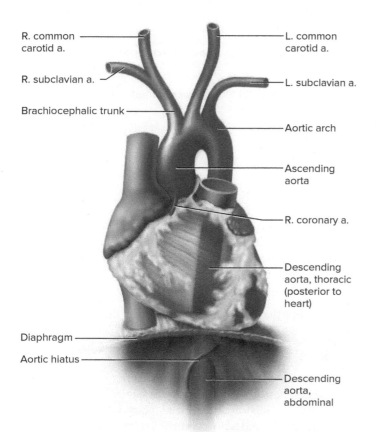

R. common carotid a.

R. subclavian a.

Brachiocephalic trunk

L. common carotid a.

L. subclavian a.

Aortic arch

Ascending aorta

R. coronary a.

Descending aorta, thoracic (posterior to heart)

Diaphragm

Aortic hiatus

Descending aorta, abdominal

FIGURE 20.26 The Thoracic Aorta. (L. = left; R. = right)

---

[10]*brachio* = arm; *cephal* = head
[11]*sub* = below; *clavi* = clavicle, collarbone
[12]*thyro* = thyroid gland; *cerv* = neck
[13]*costo* = rib; *cerv* = neck

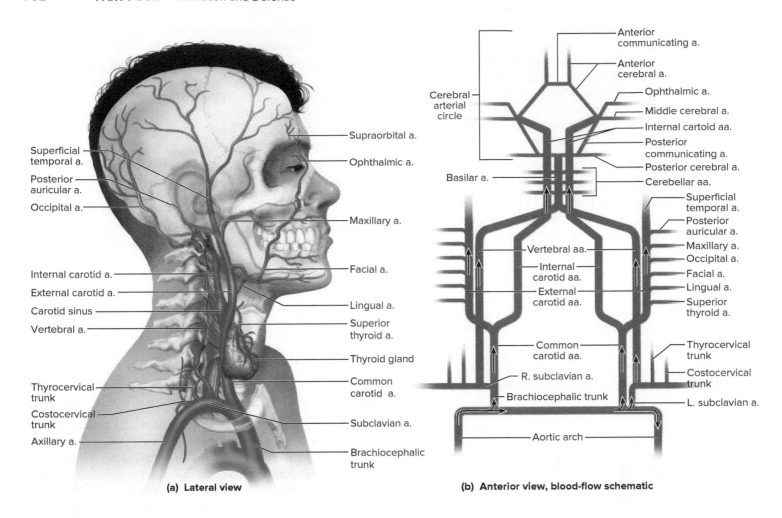

FIGURE 20.27 Superficial (Extracranial) Arteries of the Head and Neck. (a) Lateral view. (b) Blood-flow schematic, anterior view. The upper part of the schematic depicts the cerebral circulation in figure 20.28. **A&PR**

❓ *List the arteries, in order, that an erythrocyte must travel to get from the left ventricle to the skin of the left side of the forehead.*

1. The **external carotid artery** ascends the side of the head external to the cranium and supplies most extracranial structures except the orbits. It gives rise to the following arteries in ascending order:

   a. the **superior thyroid artery** to the thyroid gland and larynx;
   b. the **lingual artery** to the tongue;
   c. the **facial artery** to the skin and muscles of the face;
   d. the **occipital artery** to the posterior scalp;
   e. the **maxillary artery** to the teeth, maxilla, oral cavity, and external ear; and
   f. the **superficial temporal artery** to the chewing muscles, nasal cavity, lateral aspect of the face, most of the scalp, and the dura mater.

2. The **internal carotid artery** passes medial to the angle of the mandible and passes through the carotid canal of the temporal bone into the cranial cavity. It supplies the orbits

and about 80% of the cerebrum. Compressing the internal carotids near the mandible can therefore cause loss of consciousness (but is dangerous and must never be done for amusement, as some people do). Principal branches of the internal carotid artery **(fig. 20.28)** are

   a. the **ophthalmic artery,** which leaves the cranial cavity through the optic canal and supplies blood to the orbit, nose, and forehead;
   b. the large **middle cerebral artery,** which travels in the lateral sulcus of the cerebrum, supplies the insula, then issues numerous branches to the lateral region of the frontal, temporal, and parietal lobes of the brain; and
   c. the smaller **anterior cerebral artery,** which travels anteriorly, then turns back and arches posteriorly over the corpus callosum as far as the posterior limit of the parietal lobe; it gives off extensive branches to the frontal and parietal lobes.

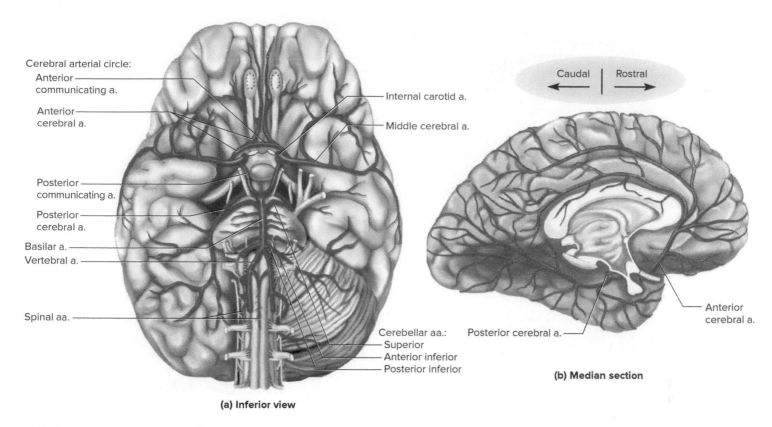

FIGURE 20.28 The Cerebral Blood Supply. (a) Inferior view of the brain showing the blood supply to the brainstem, cerebellum, and cerebral arterial circle. (b) Median section of the brain showing the more distal branches of the anterior and posterior cerebral arteries. Branches of the middle cerebral artery are distributed over the lateral surface of the cerebrum (not illustrated). **APR**

Continuation of the Vertebral Arteries

The vertebral arteries give rise to small branches that supply the spinal cord and its meninges, the cervical vertebrae, and deep muscles of the neck. They next enter the foramen magnum, supply the cranial bones and meninges, and continue as follows:

1. They converge to form a single median **basilar artery** at the junction of the medulla oblongata and pons. The basilar artery runs along the anterior aspect of the pons and gives off branches to the cerebellum, pons, and inner ear. At or near the pons–midbrain border, it divides into the following arteries.

2. Right and left **posterior cerebral arteries** arise from the basilar artery, sweep posteriorly to the rear of the brain, and serve the inferior and medial regions of the temporal and occipital lobes, the midbrain, and the thalamus.

The Cerebral Arterial Circle

In figure 20.28a and the upper part of 20.27b, you can see that a number of these arteries form a loop that encircles the pituitary gland and optic chiasm. This is called the **cerebral arterial circle** (*circle of Willis*[14]). Its components include the basilar artery;

[14]Thomas Willis (1621–75), English anatomist

internal carotid arteries; anterior, middle, and posterior cerebral arteries; and the following anastomoses that complete the loop:

1. one **anterior communicating artery** medially connecting the right and left anterior cerebral arteries; and

2. a slender, right and left **posterior communicating artery,** connecting the internal carotid and posterior cerebral arteries.

Only about 20% of people, however, have a complete cerebral arterial circle. Usually, one or more components are absent or so constricted as to provide no significant blood flow. Knowledge of the distribution of the arteries arising from the cerebral arterial circle is crucial for understanding the effects of blood clots, aneurysms, and strokes on brain function. Cerebral aneurysms occur most often in this complex of arteries or in the basilar artery proximal to the circle.

20.7c Veins of the Head and Neck

The head and neck are drained mainly by three pairs of veins—the *internal* and *external jugular veins* and *vertebral veins*. We will trace these from their origins to the *subclavian veins*.

Dural Venous Sinuses

After blood circulates through the brain, it collects in large, thin-walled, modified veins called **dural venous sinuses**—blood-filled spaces between the layers of the dura mater (**fig. 20.29**).

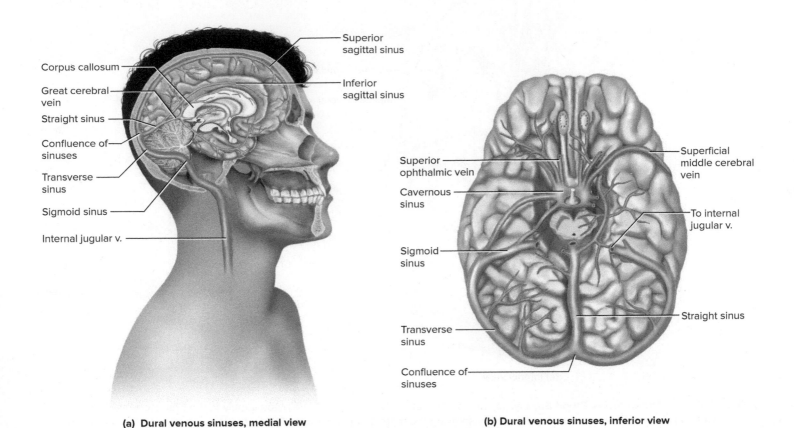

(a) **Dural venous sinuses, medial view**

(b) **Dural venous sinuses, inferior view**

FIGURE 20.29 Veins of the Head and Neck. (a) Dural venous sinuses seen in a median section of the cerebrum. (b) Dural venous sinuses seen in an inferior view of the cerebrum. (c) Superficial (extracranial) veins of the head and neck. **APR**

(c) **Superficial veins of the head and neck**

A reminder of the structure of the dura mater may be helpful in understanding these sinuses. This tough membrane between the brain and cranial bones has a *periosteal layer* against the bone and a *meningeal layer* against the brain. In a few places, a space exists between these layers to accommodate a blood-collecting sinus. Between the two cerebral hemispheres is a vertical, sickle-shaped wall of dura called the *falx cerebri,* which contains two of the sinuses. There are about 13 dural venous sinuses in all; we survey only the few most prominent ones here.

1. The **superior sagittal sinus** is contained in the superior margin of the falx cerebri and overlies the longitudinal cerebral fissure (fig. 20.29a; see also figs. 14.5, 14.7). It begins anteriorly near the crista galli of the skull and extends posteriorly to the level of the posterior occipital protuberance. Here it bends, usually to the right, and drains into a *transverse sinus.*

2. The **inferior sagittal sinus** is contained in the inferior margin of the falx cerebri and arches over the corpus callosum, deep in the longitudinal cerebral fissure. Posteriorly, it joins the *great cerebral vein* and their union forms the **straight sinus,** which continues to the rear of the head. There, the superior sagittal and straight sinuses meet in a space called the *confluence of the sinuses.*

3. Right and left **transverse sinuses** lead away from the confluence and encircle the inside of the occipital bone, leading toward the ears (fig. 20.29b); their path is marked by grooves on the inner surface of the occipital bone (see fig. 8.5b). The right transverse sinus receives blood mainly from the superior sagittal sinus, and the left one drains mainly the straight sinus. Laterally, each transverse sinus makes an S-shaped bend, the **sigmoid sinus,** then exits the cranium through the jugular foramen. From here, blood flows down the *internal jugular vein* of the neck.

4. The **cavernous sinuses** are honeycombs of blood-filled spaces on each side of the body of the sphenoid bone (fig. 20.29b). They receive blood from the *superior ophthalmic vein* of the orbit and the *superficial middle cerebral vein* of the brain, among other sources. They drain through several outlets including the transverse sinus, internal jugular vein, and facial vein. They are clinically important because infections can pass from the face and other superficial sites into the cranial cavity by this route. Also, inflammation of a cavernous sinus can injure important structures that pass through it, including the internal carotid artery and cranial nerves III to VI.

Major Veins of the Neck

Blood flows down the neck mainly through three veins on each side, all of which empty into the subclavian vein (fig. 20.29c).

1. The **internal jugular**[15] **vein** (JUG-you-lur) courses down the neck deep to the sternocleidomastoid muscle. It receives

---
[15]*jugul* = neck, throat

DEEPER INSIGHT 20.3

CLINICAL APPLICATION

Air Embolism

Injury to the dural sinuses or jugular veins presents less danger from loss of blood than from air sucked into the circulatory system. The presence of air in the bloodstream is called *air embolism* **(fig. 20.30).** This is an important concern to neurosurgeons, who sometimes operate with the patient in a sitting position. If a dural sinus is punctured, air can be sucked into the sinus and accumulate in the heart chambers, which blocks cardiac output and causes sudden death. Smaller air bubbles in the systemic circulation can cut off blood flow to the brain, lungs, myocardium, and other vital tissues. As little as 0.5 mL of air in a coronary artery can cause cardiac arrest.

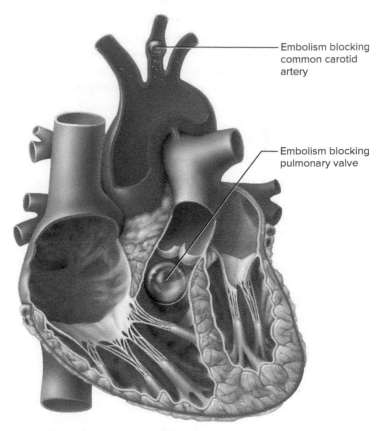

Embolism blocking common carotid artery

Embolism blocking pulmonary valve

FIGURE 20.30 Air Embolism.

most of the blood from the brain; picks up blood from the **facial vein, superficial temporal vein,** and **superior thyroid vein** along the way; passes behind the clavicle; and joins the subclavian vein (which is further traced in section 20.7e).

2. The **external jugular vein** courses down the side of the neck superficial to the sternocleidomastoid muscle and empties into the subclavian vein. It drains tributaries from

the parotid salivary gland, facial muscles, scalp, and other superficial structures. Some of this blood also follows venous anastomoses to the internal jugular vein.

3. The **vertebral vein** travels with the vertebral artery in the transverse foramina of the cervical vertebrae. Although the companion artery leads to the brain, the vertebral vein doesn't come from there. It drains the cervical vertebrae, spinal cord, and some of the small deep muscles of the neck, and empties into the subclavian vein.

Section 20.7e traces this blood flow the rest of the way to the superior vena cava and heart.

20.7d Arteries of the Thorax

The thorax is supplied by several arteries arising directly from the descending aorta and from the subclavian and axillary arteries. The thoracic aorta begins distal to the aortic arch and ends at the **aortic hiatus** (hy-AY-tus), a passage through the diaphragm. Along the way, it sends off numerous small branches to the thoracic viscera and body wall **(fig. 20.31).**

Visceral Branches of the Thoracic Aorta

Visceral branches of the thoracic aorta include the following:

1. The **bronchial arteries** vary in number and arrangement; there are usually two on the left and one on the right. The right bronchial artery usually arises from one of the left bronchial arteries or from a *posterior intercostal artery.* The bronchial arteries supply the visceral pleura, pericardium, and esophagus, and enter the lungs to supply the bronchi, bronchioles, and larger pulmonary blood vessels.

2. The **esophageal arteries** are four or five unpaired arteries that come off the anterior surface of the aorta and supply the esophagus.

3. The **mediastinal arteries** (not illustrated) are numerous small vessels that supply structures of the posterior mediastinum.

▶▶▶ **APPLY WHAT YOU KNOW**

Both the pulmonary arteries and bronchial arteries supply blood to the lungs, but when this blood emerges from the lungs, the pulmonary blood is richer in oxygen and the bronchial blood is poorer in oxygen. Explain why.

Parietal Branches of the Thoracic Aorta

The following branches supply chiefly the muscles, bones, and skin of the chest; only the first are illustrated.

1. The **posterior intercostal arteries** are nine pairs of vessels arising from the posterior side of the aorta. They course around the posterior side of the rib cage between ribs 3 through 12, then anastomose with the anterior intercostal arteries described in the next section. They supply the inter-costal, pectoralis, serratus anterior, and some abdominal muscles, as well as the vertebrae, spinal cord, meninges, breasts, skin, and subcutaneous tissue.

2. One pair of **subcostal arteries** arises from the aorta inferior to rib 12. They supply the posterior intercostal tissues, vertebrae, spinal cord, and deep muscles of the back.

3. A variable number of **superior phrenic**[16] **arteries** (FREN-ic) arise at the aortic hiatus and supply the superior and posterior regions of the diaphragm.

▶▶▶ **APPLY WHAT YOU KNOW**

The posterior intercostal arteries are larger in lactating women than in men and nonlactating females. Explain why.

Branches of the Subclavian and Axillary Arteries

The thoracic wall is also supplied by branches of the subclavian arteries and their continuations, the *axillary arteries,* in the shoulder and axillary regions. Recall that the right subclavian artery arises from the brachiocephalic trunk and the left subclavian artery arises directly from the aortic arch (see fig. 20.26). On both the right and left, the subclavian artery gives off the internal thoracic artery, then continues as the axillary artery. Further divisions of these arteries are as follows:

1. The **internal thoracic (mammary) artery** supplies the breast and anterior thoracic wall. It issues the following branches:
   a. The **pericardiophrenic artery** supplies the pericardium and diaphragm.
   b. The **anterior intercostal arteries** arise from the internal thoracic artery as it descends alongside the sternum. They travel between the ribs; supply the ribs and the intercostal and pectoral muscles, breast, and skin; and, finally, anastomose with the posterior intercostal arteries. Each sends one branch along the lower margin of the rib above it and another, parallel branch along the upper margin of the rib below it.

2. The **thoracoacromial**[17] **trunk** (THOR-uh-co-uh-CRO-me-ul) provides branches to the superior shoulder and pectoral regions.

3. The **lateral thoracic artery** supplies the pectoral, serratus anterior, and subscapularis muscles. It also issues branches to the breast and is larger in females than in males.

4. The **subscapular artery** is the largest branch of the axillary artery. It supplies the scapula and the latissimus dorsi, serratus anterior, teres major, deltoid, triceps brachii, and intercostal muscles.

---

[16]*phren* = diaphragm
[17]*thoraco* = chest; *acr* = tip, apex; *om* = shoulder

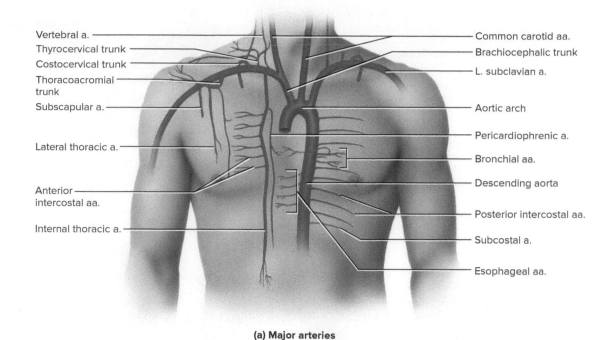

Vertebral a.
Thyrocervical trunk
Costocervical trunk
Thoracoacromial trunk
Subscapular a.
Lateral thoracic a.
Anterior intercostal aa.
Internal thoracic a.

Common carotid aa.
Brachiocephalic trunk
L. subclavian a.
Aortic arch
Pericardiophrenic a.
Bronchial aa.
Descending aorta
Posterior intercostal aa.
Subcostal a.
Esophageal aa.

(a) Major arteries

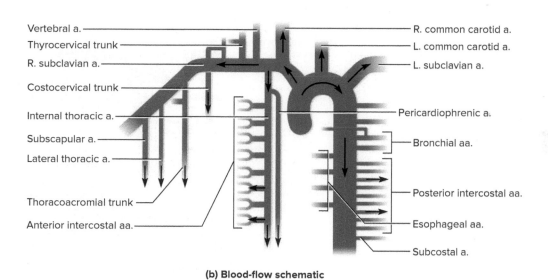

Vertebral a.
Thyrocervical trunk
R. subclavian a.
Costocervical trunk
Internal thoracic a.
Subscapular a.
Lateral thoracic a.
Thoracoacromial trunk
Anterior intercostal aa.

R. common carotid a.
L. common carotid a.
L. subclavian a.
Pericardiophrenic a.
Bronchial aa.
Posterior intercostal aa.
Esophageal aa.
Subcostal a.

(b) Blood-flow schematic

FIGURE 20.31 Arteries of the Thorax. (a) Major thoracic arteries. (b) Blood-flow schematic of the thoracic arteries.

20.7e Veins of the Thorax

The superior vena cava receives all venous drainage not only from the head and neck as already described, but also from all thoracic organs and tissues.

Tributaries of the Superior Vena Cava

The most prominent veins of the upper thorax carry blood from the shoulder region to the heart **(fig. 20.32);** they are as follows:

1. The **subclavian vein** drains the upper limb (see "Deep Veins" in section 20.8b). It begins at the lateral margin of the first rib and travels posterior to the clavicle. It receives the external jugular and vertebral veins, then ends (changes names) where it receives the internal jugular vein.

2. The **brachiocephalic vein** forms by the union of the subclavian and internal jugular veins. The right brachiocephalic is only about 2.5 cm long and the left is about 6 cm long. They

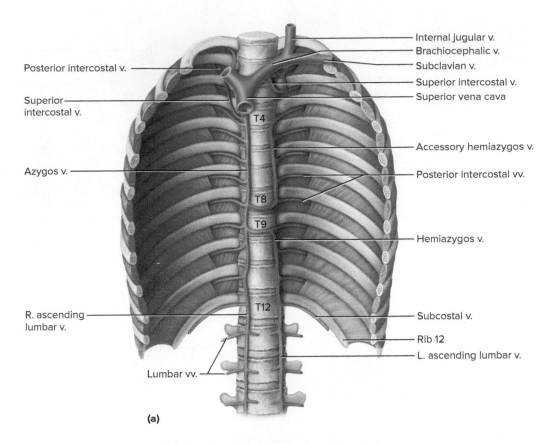

(a)

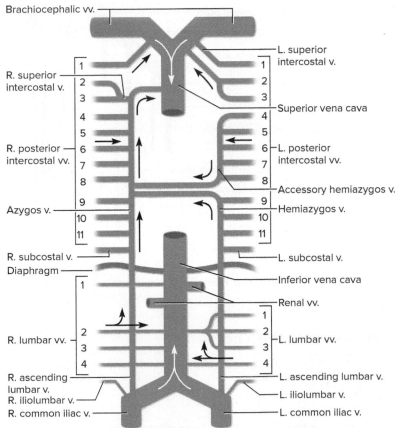

(b)

FIGURE 20.32 Venous Drainage of the Posterior Wall of the Thorax and Abdomen. (a) The azygos system of the thoracic wall. This system provides venous drainage from the wall and viscera of the thorax, but the visceral tributaries are not illustrated. (b) Blood-flow schematic of the thoracic and abdominal drainage. The components above the diaphragm constitute the azygos system. There is a great deal of individual variation in this anatomy. **APR**

receive tributaries from the vertebrae, thyroid gland, and upper thoracic wall and breast, then converge to form the next vein.

3. The **superior vena cava (SVC)** forms by the union of the right and left brachiocephalic veins. It travels inferiorly for about 7 cm and empties into the right atrium of the heart. Its main tributary is the *azygos vein*. It drains all structures superior to the diaphragm except the pulmonary circuit and coronary circulation. It also receives drainage from the abdominal cavity by way of the azygos system, described next.

The Azygos System

The principal venous drainage of the thoracic organs is by way of the *azygos system* (AZ-ih-goss) (fig. 20.32). The most prominent vein of this system is the **azygos**[18] **vein,** which ascends the right side of the posterior thoracic wall. It is named for the lack of a mate on the left. It receives the following tributaries, then empties into the superior vena cava at the level of vertebra T4.

1. The right **ascending lumbar vein** drains the right abdominal wall, then penetrates the diaphragm and enters the thoracic cavity. The azygos vein begins where the right ascending lumbar vein meets the right **subcostal vein** beneath rib 12.

2. The right **posterior intercostal veins** drain the intercostal spaces. The first (superior) one empties into the right brachiocephalic vein; intercostal veins 2 and 3 join to form the *right superior intercostal vein* before emptying into the azygos vein; and intercostal veins 4 through 11 each enter the azygos vein separately.

3. The right **esophageal, mediastinal, pericardial,** and **bronchial veins** (not illustrated) drain their respective organs into the azygos vein.

4. The **hemiazygos**[19] **vein** ascends the posterior thoracic wall on the left. It begins where the left ascending lumbar vein, having just penetrated the diaphragm, joins the subcostal vein below rib 12. The hemiazygos then receives the lower three posterior intercostal veins, esophageal veins, and mediastinal veins. At the left of vertebra T9, it crosses to the right and empties into the azygos vein.

5. The **accessory hemiazygos vein** descends the posterior thoracic wall on the left. It receives drainage from posterior intercostal veins 4 through 8 and sometimes the left bronchial veins. It crosses to the right at the level of vertebra T8 and empties into the azygos vein.

The left posterior intercostal veins 1 to 3 are the only ones on this side that do not ultimately drain into the azygos vein. The first one usually drains directly into the left brachiocephalic vein. The second and third unite to form the *left superior intercostal vein,* which empties into the left brachiocephalic vein.

20.7f Arteries of the Abdominal and Pelvic Regions

After passing through the aortic hiatus, the aorta descends through the abdominal cavity and ends at the level of vertebra L4, where it branches into the right and left common iliac arteries. The abdominal aorta is retroperitoneal.

Major Branches of the Abdominal Aorta

The abdominal aorta gives off arteries in the order listed here, from superior to inferior (**fig. 20.33**). Those named in the plural are paired left and right, whereas those named in the singular are solitary median arteries.

1. The **inferior phrenic arteries** supply the inferior surface of the diaphragm. They may arise from the aorta, celiac trunk, or renal artery. Each issues two or three small **superior suprarenal arteries** to the ipsilateral adrenal (suprarenal) gland.

2. The **celiac**[20] **trunk** (SEE-lee-ac) supplies the upper abdominal viscera (see next section).

3. The **superior mesenteric artery** supplies the intestines.

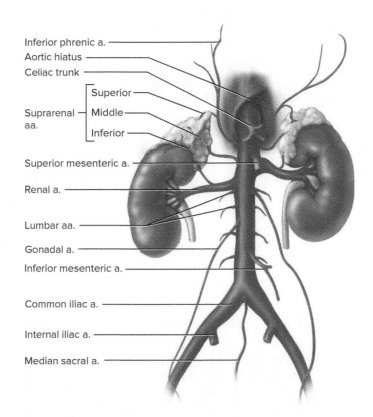

Inferior phrenic a.
Aortic hiatus
Celiac trunk
Superior
Suprarenal aa.
Middle
Inferior
Superior mesenteric a.
Renal a.
Lumbar aa.
Gonadal a.
Inferior mesenteric a.
Common iliac a.
Internal iliac a.
Median sacral a.

FIGURE 20.33 The Abdominal Aorta and Its Major Branches. APR

---

[18]unpaired; from *a* = without; *zygo* = union, mate
[19]*hemi* = half

[20]*celi* = belly, abdomen

4. The **middle suprarenal arteries** arise laterally from the aorta, usually at the same level as the superior mesenteric artery. They supply the adrenal glands.

5. The **renal arteries** supply the kidneys and issue a small **inferior suprarenal artery** to each adrenal gland.

6. The **gonadal arteries—ovarian arteries** of the female and **testicular arteries** of the male—are long, slender arteries that arise from the midabdominal aorta and descend along the posterior body wall to the female pelvic cavity or male scrotum. They supply the gonads. The gonads begin their embryonic development near the kidneys, and the gonadal arteries are then quite short. As the gonads descend to the pelvic cavity, these arteries grow and acquire their peculiar length and course.

7. The **inferior mesenteric artery** supplies the distal end of the large intestine.

8. The **lumbar arteries** arise from the lower aorta in four pairs. They supply the posterior abdominal wall (muscles, joints, and skin) and the spinal cord and other tissues in the vertebral canal.

9. The **median sacral artery,** a tiny median artery at the inferior end of the aorta, supplies the sacrum and coccyx.

10. The **common iliac arteries** arise as the aorta forks at its lower end. We will further trace these in later discussions of arteries of the pelvic region and lower limb.

Branches of the Celiac Trunk

The celiac circulation to the upper abdominal viscera is the most complex route off the abdominal aorta. Because it has numerous anastomoses, the bloodstream doesn't follow a simple linear path but divides and rejoins itself at several points. As you study the following description, locate these branches in **figure 20.34** and identify the points of anastomosis. The small size and complex pathways of these arteries are major obstacles to surgical treatment of pancreatic cancer.

The short, stubby celiac trunk, barely more than 1 cm long, is a median branch of the aorta just below the diaphragm. It immediately gives rise to three branches—the *common hepatic, left gastric,* and *splenic arteries.*

1. The **common hepatic artery** passes to the right and issues two main branches:

    a. The **gastroduodenal artery** gives off the **right gastro-omental artery** to the stomach. It then continues as the **pancreaticoduodenal artery** (PAN-cree-AT-ih-co-dew-ODD-eh-nul), which splits into two branches that pass around the anterior and posterior sides of the head of the pancreas. These anastomose with the two branches of the *inferior pancreaticoduodenal artery,* discussed under "Mesenteric Blood Supply," following shortly.

    b. The **hepatic artery proper** ascends toward the liver. It gives off the **right gastric artery,** then branches into the

right and **left hepatic arteries.** The right hepatic artery issues a **cystic artery** to the gallbladder, then the two hepatic arteries enter the liver from below.

2. The **left gastric artery** supplies the stomach and lower esophagus, arcs around the *lesser curvature* (superomedial margin) of the stomach, and anastomoses with the right gastric artery (fig. 20.34b). Thus, the right and left gastric arteries approach from opposite directions and supply this margin of the stomach. The left gastric also has branches to the lower esophagus, and the right gastric also supplies the duodenum.

3. The **splenic artery** supplies blood to the spleen, but gives off the following branches on the way there.

    a. Several small **pancreatic arteries** supply the pancreas.

    b. The **left gastro-omental artery** arcs around the *greater curvature* (inferolateral margin) of the stomach and anastomoses with the right gastro-omental artery. These two arteries stand off about 1 cm from the stomach itself and travel through the superior margin of the greater omentum, a fatty membrane suspended from the greater curvature (see figs. B.4 in atlas B, 25.3). They furnish blood to both the stomach and omentum.

    c. The **short gastric arteries** supply the upper portion (*fundus*) of the stomach.

Mesenteric Blood Supply

The mesentery is a translucent sheet that suspends the intestines and other abdominal viscera from the posterior body wall (see figs. A.8 in atlas A, 25.3). It contains numerous arteries, veins, and lymphatic vessels that supply and drain the intestines. The arterial supply arises from the *superior* and *inferior mesenteric arteries;* numerous anastomoses between these ensure adequate collateral circulation to the intestines even if one route is temporarily obstructed.

The **superior mesenteric artery (fig. 20.35a)** is the most significant intestinal blood supply, serving nearly all of the small intestine and the proximal half of the large intestine. It arises medially from the upper abdominal aorta and gives off the following branches:

1. The **inferior pancreaticoduodenal artery** branches to pass around the anterior and posterior sides of the pancreas and anastomose with the two branches of the superior pancreaticoduodenal artery.

2. Twelve to 15 **jejunal** and **ileal arteries** fan out through the mesentery to supply nearly all of the small intestine (portions called the *jejunum* and *ileum*).

3. The **ileocolic artery** (ILL-ee-oh-CO-lic) supplies the ileum, appendix, and parts of the large intestine (*cecum* and *ascending colon*).

4. The **right colic artery** also supplies the ascending colon.

5. The **middle colic artery** supplies most of the *transverse colon.*

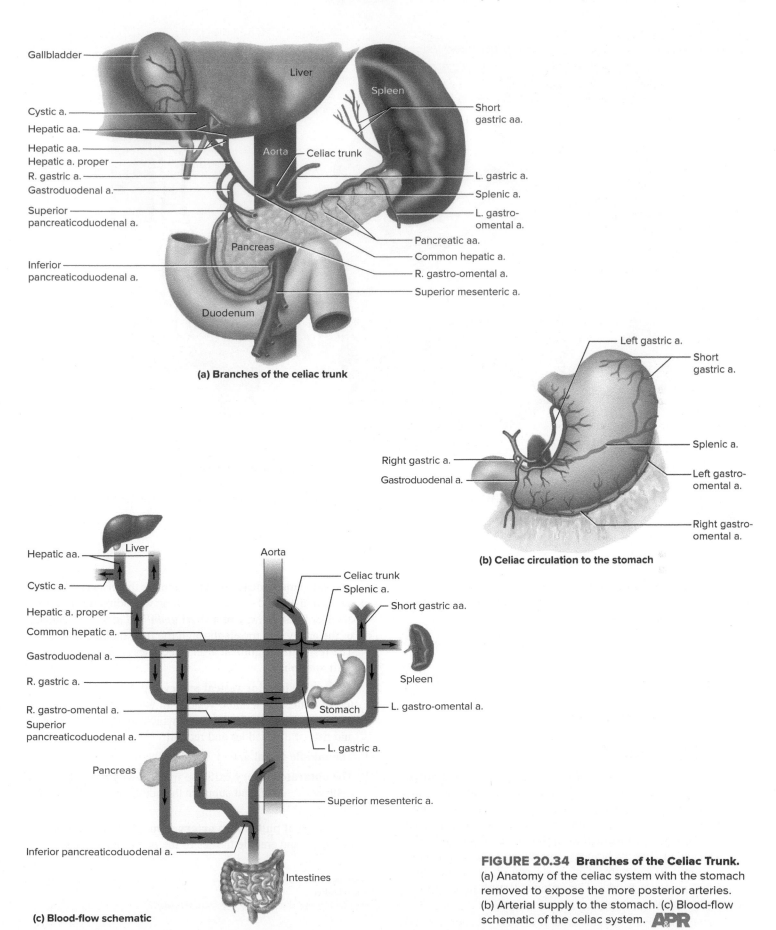

(a) Branches of the celiac trunk

(b) Celiac circulation to the stomach

(c) Blood-flow schematic

FIGURE 20.34 Branches of the Celiac Trunk.
(a) Anatomy of the celiac system with the stomach removed to expose the more posterior arteries.
(b) Arterial supply to the stomach. (c) Blood-flow schematic of the celiac system. **APR**

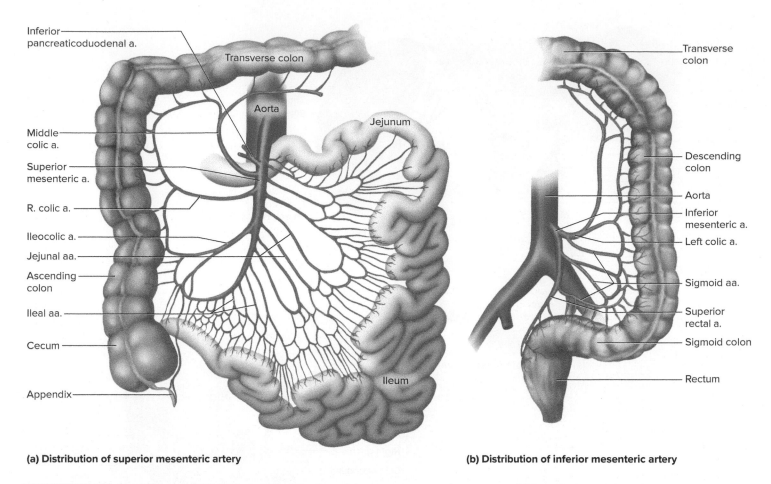

Inferior pancreaticoduodenal a.

Transverse colon

Aorta

Jejunum

Middle colic a.

Superior mesenteric a.

R. colic a.

Ileocolic a.

Jejunal aa.

Ascending colon

Ileal aa.

Cecum

Appendix

Ileum

Transverse colon

Descending colon

Aorta

Inferior mesenteric a.

Left colic a.

Sigmoid aa.

Superior rectal a.

Sigmoid colon

Rectum

(a) Distribution of superior mesenteric artery

(b) Distribution of inferior mesenteric artery

FIGURE 20.35   The Mesenteric Arteries.   (a) Distribution of the superior mesenteric artery. (b) Distribution of the inferior mesenteric artery. **APR**

The **inferior mesenteric artery** arises from the lower abdominal aorta and serves the distal part of the large intestine **(fig. 20.35b).** It gives off three main branches:

1. The **left colic artery** supplies the transverse and *descending colon.*

2. The **sigmoid arteries** supply the descending and *sigmoid colon.*

3. The **superior rectal artery** supplies the rectum.

Arteries of the Pelvic Region

The two common iliac arteries arise by branching of the aorta, descend for another 5 cm, then at the level of the sacroiliac joint, each divides into an external and internal iliac artery. The *external iliac artery* supplies mainly the lower limb (see section 20.8c). The **internal iliac artery** supplies mainly the pelvic wall and viscera. Its branches are shown only in schematic form in figure 20.42. Shortly after its origin, it divides into anterior and posterior trunks. The **anterior trunk** produces the following branches:

1. The **superior vesical**[21] **artery** supplies the urinary bladder and distal end of the ureter. It arises indirectly from the anterior trunk by way of a short *umbilical artery,* a remnant of the artery that travels through the fetal umbilical cord. The rest of the umbilical artery becomes a closed fibrous cord after birth.

2. In men, the **inferior vesical artery** supplies the bladder, ureter, prostate, and seminal vesicle. In women, the corresponding vessel is the **vaginal artery,** which supplies the vagina and part of the bladder and rectum.

3. The **middle rectal artery** supplies the rectum.

4. The **obturator artery** exits the pelvic cavity through the obturator foramen and supplies the adductor muscles of the medial thigh.

5. The **internal pudendal**[22] **artery** (pyu-DEN-dul) serves the perineum and erectile tissues of the penis and clitoris; it

---

[21]*vesic* = bladder
[22]*pudend* = literally, "shameful parts"; the external genitals

supplies blood for the vascular engorgement and erection of these organs during sexual arousal.

6. In women, the **uterine artery** is the main blood supply to the uterus and supplies some blood to the vagina. It enlarges substantially in pregnancy and is the chief source of blood to the placenta, and thus critically important to fetal development. It passes up the uterine margin, then turns laterally at the uterine tube and anastomoses with the ovarian artery, thus supplying blood to the ovary as well (see fig. 28.7).

7. The **inferior gluteal artery** supplies the gluteal muscles and hip joint.

The **posterior trunk** produces the following branches:

1. The **iliolumbar artery** supplies the lumbar body wall and pelvic bones.

2. The **lateral sacral arteries** lead to tissues of the sacral canal, skin, and muscles posterior to the sacrum. There are usually two of these, superior and inferior.

3. The **superior gluteal artery** supplies the skin and muscles of the gluteal region and the muscle and bone tissues of the pelvic wall.

20.7g Veins of the Abdominal and Pelvic Regions

The most significant route of venous drainage from all of the body below the diaphragm is the **inferior vena cava (IVC).** This is the body's largest blood vessel, having a diameter of about 3.5 cm. It forms by the union of the right and left common iliac veins at the level of vertebra L5 and drains many of the abdominal viscera as it ascends the posterior body wall. It is retroperitoneal and lies immediately to the right of the aorta.

Tributaries of the Inferior Vena Cava

The IVC picks up blood from numerous tributaries in the following ascending order **(fig. 20.36):**

1. The **internal iliac veins** drain the gluteal muscles, the medial aspect of the thigh, the urinary bladder, and rectum; the prostate and ductus deferens of the male; and the uterus and vagina of the female. They unite with the *external iliac veins,* which drain the lower limb and are described in section 20.8d. Their union forms the **common iliac veins,** which then converge to form the IVC.

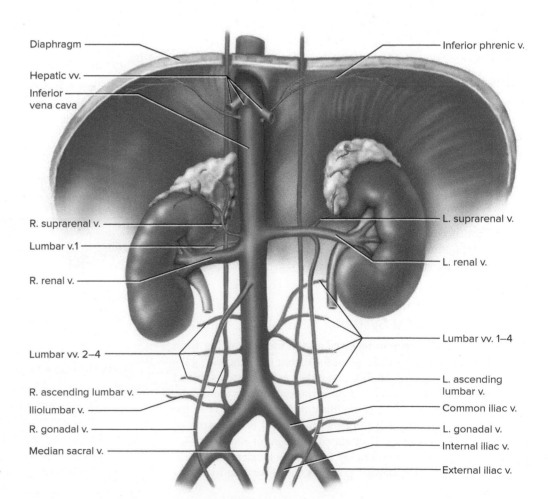

FIGURE 20.36 The Inferior Vena Cava and Its Tributaries. Compare the blood-flow schematic in figure 20.32b.

❓ *Why do the veins that drain the ovaries and testes terminate so far away from the gonads?*

Diaphragm
Hepatic vv.
Inferior vena cava
R. suprarenal v.
Lumbar v.1
R. renal v.
Lumbar vv. 2–4
R. ascending lumbar v.
Iliolumbar v.
R. gonadal v.
Median sacral v.

Inferior phrenic v.
L. suprarenal v.
L. renal v.
Lumbar vv. 1–4
L. ascending lumbar v.
Common iliac v.
L. gonadal v.
Internal iliac v.
External iliac v.

2. Four pairs of **lumbar veins** empty into the IVC as well as into the ascending lumbar veins described in the next section.

3. The **gonadal veins—ovarian veins** of the female and **testicular veins** of the male—drain the gonads. Like the gonadal arteries, and for the same reason, these are long slender vessels that end far from their origins. The left gonadal vein empties into the left renal vein, whereas the right gonadal vein empties directly into the IVC.

4. The **renal veins** drain the kidneys into the IVC. The left renal vein also receives blood from the left gonadal vein and left suprarenal veins. It is up to three times as long as the right renal vein, since the IVC lies to the right of the midline of the body.

5. The **suprarenal veins** drain the adrenal (suprarenal) glands. The right suprarenal empties directly into the IVC and the left suprarenal empties into the left renal vein.

6. The **inferior phrenic veins** drain the inferior aspect of the diaphragm.

7. Three **hepatic veins** drain the liver, extending a short distance from its superior surface to the IVC.

After receiving these inputs, the IVC penetrates the diaphragm and enters the right atrium of the heart from below (see fig. 19.5). It does not receive any thoracic drainage.

Veins of the Abdominal Wall

A pair of **ascending lumbar veins** receives blood from the common iliac veins below and from the aforementioned lumbar veins of the posterior body wall (see fig. 20.32b). The ascending lumbar veins give off anastomoses with the inferior vena cava beside them as they ascend to the diaphragm. The left ascending lumbar vein passes through the diaphragm via the aortic hiatus and continues as the hemiazygos vein above. The right ascending lumbar vein passes through the diaphragm to the right of the vertebral column and continues as the azygos vein above. The further paths of the azygos and hemiazygos veins were described earlier.

The Hepatic Portal System

The **hepatic portal system** receives all the blood draining from the abdominal digestive tract, as well as from the pancreas, gallbladder, and spleen **(fig. 20.37).** Like other portal systems, blood passes through two capillary beds in series on one trip around the systemic circulation. The first capillary bed in this case is in the intestines and other digestive organs; the second is a network of modified capillaries in the liver called the *hepatic sinusoids* (see fig. 20.6). Intestinal blood is richly laden with nutrients for a few hours after a meal. The hepatic portal system gives the liver first claim to these nutrients before they are distributed to the rest of the body. It also allows the liver to cleanse the blood of bacteria and toxins picked up from the intestines—an important function of the liver. The principal veins of the hepatic portal system are as follows:

1. The **inferior mesenteric vein** receives blood from the rectum and distal colon. It converges in a fanlike array in the mesentery and empties into the splenic vein.

2. The **superior mesenteric vein** receives blood from the entire small intestine, ascending colon, transverse colon, and stomach. It, too, exhibits a fanlike arrangement in the mesentery, then joins the splenic vein to form the hepatic portal vein.

3. The **splenic vein** drains the spleen and travels across the upper abdominal cavity toward the liver. Along the way, it picks up **pancreatic veins** from the pancreas, then picks up the inferior mesenteric vein, and ends where it meets the superior mesenteric vein.

4. The **hepatic portal vein** is the continuation beyond the convergence of the splenic and superior mesenteric veins. It travels about 8 cm upward and to the right, receives the **cystic vein** from the gallbladder, then enters the inferior surface of the liver. In the liver, it ultimately leads to the innumerable microscopic hepatic sinusoids. Blood from the sinusoids collects in the hepatic veins, and they empty into the IVC. Circulation within the liver is described in more detail in section 25.4.

5. The left and right **gastric veins** form an arc along the lesser curvature of the stomach and empty into the hepatic portal vein.

Answer the following questions to test your understanding of the preceding section:

26. Concisely contrast the destinations of the external and internal carotid arteries.

27. Briefly state the organs or parts of organs that are supplied with blood by (a) the cerebral arterial circle, (b) the celiac trunk, (c) the superior mesenteric artery, and (d) the internal iliac artery.

28. If you were dissecting a cadaver, where would you look for the internal and external jugular veins? What muscle would help you distinguish one from the other?

29. Trace the path of a blood cell from the left lumbar body wall to the superior vena cava, naming the vessels through which it would travel.

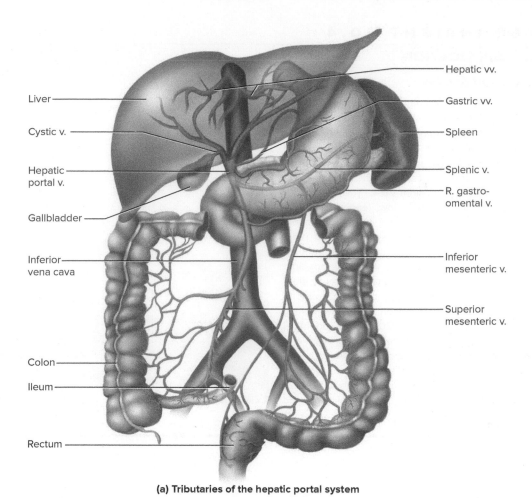

Liver

Cystic v.

Hepatic portal v.

Gallbladder

Inferior vena cava

Colon

Ileum

Rectum

Hepatic vv.

Gastric vv.

Spleen

Splenic v.

R. gastro-omental v.

Inferior mesenteric v.

Superior mesenteric v.

(a) Tributaries of the hepatic portal system

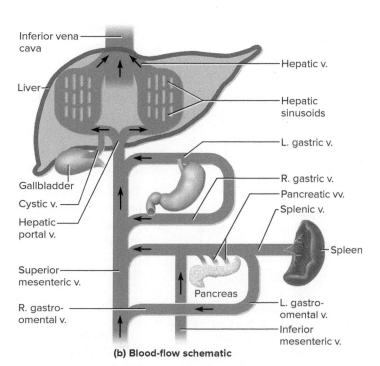

Inferior vena cava

Liver

Gallbladder

Cystic v.

Hepatic portal v.

Superior mesenteric v.

R. gastro-omental v.

Hepatic v.

Hepatic sinusoids

L. gastric v.

R. gastric v.

Pancreatic vv.

Splenic v.

Spleen

Pancreas

L. gastro-omental v.

Inferior mesenteric v.

(b) Blood-flow schematic

FIGURE 20.37 The Hepatic Portal System. (a) Tributaries of the hepatic portal system. (b) Blood-flow schematic of the system. **APR**

DEEPER INSIGHT 20.4

CLINICAL APPLICATION

Portal Hypertension and Ascites

Ascites (ah-SY-teez) is the abnormal accumulation of serous fluid in the peritoneal cavity, marked by abdominal distension **(fig. 20.38)**. It is usually associated with alcoholism, although it can have other causes such as malnutrition (see fig. 18.3), heart failure, infection, cancer, and chronic hepatitis. Excessive alcohol consumption causes *cirrhosis* of the liver—inflammation, destruction of liver cells, and their replacement by fatty and fibrous tissue (see Deeper Insight 26.4). The degenerating liver puts up excess resistance to blood flow, leading to *portal hypertension*—high blood pressure in the hepatic portal circulation. Since the spleen drains into the hepatic portal system, blood pressure backs up into the spleen as well. Both liver and spleen become enlarged (*hepatomegaly* and *splenomegaly*) and "weep" serous fluid into the peritoneal cavity. The failing liver also fails to adequately clear hormones from the blood, so aldosterone and antidiuretic hormone accumulate and stimulate increased fluid retention, further worsening the ascites. A person can retain as much as 10 to 20 liters of abdominal fluid, pressing up on the other abdominal viscera and diaphragm and producing shortness of breath. An infection called *spontaneous bacterial peritonitis (SBP)* is a frequent complication of ascites. The prognosis for recovery from ascites, especially with SBP, is poor; about 25% of patients die within one year of diagnosis, often because of continued heavy drinking.

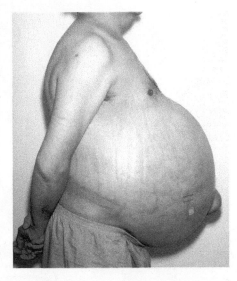

FIGURE 20.38 Ascites. The abdomen is distended with accumulated serous fluid that has filtered from the liver, spleen, and intestinal blood vessels.
Mediscan/Alamy

20.8   Systemic Vessels of the Appendicular Region

Expected Learning Outcomes

When you have completed this section, you should be able to

a. identify the principal systemic arteries and veins of the limbs; and

b. trace the flow of blood from the heart to any region of the upper or lower limb and back to the heart.

The principal vessels of the appendicular region are detailed in the following sections, 20.8a through 20.8d. Although the appendicular arteries are usually deep and well protected, the veins occur in both deep and superficial groups.

Venous pathways have more anastomoses than arterial pathways, so the route of flow is often not as clear. If all the anastomoses were illustrated, many of these venous pathways would look more like confusing networks than a clear route back to the heart. Therefore, most anastomoses—especially the highly variable and unnamed ones—are omitted from the figures to allow you to focus on the more general course of blood flow. The blood-flow schematics in several figures will also help, like road maps, to clarify these routes.

20.8a   Arteries of the Upper Limb

The upper limb is supplied by a prominent artery that changes name along its course from *subclavian* to *axillary* to *brachial artery,* then issues branches to the arm, forearm, and hand **(fig. 20.39)**.

The Shoulder and Arm

The shoulder and arm, like the head and most thoracic viscera, also receive their blood supply from arteries arising from the aortic arch. These pathways begin with the subclavian arteries, named for their proximity to the clavicles.

1. The brachiocephalic trunk arises from the aortic arch and branches into the right common carotid artery and **right subclavian artery.** The **left subclavian artery** arises directly from the aortic arch slightly distal to the brachiocephalic trunk. Each subclavian arches over the respective lung, rising as high as the base of the neck slightly superior to the clavicle. It then passes posterior to the clavicle, downward over the first rib, and ends in name only at the rib's lateral margin. In the shoulder, it gives off several small branches to the thoracic wall and viscera, which were described in section 20.7d.

2. As the artery continues past the first rib, it is named the **axillary artery.** It continues through the axillary region, gives off small thoracic branches, and ends, again in name

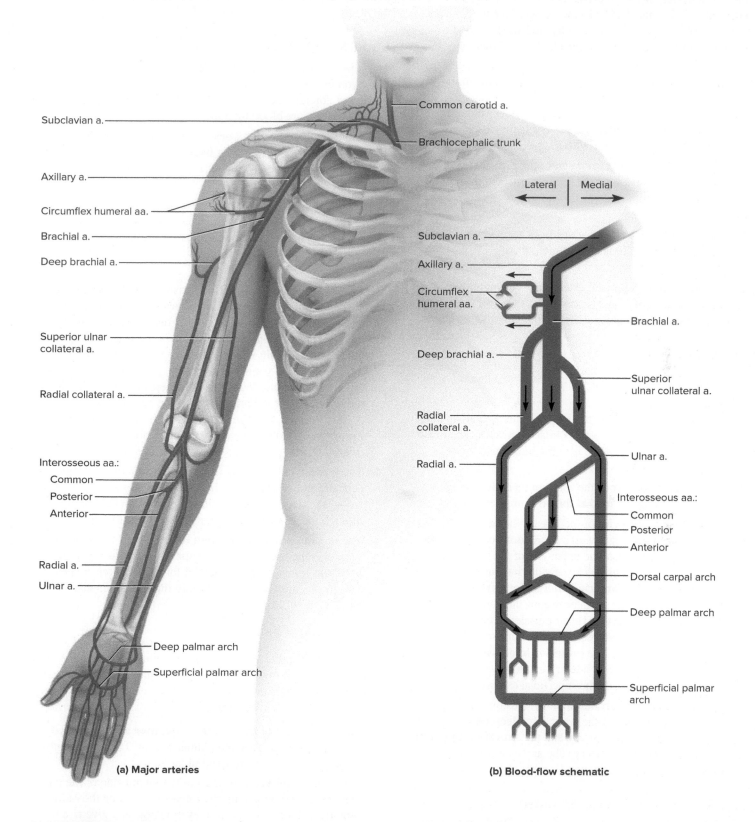

Subclavian a.

Common carotid a.

Brachiocephalic trunk

Axillary a.

Lateral   Medial

Circumflex humeral aa.

Subclavian a.

Brachial a.

Axillary a.

Deep brachial a.

Circumflex humeral aa.

Brachial a.

Superior ulnar collateral a.

Deep brachial a.

Superior ulnar collateral a.

Radial collateral a.

Radial collateral a.

Ulnar a.

Interosseous aa.:

Radial a.

Common

Interosseous aa.:

Posterior

Common

Anterior

Posterior

Anterior

Dorsal carpal arch

Radial a.

Deep palmar arch

Ulnar a.

Deep palmar arch

Superficial palmar arch

Superficial palmar arch

(a) Major arteries

(b) Blood-flow schematic

FIGURE 20.39 Arteries of the Upper Limb. (a) The major arteries, anterior view. (b) Blood-flow schematic of the upper limb. **APR**

❓ *Why are arterial anastomoses especially common at joints such as the shoulder and elbow?*

only, at the neck of the humerus. Here, it gives off a pair of **circumflex**[23] **humeral arteries,** which encircle the humerus, anastomose with each other laterally, and supply blood to the shoulder joint and deltoid muscle. Beyond this loop, it continues as the next artery.

3. The **brachial artery** (BRAY-kee-ul) continues down the median and anterior sides of the humerus and ends just distal to the elbow, supplying the anterior flexor muscles of the brachium along the way. This artery is the usual site of blood pressure measurement with the sphygmomanometer.

4. The **deep brachial artery** arises from the proximal end of the brachial artery and supplies the humerus and triceps brachii muscle. About midway down the arm, it continues as the next artery.

5. The **radial collateral artery** arises from the deep brachial artery, descends the lateral side of the arm, and empties into the radial artery slightly distal to the elbow.

6. The **superior ulnar collateral artery** arises about midway along the brachial artery and descends in the medial side of the arm. It empties into the ulnar artery slightly distal to the elbow.

The Forearm and Hand

Just distal to the elbow, the brachial artery forks into the *radial* and *ulnar arteries.*

1. The **radial artery** descends the forearm laterally, alongside the radius, nourishing the lateral forearm muscles. The most common place to take a pulse is at the radial artery just proximal to the thumb.

2. The **ulnar artery** descends the forearm medially, alongside the ulna, nourishing the medial forearm muscles.

3. The **interosseous**[24] **arteries** of the forearm lie between the radius and ulna. They begin with a short **common interosseous artery** branching from the upper end of the ulnar artery. The common interosseous quickly divides into anterior and posterior branches. The **anterior interosseous artery** travels down the anterior side of the interosseous membrane, nourishing the radius, ulna, and deep flexor muscles. It ends distally by passing through the interosseous membrane to join the posterior interosseous artery. The **posterior interosseous artery** descends along the posterior side of the interosseous membrane and nourishes mainly the superficial extensor muscles.

4. Two U-shaped **palmar arches** arise by anastomosis of the radial and ulnar arteries at the wrist. The **deep palmar arch** is fed mainly by the radial artery and the **superficial palmar arch** mainly by the ulnar artery. The arches issue smaller arteries to the palmar region and fingers.

20.8b Veins of the Upper Limb

Both superficial and deep veins drain the upper limb **(fig. 20.40).** We will trace these veins in the order of blood flow, from the hand to the axillary and subclavian veins, which, in turn, lead off toward the heart.

Superficial Veins

The superficial veins travel through the subcutaneous tissue of the limb; you may be able to see several of them through the skin of your hand, forearm, and arm **(fig. 20.41).** They are larger in diameter and carry more blood than the deep veins.

1. The **dorsal venous network** is a plexus of veins often visible through the skin on the back of the hand. It empties into the major superficial veins of the forearm, the cephalic and basilic veins.

2. The **cephalic**[25] **vein** (sef-AL-ic) arises from the lateral side of the network, travels up the lateral side of the forearm and arm to the shoulder, and joins the axillary vein there. Intravenous fluids are often administered through the distal end of this vein.

3. The **basilic**[26] **vein** (bah-SIL-ic) arises from the medial side of the network, travels up the posterior side of the forearm, and continues into the arm. It turns deeper about midway up the arm and joins the *brachial vein* at the axilla. As an aid to remembering which vein is cephalic and which is basilic, visualize your arm held straight away from the torso (abducted) with the thumb up. The cephalic vein runs along the upper side of the arm closer to the head (as suggested by *cephal,* "head"), and the name *basilic* is suggestive of the lower (basal) side of the arm (although not named for that reason; *basilic* means "prominent," as in *basilica*).

4. The **median cubital vein** is a short anastomosis between the cephalic and basilic veins that obliquely crosses the cubital fossa (anterior bend of the elbow). It is often clearly visible through the skin and is a common site for drawing blood.

5. The **median antebrachial vein** drains a network of blood vessels in the hand called the **superficial palmar venous network.** It travels up the medial forearm and terminates at the elbow, emptying variously into the basilic, median cubital, or cephalic vein.

Deep Veins

Deep veins run parallel to the arteries and often have similar names (*brachial veins* and *brachial artery,* for example). In some cases, the deep veins occur in pairs flanking the corresponding artery (such as the two *radial veins* traveling alongside the *radial artery*).

1. The **deep** and **superficial venous palmar arches** receive blood from the fingers and palmar region. They are anastomoses that join the radial and ulnar veins.

2. A pair of **radial veins** arise from the lateral side of the palmar arches and course up the forearm alongside the radius. Slightly distal to the elbow, they converge and give rise to one of the brachial veins.

---

[23]*circum* = around; *flex* = to bend
[24]*inter* = between; *osse* = bones

[25]*cephal* = head
[26]*basilic* = prominent, important

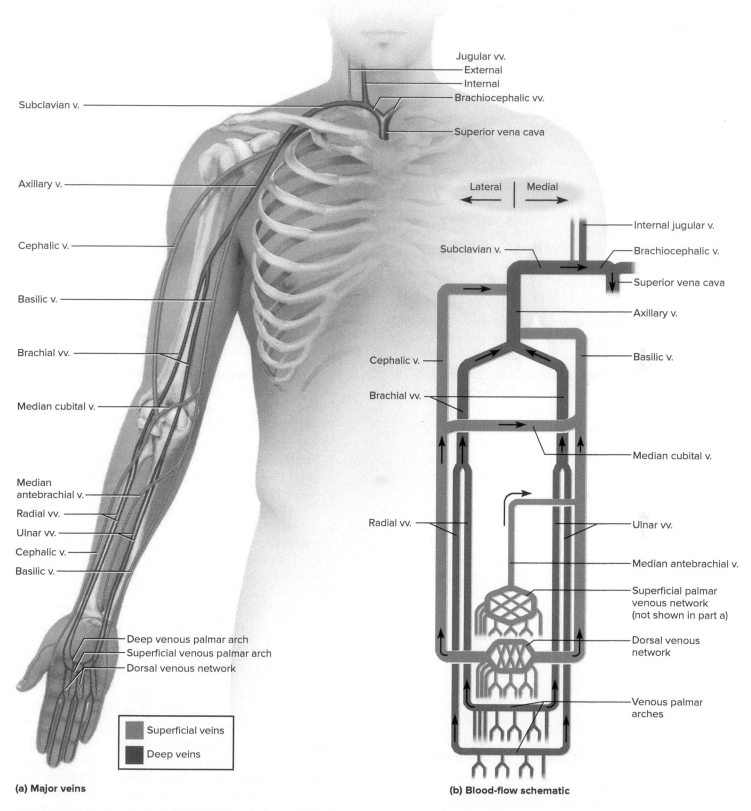

(a) Major veins

(b) Blood-flow schematic

FIGURE 20.40 Veins of the Upper Limb. (a) The major veins, anterior view. (b) Blood-flow schematic of the upper limb. Variations on this pattern are highly common. Many venous anastomoses are omitted for clarity. **APR**

❓ *Name three veins that are often visible through the skin of the upper limb.*

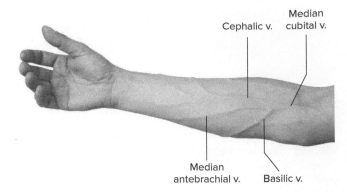

FIGURE 20.41 Superficial Veins of the Lower Arm and Upper Forearm. Anterior view. These prominent and accessible veins, especially the basilic and median cubital, are commonly used for drawing blood specimens and administering I.V. fluids and transfusions, and for cardiac catheterization.

Taborsk/Getty Images

3. A pair of **ulnar veins** arise from the medial side of the palmar arches and course up the forearm alongside the ulna. They unite near the elbow to form the other brachial vein.

4. The two **brachial veins** continue up the brachium, flanking the brachial artery, and converge into a single vein just before the axillary region.

5. The **axillary vein** forms by the union of the brachial and basilic veins. It begins at the lower margin of the teres major muscle and passes through the axillary region, picking up the cephalic vein along the way. At the lateral margin of the first rib, it changes name to the subclavian vein.

6. The **subclavian vein** continues into the shoulder posterior to the clavicle and ends where it meets the internal jugular vein of the neck. There it becomes the brachiocephalic vein described earlier. The right and left brachiocephalics converge and form the superior vena cava, which empties into the right atrium of the heart.

20.8c Arteries of the Lower Limb

As we have already seen, the aorta forks at its lower end into the right and left common iliac arteries, and each of these soon divides again into an internal and external iliac artery. We traced the internal iliac artery in section 20.7f, and we now trace the external iliac as it supplies the lower limb **(figs. 20.42, 20.43).**

Arteries from the Pelvic Region to the Knee

1. The **external iliac artery** issues small branches to the skin and muscles of the abdominal wall and pelvis, then passes deep to the inguinal ligament and becomes the femoral artery.

2. The **femoral artery** passes through the *femoral triangle* of the upper medial thigh, where its pulse can be palpated (see Deeper Insight 20.5). In the triangle, it gives off sev-

eral small arteries to the skin, then produces the following branches before descending the rest of the way to the knee.

a. The **deep femoral artery** arises from the lateral side of the femoral, within the triangle. It is the largest branch and is the major arterial supply to the thigh muscles.

b. Two **circumflex femoral arteries** arise from the deep femoral, encircle the head of the femur, and anastomose laterally. They supply mainly the femur, hip joint, and hamstring muscles.

3. The **popliteal artery** is a continuation of the femoral artery in the popliteal fossa at the back of the knee. It begins where the femoral artery emerges from an opening *(adductor hiatus)* in the tendon of the adductor magnus muscle and ends where it splits into the *anterior* and *posterior tibial arteries.* As it passes through the popliteal fossa, it gives off anastomoses called **genicular**[27] **arteries** that supply the knee joint.

Arteries of the Leg and Foot

In the leg proper, the three most significant arteries are the anterior tibial, posterior tibial, and fibular arteries.

1. The **anterior tibial artery** arises from the popliteal artery and immediately penetrates through the interosseous membrane of the leg to the anterior compartment. There, it travels lateral to the tibia and supplies the extensor muscles. Upon reaching the ankle, it gives off the following:

a. The **dorsal artery of the foot** traverses the ankle and upper medial surface of the foot and gives rise to the arcuate artery.

b. The **arcuate artery** sweeps across the foot from medial to lateral and gives off small arteries that supply the toes.

2. The **posterior tibial artery** is a continuation of the popliteal artery that passes down the leg, deep in the posterior compartment, supplying flexor muscles along the way. Inferiorly, it passes behind the medial malleolus of the ankle and into the plantar region of the foot. It gives rise to the following:

a. The **median** and **lateral plantar arteries** originate by branching of the posterior tibial artery at the ankle. The medial plantar artery supplies mainly the great toe. The lateral plantar artery sweeps across the sole of the foot and becomes the deep plantar arch.

b. The **deep plantar arch** gives off another set of small arteries to the toes.

3. The **fibular (peroneal) artery** arises from the proximal end of the posterior tibial artery near the knee. It descends through the lateral side of the posterior compartment, supplying lateral muscles of the leg along the way, and ends in a network of arteries in the heel.

---

[27]*genic* = of the knee

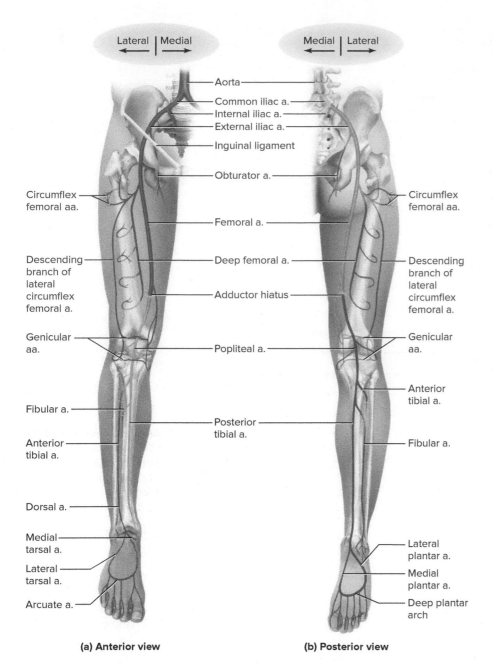

FIGURE 20.42 Arteries of the Lower Limb. (a) The major arteries in anterior view, with the foot strongly plantar flexed so its upper (dorsal) surface faces the viewer. (b) The major arteries in posterior view, with the sole of the foot facing the viewer. **APR**

(a) Anterior view

(b) Posterior view

20.8d Veins of the Lower Limb

We will follow venous drainage of the lower limb from the toes to the inferior vena cava (**figs. 20.44, 20.45**). As in the upper limb, there are deep and superficial veins with anastomoses between them. Most of the anastomoses are omitted from the illustrations.

Superficial Veins

The superficial veins of the lower thigh and leg lie in the subcutaneous tissue; thus, they are often visible through the skin and accessible with relative ease for such purposes as I.V. fluid therapy. They are particularly prone to becoming varicose veins (see fig. 20.9).

1. The **dorsal venous arch** (fig. 20.44a) is often visible through the skin on the dorsum of the foot. It collects blood from the toes and more proximal part of the foot, and has numerous anastomoses similar to the dorsal venous network of the hand. It gives rise to the following:

2. The **small (short) saphenous**[28] **vein** (sah-FEE-nus) arises from the lateral side of the arch and passes up that side of the leg as far as the knee. There, it drains into the popliteal vein.

---

[28]*saphen* = standing

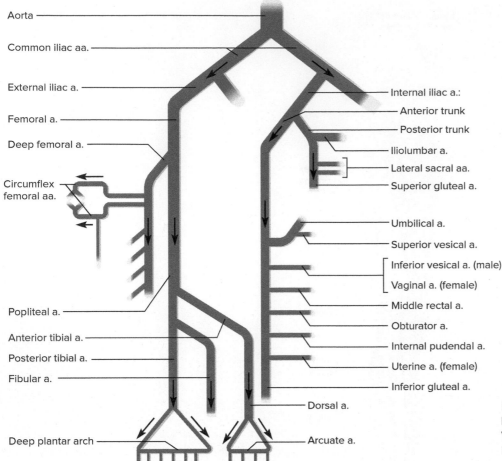

Aorta

Common iliac aa.

External iliac a.

Femoral a.

Deep femoral a.

Circumflex
femoral aa.

Popliteal a.

Anterior tibial a.

Posterior tibial a.

Fibular a.

Deep plantar arch

Internal iliac a.:
Anterior trunk
Posterior trunk
Iliolumbar a.
Lateral sacral aa.
Superior gluteal a.

Umbilical a.
Superior vesical a.
Inferior vesical a. (male)
Vaginal a. (female)
Middle rectal a.
Obturator a.
Internal pudendal a.
Uterine a. (female)
Inferior gluteal a.

Dorsal a.

Arcuate a.

FIGURE 20.43 Arterial Schematic of the Pelvic Region and Lower Limb (Anterior View). The pelvic schematic on the right is stretched for clarity. These arteries are not located as far inferiorly as the arteries depicted adjacent to them on the left.

3. The **great (long) saphenous vein,** the longest vein in the body, arises from the medial side of the arch and travels all the way up the leg and thigh to the inguinal region. It empties into the femoral vein slightly inferior to the inguinal ligament. It is commonly used as an access site for the long-term administration of intravenous fluids and for cardiac catheterization. It is a relatively accessible vein in infants and in patients in shock whose veins have collapsed. Portions of this vein are commonly used as grafts in coronary artery bypass surgery. The great and small saphenous veins are among the most common sites of varicose veins.

Deep Veins

Deep veins of the lower limb accompany the deep arteries. Some of them mirror the arrangement seen in the forelimb, with paired veins flanking the corresponding artery (such as the two *posterior tibial veins* running alongside the *posterior tibial artery*).

1. The **deep plantar venous arch** receives blood from the toes and gives rise to **lateral** and **medial plantar veins** on the respective sides of the foot. The lateral plantar vein gives

off the *fibular veins,* then crosses over to the medial side and approaches the medial plantar vein (but does not join it). The two plantar veins pass behind the medial malleolus of the ankle and continue as a pair of parallel *posterior tibial veins.*

2. The two **posterior tibial veins** pass up the leg embedded deep in the calf muscles. They converge like an inverted Y into a single vein about two-thirds of the way up the tibia.

3. The two **fibular (peroneal) veins** ascend the back of the leg and similarly converge like an inverted Y.

4. The **popliteal** vein begins near the knee by convergence of these two Ys. It passes through the popliteal fossa at the back of the knee.

5. The two **anterior tibial veins** travel up the anterior compartment of the leg between the tibia and fibula (fig. 20.44a). They arise from the medial side of the dorsal venous arch, converge just distal to the knee, then flow into the popliteal vein.

6. The **femoral vein** is a continuation of the popliteal vein into the thigh. It drains blood from the deep thigh muscles and femur.

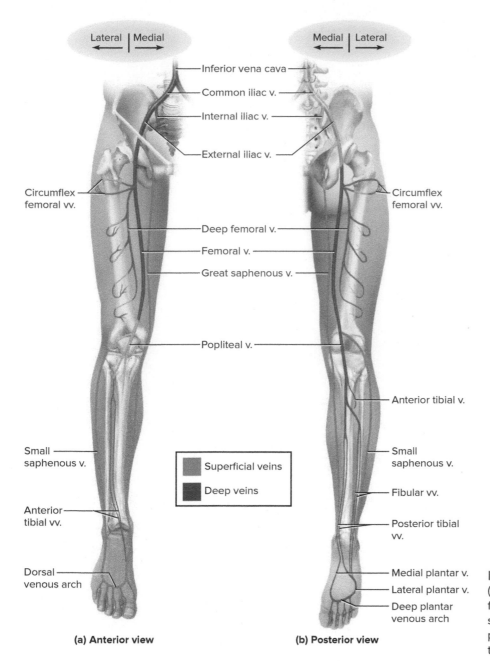

(a) Anterior view

(b) Posterior view

FIGURE 20.44 Veins of the Lower Limb.
(a) The major veins in anterior view, with the foot strongly plantar flexed so its upper (dorsal) surface faces the viewer. (b) The major veins in posterior view, with the sole of the foot facing the viewer. **APR**

7. The **deep femoral vein** drains the femur and muscles of the thigh supplied by the deep femoral artery. It receives tributaries along the shaft of the femur, then a pair of *circumflex femoral veins* that encircle the upper femur. It finally drains into the upper femoral vein.

8. The **external iliac vein** forms by the union of the femoral and great saphenous veins near the inguinal ligament.

9. The **internal iliac vein** follows the course of the internal iliac artery and its distribution. Its tributaries drain the gluteal muscles; the medial aspect of the thigh; the urinary bladder, rectum, prostate, and ductus deferens of the male; and the uterus and vagina of the female.

10. The **common iliac vein** forms by the union of the external and internal iliac veins. The right and left

common iliacs then unite to form the inferior vena cava.

▶▶▶ **APPLY WHAT YOU KNOW**

There are certain similarities between the arteries of the hand and foot. What arteries of the wrist and hand are most comparable in arrangement and function to the arcuate artery and deep plantar arch of the foot?

Deeper Insight 20.5 exemplifies the relevance of vascular anatomy to emergency first aid. The most common cardiovascular diseases are atherosclerosis and hypertension. **Table 20.2** provides links to further information on these and several other vascular diseases. See "Circulatory System" in section 29.4a for the effects of aging on the blood vessels.

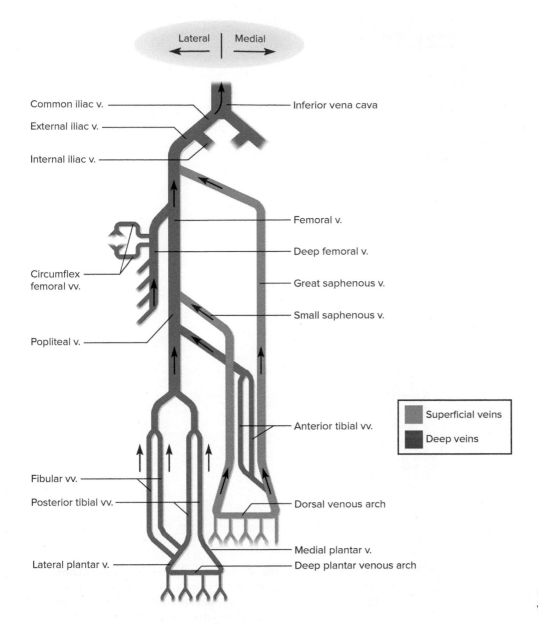

Lateral | Medial

Common iliac v.

External iliac v.

Internal iliac v.

Circumflex femoral vv.

Popliteal v.

Fibular vv.

Posterior tibial vv.

Lateral plantar v.

Inferior vena cava

Femoral v.

Deep femoral v.

Great saphenous v.

Small saphenous v.

Anterior tibial vv.

Dorsal venous arch

Medial plantar v.
Deep plantar venous arch

Superficial veins
Deep veins

FIGURE 20.45 Venous Schematic of the Lower Limb (Anterior View).

TABLE 20.2	Some Vascular Disorders
Dissecting aneurysm	Splitting of the layers of an arterial wall from each other because of the accumulation of blood between layers. Results from either a tear in the tunica interna or rupture of the vasa vasorum.
Fat embolism	The presence of fat globules traveling in the bloodstream. Globules originate from bone fractures, fatty degeneration of the liver, and other causes and may block cerebral or pulmonary blood vessels.
Orthostatic hypotension	A decrease in blood pressure that occurs when one stands, often resulting in blurring of vision, dizziness, and syncope (fainting). Results from sluggish or inactive baroreflexes.

You can find other vascular disorders described in the following places:

Thrombosis and *thromboembolism* in section 18.5f; *air embolism* in Deeper Insight 20.3; *atherosclerosis* and *arteriosclerosis* in Deeper Insight 19.4 and section 20.2a; *aneurysm* in Deeper Insight 20.1; *hypertension* and *hypotension* in section 20.2a and Deeper Insight 20.6; *varicose veins* in Deeper Insight 20.2; *circulatory shock* in section 20.4c; *transient ischemic attack (TIA)* and *stroke* in section 20.5a; and *edema* in section 20.3d.

DEEPER INSIGHT 20.5

CLINICAL APPLICATION

Arterial Pressure Points

In some places, major arteries come close enough to the body surface to be palpated. These places can be used to take a pulse, and they can serve as emergency *pressure points,* where firm pressure can be applied to temporarily reduce arterial bleeding **(fig. 20.46a).** One of these points is the *femoral triangle* of the upper medial thigh

(fig. 20.46b, c). This is an important landmark for arterial supply, venous drainage, and innervation of the lower limb. Its boundaries are the sartorius muscle laterally, the inguinal ligament superiorly, and the adductor longus muscle medially. The femoral artery, vein, and nerve run close to the surface at this point.

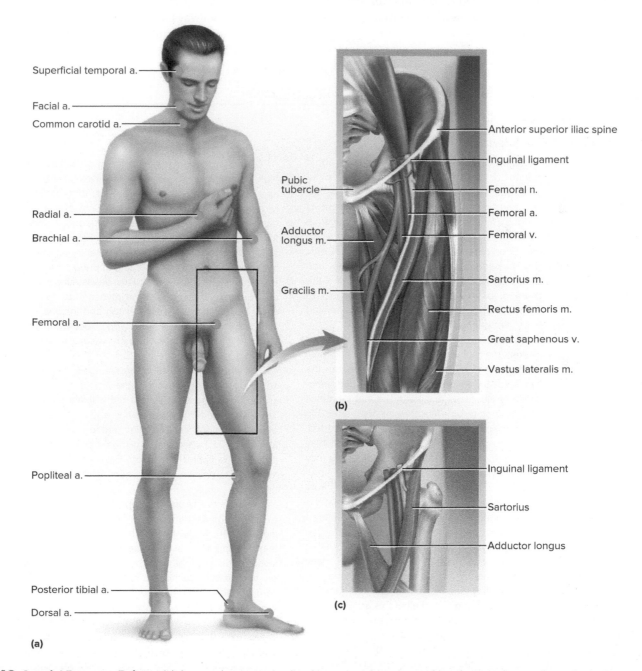

FIGURE 20.46 Arterial Pressure Points. (a) Areas where arteries lie close enough to the surface that a pulse can be palpated or pressure can be applied to reduce arterial bleeding. (b) Structures in the femoral triangle. (c) The three boundaries that define the femoral triangle.

▶▶▶ APPLY WHAT YOU KNOW

From the preceding discussion of arteries and veins of the limbs, identify an artery or vein with special relevance to each of the following clinical applications: (1) the artery from which blood pressure is usually measured; (2) the artery where a patient's pulse is most often taken; (3) a vessel where pressure should be applied to stop arterial bleeding from a laceration of the thigh; (4) upper and lower limb veins where intravenous fluid is often administered; (5) a vein where blood samples are commonly drawn; and (6) a vein from which a portion may be removed and used for a coronary artery bypass graft.

BEFORE YOU GO ON

Answer the following questions to test your understanding of the preceding section:

30. Trace one possible path of a red blood cell from the left ventricle to the toes.

31. Trace one possible path of a red blood cell from the fingers to the right atrium.

32. The subclavian, axillary, and brachial arteries are really one continuous artery. What is the reason for giving it three different names along its course?

33. State two ways in which the great saphenous vein has special clinical significance. Where is this vein located?

DEEPER INSIGHT 20.6

CLINICAL APPLICATION

Hypertension—"The Silent Killer"

Hypertension, the most common cardiovascular disease, affects about 30% of Americans over age 50, and 50% by age 74. It is a "silent killer" that can wreak its destructive effects for 10 to 20 years before the symptoms are first noticed. Hypertension is the major cause of heart failure, stroke, and kidney failure. It damages the heart because it increases the afterload, which makes the ventricles work harder to expel blood. The myocardium enlarges up to a point (the *hypertrophic response*), but eventually it becomes excessively stretched and less efficient. Hypertension strains the blood vessels and tears the endothelium, thereby creating lesions that become focal points of atherosclerosis. Atherosclerosis then worsens the hypertension and establishes an insidious positive feedback cycle.

Another positive feedback cycle involves the kidneys. Their arterioles thicken in response to the stress, their lumens become narrower, and renal blood flow declines. In response to the resulting drop in blood pressure, the kidneys release renin, which leads to the formation of the vasoconstrictor angiotensin II and the release of aldosterone, a hormone that promotes salt retention (see "The Renin–Angiotensin–Aldosterone Mechanism" in section 23.3d). These effects worsen the hypertension that already existed. If diastolic pressure exceeds 120 mm Hg, the kidneys and heart may deteriorate rapidly, blood vessels of the eye hemorrhage, blindness may ensue, and death usually follows within 2 years.

Primary hypertension, which accounts for 90% of cases, results from such a complex web of behavioral, hereditary, and other factors that it is difficult to sort out any specific underlying cause. It was once considered such a normal part of the "essence" of aging that it continues to be called by another name, *essential hypertension.* That term suggests a fatalistic resignation to hypertension as a fact of life, but this need not be. Many risk factors have been identified, and most of them are controllable.

One of the chief culprits is obesity. Each pound of extra fat requires miles of additional blood vessels to serve it, and all of this added vessel length increases peripheral resistance and blood pressure. Just carrying around extra weight, of course, also increases the workload on the heart. Even a small weight loss can significantly reduce blood pressure. Sedentary behavior is another risk factor. Aerobic exercise helps to reduce hypertension by controlling weight, reducing emotional tension, and stimulating vasodilation.

Dietary factors are also significant contributors to hypertension. Diets high in saturated fat contribute to atherosclerosis. Potassium and magnesium reduce blood pressure; thus, diets deficient in these minerals promote hypertension. The relationship of salt intake to hypertension has been a controversial subject. The kidneys compensate so effectively for excess salt intake that dietary salt has little effect on the blood pressure of most people. Reduced salt intake may, however, help to control hypertension in older people and in people with reduced renal function.

Nicotine makes a particularly devastating contribution to hypertension because it stimulates the myocardium to beat faster and harder, while it stimulates vasoconstriction and increases the afterload against which the myocardium must work. Just when the heart needs extra oxygen, nicotine causes coronary vasoconstriction and promotes myocardial ischemia.

Some risk factors cannot be changed at will—ancestry, heredity, and sex. Hypertension runs in some families. A person whose parents or siblings have hypertension is more likely than average to develop it. The incidence of hypertension is about 30% higher, and the incidence of strokes about twice as high, among blacks as among whites. From ages 18 to 54, hypertension is more common in men, but above age 65, it is more common in women. Even people at risk from these factors, however, can minimize their chances of hypertension by changing risky behaviors.

Treatments for primary hypertension include weight loss, diet, and certain drugs. Diuretics lower blood volume and pressure by promoting urination. ACE inhibitors block the formation of the vasoconstrictor angiotensin II. Beta-blockers such as propranolol also lower angiotensin II level, but do it by inhibiting the secretion of renin. Calcium channel blockers such as verapamil and nifedipine inhibit the inflow of calcium into cardiac and smooth muscle, thus inhibiting their contraction, promoting vasodilation, and reducing cardiac workload.

Secondary hypertension, which accounts for about 10% of cases, is high blood pressure that results from other identifiable disorders. These include kidney disease (which may cause renin hypersecretion), atherosclerosis, hyperthyroidism, Cushing syndrome, and polycythemia. Secondary hypertension is corrected by treating the underlying disease.

CONNECTIVE ISSUES

Effects of the **CIRCULATORY SYSTEM** on Other Organ Systems

ALL SYSTEMS
Blood delivers O_2 to all tissues and organs and removes CO_2 and other wastes from them, distributes nutrients and hormones throughout the body, and carries heat from deeper organs to the body surface for elimination.

INTEGUMENTARY SYSTEM
Dermal blood flow strongly affects overall body temperature.

LYMPHATIC AND IMMUNE SYSTEMS
Blood vessels produce tissue fluid, which becomes the lymph; blood contains the WBCs and plasma proteins employed in immunity.

SKELETAL SYSTEM
Blood delivers the minerals needed for bone deposition; delivers hormones that regulate skeletal growth; and delivers hormones to the bone marrow that stimulate RBC, WBC, and platelet production.

RESPIRATORY SYSTEM
Blood picks up O_2 from the lungs and releases CO_2 to be exhaled; low capillary blood pressure and blood oncotic pressure keep alveoli from filling with fluid.

URINARY SYSTEM
Urine production begins with blood filtration; blood carries away the water and solutes reabsorbed by the kidneys; blood pressure maintains renal function.

MUSCULAR SYSTEM
Blood removes the heat generated by exercise.

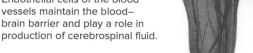

NERVOUS SYSTEM
Endothelial cells of the blood vessels maintain the blood–brain barrier and play a role in production of cerebrospinal fluid.

DIGESTIVE SYSTEM
Blood picks up absorbed nutrients and helps in reabsorption and recycling of bile salts and minerals from the intestines.

ENDOCRINE SYSTEM
Blood is the medium in which all hormones travel to their target organs.

REPRODUCTIVE SYSTEM
Blood delivers the hormones that affect reproductive function; vasodilation produces erection in sexual response; blood provides nutrients, oxygen, and other metabolic needs to the fetus and removes its wastes.

STUDY GUIDE

▶ Assess Your Learning Outcomes

To test your knowledge, discuss the following topics with a study partner or in writing, ideally from memory.

20.1 General Anatomy of the Blood Vessels

1. Definitions of *arteries, veins,* and *capillaries* with respect to the path of blood flow
2. Tunics of an artery or vein, and their general histological differences
3. Structure and functions of the endothelium
4. Location and function of the vasa vasorum
5. Three size classes of arteries; how and why they differ not just in diameter, but also histologically
6. The relationship of metarterioles to a capillary bed, and the function of the precapillary sphincters of a metarteriole
7. Location, structure, and function of the carotid sinuses, carotid bodies, and aortic bodies
8. Histology of the three types of capillaries and how it relates to their functions
9. Organization of a capillary bed and how its perfusion is regulated
10. Why veins are called *capacitance vessels* and how this relates to the structural difference between veins and arteries
11. What capillaries and postcapillary venules have in common with respect to fluid exchange
12. Structural differences between muscular venules, medium veins, and large veins
13. Structure and purpose of the venous valves, where they occur, and the reason certain veins have valves but arteries of corresponding size do not
14. How venous sinuses differ from other veins, and where they occur
15. How portal systems and anastomoses differ from simpler routes of blood flow; types of anastomoses and their purposes

20.2 Blood Pressure, Resistance, and Flow

1. The difference between blood flow and perfusion
2. How blood flow is related to resistance and pressure differences; the mathematical expression of these relationships
3. How to determine systolic pressure, diastolic pressure, and pulse pressure; how to estimate mean arterial pressure (MAP), and why MAP differs from head to foot

4. The meanings of *hypertension* and *hypotension*
5. Why arterial expansion and recoil during the cardiac cycle reduce pulse pressure and ease the strain on small arteries
6. Why arterial flow is pulsatile but capillary and venous flow are not
7. Why blood pressure rises with age
8. Variables that determine blood pressure
9. Variables that determine peripheral resistance; whether each one is directly or inversely proportional to resistance; and which of them is most changeable from moment to moment
10. Terms for widening and narrowing of a blood vessel by muscular contraction and relaxation
11. The mathematical relationship between peripheral resistance and vessel radius; why this is related to the laminar flow of blood; and why it makes vasoreflexes such a powerful influence on blood flow
12. Why blood velocity declines from aorta to capillaries and rises again from capillaries to veins, but never rises as high in veins as it was in the aorta
13. Why arterioles exert a greater influence than any other category of blood vessels on tissue perfusion
14. Three levels of control over blood pressure and flow
15. Short- and long-term mechanisms of local control of blood flow; examples of vasoactive chemicals and how they can cause reactive hyperemia
16. Angiogenesis and its importance for cancer therapy
17. The role of the vasomotor center of the medulla oblongata in controlling blood flow; baroreflexes, chemoreflexes, and the medullary ischemic reflex
18. Mechanisms of action by angiotensin II, aldosterone, natriuretic peptides, antidiuretic hormone, epinephrine, and norepinephrine on blood pressure
19. How vasomotion can change systemwide blood pressure or redirect blood flow from one region to another; circumstances that call for redirection of blood flow

20.3 Capillaries and Fluid Exchange

1. The meaning of *capillary exchange,* and substances involved in the process

2. Three routes and four mechanisms by which materials pass through capillary walls
3. Substances exchanged by simple diffusion; factors that determine whether a substance can diffuse through a capillary wall
4. Capillary transcytosis and some substances exchanged this way
5. In capillary filtration, three forces that draw fluid out of the capillaries and one force that draws fluid into them
6. The values and net effects of capillary exchange forces at the arterial and venous ends of a capillary, and how they enable a capillary to give off fluid at one end and reabsorb it at the other
7. Relative amounts of fluid given off and reabsorbed by a model capillary, and what compensates for the difference between filtration and reabsorption
8. The role of solvent drag in capillary exchange
9. Why the dynamics of capillary absorption can change from moment to moment or differ in various places in the body; examples of places where the capillaries are engaged entirely in net filtration or reabsorption
10. Chemicals that affect capillary permeability and filtration
11. Three causes of edema, and its pathological consequences

20.4 Venous Return and Circulatory Shock

1. The definition of *venous return,* and five mechanisms that drive it
2. How the skeletal muscle pump works and why it depends on venous valves
3. Why exercise increases venous return
4. Why physical inactivity can lead to venous pooling; consequences of venous pooling
5. Definition of *circulatory shock*
6. Two basic categories of circulatory shock, three forms of low venous return (LVR) shock, and situations in which each form of shock may occur
7. Why septic and anaphylactic shock cannot be strictly classified into any single category of LVR shock
8. Differences between compensated and decompensated shock

20.5 Special Circulatory Routes

1. A typical value for cerebral blood flow and why its constancy is important

STUDY GUIDE

2. How the brain regulates its blood flow and what chemical stimulus is the most potent in activating its regulatory mechanisms
3. The causes, effects, and difference between a transient ischemic attack (TIA) and cerebral vascular accident (stroke)
4. Variability of skeletal muscle perfusion; what stimuli increase perfusion to meet the demands of exercise; and why isometric contraction causes fatigue more quickly than isotonic contraction does
5. How pulmonary circulation differs from systemic circulation with respect to blood pressure, capillary exchange, relative oxygenation of arterial and venous blood, and the vasomotor response to hypoxia

20.6 Anatomy of the Pulmonary Circuit

1. The route of blood flow in the pulmonary circuit
2. Where the capillaries of the pulmonary circuit are found and the function they serve
3. How the function of the pulmonary circuit differs from that of the bronchial arteries, which also supply the lungs

20.7 Systemic Vessels of the Axial Region

1. For all named blood vessels in this outline, their anatomical location; the vessel from which they arise; the course they follow; and the organs, body regions, or other blood vessels they supply
2. The ascending aorta, aortic arch, and descending aorta, and the thoracic and abdominal segments of the descending aorta (section 20.7a)
3. Branches that arise from the ascending aorta and aortic arch: the coronary arteries, brachiocephalic trunk, left common carotid artery, and left subclavian artery (section 20.7a)
4. Four principal arteries of the neck: the common carotid, vertebral artery, thyrocervical trunk, and costocervical trunk (section 20.7b)
5. The external and internal carotid arteries; branches of the external carotid (superior thyroid, lingual, facial, occipital, maxillary, and superficial temporal arteries); and branches of the internal carotid (ophthalmic, anterior cerebral, and middle cerebral arteries) (section 20.7b)
6. Convergence of the vertebral arteries to form the basilar artery; the posterior cerebral arteries and arteries to the cerebellum, pons, and inner ear arising from the basilar artery (section 20.7b)

7. The location and constituents of the cerebral arterial circle (section 20.7b)
8. Dural venous sinuses; the superior sagittal, inferior sagittal, transverse, and cavernous sinuses; outflow from the sinus system into the internal jugular veins (section 20.7c)
9. The internal jugular, external jugular, and vertebral veins of the neck (section 20.7c)
10. Visceral branches (bronchial, esophageal, and mediastinal arteries) and parietal branches (posterior intercostal, subcostal, and superior phrenic arteries) of the thoracic aorta (section 20.7d)
11. Arteries of the thorax and shoulder that arise from the subclavian artery and its continuation, the axillary artery: the internal thoracic artery, thoracoacromial trunk, lateral thoracic artery, and subscapular artery (section 20.7d)
12. The subclavian vein, brachiocephalic vein, and superior vena cava; landmarks that define the transition from one to another (section 20.7e)
13. The azygos system of thoracic veins, especially the azygos, hemiazygos, and accessory hemiazygos veins; their tributaries, including the posterior intercostal, subcostal, esophageal, mediastinal, pericardial, bronchial, and ascending lumbar veins (section 20.7e)
14. Branches of the abdominal aorta: inferior phrenic arteries; celiac trunk; and superior mesenteric, middle suprarenal, renal, gonadal (ovarian or testicular), inferior mesenteric, lumbar, median sacral, and common iliac arteries (section 20.7f)
15. The general group of organs supplied by the celiac trunk; its three primary branches—the common hepatic, left gastric, and splenic arteries—and smaller branches given off by each of these (section 20.7f)
16. Branches of the superior mesenteric artery: inferior pancreaticoduodenal, jejunal, ileal, and right and middle colic arteries (section 20.7f)
17. Branches of the inferior mesenteric artery: left colic, sigmoid, and superior rectal arteries (section 20.7f)
18. Two main branches of the common iliac artery, the posterior and anterior trunks of the internal iliac artery, and the organs supplied by those trunks (section 20.7f)
19. Convergence of the internal and external iliac veins to form the common iliac vein; convergence of the right and left common

iliac veins to form the inferior vena cava (IVC) (section 20.7g)
20. Abdominal tributaries of the IVC: lumbar, gonadal (ovarian or testicular), renal, suprarenal, hepatic, and inferior phrenic veins (section 20.7g)
21. The ascending lumbar veins, their drainage in the abdomen, and their continuation into the thorax (section 20.7g)
22. The hepatic portal system and its tributaries: the splenic vein; the pancreatic, inferior mesenteric, and superior mesenteric veins draining into it; continuation of the splenic vein as the hepatic portal vein; the cystic vein and gastric veins draining into the hepatic portal vein; hepatic sinusoids in the liver; and hepatic veins (section 20.7g)

20.8 Systemic Vessels of the Appendicular Region

1. The main artery to the upper limb, which changes name along its course from subclavian to axillary to brachial artery; branches of the brachial artery in the arm (deep brachial and superior ulnar collateral arteries); and the radial collateral artery (section 20.8a)
2. Brachial artery branches that supply the forearm: radial and ulnar arteries; anterior and posterior interosseous arteries; and deep and superficial palmar arches (section 20.8a)
3. The dorsal venous network of the hand; median antebrachial vein; and median cubital vein (section 20.8b)
4. The venous palmar arches, and brachial, basilic, axillary, and subclavian veins (section 20.8b)
5. Continuation of the external iliac artery as the femoral artery; deep femoral and circumflex femoral branches of the femoral artery; popliteal artery; and anterior and posterior tibial arteries (section 20.8c)
6. The dorsal pedal and arcuate arteries that arise from the anterior tibial artery; fibular, medial plantar, and lateral plantar arteries; and deep plantar arch (section 20.8c)
7. The superficial dorsal venous arch, small and great saphenous veins, and popliteal vein (section 20.8d)
8. The deep plantar venous arch; the lateral and medial plantar veins; fibular and posterior tibial veins; and anterior tibial veins (section 20.8d)
9. The femoral, deep femoral, and external iliac veins (section 20.8d)

STUDY GUIDE

▶ Testing Your Recall

Answers in Appendix A

1. Blood often flows into a capillary bed from
   a. the distributing arteries.
   b. the conducting arteries.
   c. a metarteriole.
   d. an arteriovenous anastomosis
   e. the venules.

2. Plasma solutes enter the tissue fluid most easily from
   a. continuous capillaries.
   b. fenestrated capillaries.
   c. arteriovenous anastomoses.
   d. collateral vessels.
   e. venous anastomoses.

3. A blood vessel adapted to withstand a high pulse pressure would be expected to have
   a. an elastic tunica media.
   b. a thick tunica interna.
   c. one-way valves.
   d. a flexible endothelium.
   e. a rigid tunica media.

4. The substance most likely to cause a rapid drop in blood pressure is
   a. epinephrine.
   b. norepinephrine.
   c. angiotensin II.
   d. serotonin.
   e. histamine.

5. A person with a systolic blood pressure of 130 mm Hg and a diastolic pressure of 85 mm Hg would have a mean arterial pressure of about
   a. 85 mm Hg.
   b. 100 mm Hg.
   c. 108 mm Hg.
   d. 115 mm Hg.
   e. 130 mm Hg.

6. The velocity of blood flow decreases if
   a. vessel radius increases.
   b. blood pressure increases.
   c. viscosity increases.
   d. viscosity decreases.
   e. afterload increases.

7. Blood flows faster in a venule than in a capillary because venules
   a. have one-way valves.
   b. are more muscular.
   c. are closer to the heart.
   d. have higher blood pressures.
   e. have larger diameters.

8. In a case where interstitial hydrostatic pressure is negative, the only force causing capillaries to reabsorb fluid is
   a. colloid osmotic pressure of the blood.
   b. colloid osmotic pressure of the tissue fluid.
   c. capillary hydrostatic pressure.
   d. interstitial hydrostatic pressure.
   e. net filtration pressure.

9. Intestinal blood flows to the liver by way of
   a. the superior mesenteric artery.
   b. the celiac trunk.
   c. the inferior vena cava.
   d. the azygos system.
   e. the hepatic portal system.

10. The brain receives blood from all of the following vessels *except* the _____ artery or vein.
    a. basilar
    b. vertebral
    c. internal carotid
    d. internal jugular
    e. anterior communicating

11. The highest arterial blood pressure attained during ventricular contraction is called _____ pressure. The lowest attained during ventricular relaxation is called _____ pressure.

12. The capillaries of skeletal muscles are of the structural type called _____.

13. _____ shock occurs as a result of exposure to an antigen to which one is hypersensitive.

14. The role of breathing in venous return is called the _____.

15. The difference between the colloid osmotic pressure of blood and that of the tissue fluid is called _____.

16. Movement across the capillary endothelium by the uptake and release of fluid droplets is called _____.

17. All efferent fibers of the vasomotor center belong to the _____ division of the autonomic nervous system.

18. The pressure sensors in the major arteries near the head are called _____.

19. Most of the blood supply to the brain comes from a ring of arterial anastomoses called the _____.

20. The major superficial veins of the arm are the _____ on the medial side and _____ on the lateral side.

▶ Building Your Medical Vocabulary

Answers in Appendix A

State a meaning of each word element, and give a medical term from this chapter that uses it or a slight variation of it.

1. angio-

2. brachio-

3. celi-

4. fenestra-

5. jugulo-

6. -orum

7. sapheno-

8. sub-

9. thoraco-

10. vesico-

STUDY GUIDE

What's Wrong with These Statements?

Answers in Appendix A

Briefly explain why each of the following statements is false, or reword it to make it true.

1. Blood cannot get from an artery to a vein without first passing through some capillaries.

2. Blood returns from the brain to the heart by way of the external jugular veins.

3. The body's longest blood vessel is the inferior vena cava.

4. Arteries have a series of valves that ensure a one-way flow of blood.

5. If the radius of a blood vessel doubles and all other factors remain the same, blood flow through that vessel also doubles.

6. The femoral triangle is bordered by the inguinal ligament, sartorius muscle, and rectus femoris muscle.

7. The lungs receive blood exclusively from the pulmonary circuit of the circulatory system.

8. If blood capillaries fail to reabsorb all the fluid they emit, edema will occur.

9. An aneurysm is a ruptured blood vessel.

10. In the baroreflex, a drop in arterial blood pressure triggers a corrective vasodilation of the systemic blood vessels.

Testing Your Comprehension

1. It is a common lay perception that systolic blood pressure should be 100 plus a person's age. Evaluate the validity of this statement.

2. Calculate the net filtration or reabsorption pressure at a point in a hypothetical capillary assuming a hydrostatic blood pressure of 28 mm Hg, an interstitial hydrostatic pressure of –2 mm Hg, a blood COP of 25 mm Hg, and an interstitial COP of 4 mm Hg. Give the magnitude (in mm Hg) and direction (in or out) of the net pressure.

3. Aldosterone secreted by the adrenal gland must be delivered to the kidney immediately below. Trace the route that an aldosterone molecule must take from the adrenal gland to the kidney, naming all major blood vessels in the order traveled.

4. People in shock commonly exhibit paleness, cool skin, tachycardia, and a weak pulse. Explain the physiological basis for each of these signs.

5. Discuss why it is advantageous to have baroreceptors in the aortic arch and carotid sinus rather than in some other location such as the common iliac arteries.

21

THE LYMPHATIC AND IMMUNE SYSTEMS

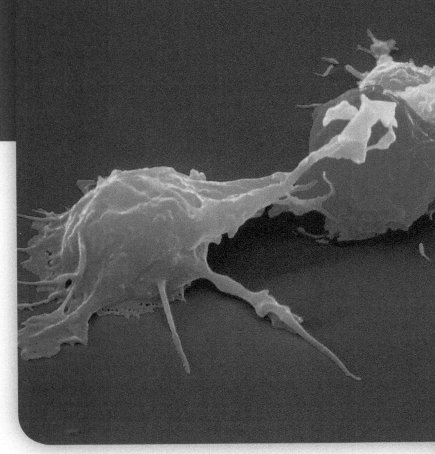

Natural killer (NK) cells (orange) attacking a human cancer cell (red)
Eye of Science/Science Source

CHAPTER OUTLINE

DEEPER INSIGHTS

Anatomy & Physiology
Revealed 4.0

Module 10: Lymphatic System

- Lymphatic organs have several features in common with exocrine glands—capsule, septa, stroma, and parenchyma. Brushing up on the meaning of those terms and their structural relationships may help you better understand anatomy of the lymphatic organs (see section 5.5b).

- The mechanisms of lymph flow are similar to those for the venous return of blood (see section 20.4a).

- Leukocytes are deeply involved in immunity and defense in various ways. You can brush up on leukocyte types, appearances, and functions most easily in table 18.6.

- The actions of immune cells against disease agents involve the processes of phagocytosis, receptor-mediated endocytosis, and exocytosis described in section 3.3f.

- The eicosanoids introduced in section 17.6 play multiple important roles in the immune processes described in this chapter.

It may come as a surprise to know that the human body harbors at least as many bacterial cells as human cells. But it shouldn't be surprising. After all, human homeostasis works wonderfully not only to sustain our lives, but also to provide a predictable, warm, wet, nutritious habitat for our internal guests. It's a wonder that the body isn't overrun and consumed by microorganisms—which indeed quickly happens when one dies and homeostasis ceases.

Many of these guest microorganisms are beneficial or even necessary to human health, but some have the potential to cause disease if they get out of hand. Furthermore, we're constantly exposed to new invaders through the food and water we consume, the air we breathe, and even the surfaces we touch. We must have a means of keeping such would-be colonists in check.

One of these defenses was discovered in 1882 by a moody, intense, Russian zoologist, Elie Metchnikoff (1845–1916). When studying the tiny transparent larvae of starfish, he observed mobile cells wandering throughout their bodies. He thought at first that they must be digestive cells, but when he saw similar cells in sea anemones ingest nonnutritive dye particles that he injected, he thought they must play a defensive role. Metchnikoff knew that mobile cells also exist in human blood and pus and quickly surround a splinter introduced through the skin, so he decided to experiment to see if the starfish cells would do the same. He impaled a starfish larva on a rose thorn, and the next morning he found the thorn crawling with cells that seemed to be trying to devour it. He later saw similar cells devouring and digesting infectious yeast in tiny transparent crustaceans called water fleas. He coined the word *phagocytosis* for this reaction and named the wandering cells *phagocytes*—terms we still use today.

Metchnikoff showed that animals from simple sea anemones and starfish to humans actively defend themselves against disease agents. His observations marked the founding of cellular and comparative immunology, and won him the scientific respect he had so long coveted. Indeed, he shared the 1908 Nobel Prize for Physiology or Medicine with Paul Ehrlich (1854–1915), who had developed the theory of humoral immunity, a process also discussed in this chapter.

This chapter focuses largely on the *immune system,* which is not an organ system but rather a population of cells that inhabit all of our organs and defend the body from agents of disease. But immune cells are especially concentrated in a true organ system, the *lymphatic system.* This is a network of organs and veinlike vessels that recover tissue fluid, inspect it for disease agents, activate immune responses, and return the fluid to the bloodstream. It is with the lymphatic system that we begin this chapter's exploration.

21.1 The Lymphatic System APR

Expected Learning Outcomes

When you have completed this section, you should be able to

a. list the functions of the lymphatic system;

b. explain how lymph forms and returns to the bloodstream;

c. name the major cells of the lymphatic system and state their functions;

d. name and describe the types of lymphatic tissue; and

e. describe the structure and function of the red bone marrow, thymus, lymph nodes, tonsils, and spleen.

The **lymphatic system (fig. 21.1)** consists of a network of vessels that penetrate nearly every tissue of the body, and a collection of tissues and organs that produce immune cells. These include the lymph nodes, spleen, thymus, tonsils, and red bone marrow.

The lymphatic system has three functions:

1. **Fluid recovery.** Fluid continually filters from blood capillaries into the tissue (interstitial) spaces. The capillaries reabsorb about 85% of it on average, but the 15% they don't absorb would, over the course of a day, amount to 2 to 4 L of water and one-quarter to one-half of the protein in the blood plasma. One would die of circulatory failure within hours if this water and protein were not returned to the bloodstream. One task of the lymphatic system is to reabsorb this excess and return it to the blood. Even partial interference with lymphatic drainage can lead to severe **lymphedema** (see fig. 20.19).

2. **Immunity.** As the lymphatic system recovers tissue fluid, it also picks up foreign cells and chemicals from the tissues. On its way back to the bloodstream, the fluid passes through lymph nodes, where immune cells stand guard against foreign matter. When they detect anything potentially harmful, they activate a protective immune response.

3. **Lipid absorption.** In the small intestine, special lymphatic vessels called *lacteals* absorb dietary lipids that are not absorbed by the blood capillaries.

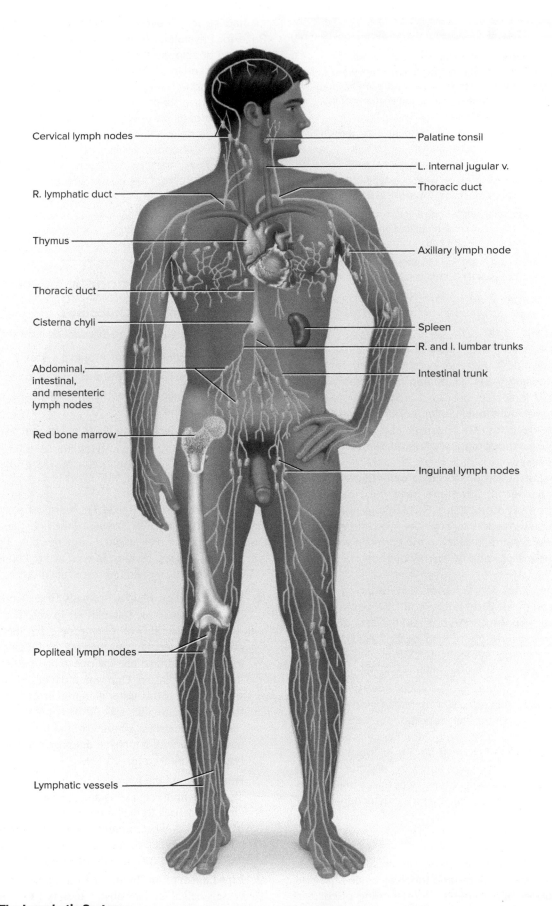

Cervical lymph nodes

Palatine tonsil

L. internal jugular v.

R. lymphatic duct

Thoracic duct

Thymus

Axillary lymph node

Thoracic duct

Cisterna chyli

Spleen

R. and l. lumbar trunks

Abdominal,
intestinal,
and mesenteric
lymph nodes

Intestinal trunk

Red bone marrow

Inguinal lymph nodes

Popliteal lymph nodes

Lymphatic vessels

FIGURE 21.1 The Lymphatic System.

The components of the lymphatic system are (1) *lymph,* the recovered fluid; (2) *lymphatic vessels,* which transport the lymph; (3) *lymphatic tissue,* composed of aggregates of lymphocytes and macrophages that populate many organs of the body; and (4) *lymphatic organs,* in which these cells are especially concentrated and which are set off from surrounding organs by connective tissue capsules.

21.1a Lymph and the Lymphatic Vessels

Lymph is usually a clear, colorless fluid, similar to blood plasma but low in protein. It originates as tissue fluid taken up by the lymphatic vessels. Its composition varies substantially from one place and time to another. After a meal, for example, lymph draining from the small intestine has a milky appearance because of its lipid content. Lymph leaving the lymph nodes contains a large number of lymphocytes—indeed, this is the main supply of lymphocytes to the bloodstream. Lymph may also contain macrophages, hormones, bacteria, viruses, cellular debris, or even traveling cancer cells.

Lymphatic Vessels

Lymph flows through a system of **lymphatic vessels (lymphatics)** similar to blood vessels. These begin with microscopic **lymphatic capillaries (terminal lymphatics),** which penetrate nearly every tissue of the body but are absent from cartilage, bone, bone marrow, and the cornea. They are closely associated with blood capillaries, but unlike them, they are closed at one end **(fig. 21.2)** and there is no through-flow of fluid like there is for capillary blood; lymph flow begins here. A lymphatic capillary consists of a sac of thin endothelial cells that loosely overlap each other like the shingles of a roof. The cells are tethered to surrounding tissue by *anchoring filaments* that prevent the sac from collapsing.

Unlike the endothelial cells of blood capillaries, lymphatic endothelial cells aren't joined by tight junctions, nor do they have a continuous basal lamina; indeed, the gaps between them are so large that bacteria, lymphocytes, and other cells and particles can enter along with the tissue fluid. Thus, the composition of lymph arriving at a lymph node is like a report on the state of the upstream tissues.

The overlapping edges of the endothelial cells act as valves that can open and close. When tissue fluid pressure is high, it pushes the flaps inward (open) and fluid flows into the capillary. When pressure is higher in the lymphatic capillary than in the tissue fluid, the flaps are pressed outward (closed).

▶▶▶APPLY WHAT YOU KNOW

Contrast the structure of a lymphatic capillary with that of a continuous blood capillary. Explain why their structural difference is related to their functional difference.

Lymphatic vessels form in the embryo by budding from the veins, so it's not surprising that the larger ones have a similar histology. They have a *tunica interna* with an endothelium and valves **(fig. 21.3),** a *tunica media* with elastic fibers and smooth muscle, and a thin outer *tunica externa.* Their walls are thinner and their valves are closer together than those of the veins.

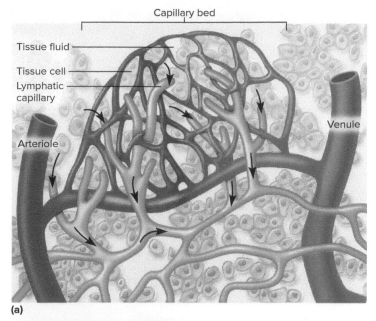

(a)

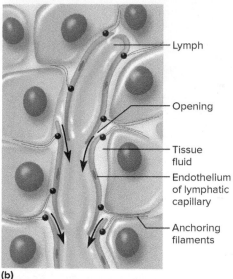

(b)

FIGURE 21.2 Lymphatic Capillaries. (a) Relationship of the lymphatic capillaries to a bed of blood capillaries. (b) Uptake of tissue fluid by a lymphatic capillary.

❓ *Why can metastasizing cancer cells get into the lymphatic system more easily than they can enter the bloodstream?*

As the lymphatic vessels converge along their path, they become larger and larger vessels with changing names. The route from the tissue fluid back to the bloodstream is: lymphatic capillaries → collecting vessels → 11 lymphatic trunks → two collecting ducts → subclavian veins. Thus, there is a continual recycling of fluid from blood to tissue fluid to lymph and back to the blood **(fig. 21.4).**

The lymphatic capillaries converge to form **collecting vessels.** These often travel alongside veins and arteries and share a common connective tissue sheath with them. At irregular intervals, they empty into lymph nodes. The lymph trickles slowly through each node, where bacteria are phagocytized and immune cells monitor the fluid for foreign antigens. It leaves the other side of

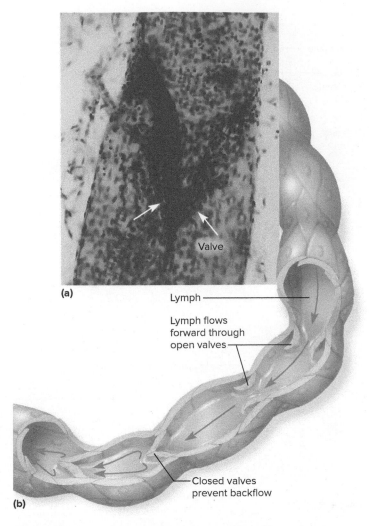

(a)

Valve

Lymph

Lymph flows
forward through
open valves

Closed valves
prevent backflow

(b)

FIGURE 21.3 Valves in the Lymphatic Vessels. (a) Photograph
of a lymphatic valve. (b) Operation of the valves to ensure a one-way
flow of lymph.

a: Dennis Strete/McGraw-Hill Education

❓ *What would be the consequence if these valves did not exist?*

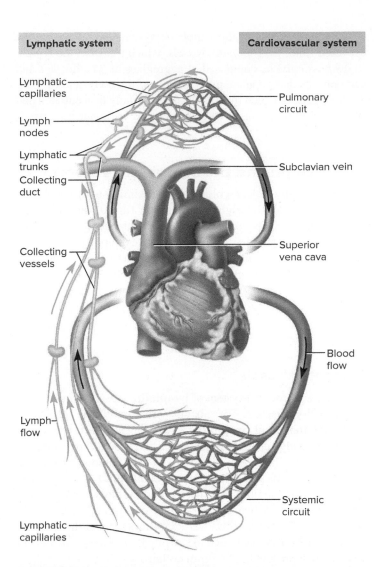

Lymphatic system

Cardiovascular system

Lymphatic
capillaries

Lymph
nodes

Lymphatic
trunks

Collecting
duct

Collecting
vessels

Lymph
flow

Lymphatic
capillaries

Pulmonary
circuit

Subclavian vein

Superior
vena cava

Blood
flow

Systemic
circuit

**FIGURE 21.4 Fluid Exchange Between the Circulatory and
Lymphatic Systems.** Blood capillaries lose fluid to the tissue
spaces. The lymphatic system picks up excess tissue fluid and
returns it to the bloodstream.

❓ *Identify two benefits in having lymphatic capillaries pick up
tissue fluid that is not reclaimed by the blood capillaries.*

the node through another collecting vessel, traveling on and often
encountering additional lymph nodes before it finally returns to
the bloodstream.

Eventually, the collecting vessels converge to form larger
lymphatic trunks, each of which drains a major portion of the
body. There are 11 of these, whose names indicate their locations and parts of the body they drain: a solitary *intestinal trunk*
and paired *jugular, subclavian, bronchomediastinal, intercostal,*
and *lumbar trunks.* The lumbar trunks drain not only the lumbar
region but also the lower limbs.

The lymphatic trunks converge to form two **collecting ducts,**
the largest of the lymphatic vessels **(fig. 21.5):**

1. The **right lymphatic duct** is formed by the convergence of
   the right jugular, subclavian, and bronchomediastinal trunks
   in the right thoracic cavity. It receives lymphatic drainage
   from the right arm and right side of the thorax and head and
   empties into the right subclavian vein.

2. The **thoracic duct,** on the left, is larger and longer. It
   begins just below the diaphragm anterior to the vertebral
   column at the level of the second lumbar vertebra. Here,
   the two lumbar trunks and the intestinal trunk join and
   form a sac called the **cisterna chyli** (sis-TUR-nuh KY-lye),
   named for the large amount of *chyle* (fatty intestinal
   lymph) that it collects after a meal. The thoracic duct then
   passes through the diaphragm with the aorta and ascends
   the mediastinum adjacent to the vertebral column. As it
   passes through the thorax, it receives additional lymph
   from the left bronchomediastinal, left subclavian, and left
   jugular trunks, then empties into the left subclavian vein.
   Collectively, this duct therefore drains all of the body
   below the diaphragm, and the left upper limb and left side
   of the head, neck, and thorax.

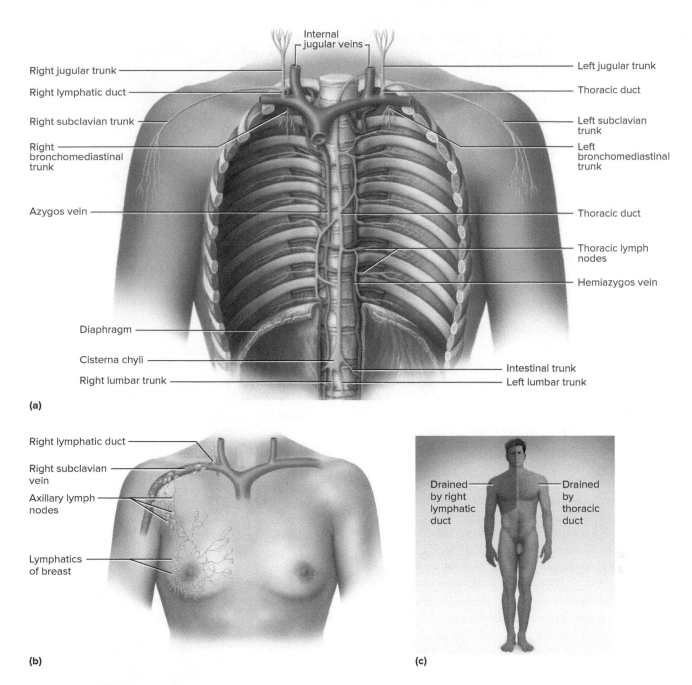

FIGURE 21.5 Lymphatics of the Thoracic Region. (a) Lymphatics of the thorax and upper abdomen and their relationship to the subclavian veins, where the lymph returns to the bloodstream. (b) Lymphatic drainage of the right mammary and axillary regions. (c) Regions of the body drained by the right lymphatic duct and thoracic duct. **APR**

❓ *Why are the axillary lymph nodes often biopsied in cases of suspected breast cancer?*

Flow of Lymph

Lymph flows under forces similar to those that govern venous return (see section 20.4a), except that the lymphatic system has no pump like the heart and lymph flows at even lower pressure and speed than venous blood. The primary mechanism of flow is rhythmic contractions of the lymphatic vessels themselves, which contract when the fluid stretches them. The valves of lymphatic vessels, like those of veins, prevent the fluid from flowing backward. Lymph flow is also produced by skeletal muscles squeezing the lymphatic vessels, like the skeletal muscle pump that moves venous blood. Since lymphatic vessels are often wrapped with an artery in a common connective tissue sheath, arterial pulsation also rhythmically squeezes the adjacent lymphatic vessels and contributes to lymph flow. A thoracic (respiratory) pump promotes the flow of lymph from the abdominal to the thoracic cavity as one inhales, just as it does in venous return. Finally, at the point where the collecting ducts empty into the subclavian veins, the rapidly flowing bloodstream draws the lymph into it. Considering these mechanisms of lymph flow, it should be apparent why physical exercise significantly increases the rate of lymphatic return.

▶▶▶ APPLY WHAT YOU KNOW

Why does it make more functional sense for the collecting ducts to connect to the subclavian veins than it would for them to connect to the subclavian arteries?

21.1b Lymphatic Cells A&PR

Another component of the lymphatic system is *lymphatic tissue,* which ranges from loosely scattered cells in the mucous membranes of the respiratory, digestive, urinary, and reproductive tracts to compact cell populations encapsulated in lymphatic organs. These tissues are composed of a variety of lymphocytes and other cells with various roles in defense and immunity:

1. **Neutrophils** are aggressively antibacterial leukocytes and are described in section 18.4b.

2. **Natural killer (NK) cells** are large lymphocytes that attack and destroy bacteria, transplanted tissues, and *host cells* (cells of one's own body) that have either become infected with viruses or turned cancerous.

3. **T lymphocytes (T cells)** are lymphocytes that mature in the thymus and later depend on thymic hormones; the *T* stands for *thymus-dependent*. There are several subclasses of T cells that will be introduced later.

4. **B lymphocytes (B cells)** are lymphocytes that differentiate into *plasma cells*—connective tissue cells that secrete antibodies. They are named for an organ in chickens (the *bursa of Fabricius*[1]) in which they were first discovered. However, you may find it more helpful to think of *B* for *bone marrow,* the site where these cells mature in humans.

5. **Macrophages** are very large, avidly phagocytotic cells of the connective tissues. They arise from monocytes that have emigrated from the bloodstream and from division of preexisting tissue macrophages. They phagocytize tissue debris, dead neutrophils, bacteria, and other foreign matter **(fig. 21.6).** They also process foreign matter and display antigenic fragments of it to certain T cells, thus alerting the immune system to the presence of an enemy. Macrophages and other cells that do this are collectively called **antigen-presenting cells (APCs).**

6. **Dendritic cells** are branched, mobile APCs found in the epidermis, mucous membranes, and lymphatic organs. They play an important role in alerting the immune system to pathogens that have breached the body surfaces. They engulf foreign matter by receptor-mediated endocytosis rather than phagocytosis, but otherwise function like macrophages. After internalizing an antigen, they migrate to a nearby lymph node and activate an immune reaction to it.

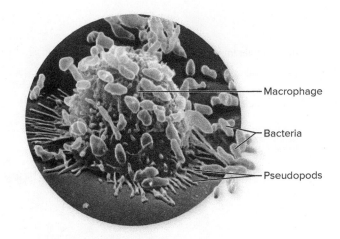

FIGURE 21.6 Macrophages Phagocytizing Bacteria. Filamentous pseudopods of the macrophages snare the rod-shaped bacteria and draw them to the cell surface, where they are phagocytized.
David M. Phillips/Science Source

7. **Reticular cells** are branched, stationary APCs that contribute to the connective tissue framework (stroma) of the lymphatic organs. (They should not be confused with reticular *fibers,* which are fine, branched collagen fibers common in lymphatic organs.)

21.1c Lymphatic Tissues

Lymphatic (lymphoid) tissues are aggregations of lymphocytes in the connective tissues of mucous membranes and various organs. The simplest form is **diffuse lymphatic tissue,** in which the lymphocytes are scattered rather than densely clustered. It is particularly prevalent in body passages that are open to the exterior—the respiratory, digestive, urinary, and reproductive tracts—where it is called **mucosa-associated lymphatic tissue (MALT).**

In some places, lymphocytes and macrophages congregate in dense masses called **lymphatic nodules (follicles) (fig. 21.7),**

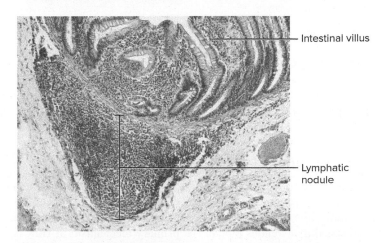

FIGURE 21.7 Lymphatic Nodule in the Mucous Membrane of the Small Intestine. This nodule is part of the mucosa-associated lymphatic tissue (MALT).
Garry DeLong/Science Source

[1]Hieronymus Fabricius (Girolamo Fabrizzi) (1537–1619), Italian anatomist

which come and go as pathogens invade the tissues and the immune system answers the challenge. Abundant lymphatic nodules are, however, a relatively constant feature of the lymph nodes (see fig. 21.10), tonsils, and appendix. In the ileum, the distal portion of the small intestine, they form clusters called **aggregated lymphoid nodules** (formerly named *Peyer patches*).

21.1d Lymphatic Organs

In contrast to the diffuse lymphatic tissue, **lymphatic (lymphoid) organs** have well-defined anatomical sites and at least a partial connective tissue capsule that separates the lymphatic tissue from neighboring tissues. These organs include the red bone marrow, thymus, lymph nodes, tonsils, and spleen. The red bone marrow and thymus are regarded as *primary lymphatic organs* because they are the sites where B and T lymphocytes, respectively, become *immunocompetent*—that is, able to recognize and respond to antigens. The lymph nodes, tonsils, and spleen are called *secondary lymphatic organs* because immunocompetent lymphocytes migrate to these organs only after they mature in the primary lymphatic organs.

Red Bone Marrow

Red bone marrow may not seem to be an organ; when aspirated from the bones for the purpose of biopsy or transfusion, it simply looks like extra-thick blood. Yet a careful microscopic examination of less disturbed marrow shows that it has a surprising degree of structure and is composed of multiple tissues, meeting the criteria of an organ, even if a very soft one.

There are two kinds of bone marrow: yellow and red. Yellow bone marrow is mainly adipose tissue and can be disregarded for present purposes, but red bone marrow is involved in hematopoiesis (blood formation) and immunity. In children, it occupies the medullary spaces of nearly all bones. In adults, it is limited to the axial skeleton and the proximal heads of the humerus and femur. Red bone marrow is an important supplier of lymphocytes to the immune system.

Red bone marrow is soft, loosely organized, highly vascular material, separated from osseous tissue by the endosteum of the bone. It produces all classes of formed elements of the blood; its red color comes from the abundance of erythrocytes. Numerous small arteries enter *nutrient foramina* on the bone surface, penetrate the bone, and empty into large *sinusoids* (45 to 80 μm wide) in the marrow **(fig. 21.8)**. The sinusoids drain into a *central longitudinal vein* that exits the bone via the same route that the arteries entered. The sinusoids are lined by endothelial cells, like other blood vessels, and are surrounded by reticular cells and reticular fibers. The blood-forming cells are attached in various ways to the reticular cells and other elements of the framework (stroma) of the marrow. The reticular cells secrete colony-stimulating factors and other signals that induce stem cells to develop into leukocytes, erythrocytes, and platelet-forming megakaryocytes. In the long bones of the limbs, aging reticular cells accumulate fat and transform into adipose cells, eventually replacing red bone marrow with yellow bone marrow.

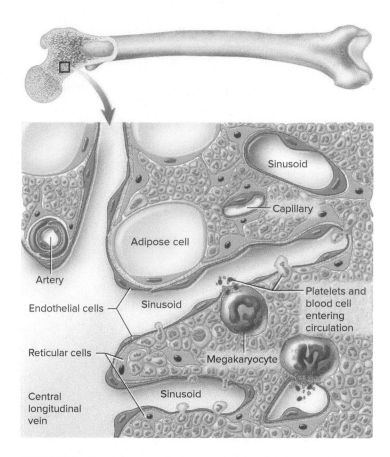

FIGURE 21.8 Histology of the Red Bone Marrow. The formed elements of blood squeeze through the endothelial cells into the sinuses, which converge on a central longitudinal vein at the lower left.

The spaces between the sinusoids are occupied by *islands (cords)* of hematopoietic tissue, composed of macrophages and blood cells in all stages of development. The macrophages destroy malformed blood cells and the nuclei discarded by developing erythrocytes. As blood cells mature, they push their way through the reticular and endothelial cells to enter the sinusoid and flow away in the bloodstream.

Thymus

The **thymus** is a member of the endocrine, lymphatic, and immune systems. It houses developing lymphocytes and secretes hormones that regulate their later activity. It is a bilobed organ located between the sternum and aortic arch in the superior mediastinum. The thymus shows a remarkable degree of degeneration (involution) with age, as described and illustrated earlier (see fig. 17.8).

The fibrous capsule of the thymus gives off trabeculae (septa) that divide the gland into several angular lobules. Each lobule has a light central *medulla* populated by T lymphocytes, surrounded by a dense, darker *cortex* **(fig. 21.9)**. Both cortex and medulla have a branching network of interconnected **epithelial cells** that play important roles in lymphocyte development discussed later; their roles differ in the two regions, so they are separately described as *cortical epithelial cells* and *medullary epithelial cells*.

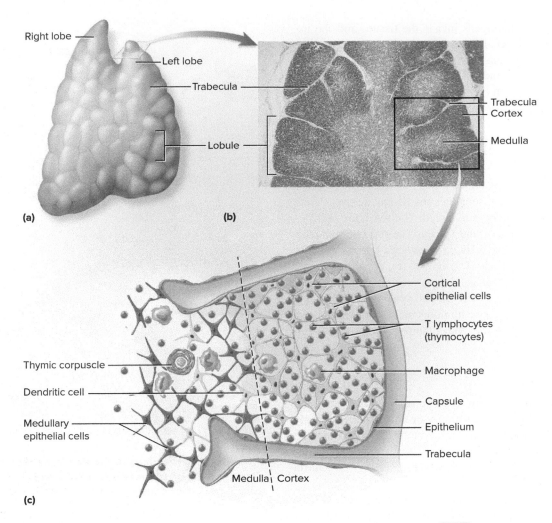

FIGURE 21.9 The Thymus. (a) Gross anatomy. (b) Histology. (c) Cellular architecture of a lobule. **APR**

b: Dennis Strete/McGraw-Hill Education

In the cortex, cortical epithelial cells and capillary *pericytes* (see fig. 20.5a) surround the blood capillaries and form a *blood–thymus barrier,* which isolates developing lymphocytes from premature exposure to blood-borne antigens. After developing in the cortex, T cells migrate to the medulla, where they spend another 3 weeks. There is no blood–thymus barrier in the medulla; mature T cells enter blood or lymphatic vessels here and leave the thymus. Some of the medullary epithelial cells are arranged in keratinized whorls called *thymic corpuscles,* which may play a role in the immune system's *self-tolerance* (restraint from attacking the body's own tissues) and are useful for identifying the thymus histologically.

Epithelial cells of the thymus secrete several signaling molecules that promote the development and action of T cells both locally (as paracrines) and systemically (as hormones); these include *thymosin, thymopoietin, thymulin, interleukins,* and *interferon.* If the thymus is removed from newborn mammals, they waste away and never develop immunity. Other lymphatic organs also seem to depend on thymosins or T cells and develop poorly in thymectomized animals. The role of the thymus in T cell development is discussed later.

Lymph Nodes

Lymph nodes (fig. 21.10) are the most numerous lymphatic organs, numbering about 450 in a typical adult. They serve two functions: to cleanse the lymph and to act as a site of T and B cell activation. A lymph node is an elongated or bean-shaped structure, usually less than 3 cm long, often with an indentation called the *hilum* on one side. It is enclosed in a fibrous capsule with trabeculae that partially divide the interior of the node into compartments. Between the capsule and parenchyma is a narrow, relatively clear space called the *subcapsular sinus,* which contains reticular fibers, macrophages, and dendritic cells. Deep to this, the gland consists mainly of a stroma of reticular connective tissue and a parenchyma of lymphocytes and antigen-presenting cells.

The parenchyma is divided into an outer C-shaped **cortex** that encircles about four-fifths of the organ, and an inner **medulla** that extends to the surface at the hilum. The cortex consists mainly of ovoid to conical lymphatic nodules. When the lymph node is fighting a pathogen, these nodules acquire light-staining **germinal centers** where B cells multiply and differentiate into plasma cells. The medulla consists largely of a branching network of *medullary*

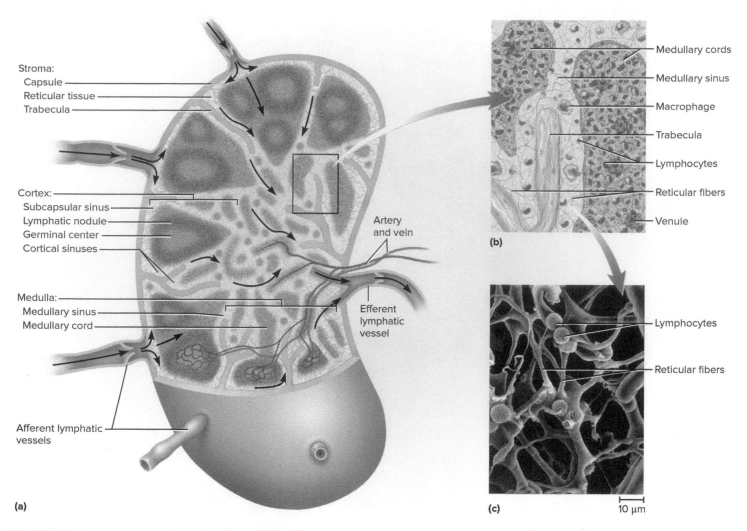

FIGURE 21.10 Anatomy of a Lymph Node. (a) Partially bisected lymph node showing pathway of lymph flow. (b) Detail of the boxed region in part (a). (c) Reticular fiber stroma and immune cells in a medullary sinus (SEM). **APR**

c: Francis Leroy, Biocosmos/Science Source

cords composed of lymphocytes, plasma cells, macrophages, reticular cells, and reticular fibers. The cortex and medulla also contain lymph-filled sinuses continuous with the subcapsular sinus.

Several **afferent lymphatic vessels** lead into the node along its convex surface. Lymph flows from these vessels into the subcapsular sinus, percolates slowly through the sinuses of the cortex and medulla, and leaves the node through one to three **efferent lymphatic vessels** that emerge from the hilum. No other lymphatic organs have afferent lymphatic vessels; lymph nodes are the only organs that filter lymph as it flows along its course. The lymph node is a bottleneck that slows down lymph flow and allows time for cleansing it of foreign matter. Macrophages and reticular cells of the sinuses remove about 99% of the impurities before the lymph leaves the node. On its way to the bloodstream, lymph flows through one lymph node after another and thus becomes quite thoroughly cleansed of impurities.

Blood vessels also penetrate the hilum. Arteries follow the medullary cords and give rise to capillary beds in the medulla

and cortex. In the *deep cortex* near the junction with the medulla, lymphocytes emigrate from the bloodstream into the parenchyma of the node. Most lymphocytes in the deep cortex are T cells.

Lymph nodes are widespread but especially concentrated in the following locations (see fig. 21.1 for an overview):

- *Cervical lymph nodes* occur in deep and superficial groups in the neck, and monitor lymph coming from the head and neck.

- *Axillary lymph nodes* are concentrated in the armpit (axilla) and receive lymph from the upper limb and breast (see fig. 21.5b).

- *Thoracic lymph nodes* occur in the thoracic cavity, especially in the mediastinum, and receive lymph from the mediastinum, lungs, and airway.

- *Abdominal lymph nodes* occur in the posterior abdominopelvic wall and receive lymph from the urinary and reproductive systems.

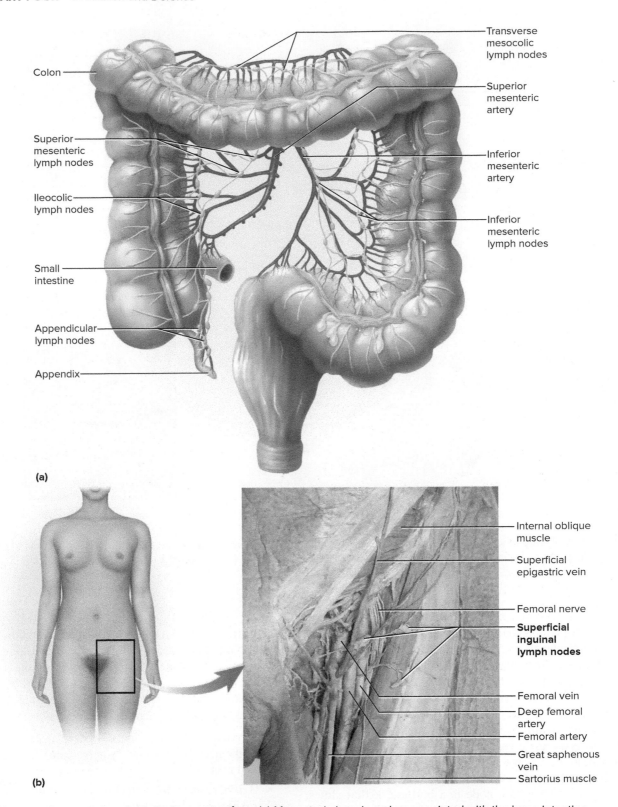

FIGURE 21.11 Some Areas of Lymph Node Concentration. (a) Mesenteric lymph nodes associated with the large intestine.
(b) Inguinal lymph nodes in the groin of a female cadaver. **APR**

b: Rebecca Gray/Don Kincaid/McGraw-Hill Education

- *Intestinal* and *mesenteric lymph nodes* are found in the mesenteries **(fig. 21.11a)** and adjacent to the appendix and intestines; they receive lymph from the digestive tract.

- *Inguinal lymph nodes* occur in the groin **(fig. 21.11b)** and receive lymph from the entire lower limb.

- *Popliteal lymph nodes* occur at the back of the knee and receive lymph from the foot and leg proper.

When a lymph node is under challenge by an antigen, it may become swollen and painful to the touch—a condition called **lymphadenitis**[2] (lim-FAD-en-EYE-tis). Physicians routinely palpate the accessible lymph nodes of the cervical, axillary, and inguinal regions for swelling. The collective term for all lymph node diseases is **lymphadenopathy**[3] (lim-FAD-eh-NOP-a-thee). Lymph nodes are common sites of metastatic cancer (see Deeper Insight 21.1).

DEEPER INSIGHT 21.1

CLINICAL APPLICATION

Lymph Nodes and Metastatic Cancer

Metastasis is a phenomenon in which cancerous cells break free of the original *primary tumor,* travel to other sites in the body, and establish new tumors (see fig. 4.22). Because of the high permeability of lymphatic capillaries, metastasizing cancer cells easily enter them and travel in the lymph. They tend to lodge in the first lymph node they encounter and multiply there, eventually destroying the node. Cancerous lymph nodes are swollen but relatively firm and usually painless. Cancer of a lymph node is called *lymphoma*.

Once a tumor is well established in one node, cells may emigrate from there and travel to the next. However, if the metastasis is detected early enough, cancer can sometimes be eradicated by removing not only the primary tumor, but also the nearest lymph nodes downstream from that point. For example, breast cancer is often treated with a combination of lumpectomy or mastectomy along with removal of the nearby axillary lymph nodes.

---

[2]*lymph* = water; *adeno* = gland; *itis* = inflammation
[3]*lymph* = water; *adeno* = gland; *pathy* = disease

Tonsils

The **tonsils** are patches of lymphatic tissue located at the entrance to the pharynx, where they guard against ingested and inhaled pathogens. Each is covered by an epithelium and has deep pits called **tonsillar crypts** lined by lymphatic nodules **(fig. 21.12).** The crypts often contain food debris, dead leukocytes, bacteria, and antigenic chemicals. Below the crypts, the tonsils are partially separated from underlying connective tissue by an incomplete fibrous capsule.

There are three main sets of tonsils: (1) a single median **pharyngeal tonsil (adenoids)** on the wall of the pharynx just behind the nasal cavity; (2) a pair of **palatine tonsils** at the posterior margin of the oral cavity; and (3) numerous **lingual tonsils,** each with a single crypt, concentrated in patches embedded in each side of the root of the tongue (see fig. 25.5a).

The palatine tonsils are the largest and most often infected. *Tonsillitis* is an acute inflammation of the palatine tonsils, usually caused by a viral or bacterial infection. Their surgical removal, called *tonsillectomy,* used to be one of the most common surgical procedures performed on children, but is less common today. Tonsillitis is now usually treated with antibiotics.

Spleen

The **spleen,** the body's largest lymphatic organ, measures up to 12 cm long and usually weighs about 150 g. It is located in the left hypochondriac region, just inferior to the diaphragm and posterolateral to the stomach **fig. 21.13;** see also atlas B, fig. B.6). It is

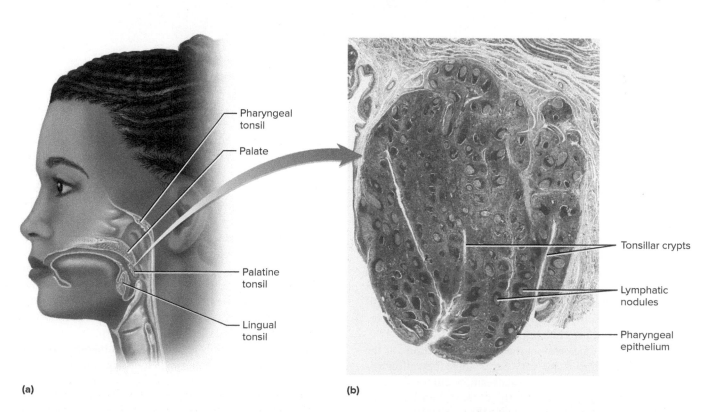

(a)   (b)

FIGURE 21.12 The Tonsils. (a) Locations of the tonsils. (b) Histology of the palatine tonsil. **APR**

b: Biophoto Associates/Science Source

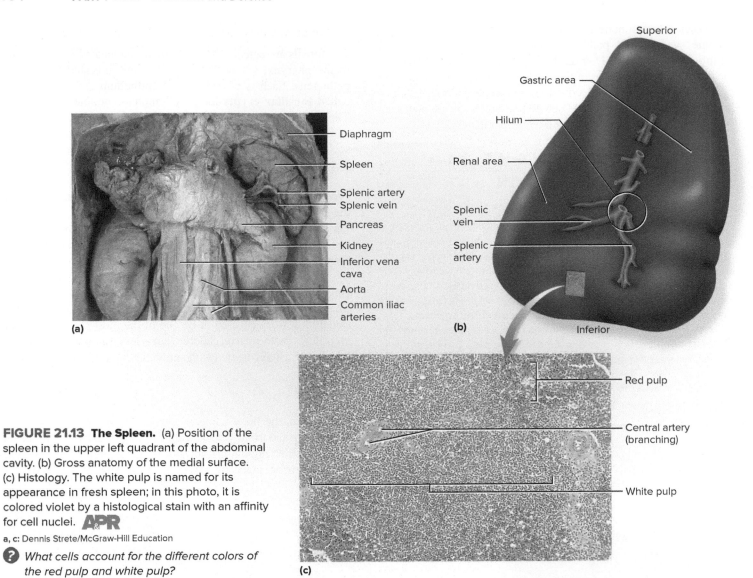

FIGURE 21.13 The Spleen. (a) Position of the spleen in the upper left quadrant of the abdominal cavity. (b) Gross anatomy of the medial surface. (c) Histology. The white pulp is named for its appearance in fresh spleen; in this photo, it is colored violet by a histological stain with an affinity for cell nuclei. **APR**

a, c: Dennis Strete/McGraw-Hill Education

❓ *What cells account for the different colors of the red pulp and white pulp?*

protected by ribs 10 through 12. The spleen fits snugly between the diaphragm, stomach, and kidney and has indentations called the *gastric area* and *renal area* where it presses against these adjacent viscera. It has a medial hilum penetrated by the splenic artery, splenic vein, and lymphatic vessels.

The parenchyma exhibits two types of tissue named for their appearance in fresh specimens (not in stained sections): **red pulp,** which consists of sinuses gorged with concentrated erythrocytes; and **white pulp,** which consists of lymphocytes and macrophages aggregated like sleeves along small branches of the splenic artery. In tissue sections, white pulp appears as an ovoid mass of lymphocytes with an arteriole passing through it. However, the three-dimensional shape is not egglike but cylindrical.

These two tissue types reflect the multiple functions of the spleen. Its blood capillaries are very permeable; they allow red blood cells (RBCs) to leave the bloodstream, accumulate in the sinuses of the red pulp, and reenter the bloodstream later. The spleen is an "erythrocyte graveyard"—old, fragile RBCs rupture as they squeeze through the capillary walls into the sinuses. Macrophages phagocytize their remains, just as they dispose of

blood-borne bacteria and other cellular debris. The spleen produces blood cells in the fetus and can resume this role in adults in the event of extreme anemia. Lymphocytes and macrophages of the white pulp monitor the blood for foreign antigens, much like the lymph nodes do the lymph. The spleen is a reservoir for a large "standing army" of monocytes, waiting in a state of emergency preparedness. In such events as microbial infection, myocardial infarction, or gaping wounds, angiotensin II stimulates the spleen to release great numbers of monocytes into the bloodstream. The monocytes help to combat pathogens and repair damaged tissues. The spleen also helps to stabilize blood volume by transferring excess plasma from the bloodstream into the lymphatic system.

The spleen is highly vascular and vulnerable to trauma and infection. A ruptured spleen can hemorrhage fatally, but is difficult to repair surgically. Therefore, a once-common procedure in such cases was its removal, *splenectomy.* A person can live without a spleen, but people with splenectomies are more susceptible to septicemia, other infections, and premature death. Like tonsillectomy, splenectomy is now performed less commonly than it used to be.

Answer the following questions to test your understanding of the preceding section:

1. List the primary functions of the lymphatic system. What do you think would be the most noticeable effect of clamping the right lymphatic duct closed?

2. How does fluid get into the lymphatic system? What prevents it from draining back out?

3. What do NK, T, and B cells have in common? How do their functions differ?

4. List five major cell types of lymphatic tissues and state the function of each.

5. Predict the relative seriousness of removing the following organs from a 2-year-old child: (a) a lymph node, (b) the spleen, (c) the thymus, (d) the palatine tonsils.

21.2   Innate Immunity

Expected Learning Outcomes

When you have completed this section, you should be able to

a. define *pathogen* and *immune system;*

b. identify the body's three lines of defense against pathogens;

c. contrast innate and adaptive immunity;

d. describe the defensive functions of various types of leukocytes and macrophages;

e. describe the immune roles of interferons and the complement system;

f. explain how fever serves a protective role against pathogens; and

g. describe the process of inflammation and explain what accounts for its cardinal signs.

For all living organisms, one of the greatest survival challenges is coping with **pathogens**[4]—viruses, bacteria, fungi, and other microorganisms that cause disease. However, the body must also defend itself from nonliving disease agents such as poison ivy toxin and allergy-producing chemicals in food, cosmetics, and latex gloves.

We can think of the body as having three lines of defense against these environmental threats:

1. The **first line of defense** consists of epithelial barriers, notably the skin and mucous membranes, which are impenetrable to most of the pathogens that daily assault us.

2. The **second line of defense** consists of protections against pathogens that break through those external barriers. These defenses include leukocytes and macrophages, antimicrobial proteins, natural killer cells, fever, and inflammation.

3. The **third line of defense** is adaptive immunity, a group of mechanisms that not only defeat a pathogen but leave the body with a memory of it, enabling one to defeat it so quickly in future encounters that the pathogen causes no illness.

Such defenses collectively compose the **immune**[5] **system,** which consists of a widely distributed population of cells that inhabit nearly every organ of the body; diverse chemicals they produce to neutralize and destroy pathogens; physical barriers to invasion such as the skin and mucous membranes; and physiological processes such as fever and inflammation. Note that unlike other body systems, this is not an organ system but a collective term for numerous defensive cells and mechanisms.

Our mechanisms of defense are divided into two broad forms called innate and adaptive immunity, although there is such extensive interaction between the two that they're not entirely separable or independent. **Innate immunity** consists of defenses we're born with (hence *innate*) and that protect us from a broad spectrum of disease agents; it encompasses the first and second lines of defense just described. **Adaptive immunity,** by contrast, constitutes the third line of defense and is distinguished by its capacity for immune memory. It *adapts* the body to the presence of a pathogen so we become less vulnerable to the illness it could otherwise cause.

Innate immunity has three characteristics that differentiate it from adaptive immunity:

1. It is a **local** effect, in most cases, warding off a pathogen at the point of invasion (such as the itchy inflammation of a rash or mosquito bite) with little effect anywhere else. Fever is an exception, having a *systemic* (body-wide) effect.

2. It is **nonspecific.** Each mechanism of innate immunity, such as the physical barrier of the skin and the antiviral effect of fever, acts against a broad spectrum of disease agents, not against one particular pathogen. Innate immunity used to be called *nonspecific defense* for this reason.

3. It **lacks memory** of any prior exposure to a pathogen, so it is no easier to defeat that pathogen on later exposures than it was the first time.

Much of our innate immunity employs three basic kinds of defense: (1) *protective proteins* such as keratin, interferons, and complement; (2) *protective cells* such as neutrophils and macrophages; and (3) *protective processes* such as fever and inflammation. We will examine these in the coming sections.

21.2a External Barriers

Our first line of defense is the skin and mucous membranes—the physical barriers to microbial invasion. When the skin is broken by a scrape or animal bite or destroyed by a burn, one of the most urgent treatment concerns is the prevention of infection. This attests to the importance of intact skin as a barrier. Its surface is composed mainly of keratin, a tough protein that few pathogens can penetrate. Furthermore, with exceptions such as the axillary and pubic areas, it is too dry and poor in nutrients to support much microbial growth. Even

---

[4]*patho* = disease, suffering; *gen* = producing

[5]*immuno* = free

those microorganisms that do adhere to the epidermis are continually cast off as we shed dead surface keratinocytes (see fig. 5.12).

The skin also is coated with diverse antimicrobial chemicals. Sweat and sebum coat it with a protective **acid mantle**—a thin film of lactic and fatty acids that inhibit bacterial growth. Sweat also contains an antibacterial peptide called **dermicidin.** Keratinocytes, neutrophils, macrophages, and other cells also produce peptides called **defensins** and **cathelicidins**[6] (ca-THEL-ih-SY-dins) that destroy bacteria, viruses, and fungi. The effects of these defenses are enhanced by vitamin D (calcitriol), pointing to the benefit of a moderate amount of sunlight exposure for one's resistance to infection. (See section 7.4b for a reminder of the role of sunlight in vitamin D synthesis.)

The digestive, respiratory, urinary, and reproductive tracts are open to the exterior, making them vulnerable to invasion, but they're protected by mucous membranes. Sticky mucus physically ensnares microorganisms. Those trapped in the respiratory mucus are moved by cilia to the pharynx, swallowed, and destroyed by stomach acid. Microorganisms are flushed from the upper digestive tract by saliva and from the lower urinary tract by urine. Mucus, tears, and saliva also contain **lysozyme,** an enzyme that destroys bacteria by dissolving their cell walls.

Beneath the epithelia of the skin and mucous membranes is a layer of areolar tissue. Its ground substance contains a giant glycosaminoglycan called **hyaluronic acid** (HI-ul-yur-ON-ic), which gives it a viscous consistency. It is normally difficult for microorganisms to migrate through this sticky tissue gel. Some pathogens overcome this obstacle, however, by producing an enzyme called *hyaluronidase,* which breaks it down to a thinner consistency that is more easily penetrated. Hyaluronidase occurs in some snake venoms and bacterial toxins and is produced by some parasitic protozoans to facilitate their invasion of the connective tissues.

21.2b Leukocytes and Macrophages

The skin and mucous membranes obviously aren't invincible barriers. They suffer frequent cuts, nicks, and scrapes and are daily breached even by such mundane activities as shaving and brushing our teeth. But when microorganisms get past these epithelial barriers, they're attacked by **phagocytes** (phagocytic cells) that have a voracious appetite for foreign matter. Leukocytes and macrophages play especially important roles in both innate and adaptive immunity and, therefore, in both the second and third lines of defense.

Leukocytes

The five types of leukocytes are illustrated and described in table 18.6. We will now examine their contributions to resistance and immunity in more detail.

1. **Neutrophils** spend most of their lives wandering in the connective tissues killing bacteria. One of their methods is simple phagocytosis and digestion—engulfing microorganisms with their pseudopods and destroying them with lysosomal enzymes (see figs. 3.12, 3.20). The other is a more complex process that produces a cloud of bactericidal chemicals.

When a neutrophil detects bacteria in the immediate area, its lysosomes migrate to the cell surface and *degranulate,* or discharge their enzymes into the tissue fluid. Here, the enzymes catalyze a reaction called the **respiratory burst:** The neutrophil rapidly absorbs oxygen and reduces it to *superoxide anions* ($O_2 \cdot^-$), which react with H^+ to form hydrogen peroxide (H_2O_2). Another lysosomal enzyme produces hypochlorite (HClO), the active ingredient in chlorine bleach, using chloride ions in the tissue fluid. Superoxide, hydrogen peroxide, and hypochlorite are highly toxic; they form a chemical **killing zone** around the neutrophil that destroys far more bacteria than the neutrophil can destroy by phagocytosis alone. Unfortunately for the neutrophil, it too is killed by these chemicals. These potent oxidizing agents can also damage connective tissues and sometimes contribute to rheumatoid arthritis.

2. **Eosinophils** are found especially in the mucous membranes, standing guard against parasites, allergens (allergy-causing antigens), and other foes. They congregate especially at sites of allergy, inflammation, or parasitic infection. They help to kill parasites such as tapeworms and roundworms, which are too big to phagocytize, by producing superoxide, hydrogen peroxide, and various toxic proteins including a neurotoxin. These agents promote the action of basophils and mast cells (see next paragraph). Eosinophils phagocytize and degrade antigen–antibody complexes. Finally, they secrete enzymes that degrade and limit the action of histamine and other inflammatory chemicals that, unchecked, could cause tissue damage.

3. **Basophils** secrete chemicals that aid the mobility and action of other leukocytes: *leukotrienes* that activate and attract neutrophils and eosinophils; the vasodilator *histamine,* which increases blood flow and speeds the delivery of leukocytes to the area; and the anticoagulant *heparin,* which inhibits the formation of blood clots that would impede leukocyte mobility. These substances are also produced by **mast cells,** a type of connective tissue cell similar to basophils. Eosinophils promote basophil and mast cell action by stimulating them to release these secretions.

4. **Lymphocytes** all look more or less alike in blood films, but there are several functional types. Three basic categories have already been mentioned: natural killer (NK) cells, T cells, and B cells. In the circulating blood, about 80% of the lymphocytes are T cells, 15% B cells, and 5% NK and stem cells. The roles of these lymphocyte types are too diverse for easy generalizations here, but are described in later sections on NK cells and adaptive immunity. NK cells are part of our innate immunity and the others function mainly in adaptive immunity. Certain lymphocytes called *helper T cells* function in both innate and adaptive immunity.

5. **Monocytes** are leukocytes that emigrate from the blood into the connective tissues and transform into macrophages. All of the body's avidly phagocytic cells except leukocytes are called the **macrophage system.** Dendritic cells are included even though they come from different stem cells

---

[6]*catheli* = universal; *cid* = kill; *in* = substance, protein

than macrophages and employ receptor-mediated endocytosis instead of phagocytosis to internalize foreign matter. Some phagocytes are wandering cells that actively seek pathogens, whereas reticular cells and others are fixed in place and phagocytize only those pathogens that come to them—although they are strategically positioned for this to occur. Macrophages are widely distributed in the loose connective tissues, but there are also specialized forms with more specific localities: *microglia* in the central nervous system, *alveolar macrophages* in the lungs, and *stellate macrophages* in the liver, for example.

21.2c Antimicrobial Proteins

Multiple types of proteins inhibit microbial reproduction and provide short-term, nonspecific resistance to pathogenic bacteria and viruses. We have already considered several at the skin surface, and now turn our attention to two families of blood-borne antimicrobial proteins.

Interferons

When certain cells (especially leukocytes) are infected with viruses, they secrete proteins called **interferons.** These are of little benefit to the cell that secretes them, but are like its "dying words" that alert neighboring cells and protect them from becoming infected. They bind to surface receptors on those cells and activate second-messenger systems within. This induces the synthesis of dozens of antiviral proteins that defend a cell by such means as breaking down viral genes and preventing viral replication. Interferons also activate NK cells and macrophages, which destroy infected cells before they can liberate a swarm of newly replicated viruses. Interferons also confer resistance to cancer, since the activated NK cells destroy malignant cells.

Complement System

The **complement system** is a group of 30 or more globulins that make powerful contributions to both innate and adaptive immunity. Immunology pioneer Paul Ehrlich (1854–1915) named it *complement* because it "completes the action of antibody," and indeed this is the principal means of pathogen destruction in antibody-mediated immunity. Since Ehrlich's time, however, the complement system has also been found important in innate immunity.

Complement proteins are synthesized mainly by the liver. They circulate in the blood in inactive form and are activated in the presence of pathogens. The inactive proteins are named with the letter *C* and a number, such as C3. Activation splits them into fragments, which are further identified by lowercase letters (C3a and C3b, for example).

Activated complement contributes to pathogen destruction by four methods: inflammation, immune clearance, phagocytosis, and cytolysis. We will examine the pathways of activation with a view to understanding how each of these goals is achieved. There are three such routes **(fig. 21.14):** the classical, alternative, and lectin pathways.

The **classical pathway** requires an antibody to get it started; thus it is part of adaptive immunity. The antibody binds to an antigen on the surface of a microorganism and changes shape,

exposing a pair of *complement-binding sites* (see fig. 21.19). Complement C1 binds to these sites and sets off a reaction cascade. Like the cascade of blood-clotting reactions, each step generates an enzyme that catalyzes the production of many more molecules at the next step; each step is an amplifying process, so many molecules of product result from a small beginning. In the classical pathway, the cascade is called **complement fixation,** since it results in the attachment of a chain of complement proteins to the antibody.

The alternative and lectin pathways require no antibodies and thus belong to our innate immunity. Complement C3 slowly and spontaneously breaks down in the blood into C3a and C3b. In the **alternative pathway,** C3b binds directly to targets such as human tumor cells, viruses, bacteria, and yeasts. This, too, triggers a reaction cascade—this time with an *autocatalytic effect* in which C3b leads to the accelerated splitting of more C3 and production of even more C3b.

Lectins are plasma proteins that bind to carbohydrates. In the **lectin pathway,** a lectin binds to certain sugars of a microbial cell surface and sets off yet another reaction cascade leading to C3b production.

As we can see, the splitting of C3 into C3a and C3b is an intersection where all three pathways converge. These two C3 fragments then produce, directly or indirectly, the end results of the complement system:

1. **Inflammation.** C3a stimulates mast cells and basophils to secrete histamine and other inflammatory chemicals. It also activates and attracts neutrophils and macrophages, the two key cellular agents of pathogen destruction in inflammation. The exact roles of these chemicals and cells are explained in the section on inflammation to follow.

2. **Immune clearance.** C3b binds antigen–antibody (Ag–Ab) complexes to red blood cells. As these RBCs circulate through the liver and spleen, the macrophages of those organs strip off and destroy the Ag–Ab complexes, leaving the RBCs unharmed. This is the principal means of clearing foreign antigens from the bloodstream.

3. **Phagocytosis.** Bacteria, viruses, and other pathogens are phagocytized and digested by neutrophils and macrophages. However, those phagocytes can't easily internalize "naked" microorganisms. C3b assists them by means of **opsonization**[7]—it coats microbial cells and serves as binding sites for phagocyte attachment. The way Elie Metchnikoff described this, opsonization "butters up" the foreign cells to make them more appetizing to phagocytes.

4. **Cytolysis.**[8] C3b splits another complement protein, C5, into C5a and C5b. C5a joins C3a in its proinflammatory actions, but C5b plays a more important role in pathogen destruction. It binds to the enemy cell and then attracts complements C6, C7, and C8. This conglomeration of proteins (now called C5b678) goes on to bind up to 17 molecules of complement C9, which form a ring called the *membrane*

---

[7]*opson* = to prepare food
[8]*cyto* = cell; *lysis* = split apart, break down

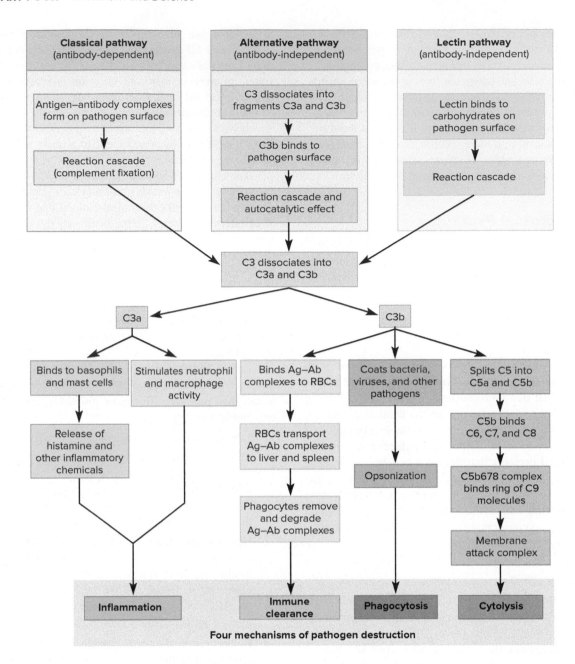

FIGURE 21.14 Complement Activation. The classical, alternative, and lectin pathways all lead to the cleavage of complement C3 into C3a and C3b. Those two fragments activate processes that lead to enhanced inflammation, immune clearance, phagocytosis, and cytolysis.

attack complex **(fig. 21.15).** The complex forms a hole in the target cell up to 10 nm wide, about the diameter of a single protein molecule. The cell can no longer maintain homeostasis; electrolytes leak out, water flows rapidly in, and the cell ruptures.

21.2d Natural Killer Cells

Natural killer (NK) cells continually patrol the body "on the look-out" for pathogens or diseased host cells. They attack and destroy bacteria, cells of transplanted organs and tissues, cells infected with viruses, and cancer cells. Upon recognition of an enemy cell, the

NK cell binds to it and releases proteins called **perforins,** which polymerize in a ring and create a hole in its plasma membrane **(fig. 21.16).** This is a kiss of death, for the hole allows a rapid inflow of water and salts. That alone may kill the target cell, but the NK cell also secretes a group of protein-degrading enzymes called **granzymes.** These enter the pore made by the perforins, destroy the target cell's enzymes, and induce apoptosis (programmed cell death).

21.2e Fever

Fever is an abnormal elevation of body temperature. It is also known as **pyrexia,** and the term *febrile* means pertaining to fever

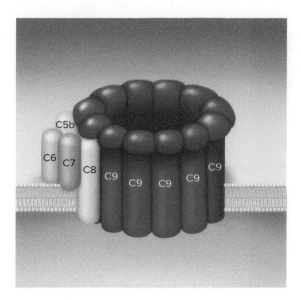

FIGURE 21.15 The Membrane Attack Complex. Complement proteins C5b, C6, C7, and C8 form an organizing center around which many C9 molecules create a ring that opens a lethal hole in the enemy cell membrane.

❓ *In what way does the action of the membrane attack complex resemble the action of perforin?*

(as in "febrile attack"). Fever results from trauma, infections, drug reactions, brain tumors, and several other causes. Because of variations in human body temperature, there is no exact criterion for what constitutes a fever—a temperature that is febrile for one person may be normal for another.

Fever is commonly regarded as an undesirable side effect of illness, and we make efforts to reduce it for the sake of comfort. However, it is usually a beneficial defense mechanism that does more good than harm. People with colds, for example, recover more

quickly and are less infective to others when they allow a fever to run its course rather than using **antipyretic** (fever-reducing) medications such as aspirin and ibuprofen. Fever is beneficial in that it (1) promotes interferon activity, (2) inhibits reproduction of bacteria and viruses, and (3) elevates metabolic rate and accelerates tissue repair.

Fever is typically initiated by **exogenous pyrogens**[9]—fever-producing agents originating outside the body, such as the surface glycolipids of bacteria and viruses. As neutrophils and macrophages attack such pathogens, they secrete a variety of polypeptides that act as **endogenous pyrogens.**[10] These in turn stimulate neurons of the anterior hypothalamus to raise the set point for body temperature—say, to 39°C (102°F) instead of the usual 37°C (**fig. 21.17**). Prostaglandin E_2 (PGE_2), secreted in the hypothalamus, enhances this effect. Aspirin and ibuprofen reduce fever by inhibiting prostaglandin synthesis, but in some circumstances, using aspirin to control fever can have deadly consequences (see Deeper Insight 21.2).

When the set point rises, a person shivers to generate heat and the cutaneous arteries constrict to reduce heat loss. In the stage of fever called *onset,* one has a rising temperature, yet experiences chills and feels cold and clammy to another's touch. In the next stage, *stadium,* the temperature oscillates around the higher set point for as long as the pathogen is present. The elevated temperature enhances the action of interferons and other antimicrobial proteins, and it inhibits bacterial reproduction.

When the infection is defeated, pyrogen secretion ceases and the hypothalamic thermostat is set back to normal. This activates heat-losing mechanisms, especially cutaneous vasodilation and

---

[9]*exo* = from outside; *genous* = arising; *pyro* = fire, heat; *gen* = producing
[10]*endo* = from within; *genous* = arising; *pyro* = fire, heat; *gen* = producing

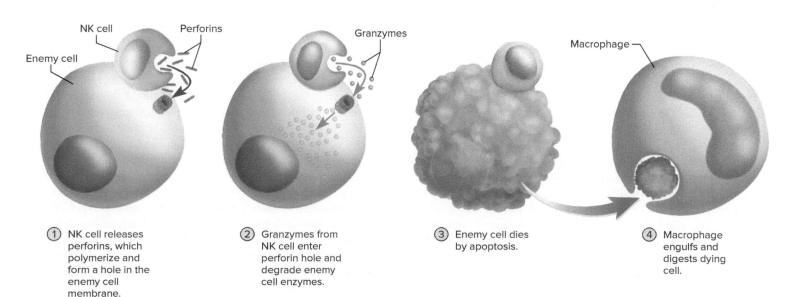

① NK cell releases perforins, which polymerize and form a hole in the enemy cell membrane.

② Granzymes from NK cell enter perforin hole and degrade enemy cell enzymes.

③ Enemy cell dies by apoptosis.

④ Macrophage engulfs and digests dying cell.

FIGURE 21.16 The Action of a Natural Killer (NK) Cell.

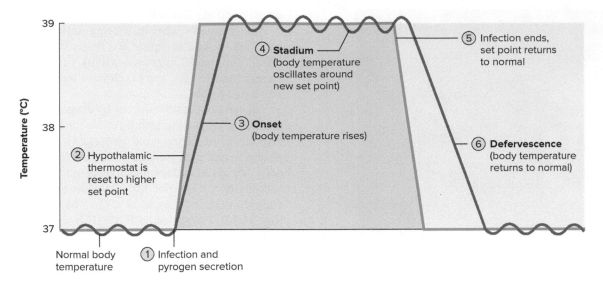

FIGURE 21.17 **The Course of a Fever.**

DEEPER INSIGHT 21.2

CLINICAL APPLICATION

Reye Syndrome

In children younger than 15, an acute viral infection such as chickenpox or influenza is sometimes followed by a serious disorder called *Reye*[11] *syndrome* (pronounced "rye"). First recognized in 1963, this disease is characterized by swelling of brain neurons and fatty infiltration of the liver and other viscera. Neurons die from hypoxia and the pressure of the swelling brain, which results in nausea, vomiting, disorientation, seizures, and coma. About 30% of victims die, and the survivors sometimes suffer mental retardation. Reye syndrome can be triggered by the use of aspirin to control fever; parents are strictly advised never to give aspirin to children with chickenpox or flulike symptoms.

---

sweating. The skin is warm and flushed during this phase. The phase of falling temperature is called *defervescence* in general, *crisis (flush)* if the temperature drops abruptly, or *lysis* if it falls slowly.

Even though most fevers are beneficial, excessively high temperature can be dangerous because it speeds up different enzymatic pathways to different degrees, causing metabolic discoordination and cellular dysfunction. Fevers above 40.5°C (105°F) can make one delirious. Convulsions and coma ensue at higher temperatures, and death or irreversible brain damage commonly results from fevers that range from 44° to 46°C (111° to 115°F).

21.2f Inflammation

Inflammation is a local defensive response to tissue injury of any kind, including trauma and infection. Its general purposes are (1) to limit the spread of pathogens and ultimately destroy them, (2) to remove the debris of damaged tissue, and (3) to initiate tissue repair. Inflammation is characterized by four **cardinal signs:** redness, swelling, heat, and pain. Some authorities list impaired use as a fifth sign, but this may or may not occur and when it does, it is mostly because of the pain.

▶▶▶**APPLY WHAT YOU KNOW**

In spite of the expression, the four "cardinal signs" of inflammation are actually a mixture of signs and symptoms. With the aid of the glossary definitions, identify which are signs and which are symptoms.

Words ending in the suffix *-itis* denote inflammation of specific organs and tissues: *arthritis, encephalitis, peritonitis, gingivitis,* and *dermatitis,* for example. Inflammation can occur anywhere in the body, but it is most common and observable in the skin, which is subject to more trauma than any other organ. Examples of cutaneous inflammation include an itchy mosquito bite, sunburn, a poison ivy rash, and the redness and blistering produced by manual labor, tight shoes, or a kitchen burn.

The following discussion will account for the four cardinal signs and explain how the three purposes of inflammation are achieved. Inflammation is mediated by several types of cells and chemicals summarized in **table 21.1.** Many of the chemicals that regulate inflammation and immunity are in a class called **cytokines**[12]—small proteins that serve as a chemical communication network among immune cells. Cytokines usually act at short

---

[11]R. Douglas Reye (1912–77), Australian pathologist

[12]*cyto* = cell; *kin* = to set in motion

TABLE 21.1	Agents of Inflammation
Cellular Agents	
Basophils	Secrete histamine, heparin, leukotrienes, and kinins
Endothelial cells	Produce cell-adhesion molecules to recruit leukocytes; secrete platelet-derived growth factor
Eosinophils*	Produce antiparasitic oxidizing agents and toxic proteins; stimulate basophils and mast cells; limit action of histamine and other inflammatory chemicals
Fibroblasts	Rebuild damaged tissue by secreting collagen, ground substance, and other tissue components
Helper T cells*	Secrete chemotactic factors and colony-stimulating factors
Macrophages*	Clean up tissue damage; phagocytize bacteria, tissue debris, dead and dying leukocytes, and pathogens
Mast cells	Same actions as basophils
Monocytes	Emigrate into inflamed tissue and become macrophages
Neutrophils	Phagocytize bacteria; secrete bactericidal oxidizing agents; secrete cytokines that activate more leukocytes
Platelets	Secrete clotting factors and platelet-derived growth factor
Chemical Agents	
Bradykinin	A kinin that stimulates vasodilation and capillary permeability, stimulates pain receptors, and is a neutrophil chemotactic factor
Chemotactic factors	Chemicals that provide a trail that neutrophils and other leukocytes can follow to specific sites of infection and tissue injury; include bradykinin, leukotrienes, and some complement proteins
Colony-stimulating factors	Hormones that raise the WBC count by stimulating leukopoiesis
Complement*	Proteins that promote phagocytosis and cytolysis of pathogens, activate and attract neutrophils and macrophages, and stimulate basophils and mast cells to secrete inflammatory chemicals
Cytokines	Small proteins produced mainly by WBCs; have autocrine, paracrine, and endocrine roles in cellular communication; act especially in inflammation and immune responses; include interleukins, interferons, colony-stimulating factors, chemotactic factors, and others
Fibrinogen	A plasma clotting protein that filters into inflamed tissue and forms fibrin, thus coagulating tissue fluid, sequestering pathogens, and forming a temporary scaffold for tissue rebuilding
Heparin	A polysaccharide secreted by basophils and mast cells that inhibits clotting of tissue fluid within the area walled off by fibrin, thus promoting free mobility of leukocytes that attack infectious microorganisms
Histamine	An amino acid derivative produced by basophils and mast cells that stimulates vasodilation and capillary permeability
Kinins	Plasma proteins that are activated by tissue injury and stimulate vasodilation, capillary permeability, and pain; include bradykinin
Leukotrienes	Eicosanoids that stimulate vasodilation, capillary permeability, and neutrophil chemotaxis, especially in inflammation and allergy
Prostaglandins	Eicosanoids that stimulate pain, fever, and vasodilation; promote neutrophil diapedesis; and enhance histamine and bradykinin action
Selectins	Cell-adhesion molecules of endothelial cells that adhere to circulating leukocytes, promoting margination and diapedesis

* These agents of inflammation have additional roles in adaptive immunity described in table 21.4.

range, either on neighboring cells (a *paracrine*[13] effect) or on the same cell that secretes them (an *autocrine*[14] effect); these terms are distinguished from the long-distance *endocrine* effects of hormones. Cytokines include interferons, interleukins, tumor necrosis factor, chemotactic factors, and other chemicals you will soon encounter in this discussion.

Inflammation involves three major processes: mobilization of the body's defenses, containment and destruction of pathogens, and tissue cleanup and repair.

Mobilization of Defenses

The most immediate requirement for dealing with tissue injury is to get defensive leukocytes to the site quickly. Damaged tissues release cytokines that stimulate the red bone marrow to release neutrophils into circulation, raising the blood neutrophil count within hours. In addition, certain cells secrete *vasoactive* chemicals

---

[13]*para* = next to; *crin* = to secrete
[14]*auto* = self; *crin* = to secrete

that dilate the blood vessels in the area of injury. Among these are histamine, leukotrienes, and other cytokines secreted by basophils, mast cells, and cells damaged by the pathogens that triggered the inflammation. The resulting increase in local blood flow is called **hyperemia.** Hyperemia not only results in the more rapid delivery of leukocytes, but also washes toxins and metabolic wastes from the tissue more rapidly.

In addition to dilating local blood vessels, the vasoactive chemicals stimulate endothelial cells of the blood capillaries and venules to contract slightly, widening the gaps between them and increasing capillary permeability. This allows for the easier movement of fluid, leukocytes, and plasma proteins from the bloodstream into the surrounding tissue. Among the helpful proteins filtering from the blood are complement, antibodies, and clotting factors, all of which aid in combating pathogens.

Endothelial cells actively recruit leukocytes. In the area of injury, they produce cell-adhesion molecules called **selectins,** which make their membranes sticky, and snag leukocytes arriving in the bloodstream. Leukocytes adhere loosely to the selectins and slowly tumble along the endothelium, sometimes coating it so thickly they obstruct blood flow. This adhesion to the vessel wall is called **margination.** The leukocytes then crawl through the gaps between the endothelial cells—an action called **diapedesis**[15] or **emigration**—and enter the tissue fluid of the damaged tissue **(fig. 21.18).** Most diapedesis occurs across the walls of the postcapillary venules. Cells and chemicals that have left the bloodstream are said to be *extravasated.*[16]

In the events that have already transpired, we can see the basis for the four cardinal signs of inflammation: (1) The heat results from the hyperemia; (2) redness is also due to hyperemia and in some cases, such as sunburn, to extravasated erythrocytes in the tissue; (3) swelling (edema) is due to the increased fluid filtration from the capillaries; and (4) pain results from direct injury to the nerves, pressure on the nerves from the edema, and stimulation of pain receptors by prostaglandins, some bacterial toxins, and a kinin called **bradykinin.**

▶▶▶ APPLY WHAT YOU KNOW

Review eicosanoid synthesis (fig. 17.24) and explain why aspirin eases the pain of inflammation.

Containment and Destruction of Pathogens

One priority in inflammation is to prevent pathogens from spreading through the body. The fibrinogen that filters into the tissue fluid clots in areas adjacent to the injury, forming a sticky mesh that sequesters (walls off and isolates) bacteria and other microorganisms. Heparin, the anticoagulant, prevents clotting in the immediate area of the injury, so bacteria or other pathogens are essentially trapped in a fluid pocket surrounded by a gelatinous

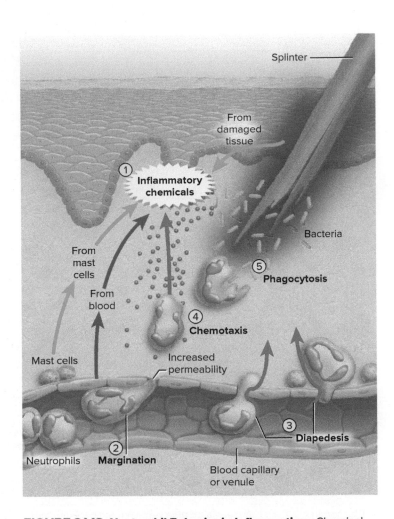

FIGURE 21.18 Neutrophil Behavior in Inflammation. Chemical messengers are released by basophils, mast cells, blood plasma, and damaged tissue. These inflammatory chemicals stimulate leukocyte margination (adhesion to the blood vessel wall), diapedesis (crawling through gaps in the wall), chemotaxis (movement toward the source of the inflammatory chemicals), and phagocytosis (engulfing bacteria or other pathogens).

capsule of clotted fluid. They are attacked by antibodies, phagocytes, and other defenses, while the surrounding areas of clotted tissue fluid prevent them from easily escaping this onslaught.

The chief enemies of bacteria are neutrophils, which accumulate in the inflamed tissue within an hour. After emigrating from the bloodstream, they exhibit **chemotaxis**—attraction to chemicals *(chemotactic factors)* that guide them to the site of injury or infection. These include bradykinin, leukotrienes, ATP released by dying cells, and ADP released by platelets. As they encounter bacteria, neutrophils avidly phagocytize and digest them, and destroy many more by the respiratory burst described earlier. The major stages of neutrophil action are summarized in figure 21.18.

Neutrophils also recruit macrophages and additional neutrophils by secreting cytokines, like shouting "Over here!" to bring in reinforcements. Activated macrophages and T cells in the inflamed tissue secrete cytokines called *colony-stimulating factors,* which promote the production of more leukocytes (leukopoiesis) by the red bone marrow. Within a few hours of onset, the neutrophil count

---

[15]*dia* = through; *pedesis* = stepping
[16]*extra* = outside; *vas* = vessel

in the blood can rise from the normal 4,000 or 5,000 cells/μL to as high as 25,000 cells/μL, a condition called **neutrophilia.** In the case of allergy or parasitic infection, an elevated eosinophil count, or **eosinophilia,** may also occur. The task of eosinophils was described earlier.

Tissue Cleanup and Repair

Monocytes are major agents of tissue cleanup and repair. They arrive within 8 to 12 hours, emigrate from the bloodstream, and turn into macrophages. Macrophages engulf and destroy bacteria, damaged host cells, and dead and dying neutrophils. They also act as antigen-presenting cells, activating the processes of adaptive immunity.

Edema also contributes to tissue cleanup. The swelling compresses veins and reduces venous drainage, while it forces open the valves of lymphatic capillaries and promotes lymphatic drainage. The lymphatics can collect and remove bacteria, dead cells, proteins, and tissue debris better than blood capillaries or venules can.

As the battle progresses, all of the neutrophils and most of the macrophages die. These dead cells, other tissue debris, and tissue fluid form a pool of yellowish fluid called **pus,** which accumulates in a tissue cavity called an **abscess.**[17] Pus is usually absorbed, but sometimes it forms a blister between the epidermis and dermis and may be released by its rupture.

Blood platelets and endothelial cells in an area of injury secrete **platelet-derived growth factor,** an agent that stimulates fibroblasts to multiply and synthesize collagen. At the same time, hyperemia delivers oxygen, amino acids, and other necessities of protein synthesis, while the heat of inflamed tissue increases metabolic rate and the speed of mitosis and tissue repair. The fibrin clot in the tissue may provide a scaffold for reconstruction. Pain also contributes importantly to recovery. It is an important alarm signal that calls our attention to the injury and makes us limit the use of a body part so it has a chance to rest and heal.

BEFORE YOU GO ON

Answer the following questions to test your understanding of the preceding section:

6. Earlier it was stated that innate immunity employs protective proteins, protective cells, and protective processes. Give three examples of each.

7. What are macrophages? Give four examples and state where they are found.

8. How do interferons and the complement system protect against disease?

9. Summarize the benefits of fever and the limits of these benefits.

10. List the cardinal signs of inflammation and state the cause of each.

---

[17]*ab* = away; *scess* (from *cedere*) = to go

21.3 Adaptive Immunity— General Aspects

Expected Learning Outcomes
When you have completed this section, you should be able to

a. identify the three distinguishing characteristics of adaptive immunity;

b. contrast cellular and humoral immunity, active and passive immunity, and natural and artificial immunity;

c. describe the chemical properties of antigens;

d. describe the structure and five types of antibodies;

e. describe and contrast the development of T and B lymphocytes; and

f. describe the general roles played by lymphocytes, antigen-presenting cells, and interleukins in the immune response.

The remainder of this chapter is concerned with *adaptive immunity* (the third line of defense). Adaptive immunity was noticed even in the fifth century BCE, when Greek historian Thucydides remarked that people who recovered from a disease often became immune to that one but remained susceptible to others. Adaptive immunity is now defined by three characteristics that distinguish it from the three that were itemized earlier (local, nonspecific, and lacking memory) for innate immunity:

1. It has a **systemic effect.** When an adaptive response is mounted against a particular threat such as a bacterial infection, it acts throughout the body to defeat that pathogen wherever it may be found.

2. It exhibits **specificity.** Adaptive immunity is directed against a specific pathogen. Immunity to one disease such as chickenpox does not confer immunity to others such as tetanus.

3. It has a **memory.** When reexposed to the same pathogen, the body reacts so quickly that there is no noticeable illness. The reaction time for inflammation and other innate defenses, by contrast, is just as long for later exposures as for the initial one.

21.3a Forms of Adaptive Immunity

In the late 1800s, it was discovered that immunity can be transferred from one animal to another by way of the blood serum. In the mid-1900s, however, it was found that serum doesn't always confer immunity; sometimes only donor lymphocytes do so. Thus, biologists came to recognize two types of adaptive immunity, called cellular and humoral immunity, although the two interact extensively and often respond to the same pathogen.

Cellular (cell-mediated) immunity employs lymphocytes that directly attack and destroy foreign cells or diseased host cells. It is a means of ridding the body of pathogens that reside inside human cells, where they are inaccessible to antibodies: intracellular viruses, bacteria, yeasts, and protozoans, for example. Cellular immunity also acts against parasitic worms, cancer cells, and cells of transplanted tissues and organs.

Humoral (antibody-mediated) immunity employs antibodies, which don't directly destroy pathogens but tag them for destruction by mechanisms described later. The expression *humoral* refers to antibodies dissolved in the body fluids ("humors"). Humoral immunity is effective against extracellular viruses, bacteria, yeasts, protozoans, and molecular (noncellular) disease agents such as toxins, venoms, and allergens. In the unnatural event of a mismatched blood transfusion, it also destroys foreign erythrocytes.

Note that humoral immunity works mainly against the *extracellular* stages of infectious microorganisms. When such microorganisms invade host cells, they are usually sheltered from attack by serum antibodies. However, the *intracellular* stages are still vulnerable to cellular immunity, which destroys them by killing the cells that harbor them. Furthermore, certain antibodies in the IgE class (explained later) bind to parasitic worms and aid in their destruction. Thus, humoral and cellular immunity sometimes attack the same microorganism in different ways or at different points in its life cycle. After our discussion of the details of the two processes, you will find cellular and humoral immunity summarized and compared in table 21.5.

Other ways of classifying immunity are active versus passive and natural versus artificial. In *active immunity,* the body makes its own antibodies or T cells against a pathogen, whereas in *passive immunity,* the body acquires them from another person or an animal that is immune to the pathogen. Either type of immunity can occur naturally or, for treatment and prevention purposes, it can be induced artificially. Thus we can recognize four classes of immunity under this scheme:

1. **Natural active immunity.** This is the production of one's own antibodies or T cells as a result of natural exposure to an antigen.

2. **Artificial active immunity.** This is the production of one's own antibodies or T cells as a result of **vaccination** against diseases such as smallpox, tetanus, or influenza. A **vaccine** consists of either dead or *attenuated* (weakened) pathogens that can stimulate an immune response but cause little or no discomfort or disease. In some cases, periodic *booster shots* are given to restimulate immune memory and maintain a high level of protection (tetanus boosters, for example). Vaccination has eliminated smallpox worldwide and greatly reduced the incidence of life-threatening childhood diseases, but many people continue to die from influenza and other diseases that could be prevented by vaccination. Even polio, once nearly eradicated worldwide, has lately made a comeback in some countries because of antivaccination superstition and politics.

3. **Natural passive immunity.** This is a temporary immunity that results from acquiring antibodies produced by another person. The only natural ways for this to happen are for a fetus to acquire antibodies from the mother through the placenta before birth, or for a baby to acquire them during breast-feeding.

4. **Artificial passive immunity.** This is a temporary immunity that results from the injection of an *immune serum* obtained from another person or from animals (such as horses) that have antibodies against a certain pathogen. Immune serum is used for emergency treatment of snakebites, botulism, tetanus, rabies, and other diseases.

Only the two forms of active immunity involve memory and thus provide future protection. Passive immunity typically lasts for only 2 or 3 weeks, until the acquired antibody is degraded. The remaining discussion is based on natural active immunity.

21.3b Antigens

An **antigen**[18] **(Ag)** is any molecule that triggers an immune response. Some antigens are free molecules such as venoms, toxins, and foodborne substances; others are components of plasma membranes and bacterial cell walls. Small universal molecules such as glucose and amino acids aren't antigenic; if they were, our immune systems would attack the nutrients and other molecules essential to our very survival. Most antigens have molecular weights over 10,000 amu and have enough structural complexity and variability to be unique to each individual: proteins, polysaccharides, glycoproteins, and glycolipids. Their uniqueness enables the body to distinguish its own ("self") molecules from those of any other individual or organism ("nonself"). The immune system learns to distinguish self-antigens from nonself-antigens so that it normally attacks only nonself-antigens.

Only certain regions of an antigen molecule, called **epitopes (antigenic determinants),** stimulate immune responses. One antigen molecule typically has several different epitopes, however, that can stimulate the simultaneous production of different antibodies.

Some molecules, called **haptens**[19] **(incomplete antigens),** are too small to be antigenic in themselves, but they can stimulate an immune response by binding to a host macromolecule and creating a unique complex that the body recognizes as foreign. After the first exposure, the hapten alone may stimulate an immune response without needing to bind to a host molecule. Many people are allergic to haptens in cosmetics, detergents, industrial chemicals, poison ivy, and animal dander. The most common drug allergy is to penicillin—a hapten that binds to host proteins in allergic individuals, creating a complex that binds to mast cells and triggers massive release of histamine and other inflammatory chemicals. This can cause death from *anaphylactic shock.*

21.3c Antibodies

Antibodies (Abs), also called **immunoglobulins (Igs),** are proteins in the gamma globulin class that play a variety of roles in defense. Some of them are integral proteins in the plasma membranes of basophils and mast cells and thus function in innate immunity. Others, with roles in adaptive immunity, are membrane proteins of B lymphocytes or *soluble antibodies* dissolved in body fluids such as blood plasma, lymph, mucus, saliva, intestinal secretions, tears, and breast milk. We have said much about antibodies already in chapter 18 (blood types) and this chapter; it is now time to take a closer look at what they are and how they work.

The basic structural unit of an antibody, called an **antibody monomer,** is composed of four polypeptides linked by disulfide (—S—S—) bonds **(fig. 21.19).** These include two **heavy chains** about 400 amino acids long and two **light chains** about half that long. Each heavy chain has a hinge region where the antibody is bent, giving the monomer a T or Y shape.

---

[18]acronym from *anti*body *gen*erating
[19]from *haptein* = to fasten

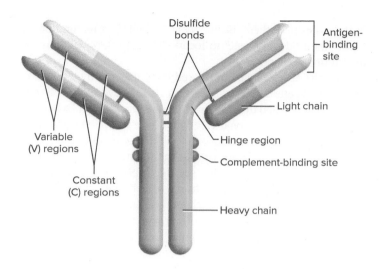

FIGURE 21.19 Antibody Structure. A molecule of IgG, a monomer.

All four chains have a **variable (V) region** that gives an antibody its uniqueness. The V regions of each heavy and light chain pair combine to form an **antigen-binding site** on each arm. These sites are where the antibody attaches to the epitopes of antigen molecules. The rest of each chain is a **constant (C) region,** which has the same amino acid sequence, or nearly so, in all antibodies of a given class (within one person). The C region determines the mechanism of an antibody's action—for example, whether it can bind complement proteins.

There are five classes of antibodies named **IgA, IgD, IgE, IgG,** and **IgM** after the structures of their C regions (*alpha, delta, epsilon, gamma,* and *mu*). As shown in **table 21.2,** IgD, IgE, and IgG are monomers; IgA has a monomer form as well as a *dimer* composed of two cojoined monomers; and IgM has a monomer form as well as a *pentamer* composed of five monomers. The surface antigen receptors of B cells are IgD and IgM molecules. IgG is particularly important in the immunity of the newborn because it crosses the placenta with relative ease. Thus, it transfers immunity from the mother to her fetus. In addition, an infant acquires some maternal IgA through breast milk and colostrum (the fluid secreted for the first 2 or 3 days of breast-feeding).

The human immune system is believed capable of producing at least 10 billion and perhaps up to 1 trillion different antibodies. Any one person has a much smaller subset of these, but such an enormous potential helps to explain why we can deal with the tremendous diversity of antigens that exist in our environment. Yet such huge numbers may seem puzzling, because we're accustomed to thinking of each protein in the body being encoded by one gene, and we have only slightly more than 20,000 genes, most of which have nothing to do with immunity. How can so few genes generate so many antibodies? Obviously there cannot be a different gene for each one. One means of generating diversity is that the genome contains several hundred DNA segments that are shuffled and combined in various ways to produce antibody genes unique to each clone of B cells. This process is called **somatic recombination,** because it forms new combinations of DNA base sequences in somatic (nonreproductive) cells. Another mechanism

TABLE 21.2	The Five Classes of Antibodies		
Class	**Structure**		**Location and Function**
IgA	Monomer	Dimer	Found as a monomer in blood plasma and mainly as a dimer in mucus, tears, milk, saliva, and intestinal secretions. Sometimes also forms trimers and tetramers. Prevents pathogens from adhering to epithelia and penetrating underlying tissues. Provides passive immunity to the newborn.
IgD	Monomer		A transmembrane protein of B cells; functions in activation of B cells by antigens.
IgE	Monomer		A transmembrane protein of basophils and mast cells. Stimulates them to release histamine and other mediators of inflammation and allergy; important in immediate hypersensitivity reactions and in attracting eosinophils to sites of parasitic infection.
IgG	Monomer		Constitutes about 80% of circulating antibodies in blood plasma. The predominant antibody secreted in the secondary immune response. IgG and IgM are the only antibodies with significant complement-fixation activity. Crosses placenta and confers temporary immunity on the fetus. Includes the anti-D antibodies of the Rh blood group.
IgM	Monomer	Pentamer	Constitutes about 10% of circulating antibodies in plasma. Monomer is a transmembrane protein of B cells, where it functions as part of the antigen receptor. Pentamer occurs in blood plasma and lymph. The predominant antibody secreted in the primary immune response; very strong agglutinating and complement-fixation abilities; includes the anti-A and anti-B agglutinins of the ABO blood group.

of generating diversity is that B cells in the germinal centers of lymphatic nodules undergo exceptionally high rates of mutation, a process called **somatic hypermutation**—not just recombining preexisting DNA but creating wholly new DNA sequences. These and other mechanisms explain how we can produce such a tremendous variety of antibodies with a limited number of genes.

21.3d Lymphocytes

The major cells of the adaptive immune system are lymphocytes, macrophages, and dendritic cells, which are especially concentrated at strategic places such as the lymphatic organs, skin, and mucous membranes. Lymphocytes fall into three classes: natural killer (NK) cells, T lymphocytes, and B lymphocytes. We have already discussed the role of NK cells in innate immunity. Here, we must take a closer look at T and B lymphocytes, the principal agents of adaptive immunity.

T Lymphocytes (T Cells)

The life history of a T cell basically involves three stages and three anatomical stations in the body **(fig. 21.20).** We can loosely think

of these stages as their "birth," their "training" or maturation, and finally their "deployment" to locations where they will carry out their immune function.

T cells are produced in the red bone marrow by the hematopoietic stem cells described in section 18.1e. Newborn T cells enter the bloodstream and travel to the thymus—the "school" where they mature into fully functional T cells and face two harsh "graduation exams" that test their usefulness to the immune system.

On arrival, T cells go first to the thymic cortex and cluster on the cortical epithelial cells (see fig. 21.9). The epithelial cells test these young lymphocytes to see which ones will be capable of later recognizing foreign antigens and antigen-presenting cells (APCs). If a T cell possesses the proper receptors to recognize them, it receives a protective signal from the epithelial cell that spares its life. T cells that can't recognize them receive no life-sparing signal. They do, however, get a chance to "retake the test"; they can reshuffle the DNA for their antigen receptors and try again. But if they fail once more, they're doomed. Within 3 or 4 days, these useless T cells die by apoptosis and the cortical macrophages phagocytize them. T cells that pass the test, demonstrating their ability to respond to antigens, are called **immunocompetent.**

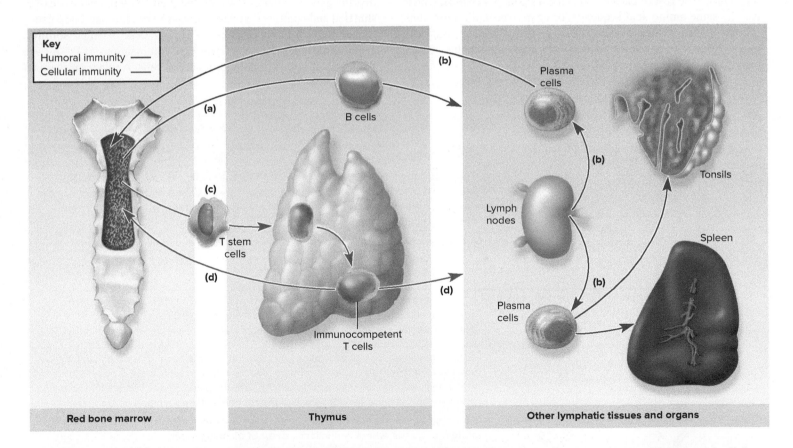

FIGURE 21.20 The Life History and Migrations of B and T Cells. Humoral immunity is represented by the violet pathways and cellular immunity by the red. (a) B cells achieve immunocompetence in the red bone marrow (left), and many emigrate to lymphatic tissues and organs, including the lymph nodes, tonsils, and spleen (right). (b) Plasma cells develop in the lymph nodes (among other sites) and emigrate to the bone marrow and other lymphatic organs, where they spend a few days secreting antibodies. (c) T stem cells emigrate from the bone marrow and attain immunocompetence in the thymus. (d) Immunocompetent T cells emigrate from the thymus and recolonize the bone marrow or colonize various lymphatic organs (right).

The cortical process of selecting the few T cells that prove their immunocompetence is called **positive selection.** Only a small percentage of them pass this cortical "exit exam" and get the opportunity to move on to "graduate school," the medulla. This explains why the medulla of the thymus looks so much lighter than the cortex in histological sections (see fig. 21.9b), somewhat like graduate school enrollments compared to undergraduate.

But like graduate students, the T cells in the medulla face yet another difficult test. Even more T cells are doomed to fail and possibly die. Here, their examiners are macrophages and reticular cells. Unlike the cortical epithelial cells, these are derived from bone marrow and test the T cells in a different way. Their role is to weed out T cells that react to the antigens of one's own body or to one's own APCs even in the absence of antigen. Such overreactive T cells could be a future threat if they attacked one's own tissues. Owing to the imperfections of the immune system, this sometimes happens anyway, causing notorious *autoimmune diseases* described later in section 21.6b. But to minimize that risk, macrophages and reticular cells present the T cells with self-antigens and antigen-binding proteins called MHCs (explained shortly). In one theory, T cells that react too strongly to these are killed by apoptosis. There is also evidence, however, that the thymic corpuscles secrete a signal (cytokine) that renders these self-reactive T cells permanently inactive (a state called **anergy**[20]) or converts them to *regulatory T cells* that moderate the activity of the *cytotoxic (killer) T cells* that actually attack foreign cells. In any event, elimination or conversion of self-reactive T cells is called **negative selection,** and it leaves the immune system in a state of **self-tolerance**—restraint from attacking one's own tissues.

Only about 2% of the T cells survive both positive and negative selection; 98% are eliminated, especially by positive selection. (And you think *your* final exams are tough!) The few survivors multiply and form *clones* of identical T cells programmed to respond to a particular antigen. These cells, which are immunocompetent but haven't yet encountered an enemy (foreign antigen), constitute the **naive lymphocyte pool.** Naive T cells leave the thymus by way of blood and lymphatic vessels (there is no blood–thymus barrier in the medulla), disperse throughout the body, and colonize lymphatic tissues and organs everywhere (the lymph nodes, tonsils, bone marrow, and so forth) (fig. 21.20d). They become especially concentrated in the deep cortex of the lymph nodes. They are now ready to do battle.

B Lymphocytes (B Cells)

B cell maturation occurs entirely within the red bone marrow. Adults produce about 50 million B cells per day, but only 10% enter the general circulation. The other 90% are apparently destroyed in the course of positive and negative selection in the bone marrow. Self-tolerant B cells that survive selection go on to multiply and generate immunocompetent B cell clones. These cells disperse throughout the body and colonize the same organs

as T cells (fig. 21.20a, b). They are abundant in the lymphatic nodules of the lymph nodes and in the spleen, bone marrow, and mucous membranes.

21.3e Antigen-Presenting Cells

Although the function of T cells is to recognize and attack foreign antigens, they usually can't do this on their own. They require the help of **antigen-presenting cells (APCs).** In addition to their other roles, dendritic cells, macrophages, reticular cells, and B cells function as APCs.

APC function hinges on a family of genes called the **major histocompatibility complex (MHC)** on chromosome 6. These genes code for **MHC proteins**—proteins on the APC surface that are shaped a little like hotdog buns, with an elongated groove for holding the "hotdog" of the foreign antigen. MHC proteins are structurally unique to every person except for identical twins. They act as "identification tags" that label every cell of your body as belonging to you.

When an APC encounters an antigen, it internalizes it by endocytosis, digests it into molecular fragments, and displays the relevant fragments (its epitopes) in the grooves of the MHC proteins **(fig. 21.21a).** These steps are called **antigen processing.** Wandering T cells regularly inspect APCs for displayed antigens **(fig. 21.21b).** If an APC displays a self-antigen, the T cells disregard it. If it displays a nonself-antigen, however, they initiate an attack. APCs thus alert the immune system to the presence of a foreign antigen. The key to a successful defense is then to quickly mobilize immune cells against it.

With so many cell types involved in immunity, it's not surprising that they require chemical messengers to coordinate their activities. Lymphocytes and APCs talk to each other with cytokines called **interleukins**[21]—chemical signals from one leukocyte (or leukocyte derivative) to another.

With this introduction to the main actors in immunity, we can now look at the more specific features of cellular and humoral immunity. Since the terminology of immune cells and chemicals is quite complex, you may find it helpful to refer often to table 21.4 as you read the following discussions.

BEFORE YOU GO ON

Answer the following questions to test your understanding of the preceding section:

11. How does adaptive immunity differ from innate immunity?

12. How does humoral immunity differ from cellular immunity?

13. Contrast active and passive immunity. Give natural and artificial examples of each.

14. What structural properties distinguish antigenic molecules from those that are not antigenic?

15. Describe the structure of an antibody monomer and state what part of it binds to antigens.

---

[20]*an* = without; *erg* = action, work

[21]*inter* = between; *leuk* = leukocytes

16. What is an immunocompetent lymphocyte? What does a lymphocyte have to produce in order to become immunocompetent?

17. What role does the thymus play in the life history of a T cell?

18. What role does an antigen-presenting cell play in the activation of a T cell?

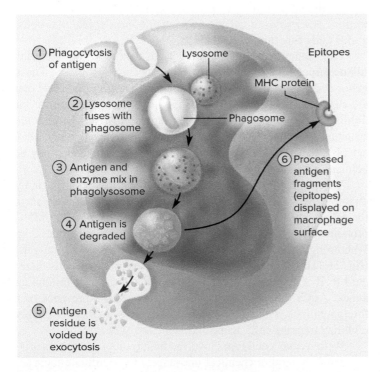

① Phagocytosis of antigen
② Lysosome fuses with phagosome
③ Antigen and enzyme mix in phagolysosome
④ Antigen is degraded
⑤ Antigen residue is voided by exocytosis
⑥ Processed antigen fragments (epitopes) displayed on macrophage surface

Lysosome
Epitopes
MHC protein
Phagosome

(a)

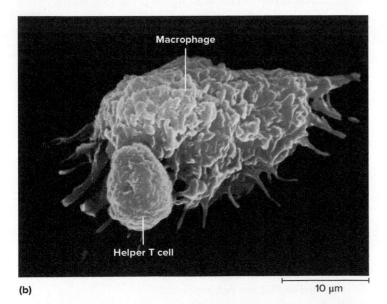

Macrophage

Helper T cell

10 μm

(b)

FIGURE 21.21 The Action of Antigen-Presenting Cells (APCs).
(a) Stages in the processing and presentation of an antigen by an APC such as a macrophage. (b) Macrophage presenting processed antigen to helper T cell.

b: CNRI/Science Source

21.4 Cellular Immunity A&PR

Expected Learning Outcomes

When you have completed this section, you should be able to

a. list the types of lymphocytes involved in cellular immunity and describe the roles they play;

b. describe the process of antigen presentation and T cell activation;

c. describe how T cells destroy enemy cells; and

d. explain the role of memory cells in cellular immunity.

Cellular (cell-mediated) immunity is a form of adaptive immunity in which T lymphocytes directly attack and destroy diseased or foreign cells, and the immune system remembers the antigens of those invaders and prevents them from causing disease in the future. There are at least 15 kinds of T cells with new ones being discovered continually, but the 4 principal types important to our discussion are these:

1. **Cytotoxic T (T_C) cells** are the "effectors" of cellular immunity that carry out the attack on foreign cells.

2. **Helper T (T_H) cells** promote the action of T_C cells as well as play key roles in humoral and innate immunity. All other T cells are involved in cellular immunity only.

3. **Regulatory T (T_R) cells,** or **T-regs,** limit the immune response by inhibiting multiplication and cytokine secretion by other T cells. Once a pathogen is defeated, it is important to down-regulate T_C activity, because otherwise T_C cells would continue to produce inflammatory cytokines that could cause extensive tissue damage in the long term. T_R cells prevent this and reduce the risk of developing autoimmune diseases.

4. **Memory T (T_M) cells** are descended from T_C cells and are responsible for memory in cellular immunity. Thus, they sustain the body's vigilance against a given pathogen without causing the damage that a persistent population of T_C cells would do.

T_C cells are also known as T8, CD8, or CD8+ cells because they have a surface glycoprotein called CD8. T_H and T_R cells are also known as T4, CD4, or CD4+ cells, after their glycoprotein, CD4. (*CD* stands for *cluster of differentiation,* a classification system for many cell surface molecules.) These glycoproteins are cell-adhesion molecules that enable T cells to bind to other cells in the events to be described shortly.

Both cellular and humoral immunity occur in three stages that we can think of as recognition, attack, and memory (or "the three *R*s of immunity"—recognize, react, and remember). In cellular immunity, the events of each stage are as follows.

21.4a Recognition

The recognition phase has two aspects: antigen presentation and T cell activation.

Antigen Presentation

When an antigen-presenting cell (APC) encounters and processes an antigen, it typically migrates to the nearest lymph node and displays it to the T cells. Cytotoxic and helper T cells patrol the lymph nodes and other tissues as if looking for trouble. When they encounter a cell displaying an antigen on an MHC protein, they initiate an immune response. T cells respond to two classes of MHC proteins:

1. *MHC-I proteins* occur on every nucleated cell of the body (not erythrocytes). These proteins are constantly produced by the cell and transported to the plasma membrane. Along the way, they pick up small peptides in the cytoplasm and display them once they are installed in the membrane. If the peptides are normal self-antigens, they don't elicit a T cell response. If they are viral proteins or abnormal antigens made by cancer cells, however, they do. In this case, the Ag–MHC protein complex is like a tag on the host cell that says, "I'm diseased; kill me." Infected or malignant cells are then destroyed before they can do further harm to the body.

2. *MHC-II proteins* (also called *human leukocyte antigens, HLAs*) occur only on APCs and display only foreign antigens.

As T cells mature in the thymus and undergo the positive and negative selection described earlier, they become limited to recognizing a specific class of MHC protein. This process, called **MHC restriction,** results in T_C cells responding only to MHC-I proteins and T_H cells only to MHC-II **(table 21.3).**

T Cell Activation

T cell activation is shown in **figure 21.22.** It begins when a T_C or T_H cell binds to an MHC protein displaying an epitope that the T cell is programmed to recognize. Before the response can go any further, the T cell must bind to another protein, related to interleukins, found on the surface of APCs in damaged or infected tissues. In a sense, the T cell has to check twice to see if it really has bound to an APC displaying a suspicious antigen. This signaling process, called **costimulation,** helps to ensure that the immune system doesn't launch an attack in the absence of an enemy, which could turn against one's own body with injurious consequences.

Lack of costimulation drives the T cell into *anergy,* a state of inactivity and ineffectiveness. Successful costimulation, in

TABLE 21.3	Comparison of the Responses of Cytotoxic and Helper T Cells	
Characteristic	**T_C Cells**	**T_H Cells**
Cells capable of stimulating a response	Any nucleated cell	Antigen-presenting cells
MHC protein	MHC-I	MHC-II

① **Antigen recognition**
T cell binds to an APC displaying an antigen fragment (epitope).

② **Costimulation**
T cell binds to a second protein on the APC.

③ **Clonal selection**
T cell undergoes repeated mitosis and produces a large number of effector cells and memory T cells.

④ **Attack**
Effector T_C cells attack and destroy abnormal cells with a lethal hit; T_H cells secrete interleukins that stimulate multiple forms of attack.

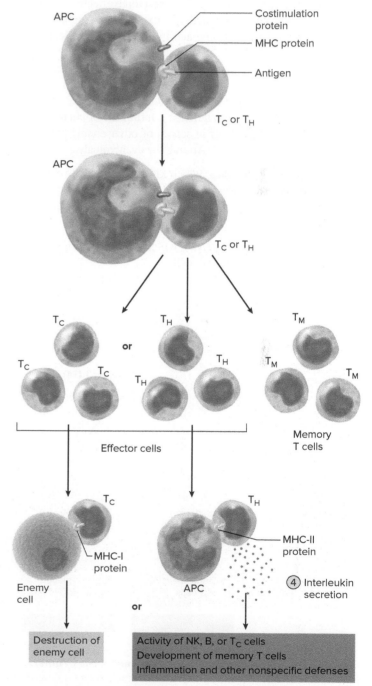

FIGURE 21.22 T Cell Activation.

contrast, activates the process of **clonal selection:** The T cell undergoes repeated mitosis, giving rise to a clone of identical T cells programmed against the same epitope. Some cells in the clone become effector cells that carry out an immune attack, and some become memory T (T_M) cells.

21.4b Attack

Helper and cytotoxic T cells play different roles in the attack phase. Helper T (T_H) cells are necessary for most immune responses. They play a central coordinating role in both humoral and cellular immunity **(fig. 21.23).** When a T_H cell recognizes an Ag–MHC protein complex, it secretes interleukins that exert three effects: (1) to attract neutrophils and natural killer cells; (2) to attract macrophages, stimulate their phagocytic activity, and inhibit them from leaving the area; and (3) to stimulate T and B cell mitosis and maturation.

Cytotoxic T (T_C) cells are the only T lymphocytes that directly attack and kill other cells **(fig. 21.24).** When a T_C cell recognizes a complex of antigen and MHC-I protein on a diseased or foreign cell, it "docks" on that cell, delivers a **lethal hit** of chemicals that will destroy it, and goes off in search of other enemy cells while the chemicals do their work. Among these chemicals are

- *perforin* and *granzymes,* which kill the target cell in the same manner as we saw earlier for NK cells (see fig. 21.16);

- *interferons,* which inhibit viral replication and recruit and activate macrophages, among other effects; and

- *tumor necrosis factor (TNF),* which aids in macrophage activation and kills cancer cells.

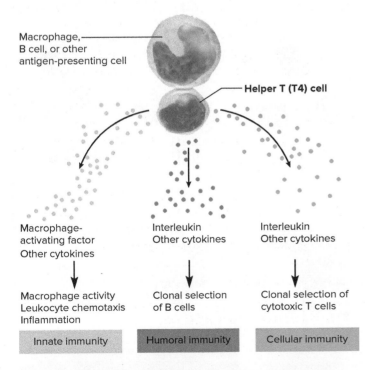

FIGURE 21.23 The Central Role of Helper T Cells in Innate, Humoral, and Cellular Immunity.

❓ *Why does AIDS reduce the effectiveness of all three defenses listed across the bottom of the figure?* (Hint: *See section 21.6c.*)

Labels in figure:
Macrophage, B cell, or other antigen-presenting cell
Helper T (T4) cell
Macrophage-activating factor / Other cytokines
Interleukin / Other cytokines
Interleukin / Other cytokines
Macrophage activity / Leukocyte chemotaxis / Inflammation
Clonal selection of B cells
Clonal selection of cytotoxic T cells
Innate immunity | Humoral immunity | Cellular immunity

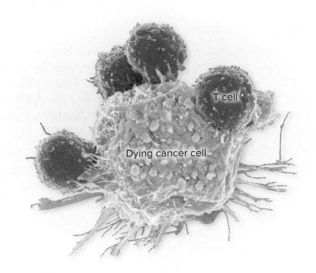

FIGURE 21.24 Destruction of a Cancer Cell by Cytotoxic T Cells.
Steve Gschmeissner/Science Source

Labels: T cell; Dying cancer cell

As more and more cells are recruited by helper T cells, the immune response exerts an overwhelming force against the pathogen. The **primary response,** seen on first exposure to a particular pathogen, peaks in about a week and then gradually declines.

▶▶▶APPLY WHAT YOU KNOW

How is a cytotoxic T cell like a natural killer (NK) cell? How are they different?

21.4c Memory

The primary response is followed by immune memory. Following clonal selection, some T cells become memory cells. These cells are long-lived and much more numerous than naive T cells. Aside from their sheer numbers, they also require fewer steps to be activated, and therefore respond to antigens more rapidly. Upon reexposure to the same pathogen later in life, memory cells mount a quick attack called the **T cell recall response.** This time-saving response destroys a pathogen so quickly that no noticeable illness occurs—that is, the person is immune to the disease.

BEFORE YOU GO ON

Answer the following questions to test your understanding of the preceding section:

19. Name four types of lymphocytes involved in cellular immunity. Which of these is also essential to humoral immunity?

20. What are the three phases of an immune response?

21. Explain why cytotoxic T cells are activated by a broader range of host cells than are helper T cells.

22. Describe some ways in which cytotoxic T cells destroy target cells.

21.5 Humoral Immunity

Expected Learning Outcomes

When you have completed this section, you should be able to

a. explain how B cells recognize and respond to an antigen;

b. describe the actions of antibodies against disease agents;

c. explain the mechanism of memory in humoral immunity; and

d. compare and contrast cellular and humoral immunity.

Humoral immunity is a more indirect method of defense than cellular immunity. Instead of directly attacking enemy cells, the B lymphocytes of humoral immunity produce antibodies that bind to antigens and tag them for destruction by other means. But like cellular immunity, humoral immunity works in three stages: recognition, attack, and memory.

21.5a Recognition

An immunocompetent B cell has thousands of surface receptors for one antigen. B cell activation begins when an antigen binds to several of these receptors, links them together, and is taken into the cell by receptor-mediated endocytosis (compare fig. 3.21). One reason small molecules are not antigenic is that they're too small to link multiple receptors together. After endocytosis, the B cell processes (digests) the antigen, links some of the epitopes to its MHC-II proteins, and displays these on the cell surface. Thus, the B cell itself acts as an antigen-presenting cell.

Usually, the B cell response goes no further unless a helper T cell binds to this Ag–MHC protein complex. (Some B cells are directly activated by antigens without the help of a T_H cell.) When a T_H cell binds to the complex, it secretes interleukins that activate the B cell. This triggers clonal selection—B cell mitosis giving rise to a battalion of identical B cells programmed against that antigen **(fig. 21.25).**

Most cells of the clone differentiate into **plasma cells.** These are larger than B cells and contain an abundance of rough endoplasmic reticulum **(fig. 21.26).** Plasma cells develop mainly in the germinal centers of the lymphatic nodules of the lymph nodes. About 10% of them remain in the lymph nodes, but the rest leave the nodes, take up residence in the bone marrow and elsewhere, and there produce antibodies until they die.

The job of a plasma cell is to synthesize and secrete antibodies, which it churns out at the remarkable rate of 2,000 molecules per second over a life span of 4 to 5 days. These antibodies travel throughout the body in the blood and other body fluids. The first time you're exposed to a particular antigen, your plasma cells produce mainly an antibody class called IgM. In later exposures to the same antigen, they produce mainly IgG.

21.5b Attack

Once released by a plasma cell, antibodies use four mechanisms to render antigens harmless:

1. **Neutralization** means the masking of critical regions of an antigen molecule by antibodies. Only certain regions of an antigen are pathogenic—for example, the parts of a toxin molecule or virus that enable these agents to bind to human cells. Antibodies can neutralize an antigen by masking these active regions.

2. **Complement fixation** is an action in which antibodies bind complement proteins to an enemy cell, leading to its destruction. IgM and IgG bind to enemy cells and change shape, exposing their complement-binding sites (see fig. 21.19). This initiates the binding of complement to the enemy cell surface and leads to inflammation, phagocytosis, immune clearance, and cytolysis, as described earlier (see fig. 21.14). Complement fixation is the primary mechanism of defense against foreign cells such as bacteria and mismatched erythrocytes. It opsonizes bacteria and makes it easier for phagocytes to ingest and destroy them.

3. **Agglutination** is the clumping of enemy cells by antibodies, described earlier in the discussion of ABO and Rh blood types (see section 18.3a). It is effective not only in mismatched blood transfusions, but more importantly as a defense against bacteria. An antibody molecule has 2 to 10 binding sites; thus, it can bind to antigen molecules on two or more enemy cells at once and stick them together **(fig. 21.27a).** This immobilizes microbes and other alien cells and prevents them from spreading through the tissues. Further, neutrophils and macrophages can phagocytize agglutinated clusters of bacteria more efficiently than phagocytizing bacteria one at a time.

4. **Precipitation** is a similar process in which antigen molecules (not whole cells) are clumped by adhesion to antibodies **(fig. 21.27b).** This creates large Ag–Ab complexes that can be removed by immune clearance or phagocytized by eosinophils.

You will note that antibodies don't directly destroy an antigen in any of these mechanisms. They render it harmless by the mechanisms just stated and mark it for destruction by other agents such as complement, macrophages, or eosinophils.

▶▶▶APPLY WHAT YOU KNOW

Explain why IgM has a stronger power of agglutination than antibodies of any other class.

21.5c Memory

When a person is exposed to a particular antigen for the first time, the humoral immune reaction is called the **primary response.** The appearance of protective antibodies is delayed

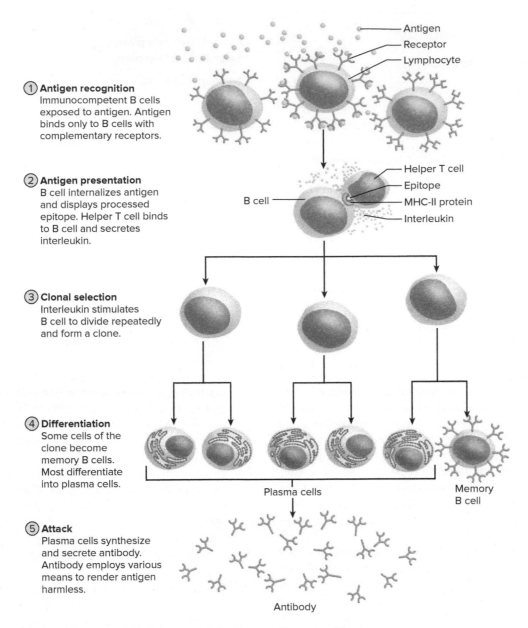

① **Antigen recognition**
Immunocompetent B cells exposed to antigen. Antigen binds only to B cells with complementary receptors.

Antigen
Receptor
Lymphocyte

② **Antigen presentation**
B cell internalizes antigen and displays processed epitope. Helper T cell binds to B cell and secretes interleukin.

Helper T cell
Epitope
B cell
MHC-II protein
Interleukin

③ **Clonal selection**
Interleukin stimulates B cell to divide repeatedly and form a clone.

④ **Differentiation**
Some cells of the clone become memory B cells. Most differentiate into plasma cells.

Plasma cells
Memory B cell

⑤ **Attack**
Plasma cells synthesize and secrete antibody. Antibody employs various means to render antigen harmless.

Antibody

FIGURE 21.25 Clonal Selection and Ensuing Events of the Humoral Immune Response.

for 3 to 6 days while naive B cells multiply and differentiate into plasma cells. As the plasma cells begin secreting antibody, the **antibody titer** (level in the blood plasma) begins to rise **(fig. 21.28).** IgM appears first, peaks in about 10 days, and soon declines. IgG levels rise as IgM declines, but even the IgG titer drops to a low level within a month.

The primary response, however, leaves one with an immune memory of the antigen. During clonal selection, some members of the clone become **memory B cells** rather than plasma cells (see fig. 21.25). Memory B cells, found mainly in the germinal centers of the lymph nodes, mount a very quick **secondary,** or **anamnestic,**[22] **response** (an-am-NESS-tic) if reexposed to the

same antigen. Plasma cells form within hours, so the IgG titer rises sharply and peaks within a few days. The response is so rapid that the antigen has little chance to exert a noticeable effect on the body, and no illness results. A low level of IgM is also secreted and quickly declines, but IgG remains elevated for weeks to years, conferring lasting protection. Memory doesn't last as long in humoral immunity, however, as it does in cellular immunity.

Table 21.4 summarizes many of the cellular and chemical agents involved in humoral and cellular immunity. **Table 21.5** compares the main features of humoral and cellular immunity. Remember that these two processes often occur simultaneously, and in conjunction with inflammation as a three-pronged attack on the same pathogen.

[22]*ana* = back; *mnes* = remember

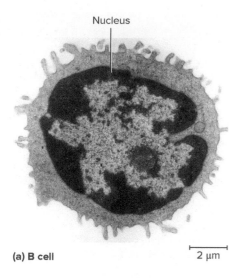

(a) B cell

2 μm

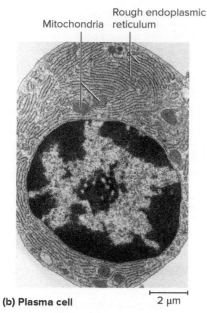

Mitochondria
Rough endoplasmic reticulum

(b) Plasma cell 2 μm

FIGURE 21.26 B Cell and Plasma Cell. (a) B cells have little cytoplasm and scanty organelles. (b) A plasma cell, which differentiates from a B cell, has an abundance of rough endoplasmic reticulum.

a, b: Don W. Fawcett/Science Source

 What does this endoplasmic reticulum do in the plasma cell?

BEFORE YOU GO ON

Answer the following questions to test your understanding of the preceding section:

23. What is the difference between a B cell and a plasma cell?

24. Describe four ways in which an antibody acts against an antigen.

25. Why does the secondary immune response prevent a pathogen from causing disease, while the primary immune response does not?

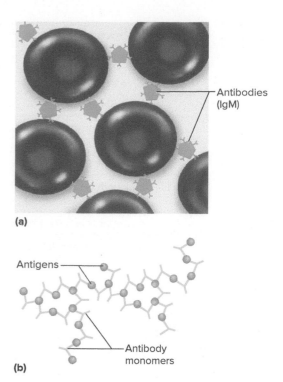

Antibodies (IgM)

(a)

Antigens

Antibody monomers

(b)

FIGURE 21.27 Agglutination and Precipitation by Antibodies. (a) Agglutination of foreign erythrocytes by IgM, a pentamer. (b) A precipitated antigen–antibody complex involving a free molecular antigen and an antibody monomer such as IgG.

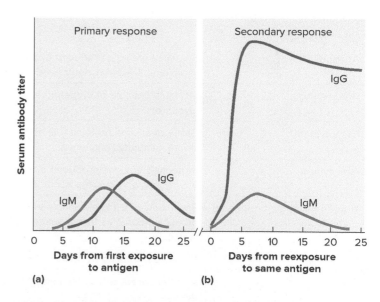

Primary response

Secondary response

IgG

IgG

IgM

IgM

Days from first exposure to antigen

Days from reexposure to same antigen

(a)

(b)

FIGURE 21.28 The Primary and Secondary (Anamnestic) Responses in Humoral Immunity. (a) The primary response, seen on first exposure to a given antigen. (b) The secondary response, seen in an immune person on reexposure. The individual is exposed to antigen on day 0 in both cases. Note the differences in the speed of response, the height of the antibody titer, and the rate of decline in antibody titer.

TABLE 21.4	Agents of Adaptive Immunity
Cellular Agents	
B cells	Serve as antigen-presenting cells in humoral immunity; differentiate into antibody-secreting plasma cells
CD4 (T4) cells*	T lymphocytes with CD4 surface glycoproteins; helper and regulatory T cells
CD8 (T8) cells	T lymphocytes with CD8 surface glycoproteins; cytotoxic T cells
Cytotoxic T (killer T, T_C, or CD8) cells	Effectors of cellular immunity; directly attack and destroy enemy cells; produce perforin, granzymes, interferon, tumor necrosis factor, and other cytokines
Dendritic cells	Branched, mobile APCs of the skin, mucous membranes, and lymphatic tissues; internalize antigen, migrate to lymph nodes, and present it to T_H and T_C cells
Eosinophils*	Phagocytize and degrade Ag–Ab complexes
Helper T (T_H) cells*	Play a central regulatory role in innate, humoral, and cellular immunity; recognize antigen fragments displayed by APCs with MHC-II proteins; secrete interleukins that activate B, T_C, and NK cells, neutrophils, and macrophages
Macrophages*	Phagocytize pathogens and expended or damaged host cells; act as antigen-presenting cells (APCs)
Memory B cells	Activated B cells that do not immediately differentiate into plasma cells; act as a pool of B cells that can execute a quick secondary response upon reexposure to the same antigen that initially activated them
Memory T cells	Activated T cells that do not immediately differentiate into effector T cells; act as a pool of T cells that can execute a quick T cell recall response upon reexposure to the same antigen that initially activated them
Naive lymphocytes	Immunocompetent lymphocytes that are capable of responding to an antigen but have not yet encountered one
Plasma cells	Develop from B cells that have been activated by helper T cells; synthesize and secrete antibodies
Regulatory T (T_R) cells (T-regs)	T cells that inhibit other T cells from multiplying or secreting cytokines; important especially in preventing autoimmune diseases but may also play defensive roles against infection and cancer and protect the fetus from maternal immune responses
Reticular cells	Fixed cells in the stroma of the lymph nodes and other lymphatic organs; act as APCs in the thymus, with a role in maturation of T cells
Chemical Agents	
Antibody (Ab)	A gamma globulin produced by plasma cells in response to an antigen; counteracts antigen by means of complement fixation, neutralization of toxins, agglutination, or precipitation
Antigen (Ag)	Molecule capable of triggering an immune response; usually a protein, polysaccharide, glycolipid, or glycoprotein
Complement*	Group of plasma proteins that help to destroy pathogens by cytolysis, phagocytosis, immune clearance, or innate immunity (inflammation)
Granzyme	Proteolytic enzyme produced by NK and T_C cells; enters the pore made by perforins, degrades enzymes of the enemy cell, and induces apoptosis
Hapten (incomplete antigen)	Small molecule initially unable to trigger an immune response by itself but able to bind to host molecules and produce a complex that is antigenic; may subsequently activate an immune response without binding to a host molecule
Interleukin	Cytokine produced by leukocytes and macrophages to stimulate other leukocytes
Perforin	A protein produced by NK and T_C cells that binds to target cells, produces a hole, and admits granzymes into the cell
Tumor necrosis factor (TNF)	Cytokine secreted by T_C cells that activates macrophages and kills cancer cells

*These agents have additional roles in inflammation described in table 21.1.

TABLE 21.5	Some Comparisons Between Cellular and Humoral Immunity	
Characteristic	Cellular Immunity	Humoral Immunity
Disease agents	Intracellular viruses, bacteria, yeasts, and protozoans; parasitic worms; cancer cells; transplanted tissues and organs	Extracellular viruses, bacteria, yeasts, and protozoans; toxins, venoms, and allergens; mismatched RBCs
Effector cells	Cytotoxic T cells	Plasma cells (develop from B cells)
Other cells involved in attack	Helper T cells	Helper T cells
Antigen-presenting cells	B cells, macrophages, dendritic cells, nearly all cells	B cells
MHC proteins	MHC-I and MHC-II	MHC-II only
Chemical agents of attack	Perforins, granzymes, interferons, tumor necrosis factor	Antibodies, complement
Mechanisms of counteracting or destroying pathogens	Cytolysis, phagocytosis, apoptosis	Cytolysis, phagocytosis, immune clearance, inflammation, neutralization, agglutination, precipitation
Memory	T cell recall response	Secondary (anamnestic) response

21.6 Immune System Disorders

Expected Learning Outcomes

When you have completed this section, you should be able to

a. distinguish between the four classes of immune hypersensitivity and give an example of each;

b. explain the cause of anaphylaxis and distinguish local anaphylaxis from anaphylactic shock;

c. state some reasons immune self-tolerance may fail, and give examples of the resulting diseases; and

d. describe the pathology of immunodeficiency diseases, especially AIDS.

Because the immune system involves complex cellular interactions controlled by numerous chemical messengers, there are many points at which things can go wrong. The immune response may be too vigorous, too weak, or misdirected against the wrong targets. A few disorders are summarized here to illustrate the consequences.

21.6a Hypersensitivity

Hypersensitivity is an excessive, harmful immune reaction to antigens. It includes reactions to tissues transplanted from another person *(alloimmunity),* abnormal reactions to one's own tissues *(autoimmunity),* and **allergies,**[23] which are reactions to environmental antigens. Such antigens, called **allergens,** occur in mold, dust, pollen, vaccines, bee and wasp venoms, animal dander, toxins from poison ivy and other plants, and foods such as nuts, milk, eggs, and shellfish. Drugs such as penicillin, tetracycline, and insulin are allergenic to some people.

One classification system recognizes four kinds of hypersensitivity, distinguished by the types of immune agents (antibodies or T cells) involved and their methods of attack on the antigen. In this system, type I is also characterized as *acute (immediate)*

hypersensitivity because the response is very rapid, whereas types II and III are characterized as *subacute* because they exhibit a slower onset (1–3 hours after exposure) and last longer (10–15 hours). Type IV is a delayed cell-mediated response, whereas the other three are quicker antibody-mediated responses.

- **Type I (acute) hypersensitivity** includes the most common allergies. Some authorities use the word *allergy* for type I reactions only, and others use it for all four types. Type I is an IgE-mediated reaction that begins within seconds of exposure and usually subsides within 30 minutes, although it can be severe and even fatal. Allergens bind to IgE on the membranes of basophils and mast cells and stimulate them to secrete histamine and other inflammatory and vasoactive chemicals. These chemicals trigger glandular secretion, vasodilation, increased capillary permeability, smooth muscle spasms, and other effects. The clinical signs include local edema, mucus hypersecretion and congestion, watery eyes, a runny nose, hives (red itchy skin), and sometimes cramps, diarrhea, and vomiting. Some examples of type I hypersensitivity are food allergies and **asthma,**[24] a local inflammatory reaction to inhaled allergens (see Deeper Insight 21.3).

  Anaphylaxis[25] (AN-uh-fih-LAC-sis) is an immediate and intense type I reaction. Local anaphylaxis can be relieved with antihistamines. **Anaphylactic shock** is a severe, widespread acute hypersensitivity that occurs when an allergen such as bee venom or penicillin is introduced to the bloodstream of an allergic individual, or when a person ingests certain foods (such as peanuts) to which he or she is allergic. It is characterized by bronchoconstriction, dyspnea (labored breathing), widespread vasodilation, circulatory shock, and sometimes sudden death. Antihistamines are inadequate by themselves to counter anaphylactic shock, but epinephrine relieves the symptoms by dilating the bronchioles, increasing cardiac output, and restoring blood pressure. Fluid therapy and respiratory support are sometimes required.

---

[23]*allo* = altered; *erg* = action, reaction

[24]*asthma* = panting
[25]*ana* = against; *phylax* = prevention

DEEPER INSIGHT 21.3

CLINICAL APPLICATION

Asthma

Asthma, a type I hypersensitivity, is the most common chronic illness of children, especially boys. It is the leading cause of school absenteeism and childhood hospitalization in the United States. About half of all cases develop before age 10 and only 15% after age 40. In the United States, it affects about 5% of adults and up to 10% of children, and takes about 3,400 lives per year. Moreover, asthma is on the rise; there are many more cases and deaths now than there were decades ago.

In *allergic (extrinsic) asthma,* the most common form, a respiratory crisis is triggered by allergens in pollen, mold, animal dander, food, dust mites, or cockroaches. The allergens stimulate plasma cells to secrete IgE, which binds to mast cells of the respiratory mucosa. Reexposure to the allergen causes the mast cells to release a complex mixture of inflammatory chemicals, which trigger intense airway inflammation. *Nonallergic (intrinsic) asthma* isn't caused by allergens but can be triggered by infections, drugs, air pollutants, cold dry air, exercise, or emotions. This form is more common in adults than in children, but the effects are much the same.

Within minutes, the bronchioles constrict spasmodically *(bronchospasm),* causing severe coughing, wheezing, and sometimes suffocation. A second respiratory crisis often occurs 6 to 8 hours later. Interleukins attract eosinophils to the bronchial tissue, where they secrete proteins that paralyze the respiratory cilia, severely damage the epithelium, and

lead to scarring and extensive long-term damage to the lungs. The bronchioles also become edematous and plugged with thick, sticky mucus. People who die of asthmatic suffocation typically show airways so plugged with gelatinous mucus that they couldn't exhale. The lungs remain hyperinflated even at autopsy.

Asthma is treated with epinephrine and other β-adrenergic stimulants to dilate the airway and restore breathing, and with inhaled corticosteroids or nonsteroidal anti-inflammatory drugs to minimize airway inflammation and long-term damage. The treatment regimen can be very complicated, often requiring more than eight different medications daily, and compliance is therefore difficult for children and patients with low income or educational attainment.

Asthma runs in families and seems to result from a combination of heredity and environmental irritants. In the United States, asthma is most common, paradoxically, in two groups: (1) inner-city children who are exposed to crowding, poor sanitation, and poor ventilation, and who don't often go outside or get enough exercise; and (2) children from extremely clean homes, perhaps because they have had too little opportunity to develop normal immunities. Asthma is also more common in countries where vaccines and antibiotics are widely used. It is less common in developing countries and in farm children of the United States.

- **Type II (antibody-dependent cytotoxic) hypersensitivity** occurs when IgG or IgM attacks antigens bound to cell surfaces. The reaction leads to complement activation and either lysis or opsonization of the target cell. Macrophages phagocytize and destroy opsonized platelets, erythrocytes, or other cells. Examples of cell destruction by type II reactions are blood transfusion reactions and some drug reactions. In some other type II responses, an antibody binds to cell surface receptors and either interferes with their function as in myasthenia gravis, or overstimulates the cell as in toxic goiter. (See table 21.6 for further information on these diseases.)

- **Type III (immune complex) hypersensitivity** occurs when IgG or IgM forms antigen–antibody complexes that precipitate beneath the endothelium of the blood vessels or in other tissues. At the sites of deposition, these complexes activate complement and trigger intense inflammation, causing tissue destruction. Two examples of type III hypersensitivity are the autoimmune diseases acute glomerulonephritis and systemic lupus erythematosus, a widespread inflammation of the connective tissues (see table 21.6).

- **Type IV (delayed) hypersensitivity** is a cell-mediated reaction in which the signs appear about 12 to 72 hours after exposure. It begins when APCs in the lymph nodes display antigens to helper T cells, and these T cells secrete interferon and other cytokines that activate cytotoxic T cells and macrophages. The result is a mixture of nonspecific and immune responses. Type IV reactions include allergies to haptens in cosmetics and poison ivy; graft rejection; the tuberculosis skin test; and the beta cell destruction that causes type 1 diabetes mellitus.

21.6b Autoimmune Diseases

Autoimmune diseases are failures of self-tolerance—the immune system fails to distinguish self-antigens from foreign ones and produces **autoantibodies** that attack the body's own tissues. Autoimmunity is usually prevented by negative selection of developing T and B cells, but there are at least three reasons why self-tolerance may fail:

1. **Cross-reactivity.** Some antibodies against foreign antigens react to similar self-antigens. In rheumatic fever, for example, a streptococcus infection stimulates production of antibodies that react not only against the bacteria but also against antigens of the heart tissue. It often results in scarring and stenosis (narrowing) of the mitral and aortic valves.

2. **Abnormal exposure of self-antigens to the blood.** Some of our native antigens are normally not exposed to the blood. For example, a blood–testis barrier (BTB) normally isolates sperm cells from the blood. Breakdown of the BTB can cause sterility when sperm first form in adolescence and activate the production of autoantibodies.

3. **Change in the structure of self-antigens.** Viruses and drugs may change the structure of self-antigens and cause the immune system to perceive them as foreign. One theory of type 1 diabetes mellitus is that a viral infection alters the antigens of the insulin-producing beta cells of the pancreatic islets, which leads to an autoimmune attack on the cells.

Evidence is emerging that not all self-reactive T cells are eliminated by clonal deletion in the thymus. We all apparently have at least some T cells poised to attack our own tissues, but regulatory T (T_R) cells keep them in check and normally prevent autoimmune disease.

21.6c Immunodeficiency Diseases

In the foregoing diseases, the immune system reacts too vigorously or directs its attack against the wrong targets. In immunodeficiency diseases, by contrast, the immune system fails to respond vigorously enough.

Severe Combined Immunodeficiency Disease

Severe combined immunodeficiency disease (SCID) is a group of disorders caused by recessive alleles that result in a scarcity or absence of both T and B cells. Children with SCID are highly vulnerable to opportunistic infections and must live in protective enclosures. The most publicized case was David Vetter, who spent his life in sterile plastic chambers and suits **(fig. 21.29)**, finally succumbing at age 12 to cancer triggered by a viral infection. Children with SCID are sometimes helped by transplants of bone marrow or fetal thymus, but in some cases the transplanted cells fail to survive and multiply, or transplanted T cells attack the patient's tissues (the *graft-versus-host response*). David contracted the fatal virus from his sister through a bone marrow transplant.

Acquired Immunodeficiency Syndrome

Other immunodeficiency diseases are nonhereditary and contracted after birth. The best-known example is **acquired immunodeficiency syndrome (AIDS),** a group of conditions in which infection with the **human immunodeficiency virus (HIV)** severely depresses the immune response.

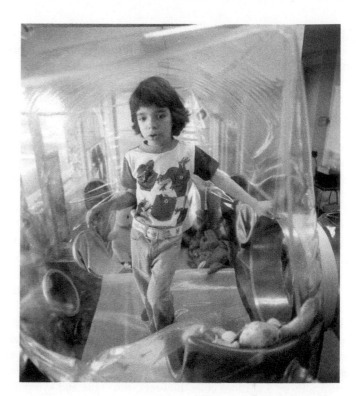

FIGURE 21.29 Boy with Severe Combined Immunodeficiency Disease. David Vetter lived with SCID from birth (1971) to age 12 and had to spend his entire life in sterile enclosures.

Source: Texas Children's Hospital

HIV **(fig. 21.30)** has an inner core consisting of a protein *capsid* that encloses two molecules of RNA, two molecules of an enzyme called *reverse transcriptase,* and a few other enzyme molecules. The capsid is enclosed in another layer of viral protein, the *matrix*. External to this is a *viral envelope* composed of phospholipids and glycoproteins derived from the host cell.

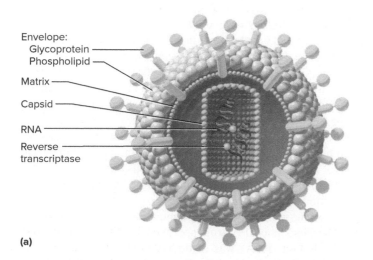

Envelope:
Glycoprotein
Phospholipid

Matrix

Capsid

RNA

Reverse
transcriptase

(a)

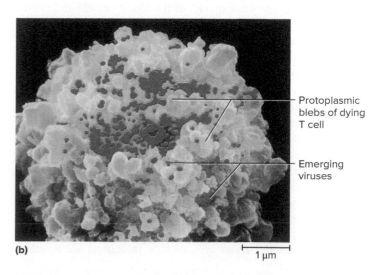

Protoplasmic
blebs of dying
T cell

Emerging
viruses

(b)

1 μm

FIGURE 21.30 The Human Immunodeficiency Virus (HIV). (a) Structure of the virus. (b) Viruses emerging from a dying helper T cell. Each virus can now invade a new helper T cell and produce a similar number of descendants.

b: NIBSC/SPL/Science Source

Like other viruses, HIV can be replicated only by a living host cell. It invades helper T (CD4) cells, dendritic cells, and macrophages. HIV adheres to a target cell by means of one of its envelope glycoproteins and "tricks" the target cell into internalizing it by receptor-mediated endocytosis. Within the host cell, reverse transcriptase uses the viral RNA as a template to synthesize DNA—the opposite of the usual process of genetic transcription. Viruses that carry out this RNA → DNA reverse transcription are called *retroviruses*.[26] The new DNA is inserted into the host cell's DNA, where it may lie dormant for months to years. When activated, however, it induces the host cell to produce new viral RNA, capsid proteins, and matrix proteins. As the new viruses emerge from the host cell (fig. 21.30b), they are coated with bits of the cell's plasma membrane, forming the new viral envelope. The new viruses then adhere to more host cells and repeat the process.

By destroying T_H cells, HIV strikes at a central coordinating agent of innate, humoral, and cellular immunity (see fig. 21.23). After an incubation period ranging from a few months to 12 years, the patient begins to experience flulike episodes of chills and fever as HIV attacks T_H cells. At first, antibodies against HIV are produced and the T_H count returns nearly to normal. As the virus destroys more and more cells, however, the signs and symptoms become more pronounced: night sweats, fatigue, headache, extreme weight loss, and lymphadenitis.

A normal T_H count is 600 to 1,200 cells/μL, but a criterion of AIDS is a count less than 200/μL. One can be HIV-positive for 10 years or longer without having AIDS. As T_H cells become severely depleted, however, a person falls vulnerable to opportunistic infections with such pathogens as *Toxoplasma* (a protozoan previously known mainly for causing birth defects), *Pneumocystis* (a group of respiratory fungi), herpes simplex virus, cytomegalovirus (which can cause blindness), and tuberculosis bacteria. White patches may appear in the mouth, caused by *Candida* (thrush) or Epstein–Barr[27] virus (leukoplakia). A cancer called Kaposi[28] sarcoma, rare in the general population but common in AIDS patients, originates in the endothelial cells of the blood vessels and causes bruiselike purple lesions visible in the skin, mouth, respiratory tract, and elsewhere (**fig. 21.31**).

Patients with AIDS show no response to standard skin tests for delayed hypersensitivity. Slurred speech, loss of motor and cognitive functions, and dementia may occur as HIV invades the brain by way of infected phagocytes (microglia) and induces them to release toxins that destroy neurons and astrocytes.

HIV is transmitted through blood, semen, vaginal secretions, and breast milk. It can be transmitted from mother to fetus through the placenta or from mother to infant during childbirth or nursing. HIV occurs in saliva and tears, but is apparently not transmitted by those fluids. The most common means of transmission are sexual intercourse (vaginal, anal, or oral), contaminated blood products, and drug injections with contaminated needles. Worldwide, about 75% of HIV infections are acquired

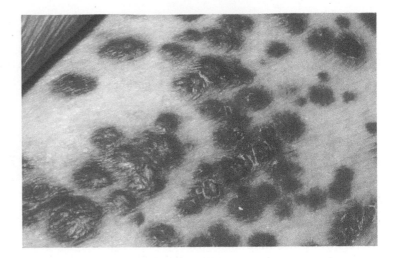

FIGURE 21.31 Kaposi Sarcoma. Typical skin lesions.

Source: National Cancer Institute (NCI)

through heterosexual, predominantly vaginal intercourse. In the United States, most cases occur in men who have sex with other men, but adolescents are the fastest-rising group of AIDS patients because of the exchange of unprotected sexual intercourse for drugs. The sharing of needles for drug use remains the chief means of transmission in urban ghettos. Since 1984, all blood donated for transfusion has been tested for HIV, and the risk of infection from transfusions is now less than 1%. HIV cannot be contracted by donating blood.

AIDS is not known to be transmitted through casual contact—for example, to family members, friends, coworkers, classmates, or medical personnel in charge of AIDS patients. It is not transmitted by kissing or by mosquitoes or other blood-sucking arthropods.

HIV survives poorly outside the human body. It is destroyed by laundering; dishwashing; exposure to heat (50°C [135°F] for at least 10 minutes); chlorination of swimming pools and hot tubs; and disinfectants such as bleach, Lysol, hydrogen peroxide, rubbing alcohol, and germicidal skin cleansers such as Betadine and Hibiclens. A properly used, undamaged latex condom is an effective barrier to HIV, but animal membrane condoms have gaps too large to block HIV transmission.

The AIDS epidemic triggered an effort of unprecedented intensity to find a vaccine or cure. HIV is a difficult pathogen to attack. Since it hides within host cells, it usually escapes recognition by the immune system. In the brain, it is protected by the blood–brain barrier. About 1% of HIV's genes mutate every year. Such rapid mutation is a barrier to both natural immunity and development of a vaccine. Even when immune cells do become sensitized to HIV, the virus soon evolves new surface antigens that escape recognition. The high mutation rate also would quickly make today's vaccine ineffective against tomorrow's strain of the virus.

The first anti-HIV drug approved by the Food and Drug Administration (FDA) was azidothymidine (AZT, or Retrovir), which inhibited reverse transcriptase and prolonged the lives of some HIV-positive individuals. In 1996, a family of drugs called protease inhibitors became available, typically used in a "triple cocktail" combining these with two reverse transcriptase inhibitors.

---

[26]*retr* = an acronym from reverse transcription
[27]M. A. Epstein (1921–), British physician; Y. M. Barr (1932–2016), British virologist
[28]Moritz Kaposi (1837–1902), Austrian physician

But by 1997, HIV had evolved resistance even to those drugs and they were failing in more than half of all patients. Two newer families of drugs for AIDS are *fusion inhibitors,* which interfere with the ability of HIV to invade host cells, and *integrase inhibitors,* which block the incorporation of HIV genes into human DNA. Today, at least 24 anti-HIV drugs are on the market, typically used in combinations of three or more. Such drug combinations have substantially reduced AIDS morbidity and mortality (disease and death) and reduced the hospital and hospice census. There is no cure for AIDS yet, but for those with access to antiretroviral therapy (ART), life expectancy at diagnosis is now close to that of uninfected persons. ART has saved the lives of millions of patients, but it requires lifelong drug therapy and a complicated regimen. Compliance is difficult for some, especially the homeless, drug abusers, the poorly nourished, and persons unable to pay for treatment. The major unresolved questions in AIDS therapy today are when to start drug treatment, which drugs to use, when to switch drugs, how to improve patient compliance, and how to make therapy available in impoverished nations where AIDS is especially rampant and people can't adhere well to complicated treatment regimens.

One obstacle to treatment and prevention is the lack of animal models for vaccine and drug research and development. Most animals aren't susceptible to HIV. The chimpanzee is an exception, but chimpanzees are difficult to maintain, and there are economic barriers and ethical controversies surrounding their use.

There also remain a number of unanswered questions about the basic biology of HIV. It is still unknown, for example, why there are such strikingly different patterns of heterosexual versus homosexual transmission in different countries, and why some people succumb so rapidly to infection but others can be HIV-positive for years without developing AIDS. AIDS remains a stubborn problem sure to challenge virologists and epidemiologists for many years to come.

We have surveyed the major classes of immune system disorders and a few particularly notorious immune diseases. A few additional lymphatic and immune system disorders are described in **table 21.6.** The effects of aging on the immune system are described in section 29.4a.

BEFORE YOU GO ON

Answer the following questions to test your understanding of the preceding section:

26. How does subacute hypersensitivity differ from acute hypersensitivity? Give an example of each.
27. Aside from the time required for a reaction to appear, how does delayed hypersensitivity differ from the acute and subacute types?
28. State some reasons why antibodies may begin attacking self-antigens to which they did not previously respond. What are these self-reactive antibodies called?
29. What is the distinction between a person who has an HIV infection and a person who has AIDS?
30. How does a reverse transcriptase inhibitor such as AZT slow the progress of AIDS?

TABLE 21.6	Some Disorders of the Lymphatic and Immune Systems
Contact dermatitis	A form of delayed hypersensitivity that produces skin lesions limited to the site of contact with an allergen or hapten; includes responses to poison ivy, cosmetics, latex, detergents, industrial chemicals, and some topical medicines.
Hives (urticaria[29])	An allergic skin reaction characterized by a "wheal-and-flare" reaction—white blisters (wheals) surrounded by reddened areas (flares), usually with itching. Caused by local histamine release in response to allergens. Can be triggered by food or drugs, but sometimes by nonimmunological factors such as cold, friction, or emotional stress.
Hodgkin[30] disease	A lymph node malignancy, with early symptoms including enlarged painful nodes, especially in the neck, and fever; often progresses to neighboring lymph nodes. Radiation and chemotherapy cure about 75% of patients.
Splenomegaly[31]	Enlargement of the spleen, sometimes without underlying disease but often indicating infections, autoimmune diseases, heart failure, cirrhosis, Hodgkin disease, and other cancers. The enlarged spleen may "hoard" erythrocytes, causing anemia, and may become fragile and subject to rupture.
Systemic lupus erythematosus[32]	Formation of autoantibodies against DNA and other nuclear antigens, resulting in accumulation of antigen–antibody complexes in blood vessels and other organs, where they trigger widespread connective tissue inflammation. Named for skin lesions once likened to a wolf bite. Causes fever, fatigue, joint pain, weight loss, intolerance of bright light, and a "butterfly rash" across the nose and cheeks. Death may result from renal failure.

You can find other lymphatic and immune system disorders described in the following places:

Rheumatoid arthritis in Deeper Insight 9.5; *myasthenia gravis* in Deeper Insight 11.4; *toxic goiter* in section 17.7a; *type 1 diabetes mellitus* in section 17.7e; *rheumatic fever* in Deeper Insight 19.3; *edema* in section 20.3d; *asthma* in Deeper Insight 21.3; *lymphadenitis* in section 21.1d; *allergy, anaphylaxis, severe combined immunodeficiency disease (SCID),* and *acquired immunodeficiency syndrome (AIDS)* in section 21.6; and *acute glomerulonephritis* in table 23.3.

[29]*urtica* = nettle
[30]Thomas Hodgkin (1798–1866), British physician
[31]*megaly* = enlargement
[32]*lupus* = wolf; *erythema* = redness

DEEPER INSIGHT 21.4

CLINICAL APPLICATION

Neuroimmunology and the Mind–Body Connection

Neuroimmunology is a relatively new branch of medicine concerned with the relationship between mind and body in health and disease. It is attempting especially to understand how a person's state of mind influences health and illness through a three-way communication between the nervous, endocrine, and immune systems.

The sympathetic nervous system issues nerve fibers to the spleen, thymus, lymph nodes, and aggregated lymphoid nodules of the ileum, where nerve fibers contact T cells, B cells, and macrophages. These immune cells have adrenergic receptors for norepinephrine and many other neurotransmitters such as neuropeptide Y, substance P, and vasoactive intestinal peptide (VIP). These neurotransmitters have been shown to influence immune cell activity in various ways. Epinephrine, for example, reduces the lymphocyte count and inhibits NK cell activity, thus suppressing both innate and adaptive immunity. Cortisol, another stress hormone, inhibits T cell and macrophage activity, antibody production, and the secretion of inflammatory chemicals. It also induces atrophy of the thymus, spleen, and lymph nodes and reduces the number of circulating lymphocytes, macrophages, and eosinophils. Thus, it is not surprising that prolonged stress increases susceptibility to illnesses such as infections and cancer. The existence of lymphatic vessels in the central nervous system, discovered only recently, has intriguing implications for direct effects of the brain on the immune system.

The immune system also sends messages to the nervous and endocrine systems. Immune cells synthesize numerous hormones and neurotransmitters that we normally associate with endocrine and nerve cells. B lymphocytes produce adrenocorticotropic hormone (ACTH) and enkephalins; T lymphocytes produce growth hormone, thyroid-stimulating hormone, luteinizing hormone, and follicle-stimulating hormone; and monocytes secrete prolactin, VIP, and somatostatin. The interleukins and tumor necrosis factor (TNF) secreted by immune cells produce feelings of fatigue and lethargy when we are sick, and stimulate the hypothalamus to secrete corticotropin-releasing hormone, leading to ACTH and cortisol secretion. It remains uncertain and controversial whether the quantities of some of these substances produced by immune cells are enough to have far-reaching effects on the body, but it seems increasingly possible that immune cells influence nervous and endocrine functions in ways that affect recovery from illness.

Although neuroimmunology has met with some skepticism among physicians, there is less and less room for doubt about the importance of a person's state of mind to immune function. People under stress, such as medical students during examination periods and people caring for relatives with Alzheimer disease, show more respiratory infections than other people and respond less effectively to hepatitis and flu vaccines. The attitudes, coping abilities, and social support systems of patients significantly influence survival time even in such serious diseases as AIDS and breast cancer. Women with breast cancer die at significantly higher rates if their husbands or partners cope poorly with stress and respond to the patient's illness with indifference, denial, or worse. Attitudes such as optimism, cheer, depression, resignation, or despair in the face of disease significantly affect immune function. Religious beliefs can also influence the prospect of recovery. Indeed, ardent believers in voodoo sometimes die just from the belief that someone has cast a spell on them. The stress of hospitalization can counteract the treatment one gives to a patient, and neuroimmunology has obvious implications for treating patients in ways that minimize their stress and thereby promote recovery.

CONNECTIVE ISSUES

Effects of the **LYMPHATIC AND IMMUNE SYSTEMS** on Other Organ Systems

ALL SYSTEMS

Lymphatic vessels drain excess tissue fluid, prevent edema, and remove cellular debris and pathogens. The immune system monitors all organs and provides defense against pathogens. Natural killer cells patrol the body and protect against cancer. All systems are subject to a variety of hypersensitivity and autoimmune disorders.

INTEGUMENTARY SYSTEM

The immune system includes dendritic cells of the epidermis, which guard against pathogens. The skin is a common site of inflammation. Autoimmunity causes pemphigus vulgaris and some other skin diseases. Hypersensitivity causes skin eruptions such as hives and dermatitis.

SKELETAL SYSTEM

Autoimmunity causes rheumatoid arthritis.

MUSCULAR SYSTEM

Autoimmunity causes myasthenia gravis, leading to muscle weakness and paralysis.

NERVOUS SYSTEM

Microglia cells scour the central nervous system for pathogens and tissue debris.

ENDOCRINE SYSTEM

Lymph transports some hormones. Autoimmunity is a factor in type 1 diabetes mellitus. Type II hypersensitivity causes toxic goiter of the thyroid. Immune cells secrete numerous hormones.

CIRCULATORY SYSTEM

Lymphatic vessels return fluid and lymphocytes to the bloodstream; the spleen disposes of expired RBCs; lymphatic organs filter pathogens and debris from the blood. Autoimmunity damages heart valves in rheumatic fever, and immune hypersensitivity causes circulatory failure in anaphylactic shock.

RESPIRATORY SYSTEM

Alveolar macrophages remove debris from the lungs; pulmonary lymphatic vessels are especially abundant and are needed to prevent fluid accumulation in the lungs. Immune hypersensitivity has effects ranging from respiratory congestion to asthma.

URINARY SYSTEM

Lymphatics absorb fluid and proteins in the kidneys, which is essential to enabling kidneys to concentrate the urine and conserve water. Autoimmunity causes acute glomerulonephritis.

DIGESTIVE SYSTEM

Lymphatic vessels called lacteals in the small intestine absorb nearly all dietary lipids and fat-soluble vitamins.

REPRODUCTIVE SYSTEM

Immunity to cells that are genetically different from other body cells requires the testes and ovaries to have barriers that protect sperm and eggs from immune destruction. A mismatch in Rh type can cause antibodies to attack fetal RBCs, causing hemolytic disease of the newborn.

STUDY GUIDE

▶ Assess Your Learning Outcomes

To test your knowledge, discuss the following topics with a study partner or in writing, ideally from memory.

21.1 The Lymphatic System

1. Functions and basic constituents of the lymphatic system
2. The definition, appearance, and composition of lymph
3. How lymph is produced; characteristics of lymphatic capillaries that allow cells and other large particles to enter the lymph
4. Lymphatic collecting vessels, trunks, and collecting ducts; the similarity of lymphatic vessels to some blood vessels; and their relationship to the lymph nodes
5. Names of the 11 lymphatic trunks and two collecting ducts; the body regions drained by them; and the two points at which lymph empties into the bloodstream
6. Mechanisms that propel the flow of lymph
7. Six types of cells found in lymphatic tissue, and their functions
8. The nature of diffuse lymphatic tissue and where it is found; what *MALT* stands for and where it is found
9. How lymphatic nodules differ from diffuse lymphatic tissue; the name of the clusters of lymphatic nodules found in the distal small intestine
10. How lymphatic organs differ from diffuse lymphatic tissue and lymphatic nodules; the two primary lymphatic organs and three secondary lymphatic organs, and why they are called this
11. Structure and function of red bone marrow
12. The location, gross anatomy, and histology of the thymus; the functional difference between its cortex and medulla; the functions of its epithelial cells; and the necessity of the thymus to immunity
13. Structure and function of lymph nodes; the significance of lymph nodes having both afferent and efferent lymphatic vessels, unlike any other lymphatic organs; the approximate number of lymph nodes and seven regions in which they are especially concentrated; and the meaning of *lymphadenitis* and *lymphadenopathy*
14. Types of tonsils, where they are located, and their structure and function; the most common cause of tonsillitis

15. Location, gross anatomy, and histology of the spleen; the difference between the red and white pulp; and functions associated with each type of pulp

21.2 Innate Immunity

1. Three lines of defense against pathogens
2. The definition of *immune system;* components of the system
3. Differences between innate and adaptive immunity; defining characteristics of the former
4. Three properties of the skin that make it an effective barrier to pathogens; the roles of organic acids and antimicrobial peptides in its barrier function
5. How the mucous membranes resist microbial invasion
6. Mechanisms by which each WBC type combats pathogens and illness, including the chemicals that some of them secrete in the performance of these functions
7. The one type of lymphocyte that is involved in innate immunity
8. Types of macrophages; their origin and functions
9. Interferons, their source, and how they oppose the spread of viruses
10. Complement proteins, their source, and how they are named
11. Three pathways of complement activation; how each is initiated; which pathways function in innate and adaptive immunity; and four mechanisms of pathogen destruction aided by complement
12. The actions of natural killer cells and the roles of perforins and granzymes in defense
13. Benefits of fever (pyrexia) and why the body's defenses may be compromised by antipyretic drugs; sources of pyrogens and how they trigger the onset of fever; the stages and course of a fever and how it combats pathogens; and the danger of excessive fever
14. Four cardinal signs of inflammation; chemicals that mobilize the body's defenses and initiate inflammation; and specific actions of these chemicals
15. The neutrophil actions of margination, diapedesis, chemotaxis, phagocytosis, the respiratory burst, and cytokine secretion
16. Other mechanisms of pathogen containment and destruction in inflammation

17. Examples of inflammatory cytokines and their roles
18. How hyperemia, bradykinin, and other factors account for the four cardinal signs of inflammation
19. The recruitment and action of macrophages
20. The formation, composition, and fate of pus
21. Mechanisms of tissue repair carried out after a pathogen is defeated

21.3 Adaptive Immunity—General Aspects

1. The three defining characteristics of adaptive immunity
2. Two basic forms of adaptive immunity, the differences between them, and the types of pathogens each one attacks
3. How adaptive immunity is classified as active or passive and as natural or artificial; which types result in immune memory and lasting protection, and which do not
4. The definition of *antigen* and the chemical characteristics of antigens
5. The role of the epitope in the antigenicity of a molecule
6. Haptens and how they become antigenic
7. The definition of *antibody* and where antibodies occur
8. Structure of the antibody monomer
9. The five antibody classes and their structural and functional differences
10. The life history of T cells including their origin; migration to the thymus; the sites, processes, and purposes of positive and negative selection; and dispersal of the naive lymphocyte pool
11. The meanings of *immunocompetence* and *self-tolerance*, how these are attained, and their importance to immunity
12. The life history of B cells including their origin, positive and negative selection, and dispersal
13. The necessity of antigen-presenting cells (APCs) to immunity; cell types that serve as APCs; the mechanism of antigen processing; and the role of MHC proteins in antigen presentation
14. Interleukins and their role in immunity

21.4 Cellular Immunity

1. Four classes of T lymphocytes involved in cellular immunity, and the function of each
2. Three fundamental stages of cellular immunity

STUDY GUIDE

3. What an APC does when it detects a foreign antigen; functional differences between MHC-I and MHC-II proteins; and the meaning of *MHC restriction*
4. Antigen recognition, costimulation, and clonal selection of a T cell; differentiation of selected T cells into effector cells and memory cells
5. How activated T_H cells stimulate neutrophils, NK cells, and macrophages
6. How activated T_C cells destroy target cells; the roles of interferons, perforin, granzymes, and tumor necrosis factor
7. Characteristics of immune memory and the T cell recall response in cellular immunity

21.5 Humoral Immunity

1. Similarities and differences between humoral and cellular immunity

2. How an immunocompetent B cell responds when it encounters a foreign antigen; the roles of MHC-II proteins and a T_H cell in its response
3. Clonal selection of activated B cell and differentiation of memory cells and plasma cells; the difference between a plasma cell and a B cell
4. Four mechanisms by which antibodies combat antigens
5. The secondary (anamnestic) response in humoral immune memory

21.6 Immune System Disorders

1. Three principal things that can go wrong with immune function
2. Hypersensitivity; names and characteristics of its four types, and examples of disorders of each type

3. The basic cause of autoimmune diseases; what normally prevents them; and three reasons why an autoimmune disease may appear, with an example of each
4. The basic cause of immunodeficiency diseases and the specific cause of severe combined immunodeficiency disease (SCID)
5. The pathology of acquired immunodeficiency syndrome (AIDS), including the structure of the human immunodeficiency virus (HIV); its mode of action; its effect on helper T cell count; the diseases to which AIDS makes a person more susceptible; how HIV is and is not transmitted; and treatment approaches to AIDS

▶ Testing Your Recall

Answers in Appendix A

1. The only lymphatic organ with both afferent and efferent lymphatic vessels is
   a. the spleen.
   b. a lymph node.
   c. a tonsil.
   d. a lymphatic follicle.
   e. the thymus.

2. Which of the following cells are involved in innate immunity but not in adaptive immunity?
   a. helper T cells
   b. cytotoxic T cells
   c. natural killer cells
   d. B cells
   e. plasma cells

3. The respiratory burst is used by _____ to kill bacteria.
   a. neutrophils
   b. basophils
   c. mast cells
   d. NK cells
   e. cytotoxic T cells

4. Which of these is a macrophage?
   a. a microglial cell
   b. a plasma cell
   c. a reticular cell
   d. a helper T cell
   e. a mast cell

5. The cytolytic action of the complement system is most similar to the action of
   a. interleukin-1.
   b. platelet-derived growth factor.
   c. granzymes.
   d. perforin.
   e. IgE.

6. _____ become antigenic by binding to larger host molecules.
   a. Epitopes
   b. Haptens
   c. Interleukins
   d. Pyrogens
   e. Cell-adhesion molecules

7. Which of the following correctly states the order of events in humoral immunity? Let
   1 = antigen display,
   2 = antibody secretion,
   3 = secretion of interleukin,
   4 = clonal selection, and
   5 = endocytosis of an antigen.
   a. 3–4–1–5–2
   b. 5–3–1–2–4
   c. 3–5–1–4–2
   d. 5–3–1–4–2
   e. 5–1–3–4–2

8. The cardinal signs of inflammation include all of the following *except*
   a. redness.
   b. swelling.
   c. heat.
   d. fever.
   e. pain.

9. A helper T cell can bind only to another cell that has
   a. MHC-II proteins.
   b. an epitope.
   c. an antigen-binding site.
   d. a complement-binding site.
   e. a CD4 protein.

10. Which of the following results from a lack of self-tolerance?
    a. SCID
    b. AIDS
    c. systemic lupus erythematosus
    d. anaphylaxis
    e. asthma

11. Any microorganism capable of causing disease is called a/an _____.

12. Mucous membranes contain an antibacterial enzyme called _____.

13. _____ is a condition in which one or more lymph nodes are swollen and painful to the touch.

STUDY GUIDE

14. The movement of leukocytes through a capillary or venule wall is called _____.

15. In the process of _____, complement proteins coat bacteria and serve as binding sites for phagocytes.

16. Any substance that triggers a fever is called a/an _____.

17. The chemical signals produced by leukocytes to stimulate other leukocytes are called _____.

18. Part of an antibody called the _____ binds to part of an antigen called the _____.

19. Self-tolerance results from a process called _____, in which lymphocytes programmed to react against self-antigens die.

20. Any disease in which antibodies attack one's own tissues is called a/an _____ disease.

▶ Building Your Medical Vocabulary

Answers in Appendix A

State a meaning of each word element, and give a medical term from this chapter that uses it or a slight variation of it.

1. ana-

2. crino-

3. extra-

4. -genous

5. immuno-

6. kino-

7. lympho-

8. -megaly

9. -pathy

10. pyro-

▶ What's Wrong with These Statements?

Answers in Appendix A

Briefly explain why each of the following statements is false, or reword it to make it true.

1. Some bacteria employ lysozyme to liquefy the tissue gel and make it easier for them to get around.

2. The thymus is the principal birthplace of all lymphocytes.

3. Interferons are named that because they interfere with the mechanisms of inflammation.

4. T lymphocytes are involved only in cell-mediated immunity.

5. The fundamental purpose of negative selection is to eliminate T cells that cannot recognize or respond to foreign antigens.

6. One function of the thymus and spleen is to filter incoming lymph and remove pathogens and other impurities from it.

7. All mechanisms of antibody action ultimately depend on complement fixation as an intermediate step.

8. Anyone who is HIV-positive is considered to have AIDS.

9. Anergy is a frequent cause of autoimmune diseases.

10. B cells that circulate freely in the bloodstream are called plasma cells.

▶ Testing Your Comprehension

1. David Vetter, the boy with SCID discussed in section 21.6c, died of infection with the Epstein–Barr virus, which had lurked unsuspected in his sister's bone marrow. (a) Why was David's sister chosen as a bone marrow donor rather than someone else? (b) Considering that the virus was fatal to David, why had it not caused any illness in his sister and, indeed, existed in her with no one being aware of it? (c) Do you think a cord blood transfusion (see Deeper Insight 18.3) may have been a better option for David than the marrow transplant? Discuss your reasoning.

2. In treating a woman for malignancy in the right breast, the surgeon removes some of her axillary lymph nodes. Following surgery, the patient experiences edema of her right arm. Explain why.

3. A girl with a defective heart receives a new heart transplanted from another child who was killed in an accident. The patient is given an antilymphocyte serum containing antibodies against her lymphocytes. The transplanted heart is not rejected, but the patient dies of an overwhelming bacterial infection. Explain why the antilymphocyte serum was given and why the patient was so vulnerable to infection.

4. A burn research center uses mice for studies of skin grafting. To prevent graft rejection, the mice are thymectomized at birth. Even though B cells don't develop in the thymus, these mice show no humoral immune response and are very susceptible to infection. Explain why the removal of the thymus would improve the success of skin grafts but adversely affect humoral immunity.

5. Contrast the structure of a B cell with that of a plasma cell, and explain how their structural difference relates to their functional difference.

CHAPTER

22

THE RESPIRATORY SYSTEM

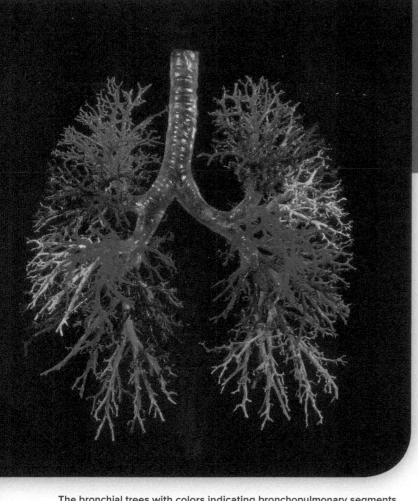

The bronchial trees with colors indicating bronchopulmonary segments

Mediscan/Alamy

Anatomy & Physiology
Revealed 4.0

Module 11: Respiratory System

Breath represents life. The first breath of a baby and the last gasp of a dying person are two of the most dramatic moments of human experience. But why do we breathe? It comes down to the fact that most of our metabolism directly or indirectly requires ATP. Most ATP synthesis requires oxygen and generates carbon dioxide—thus driving the need to breathe in order to supply the former and eliminate the latter. The respiratory system consists essentially of tubes that deliver air to the lungs, where oxygen diffuses into the blood and carbon dioxide diffuses out.

The respiratory and cardiovascular systems collaborate to deliver oxygen to tissues throughout the body and transport carbon dioxide to the lungs for elimination. Not only do these two systems have a close spatial relationship in the thoracic cavity, but they also have such a close functional relationship that they're often jointly called the *cardiopulmonary system*. A disorder that affects the lungs has direct and pronounced effects on the heart, and vice versa. As discussed in the next two chapters, the respiratory system also collaborates closely with the urinary system to regulate the body's acid–base balance, which is why we consider these systems consecutively in this group of chapters.

22.1 Anatomy of the Respiratory System

Expected Learning Outcomes
When you have completed this section, you should be able to

a. state the functions of the respiratory system;

b. name and describe the organs of this system;

c. trace the flow of air from the nose to the pulmonary alveoli; and

d. relate the function of any portion of the respiratory tract to its gross and microscopic anatomy.

The term *respiration* can mean ventilation of the lungs (breathing) or the use of oxygen in cellular metabolism. In this chapter, we are concerned with the first process. Cellular respiration was introduced in chapter 2 and is considered more fully in chapter 26.

The **respiratory system** is an organ system that rhythmically takes in air and expels it from the body, thereby supplying the body with oxygen and expelling the carbon dioxide that it generates. However, it has a broader range of functions than is commonly supposed:

1. **Gas exchange.** It provides for oxygen and carbon dioxide exchange between the blood and air.

2. **Communication.** It serves for speech and other vocalization (laughing, crying).

3. **Olfaction.** It provides the sense of smell, which is important in social interactions, food selection, and avoiding danger (such as a gas leak or spoiled food).

4. **Acid–base balance.** By eliminating CO_2, it helps to control the pH of the body fluids. Excess CO_2 reacts with water and generates carbonic acid; therefore, if respiration doesn't keep pace with CO_2 production, acid accumulates and the body fluids have an abnormally low pH *(acidosis)*.

5. **Blood pressure regulation.** The lungs carry out a step in synthesizing *angiotensin II,* which helps to regulate blood pressure.

6. **Platelet production.** More than half of one's blood platelets are made by megakaryocytes in the lungs (not in the bone marrow).

7. **Blood and lymph flow.** Breathing creates pressure gradients between the thorax and abdomen that promote the flow of lymph and venous blood.

8. **Blood filtration.** The lungs filter small blood clots from the bloodstream and dissolve them, preventing clots from obstructing more vital pathways such as the coronary, cerebral, and renal circulation.

9. **Expulsion of abdominal contents.** Breath-holding and abdominal contraction help to expel abdominal contents during urination, defecation, and childbirth.

The principal organs of the respiratory system are the nose, pharynx, larynx, trachea, bronchi, and lungs (**fig. 22.1**). Within the lungs, air flows along a dead-end pathway consisting essentially of bronchi → bronchioles → alveoli (with some refinements to be introduced later). Incoming air stops in the *alveoli* (millions of tiny, thin-walled air sacs), exchanges gases with the bloodstream through the alveolar wall, and then flows back out.

The **conducting zone** of the respiratory system consists of those passages that serve only for airflow, essentially from the nostrils through the major bronchioles. The walls of these passages

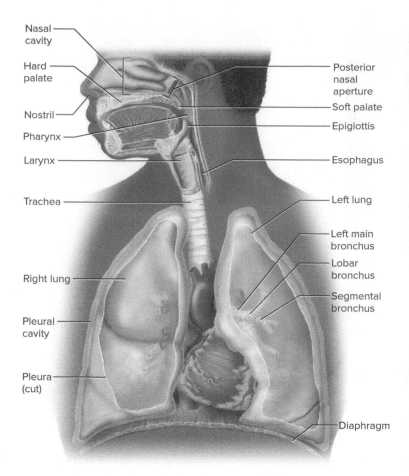

Nasal cavity
Hard palate
Nostril
Pharynx
Larynx
Trachea
Right lung
Pleural cavity
Pleura (cut)

Posterior nasal aperture
Soft palate
Epiglottis
Esophagus
Left lung
Left main bronchus
Lobar bronchus
Segmental bronchus
Diaphragm

FIGURE 22.1 The Respiratory System. APR

are too thick for adequate diffusion of oxygen from the air into the blood. The **respiratory zone** consists of the alveoli and other gas-exchange regions of the distal airway. The airway from the nose through the larynx is often called the **upper respiratory tract** (that is, the respiratory organs in the head and neck), and the regions from the trachea through the lungs compose the **lower respiratory tract** (the respiratory organs of the thorax). However, these are inexact terms and various authorities place the dividing line between the upper and lower tracts at different points.

22.1a The Nose

The **nose** has several functions: It warms, cleanses, and humidifies inhaled air; it detects odors; and it serves as a resonating chamber that amplifies the voice. It extends from a pair of anterior openings called the **nostrils,** or **nares** (NAIR-eze) (singular, *naris*), to a pair of posterior openings called the **posterior nasal apertures,** or **choanae**[1] (co-AH-nee).

The facial part of the nose is shaped by bone and hyaline cartilage. Its superior half is supported by a pair of small nasal bones medially and the maxillae laterally. The inferior half is supported by the **lateral** and **alar cartilages (fig. 22.2).** By palpating your own nose, you can easily find the boundary between the bone above and

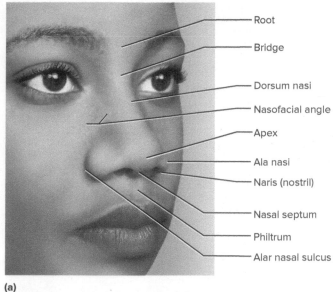

Root
Bridge
Dorsum nasi
Nasofacial angle
Apex
Ala nasi
Naris (nostril)
Nasal septum
Philtrum
Alar nasal sulcus

(a)

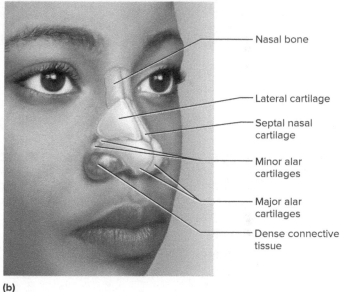

Nasal bone
Lateral cartilage
Septal nasal cartilage
Minor alar cartilages
Major alar cartilages
Dense connective tissue

(b)

FIGURE 22.2 Anatomy of the Nasal Region. (a) Surface anatomy. (b) Connective tissues that shape the nose.

Joe DeGrandis/McGraw-Hill Education

the more flexible cartilage below. The flared portion on each side of the lower end of the nose, called the **ala nasi**[2] (AIL-ah NAZE-eye), is shaped by the alar cartilages and dense connective tissue.

The internal chamber of the nose, called the **nasal cavity,** is divided into right and left halves called **nasal fossae** (FAW-see) **(fig. 22.3).** The dividing wall is a vertical plate, the **nasal septum,** composed of bone and hyaline cartilage. The vomer forms the inferior part of the septum, the perpendicular plate of the ethmoid bone forms its superior part, and the *septal cartilage* forms its anterior part. The ethmoid and sphenoid bones compose the roof of

---

[1]*choana* = funnel

[2]*ala* = wing; *nasi* = of the nose

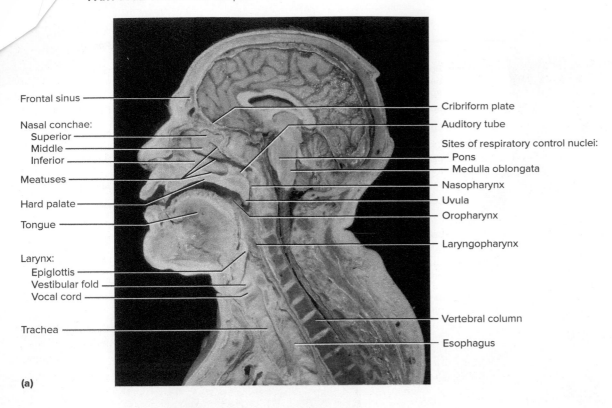

(a)

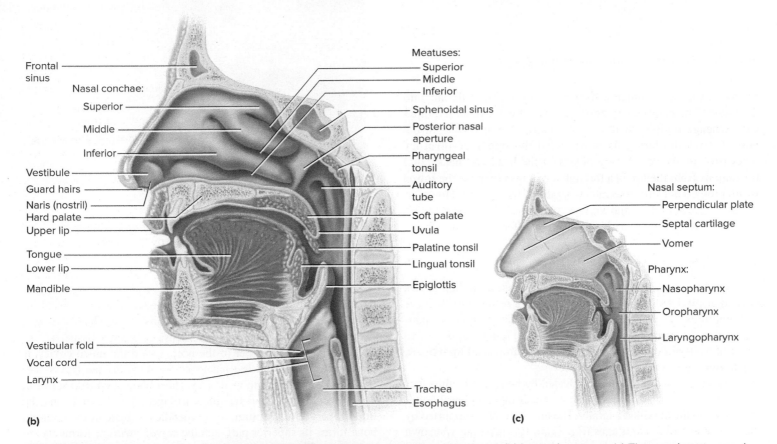

(b)

(c)

FIGURE 22.3 Anatomy of the Upper Respiratory Tract. (a) Median section of the head. (b) Internal anatomy. (c) The nasal septum and regions of the pharynx.

a: Rebecca Gray/McGraw-Hill Education

❓ *Draw a line across part (a) of this figure to indicate the boundary between the upper and lower respiratory tract.*

the nasal cavity, and the hard palate forms its floor. The palate separates the nasal cavity from the oral cavity and allows you to breathe while chewing food. The paranasal sinuses and the naso-lacrimal ducts of the orbits drain into the nasal cavity (see figs. 8.8, 16.24, respectively).

The nasal cavity begins with a small dilated chamber called the **vestibule** just inside the nostril, bordered by the ala nasi. This space is lined with stratified squamous epithelium like the facial skin, and has stiff **guard hairs,** or **vibrissae** (vy-BRISS-ee), that block debris from entering the nose. Posterior to the vestibule, the nasal cavity expands into a much larger chamber, but it doesn't have much open space. Most of it is occupied by three folds of tissue—the **superior, middle,** and **inferior nasal conchae**[3] (CON-kee), or **turbinates**—that project from the lateral walls toward the septum (fig. 22.3; see also fig. 8.7 for a frontal view). Beneath each concha is a narrow air passage called a **meatus** (me-AY-tus). The narrowness of these passages and the turbulence caused by the conchae ensure that most air contacts the mucous membrane on its way through. As it does, most dust in the air sticks to the mucus and the air picks up moisture and heat from the mucosa. The conchae thus enable the nose to cleanse, warm, and humidify the air more effectively than if the air had an unobstructed flow through a cavernous space.

Past the vestibule, the mucosa (mucous membrane) of the nasal cavity consists of a ciliated pseudostratified columnar epithelium overlying a loose connective tissue lamina propria (see figs. 5.7, 5.33). Over most of the mucosa, the epithelium is called the **respiratory epithelium.** Its **ciliated cells** are capped with a fringe of about 200 motile cilia per cell and coated with a layer of mucus. The second most abundant cells of the epithelium are the wine-glass-shaped **goblet cells,** which secrete most of the mucus. In lesser numbers, the respiratory epithelium also contains endocrine cells, chemosensory *brush cells,* and basal stem cells.

Inhaled dust, pollen, bacteria, and other foreign matter are trapped in the sticky blanket of mucus covering the epithelium. The cilia of the epithelium beat in waves that drive this debris-laden mucus posteriorly to the pharynx, where it is swallowed. The particulate debris is either digested or passes through the digestive tract rather than contaminating the lungs.

A small area of nasal mucosa has an **olfactory epithelium,** concerned with the sense of smell. It covers about 5 cm^2 in the roof of the nasal fossa and adjacent parts of the septum and superior concha. Its structure and function are detailed in section 16.3b (see fig. 16.7). A notable contrast with the respiratory epithelium is that the cilia of the olfactory epithelium are immobile. They lie flattened against the mucosal surface like a plate of spaghetti noodles and serve to bind odor molecules, not to propel mucus.

The lamina propria of the nasal cavity is loose (areolar) connective tissue. In the respiratory mucosa, it contains glands that supplement the mucus produced by the goblet cells. In the olfactory mucosa, the lamina propria has large serous **olfactory glands.** These secrete a watery serous fluid that bathes the olfactory cilia and facilitates the diffusion of odor molecules from inhaled air to their receptors on the cilia.

The lamina propria contains large blood vessels that help to warm the air. The inferior concha has an especially extensive venous plexus called the **erectile tissue (swell body).** Every 30 to 60 minutes, the erectile tissue on one side swells with blood and restricts airflow through that fossa. Most air is then directed through the other nostril, allowing the engorged side time to recover from drying. Thus, the preponderant flow of air shifts between the right and left nostrils once or twice each hour. If one nostril is blocked and the other nasal fossa is over-ventilated for several days, its pseudostratified columnar epithelium changes to stratified squamous, which better resists drying. This is an example of the *metaplasia* explained in section 5.6b.

22.1b The Pharynx

The **pharynx** (FAIR-inks, FAR-inks) is a muscular funnel extending about 13 cm (5 in.) from the posterior nasal apertures to the larynx. It has three regions: the *nasopharynx, oropharynx,* and *laryngopharynx* (fig. 22.3c).

The **nasopharynx** is distal to the posterior nasal apertures and superior to the soft palate. It receives the auditory (pharyngotympanic or eustachian) tubes from the middle ears and houses the pharyngeal tonsil. Inhaled air turns 90° downward as it passes through the nasopharynx. Relatively large particles (>10 μm) generally can't make the turn because of their inertia. They collide with the wall of the nasopharynx and stick to the mucosa near the tonsil, which is well positioned to respond to airborne pathogens.

The **oropharynx** is a space between the posterior margin of the soft palate and the epiglottis.

The **laryngopharynx** (la-RIN-go-FAIR-inks) lies mostly posterior to the larynx, extending from the superior margin of the epiglottis to the inferior margin of the cricoid cartilage. The esophagus begins at that point.

The nasopharynx passes only air and is lined by pseudostratified columnar epithelium, whereas the oropharynx and laryngopharynx pass air, food, and drink and are lined by more abrasion-resistant stratified squamous epithelium. Muscles of the pharynx play necessary roles in swallowing and speech.

22.1c The Larynx

The **larynx** (LAIR-inks) is a cartilaginous chamber about 4 cm (1.5 in.) long **(fig. 22.4).** Its primary function is to keep food and drink out of the airway, but it evolved the additional role of sound production *(phonation)* in many animals; hence, we colloquially think of it as the "voice box."

The superior opening of the larynx is guarded by a flap of tissue called the **epiglottis**[4] just posterior to the root of the tongue. At rest, the epiglottis stands almost vertically. During swallowing, however, *extrinsic muscles* of the larynx pull the larynx upward toward the epiglottis, the tongue pushes the epiglottis downward to meet it, and the epiglottis closes the airway and directs food and drink into the esophagus behind it. The *vestibular folds* of the larynx, discussed shortly, play a greater role in keeping food and drink out of the airway, however.

---

[3]*concha* = seashell

[4]*epi* = above, upon; *glottis* = back of the tongue

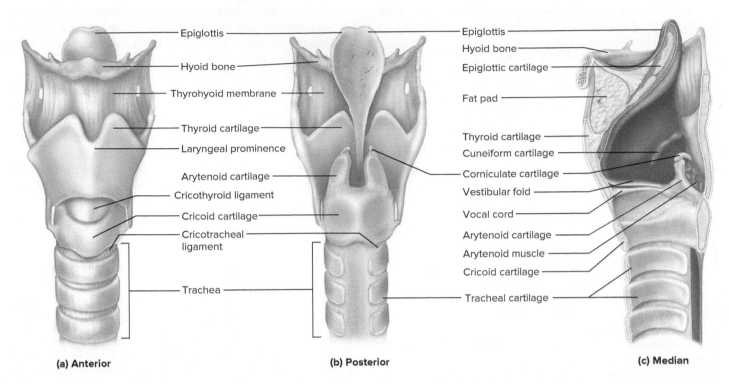

FIGURE 22.4 Anatomy of the Larynx. (a) Anterior aspect. (b) Posterior aspect. (c) Median section with most muscles removed in order to show the cartilages. **APR**

❓ *Which three cartilages in this figure are more mobile than any of the others?*

In infants, the larynx is relatively high in the throat and the epiglottis touches the soft palate. This creates a more or less continuous airway from the nasal cavity to the larynx and allows an infant to breathe continually while swallowing. The epiglottis deflects milk away from the airstream, like rain running off a tent while it remains dry inside. By age 2, the root of the tongue becomes more muscular and forces the larynx to descend to a lower position. It then becomes impossible to breathe and swallow at the same time without choking.

The framework of the larynx consists of nine cartilages. The first three are solitary and relatively large. The most superior one, the **epiglottic cartilage,** is a spoon-shaped supportive plate of elastic cartilage in the epiglottis. The largest, the **thyroid**[5] **cartilage,** is named for its shieldlike shape. It broadly covers the anterior and lateral aspects of the larynx. The "Adam's apple" is an anterior peak of the thyroid cartilage called the *laryngeal prominence.* Testosterone stimulates the growth of this prominence, which is therefore larger in males than in females. Inferior to the thyroid cartilage is a ringlike **cricoid**[6] **cartilage** (CRY-coyd). The thyroid and cricoid cartilages essentially constitute the "box" of the voice box.

The remaining cartilages are smaller and occur in three pairs. Posterior to the thyroid cartilage are the two **arytenoid**[7] **cartilages** (AR-ih-TEE-noyd), and attached to their upper ends is a pair

of little horns, the **corniculate**[8] **cartilages** (cor-NICK-you-late). The arytenoid and corniculate cartilages function in speech, as explained shortly. A pair of **cuneiform**[9] **cartilages** (cue-NEE-ih-form) supports the soft tissues between the arytenoids and the epiglottis.

A group of fibrous ligaments binds the cartilages of the larynx together and forms a suspension system for the upper airway. A broad sheet called the **thyrohyoid membrane** suspends the larynx from the hyoid bone above it. Below, the **cricothyroid ligament** suspends the cricoid cartilage from the thyroid cartilage. This is the most clinically important of all these ligaments, as this is where emergency incisions are made in a *tracheotomy* to restore breathing when the airway above it is obstructed (see Deeper Insight 22.1). The **cricotracheal ligament** suspends the trachea from the cricoid cartilage. All of these are collectively called the *extrinsic ligaments* because they link the larynx to other organs. The *intrinsic ligaments* are contained entirely within the larynx and link its nine cartilages to each other; they include ligaments of the vocal cords and vestibular folds.

The interior wall of the larynx has two folds on each side that stretch from the thyroid cartilage in front to the arytenoid cartilages in back. The superior **vestibular folds** (fig. 22.4c) play no role in speech but close the larynx during swallowing. They are supported by the **vestibular ligaments.** The inferior **vocal cords (vocal folds)** produce sound when air passes between them. They

---

[5]*thyr* = shield; *oid* = resembling
[6]*crico* = ring; *oid* = resembling
[7]*aryten* = ladle; *oid* = resembling

[8]*corni* = horn; *cul* = little; *ate* = possessing
[9]*cune* = wedge; *form* = shape

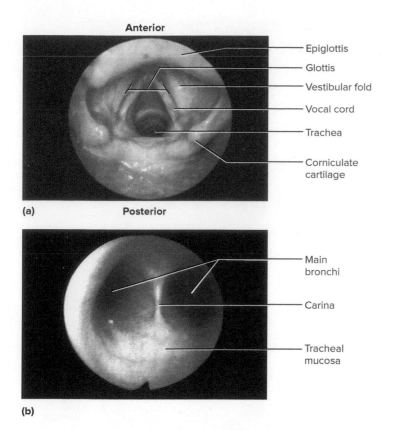

Anterior

— Epiglottis

— Glottis

— Vestibular fold

— Vocal cord

— Trachea

— Corniculate cartilage

(a)

Posterior

— Main bronchi

— Carina

— Tracheal mucosa

(b)

FIGURE 22.5 Endoscopic Views of the Respiratory Tract.
(a) Superior view of the larynx, seen with a laryngoscope. (b) Lower end of the trachea, where it forks into the two primary bronchi, seen with a bronchoscope.

a: CNRI/Science Photo Library; **b:** BSIP/Newscom

contain the **vocal ligaments** and are covered with stratified squamous epithelium, best suited to endure vibration and contact between the cords. The vocal cords and the opening between them are collectively called the **glottis (fig. 22.5a).**

The walls of the larynx are quite muscular. The superficial *extrinsic muscles* connect the larynx to the hyoid bone and elevate the larynx during swallowing. Also called the *infrahyoid group,* they are named and described in table 10.2.

The deeper *intrinsic muscles* control the vocal cords by pulling on the corniculate and arytenoid cartilages, causing the cartilages to pivot. Depending on their direction of rotation, the arytenoid cartilages abduct or adduct the vocal cords **(fig. 22.6).** Air forced between the adducted vocal cords vibrates them, producing a high-pitched sound when the cords are relatively taut and a lower-pitched sound when they are more slack. In adult males, the vocal cords are usually longer and thicker, vibrate more slowly, and produce lower-pitched sounds than in females. Loudness is determined by the force of the air passing between the vocal cords. Although the vocal cords alone produce sound, they don't produce intelligible speech; some anatomists have likened their sound to a hunter's duck call. The crude sounds from the larynx are formed into words by actions of the pharynx, oral cavity, tongue, and lips.

22.1d The Trachea

The **trachea** (TRAY-kee-uh), or "windpipe," is a tube about 12 cm (4.5 in.) long and 2.5 cm (1 in.) in diameter, anterior to the esophagus **(fig. 22.7a).** It is supported by 16 to 20 C-shaped rings of hyaline cartilage. The trachea is named for the corrugated texture imparted

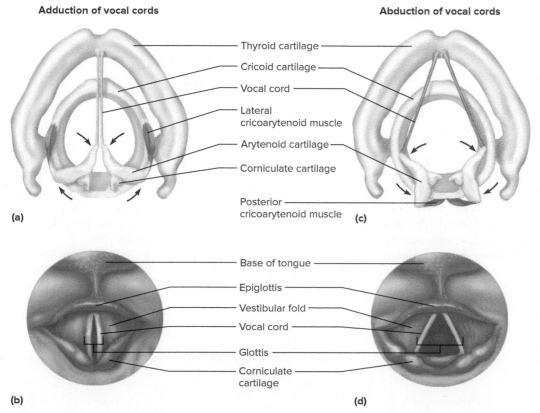

Adduction of vocal cords

Abduction of vocal cords

— Thyroid cartilage —

— Cricoid cartilage —

— Vocal cord —

— Lateral cricoarytenoid muscle

— Arytenoid cartilage —

— Corniculate cartilage

Posterior — cricoarytenoid muscle

Anterior

Posterior

(a)

(c)

— Base of tongue —

— Epiglottis —

— Vestibular fold —

— Vocal cord —

— Glottis —

— Corniculate cartilage

(b)

(d)

FIGURE 22.6 Action of Some of the Intrinsic Laryngeal Muscles on the Vocal Cords.
(a) Adduction of the vocal cords by the *lateral cricoarytenoid muscles.* (b) Adducted vocal cords seen with the laryngoscope. (c) Abduction of the vocal cords by the *posterior cricoarytenoid muscles.* (d) Abducted vocal cords seen with the laryngoscope. The intrinsic muscles are much more numerous and complex than these two pairs isolated for illustration.

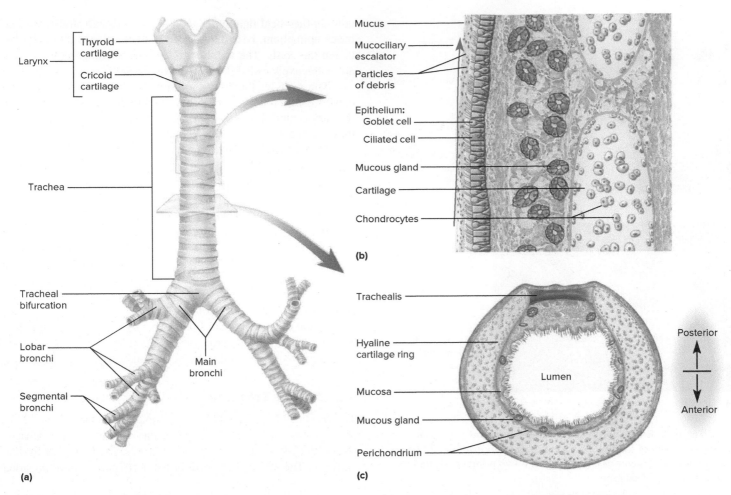

FIGURE 22.7 Anatomy of the Lower Respiratory Tract. (a) Anterior view. (b) Longitudinal section of the trachea showing the action of the mucociliary escalator. (c) Cross section of the trachea showing the C-shaped tracheal cartilage. **APR**

 Why do inhaled objects more often go into the right main bronchus than into the left?

by these rings;[10] you should be able to palpate a few of these between your larynx and sternum. Like the wire spiral in a vacuum cleaner hose, the cartilage rings reinforce the trachea and keep it from collapsing when you inhale. The open part of the C faces posteriorly, where it is spanned by a smooth muscle, the **trachealis (fig. 22.7c).** The gap in the C allows room for the esophagus to expand as swallowed food passes by. The trachealis contracts or relaxes to adjust airflow.

The inner lining of the trachea is a pseudostratified columnar epithelium composed mainly of mucus-secreting goblet cells, ciliated cells, and short basal stem cells **(figs. 22.7b, 22.8).** The mucus traps inhaled particles and the upward beating of the cilia drives the debris-laden mucus toward the pharynx, where it is swallowed. This mechanism of debris removal is called the **mucociliary escalator.**

The connective tissue beneath the tracheal epithelium contains lymphatic nodules, mucous and serous glands, and the tracheal cartilages. The outermost layer of the trachea, called the **adventitia,** is fibrous connective tissue that blends into the adventitia of other organs of the mediastinum, especially the esophagus.

[10]*trache* = rough

DEEPER INSIGHT 22.1

CLINICAL APPLICATION

Tracheotomy

The functional importance of the nasal cavity becomes especially obvious when it is bypassed. If the upper airway is obstructed, it may be necessary to make a temporary opening in the trachea inferior to the larynx and insert a tube to allow airflow—a procedure called *tracheotomy.* (A permanent opening is called a *tracheostomy.*) Life-saving tracheotomies are performed hundreds of times per day in the United States alone. They prevent asphyxiation, but the inhaled air bypasses the nasal cavity and thus is not humidified. If the opening is left for long, the mucous membranes of the respiratory tract dry out and become encrusted, interfering with the clearance of mucus from the tract and promoting infection. When a patient is on a ventilator and air is introduced directly into the trachea *(intubation)*, the air must be filtered and humidified by the apparatus to prevent respiratory tract damage.

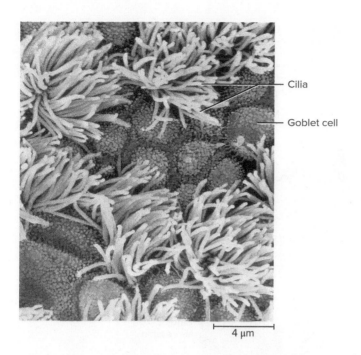

Cilia

Goblet cell

4 μm

FIGURE 22.8 The Tracheal Epithelium Showing Ciliated Cells and Nonciliated Goblet Cells (SEM). The small bumps on the goblet cells are microvilli.

Prof. P.M. Motta/Univ. "La Sapienza," Rome/Science Source

 What is the function of the goblet cells?

At the level of the sternal angle, the trachea ends at a fork called the *tracheal bifurcation,* where it gives off the right and left *main bronchi.* The lowermost tracheal cartilage has an internal median ridge called the **carina**[11] (ca-RY-na) that directs the airflow to the right and left **(fig. 22.5b).**

22.1e The Lungs and Bronchial Tree

Each **lung** is a somewhat conical organ with a broad, concave **base** resting on the diaphragm and a blunt peak called the **apex** projecting slightly above the clavicle **(fig. 22.9).** The broad **costal surface** is pressed against the rib cage, and the smaller concave **mediastinal surface** faces medially. The mediastinal surface exhibits a slit called the **hilum** through which the lung receives the main bronchus, blood vessels, lymphatics, and nerves. These structures constitute the **root** of the lung.

The lungs are crowded by adjacent organs and neither fill the entire rib cage, nor are they symmetrical **(fig. 22.10).** Inferior to the lungs and diaphragm, much of the space within the rib cage is occupied by the liver, spleen, and stomach (see fig. B.5 in atlas B). The right lung is shorter than the left because the liver rises higher on the right. The left lung, although taller, is narrower than the right because the heart tilts toward the left and occupies more space on this side of the mediastinum. On the medial surface, the left lung has an indentation called the **cardiac impression** where

the heart presses against it; part of this is visible anteriorly as a crescent-shaped **cardiac notch** in the margin of the lung. The right lung has three lobes—**superior, middle,** and **inferior.** A deep groove called the **horizontal fissure** separates the superior and middle lobes, and a similar **oblique fissure** separates the middle and inferior lobes. The left lung has only a **superior** and **inferior lobe** and a single oblique fissure.

The Bronchial Tree

Each lung has a branching system of air tubes called the **bronchial tree,** extending from the main bronchus to about 65,000 *terminal bronchioles.* Arising from the fork in the trachea, the **right main (primary) bronchus** (BRON-cus) is 2 to 3 cm long. It is slightly wider and more vertical than the left one; consequently, *aspirated* (inhaled) foreign objects lodge in the right bronchus more often than in the left. The right main bronchus gives off three branches—the **superior, middle,** and **inferior lobar (secondary) bronchi**—one to each lobe of the lung. The **left main bronchus** is about 5 cm long and slightly narrower and more horizontal than the right. It gives off superior and inferior lobar bronchi to the two lobes of the left lung.

In both lungs, the lobar bronchi branch into **segmental (tertiary) bronchi.** There are 10 of these in the right lung and 8 in the left. Each one ventilates a functionally independent unit of lung tissue called a **bronchopulmonary segment.** This chapter's opening photo shows a cast of the bronchial trees made by the corrosion cast technique described in chapter 3, with each bronchopulmonary segment injected with a different color of resin.

The main bronchi are supported, like the trachea, by rings of hyaline cartilage, whereas the cartilages transition to overlapping crescent-shaped plates by the time we reach the lobar and segmental bronchi. All of the bronchi are lined with ciliated pseudostratified columnar epithelium, but the cells grow shorter and the epithelium thinner as we progress distally. The lamina propria has an abundance of mucous glands and lymphatic nodules (*mucosa-associated lymphatic tissue, MALT*), favorably positioned to intercept inhaled pathogens. All divisions of the bronchial tree have a substantial amount of elastic connective tissue, which contributes to the recoil that expels air from the lungs in each respiratory cycle. The mucosa also has a well-developed layer of smooth muscle, the *muscularis mucosae,* which contracts or relaxes to constrict or dilate the airway, thus regulating airflow.

Bronchioles (BRON-kee-olz) are continuations of the airway that lack supportive cartilage and are 1 mm or less in diameter. The portion of the lung ventilated by one bronchiole is called a **pulmonary lobule.** Bronchioles have a ciliated cuboidal epithelium and a well-developed layer of smooth muscle in their walls. Spasmodic contractions of this muscle at death cause the bronchioles to exhibit a wavy lumen in most histological sections.

Each bronchiole divides into 50 to 80 **terminal bronchioles,** the final branches of the conducting zone **(fig. 22.11).** These measure 0.5 mm or less in diameter and have no mucous glands or goblet cells. They do have cilia, however, so that mucus draining into them from the more proximal air passages can be driven back by the mucociliary escalator, preventing congestion of the terminal bronchioles and alveoli.

---

[11]*carina* = keel

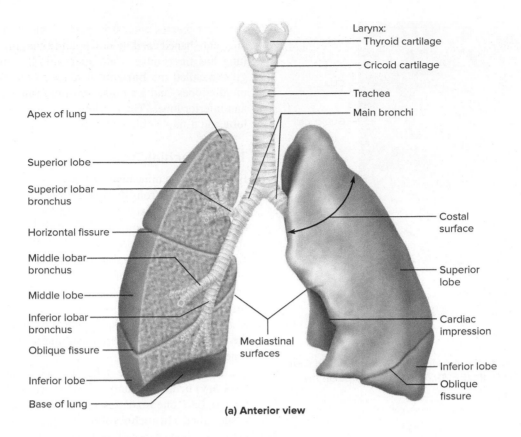

Larynx:
Thyroid cartilage
Cricoid cartilage
Trachea
Main bronchi

Apex of lung

Superior lobe

Superior lobar bronchus

Horizontal fissure

Middle lobar bronchus

Middle lobe

Inferior lobar bronchus

Oblique fissure

Inferior lobe

Base of lung

Mediastinal surfaces

Costal surface

Superior lobe

Cardiac impression

Inferior lobe

Oblique fissure

(a) Anterior view

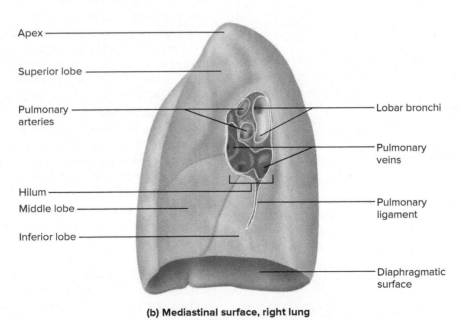

Apex

Superior lobe

Pulmonary arteries

Hilum

Middle lobe

Inferior lobe

Lobar bronchi

Pulmonary veins

Pulmonary ligament

Diaphragmatic surface

(b) Mediastinal surface, right lung

FIGURE 22.9 Gross Anatomy of the Lungs. (a) Anterior view, with frontal section through right lung. (b) Mediastinal surface of right lung, showing hilum. **APR**

Each terminal bronchiole gives off two or more smaller **respiratory bronchioles,** which have alveoli budding from their walls. They are considered the beginning of the respiratory zone because their alveoli participate in gas exchange. Their walls have scanty smooth muscle, and the smallest of them are nonciliated. Each respiratory bronchiole divides into 2 to 10 elongated, thin-walled passages called **alveolar ducts,** which also have alveoli along their walls. The alveolar ducts and smaller divisions have nonciliated simple squamous epithelia. The ducts end in **alveolar sacs,** which are clusters of alveoli arrayed around a central space called the **atrium.** The distinction between an alveolar duct and atrium is their shape—an elongated duct, or an atrium with about equal length and width. It is often a subjective judgment whether to regard a space as an alveolar duct or atrium.

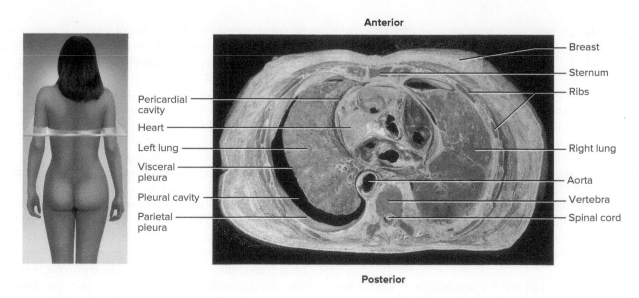

Anterior

Posterior

FIGURE 22.10 Cross Section Through the Thoracic Cavity. This photograph is oriented the same way as the reader's body. The pleural cavity is especially evident where the left lung has shrunken away from the thoracic wall, but in a living person the lung fully fills this space, the parietal and visceral pleurae are pressed together, and the pleural cavity is only a potential space between the membranes, as on the right side of this photograph.

Rebecca Gray/Don Kincaid/McGraw-Hill Education

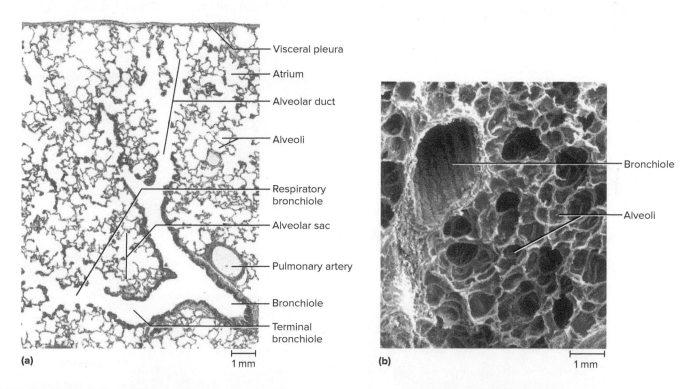

(a)

(b)

FIGURE 22.11 Histology of the Lung. (a) Light micrograph. (b) Scanning electron micrograph. Note the spongy texture of the lung.

a: MICROSCAPE/Science Source; **b:** Biophoto Associates/Science Source

Branches of the *pulmonary artery* closely follow the bronchial tree on their way to the alveoli. The *bronchial arteries* service the bronchi, bronchioles, and some other pulmonary and thoracic tissues (see section 20.7d); they don't extend to the alveoli.

In summary, the path of airflow is as follows. The first several passages belong to the conducting zone, where there are no alveoli and the tissue walls are too thick for any significant exchange of oxygen or carbon dioxide with the blood: nasal cavity → pharynx → trachea → main bronchus → lobar bronchus → segmental bronchus → bronchiole → terminal bronchiole. Then begins the respiratory zone, where all of the passages have alveoli along their walls (or are themselves alveoli) and thus engage in gas exchange: respiratory bronchiole → alveolar duct → atrium → alveolus.

Alveoli

The functional importance of human lung structure is best appreciated by comparison to the lungs of a few other animals. In frogs and other amphibians, the lung is a simple hollow sac, like an inflated balloon, lined with blood vessels. This is sufficient to meet the oxygen needs of animals with low metabolic rates. Mammals, with their high metabolic rates, could never have evolved with such a simple lung. Rather than consisting of one large sac, each human lung is a spongy mass composed of 150 million little sacs, the alveoli. These provide about 70 m^2 of gas-exchange surface per lung—about equal to the floor area of a handball court or a room 8.4 m (25 ft) square.

An **alveolus** (AL-vee-OH-lus) is a pouch about 0.2 to 0.5 mm in diameter (**fig. 22.12**). Thin, broad cells called **squamous (type I) alveolar cells** cover about 95% of the alveolar surface area. Their thinness allows for rapid gas diffusion between the air and blood. The other 5% is covered by round to cuboidal **great (type II) alveolar cells.** Squamous alveolar cells cover so much more surface area because they're so thin and spread out, even though they're far outnumbered by the great alveolar cells. If you visualize a ball of dough as representing a great alveolar cell, the same amount of dough rolled out into a thin sheet would be analogous to a squamous alveolar cell. Great alveolar cells have two functions: (1) They repair the alveolar epithelium when the squamous cells are damaged; and (2) they secrete *pulmonary surfactant,* a mixture of phospholipids and protein that coats the alveoli and smallest bronchioles and prevents the bronchioles from collapsing when one exhales. This surfactant function is later explained in greater detail.

The most numerous of all lung cells are **alveolar macrophages (dust cells),** which wander the lumens of the alveoli and connective tissue between them. These cells keep the alveoli free of debris by phagocytizing dust particles that escape entrapment by mucus in the more proximal parts of the respiratory tract. In lungs that are infected or bleeding, the macrophages also phagocytize bacteria and loose blood cells. As many as 100 million alveolar macrophages perish each day as they ride up the mucociliary escalator to be swallowed and digested, thus ridding the lungs of their load of debris.

Each alveolus is surrounded by a web of blood capillaries supplied by small branches of the pulmonary artery. The barrier between the alveolar air and blood, called the **respiratory membrane,** consists only of the squamous alveolar cell, the squamous endothelial cell of the capillary, and their shared basement

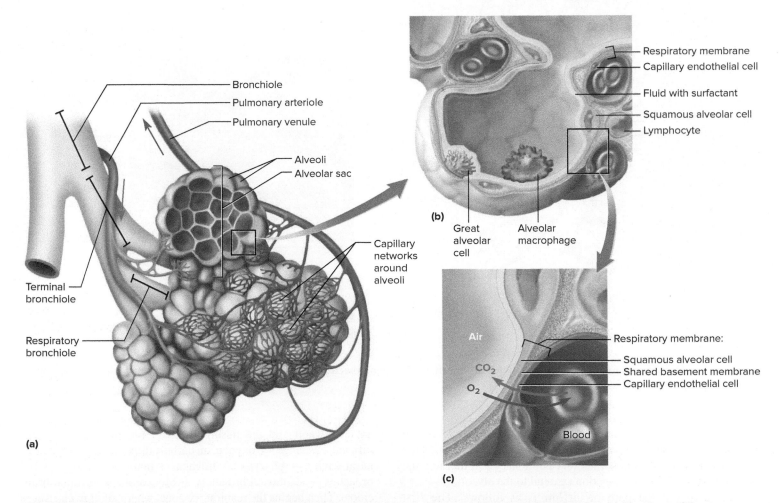

FIGURE 22.12 Pulmonary Alveoli. (a) Clusters of alveoli and their blood supply. (b) Structure of an alveolus. (c) Structure of the respiratory membrane.

membrane. These have a total thickness of only 0.5 µm, just 1/15 the diameter of a single erythrocyte.

It is crucial to prevent fluid from accumulating in the alveoli, because gases diffuse too slowly through liquid to sufficiently aerate the blood. Except for a thin film of moisture on the alveolar wall, the alveoli are kept dry by the absorption of excess water by the blood capillaries. The mean blood pressure in these capillaries is only 10 mm Hg compared to 30 mm Hg at the arterial end of the average capillary elsewhere. This low blood pressure is greatly over-ridden by the oncotic pressure that retains fluid in the capillaries (see the principles of capillary fluid exchange in section 20.3), so the osmotic uptake of water overrides filtration and keeps the alveoli free of excess fluid. The low capillary blood pressure also prevents rupture of the delicate respiratory membrane. The lungs also have a more extensive lymphatic drainage than any other organ in the body.

22.1f The Pleurae

A serous membrane, the **pleura** (PLOOR-uh), lines the thoracic wall and forms the surface of the lung. It has two layers, visceral and parietal. The **visceral pleura** forms the surface of the lung and extends even into the fissures between the lobes. At the hilum, it turns back on itself and forms the **parietal pleura,** which adheres to the mediastinum, inner surface of the rib cage, and superior surface of the diaphragm (see fig. 22.10). An extension of the parietal pleura, the *pulmonary ligament,* connects it to the diaphragm.

The space between the parietal and visceral pleurae is called the **pleural cavity.** The pleural cavity doesn't *contain* the lung; rather, it wraps around the lung, much like the pericardium wraps around the heart. The pleural cavity contains nothing but a thin film of lubricating **pleural fluid;** the cavity is only a *potential space,* meaning there is normally no room between the membranes. How-ever, under pathological conditions such as chest wounds or seep-age of fluid into the space *(pleural effusion),* the pleural cavity can fill with air or liquid, as discussed later in this chapter.

The pleurae and pleural fluid have three functions:

1. **Reduction of friction.** Pleural fluid acts as a lubricant that enables the lungs to expand and contract with minimal fric-tion. Infection of the pleurae can produce a condition called *pleurisy,* in which the pleurae roughen and rub together, making each breath a painful experience.

2. **Creation of a pressure gradient.** The pleurae play a role, explained later, in the creation of a pressure gradient that expands the lungs when one inhales.

3. **Compartmentalization.** The pleurae, mediastinum, and pericardium compartmentalize the thoracic organs and prevent infections of one organ from spreading easily to neighboring organs.

BEFORE YOU GO ON

Answer the following questions to test your understanding of the preceding section:

1. A dust particle is inhaled and gets into an alveolus without being trapped along the way. Describe the path it takes, naming all air passages from external naris to alveolus. What would happen to it after arrival in the alveolus?

2. Describe the histology of the epithelium and lamina propria of the nasal cavity and the functions of the cell types present.

3. Palpate two of your laryngeal cartilages and name them. Name the ones that cannot be palpated on a living person.

4. Describe the roles of the intrinsic muscles, corniculate cartilages, and arytenoid cartilages in speech.

5. Contrast the epithelium of the bronchioles with that of the alveoli and explain how the structural difference is related to their functional difference.

6. Explain why it is fallacious to say, as some sources do, that the lungs are contained in the pleural cavities.

22.2 Pulmonary Ventilation

Expected Learning Outcomes

When you have completed this section, you should be able to

a. name the muscles of respiration and describe their roles in breathing;

b. describe the brainstem centers that control breathing and the inputs they receive from other levels of the nervous system;

c. explain how pressure gradients account for the flow of air into and out of the lungs, and how those gradients are produced;

d. identify the sources of resistance to airflow and discuss their relevance to respiration;

e. explain the significance of anatomical dead space to alveolar ventilation;

f. define the clinical measurements of pulmonary volume and capacity; and

g. define terms for various deviations from the normal pattern of breathing.

With the foregoing anatomical background, our next objective is to understand how the lungs are ventilated. Breathing, or pulmonary ventilation, consists of a repetitive cycle of **inspiration** (inhaling) and **expiration** (exhaling). One complete breath, in and out, is called a **respiratory cycle.**

We must distinguish at times between quiet and forced respira-tion. **Quiet respiration** refers to relaxed, unconscious, automatic breathing, the way one would breathe when reading a book or lis-tening to a class lecture and not thinking about breathing. **Forced respiration** means unusually deep or rapid breathing, as in a state of exercise or when singing, playing a wind instrument, blowing up a balloon, coughing, or sneezing.

The lungs don't ventilate themselves. The only muscle they contain is smooth muscle in the walls of the bronchi and bronchi-oles. This muscle adjusts the diameter of the airway and affects the speed of airflow, but it doesn't create the airflow. That job belongs to the skeletal muscles of the trunk.

Air, like other fluids, flows down a pressure gradient from a point of higher pressure to one of lower pressure. Recall the syringe analogy (see fig. 19.18), in which we saw how an increase in the volume of a space reduces its pressure and results in an inflow of fluid. The action of the respiratory muscles is much like that of the syringe plunger—at one moment, to increase the volume and lower the pressure in the thoracic cavity, so air flows in; at the next moment, to reduce thoracic volume and raise pressure, so air flows out. We will next examine these muscular actions, how the nervous system controls them, and how the variables of pressure and resistance affect airflow and pulmonary ventilation.

22.2a The Respiratory Muscles

The principal muscles of respiration are the diaphragm and intercostal muscles (**fig. 22.13**). The diaphragm is the prime mover (see table 10.4); it alone produces about two-thirds of the pulmonary

airflow. When relaxed, it bulges upward to its farthest extent, pressing against the base of the lungs. The lungs are at their minimum volume. When the diaphragm contracts, it tenses and flattens somewhat, dropping about 1.5 cm in relaxed inspiration and as much as 12 cm in deep breathing. Not only does its descent enlarge the superior-to-inferior dimension of the thoracic cage, but its flattening also pushes outward on the sternum and ribs and enlarges the anterior-to-posterior dimension. Enlargement of the thoracic cavity lowers its internal pressure and produces an inflow of air. When the diaphragm relaxes, it bulges upward again, compresses the lungs, and expels air.

Several other muscles aid the diaphragm as synergists. Chief among these are the internal and external intercostal muscles between the ribs. Their primary function is to stiffen the thoracic cage during respiration and prevent it from collapsing when the diaphragm descends. However, they also contribute to enlargement and contraction of the thoracic cage and add about one-third of the air that ventilates the lungs. During quiet breathing, the scalene muscles of the neck fix ribs 1 and 2 (hold them stationary),

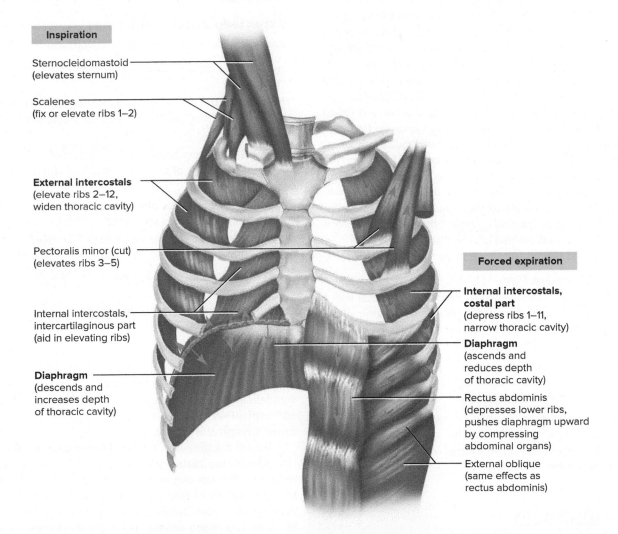

FIGURE 22.13 The Respiratory Muscles. Boldface indicates the principal respiratory muscles; the others are accessory. Arrows indicate the direction of muscle action. Muscles listed on the left are active during inspiration and those on the right are active during forced expiration. Note that the diaphragm is active in both phases, and different parts of the internal intercostal muscles serve for inspiration and expiration. Some other accessory muscles not shown here are discussed in the text.

while the external intercostal muscles pull the other ribs upward. Since most ribs are anchored at both ends—by their attachment to the vertebral column at the proximal (posterior) end and their attachment through the costal cartilage to the sternum at the distal (anterior) end—they swing upward like the handles on a bucket and thrust the sternum forward. These actions increase both the transverse (left to right) and anteroposterior diameters of the chest. In deep breathing, the anteroposterior dimension can increase as much as 20% as the chest swells.

Other muscles of the chest and abdomen also aid in breathing, especially during forced respiration; thus they are considered *accessory muscles* of respiration. Deep inspiration is aided by the erector spinae, which arches the back and increases chest diameter, and by several muscles that elevate the upper ribs: the sternocleidomastoids and scalenes of the neck; the pectoralis minor, pectoralis major, serratus anterior, and serratus posterior superior of the chest; and the *intercartilaginous part* of the internal intercostals (the anterior part between the costal cartilages). Although the scalenes merely fix the upper ribs during quiet respiration, they elevate them during forced inspiration.

Normal expiration is an energy-saving passive process achieved by the elasticity of the lungs and thoracic cage. The bronchial tree, the attachments of the ribs to the spine and sternum, and the tendons of the diaphragm and other respiratory muscles spring back when the muscles relax. As these structures recoil, the thoracic cage diminishes in size, the air pressure in the lungs rises above the atmospheric pressure outside, and the air flows out. The only muscular effort involved in normal expiration is a braking action—that is, the muscles relax gradually rather than abruptly, thus preventing the lungs from recoiling too suddenly. This makes the transition from inspiration to expiration smoother.

In forced expiration, the rectus abdominis pulls down on the sternum and lower ribs, while the *interosseous part* of the internal intercostals (the lateral part between the ribs proper) and the serratus posterior inferior pull the other ribs downward. These actions reduce the chest dimensions and expel air more rapidly and thoroughly than usual. Other lumbar, abdominal, and even pelvic muscles contribute to forced expiration by raising the pressure in the abdominal cavity and pushing some of the viscera, such as the stomach and liver, up against the diaphragm. This increases the pressure in the thoracic cavity and thus helps to expel air. Such "abdominal breathing" is particularly important in singing and public speaking.

Not only does abdominal pressure affect thoracic pressure, but the opposite is also true. Depression of the diaphragm raises abdominal pressure and helps to expel the contents of certain abdominal organs, thus aiding in childbirth, urination, defecation, and vomiting. During such actions, we often consciously or unconsciously employ the **Valsalva**[12] **maneuver.** This consists of taking a deep breath, holding it by closing the glottis, and then contracting the abdominal muscles to raise abdominal pressure and push the organ contents out.

22.2b Neural Control of Breathing

The heartbeat and breathing are the two most conspicuously rhythmic processes in the body. The heart, we have seen, has an internal pacemaker, but the lungs do not. No autorhythmic pacemaker cells for respiration have been found that are analogous to those of the heart, and the exact mechanism for setting the rhythm of respiration remains obscure. But we do know that breathing depends on repetitive stimuli from the brain. It ceases if the nerve connections to the thoracic muscles are severed or if the spinal cord is severed high on the neck. There are two reasons for this dependence on the brain: (1) Skeletal muscles, unlike cardiac muscle, can't contract without nervous stimulation. (2) Breathing involves the well-orchestrated action of multiple muscles and thus requires a central coordinating mechanism.

Breathing is controlled at two levels of the brain. One is cerebral and conscious, enabling us to inhale or exhale at will. The other is unconscious and automatic. Most of the time, we breathe without thinking about it—fortunately, for we otherwise couldn't go to sleep without fear of respiratory arrest (see Deeper Insight 22.2).

Brainstem Respiratory Centers

The automatic, unconscious cycle of breathing is controlled by three pairs of respiratory centers in the reticular formation of the medulla oblongata and pons **(fig. 22.14)**. There is one of each on the right and left sides of the brainstem; the two sides communicate with each other so that the respiratory muscles contract symmetrically.

1. The **ventral respiratory group (VRG)** is the primary generator of the respiratory rhythm. It is an elongated neural network in the medulla with two commingled webs of neurons—**inspiratory (I) neurons** and **expiratory (E) neurons**—each forming a reverberating neural circuit (see fig. 12.32). In quiet breathing (called *eupnea*), the I neuron circuit fires for about 2 seconds at a time, issuing nerve signals to integrating centers in the spinal cord. The spinal centers relay signals by way of the phrenic nerves to the diaphragm and by way of intercostal nerves to the external intercostal muscles. Contraction of these muscles enlarges the thoracic cage and causes inspiration. As long as the I neurons are firing, they also inhibit the E neurons. Eventually, however, the I neurons stop firing, either because of fatigue or because they're inhibited by signals from an outside source. As their activity wanes, the E neurons begin firing. They further inhibit the I neurons, allowing the inspiratory muscles to relax. Elastic recoil of the thoracic cage expels air from the lungs. Relaxed expiration normally lasts about 3 seconds. Then the E neuron activity wanes, the I neurons resume firing, and the cycle repeats itself. In eupnea, this oscillating pattern of neural activity, alternating between the I neuron and E neuron circuits, produces a respiratory rhythm of about 12 breaths per minute.

---

[12]Antonio Maria Valsalva (1666–1723), Italian anatomist

2. The **dorsal respiratory group (DRG)** is one of the mechanisms that modifies this basic respiratory rhythm. It is a web of neurons that extends for much of the length of the medulla between the VRG and the central canal of the brainstem. Obviously, we don't always breathe at the same rate. Breathing can be faster or slower, shallower or deeper, as the DRG and other mechanisms modulate the VRG's activity. The DRG is an integrating center that receives input from several sources detailed in the coming discussion: a respiratory center in the pons (the PNG discussed next); a chemosensitive center of the anterior medulla oblongata; chemoreceptors in certain major arteries; stretch and irritant receptors in the airway; and higher brainstem centers that allow for emotional influences on breathing. The DRG issues output to the VRG that modifies the respiratory rhythm to adapt to varying conditions.

3. The **pontine respiratory group (PRG)** on each side of the pons receives input from higher brain centers including the hypothalamus, limbic system, and cerebral cortex, and issues output to both the DRG and VRG. By acting on those centers in the medulla, it hastens or delays the transition from inspiration to expiration, making each breath shorter and shallower, or longer and deeper. The PRG adapts breathing to special circumstances such as sleep, exercise, vocalization, and emotional responses (for example, in crying, gasping, or laughing).

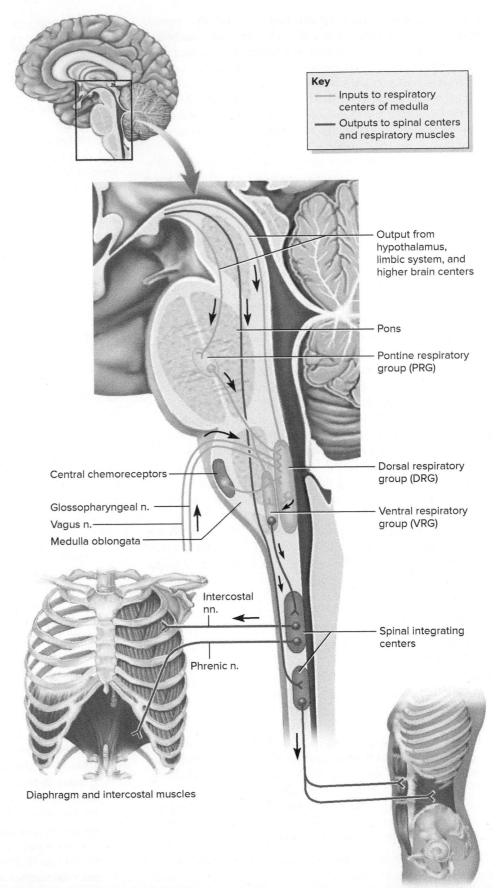

Key
— Inputs to respiratory centers of medulla
— Outputs to spinal centers and respiratory muscles

Output from hypothalamus, limbic system, and higher brain centers

Pons

Pontine respiratory group (PRG)

Dorsal respiratory group (DRG)

Ventral respiratory group (VRG)

Spinal integrating centers

Central chemoreceptors

Glossopharyngeal n.

Vagus n.

Medulla oblongata

Intercostal nn.

Phrenic n.

Diaphragm and intercostal muscles

Accessory muscles of respiration

FIGURE 22.14 Respiratory Control Centers in the Central Nervous System. See text for explanation of these centers and control pathways.

DEEPER INSIGHT 22.2

CLINICAL APPLICATION

Ondine's Curse

In German legend, there was a water nymph named Ondine who took a mortal lover. When her lover proved unfaithful, the king of the nymphs put a curse on him that took away his automatic physiological functions. Consequently, he had to remember to take each breath, and he couldn't go to sleep or he would die of suffocation—which, as exhaustion overtook him, was indeed his fate.

Some people suffer a disorder called *Ondine's curse,* in which the automatic respiratory functions are disabled. This can result from accidents of neurosurgery, brainstem damage from polio, or mutation of a gene that codes for chemoreceptors in the medulla oblongata and blunts the response to CO_2 accumulation. Victims of Ondine's curse must remember to take each breath and can't go to sleep without the aid of a mechanical ventilator.

▶▶▶ APPLY WHAT YOU KNOW

Some authorities refer to the respiratory rhythm as an autonomic function. Discuss whether you think this is an appropriate word for it. What are the effectors of the autonomic nervous system? (See chapter 15.) What are the effectors that ventilate the lungs? What bearing might this have on the question?

Central and Peripheral Input to the Respiratory Centers

Variations in the respiratory rhythm are possible because the respiratory centers of the medulla and pons receive input from several other levels of the nervous system and therefore respond to the body's varying physiological needs. For example, anxiety can trigger a bout of uncontrollable *hyperventilation* in some people, a state in which breathing is so rapid that it expels CO_2 from the body faster than it's produced. As blood CO_2 levels drop, the pH rises and causes the cerebral arteries to constrict. This reduces cerebral perfusion and may cause dizziness or fainting. Hyperventilation can be brought under control by having a person rebreathe the expired CO_2 from a paper bag held over the nose and mouth.

Multiple sensory receptors also provide information to the respiratory centers:

- **Central chemoreceptors** are brainstem neurons that respond especially to changes in the pH of the cerebrospinal fluid. They are concentrated on each side of the medulla oblongata at a point only 0.2 mm beneath its anterior surface. The pH of the CSF reflects the CO_2 level in the blood, so by regulating respiration to maintain a stable CSF pH, the respiratory centers also ensure a stable blood CO_2 level.

- **Peripheral chemoreceptors** are located in the carotid and aortic bodies of the large arteries above the heart (**fig. 22.15**). They respond to the O_2 and CO_2 content of the blood, but most of all to pH. The carotid bodies communicate with the

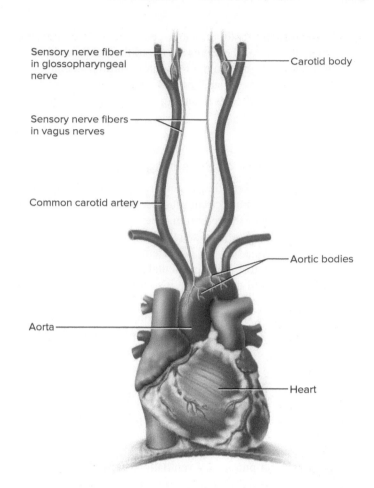

FIGURE 22.15 The Peripheral Chemoreceptors of Respiration. Peripheral chemoreceptors in the aortic arch and carotid bodies monitor blood gas concentrations and blood pH. They send signals about blood chemistry to the dorsal respiratory group of the medulla oblongata through sensory fibers in the vagus and glossopharyngeal nerves.

brainstem by way of the glossopharyngeal nerves, and the aortic bodies by way of the vagus nerves. Sensory fibers in these nerves enter the medulla and synapse with neurons of the DRG.

- **Stretch receptors** are found in the smooth muscle of the bronchi and bronchioles and in the visceral pleura. They respond to inflation of the lungs and signal the DRG by way of the vagus nerves. Excessive inflation triggers the **inflation (Hering–Breuer)[13] reflex,** a protective somatic reflex that strongly inhibits the I neurons and stops inspiration. In infants, this may be a normal mechanism of transition from inspiration to expiration, but after infancy it is activated only by extreme stretching of the lungs.

- **Irritant receptors** are nerve endings amid the epithelial cells of the airway. They respond to smoke, dust, pollen,

---

[13]Heinrich Ewald Hering (1866–1948), German physiologist; Josef Breuer (1842–1925), Austrian physician

chemical fumes, cold air, and excess mucus. They transmit signals by way of the vagus nerves to the DRG, and the DRG returns signals to the respiratory and bronchial muscles, resulting in such protective reflexes as broncho-constriction, shallower breathing, breath-holding *(apnea)*, or coughing.

Voluntary Control of Breathing

Voluntary control of breathing is important in singing, speaking, breath-holding, and other circumstances. Such control originates in the motor cortex of the cerebrum. The output neurons send impulses down the corticospinal tracts to the integrating centers in the spinal cord, bypassing the brainstem centers. There are limits to voluntary control. Temperamental children may threaten to hold their breath until they die, but it's impossible to do so. Holding one's breath raises the CO_2 level of the blood until a *breaking point* is reached when automatic controls override one's will. This forces a person to resume breathing even if he or she has lost consciousness.

22.2c Pressure, Resistance, and Airflow

Now that we know the neuromuscular aspects of breathing, we'll explore how the expansion and contraction of the thoracic cage produce airflow into and out of the lungs.

Understanding pulmonary ventilation, the transport of gases in the blood, and the exchange of gases with the tissues draws on certain *gas laws* of physics. These are named after their discoverers and are not intuitively easy to remember by name. **Table 22.1** lists them for your convenience and may be a helpful reference as you progress through respiratory physiology.

TABLE 22.1	The Gas Laws of Respiratory Physiology
Boyle's law[14]	The pressure of a given quantity of gas is inversely proportional to its volume (assuming a constant temperature).
Charles's law[15]	The volume of a given quantity of gas is directly proportional to its absolute temperature (assuming a constant pressure).
Dalton's law[16]	The total pressure of a gas mixture is equal to the sum of the partial pressures of its individual gases.
Henry's law[17]	At the air–water interface, the amount of gas that dissolves in water is determined by its solubility in water and its partial pressure in the air (assuming a constant temperature).

[14]Robert Boyle (1627–91), Anglo–Irish physicist and chemist
[15]Jacques A. C. Charles (1746–1823), French physicist
[16]John Dalton (1766–1844), English physicist and chemist
[17]William Henry (1774–1836), English chemist

Pressure and Airflow

Respiratory airflow is governed by the same principles of flow, pressure, and resistance as blood flow. As we saw in section 20.2, the flow (F) of a fluid is directly proportional to the pressure difference between two points (ΔP) and inversely proportional to resistance (R):

$$F \propto \Delta P/R.$$

For the moment, we'll focus especially on ΔP, the pressure gradient that produces airflow. We'll deal with resistance later.

The pressure that drives inspiration is **atmospheric (barometric) pressure**—the weight of the air above us. At sea level, this averages 760 mm Hg, or by definition, *1 atmosphere (1 atm)*. It fluctuates with the weather from day to day and is lower at higher elevations, but we'll use the average sea-level value as a reference point for discussion.

One way to change the pressure of an enclosed gas is to change the volume of its container. This fact is summarized by **Boyle's law:** Assuming a constant temperature, *the pressure of a given quantity of gas is inversely proportional to its volume*. If the lungs contain a quantity of gas and lung volume increases, their internal pressure (**intrapulmonary pressure**) falls. Conversely, if lung volume decreases, intrapulmonary pressure rises. (Compare this to the syringe analogy.)

If the intrapulmonary pressure falls below the atmospheric pressure, then air tends to flow down its pressure gradient into the lungs. Conversely, if intrapulmonary pressure rises above atmospheric pressure, air flows out. Therefore, all we have to do to breathe is to cyclically raise and lower the intrapulmonary pressure, employing the neuromuscular mechanisms recently described.

When dealing with respiratory airflow and thoracic pressures generated by the foregoing muscle actions, we must use a new unit of measurement, different from what you're accustomed to. In recent chapters, we used *millimeters of mercury (mm Hg)* as a measure of blood pressure, and we'll use it again later in this chapter when we speak of atmospheric pressure and blood gases. Millimeters of mercury is a measure of how high up a vacuum tube a force such as blood pressure or the weight of the atmosphere can push a column of mercury. Mercury is a very heavy liquid, so we use it because pressures can be measured with a relatively short column of mercury, as in the sphygmomanometer of a doctor's office. But the pressures in respiratory airflow are so small that they couldn't move a mercury column much at all; mercury-based instruments aren't sensitive enough. Respiratory physiologists therefore traditionally used water columns, which are more sensitive, and we measure these pressures in *centimeters of water (cm H_2O)*. (1 mm Hg $\approx$ 13.6 mm H_2O $\approx$ 1.4 cm H_2O.) Small pressure changes will move a column of water more than a column of mercury; one can see them and measure them more accurately (although now they're measured with electronic instruments rather than water-filled tubes).

Since respiratory airflow is driven by a *difference* between surrounding (ambient) atmospheric pressure and pressures in the chest, the following discussion is based on *relative* pressures. If we speak of pressure in the pulmonary alveoli reaching –2 cm H_2O during inspiration, we mean it falls 2 cm H_2O below the ambient atmospheric pressure; if it rises to +3 cm H_2O during expiration, it is 3 cm H_2O above ambient atmospheric pressure.

Inspiration

Now consider the flow of air into the lungs—inspiration. **Figure 22.16** traces the events and pressure changes that occur throughout a respiratory cycle.

At the beginning (step ① in the figure), there is no movement of the thoracic cage, no difference between the air pressure within the lungs and the ambient atmospheric pressure, and no airflow. What happens when the thoracic cage expands? Why don't the lungs remain the same size and simply occupy less space in the chest? Consider the two layers of the pleura: the parietal pleura lining the rib cage and the visceral pleura on the lung surface. They aren't anatomically attached to each other along their surfaces, but they're wet and cling together like sheets of wet paper. The space between them (*pleural cavity*) is only about 10 to 30 μm wide (about the width of one typical cell). At the end of a normal expiration, the chest wall (including the parietal pleura) tends to expand outward because of its elasticity while the lungs, because of their elasticity, tend to recoil inward. Thus, the lungs and chest wall are pulling in opposite directions. This creates a negative **intrapleural pressure,** averaging about –5 cm H_2O, between the parietal and visceral pleurae.

When the ribs swing up and out during inspiration (step ② in the figure), the parietal pleura follows. If not for the cohesion of water, this could pull the chest wall away from the lungs; but because the two wet membranes cling to each other, it only reduces the intrapleural pressure a little more, to about –8 cm H_2O. As the visceral pleura (lung surface) is pulled outward, it stretches the alveoli just below the surface of the lung. Those alveoli are mechanically linked to deeper ones by their walls, and stretch the deeper ones as well. Thus the entire lung expands along with the thoracic cage. As in the syringe analogy, the alveoli increase in volume and decrease in pressure. Pressure within the alveoli, the **intrapulmonary (alveolar) pressure,** drops to an average of –1 cm H_2O. So now there is a pressure gradient from the ambient pressure at the nostrils to the negative pressure in the alveoli. Air flows down its gradient and ventilates the lungs. In short, we inhale.

Yet this isn't the only force that expands the lungs. Another is warming of the inhaled air. As we see from **Charles's law** (see table 22.1), the volume of a given quantity of gas is directly proportional to its absolute temperature. Inhaled air is warmed to 37°C (99°F) by the time it reaches the alveoli. This means that on a cool North American day when the outdoor temperature is, say, 16°C (60°F), the air temperature would increase by 21°C (39°F) during inspiration, becoming comparable to air temperature in the tropics. An inhaled volume of 500 mL will expand to 536 mL and this thermal expansion will contribute to inflation of the lungs.

When the respiratory muscles stop contracting, the inflowing air quickly achieves an intrapulmonary pressure equal to atmospheric pressure, and flow stops. In quiet breathing, the dimensions of the thoracic cage increase by only a few millimeters in each direction, but this is enough to increase its total volume by about 500 mL. Typically, about 500 mL of air therefore flows into the respiratory tract.

▶▶▶ APPLY WHAT YOU KNOW

When you inhale, does your chest expand because your lungs inflate, or do your lungs inflate because your chest expands? Explain.

Expiration

Relaxed expiration is a passive process achieved, as we have seen, mainly by the elastic recoil of the thoracic cage. This recoil compresses the lungs and raises the intrapulmonary pressure to about +1 cm H_2O (step ③ in the figure). Air thus flows down its pressure gradient, out of the lungs. In forced breathing, the accessory muscles raise intrapulmonary pressure as high as +40 cm H_2O.

The effect of pulmonary elasticity is evident in a pathological state of pneumothorax and atelectasis. **Pneumothorax** is the presence of air in the pleural cavity. If the thoracic wall is punctured between the ribs, for example, inspiration sucks air through the wound into the pleural cavity and the visceral and parietal pleurae separate; what was a *potential space* between them becomes an air-filled cavity. Without the negative intrapleural pressure to keep the lungs inflated, the lungs recoil and collapse. The collapse of part or all of a lung is called **atelectasis**[18] (AT-eh-LEC-ta-sis). Atelectasis can also result from airway obstruction—for example, by a lung tumor, aneurysm, swollen lymph node, or aspirated object. Blood absorbs gases from the alveoli distal to the obstruction, and that part of the lung collapses because it can't be reinflated.

Resistance to Airflow

Pressure is one determinant of airflow; the other is resistance. The greater the resistance, the slower the flow. But what governs resistance? Two factors are of particular importance: diameter of the bronchioles and pulmonary compliance.

Like arterioles, the large number of bronchioles, their small diameter, and their ability to change diameter make them the primary means of controlling resistance. The trachea and bronchi can also change diameter to a degree, but are more constrained by the supporting cartilages in their walls. An increase in the diameter of a bronchus or bronchiole is called **bronchodilation** (BRON-co-dy-LAY-shun) and a reduction in diameter is called **bronchoconstriction.** Epinephrine and the sympathetic nerves (norepinephrine) stimulate bronchodilation and increase airflow. Histamine, parasympathetic nerves (acetylcholine), cold air, and chemical irritants are among the factors that stimulate bronchoconstriction. Many people have suffocated from the extreme bronchoconstriction brought on by anaphylactic shock or asthma (see Deeper Insight 21.3).

---

[18]*atel* = imperfect, incomplete; *ectasis* = expansion

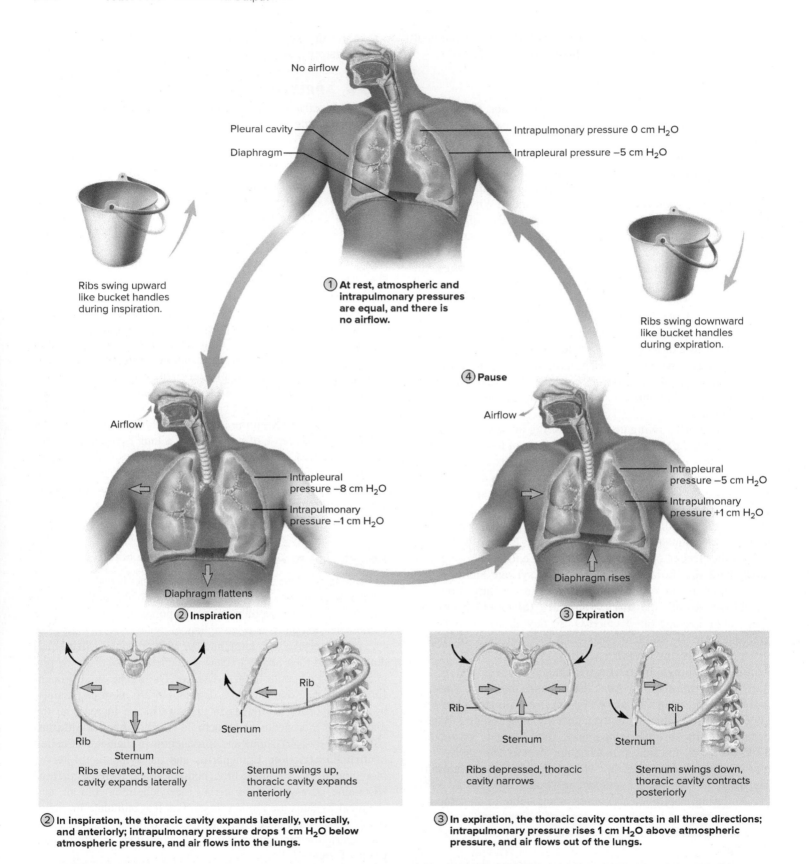

No airflow

Pleural cavity

Diaphragm

Intrapulmonary pressure 0 cm H_2O

Intrapleural pressure −5 cm H_2O

Ribs swing upward like bucket handles during inspiration.

① **At rest, atmospheric and intrapulmonary pressures are equal, and there is no airflow.**

Ribs swing downward like bucket handles during expiration.

④ **Pause**

Airflow

Airflow

Intrapleural pressure −8 cm H_2O

Intrapulmonary pressure −1 cm H_2O

Intrapleural pressure −5 cm H_2O

Intrapulmonary pressure +1 cm H_2O

Diaphragm flattens

Diaphragm rises

② **Inspiration**

③ **Expiration**

Rib

Sternum

Rib

Sternum

Rib

Sternum

Rib

Sternum

Ribs elevated, thoracic cavity expands laterally

Sternum swings up, thoracic cavity expands anteriorly

Ribs depressed, thoracic cavity narrows

Sternum swings down, thoracic cavity contracts posteriorly

② In inspiration, the thoracic cavity expands laterally, vertically, and anteriorly; intrapulmonary pressure drops 1 cm H_2O below atmospheric pressure, and air flows into the lungs.

③ In expiration, the thoracic cavity contracts in all three directions; intrapulmonary pressure rises 1 cm H_2O above atmospheric pressure, and air flows out of the lungs.

FIGURE 22.16 The Respiratory Cycle. All pressures given here are relative to atmospheric pressure external to the body, which is considered to be zero as a point of reference. Note that pressures governing respiratory airflow are measured in cm H_2O (centimeters of water), not mm Hg. Like bucket handles, each rib is attached at both ends (to the spine and sternum) and swings up and down during inspiration and expiration. **APR**

Pulmonary compliance means the ease with which the lungs expand, or more exactly, the change in lung volume relative to a given pressure change. Inspiratory effort may produce the same intrapleural pressure in two people, but the lungs will expand less in a person with poorer compliance (stiffer lungs), or at least that person must expend more effort to inflate the lungs to the same degree as the other. Think of the difference in effort it takes to blow up a brand-new party balloon (with low compliance) versus blowing up one that has been inflated before. Pulmonary compliance is reduced by degenerative lung diseases such as tuberculosis and black lung disease, in which the lungs are stiffened by scar tissue. In such conditions, the thoracic cage expands normally but the lungs expand relatively little.

A major limitation on pulmonary compliance is the thin film of water on the respiratory epithelium, especially from the respiratory bronchioles to the alveoli. This film is necessary for gas exchange, but creates a potential problem for pulmonary ventilation. Water molecules are attracted to each other by hydrogen bonds, creating surface tension, as we saw in section 2.2a. You can appreciate the strength of this attraction if you reflect on the difficulty of separating two sheets of wet paper compared with two sheets of dry paper. Surface tension draws the walls of the airway inward toward the lumen. If it went unchecked, parts of the airway would collapse with each expiration and would strongly resist reinflation. This is especially so in small airways such as the respiratory bronchioles and alveolar ducts leading to the alveoli.

The solution to this problem takes us back to the great alveolar cells and their surfactant. A surfactant is an agent that disrupts the hydrogen bonds of water and reduces surface tension; soaps and detergents are everyday examples. The pulmonary surfactant is composed of amphipathic proteins and phospholipids. These molecules are partially hydrophobic, so they spread out over the surface of the water film, partially embedded in it like ice cubes floating in a bowl of water. As the small airways deflate, the surfactants are squeezed closer together, like the ice cubes being pushed together into a smaller area. If the air spaces were covered with a film of water only, they could continue collapsing, because water molecules can pile up into a thicker film of moisture. The physical structure of the surfactants resists compression, however. They can't pile up into a thicker layer because their hydrophilic regions resist separation from the water below. As they become crowded into a small area and resist layering, they retard and then halt the collapse of the airway.

Deep breathing spreads pulmonary surfactant throughout the small airways. Patients recently out of surgery are encouraged to breathe deeply, even though it may hurt, in order to promote this spread of surfactant up the alveolar ducts and small bronchioles. Those who don't adhere to their breathing exercises can experience collapse of portions of the lung that are not adequately coated with surfactant.

The importance of this surfactant is especially apparent when it's lacking. Premature infants often have a surfactant deficiency and great difficulty breathing (see section 29.3b). The resulting *infant respiratory distress syndrome (IRDS)* can be treated by administering artificial surfactant.

22.2d Alveolar Ventilation

Air that actually enters the alveoli becomes available for gas exchange, but not all inhaled air gets that far. About 150 mL of it fills the conducting zone of the airway. Since this air cannot exchange gases with the blood, the conducting zone is called the **anatomical dead space.** The dead space is about 1 mL per pound of body weight in a healthy person. In some pulmonary diseases, however, it can be substantially greater. Some alveoli may be unable to exchange gases because they lack blood flow or because the pulmonary membrane is thickened by edema or fibrosis. **Physiological (total) dead space** is the sum of anatomical dead space and any pathological dead space that may exist.

The anatomical dead space varies with circumstances. In a state of relaxation, parasympathetic stimulation keeps the airway somewhat constricted. This minimizes the dead space so more of the inhaled air ventilates the alveoli. In a state of arousal or exercise, by contrast, the sympathetic nervous system dilates the airway, which increases airflow. The increased airflow outweighs the air that is wasted by filling the increased dead space.

If a person inhales 500 mL of air and 150 mL of it stays in the dead space, then 350 mL ventilates the alveoli. Multiplying this by the respiratory rate gives the **alveolar ventilation rate (AVR)**—for example,

$$350 \text{ mL/breath} \times 12 \text{ breaths/min.} = 4{,}200 \text{ mL/min.}$$

Of all measures of pulmonary ventilation, this one is most directly relevant to the body's ability to get oxygen to the tissues and dispose of carbon dioxide.

The air current taken in by inspiration never actually enters the alveoli. This *bulk flow* of air gets only as far as the terminal bronchioles. Beyond this point, the air passages are so narrow and their resistance to flow is so great that bulk flow ceases. Oxygen completes its journey to the alveoli, and carbon dioxide leaves them, by simple diffusion. Pulsation of the pulmonary arteries generated by the heartbeat probably compresses adjacent airways and accelerates this process, however.

The lungs never completely empty during expiration. There is always some leftover air called the *residual volume,* typically about 1,300 mL that one cannot exhale even with maximum effort. Residual air mixes with fresh air arriving on the next inspiration, so the same oxygen-depleted air doesn't remain in the lungs cycle after cycle. It takes about 90 seconds, or approximately 18 breaths at an average rate and depth of breathing, to completely replace all pulmonary air.

22.2e Measurement of Pulmonary Ventilation

Clinicians often measure a patient's pulmonary ventilation in order to assess the severity of a respiratory disease or monitor the patient's improvement or deterioration. The process of making such measurements is called **spirometry.**[19] It entails

---

[19]*spiro* = breath; *metry* = process of measuring

having the subject breathe into a device called a **spirometer** (fig. 22.17a), which recaptures the expired breath and records such variables as the rate and depth of breathing, speed of expiration, and rate of oxygen consumption. Representative measurements for a healthy adult male are given in **table 22.2** and explained in **figure 22.17b.** Female values are somewhat lower because of smaller average body size.

Four of these values are called *respiratory volumes:* tidal volume, inspiratory reserve volume, expiratory reserve volume, and residual volume. **Tidal volume (TV)** is the amount of air inhaled and exhaled in one cycle; in quiet breathing, it averages about 500 mL. Beyond the amount normally inhaled, it's typically possible to inhale another 3,000 mL with maximum effort; this is the **inspiratory reserve volume (IRV).** Similarly, with maximum

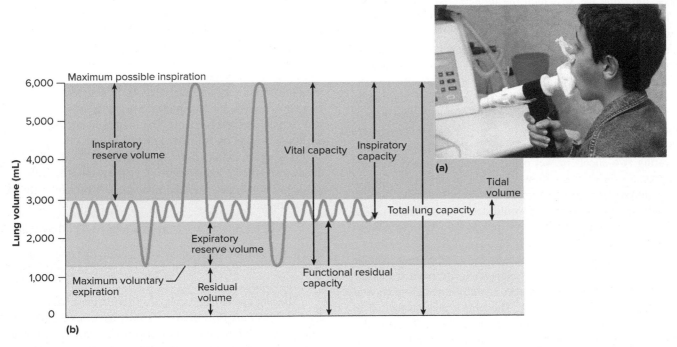

FIGURE 22.17 Respiratory Volumes and Capacities. (a) Subject breathing into a spirometer. (b) An idealized spirogram. The wavy line indicates inspiration when it rises and expiration when it falls. Compare with table 22.2.

a: BSIP/Science Source

? *Why is a nose clip necessary for obtaining a valid spirogram?*

TABLE 22.2	Respiratory Volumes and Capacities for an Average Young Adult Male		
Measurement	**Typical Value**	**Definition**	
Respiratory Volumes			
Tidal volume (TV)	500 mL	Amount of air inhaled and exhaled in one cycle during quiet breathing	
Inspiratory reserve volume (IRV)	3,000 mL	Amount of air in excess of tidal volume that can be inhaled with maximum effort	
Expiratory reserve volume (ERV)	1,200 mL	Amount of air in excess of tidal volume that can be exhaled with maximum effort	
Residual volume (RV)	1,300 mL	Amount of air remaining in the lungs after maximum expiration; the amount that can never be voluntarily exhaled	
Respiratory Capacities			
Vital capacity (VC)	4,700 mL	The amount of air that can be inhaled and then exhaled with maximum effort; the deepest possible breath (VC = ERV + TV + IRV)	
Inspiratory capacity (IC)	3,500 mL	Maximum amount of air that can be inhaled after a normal tidal expiration (IC = TV + IRV)	
Functional residual capacity (FRC)	2,500 mL	Amount of air remaining in the lungs after a normal tidal expiration (FRC = RV + ERV)	
Total lung capacity (TLC)	6,000 mL	Maximum amount of air the lungs can contain (TLC = RV + VC)	

effort, one can normally exhale another 1,200 mL beyond the normal amount; this difference is the **expiratory reserve volume (ERV).** Even after a maximum voluntary expiration, there remains a **residual volume (RV)** of about 1,300 mL. This air allows gas exchange with the blood to continue even between the times one inhales fresh air.

Four other measurements, called *respiratory capacities,* are obtained by adding two or more of the respiratory volumes: **vital capacity (VC)** (ERV + TV + IRV), **inspiratory capacity** (TV + IRV), **functional residual capacity** (RV + ERV), and **total lung capacity** (RV + VC). Vital capacity, the maximum ability to ventilate the lungs in one breath, is an especially important measure of pulmonary health.

Spirometry helps to assess and distinguish between *restrictive* and *obstructive* lung disorders. **Restrictive disorders** are those that reduce pulmonary compliance, thus limiting the amount to which the lungs can be inflated. They show in spirometry as a reduced vital capacity. Any disease that produces pulmonary fibrosis has a restrictive effect: black lung disease and tuberculosis, for example. **Obstructive disorders** are those that interfere with airflow by narrowing or blocking the airway. They make it harder to inhale or exhale a given amount of air. Asthma and chronic bronchitis are the most common examples. Obstructive disorders can be measured by having the subject exhale as rapidly as possible into a spirometer and measuring **forced expiratory volume (FEV)**—the volume of air or the percentage of the vital capacity that can be exhaled in a given time interval. A healthy adult should be able to expel 75% to 85% of the vital capacity in 1.0 second (a value called the $FEV_{1.0}$). At home, asthma patients and others can monitor their respiratory function by blowing into a handheld meter that roughly measures **peak flow,** the maximum speed of expiration.

The amount of air inhaled per minute is the **minute respiratory volume (MRV).** MRV largely determines the alveolar ventilation rate. It can be measured directly with a spirometer or obtained by multiplying tidal volume by respiratory rate. For example, if a person has a tidal volume of 500 mL per breath and a rate of 12 breaths per minute, the MRV would be $500 \times 12 = 6,000$ mL/min. During heavy exercise, MRV may be as high as 125 to 170 L/min. This is called **maximum voluntary ventilation (MVV),** formerly called *maximum breathing capacity.*

22.2f Variations in the Respiratory Rhythm

Relaxed, quiet breathing is called **eupnea**[20] (YOOP-nee-uh). It is typically characterized by a tidal volume of about 500 mL and a respiratory rate of 12 to 15 breaths per minute. Conditions ranging from exercise or anxiety to various disease states can cause deviations such as abnormally fast, slow, or labored breathing. **Table 22.3** defines the clinical terms for several such variations. You should familiarize yourself with these before proceeding, because later discussions in this chapter assume a working knowledge of some of these terms.

TABLE 22.3	Variations in the Respiratory Rhythm
Apnea[21] (AP-nee-uh)	Temporary cessation of breathing (one or more skipped breaths)
Dyspnea[22] (DISP-nee-uh)	Labored, gasping breathing; shortness of breath
Hyperpnea[23] (HY-purp-NEE-uh)	Increased rate and depth of breathing in response to exercise, pain, or other conditions
Hyperventilation	Increased pulmonary ventilation in excess of metabolic demand, frequently associated with anxiety; expels CO_2 faster than it is produced, thus lowering the blood CO_2 concentration and raising the blood pH
Hypoventilation[24]	Reduced pulmonary ventilation; leads to an increase in blood CO_2 concentration if ventilation is insufficient to expel CO_2 as fast as it is produced
Kussmaul[25] respiration	Deep, rapid breathing often induced by acidosis; seen in diabetes mellitus
Orthopnea[26] (or-thop-NEE-uh)	Dyspnea that occurs when a person is lying down or in any position other than standing or sitting erect; seen in heart failure, asthma, emphysema, and other conditions
Respiratory arrest	Permanent cessation of breathing (unless there is medical intervention)
Tachypnea[27] (tack-ip-NEE-uh)	Accelerated respiration

Other variations in pulmonary ventilation serve the purposes of speaking, expressing emotion (laughing, crying), yawning, hiccuping, expelling noxious fumes, coughing, sneezing, and expelling abdominal contents. Coughing is induced by irritants in the lower respiratory tract. To cough, we close the glottis and contract the respiratory and abdominal muscles, producing high pressure in the lower respiratory tract. We then suddenly open the glottis and release an explosive burst of air at speeds over 900 km/h (600 mi./h). This drives mucus and foreign matter toward the pharynx and mouth. Sneezing is triggered by irritants in the nasal cavity. Its mechanism is similar to coughing except that the glottis is continually open, the soft palate and tongue block the flow of air while thoracic pressure builds, and then the soft palate is depressed to direct part of the airstream through the nose. These actions are coordinated by coughing and sneezing centers in the medulla oblongata.

[20]*eu* = easy, normal; *pnea* = breathing
[21]*a* = without; *pnea* = breathing
[22]*dys* = difficult, abnormal, painful; *pnea* = breathing
[23]*hyper* = above normal
[24]*hypo* = below normal
[25]Adolph Kussmaul (1822–1902), German physician
[26]*ortho* = straight, erect; *pnea* = breathing
[27]*tachy* = fast; *pnea* = breathing

Answer the following questions to test your understanding of the preceding section:

7. Explain why contraction of the diaphragm causes inspiration but contraction of the transverse abdominal muscle causes expiration.

8. Which brainstem respiratory nucleus is indispensable to respiration? What do the other nuclei do?

9. Explain why Boyle's law is relevant to the action of the respiratory muscles.

10. Explain why eupnea requires little or no action by the muscles of expiration.

11. Identify a benefit and a disadvantage of normal (nonpathological) bronchoconstriction.

12. Suppose a healthy person has a tidal volume of 650 mL, an anatomical dead space of 160 mL, and a respiratory rate of 14 breaths per minute. Calculate her alveolar ventilation rate.

13. Suppose a person has a total lung capacity of 5,800 mL, a residual volume of 1,200 mL, an inspiratory reserve volume of 2,400 mL, and an expiratory reserve volume of 1,400 mL. Calculate his tidal volume.

22.3 Gas Exchange and Transport

Expected Learning Outcomes

When you have completed this section, you should be able to

a. define *partial pressure* and discuss its relationship to a gas mixture such as air;

b. contrast the composition of inspired and alveolar air;

c. discuss how partial pressure affects gas transport by the blood;

d. describe the mechanisms of transporting O_2 and CO_2;

e. describe the factors that govern gas exchange in the lungs and systemic capillaries;

f. explain how gas exchange is adjusted to the metabolic needs of different tissues; and

g. discuss the effect of blood gases and pH on the respiratory rhythm.

Ultimately, respiration is about gases, especially oxygen and carbon dioxide. We will turn our attention now to the behavior of these gases in the human body: how oxygen is obtained from inspired air and delivered to the tissues, and how carbon dioxide is removed from the tissues and released into the expired air. First, however, it is necessary to understand the composition of the air we inhale and how gases behave in contact with the water film that lines the alveoli.

22.3a Composition of Air

Air consists of about 78.6% nitrogen; 20.9% oxygen; 0.04% carbon dioxide; several quantitatively minor gases such as argon, neon, helium, methane, and ozone; and a variable amount of water vapor. Water vapor constitutes from 0% to 4%, depending on temperature and humidity; we will use a value of 0.5%, typical of a cool clear day.

Total atmospheric pressure is a sum of the contributions of these individual gases—a principle known as **Dalton's law** (see table 22.1). The separate contribution of each gas in a mixture is called its **partial pressure** and is symbolized with a P followed by the formula of the gas, such as P_{O_2}. As we are now concerned with atmospheric pressures and how they influence the partial pressures of blood gases, we return to mm Hg as our unit of measurement (not cm H_2O as when we were considering pulmonary ventilation). If we assume the average sea-level atmospheric pressure of 760 mm Hg and oxygen is 20.9% of the atmosphere, then P_{O_2} is simply

$$0.209 \times 760 \text{ mm Hg} = 159 \text{ mm Hg.}$$

Applying Dalton's law to the aforementioned mixture of gases in the air gives us the following:

$$P_{N_2} + P_{O_2} + P_{H_2O} + P_{CO_2}$$

$$\approx 597 + 159 + 3.7 + 0.3$$

$$= 760.0 \text{ mm Hg.}$$

These values change dramatically at higher altitude (see Deeper Insight 22.3).

This is the composition of the air we inhale, but it's not the composition of air in the alveoli. Alveolar air can be sampled with an apparatus that collects the last 10 mL of expired air. As we see in **table 22.4,** its composition differs from that of the atmosphere because of three influences: (1) It is humidified by contact with the mucous membranes, so its P_{H_2O} is more than 10 times higher than that of the inhaled air. (2) Freshly inspired air mixes with residual air left from the previous respiratory cycle, so its oxygen is diluted and it is enriched with CO_2 from the residual air. (3) Alveolar air

TABLE 22.4	Composition of Inspired (Atmospheric) and Alveolar Air			
Gas	Inspired Air*		Alveolar Air	
N_2	78.6%	597 mm Hg	74.9%	569 mm Hg
O_2	20.9%	159 mm Hg	13.7%	104 mm Hg
H_2O	0.5%	3.7 mm Hg	6.2%	47 mm Hg
CO_2	0.04%	0.3 mm Hg	5.3%	40 mm Hg
Total	100%	760 mm Hg	100%	760 mm Hg

* Typical values for a cool clear day; values vary with temperature and humidity. Other gases present in small amounts are disregarded.

DEEPER INSIGHT 22.3

MEDICAL HISTORY

The Flight of the Zenith

As any aviator or mountain hiker knows, the composition of air changes dramatically from sea level to high altitude. This was all too sadly realized by French physician Paul Bert (1833–86), who is commonly recognized as the founder of aerospace medicine. He invented the first pressure chamber capable of simulating the effects of high altitude, and undertook a variety of experiments on human and animal subjects to test the effects of variation in oxygen partial pressure. In 1875, balloonist Gaston Tissandier set out from Paris in a hot-air balloon named the *Zenith* with two of Bert's protégés in physiology. Their aim was to investigate the effects of the low oxygen pressures attainable only by ascending to a very high altitude. They ignored Bert's advice to breathe supplemental oxygen continually, rather than only when they felt the need for it. As they ascended, they observed each other and took notes. Seeing no ill effects, they continued to throw out ballast and go higher, eventually to 28,000 feet. But after passing 24,000 feet, they experienced stupefaction, muscular paralysis, euphoria, and finally unconsciousness. The balloon eventually descended on its own with two of the three men dead; only Tissandier lived to write about it.

exchanges O_2 and CO_2 with the blood. Thus, the P_{O_2} of alveolar air is about 65% that of inhaled air, and its P_{CO_2} is more than 130 times higher.

▶▶▶**APPLY WHAT YOU KNOW**

Expired air considered as a whole (not just the last 10 mL) is about 15.3% O_2 and 4.2% CO_2. Why would these values differ from the ones for alveolar air?

22.3b Alveolar Gas Exchange **A&PR**

Air in the alveolus is in contact with the film of water covering the alveolar epithelium. For oxygen to get into the blood, it must dissolve in this water and pass through the respiratory membrane separating the air from the bloodstream. For carbon dioxide to leave the blood, it must pass the other way and diffuse out of the water film into the alveolar air. This back-and-forth traffic of O_2 and CO_2 across the respiratory membrane is called **alveolar gas exchange.**

The reason O_2 diffuses in one direction and CO_2 in the other is that each gas diffuses down its own partial pressure gradient. Whenever air and water are in contact with each other, gases diffuse down their gradients until the partial pressure of each gas in the air is equal to its partial pressure in the water. If a gas has a greater partial pressure in the water than in the air, it diffuses into the air; the smell of chlorine near a swimming pool is evidence of

this. If the partial pressure of the gas is greater in the air, it diffuses into the water.

Henry's law states that *at the air–water interface, for a given temperature, the amount of gas that dissolves in the water is determined by its solubility in water and its partial pressure in the air* (**fig. 22.18**). Thus, the greater the P_{O_2} in the alveolar air, the more O_2 the blood picks up. And since blood arriving at an alveolus has a higher P_{CO_2} than air, it releases CO_2 into the alveolar air. At the alveolus, the blood is said to *unload* CO_2 and *load* O_2. Each gas in a mixture behaves independently; the diffusion of one gas doesn't influence the diffusion of another.

Both O_2 loading and CO_2 unloading involve erythrocytes (RBCs). The efficiency of these processes therefore depends on

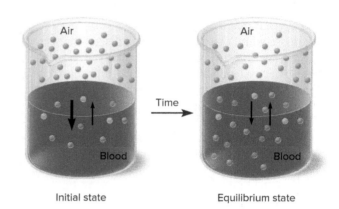

Initial state   Equilibrium state

(a) Oxygen

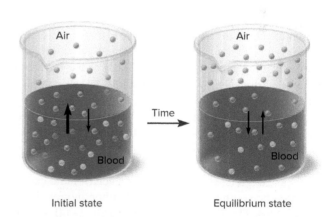

Initial state   Equilibrium state

(b) Carbon dioxide

FIGURE 22.18 Henry's Law and Its Relationship to Alveolar Gas Exchange. (a) The P_{O_2} of alveolar air is initially higher than the P_{O_2} of the blood arriving at an alveolus. Oxygen diffuses into the blood until the two are in equilibrium. (b) The P_{CO_2} of the arriving blood is initially higher than the P_{CO_2} of alveolar air. Carbon dioxide diffuses into the alveolus until the two are in equilibrium.

how long an RBC spends in an alveolar capillary compared with how long it takes for each gas to be fully loaded or unloaded—that is, for them to reach equilibrium concentrations in the capillary blood. It takes about 0.25 second to reach equilibrium. At rest, when blood circulates at its slowest speed, an RBC takes about 0.75 second to pass through an alveolar capillary—plenty of time to pick up a maximum load of oxygen. Even in vigorous exercise, when the blood flows faster, an erythrocyte is in the alveolar capillary for about 0.3 second, which is still adequate.

Several variables affect the efficiency of alveolar gas exchange, and under abnormal conditions, some of these can prevent the complete loading and unloading of gases:

- **Pressure gradients of the gases.** P_{O_2} is about 104 mm Hg in alveolar air and 40 mm Hg in blood arriving at an alveolus. Oxygen therefore diffuses from the air into the blood, where it reaches a P_{O_2} of 104 mm Hg. Before the blood leaves the lung, however, this drops to about 95 mm Hg. This oxygen dilution occurs because the pulmonary veins anastomose with bronchial veins in the lungs, so there is some mixing of the oxygen-rich pulmonary blood with oxygen-poor systemic blood. Even though the blood is 100% saturated with oxygen as it leaves the alveolar capillaries, it is nearly impossible for it to remain 100% saturated by the time it leaves the lungs.

  P_{CO_2} is about 46 mm Hg in blood arriving at the alveolus and 40 mm Hg in alveolar air. CO_2 therefore diffuses from the blood into the alveoli. These changes are summarized here and in the yellow zone of **figure 22.19.**

Blood entering lungs		*Blood leaving lungs*	
P_{O_2}	40 mm Hg	P_{O_2}	95 mm Hg
P_{CO_2}	46 mm Hg	P_{CO_2}	40 mm Hg

  These gradients differ under special circumstances such as high elevation and *hyperbaric oxygen therapy* (treatment with oxygen at >1 atm of pressure) (**fig. 22.20**). At high elevations, the partial pressures of all atmospheric gases are lower. Atmospheric P_{O_2}, for example, is 159 mm Hg at sea level but only 110 mm Hg at 3,000 m (10,000 feet). The O_2 gradient from air to blood is proportionately less, so as we can predict from Henry's law, less O_2 diffuses into the blood. In a hyperbaric oxygen chamber, by contrast, a patient is exposed to 3 to 4 atm of oxygen to treat such conditions as gangrene (to kill anaerobic bacteria) and carbon monoxide poisoning (to displace the carbon monoxide from hemoglobin). The P_{O_2} ranges from 2,300 to 3,000 mm Hg. Thus, there is a very steep gradient of P_{O_2} from alveolus to blood and diffusion into the blood is accelerated.

- **Solubility of the gases.** Gases differ in their ability to dissolve in water. Carbon dioxide is about 20 times as soluble as oxygen, and oxygen is about twice as soluble as nitrogen. Even though the pressure gradient of O_2 is much greater than that of CO_2 across the respiratory membrane, equal amounts of the two gases are exchanged because CO_2 is so much more soluble and diffuses more rapidly.

- **Membrane thickness.** The respiratory membrane between the blood and alveolar air is only 0.5 μm thick in most places—much less than the 7 to 8 μm diameter of a single RBC. Thus, it presents little obstacle to diffusion (**fig. 22.21a**). In such heart conditions as left ventricular failure, however, blood pressure builds up in the lungs and promotes capillary filtration into the connective tissues, causing the respiratory membranes to become edematous and thickened (similar to their condition in pneumonia; **fig. 22.21b**). The gases have farther to travel between blood and air, so oxygen can't get to the RBCs quickly enough to fully load their hemoglobin. Under these circumstances, blood leaving the lungs has an unusually low P_{O_2} and high P_{CO_2}.

- **Membrane area.** In good health, each lung has about 70 m² of respiratory membrane available for gas exchange. Since the alveolar capillaries contain a total of only 100 mL of blood at any one time, this blood is spread very thinly. Several pulmonary diseases, however, decrease the alveolar surface area and thus lead to low blood P_{O_2}—for example, emphysema (**fig. 22.21c**) and lung cancer.

- **Ventilation–perfusion coupling.** Gas exchange requires not only good ventilation of the alveoli but also good perfusion of their capillaries. *Ventilation–perfusion coupling* refers to physiological responses that match airflow to blood flow and vice versa. For example, if part of a lung were poorly ventilated because of tissue destruction or an airway obstruction, it would be pointless to direct much blood to that tissue. Poor ventilation leads to a low P_{O_2} in that region of the lung. This stimulates local vasoconstriction, rerouting the blood to better-ventilated areas of the lung where it can pick up more oxygen (left side of **fig. 22.22a**). In contrast, increased ventilation raises the local blood P_{O_2} and this stimulates vasodilation, increasing blood flow to that region to take advantage of the oxygen availability (right side of same figure). These reactions of the pulmonary arteries are opposite from the reactions of systemic arteries, which dilate in response to hypoxia. Furthermore, changes in the blood flow to a region of a lung stimulate bronchoconstriction or dilation, adjusting ventilation so that air is directed to the best-perfused parts of the lung (**fig. 22.22b**).

22.3c Gas Transport

Gas transport is the process of carrying gases from the alveoli to the systemic tissues and vice versa. This section explains how the blood loads and transports O_2 and CO_2.

Oxygen

Arterial blood carries about 20 mL of oxygen per deciliter. About 98.5% of it is bound to hemoglobin in the RBCs and 1.5% is dissolved in the blood plasma. Hemoglobin is specialized for oxygen transport. It consists of four protein (globin) chains, each with one heme group (see fig. 18.5). Each heme can bind 1 O_2 to the iron atom at its center; thus, one

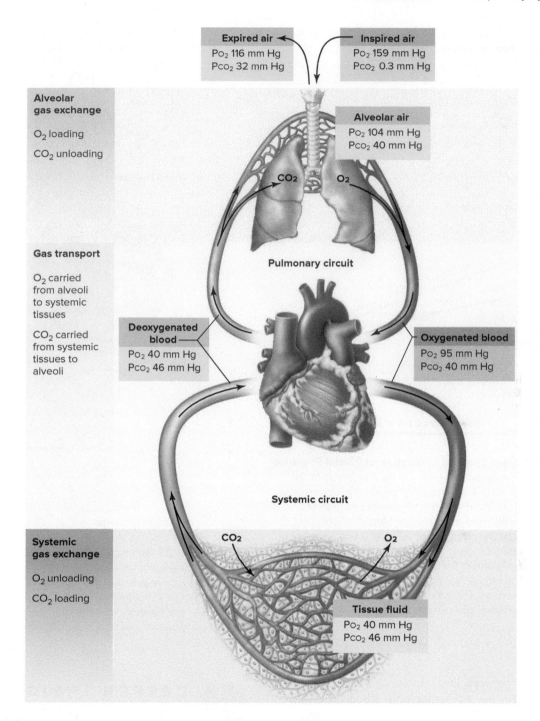

FIGURE 22.19 Changes in Po$_2$ and Pco$_2$ Along the Circulatory Route. APR

? *Trace the partial pressure of oxygen from inspired air to expired air and explain each change in Po$_2$ along the way. Do the same for Pco$_2$.*

Labels within the figure:

Expired air
Po$_2$ 116 mm Hg
Pco$_2$ 32 mm Hg

Inspired air
Po$_2$ 159 mm Hg
Pco$_2$ 0.3 mm Hg

Alveolar gas exchange

O$_2$ loading

CO$_2$ unloading

Alveolar air
Po$_2$ 104 mm Hg
Pco$_2$ 40 mm Hg

CO$_2$ O$_2$

Pulmonary circuit

Gas transport

O$_2$ carried from alveoli to systemic tissues

CO$_2$ carried from systemic tissues to alveoli

Deoxygenated blood
Po$_2$ 40 mm Hg
Pco$_2$ 46 mm Hg

Oxygenated blood
Po$_2$ 95 mm Hg
Pco$_2$ 40 mm Hg

Systemic circuit

Systemic gas exchange

O$_2$ unloading

CO$_2$ loading

CO$_2$ O$_2$

Tissue fluid
Po$_2$ 40 mm Hg
Pco$_2$ 46 mm Hg

hemoglobin molecule can carry up to 4 O$_2$. If one or more molecules of O$_2$ are bound to hemoglobin, the compound is called **oxyhemoglobin (HbO$_2$),** whereas hemoglobin with no oxygen bound to it is **deoxyhemoglobin (HHb).** When hemoglobin is 100% saturated, every molecule of it carries 4 O$_2$; if it is 75% saturated, there is an average of 3 O$_2$ per hemoglobin molecule; if it is 50% saturated, there is an average of 2 O$_2$ per hemoglobin; and so forth. The poisonous effect of carbon monoxide stems from its competition for the O$_2$ binding site (see Deeper Insight 22.4).

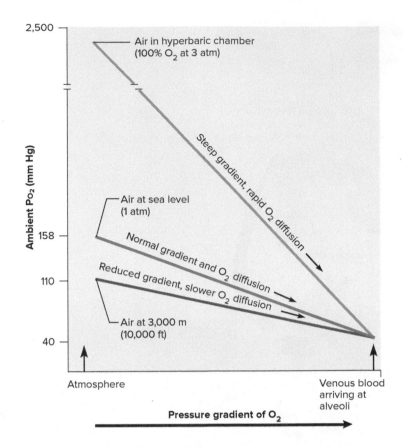

FIGURE 22.20 Oxygen Loading in Relation to Partial Pressure Gradient. The rate of loading depends on the steepness of the gradient from alveolar air to the venous blood arriving at the alveolar capillaries. Compared with the oxygen gradient at sea level (blue line), the gradient is less steep at high elevation (red line) because the Po_2 of the atmosphere is lower. Thus, oxygen loading of the pulmonary blood is slower. In a hyperbaric chamber with 100% oxygen, the gradient from air to blood is very steep (green line), and oxygen loading is correspondingly rapid. This is an illustration of Henry's law and has important effects in diving, aviation, mountain climbing, and oxygen therapy.

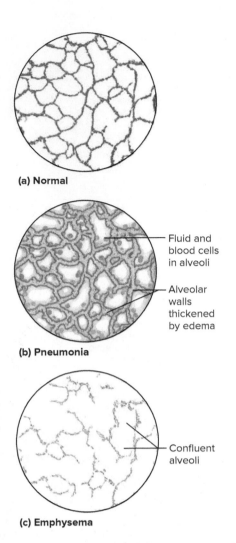

FIGURE 22.21 Pulmonary Alveoli in Health and Disease. (a) In a healthy lung, the alveoli are small and have thin respiratory membranes. (b) In pneumonia, the respiratory membranes (alveolar walls) are thick with edema, and the alveoli contain fluid and blood cells. (c) In emphysema, alveolar membranes break down and neighboring alveoli join to form larger, fewer alveoli with less total surface area.

The relationship between hemoglobin saturation and ambient Po_2 is shown by the **oxyhemoglobin dissociation curve** (fig. 22.23). As you can see, it isn't a simple linear relationship. At low Po_2, the curve rises slowly; then there is a rapid increase in oxygen loading as Po_2 rises farther. This reflects the way hemoglobin loads oxygen. When the first heme group binds O_2, hemoglobin changes shape in a way that facilitates uptake of the second O_2 by another heme group. This, in turn, promotes the uptake of the third and then the fourth O_2—hence the rapidly rising midportion of the curve. At high Po_2 levels, the curve levels off because the hemoglobin approaches 100% saturation and cannot load much more oxygen.

▶▶▶**APPLY WHAT YOU KNOW**

Is oxygen loading a positive or negative feedback process? Explain.

 DEEPER INSIGHT 22.4

CLINICAL APPLICATION

Carbon Monoxide Poisoning

The lethal effect of carbon monoxide (CO) is well known. This colorless, odorless gas occurs in cigarette smoke, engine exhaust, and fumes from gas furnaces and space heaters. It binds to the iron of hemoglobin to form *carboxyhemoglobin (HbCO)*. Thus, it competes with oxygen for the same binding site. Not only that, but it binds 210 times as tightly as oxygen. Thus, CO tends to tie up hemoglobin for a long time. Less than 1.5% of the hemoglobin is occupied by carbon monoxide in most nonsmokers, but this figure rises to as much as 3% in residents of heavily polluted cities and 10% in heavy smokers. An ambient concentration of 0.1% CO is enough to bind 50% of a person's hemoglobin, and a concentration of 0.2% is quickly lethal.

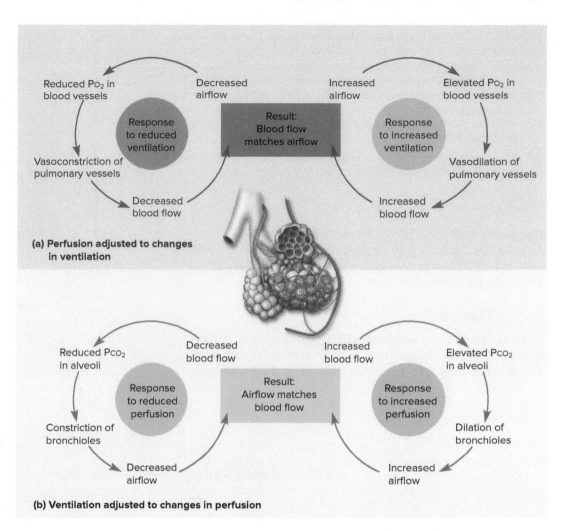

FIGURE 22.22 Ventilation–Perfusion Coupling. Negative feedback loops adjust airflow and blood flow to each other. (a) Blood circulation can be adjusted to match above- or below-normal ventilation of a part of the lung. (b) Ventilation can be adjusted to match above- or below-normal blood circulation to a part of the lung.

(a) Perfusion adjusted to changes in ventilation

Reduced P_{O_2} in blood vessels

Decreased airflow

Increased airflow

Elevated P_{O_2} in blood vessels

Response to reduced ventilation

Result: Blood flow matches airflow

Response to increased ventilation

Vasoconstriction of pulmonary vessels

Vasodilation of pulmonary vessels

Decreased blood flow

Increased blood flow

(b) Ventilation adjusted to changes in perfusion

Reduced P_{CO_2} in alveoli

Decreased blood flow

Increased blood flow

Elevated P_{CO_2} in alveoli

Response to reduced perfusion

Result: Airflow matches blood flow

Response to increased perfusion

Constriction of bronchioles

Dilation of bronchioles

Decreased airflow

Increased airflow

Carbon Dioxide

Carbon dioxide is transported in three forms: carbonic acid, carbamino compounds, and dissolved gas.

1. About 90% of the CO_2 is hydrated (reacts with water) to form **carbonic acid,** which then dissociates into bicarbonate and hydrogen ions:

$$CO_2 + H_2O \longrightarrow H_2CO_3 \longrightarrow HCO_3^- + H^+.$$

More will be said about this reaction shortly.

2. About 5% binds to the amino groups of plasma proteins and hemoglobin to form **carbamino compounds**—chiefly **carbaminohemoglobin (HbCO$_2$).** The reaction with hemoglobin can be symbolized Hb + $CO_2 \longrightarrow$ HbCO$_2$. Carbon dioxide doesn't compete with oxygen because CO_2 and O_2 bind to different sites on the hemoglobin molecule—oxygen to the heme moiety and CO_2 to the polypeptide chains. Hemoglobin can therefore transport both O_2 and CO_2 simultaneously. As we will see, however, each gas somewhat inhibits transport of the other.

3. The remaining 5% of the CO_2 is carried in the blood as dissolved gas, like the CO_2 in sparkling wines and carbonated beverages.

The relative amounts of CO_2 exchanged between the blood and alveolar air differ from the percentages just given. About 70% of the *exchanged* CO_2 comes from carbonic acid, 23% from carbamino compounds, and 7% from the dissolved gas. That is, blood gives up the dissolved CO_2 gas and CO_2 from the carbamino compounds more easily than it gives up the CO_2 in bicarbonate.

22.3d Systemic Gas Exchange

Systemic gas exchange is the unloading of O_2 and loading of CO_2 at the systemic capillaries (see fig. 22.19, bottom; **fig. 22.24**).

Carbon Dioxide Loading

Aerobic respiration produces a molecule of CO_2 for each O_2 it consumes. The tissue fluid therefore contains a relatively high P_{CO_2} and there is typically a CO_2 gradient of 46 → 40 mm Hg from tissue fluid to blood. Consequently, CO_2 diffuses into the bloodstream, where it is carried in the three forms already noted. Most of it reacts with water to produce bicarbonate ions (HCO_3^-) and hydrogen ions (H^+). This reaction occurs slowly in the blood plasma but much faster in the RBCs, where it is catalyzed by the enzyme *carbonic anhydrase.* An antiport called the *chloride–bicarbonate exchanger*

FIGURE 22.23 The Oxyhemoglobin Dissociation Curve. This curve shows the relative amount of hemoglobin that is saturated with oxygen (*y*-axis) as a function of ambient (surrounding) oxygen partial pressure (*x*-axis). As it passes through the alveolar capillaries where the P_{O_2} is high, hemoglobin becomes saturated with oxygen. As it passes through the systemic capillaries where the P_{O_2} is low, it typically gives up about 22% of its oxygen (color bar at top of graph). This percentage is called the *utilization coefficient.*

> ❓ *What would be the approximate utilization coefficient if the systemic tissues had a P_{O_2} of 30 mm Hg?*

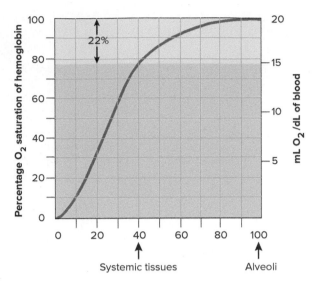

then pumps most of the HCO_3^- out of the RBC in exchange for Cl^- from the blood plasma. This exchange is called the **chloride shift.** Most of the H^+ binds to hemoglobin or oxyhemoglobin, which thus buffers the intracellular pH.

Oxygen Unloading

When H^+ binds to oxyhemoglobin (HbO_2), it reduces the affinity of hemoglobin for O_2 and tends to make hemoglobin release it. Oxygen consumption by respiring tissues keeps the P_{O_2} of tissue

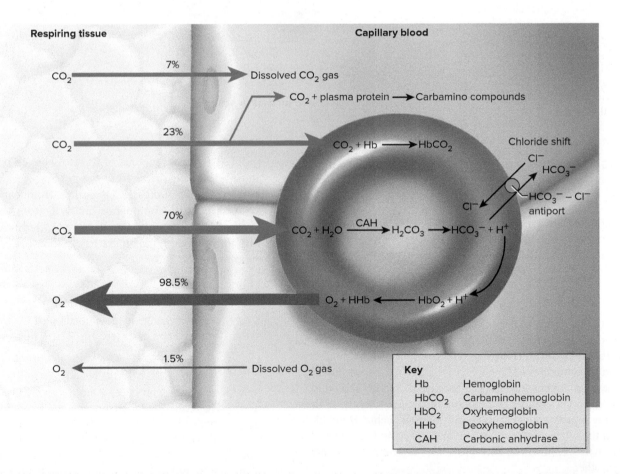

FIGURE 22.24 Systemic Gas Exchange. Blue arrows show the three mechanisms of CO_2 loading and transport; their thickness represents the relative amounts of CO_2 loaded in each of the three forms. Red arrows show the two mechanisms of O_2 unloading; their thickness indicates the relative amounts unloaded by each mechanism. Note that CO_2 loading releases hydrogen ions in the erythrocyte, and hydrogen ions promote O_2 unloading.

fluid relatively low, so there is typically a pressure gradient of about 95 → 40 mm Hg of oxygen from the arterial blood to the tissue fluid. Thus, the liberated oxygen—along with some that was carried as dissolved gas in the plasma—diffuses from the blood into the tissue fluid.

As blood arrives at the systemic capillaries, its oxygen concentration is about 20 mL/dL and the hemoglobin is about 97% saturated. As it leaves the capillaries of a typical resting tissue, its oxygen concentration is about 15.6 mL/dL and the hemoglobin is about 75% saturated. Thus, it has given up 4.4 mL/dL—about 22% of its oxygen load. This fraction is called the **utilization coefficient** (see fig. 22.23). The oxygen remaining in the blood after it passes through the capillary bed provides a **venous reserve** of oxygen, which can sustain life for 4 to 5 minutes even in the event of respiratory arrest. At rest, the circulatory system releases oxygen to the tissues at an overall rate of about 250 mL/min.

22.3e Alveolar Gas Exchange Revisited

The processes illustrated in figure 22.24 make it easier to understand alveolar gas exchange more fully. As shown in **figure 22.25,** the reactions that occur in the lungs are essentially the reverse of

systemic gas exchange. As hemoglobin loads oxygen, its affinity for H^+ declines. Hydrogen ions dissociate from the hemoglobin and bind with bicarbonate ions (HCO_3^-) transported from the plasma into the RBCs. Chloride ions are transported back out of the RBC (a reverse chloride shift). The reaction of H^+ and HCO_3^- reverses the hydration reaction and generates free CO_2. This diffuses into the alveolus to be exhaled—as does the CO_2 released from carbaminohemoglobin and CO_2 gas that was dissolved in the plasma.

22.3f Adjustment to the Metabolic Needs of Tissues

Hemoglobin doesn't unload the same amount of oxygen to all tissues. Some tissues need more and some less, depending on their state of activity. Hemoglobin responds to such variations and unloads more oxygen to the tissues that need it most. In exercising skeletal muscles, for example, the utilization coefficient may be as high as 80%. Four factors adjust the rate of oxygen unloading to the metabolic rates of different tissues:

1. **Ambient Po_2.** Since an active tissue consumes oxygen rapidly, the Po_2 of its tissue fluid remains low. From the

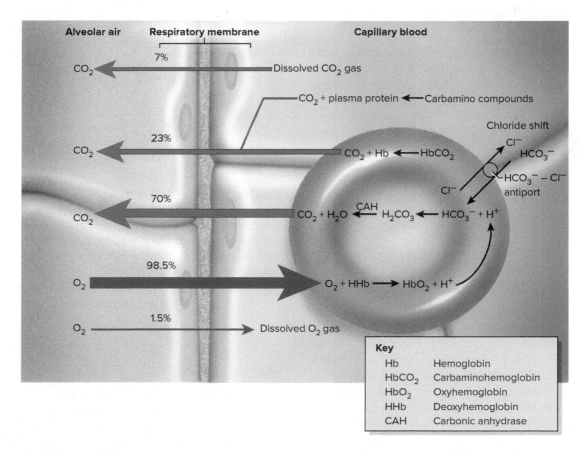

FIGURE 22.25 Alveolar Gas Exchange. Arrow colors and thicknesses represent the same variables as in the preceding figure. Note that O_2 loading promotes the decomposition of carbonic acid into H_2O and CO_2, and most exhaled CO_2 comes from the erythrocytes.

In what fundamental way does this differ from the preceding figure? Following alveolar gas exchange, will the blood contain a higher or lower concentration of bicarbonate ions than it did before?

oxyhemoglobin dissociation curve (see fig. 22.23), you can see that at a low P_{O_2}, HbO_2 releases more oxygen.

2. **Temperature.** When temperature rises, the oxyhemoglobin dissociation curve shifts to the right (**fig. 22.26a**); in other words, elevated temperature promotes oxygen unloading. Active tissues are warmer than less active ones and thus extract more oxygen from the blood passing through them.

3. **Ambient pH.** Active tissues also generate extra CO_2, which raises the H^+ concentration and lowers the pH of the blood. Hydrogen ions weaken the bond between hemoglobin and oxygen and thereby promote oxygen unloading—a phenomenon called the **Bohr**[28] **effect.** This can also be seen in the oxyhemoglobin dissociation curve, where a drop in pH shifts the curve to the right (**fig. 22.26b**). The effect is less pronounced at the high P_{O_2} present in the lungs, so pH has relatively little effect on pulmonary oxygen loading. In the systemic capillaries, however, P_{O_2} is lower and the Bohr effect is more pronounced.

4. **BPG.** Erythrocytes have no mitochondria and meet their energy needs solely by anaerobic fermentation. One of their metabolic intermediates is **bisphosphoglycerate (BPG),** which binds to hemoglobin and promotes oxygen unloading. An elevated body temperature (as in fever) stimulates BPG synthesis, as do thyroxine, growth hormone, testosterone, and epinephrine. All of these hormones thus promote oxygen unloading to the tissues.

The rate of CO_2 loading is also adjusted to varying needs of the tissues. A low level of oxyhemoglobin (HbO_2) enables the blood to transport more CO_2, a phenomenon known as the **Haldane**[29] **effect.** This occurs for two reasons: (1) HbO_2 doesn't bind CO_2 as well as deoxyhemoglobin (HHb) does. (2) HHb binds more hydrogen ions than HbO_2 does, and by removing H^+ from solution, HHb shifts the carbonic acid reaction to the right:

$$H_2O + CO_2 \longrightarrow HCO_3^- + H^+.$$

A high metabolic rate keeps oxyhemoglobin levels relatively low and thus allows more CO_2 to be transported by these two mechanisms.

22.3g Blood Gases and the Respiratory Rhythm

Normally the systemic arterial blood has a P_{O_2} of 95 mm Hg, a P_{CO_2} of 40 mm Hg, and a pH of 7.40 ± 0.05. The rate and depth of breathing are adjusted to maintain these values. This is possible because the brainstem respiratory centers receive input from central and peripheral chemoreceptors that monitor the composition of the blood and CSF, as described earlier in this chapter. Of these three chemical stimuli, the most potent stimulus for breathing is pH, followed by CO_2; perhaps surprisingly, the least significant is O_2.

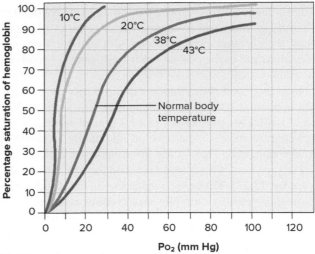

(a) Effect of temperature

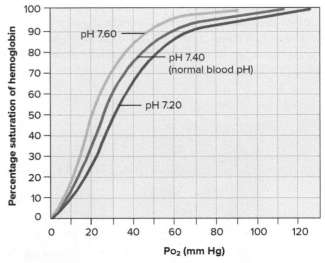

(b) Effect of pH

FIGURE 22.26 Effects of Temperature and pH on Oxyhemoglobin Dissociation. (a) For a given P_{O_2}, hemoglobin unloads more oxygen at higher temperatures. (b) For a given P_{O_2}, hemoglobin unloads more oxygen at lower pH (the Bohr effect). Both mechanisms cause hemoglobin to release more oxygen to tissues with higher metabolic rates.

? *Why is it physiologically beneficial to the body that the curves in part (a) shift to the right as temperature increases?*

Hydrogen Ions

Ultimately, pulmonary ventilation is adjusted to maintain the pH of the brain. The central chemoreceptors in the medulla oblongata mediate about 75% of the change in respiration induced by pH shifts, and yet H^+ doesn't cross the blood–brain barrier very easily. However, CO_2 does, and once it's in the CSF, it reacts with water to produce carbonic acid, and the carbonic acid dissociates into bicarbonate and hydrogen ions. The CSF contains relatively little protein to buffer the hydrogen ions, so most H^+ remains free, and

[28]Christian Bohr (1855–1911), Danish physiologist
[29]John Scott Haldane (1860–1936), Scottish physiologist

it strongly stimulates the central chemoreceptors. Hydrogen ions are also a potent stimulus to the peripheral chemoreceptors, which mediate about 25% of the respiratory response to pH changes.

How do we know it is the H^+ that stimulates the central chemoreceptors and not primarily the CO_2 that diffuses into the CSF? Experimentally, it is possible to vary the pH or the P_{CO_2} of the CSF while holding the other variable steady. When pH alone changes, there is a strong effect on respiration; when P_{CO_2} alone changes, the effect is weaker. Therefore, even though these two variables usually change together, we can see that the chemoreceptors react primarily to the H^+.

A blood pH lower than 7.35 is called **acidosis** and a pH greater than 7.45 is called **alkalosis.** The P_{CO_2} of arterial blood normally ranges from 37 to 43 mm Hg. A P_{CO_2} less than 37 mm Hg is called **hypocapnia,**[30] and is the most common cause of alkalosis. The most common cause of acidosis is **hypercapnia,** a P_{CO_2} greater than 43 mm Hg. When these pH imbalances occur because the rate of pulmonary ventilation doesn't match the rate of CO_2 production, they are called *respiratory acidosis* and *respiratory alkalosis* (further discussed under "Disorders of Acid–Base Balance" in section 24.3).

The corrective homeostatic response to acidosis is hyperventilation, "blowing off" CO_2 faster than the body produces it. As CO_2 is eliminated from the body, the carbonic acid reaction shifts to the left:

$$CO_2 + H_2O \longleftarrow H_2CO_3 \longleftarrow HCO_3^- + H^+.$$

Thus, the H^+ on the right is consumed, and as H^+ concentration declines, the pH rises and ideally returns the blood from the acidotic range to normal.

The corrective response to alkalosis is hypoventilation, which allows CO_2 to accumulate in the body fluids faster than we exhale it. Hypoventilation shifts the reaction to the right, raising the H^+ concentration and lowering the pH to normal:

$$CO_2 + H_2O \longrightarrow H_2CO_3 \longrightarrow HCO_3^- + H^+.$$

Although pH changes usually result from P_{CO_2} changes, they can have other causes. In diabetes mellitus, for example, rapid fat oxidation releases acidic ketone bodies, causing an abnormally low pH called *ketoacidosis.* Ketoacidosis tends to induce a form of dyspnea called *Kussmaul respiration* (see table 22.3). Hyperventilation cannot reduce the level of ketone bodies in the blood, but by blowing off CO_2, it reduces the concentration of CO_2-generated H^+ and compensates to some degree for the H^+ released by the ketone bodies.

Carbon Dioxide

Although the arterial P_{CO_2} has a strong influence on respiration, we have seen that it's mostly an indirect one, mediated through its effects on the pH of the CSF. Yet the experimental evidence described earlier shows that CO_2 has some effect even when pH remains stable. At the beginning of exercise, the rising blood CO_2 level may directly stimulate the peripheral chemoreceptors and trigger an increase in ventilation more quickly than the central chemoreceptors do.

Oxygen

The partial pressure of oxygen usually has little effect on respiration. Even in eupnea, the hemoglobin is at least 97% saturated with O_2, so little can be added by increasing pulmonary ventilation. Arterial P_{O_2} significantly affects respiration only if it drops below 60 mm Hg. At low elevations, such a low P_{O_2} seldom occurs even in prolonged holding of the breath. A moderate drop in P_{O_2} does stimulate the peripheral chemoreceptors, but another effect overrides this: As the level of HbO_2 falls, hemoglobin binds more H^+ (see fig. 22.24). This raises the blood pH, which inhibits respiration and counteracts the effect of low P_{O_2}.

At about 10,800 feet (3,300 m), arterial P_{O_2} falls to 60 mm Hg and the stimulatory effect of hypoxemia on the carotid bodies overrides the inhibitory effect of the pH increase. This produces heavy breathing in people who aren't acclimated to high elevation. Long-term hypoxemia can lead to a condition called **hypoxic drive,** in which respiration is driven more by the low P_{O_2} than by CO_2 or pH. This occurs in situations such as emphysema and pneumonia, which interfere with alveolar gas exchange, and in mountain climbing of at least 2 or 3 days' duration.

Respiration and Exercise

It is common knowledge that we breathe more heavily during exercise, and it's tempting to think this occurs because exercise raises CO_2 levels, lowers the blood pH, and lowers blood O_2 levels. However, this is not true; all these values remain essentially the same in exercise as they do at rest. It appears that the increased respiration has other causes: (1) When the brain sends motor commands to the muscles (via the lower motor neurons of the spinal cord), it also sends this information to the respiratory centers, so they increase pulmonary ventilation in anticipation of the needs of the exercising muscles. In contrast to homeostasis by negative feedback, this is considered a *feed-forward* mechanism, in which signals are transmitted to the effectors (brainstem respiratory centers) to produce a change *in anticipation* of need. (2) Exercise stimulates proprioceptors of the muscles and joints, and they transmit excitatory signals to the brainstem respiratory centers. Thus, the respiratory centers increase breathing because they're informed that the muscles have been told to move or are actually moving. The increase in pulmonary ventilation keeps blood gas values at their normal levels in spite of the elevated O_2 consumption and CO_2 generation by the muscles.

In summary, the main chemical stimulus to pulmonary ventilation is the H^+ in the CSF and tissue fluid of the brain. These hydrogen ions arise mainly from CO_2 diffusing into the CSF and brain and generating H^+ through the carbonic acid reaction. Therefore, the P_{CO_2} of the arterial blood is an important driving force in respiration, even though its action on the chemoreceptors is indirect. Ventilation is adjusted to maintain arterial pH at about 7.40 and arterial P_{CO_2} at about 40 mm Hg. This automatically ensures that the blood is at least 97% saturated with O_2 as well.

---

[30]*capn* = smoke

Under ordinary circumstances, arterial P_{O_2} has relatively little effect on respiration. When it drops below 60 mm Hg, however, it excites the peripheral chemoreceptors and stimulates an increase in ventilation. This can be significant at high elevations and in certain lung diseases. The increase in respiration during exercise results from the expected or actual activity of the muscles, not from any change in blood gas pressures or pH.

BEFORE YOU GO ON

Answer the following questions to test your understanding of the preceding section:

14. Why is the composition of alveolar air different from that of the atmosphere?

15. What four factors affect the efficiency of alveolar gas exchange?

16. Explain how perfusion of a pulmonary lobule changes if it is poorly ventilated.

17. How is most oxygen transported in the blood, and why does carbon monoxide interfere with this?

18. What are the three ways in which blood transports CO_2?

19. Give two reasons why highly active tissues can extract more oxygen from the blood than less active tissues do.

20. Define *hypocapnia* and *hypercapnia*. Name the pH imbalances that result from these conditions and explain the relationship between P_{CO_2} and pH.

21. What is the most potent chemical stimulus to respiration, and where are the most effective chemoreceptors for it located?

22. Explain how changes in pulmonary ventilation can correct pH imbalances.

22.4   Respiratory Disorders

Expected Learning Outcomes

When you have completed this section, you should be able to

a. describe the forms and effects of oxygen deficiency and oxygen excess;

b. describe the chronic obstructive pulmonary diseases and their consequences; and

c. explain how lung cancer begins, progresses, and exerts its lethal effects.

The delicate lungs are exposed to a wide variety of inhaled pathogens and debris, so it's not surprising that they're prone to a host of diseases. Several already have been mentioned in this chapter and some others are briefly described in **table 22.5.** The effects of aging on the respiratory system are discussed in section 29.4a.

22.4a Oxygen Imbalances

Hypoxia is a deficiency of oxygen in a tissue or the inability to use oxygen. It's not a respiratory disease in itself but is often a consequence of respiratory diseases. Hypoxia is classified according to cause:

- **Hypoxemic hypoxia,** a state of low arterial P_{O_2}, is usually due to inadequate pulmonary gas exchange. Some of its root causes include atmospheric deficiency of oxygen at high elevations; impaired ventilation, as in drowning or aspiration of foreign matter; respiratory arrest; and degenerative lung diseases. It also occurs in carbon monoxide poisoning, which prevents hemoglobin from transporting oxygen.

- **Ischemic hypoxia** results from inadequate blood circulation, as in congestive heart failure.

- **Anemic hypoxia** is due to anemia and the resulting inability of the blood to carry adequate oxygen.

- **Histotoxic hypoxia** occurs when a metabolic poison such as cyanide prevents the tissues from using the oxygen delivered to them.

Hypoxia is often marked by **cyanosis,** blueness of the skin. Whatever the cause, its primary danger is the necrosis of oxygen-starved tissues. This is especially critical in organs with the highest metabolic demands, such as the brain, heart, and kidneys.

An oxygen excess is also dangerous. It is safe to breathe 100% oxygen at 1 atm for a few hours, but **oxygen toxicity** rapidly develops when pure oxygen is breathed at 2.5 atm or greater. Excess oxygen generates hydrogen peroxide and free radicals that destroy enzymes and damage nervous tissue; thus, it can lead to seizures, coma, and death. This is why scuba divers breathe a mixture of oxygen and nitrogen rather than pure compressed oxygen (see Deeper Insight 22.5). Hyperbaric oxygen was formerly used to treat premature infants for respiratory distress syndrome, but it caused retinal deterioration and blinded many infants before the practice was discontinued.

22.4b Chronic Obstructive Pulmonary Diseases

Chronic obstructive pulmonary diseases (COPDs) are defined by a long-term obstruction of airflow and substantial reduction of pulmonary ventilation. The major COPDs are *chronic bronchitis* and *emphysema.* COPDs are leading causes of adult mortality in the United States. They are almost always caused by cigarette smoking, but occasionally result from air pollution, occupational exposure to airborne irritants, or a hereditary defect. Most COPD patients exhibit mixed chronic bronchitis and emphysema, but one form or the other often predominates.

Chronic bronchitis is severe, persistent inflammation of the lower respiratory tract. Goblet cells of the bronchial mucosa enlarge and secrete excess mucus, while at the same time, the cilia are immobilized and unable to discharge it. Thick, stagnant mucus accumulates in the lungs and furnishes a growth medium for bacteria. Furthermore, tobacco smoke incapacitates the alveolar

TABLE 22.5	Some Disorders of the Respiratory System
Acute rhinitis	The common cold. Caused by many types of viruses that infect the upper respiratory tract. Symptoms include congestion, increased nasal secretion, sneezing, and dry cough. Transmitted especially by contact of contaminated hands with mucous membranes; not transmitted orally.
Adult respiratory distress syndrome	Acute lung inflammation and alveolar injury stemming from trauma, infection, burns, aspiration of vomit, inhalation of noxious gases, drug overdoses, and other causes. Alveolar injury is accompanied by severe pulmonary edema and hemorrhaging, followed by fibrosis that progressively destroys lung tissue. Fatal in about 40% of cases under age 60 and in 60% of cases over age 65.
Pneumonia	A lower respiratory infection caused by any of several viruses, fungi, or protozoans, but most often the bacterium *Streptococcus pneumoniae*. Causes filling of alveoli with fluid and dead leukocytes and thickening of the respiratory membrane, which interferes with gas exchange and causes hypoxemia. Especially dangerous to infants, the elderly, and people with compromised immune systems, such as AIDS and leukemia patients.
Sleep apnea	Cessation of breathing for 10 seconds or longer during sleep; sometimes occurs hundreds of times per night, often accompanied by restlessness and alternating with snoring. Can result from altered function of CNS respiratory centers, airway obstruction, or both. Over time, may lead to daytime drowsiness, hypoxemia, polycythemia, pulmonary hypertension, congestive heart failure, and cardiac arrhythmia. Most common in obese people and men.
Tuberculosis (TB)	Pulmonary infection with the bacterium *Mycobacterium tuberculosis*, which invades the lungs by way of air, blood, or lymph. Stimulates the lung to form fibrous nodules called tubercles around the bacteria. Progressive fibrosis compromises the elastic recoil and ventilation of the lungs and causes pulmonary hemorrhaging as it invades blood vessels. Especially common among impoverished and homeless people and becoming increasingly common among people with AIDS.

You can find other respiratory system disorders described in the following places:

Cystic fibrosis in Deeper Insight 3.2; *pulmonary hypertension* and *pulmonary edema* in section 19.5d; *cor pulmonale* in sections 19.6d and 22.4b; *asthma* in Deeper Insight 21.3; *Ondine's curse* in Deeper Insight 22.2; *pneumothorax* and *atelectasis* in section 22.2c; *apnea, dyspnea, orthopnea, hyperpnea, tachypnea, hyper-* and *hypoventilation, Kussmaul respiration,* and *respiratory arrest* in table 22.3; *carbon monoxide poisoning* in Deeper Insight 22.4; *hypoxia, COPDs (emphysema* and *chronic bronchitis),* and *lung cancer* in section 22.4; *decompression sickness* in Deeper Insight 22.5; *respiratory acidosis* and *alkalosis* in section 24.3d; and *infant respiratory distress syndrome* in section 29.3b.

macrophages and reduces one's defense against respiratory infection. Smokers with chronic bronchitis develop a chronic cough and bring up a thick mixture of mucus and cellular debris called **sputum** (SPEW-tum). Since blood flowing through congested areas of the lung cannot load a normal amount of oxygen, the ventilation–perfusion ratio is reduced and such patients commonly exhibit hypoxemia and cyanosis.

In **emphysema**[31] (EM-fih-SEE-muh), alveolar walls break down and alveoli converge into fewer and larger spaces (see fig. 22.21c). Thus, there is much less respiratory membrane available for gas exchange. In severe cases, the lungs are flabby and cavitated with spaces as big as grapes or even ping-pong balls. The severity of the disease may not be fully appreciated by looking only at histological specimens, since such large spaces are not seen on microscope slides. The lungs also become fibrotic and less elastic. The air passages open adequately during inspiration, but they tend to collapse and obstruct the outflow of air. Air becomes trapped in the lungs, and over a period of time a person becomes barrel-chested. The overly stretched thoracic muscles contract weakly, which further contributes to the difficulty of expiration. Since proportionate amounts of alveolar wall and capillaries are both destroyed, the ventilation–perfusion ratio of the lung is relatively normal, and persons with emphysema don't necessarily show the cyanosis that typifies chronic bronchitis. People with emphysema can become exhausted and emaciated because they expend three to four times the normal amount of energy just to breathe. Even slight physical exertion, such as walking across a room, can cause severe shortness of breath.

▶▶▶APPLY WHAT YOU KNOW

Explain how the length–tension relationship of skeletal muscle (see fig. 11.12 and associated text) accounts for the weakness of the respiratory muscles in emphysema.

COPD tends to reduce vital capacity and causes hypoxemia, hypercapnia, and respiratory acidosis. Hypoxemia stimulates the kidneys to secrete erythropoietin, which leads to accelerated erythrocyte production and polycythemia (see fig. 18.8). As the blood thickens and lung tissue deteriorates, the right ventricle has to work harder to force blood through the lungs. Like any heavily used muscle, it enlarges and may eventually fail. Such ventricular hypertrophy and failure resulting from obstructed pulmonary circulation is called **cor pulmonale.**[32]

[31]*emphys* = inflamed

[32]*cor* = heart; *pulmo* = lung

22.4c Smoking and Lung Cancer

Lung cancer (**fig. 22.27**) accounts for more deaths than any other form of cancer. The most important cause of lung cancer is cigarette smoking, distantly followed by air pollution. Cigarette smoke contains at least 60 carcinogenic compounds. Lung cancer commonly follows or accompanies COPD.

There are three forms of lung cancer, the most common of which is **squamous-cell carcinoma.** In its early stage, basal cells of the bronchial epithelium multiply and the ciliated pseudostratified epithelium transforms into the stratified squamous type. As the dividing epithelial cells invade the underlying tissues of the bronchial wall, the bronchus develops bleeding lesions. Dense masses of keratin and malignant squamous cells appear in the lung parenchyma and replace functional respiratory tissue.

A second form of lung cancer, nearly as common, is **adenocarcinoma,**[33] which originates in the mucous glands of the lamina propria. The least common (10% to 20% of lung malignancies) but most dangerous form is **small-cell (oat-cell) carcinoma,** named for clusters of cells that resemble oat grains. This originates in the main bronchi but invades the mediastinum and metastasizes quickly to other organs.

Over 90% of lung tumors originate in the mucous membranes of the large bronchi. As a tumor invades the bronchial wall and grows around it, it compresses the airway and may cause atelectasis (collapse) of more distal parts of the lung. Growth of the tumor produces a cough, but coughing is such an everyday occurrence among smokers it seldom causes much alarm. Often, the first sign of serious trouble is coughing up blood. Lung cancer metastasizes so rapidly that it has usually spread to other organs by the time it's diagnosed. Common sites of metastasis are the pericardium, heart, bones, liver, lymph nodes, and brain. The chance of recovery is poor relative to other cancers, but is improving with advances in treatment. About 18% of patients survive for 5 years after diagnosis.

The popular use of recreational marijuana and its legalization in some states has sparked attention to it as a risk factor for lung cancer. Marijuana smokers inhale more deeply and hold it longer than cigarette smokers do, and they smoke the marijuana "joint" down to its last nub, loaded with tar and other carcinogens. Studies to date have been too limited to establish a significant correlation between marijuana use and lung cancer. Ongoing investigations aim to improve study methods and survey older people with a long history of marijuana use. The growing popularity of electronic cigarettes ("vaping") is also cause for concern. It has been associated with a serious lung disease called *popcorn lung,* but the composition of vaping liquids has undergone changes and the jury is still out on the seriousness of this public health risk.

[33]*adeno* = gland; *carcino* = cancer; *oma* = tumor

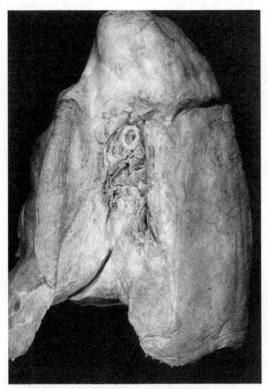

(a) Healthy lung, mediastinal surface

(b) Smoker's lung with carcinoma

Tumors

FIGURE 22.27 Effects of Smoking. (a) Photograph of a healthy lung, mediastinal surface. (b) Photograph of a smoker's lung with carcinoma.

a: Dennis Strete/McGraw-Hill Education; b: Biophoto Associates/Science Source

BEFORE YOU GO ON

Answer the following questions to test your understanding of the preceding section.

23. Describe the four classes of hypoxia.

24. Name and compare the two COPDs and describe some pathological effects that they have in common.

25. In what lung tissue does lung cancer originate? How does it kill?

DEEPER INSIGHT 22.5

CLINICAL APPLICATION

Diving Physiology and Decompression Sickness

Because of the popularity of scuba diving, many people know something about the scientific aspects of breathing under high pressure. But diving is by no means a new fascination. As early as the fifth century BCE, Aristotle described divers using snorkels and taking containers of air underwater in order to stay down longer. Some Renaissance artists depicted divers many meters deep breathing from tubes to the water surface. In reality, this would be physically impossible. For one thing, such tubes would have so much dead space that fresh air from the surface wouldn't reach the diver. The short snorkels used today are about the maximum length that will work for surface breathing. Another reason snorkels can't be used at greater depths is that water pressure increases by 1 atm for every 10 m of depth, and even at 1 m the pressure is so great that a diver can't expand the chest muscles without help. This is one reason why scuba divers use pressurized air tanks. The tanks create a positive intrapulmonary pressure and enable the diver to inhale with only slight assistance from the thoracic muscles. Scuba tanks also have regulators that adjust the outflow pressure to the diver's depth and the opposing pressure of the surrounding water.

But breathing pressurized (hyperbaric) gas presents its own problems. Divers can't use pure oxygen because of the problem of oxygen toxicity. Instead, they use compressed air—a mixture of 21% oxygen and 79% nitrogen. On land, nitrogen presents no physiological problems; it dissolves poorly in blood and it is physiologically inert. But under hyperbaric conditions, larger amounts of nitrogen dissolve in the blood. (Which of the gas laws in table 22.1 applies here?) Even more dissolves in adipose tissue and the myelin of the brain, since nitrogen is more soluble in lipids. In the brain, it causes *nitrogen narcosis,* or what scuba inventor Jacques Cousteau (1910–1997) termed "rapture of the deep." A diver can become dizzy, euphoric, and dangerously disoriented; for every 15 to 20 m of depth, the effect is said to be equivalent to that of one martini on an empty stomach.

Strong currents, equipment failure, and other hazards sometimes make scuba divers panic, hold their breath, and quickly swim to the surface (a *breath-hold ascent*). Ambient (surrounding) pressure falls rapidly as a diver ascends, and the air in the lungs expands just as rapidly. (Which gas law is demonstrated here?) It is imperative that an ascending diver keep his or her airway open to exhale the expanding gas; otherwise it's likely to cause *pulmonary barotrauma*—ruptured alveoli. Then, when the diver takes a breath of air at the surface, alveolar air goes directly into the bloodstream and causes air embolism (see Deeper Insight 20.3).

After passing through the heart, the emboli enter the cerebral circulation because the diver is head-up and air bubbles rise in liquid. The resulting cerebral embolism can cause motor and sensory dysfunction, seizures, unconsciousness, and drowning.

Barotrauma can be fatal even at the depths of a backyard swimming pool. In one case, children trapped air in a bucket 1 m underwater and then swam under the bucket to breathe from the air space. Because the bucket was under water, the air in it was compressed. One child filled his lungs under the bucket, did a "mere" 1 m breath-hold ascent, and his alveoli ruptured. He died in the hospital, partly because the case was mistaken for drowning and not treated for what it really was. This would not have happened to a person who inhaled at the surface, did a breath-hold dive, and then resurfaced—nor is barotrauma a problem for those who do breath-hold dives to several meters. (Why? What is the difference?)

Even when not holding the breath, but letting the expanding air escape from the mouth, a diver must ascend slowly and carefully to allow for decompression of the nitrogen that has dissolved in the tissues. *Decompression tables* prescribe safe rates of ascent based on the depth and the length of time a diver has been down. When pressure drops, nitrogen dissolved in the tissues can go either of two places—it can diffuse into the alveoli and be exhaled, or it can form bubbles like the CO_2 in a bottle of soda when the cap is removed. The diver's objective is to ascend slowly, allowing for the former and preventing the latter. If a diver ascends too rapidly, nitrogen "boils" from the tissues—especially in the 3 m just below the surface, where the relative pressure change is greatest. A diver may double over in pain from bubbles in the joints, bones, and muscles—a disease called the *bends* or *decompression sickness (DCS)*. Nitrogen bubbles in the pulmonary capillaries cause *chokes*—substernal pain, coughing, and dyspnea. DCS is sometimes accompanied by mood changes, seizures, numbness, and itching. These symptoms usually occur within an hour of surfacing, but they are sometimes delayed for up to 36 hours. DCS is treated by putting the individual in a hyperbaric chamber to be recompressed and then *slowly* decompressed.

DCS is also called *caisson disease.* A caisson is a watertight underwater chamber filled with pressurized air. Caissons are used in underwater construction work on bridges, tunnels, ships' hulls, and so forth. Caisson disease was first reported in the late 1800s among workmen building the foundations of the Brooklyn Bridge.

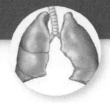

CONNECTIVE ISSUES

Effects of the **RESPIRATORY SYSTEM** on Other Organ Systems

ALL SYSTEMS
Delivers oxygen to the tissues and removes their carbon dioxide; maintains proper acid–base balance in the tissues

INTEGUMENTARY SYSTEM
Respiratory disorders can cause such skin discolorations as the cyanosis of hypoxemia or the cherry-red color of carbon monoxide poisoning.

SKELETAL SYSTEM
Any respiratory disorder that causes hypoxemia stimulates accelerated erythropoiesis in the red bone marrow.

MUSCULAR SYSTEM
Acid–base imbalances of respiratory origin can affect neuromuscular function.

NERVOUS SYSTEM
Respiration affects the pH of the cerebrospinal fluid, which in turn affects neural function with effects ranging from hyperexcitability to depressed excitability and coma.

ENDOCRINE SYSTEM
Lungs produce angiotensin-converting enzyme (ACE), which converts angiotensin I to the hormone angiotensin II; hypoxemia stimulates secretion of erythropoietin.

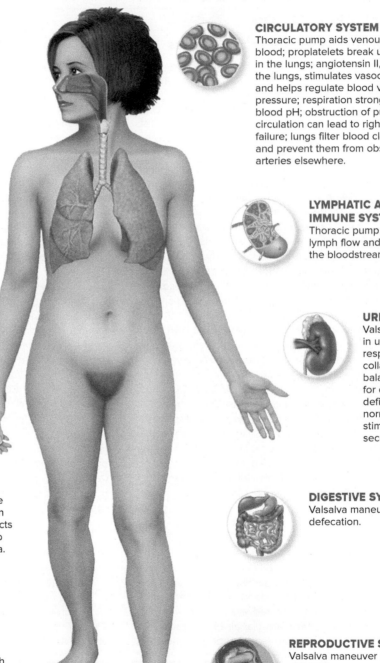

CIRCULATORY SYSTEM
Thoracic pump aids venous return of blood; proplatelets break up into platelets in the lungs; angiotensin II, produced in the lungs, stimulates vasoconstriction and helps regulate blood volume and pressure; respiration strongly influences blood pH; obstruction of pulmonary circulation can lead to right-sided heart failure; lungs filter blood clots and emboli and prevent them from obstructing vital arteries elsewhere.

LYMPHATIC AND IMMUNE SYSTEMS
Thoracic pump promotes lymph flow and its return to the bloodstream.

URINARY SYSTEM
Valsalva maneuver aids in urination; urinary and respiratory systems collaborate in acid–base balance and compensate for each other's deficiencies in maintaining normal pH; hypoxemia stimulates kidneys to secrete erythropoietin.

DIGESTIVE SYSTEM
Valsalva maneuver aids in defecation.

REPRODUCTIVE SYSTEM
Valsalva maneuver aids in childbirth.

STUDY GUIDE

▶ Assess Your Learning Outcomes

To test your knowledge, discuss the following topics with a study partner or in writing, ideally from memory.

22.1 Anatomy of the Respiratory System

1. Two meanings of the word *respiration*
2. Functions of the respiratory system
3. The distinction between the respiratory and conducting divisions of this system, and constituents of each division
4. The distinction between the upper and lower respiratory tract and the dividing line between them
5. The extent of the nasal cavity, names of its anterior and posterior openings, and names of the two chambers separated by the nasal septum, and histology of its mucosa
6. Names and functions of the scroll-like folds that arise from each lateral wall of the nasal cavity
7. Anatomy and functions of the pharynx, larynx, and trachea
8. Gross anatomy of the lungs; how the right and left lungs differ; and the structures that enter or leave through the hilum
9. Divisions of the bronchial tree from main bronchus to segmental bronchi, and histological changes along the way
10. How bronchioles differ from bronchi; two types of bronchioles; and how the two differ in histology and function
11. Alveolar ducts and alveoli; cell types of the alveoli and their functions; the relationship of pulmonary blood vessels to the alveoli; and the structure of the respiratory membrane in relation to its function
12. The parietal and visceral pleurae, pleural cavity, and pleural fluid

22.2 Pulmonary Ventilation

1. The two phases of the respiratory cycle
2. Actions of the respiratory muscles; the prime mover and synergists of respiration
3. Locations and functions of the brainstem respiratory centers; their connections with each other and with other levels of the CNS; and routes of CNS output to the respiratory muscles
4. Locations and roles of the central and peripheral chemoreceptors, stretch receptors, and irritant receptors in modulating the respiratory rhythm

5. The neural pathway for voluntary control of respiration
6. The mathematical relationship of airflow, pressure, and resistance
7. Actions of the sternum and rib cage during the respiratory cycle
8. Why the pressures driving respiratory airflow are measured in cm H_2O rather than mm Hg like other pressures considered in this and previous chapters
9. How and why intrapulmonary pressure changes relative to atmospheric pressure during inspiration; how Boyle's and Charles's laws relate to pulmonary ventilation
10. The role of elastic recoil of the thorax in expiration; how and why intrapulmonary pressure changes relative to atmospheric pressure in expiration
11. How pulmonary ventilation is affected by bronchodilation, bronchoconstriction, pulmonary compliance, and alveolar surfactant
12. A typical adult tidal volume; how much of this ventilates the alveoli and how much remains in the anatomical dead space; and how to calculate alveolar ventilation rate
13. Use of the spirometer to measure pulmonary ventilation; the meanings and typical values of the four respiratory volumes and four capacities
14. How to determine forced expiratory volume, minute respiratory volume, and maximum voluntary ventilation
15. The difference between restrictive and obstructive disorders of respiration, their respective effects on certain respiratory volumes and capacities, and examples of each
16. Definitions of *eupnea, dyspnea, hyperpnea, hyperventilation, hypoventilation, Kussmaul respiration, orthopnea, respiratory arrest,* and *tachypnea*

22.3 Gas Exchange and Transport

1. Composition of the atmosphere and average partial pressures of its constituent gases at sea level; the application of Dalton's law to partial pressures and total atmospheric pressure
2. Differences between the composition of atmospheric air and alveolar air, and reasons for the differences

3. Why gas exchange depends on the ability of the gases to dissolve in water; the application of Henry's law to the air–water interface in the alveoli
4. Four variables that determine the rate of O_2 loading and CO_2 unloading by blood passing through the alveolar capillaries
5. How ventilation–perfusion coupling matches pulmonary airflow to blood flow for optimal gas exchange
6. The two modes of O_2 transport in the blood and the relative amounts of O_2 transported by each; where O_2 binds to the hemoglobin molecule; how much O_2 a hemoglobin molecule can carry; and what hemoglobin is called when O_2 is bound to it
7. Interpretation of the oxyhemoglobin dissociation curve, including the reason for its shape and how it can be used to show the amount of O_2 unloading as hemoglobin passes through a typical systemic tissue
8. Three modes of CO_2 transport in the blood and the relative amounts of CO_2 transported by each; where CO_2 binds to hemoglobin; and what hemoglobin is called when CO_2 is bound to it
9. How carbonic anhydrase (CAH) and the chloride shift aid in the loading of CO_2 from the tissue fluids; the reaction catalyzed by CAH
10. How the loading of CO_2 in systemic tissues influences the unloading of O_2; the meaning of the *utilization coefficient* and a typical resting value
11. How the loading of O_2 in the lungs influences the unloading of CO_2
12. Four mechanisms that adjust the amount of O_2 unloaded by hemoglobin to the needs of individual tissues
13. How the Haldane effect modifies CO_2 loading in relation to the metabolic rates of individual tissues
14. Three factors that stimulate the central and peripheral chemoreceptors, and their relative influences on breathing

STUDY GUIDE

15. The normal pH range of the blood; terms for deviations above and below this range; terms for the CO_2 imbalances that cause these pH deviations; and how the body homeostatically regulates blood pH
16. The mechanism by which exercise increases respiration

22.4 Respiratory Disorders

1. The definition of *hypoxia;* its four varieties and the cause of each; and the consequences of uncorrected hypoxia
2. The mechanism and effects of oxygen toxicity

3. The names, most common cause, and pathology of the two chronic obstructive pulmonary diseases (COPDs)
4. The most common cause of lung cancer, and the names and pathological differences between the three forms of lung cancer

▶ Testing Your Recall

Answers in Appendix A

1. The nasal cavity is divided by the nasal septum into right and left
   a. nares.
   b. vestibules.
   c. fossae.
   d. choanae.
   e. conchae.

2. The intrinsic laryngeal muscles regulate speech by rotating
   a. the extrinsic laryngeal muscles.
   b. the corniculate cartilages.
   c. the arytenoid cartilages.
   d. the hyoid bone.
   e. the vocal cords.

3. The largest air passages that engage in gas exchange with the blood are
   a. the respiratory bronchioles.
   b. the terminal bronchioles.
   c. the primary bronchi.
   d. the alveolar ducts.
   e. the alveoli.

4. Respiratory arrest would most likely result from a tumor of the
   a. pons.
   b. midbrain.
   c. thalamus.
   d. cerebellum.
   e. medulla oblongata.

5. Which of these values is normally highest?
   a. tidal volume
   b. inspiratory reserve volume
   c. expiratory reserve volume
   d. residual volume
   e. vital capacity

6. The _____ protects the lungs from injury by excessive inspiration.
   a. pleura
   b. rib cage
   c. inflation reflex
   d. Haldane effect
   e. Bohr effect

7. According to _____, the warming of air as it is inhaled helps to inflate the lungs.
   a. Boyle's law
   b. Charles's law
   c. Dalton's law
   d. the Bohr effect
   e. the Haldane effect

8. Poor blood circulation causes _____ hypoxia.
   a. ischemic
   b. histotoxic
   c. hemolytic
   d. anemic
   e. hypoxemic

9. Most of the CO_2 that diffuses from the blood into an alveolus comes from
   a. dissolved gas.
   b. carbaminohemoglobin.
   c. carboxyhemoglobin.
   d. carbonic acid.
   e. expired air.

10. The duration of an inspiration is set by
    a. the pneumotaxic center.
    b. the phrenic nerves.
    c. the vagus nerves.
    d. the I neurons.
    e. the E neurons.

11. The superior opening into the larynx is guarded by a tissue flap called the _____.

12. Within each lung, the airway forms a branching complex called the _____.

13. The great alveolar cells secrete a phospholipid–protein mixture called _____.

14. Intrapulmonary pressure must be lower than _____ pressure for inspiration to occur.

15. _____ disorders reduce the speed of airflow through the airway.

16. Some inhaled air does not participate in gas exchange because it fills the _____ of the respiratory tract.

17. Inspiration depends on the ease of pulmonary inflation, called _____, whereas expiration depends on _____, which causes pulmonary recoil.

18. Inspiration is caused by the firing of I neurons in the _____ of the medulla oblongata.

19. The matching of airflow to blood flow in any region of the lung is called _____.

20. A blood pH > 7.45 is called _____ and can be caused by a CO_2 deficiency called _____.

STUDY GUIDE

▶ Building Your Medical Vocabulary

Answers in Appendix A

State a meaning of each word element, and give a medical term from this chapter that uses it or a slight variation of it.

1. atel-

2. capni-

3. carcino-

4. corni-

5. eu-

6. -meter

7. naso-

8. -pnea

9. spiro-

10. thyro-

▶ What's Wrong with These Statements?

Answers in Appendix A

Briefly explain why each of the following statements is false, or reword it to make it true.

1. The phrenic nerves fire during inspiration only.

2. There is one segmental bronchus for each lobe of the lung.

3. The most abundant cells in the lung are the squamous alveolar cells.

4. If you increase the volume of a given quantity of gas, its pressure increases.

5. Atelectasis is always preceded by pneumothorax.

6. The greatest effect of accelerated breathing is to increase the oxygen content of the blood.

7. Oxygen is the only gas we inhale from the atmosphere, since we can't use the nitrogen or other gases in it.

8. Most of the air one inhales never makes it to the alveoli.

9. The lower the P_{CO_2} of the blood is, the lower its pH is.

10. Most of the CO_2 transported by the blood is in the form of dissolved gas.

▶ Testing Your Comprehension

1. Discuss how the different functions of the conducting division and respiratory division relate to differences in their histology.

2. State whether hyperventilation would raise or lower each of the following—the blood P_{O_2}, P_{CO_2}, and pH—and explain why. Do the same for emphysema.

3. Some competitive swimmers hyperventilate before a race, thinking they can "load up extra oxygen" and hold their breaths longer underwater. While they can indeed hold their breaths longer, it is not for the reason they think. Furthermore, some have lost consciousness and drowned because of this practice. What is wrong with this thinking, and what accounts for the loss of consciousness?

4. Consider a man in good health with a 650 mL tidal volume and a respiratory rate of 11 breaths per minute. Report his minute respiratory volume in liters per minute. Assuming his anatomical dead space is 185 mL, calculate his alveolar ventilation rate in liters per minute.

5. An 83-year-old woman is admitted to the hospital, where a critical care nurse attempts to insert a nasoenteric tube ("stomach tube") for feeding. The patient begins to exhibit dyspnea, and a chest X-ray reveals air in the right pleural cavity and a collapsed right lung. The patient dies 5 days later from respiratory complications. Name the conditions revealed by the X-ray and explain how they could have resulted from the nurse's procedure.

23

THE URINARY SYSTEM

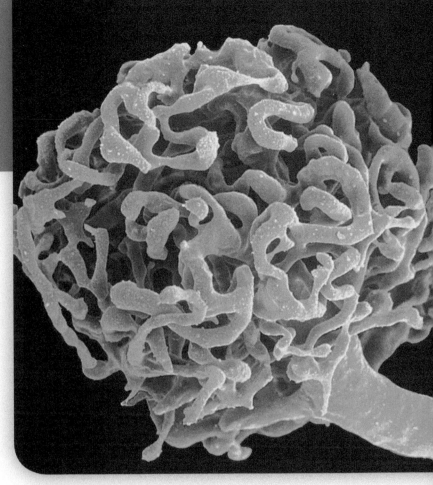

The renal glomerulus, a mass of capillaries where the kidney filters the blood (SEM of a vascular cast)

SPL/Science Source

Anatomy & Physiology *Revealed* 4.0

Module 13: Urinary System

To live is to metabolize, and metabolism unavoidably produces a variety of waste products that are not merely unneeded by the body, but indeed toxic if allowed to accumulate. We rid the body of some of these wastes through the respiratory and digestive tracts and the sweat glands, but the urinary system is the principal means of waste excretion. The kidneys are glands that separate metabolic wastes from the blood. The rest of the urinary system serves only for the transport, storage, and elimination of urine. Most of our focus in this chapter is therefore on the kidneys.

Their task goes far beyond waste excretion. As we will see, the kidneys also play indispensable roles in regulating blood volume, pressure, and composition. In performing these tasks, they have a very close physiological relationship with the endocrine, circulatory, and respiratory systems, covered in recent chapters.

Anatomically, the urinary system is closely associated with the reproductive system. In many animals, the eggs and sperm are emitted through the urinary tract, and the two systems have a shared embryonic development and adult anatomical relationship. This is reflected in humans, where the systems develop together in the embryo and, in the male, the urethra continues to serve as a passage for both urine and sperm. Thus, the urinary and reproductive systems are often collectively called the *urogenital (U–G) system,* and *urologists* treat both urinary and male reproductive disorders. We examine the anatomical relationship between the urinary and reproductive systems in chapter 27, but the physiological link to the circulatory and respiratory systems is more important to consider at this time.

23.1 Functions of the Urinary System

Expected Learning Outcomes

When you have completed this section, you should be able to

a. name and locate the organs of the urinary system;

b. list several functions of the kidneys in addition to urine formation;

c. name the major nitrogenous wastes and identify their sources; and

d. define *excretion* and identify the systems that excrete wastes.

The **urinary system** consists of six principal organs: two **kidneys,** two **ureters,** the **urinary bladder,** and the **urethra** (**fig. 23.1**). The urinary tract has important spatial relationships with the vagina and uterus in females and the prostate in males. These relationships are best appreciated from the sagittal views of figures 27.10 and 28.1 and can be seen in the cadaver in figure B.14 of atlas B.

23.1a Functions of the Kidneys APR

Although the primary function of the kidneys is excretion, they play more roles than are commonly realized:

- They filter the blood and excrete the toxic metabolic wastes.

- They regulate blood volume, pressure, and osmolarity by regulating water output.

- They regulate the electrolyte and acid–base balance of the body fluids.

- They secrete the hormone *erythropoietin,* which stimulates the production of red blood cells and thus supports the oxygen-carrying capacity of the blood.

- They help to regulate calcium homeostasis and bone metabolism by participating in the synthesis of calcitriol.

- They clear hormones and drugs from the blood and thereby limit their action.

- They detoxify free radicals.

- In conditions of extreme starvation, they help to support the blood glucose level by synthesizing glucose from amino acids.

In view of such diverse roles, it is easy to see why renal failure can lead to the collapse of many other physiological functions as well.

23.1b Nitrogenous Wastes

A **waste** is any substance that is useless to the body or present in excess of the body's needs. A **metabolic waste,** more specifically, is a waste substance produced by the body. The food residue in feces, for example, is a waste but not a metabolic waste, since it wasn't produced by the body and, indeed, never entered the body's tissues.

Among the most toxic of our metabolic wastes are small nitrogen-containing compounds called **nitrogenous wastes** (**fig. 23.2**). About 50% of the nitrogenous waste is urea, a by-product of protein catabolism. Proteins are hydrolyzed to amino acids, then the —NH_2 group is removed from each amino acid. The —NH_2 forms ammonia, which is exceedingly toxic but

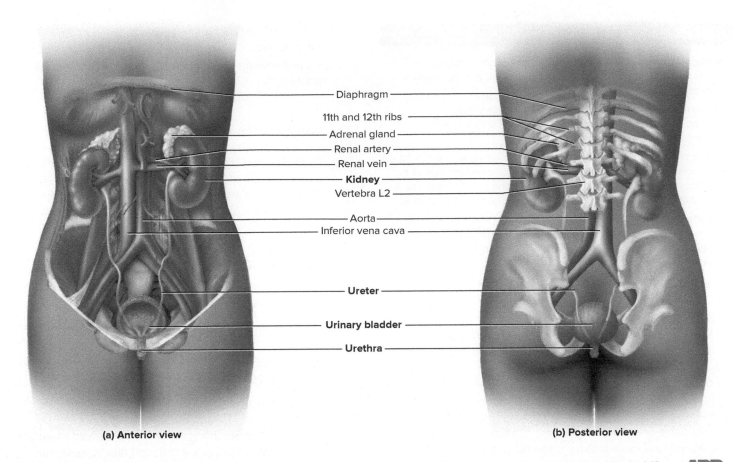

(a) Anterior view

(b) Posterior view

FIGURE 23.1 The Urinary System. (a) Anterior view. (b) Posterior view. Organs of the urinary system are indicated in boldface. **A&PR**

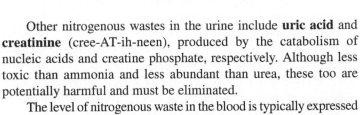

FIGURE 23.2 The Major Nitrogenous Wastes.

❓ *How is each of these wastes produced in the body?*

which the liver quickly converts to urea, $CO(NH_2)_2$, a somewhat less toxic waste:

$$2\ NH_3 + CO_2 \longrightarrow H_2N\overset{\displaystyle O}{\overset{\displaystyle \|}{-}C-}NH_2 + H_2O$$

Other nitrogenous wastes in the urine include **uric acid** and **creatinine** (cree-AT-ih-neen), produced by the catabolism of nucleic acids and creatine phosphate, respectively. Although less toxic than ammonia and less abundant than urea, these too are potentially harmful and must be eliminated.

The level of nitrogenous waste in the blood is typically expressed as **blood urea nitrogen (BUN).** The normal concentration of blood urea is 10 to 20 mg/dL. An elevated BUN is called **azotemia**[1] (AZ-oh-TEE-me-uh) and may indicate renal insufficiency. It can progress to **uremia** (you-REE-me-uh), a syndrome of diarrhea, vomiting, dyspnea, and cardiac arrhythmia stemming from the toxicity of the nitrogenous wastes. Convulsions, coma, and death can follow within a few days. Deeper Insight 23.5 discusses treatments for renal insufficiency.

23.1c Excretion

Excretion is the process of separating wastes from the body fluids and eliminating them from the body. It is carried out by four organ systems:

1. The respiratory system excretes carbon dioxide, small amounts of other gases, and water.

---

[1]*azot* = nitrogen; *emia* = blood condition

2. The integumentary system excretes water, inorganic salts, lactate, and urea in the sweat.

3. The digestive system not only *eliminates* food residue (which is not a process of excretion) but also actively *excretes* water, salts, carbon dioxide, lipids, bile pigments, cholesterol, and other metabolic wastes.

4. The urinary system excretes a broad variety of metabolic wastes, toxins, drugs, hormones, salts, hydrogen ions, and water.

BEFORE YOU GO ON

Answer the following questions to test your understanding of the preceding section:

1. State at least four functions of the kidneys other than forming urine.

2. List four nitrogenous wastes and their metabolic sources.

3. Name some wastes eliminated by three systems other than the urinary system.

23.2 Anatomy of the Kidney APR

Expected Learning Outcomes

When you have completed this section, you should be able to

a. describe the location and general appearance of the kidneys;

b. identify the external and internal features of the kidney;

c. trace the flow of blood through the kidney;

d. trace the flow of fluid through the renal tubules; and

e. describe the nerve supply to the kidney.

23.2a Position and Associated Structures

The kidneys lie against the posterior abdominal wall at the level of vertebrae T12 to L3. The right kidney is slightly lower than the left because of the space occupied by the large right lobe of the liver above it. Rib 12 crosses the approximate middle of the left kidney. The kidneys are retroperitoneal, along with the ureters, urinary bladder, renal artery and vein, and the adrenal glands (**fig. 23.3**).

23.2b Gross Anatomy

Each kidney weighs about 150 g and measures about 11 cm long, 6 cm wide, and 3 cm thick—about the size of a bar of bath soap. The lateral surface is convex, and the medial surface is concave and has a slit, the **hilum,** that admits the renal nerves, blood vessels, lymphatics, and ureter.

The kidney is protected by three layers of connective tissue (fig. 23.3b): (1) A fibrous **renal fascia,** immediately deep to the parietal peritoneum, binds the kidney and associated organs to the abdominal wall; (2) the **perirenal fat capsule,** a layer of adipose tissue, cushions the kidney and holds it in place; and (3) the **fibrous capsule** encloses the kidney like a cellophane wrapper

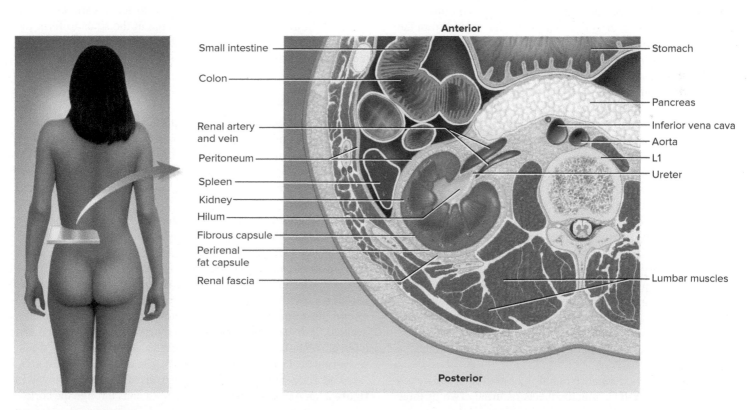

FIGURE 23.3 Retroperitoneal Position of the Kidney. Cross section of the abdomen at the level of vertebra L1.

? *If the kidney were not retroperitoneal, where on this figure would you have to relocate it?*

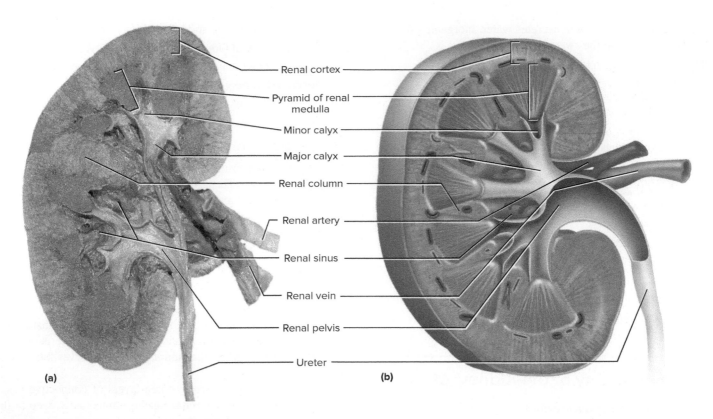

FIGURE 23.4 Gross Anatomy of the Kidney. Posterior views. (a) Photograph of frontal section. (b) Major anatomical features. The adipose tissue that normally fills in the renal sinus is omitted to better reveal the other structures that occupy the sinus. **APR**

a: Rebecca Gray/McGraw-Hill Education

anchored at the hilum, and protects it from trauma and infection. The kidneys are suspended by collagen fibers that extend from the fibrous capsule, through the fat, to the renal fascia. The renal fascia is fused with the peritoneum anteriorly and with the fascia of the lumbar muscles posteriorly. In spite of all this, the kidneys drop about 3 cm when one goes from lying down to standing, as when getting out of bed in the morning. Under some circumstances, they become detached and drift even lower, with pathological results (see nephroptosis, or "floating kidney," in table 23.3).

The renal parenchyma—the glandular tissue that forms the urine—appears C-shaped in frontal section **(fig. 23.4).** It encircles a medial cavity, the **renal sinus,** occupied by blood and lymphatic vessels, nerves, and urine-collecting structures. Adipose tissue fills the remaining space in the sinus and holds these structures in place.

The parenchyma is divided into two zones: an outer **renal cortex** about 1 cm thick and an inner **renal medulla** facing the sinus. The boundary between the cortex and medulla is called the **corticomedullary junction.** Extensions of the cortex called **renal columns** project toward the sinus and divide the medulla into 6 to 10 **renal pyramids.** Each pyramid is conical, with a broad base facing the cortex and a blunt point called the **renal papilla** facing the sinus. One pyramid and the overlying cortex constitute one *lobe* of the kidney.

The papilla of each renal pyramid is nestled in a cup called a **minor calyx**[2] (CAY-lix), which collects its urine. Two or three minor calyces (CAY-lih-seez) converge to form a **major calyx,** and two or three major calyces converge in the sinus to form the funnel-like **renal pelvis.**[3] The ureter is a tubular continuation of the renal pelvis that drains the urine down to the urinary bladder.

23.2c Renal Circulation

The kidneys account for only 0.4% of the body weight, but receive about 1.1 liters of blood per minute, or 21% of the cardiac output (the *renal fraction*)—more for the purpose of waste removal than to meet the metabolic demands of the kidney tissue. This is a hint of how important the kidneys are in regulating blood volume and composition.

The larger divisions of the renal circulation are shown in **figure 23.5.** Each kidney is supplied by a **renal artery** arising from the aorta. Just before or after entering the hilum, the renal artery divides into a few **segmental arteries,** and each of these further divides into a few **interlobar arteries.** An interlobar artery penetrates each renal column and travels between the pyramids toward the corticomedullary junction. Along the way, it branches again to form **arcuate arteries,** which make a sharp 90° bend and travel along the base of the pyramid. Each arcuate artery gives rise to several **cortical radiate arteries,** which pass upward into the cortex.

The finer branches of the renal circulation are shown in **figure 23.6.** As a cortical radiate artery ascends through the cortex,

---

[2]*calyx* = cup

[3]*pelvis* = basin

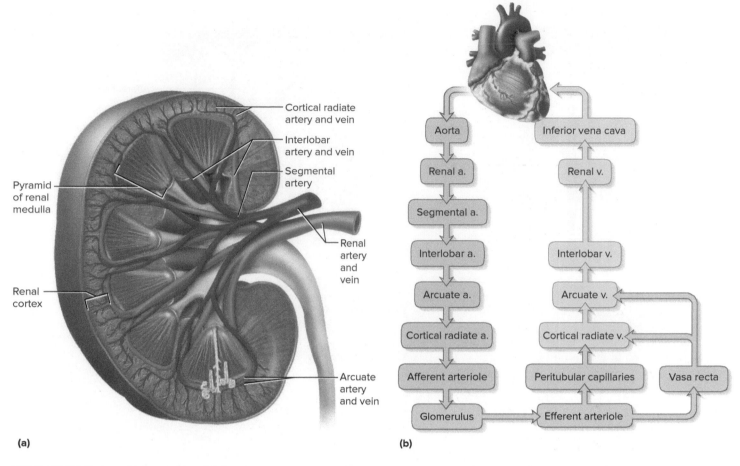

(a)

(b)

FIGURE 23.5 Renal Circulation. (a) The larger blood vessels of the kidney. (b) Flowchart of renal circulation. The pathway through the vasa recta (instead of peritubular capillaries) applies only to the juxtamedullary nephrons. Pink indicates the arterial supply to the nephrons; violet indicates the portal system of connected capillary beds; and blue indicates venous drainage of the kidney.

a series of **afferent arterioles** arise from it at nearly right angles like limbs arising from the trunk of a pine tree. Each afferent arteriole supplies one functional unit of the kidney called a **nephron**[4] (NEF-ron). The afferent arteriole leads to a ball of capillaries called a **glomerulus**[5] (glo-MERR-you-lus), enclosed in a sphere called the *glomerular capsule.* Blood leaves the glomerulus by way of an **efferent arteriole.**

The efferent arteriole usually leads to a plexus of **peritubular capillaries,** named for the fact that they form a network around another part of the nephron, the *renal tubule.* The renal tubule reabsorbs most of the water and solutes that filter out of the blood at the glomerulus and returns these to the bloodstream by way of these peritubular capillaries. The peritubular capillaries carry it away to the **cortical radiate veins, arcuate veins, interlobar veins,** and the **renal vein,** in that order. These veins travel parallel to the arteries of the same names. (There are, however, no segmental veins corresponding to the segmental arteries.) The renal vein leaves the hilum and drains into the inferior vena cava.

The renal medulla receives only 1% to 2% of the total renal blood flow, supplied by a network of vessels called the **vasa recta**[6] (VAH-za REC-ta). These arise from the efferent arterioles of the nephrons closest to the medulla. Here, the efferent arterioles descend immediately into the medulla and give rise to the vasa recta instead of peritubular capillaries. Capillaries of the vasa recta lead into venules that ascend and empty into the arcuate and cortical radiate veins. Capillaries of the vasa recta are wedged into the tight spaces between the medullary parts of the renal tubule, and carry away water and solutes reabsorbed by those sections of the tubule. Figure 23.5b summarizes the route of renal blood flow.

23.2d The Nephron APR

Each kidney has about 1.2 million nephrons. To understand how just one of these works is to understand nearly everything about how the whole kidney works. Each nephron is composed of two principal parts: a *renal corpuscle,* which filters the blood

---

[4]*nephro* = kidney
[5]*glomer* = ball; *ulus* = little

[6]*vasa* = vessels; *recta* = straight

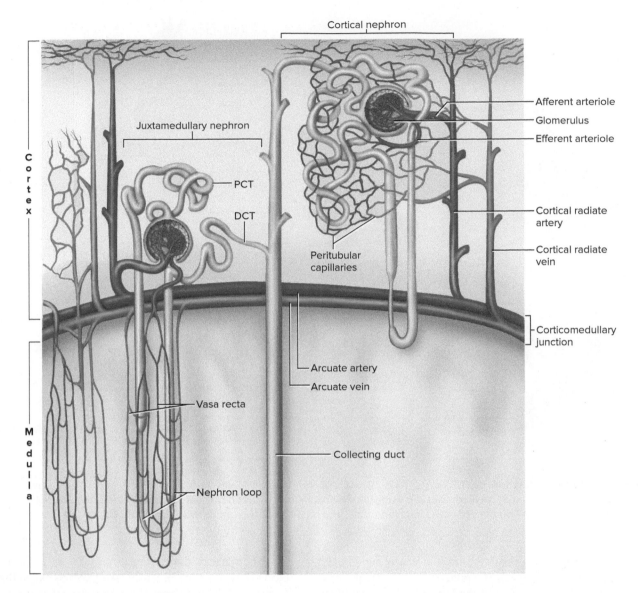

FIGURE 23.6 Microcirculation of the Kidney. For clarity, vasa recta are shown only on the left and peritubular capillaries only on the right. In the juxtamedullary nephron (left), the efferent arteriole gives rise to the vasa recta of the medulla. In the cortical nephron (right), the nephron loop barely dips into the renal medulla and the efferent arteriole gives rise to peritubular capillaries. (DCT = distal convoluted tubule; PCT = proximal convoluted tubule)

plasma, and a long coiled *renal tubule,* which converts the filtrate to urine.

The Renal Corpuscle

The **renal corpuscle (fig. 23.7)** consists of the glomerulus described earlier and a two-layered **glomerular capsule** (formerly called the *Bowman capsule*) that encloses it. The parietal (outer) layer is a simple squamous epithelium, and the visceral (inner) layer consists of elaborate cells called **podocytes**[7] wrapped around the capillaries of the glomerulus. The two layers are separated by a filtrate-collecting **capsular space.** In tissue sections, this space appears as an empty circular or C-shaped space around the glomerulus.

Opposite sides of the renal corpuscle are called the vascular and urinary poles. At the **vascular pole,** the afferent arteriole enters the capsule, bringing blood to the glomerulus, and the efferent arteriole leaves the capsule and carries blood away. The afferent arteriole is significantly larger than the efferent arteriole. Thus, the glomerulus has a large inlet and a small outlet—a point whose functional significance will become apparent later. At the **urinary pole,** the parietal wall of the capsule turns away from the corpuscle and gives rise to the renal tubule. The simple squamous epithelium of the capsule becomes simple cuboidal in the tubule.

[7]*podo* = foot; *cyte* = cell

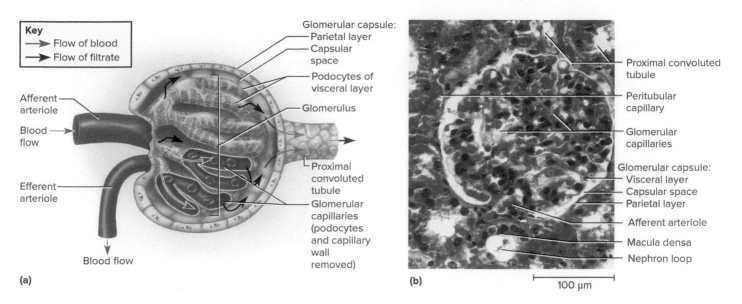

FIGURE 23.7 The Renal Corpuscle. (a) Anatomy of the corpuscle. (b) Light micrograph of the renal corpuscle and sections of the surrounding renal tubule. **APR**

b: Alvin Telser/McGraw-Hill Education

The Renal Tubule

The **renal tubule** is a duct that leads away from the glomerular capsule and ends at the tip of a medullary pyramid. It is about 3 cm long and divided into four regions: the *proximal convoluted tubule, nephron loop, distal convoluted tubule,* and *collecting duct* **(fig. 23.8).** The first three of these are parts of one nephron; the collecting duct receives fluid from many nephrons. Each region has unique physiological properties and roles in the production of urine.

1. The **proximal convoluted tubule (PCT)** arises from the glomerular capsule. It is the longest and most coiled of the four regions and therefore dominates histological sections of renal cortex. It has a simple cuboidal epithelium with prominent microvilli (a brush border), which attests to the great deal of absorption that occurs here. The microvilli give the epithelium a distinctive shaggy look.

2. The **nephron loop** (formerly called the *loop of Henle*) is a long U-shaped portion of the renal tubule found mostly in the medulla. It begins where the PCT straightens out and dips toward or into the medulla, forming the **descending limb** of the loop. At its deep end, the loop turns 180° and forms the **ascending limb,** which returns to the cortex, traveling parallel and close to the descending limb. The loop is divided into thick and thin segments. The **thick segments** have a simple cuboidal epithelium. They form the initial part of the descending limb and part or all of the ascending limb. The cells here are heavily engaged in active transport of salts, so they have very high metabolic

activity and are loaded with mitochondria, accounting for their thickness. The **thin segment** has a simple squamous epithelium. It forms most of the descending limb, and in some nephrons, it rounds the bend and continues partway up the ascending limb. The cells here have low metabolic activity, but the thin segment of the descending limb is very permeable to water.

3. The **distal convoluted tubule (DCT)** begins shortly after the ascending limb reenters the cortex. It is shorter and less coiled than the proximal convoluted tubule, so fewer sections of it are seen in histological sections. It has a cuboidal epithelium with smooth-surfaced cells nearly devoid of microvilli. The DCT is the end of the nephron.

4. The **collecting duct** receives fluid from the DCTs of several nephrons as it passes back into the medulla. Numerous collecting ducts converge toward the tip of a medullary pyramid, and near the papilla, they merge to form a larger **papillary duct.** About 30 papillary ducts end in pores at the conical tip of each papilla. Urine drains from these pores into the minor calyx that encloses the papilla. The collecting and papillary ducts are lined with simple cuboidal epithelium.

The flow of fluid from the point where the glomerular filtrate is formed to the point where urine leaves the body is: glomerular capsule → proximal convoluted tubule → nephron loop → distal convoluted tubule → collecting duct → papillary duct → minor calyx → major calyx → renal pelvis → ureter → urinary bladder → urethra.

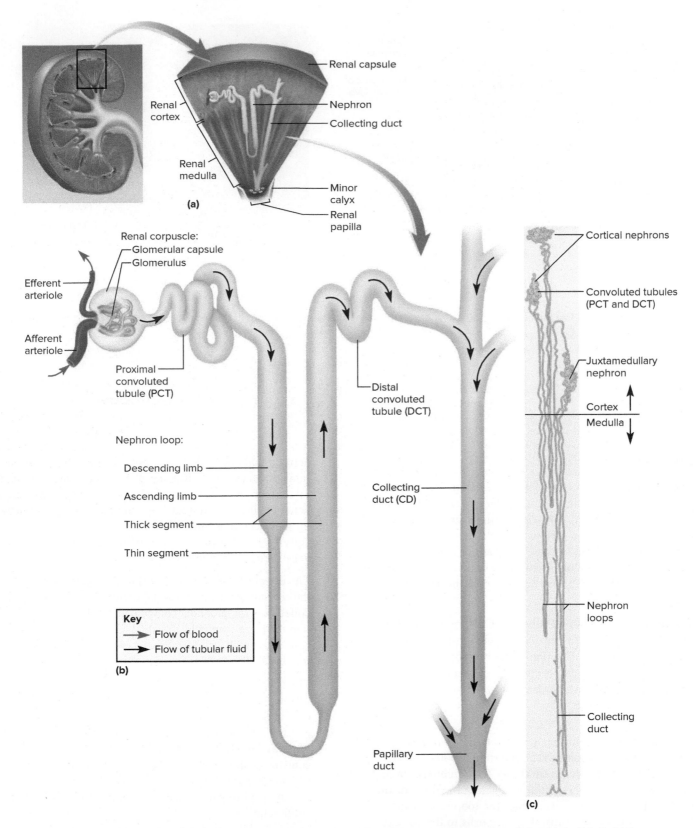

FIGURE 23.8 Microscopic Anatomy of the Nephron. (a) Location of the nephrons in one wedge-shaped lobe of the kidney. (b) Structure of a nephron. For clarity, the nephron is stretched out to separate the convoluted tubules. The nephron loop is greatly shortened for the purpose of illustration. (c) The true proportions of the nephron loops relative to the convoluted tubules. Three nephrons are shown. Their proximal and distal convoluted tubules are commingled in a single tangled mass in each nephron. Note the extreme lengths of the nephron loops. **APR**

Juxtamedullary and Cortical Nephrons

Not all nephrons are identical. Those close to the medulla are called **juxtamedullary**[8] **nephrons.** They have very long nephron loops that extend as far as the apex of the renal pyramid. The remaining nephrons, farther from the medulla, are called **cortical nephrons.** They have relatively short nephron loops that dip only slightly into the outer medulla before turning back (see fig. 23.6) or turn back even before leaving the cortex. Some of them have no nephron loops at all. As you will see later, nephron loops are responsible for maintaining an osmotic gradient in the medulla that helps the body conserve water. Although only 15% of the nephrons are juxtamedullary, they are almost solely responsible for maintaining this gradient.

23.2e Renal Innervation

Wrapped around each renal artery is a **renal plexus** of nerves and ganglia (see fig. 15.6). The plexus follows branches of the renal artery into the parenchyma of the kidney, issuing nerve fibers to the blood vessels and convoluted tubules of the nephrons. The renal plexus carries sympathetic innervation from the abdominal aortic plexus (especially its superior mesenteric and celiac ganglia) as well as afferent pain fibers from the kidneys en route to the spinal cord. Stimulation by the sympathetic fibers of the renal plexus tends to reduce glomerular blood flow and therefore the rate of urine production, although these rates are influenced by other factors as well. Another role of the sympathetic fibers is to respond to falling blood pressure by stimulating the kidneys to secrete *renin,* an enzyme that activates hormonal mechanisms for restoring blood pressure. The kidneys also receive parasympathetic innervation from branches of the vagus nerve, but its function is unknown.

> **BEFORE YOU GO ON**
>
> Answer the following questions to test your understanding of the preceding section:
>
> 4. Arrange the following in order from the most numerous to the least numerous structures in a kidney: glomeruli, major calyces, minor calyces, cortical radiate arteries, interlobar arteries.
>
> 5. Trace the path taken by one red blood cell from the renal artery to the renal vein.
>
> 6. Consider one molecule of urea in the urine. Trace the route that it took from the point where it left the bloodstream to the point where it left the body.

[8]*juxta* = next to

23.3 Urine Formation I: Glomerular Filtration APR

Expected Learning Outcomes
When you have completed this section, you should be able to

a. describe the process by which the kidney filters the blood plasma, including the relevant cellular structure of the glomerulus;

b. Explain the forces that promote and oppose filtration, and calculate the filtration pressure if given the magnitude of these forces; and

c. describe how the nervous system, hormones, and the nephron itself regulate filtration.

The kidney converts blood plasma to urine in four stages: glomerular filtration, tubular reabsorption, tubular secretion, and water conservation **(fig. 23.9).** These are the themes of the next three sections of the chapter. As we trace fluid through the nephron, we will refer to it by different names that reflect its changing composition: (1) The fluid in the capsular space, called **glomerular filtrate,** is similar to blood plasma except that it has almost no protein. (2) The fluid from the proximal convoluted tubule through the distal convoluted tubule is called **tubular fluid.** It differs from the glomerular filtrate because of substances removed and added by the tubule cells. (3) The fluid is called **urine** once it enters the collecting duct, since it undergoes little alteration beyond that point except for a change in water content.

23.3a The Filtration Membrane

Glomerular filtration, discussed in this section, is a process in which water and some solutes in the blood plasma pass from capillaries of the glomerulus into the capsular space of the nephron. To do so, fluid passes through three barriers that constitute a **filtration membrane (fig. 23.10):**

1. **The fenestrated endothelium of the capillary.** Endothelial cells of the glomerular capillaries are honeycombed with large filtration pores about 70 to 90 nm in diameter (see fig. 20.5b). Like fenestrated capillaries elsewhere, these are highly permeable, although their pores are small enough to exclude blood cells from the filtrate.

2. **The basement membrane.** This consists of a proteoglycan gel. Passing large molecules through it would be like trying to grind sand through a kitchen sponge: A few grains may penetrate its small spaces and reach the other side, but most would be held back. On the basis of size alone, the basement membrane excludes molecules larger than 8 nm. Even some smaller molecules, however, are held back by a negative charge on the proteoglycans. Blood albumin is slightly

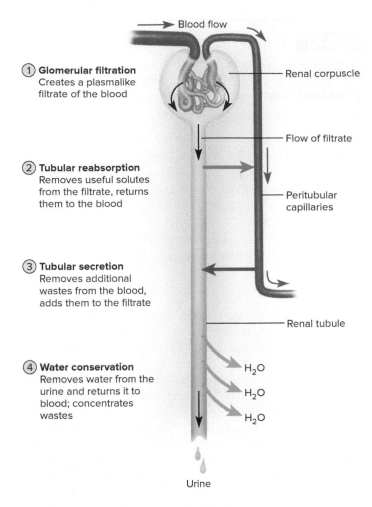

Blood flow

① Glomerular filtration
Creates a plasmalike
filtrate of the blood

Renal corpuscle

Flow of filtrate

② Tubular reabsorption
Removes useful solutes
from the filtrate, returns
them to the blood

Peritubular
capillaries

③ Tubular secretion
Removes additional
wastes from the blood,
adds them to the filtrate

Renal tubule

④ Water conservation
Removes water from the
urine and returns it to
blood; concentrates
wastes

H_2O

H_2O

H_2O

Urine

FIGURE 23.9 Basic Stages of Urine Formation.

smaller than 7 nm, but it is also negatively charged and thus repelled by the basement membrane. Although the blood plasma is 7% protein, the glomerular filtrate is only 0.03% protein. It has traces of albumin and smaller polypeptides, including some hormones.

3. **Filtration slits.** A podocyte of the glomerular capsule is shaped somewhat like an octopus, with a bulbous cell body and several thick arms. Each arm has numerous extensions called **foot processes (pedicels[9])** that wrap around the capillaries and interdigitate with each other, like wrapping your hands around a pipe and lacing your fingers together. The foot processes have negatively charged **filtration slits** about 30 nm wide between them, which are an additional obstacle to large anions.

Almost any molecule smaller than 3 nm can pass freely through the filtration membrane into the capsular space **(fig. 23.11)**. This includes water, electrolytes, glucose, fatty acids, amino acids, nitrogenous wastes, and vitamins. Such solutes have about the same concentration in the glomerular filtrate as in the blood plasma. Some solutes of low molecular weight are retained in the bloodstream, however, because they're bound to plasma proteins that can't get through the membrane. For example, most calcium, iron, and thyroid hormone in the blood are bound to proteins that retard their filtration by the kidneys. The small fraction that is unbound, however, passes freely through the membrane and appears in the urine.

Kidney infections and trauma can damage the filtration membrane and allow albumin or blood cells to filter through. Kidney disease is sometimes marked by the presence of protein (especially albumin) or blood in the urine—conditions called **proteinuria (albuminuria)** and **hematuria,**[10] respectively. Distance runners and competitive swimmers often experience temporary proteinuria and hematuria. Strenuous exercise greatly reduces perfusion of the kidneys, and the glomerulus deteriorates under the prolonged hypoxia, thus leaking protein and sometimes blood into the filtrate.

23.3b Filtration Pressure

Glomerular filtration follows the same principles that govern filtration in other blood capillaries (see section 20.3c), but there are significant differences in the magnitude of the forces involved:

- The blood hydrostatic pressure (BHP) is much higher here than elsewhere—about 60 mm Hg compared with 10 to 15 mm Hg in most other capillaries. This results from the fact that the afferent arteriole is substantially larger than the efferent arteriole, giving the glomerulus a large inlet and small outlet (fig. 23.10a).

- The hydrostatic pressure in the capsular space is about 18 mm Hg, compared with the slightly negative interstitial pressures elsewhere. This results from the high rate of filtration and continual accumulation of fluid in the capsule.

- The colloid osmotic pressure (COP) of the blood is about the same here as anywhere else, 32 mm Hg.

- The glomerular filtrate is almost protein-free and has no significant COP. (This can change markedly in kidney diseases that allow protein to filter into the capsular space.)

On balance, then, we have a high outward pressure of 60 mm Hg, opposed by two inward pressures of 18 and 32 mm Hg **(fig. 23.12),** giving a **net filtration pressure (NFP)** of

$$60_{out} - 18_{in} - 32_{in} = 10 \text{ mm Hg}_{out}.$$

---

[9]*pedi* = foot; *cel* = little

[10]*hemat* = blood; *ur* = urine; *ia* = condition

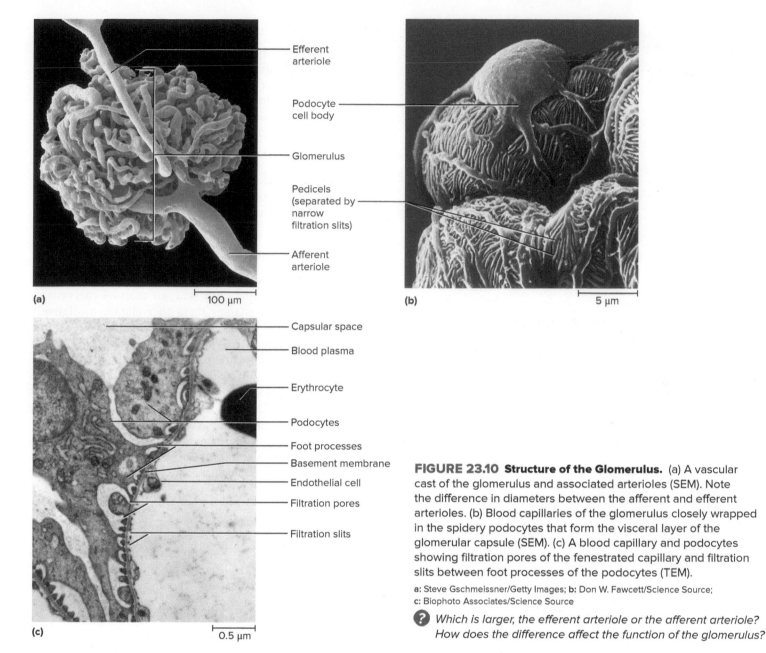

Efferent arteriole

Podocyte cell body

Glomerulus

Pedicels (separated by narrow filtration slits)

Afferent arteriole

(a)   100 μm

(b)   5 μm

Capsular space

Blood plasma

Erythrocyte

Podocytes

Foot processes

Basement membrane

Endothelial cell

Filtration pores

Filtration slits

(c)   0.5 μm

FIGURE 23.10 Structure of the Glomerulus. (a) A vascular cast of the glomerulus and associated arterioles (SEM). Note the difference in diameters between the afferent and efferent arterioles. (b) Blood capillaries of the glomerulus closely wrapped in the spidery podocytes that form the visceral layer of the glomerular capsule (SEM). (c) A blood capillary and podocytes showing filtration pores of the fenestrated capillary and filtration slits between foot processes of the podocytes (TEM).

a: Steve Gschmeissner/Getty Images; b: Don W. Fawcett/Science Source; c: Biophoto Associates/Science Source

? *Which is larger, the efferent arteriole or the afferent arteriole? How does the difference affect the function of the glomerulus?*

In most blood capillaries, the BHP drops low enough at the venous end that osmosis overrides filtration and the capillaries reabsorb fluid. Although BHP also drops along the course of the glomerular capillaries, it remains high enough that these capillaries are engaged solely in filtration. They reabsorb little or no fluid.

The high blood pressure in the glomeruli makes the kidneys especially vulnerable to hypertension, which can have devastating effects on renal function. Hypertension ruptures glomerular capillaries and leads to scarring of the kidneys *(nephrosclerosis)*. It promotes atherosclerosis of the renal blood vessels just as it does elsewhere in the body and thus diminishes renal blood supply. Over time, hypertension often leads to renal failure and renal failure leads to worsening hypertension in an insidious positive feedback loop.

23.3c Glomerular Filtration Rate

Glomerular filtration rate (GFR) is the amount of filtrate formed per minute by the two kidneys combined. For every 1 mm Hg of net filtration pressure, the kidneys of a young adult male produce about 12.5 mL of filtrate per minute. This value, called the *filtration coefficient (K_f)*, depends on the permeability and surface area of the filtration barrier. K_f is about 10% lower in women than in men. For males,

$$\text{GFR} = \text{NFP} \times K_f = 10 \times 12.5 = 125 \text{ mL/min.}$$

In young adult females, the GFR is about 105 mL/min.

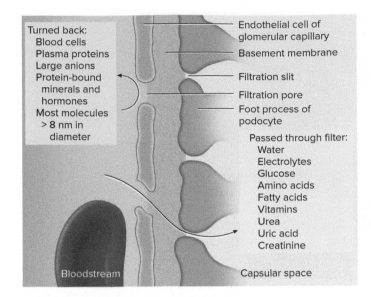

FIGURE 23.11 The Glomerular Filtration Membrane.
Small solutes pass through the membrane into the filtrate (right) and larger particles are turned back and retained in the bloodstream (left).

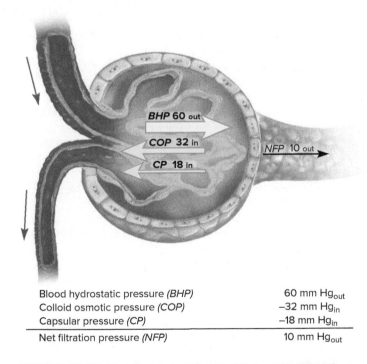

Blood hydrostatic pressure (BHP)	60 mm Hg$_{out}$
Colloid osmotic pressure (COP)	−32 mm Hg$_{in}$
Capsular pressure (CP)	−18 mm Hg$_{in}$
Net filtration pressure (NFP)	10 mm Hg$_{out}$

FIGURE 23.12 The Forces Involved in Glomerular Filtration.

These rates are equivalent to 180 L/day in males and 150 L/day in females—impressive numbers considering that this is about 60 times the amount of blood in the body and 50 to 60 times the amount of filtrate produced by all other capillaries combined. Obviously, only a small portion of this is eliminated as urine. An average adult reabsorbs 99% of the filtrate and excretes 1 to 2 L of urine per day.

23.3d Regulation of Glomerular Filtration

GFR must be precisely controlled. If it's too high, fluid flows through the renal tubules too rapidly for them to reabsorb the usual amount of water and solutes. Urine output rises and creates a threat of dehydration and electrolyte depletion. If GFR is too low, fluid flows sluggishly through the tubules, they reabsorb wastes that should be eliminated in the urine, and azotemia may occur.

The only way to adjust GFR from moment to moment is to change glomerular blood pressure. This is achieved by three homeostatic mechanisms: renal autoregulation, sympathetic control, and hormonal control.

Renal Autoregulation

Renal autoregulation is the ability of the nephrons to adjust their own blood flow and GFR without external (nervous or hormonal) control. It enables them to maintain a relatively stable GFR in spite of changes in arterial blood pressure. If the mean arterial pressure (MAP) rose from 100 to 125 mm Hg and there were no renal autoregulation, urine output would increase from the normal 1 to 2 L/day to more than 45 L/day. Because of renal autoregulation, however, urine output increases only a few percent even if MAP rises as high as 160 mm Hg. Renal autoregulation thus helps to ensure stable fluid and electrolyte balance in spite of the many circumstances that substantially alter one's blood pressure. There are two mechanisms of autoregulation: the myogenic mechanism and tubuloglomerular feedback.

The Myogenic[11] Mechanism This mechanism of stabilizing the GFR is based on the tendency of smooth muscle to contract when stretched. When arterial blood pressure rises, it stretches the afferent arteriole. The arteriole constricts and prevents blood flow into the glomerulus from changing very much. Conversely, when blood pressure falls, the afferent arteriole relaxes and allows blood to flow more easily into the glomerulus. Either way, glomerular blood flow and filtration remain fairly stable.

Tubuloglomerular Feedback This is a mechanism by which the glomerulus receives feedback on the status of the downstream tubular fluid and adjusts filtration to regulate its composition, stabilize nephron performance, and compensate for fluctuations in blood pressure. It involves a structure, the **juxtaglomerular apparatus** (JUX-tuh-glo-MER-you-lur), found at the very end of the nephron loop where it has just reentered the renal cortex. Here, the loop contacts the afferent and efferent arterioles at the vascular pole of the renal corpuscle (**fig. 23.13**).

---

[11]*myo* = muscle; *genic* = produced by

Granular cells are named for the fact that they contain granules of *renin*, which they secrete in response to a drop in blood pressure. This initiates a renin–angiotensin–aldosterone mechanism, explained shortly, which restores blood pressure and supports blood volume.

Two important points must be noted about renal autoregulation. First, it doesn't completely prevent changes in GFR. Like any other homeostatic mechanism, it maintains a *dynamic equilibrium;* the GFR fluctuates within narrow limits. Changes in blood pressure *do* affect GFR and urine output. Second, renal autoregulation cannot compensate for extreme blood pressure variations. Over an MAP range of 90 to 180 mm Hg, the GFR remains quite stable. Below 70 mm Hg, however, glomerular filtration and urine output cease. This can happen in hypovolemic shock.

Sympathetic Control

Sympathetic nerve fibers richly innervate the renal blood vessels. In strenuous exercise or acute conditions such as circulatory shock, sympathetic stimulation and adrenal epinephrine constrict the afferent arterioles. This reduces GFR and urine output while redirecting blood from the kidneys to the heart, brain, and skeletal muscles, where it is more urgently needed. Under such conditions, GFR may be as low as a few milliliters per minute.

The Renin–Angiotensin–Aldosterone Mechanism

Any substantial drop in blood pressure due to bleeding, dehydration, or other cause is detected by the baroreceptors in the aorta

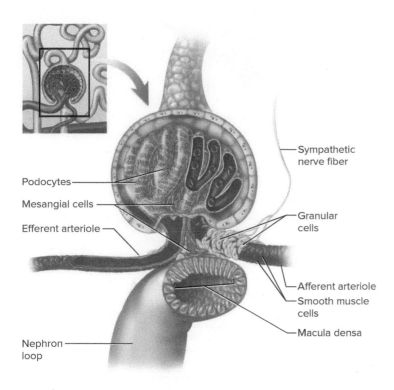

FIGURE 23.13 The Juxtaglomerular Apparatus.

Podocytes
Mesangial cells
Efferent arteriole
Nephron loop
Sympathetic nerve fiber
Granular cells
Afferent arteriole
Smooth muscle cells
Macula densa

Tubuloglomerular feedback begins with the **macula densa,**[12] a patch of slender, closely spaced sensory cells on one side of the loop. When the GFR is very high, the sodium chloride level in the nephron loop is also sharply elevated. Cells of the macula densa absorb Na^+, K^+, and Cl^-, and water follows osmotically; the cells swell and secrete ATP from their basal surfaces. The ATP is metabolized to adenosine by nearby **mesangial**[13] **cells** (mez-AN-jee-ul), which pack the spaces between the arterioles and within the glomerulus.

Adenosine acts as a paracrine messenger that stimulates nearby **granular (juxtaglomerular) cells.** These are modified smooth muscle cells wrapped around the afferent arteriole and to a lesser extent the efferent arteriole. They respond to a rising adenosine level by constricting the afferent arteriole. That reduces blood flow into the glomerulus, thereby reducing GFR and completing the negative feedback loop **(fig. 23.14).** The mesangial cells of the glomerulus may also contract, constricting the glomerular capillaries and reducing filtration. Mesangial cells also form a supportive matrix for the glomerulus and phagocytize tissue debris, preventing the glomerular filtration membrane from clogging up.

Just beyond the juxtaglomerular apparatus, the distal convoluted tubule has a limited capacity for NaCl reabsorption. The tubuloglomerular feedback process may help to prevent overloading the distal convoluted tubule with NaCl, and thus prevent excessive NaCl and water loss in the urine.

[12]*macula* = spot, patch; *densa* = dense
[13]*mes* = in the middle; *angi* = vessel

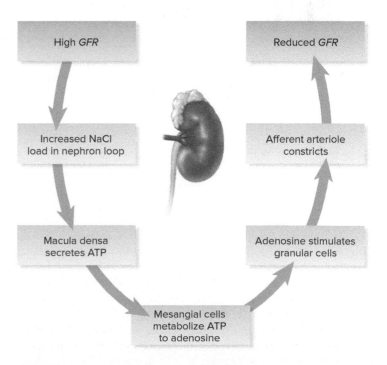

High *GFR* → Increased NaCl load in nephron loop → Macula densa secretes ATP → Mesangial cells metabolize ATP to adenosine → Adenosine stimulates granular cells → Afferent arteriole constricts → Reduced *GFR*

FIGURE 23.14 Tubuloglomerular Feedback.

and carotid arteries. They transmit a signal to the brainstem, leading to various corrective sympathetic reflexes (see fig. 20.14). One such response is that sympathetic fibers stimulate the granular cells to secrete the enzyme **renin** (REE-nin). Renin acts on *angiotensinogen,* a protein in the blood plasma, to split off a 10-amino-acid peptide called angiotensin I. In the lungs and kidneys, **angiotensin-converting enzyme (ACE)** removes two more amino acids, converting it to **angiotensin II,** a hormone that acts in several ways to restore fluid volume and blood pressure **(fig. 23.15):**

- It is a potent vasoconstrictor. Widespread vasoconstriction raises the mean arterial blood pressure throughout the body.

- In the kidneys, it constricts the efferent arterioles and to a somewhat lesser degree, the afferent arterioles. By constricting the glomerular outlet more than the inlet, it raises glomerular blood pressure and GFR, or at least prevents a drastic reduction in GFR, thus ensuring continued filtration of wastes from the blood even when blood pressure has fallen.

- Constriction of the efferent arteriole lowers the blood pressure (BP) in the peritubular capillaries downstream from them. Since capillary BP normally opposes fluid reabsorption, this reduction in BP strongly enhances the reabsorption of NaCl and water from the nephron. More water is returned to the bloodstream instead of being lost in the urine.

- Angiotensin II stimulates the adrenal cortex to secrete aldosterone, which promotes sodium and water reabsorption by the distal convoluted tubule and collecting duct. Angiotensin II also directly stimulates sodium and water reabsorption in the proximal convoluted tubule.

- It stimulates the posterior pituitary gland to secrete antidiuretic hormone, which promotes water reabsorption by the collecting duct.

- It stimulates the sense of thirst and encourages water intake.

Some of these effects are explained more fully later in this chapter and in section 24.2a. Collectively, they raise blood pressure by reducing water loss, encouraging water intake, and constricting blood vessels.

▶▶▶APPLY WHAT YOU KNOW

Would you expect ACE inhibitors to increase or reduce urine output? Why? (ACE inhibitors are explained under "Hormonal Control" in section 20.2c.)

To summarize the events thus far: Glomerular filtration occurs because the high blood pressure of the glomerular capillaries overrides the colloid osmotic pressure of the blood. The filtration membrane allows most plasma solutes into the capsular space while retaining blood cells and protein in the bloodstream. Glomerular filtration is maintained at a fairly steady rate of about 105 to 125 mL/min. (female and male, respectively) in spite of variations in systemic blood pressure. Stability is

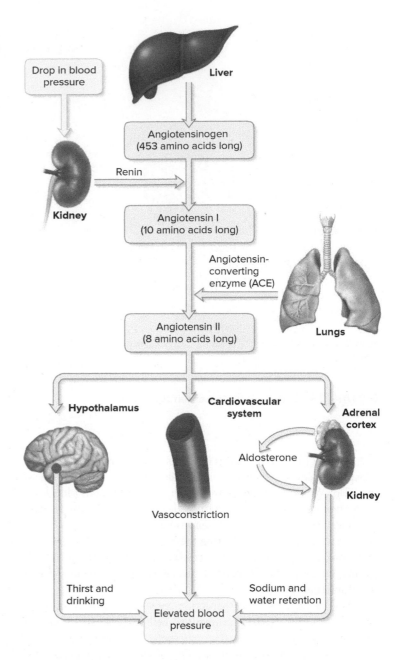

FIGURE 23.15 The Renin–Angiotensin–Aldosterone Mechanism. This chain of events is activated by a drop in blood pressure and acts to raise it again.

achieved by renal autoregulation, sympathetic control, and hormonal control.

BEFORE YOU GO ON

Answer the following questions to test your understanding of the preceding section:

7. Name the four major processes in urine production.

8. Trace the movement of a urea molecule from the blood to the capsular space, and name the barriers it passes through.

9. Calculate the net filtration pressure in a patient whose blood COP is only 10 mm Hg because of hypoproteinemia. Assume other relevant variables to be normal.

10. Assume a person is moderately dehydrated and has low blood pressure. Describe the homeostatic mechanisms that would help the kidneys maintain a normal GFR.

23.4 Urine Formation II: Tubular Reabsorption and Secretion

Expected Learning Outcomes

When you have completed this section, you should be able to

a. describe how the renal tubules reabsorb useful solutes from the glomerular filtrate and return them to the blood;

b. describe how the tubules secrete solutes from the blood into the tubular fluid; and

c. describe how the nephron regulates water excretion.

Conversion of the glomerular filtrate to urine involves the removal and addition of chemicals by tubular reabsorption and secretion, to be described in this section. Here we trace the course of the tubular fluid through the nephron, from proximal convoluted tubule through distal convoluted tubule, and see how the filtrate is modified at each point along the way. Refer to figure 23.9 to put these processes into perspective.

23.4a The Proximal Convoluted Tubule

The proximal convoluted tubule (PCT) reabsorbs about 65% of the glomerular filtrate, while it also removes some substances from the blood and secretes them into the tubule for disposal in the urine. The importance of the PCT is reflected in its relatively great length and prominent microvilli, which increase its absorptive surface area. Its cells also contain abundant large mitochondria that provide ATP for active transport. Of all the calories you consume and ATP you use each day, about 6% goes just for driving these processes in the PCTs of your kidneys.

Tubular Reabsorption

Tubular reabsorption is the process of reclaiming water and solutes from the tubular fluid and returning them to the blood. The PCT reabsorbs a greater variety of chemicals than any other part of the nephron.

There are two routes of reabsorption: (1) the **transcellular**[14] **route,** in which substances pass through the cytoplasm and out the base of the epithelial cells; and (2) the **paracellular**[15] **route,**

in which substances pass through gaps between the cells. The "tight" junctions between the epithelial cells are quite leaky and allow significant amounts of water to pass through. As it travels through the epithelium, water carries with it a variety of dissolved solutes—a process called **solvent drag.** Whether by the transcellular or paracellular route, water and solutes enter the tissue fluid at the base of the epithelium, and from there they are taken up by the peritubular capillaries. In the following discussion and **figure 23.16,** we examine mechanisms of reabsorption.

Sodium Chloride   Sodium reabsorption is the key to almost everything else, because it creates an osmotic and electrical gradient that drives the reabsorption of water and the other solutes. It is the most abundant cation in the glomerular filtrate, with a concentration of 140 mEq/L in the fluid entering the proximal convoluted tubule and only 12 mEq/L in the cytoplasm of the epithelial cells. This is a very steep concentration gradient favoring its transport into the epithelial cells.

Two types of transport proteins in the apical cell surface are responsible for sodium uptake: (1) various *symports* that simultaneously bind Na^+ and another solute such as glucose, amino acids, or lactate; and (2) an Na^+–H^+ *antiport* that pulls Na^+ into the cell while pumping H^+ out of the cell into the tubular fluid. This antiport is a means not only of reabsorbing sodium, but also of eliminating acid from the body fluids. Angiotensin II activates the Na^+–H^+ antiport and thereby exerts a strong influence on sodium reabsorption.

Sodium is prevented from accumulating in the epithelial cells by Na^+–K^+ pumps in the basal domain of the plasma membrane, which pump Na^+ out into the extracellular fluid. From there, it is picked up by the peritubular capillaries and returned to the bloodstream. These Na^+–K^+ pumps, like those anywhere, are ATP-consuming active transport pumps. Although the sodium-transporting symports in the apical membrane don't consume ATP, they are considered an example of **secondary active transport** because of their dependence on the Na^+–K^+ pumps at the base of the cell.

Chloride ions, being negatively charged, follow Na^+ because they're electrically attracted to it. There also are various antiports in the apical cell membrane that absorb Cl^- in exchange for other anions that they eject into the tubular fluid. Chloride and potassium ions are driven out through the basal cell surface by a K^+–Cl^- symport. Both Na^+ and Cl^- also pass through the tubule epithelium by the paracellular route.

Other Electrolytes   Potassium, magnesium, and phosphate ions pass through the paracellular route with water. Phosphate is also cotransported into the epithelial cells with Na^+. Roughly 52% of the filtered calcium is reabsorbed by the paracellular route and 14% by the transcellular route in the PCT. Calcium absorption here is independent of hormonal influence, but another 33% of the calcium is reabsorbed later in the nephron under the influence of parathyroid hormone, to be discussed shortly. The remaining 1%, normally, is excreted in the urine.

---

[14]*trans* = across
[15]*para* = next to

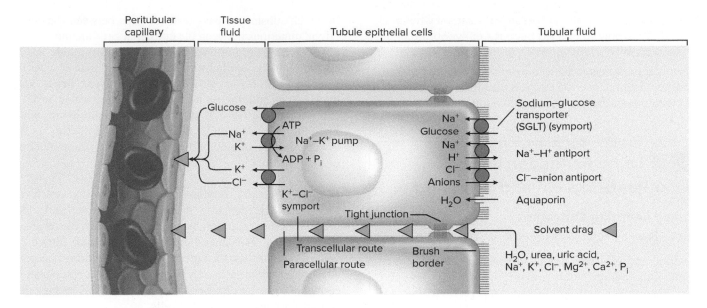

FIGURE 23.16 Reabsorption in the Proximal Convoluted Tubule. Water and solutes in the tubular fluid (right) are carried through the tubule epithelium by various means including symports, antiports, aquaporins, and the paracellular route between cells. They enter the tissue fluid at the base of the epithelium and are picked up by the peritubular capillaries (left). Many other solutes not shown here are reabsorbed by similar means.

? *How would increased Na^+ reabsorption affect the pH of the urine? Where is the clue to this in the figure?*

Glucose   Glucose is cotransported with Na^+ by symports called **sodium–glucose transporters (SGLTs).** It is then removed from the basolateral surface of the cell by facilitated diffusion. Normally, all glucose in the tubular fluid is reabsorbed and there is none in the urine.

Nitrogenous Wastes   Urea passes through the epithelium with water. The nephron as a whole reabsorbs 40% to 60% of the urea in the tubular fluid, but since it reabsorbs 99% of the water, urine has a substantially higher urea concentration than blood or glomerular filtrate. When blood enters the kidney, its urea concentration is about 20 mg/dL; when it leaves the kidney, it is typically down to 10.4 mg/dL. Thus, the kidney removes about half of the urea, keeping its concentration down to a safe level but not completely clearing the blood of it.

The PCT reabsorbs nearly all the uric acid entering it, but later parts of the nephron secrete it back into the tubular fluid. Creatinine isn't reabsorbed at all, but stays in the tubule and is all passed in the urine.

Water   The kidneys reduce about 180 L of glomerular filtrate to 1 or 2 L of urine each day, so water reabsorption is a significant function. About two-thirds of the water is reabsorbed by the PCT. The reabsorption of all the salt and organic solutes as just described makes the tubule cells and tissue fluid hypertonic to the tubular fluid. Water follows the solutes by osmosis through both the paracellular and transcellular routes. Transcellular absorption occurs by way of water channels called **aquaporins** in the apical and basolateral domains of the plasma membrane, enabling water to enter the tubule cells at

the apical surface and leave them (to return to the blood) via the basolateral surface.

Because the PCT reabsorbs proportionate amounts of solutes and water, the osmolarity of the tubular fluid remains unchanged here. Elsewhere in the nephron, water reabsorption varies continually because of the action of hormones responding to the body's state of hydration. In the PCT, however, water is reabsorbed at a constant rate called **obligatory water reabsorption.**

Uptake by the Peritubular Capillaries

After water and solutes leave the basal surface of the tubule epithelium, they are reabsorbed by the peritubular capillaries. The mechanisms of capillary absorption are osmosis and solvent drag. Three factors promote osmosis into these capillaries: (1) The accumulation of reabsorbed fluid on the basal side of the epithelium cells creates a high tissue fluid pressure that physically drives water into the capillaries. (2) The narrowness of the efferent arteriole lowers the blood hydrostatic pressure (BHP) from 60 mm Hg in the glomerulus to only 8 mm Hg in the peritubular capillaries, so there is less resistance to reabsorption here than in most systemic capillaries. (3) As blood passes through the glomerulus, a lot of water is filtered out but nearly all of the protein remains in the blood. Therefore, the blood has an elevated colloid osmotic pressure (COP) by the time it leaves the glomerulus. With a high COP and low BHP in the capillaries and a high hydrostatic pressure in the tissue fluid, the balance of forces in the peritubular capillaries strongly favors reabsorption. This tendency is even further accentuated by angiotensin II. By constricting the afferent and efferent arterioles, this hormone reduces blood pressure in the

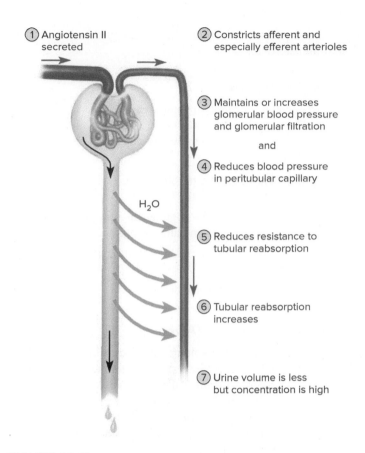

FIGURE 23.17 The Effect of Angiotensin II on Tubular Reabsorption.

① Angiotensin II secreted

② Constricts afferent and especially efferent arterioles

③ Maintains or increases glomerular blood pressure and glomerular filtration

and

④ Reduces blood pressure in peritubular capillary

⑤ Reduces resistance to tubular reabsorption

⑥ Tubular reabsorption increases

⑦ Urine volume is less but concentration is high

H_2O

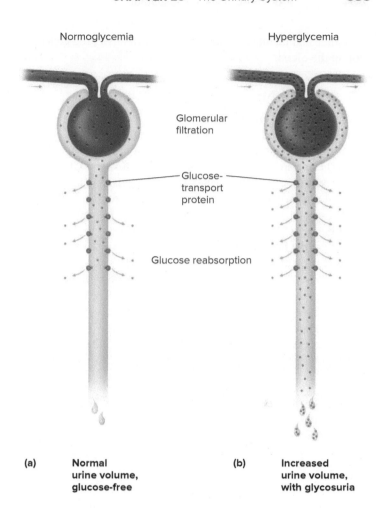

Normoglycemia   Hyperglycemia

Glomerular filtration

Glucose-transport protein

Glucose reabsorption

(a) Normal urine volume, glucose-free

(b) Increased urine volume, with glycosuria

FIGURE 23.18 The Transport Maximum. (a) At a normal blood glucose concentration (normoglycemia), all glucose filtered by the glomerulus is reabsorbed by glucose-transport proteins in the proximal convoluted tubule, and the urine is glucose-free. (b) At a high blood glucose concentration (hyperglycemia), more glucose is filtered than the transport proteins, now saturated, are able to absorb. The glomerular filtration of glucose now exceeds the transport maximum (T_m) of the renal tubule. Excess glucose escapes reabsorption and appears in the urine (glycosuria).

peritubular capillaries and thereby reduces their resistance to fluid reabsorption **(fig. 23.17).**

The Transport Maximum

There is a limit to the amount of solute that the renal tubule can reabsorb because there are limited numbers of transport proteins in the plasma membranes. If all the transporters are occupied as solute molecules pass through, some solute will escape reabsorption and appear in the urine. The maximum rate of reabsorption is the **transport maximum (T_m)**, which is reached when the transporters are saturated (see fig. 3.16).

Each solute reabsorbed by the renal tubule has its own T_m. Glucose, for example, has a T_m of 320 mg/min. It normally enters the renal tubule at a rate of 125 mg/min., well within the T_m; thus all of it is reabsorbed. But at blood glucose levels above 220 mg/dL, glucose is filtered faster than the renal tubule can reabsorb it, and the excess passes in the urine—a condition called **glycosuria**[16] (GLY-co-SOOR-ee-uh) **(fig. 23.18).** In untreated diabetes mellitus, the plasma glucose concentration may exceed 400 mg/dL, so glycosuria is one of the classic signs of this disease.

Tubular Secretion

Tubular secretion is a process in which the renal tubule extracts chemicals from the capillary blood and secretes them into the tubular fluid (see fig. 23.9). In the proximal convoluted tubule and nephron loop, it serves three purposes: (1) It contributes to acid–base balance by secreting varying proportions of hydrogen to bicarbonate ions, as detailed in section 24.3. (2) It extracts wastes from the blood, including urea, uric acid, bile acids, ammonia, and a little creatinine. Uric acid secretion compensates for its reabsorption earlier in the PCT and accounts for all of the uric acid in the urine. (3) It clears drugs and contaminants from the blood, such as morphine, penicillin, and aspirin. One reason why so many drugs must be taken three or four times a day is to keep pace with this

---

[16]*glycos* = sugar; *uria* = urine condition

clearance and maintain a therapeutically effective drug concentration in the blood.

23.4b The Nephron Loop

The primary function of the nephron loop is to generate an osmotic gradient that enables the collecting duct to concentrate the urine and conserve water, as discussed later. But in addition, the loop reabsorbs about 25% of the Na^+, K^+, and Cl^- and 15% of the water in the glomerular filtrate. Cells in the thick segment of the ascending limb of the loop have proteins in the apical membranes that simultaneously bind 1 Na^+, 1 K^+, and 2 Cl^- from the tubular fluid and cotransport them into the cytoplasm. These ions leave the basolateral cell surfaces by active transport of Na^+ and diffusion of K^+ and Cl^-. Potassium reenters the cell by means of the Na^+–K^+ pump and then reenters the tubular fluid, but NaCl remains in the tissue fluid of the renal medulla. The thick segment is impermeable to water; thus water cannot follow the reabsorbed electrolytes, and tubular fluid becomes very dilute (200 mOsm/L) by the time it passes from the nephron loop into the distal convoluted tubule.

23.4c The Distal Convoluted Tubule and Collecting Duct

Fluid arriving in the DCT still contains about 20% of the water and 7% of the salts from the glomerular filtrate. If this were all passed as urine, it would amount to 36 L/day, so a great deal of fluid reabsorption is still to come. The DCT and collecting duct reabsorb variable amounts of water and salts and are regulated by several hormones—particularly aldosterone, natriuretic peptides, antidiuretic hormone, and parathyroid hormone.

There are two kinds of cells in the DCT and collecting duct. The **principal cells** are the more abundant; they have receptors for the foregoing hormones and are involved chiefly in salt and water balance. **Intercalated cells** are fewer in number. They reabsorb K^+ and secrete H^+ into the tubule and are involved mainly in acid–base balance, as discussed in section 24.3c. The major hormonal influences on the DCT and collecting duct are as follows.

Aldosterone

Aldosterone, the "salt-retaining hormone," is a steroid secreted by the adrenal cortex when the blood Na^+ concentration falls or its K^+ concentration rises. A drop in blood pressure also induces aldosterone secretion, but indirectly—it stimulates the kidney to secrete renin; this leads to the production of angiotensin II; and angiotensin II stimulates aldosterone secretion (see fig. 23.15).

Aldosterone acts on the thick segment of the ascending limb of the nephron loop, on the DCT, and on the cortical portion of the collecting duct. It stimulates these segments of the nephron to reabsorb Na^+ and secrete K^+. Water and Cl^- follow the Na^+, so the net effect is that the body retains NaCl and water, urine volume is reduced, and the urine has an elevated K^+ concentration. Water retention helps to maintain blood

volume and pressure. Section 24.2a deals further with the action of aldosterone.

Natriuretic Peptides

The heart secretes natriuretic peptides in response to high blood pressure. These hormones exert four actions that result in the excretion of more salt and water in the urine, thereby reducing blood volume and pressure:

1. They dilate the afferent arteriole and constrict the efferent arteriole, which increases the GFR.
2. They antagonize the renin–angiotensin–aldosterone mechanism by inhibiting renin and aldosterone secretion.
3. They inhibit the secretion of antidiuretic hormone and its action on the kidney.
4. They inhibit NaCl reabsorption by the collecting duct.

Antidiuretic Hormone (ADH)

Dehydration, loss of blood volume, and rising blood osmolarity stimulate arterial baroreceptors and hypothalamic osmoreceptors. In response, the posterior pituitary gland secretes ADH. ADH makes the collecting duct more permeable to water, so water in the tubular fluid reenters the tissue fluid and blood rather than being lost in the urine. Its mechanisms of doing so are described in the next section (23.5).

Parathyroid Hormone (PTH)

A calcium deficiency (hypocalcemia) stimulates the parathyroid glands to secrete PTH, which acts in several ways to restore calcium homeostasis. Its effect on bone metabolism was described in chapter 7 (section 7.4b). In the kidney, it acts on the PCT to inhibit phosphate reabsorption and acts on the DCT and thick segment of the nephron loop to increase calcium reabsorption. On average, about 25% of the filtered calcium is reabsorbed by the thick segment and 8% by the DCT. PTH therefore increases the phosphate content of the urine and lowers its calcium content. This helps minimize further calcium loss. Because phosphate isn't retained along with the calcium, the calcium ions stay in circulation rather than precipitating into the bone tissue as calcium phosphate. Calcitriol and calcitonin have similar but weaker effects on the DCT. PTH also stimulates calcitriol synthesis by the epithelial cells of the PCT.

In summary, the PCT reabsorbs about 65% of the glomerular filtrate and returns it to the blood of the peritubular capillaries. Much of this reabsorption occurs by osmotic and cotransport mechanisms linked to the active transport of sodium ions. The nephron loop reabsorbs another 25% of the filtrate, although its primary role is to aid the function of the collecting duct. The DCT reabsorbs more sodium chloride and water, but its rates of reabsorption are subject to control by hormones, especially aldosterone and natriuretic peptides. These tubules also extract drugs, wastes, and some other solutes from the blood and secrete them into the tubular fluid. The DCT essentially completes the process of determining the chemical composition of the urine. The principal function left to the collecting duct is to conserve water.

Answer the following questions to test your understanding of the preceding section:

11. The reabsorption of water, Cl⁻, and glucose by the PCT is linked to the reabsorption of Na⁺, but in three very different ways. Contrast these three mechanisms.

12. Explain why a substance appears in the urine if its rate of glomerular filtration exceeds the T_m of the renal tubule.

13. Contrast the effects of aldosterone and natriuretic peptides on the renal tubule.

23.5 Urine Formation III: Water Conservation

Expected Learning Outcomes

When you have completed this section, you should be able to

a. explain how the collecting duct and antidiuretic hormone regulate the volume and concentration of urine; and

b. explain how the kidney maintains an osmotic gradient in the renal medulla that enables the collecting duct to function.

The kidney serves not just to eliminate metabolic waste from the body but also to prevent excessive water loss in doing so, and thus to support the body's fluid balance. As the kidney returns water to the tissue fluid and bloodstream, the fluid remaining in the renal tubule, and ultimately passed as urine, becomes more and more concentrated. In this section, we examine the kidney's mechanisms for conserving water and concentrating the urine.

23.5a The Collecting Duct

The collecting duct (CD) begins in the cortex, where it receives tubular fluid from numerous nephrons. As it passes through the medulla, it usually reabsorbs water and concentrates the urine. When urine enters the upper end of the CD, it is isotonic with blood plasma (300 mOsm/L), but by the time it leaves the lower end, it can be up to four times as concentrated—that is, highly hypertonic to the plasma. This ability to concentrate wastes and control water loss was crucial to the evolution of terrestrial animals such as ourselves (see Deeper Insight 23.1).

DEEPER INSIGHT 23.1

EVOLUTIONARY MEDICINE

The Kidney and Life on Dry Land

Physiologists first suspected that the nephron loop played a role in water conservation because of their studies of a variety of animal species. Animals that must conserve water have longer, more numerous nephron loops than animals with little need to conserve it. Fish and amphibians lack nephron loops and produce urine that is isotonic to their blood plasma. Aquatic mammals such as beavers have short nephron loops and only slightly hypertonic urine.

But the kangaroo rat, a desert rodent, provides an instructive contrast. It lives on seeds and other dry foods and can go its whole life without drinking water. Its kidneys are so efficient that it can live entirely on the water produced by aerobic respiration. They have extremely long nephron loops and produce urine that is 10 to 14 times as concentrated as the blood plasma (compared with 4 times, at most, in humans).

Comparative studies thus suggested a hypothesis for the function of the nephron loop and prompted many years of difficult research that led to the discovery of the countercurrent multiplier mechanism for water conservation. This shows how comparative anatomy provides suggestions and insights into function and why physiologists don't study human function in isolation from other species.

Two facts enable the collecting duct to produce such hypertonic urine: (1) The osmolarity of the extracellular fluid is four times as high in the lower medulla as it is in the cortex, and (2) the medullary portion of the CD is more permeable to water than to solutes. Therefore, as urine passes down the CD through the increasingly hypertonic medulla, water leaves the tubule by osmosis, most NaCl and other wastes remain behind, and the urine becomes more and more concentrated (**fig. 23.19**).

23.5b Control of Water Loss

Just how concentrated the urine becomes depends on the body's state of hydration. For example, if you drink a large volume of water, you soon produce a large volume of hypotonic urine—a response called *water diuresis*[17] (DY-you-REE-sis). Under such conditions, the cortical portion of the CD reabsorbs NaCl but is impermeable to water. Salt is removed from the urine, water stays in it, and urine osmolarity may be as low as 50 mOsm/L.

Dehydration, on the other hand, causes the urine to be scanty and more concentrated. The high blood osmolarity of a dehydrated person stimulates the pituitary to release ADH. ADH increases water reabsorption (reduces urine output) by two mechanisms. (1) Within seconds, cells of the collecting duct transfer aquaporins from storage vesicles in the cytoplasm to the apical cell surface and the cells begin taking up more water from the tubular fluid. (2) If the ADH level remains elevated for ≥24 hours, it induces the cell to transcribe the aquaporin gene and manufacture more aquaporins, further raising the water permeability of the collecting duct.

---

[17]*diuresis* = passing urine

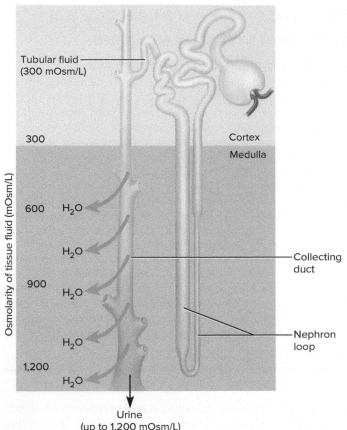

Tubular fluid
(300 mOsm/L)

300

Cortex

Medulla

600   H₂O

H₂O

Collecting
duct

900   H₂O

H₂O

Nephron
loop

1,200

H₂O

Urine
(up to 1,200 mOsm/L)

FIGURE 23.19 Water Reabsorption by the Collecting Duct. Note that the osmolarity of the tissue fluid increases fourfold from 300 mOsm/L in the cortex to 1,200 mOsm/L deep in the medulla. Urine concentration increases proportionately as water leaves the duct through its aquaporins.

By contrast, when you're well hydrated, ADH secretion falls; the tubule cells remove aquaporins from the plasma membrane and store them in cytoplasmic vesicles. The duct is then less permeable to water, so more water remains in the duct and you produce abundant, dilute urine.

In extreme cases, the blood pressure of a dehydrated person is low enough to significantly reduce the glomerular filtration rate. When the GFR is low, fluid flows more slowly through the renal tubules and there is more time for tubular reabsorption. Less salt remains in the urine as it enters the CD, so there is less opposition to the osmosis of water out of the duct and into the ECF. More water is reabsorbed and less urine is produced.

23.5c The Countercurrent Multiplier

The ability of the CD to concentrate urine depends on the osmotic gradient of the renal medulla. It may seem surprising that the ECF osmolarity is four

times as great deep in the medulla as in the cortex. We would expect salt to diffuse toward the cortex until it was evenly distributed through the kidney. However, there is a mechanism that overrides this: The nephron loop acts as a **countercurrent multiplier,** which continually recaptures salt and returns it to the deep medullary tissue. It is called a *multiplier* because it multiplies the osmolarity deep in the medulla, and a *countercurrent* mechanism because it is based on fluid flowing in opposite directions in two adjacent tubules—downward in the descending limb and upward in the ascending limb.

Figure 23.20 shows how this works. Steps ② through ⑤ form a positive feedback loop. As fluid flows down the descending limb of the nephron loop, it passes through an environment of increasing osmolarity. Most of the descending limb is very permeable to water but not to NaCl; therefore, water passes by osmosis from the tubule into the ECF, leaving NaCl behind. The tubule contents increase in osmolarity, reaching about 1,200 mOsm/L by the time the fluid rounds the bend at the lower end of the loop.

Most or all of the ascending limb (its thick segment), by contrast, is impermeable to water, but has pumps that cotransport Na⁺, K⁺, and Cl⁻ into the ECF. This keeps the osmolarity of the renal medulla high. Since water remains in the tubule, the tubular fluid becomes more and more dilute as it approaches the cortex and is only about 100 mOsm/L at the top of the loop.

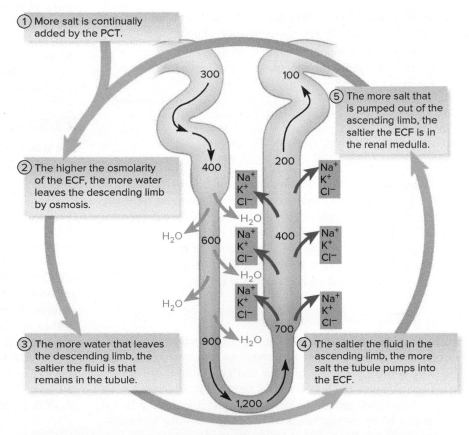

① More salt is continually added by the PCT.

⑤ The more salt that is pumped out of the ascending limb, the saltier the ECF is in the renal medulla.

② The higher the osmolarity of the ECF, the more water leaves the descending limb by osmosis.

③ The more water that leaves the descending limb, the saltier the fluid is that remains in the tubule.

④ The saltier the fluid in the ascending limb, the more salt the tubule pumps into the ECF.

FIGURE 23.20 The Countercurrent Multiplier of the Nephron Loop. The numbers in the tubule are in mOsm/L.

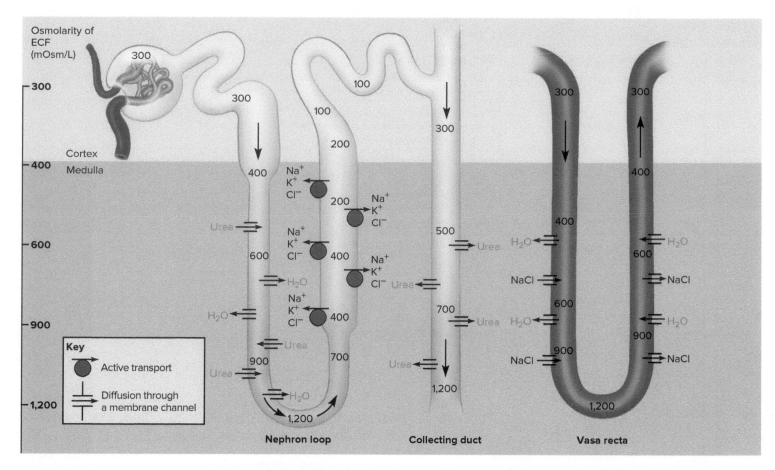

FIGURE 23.21 Functional Relationship of the Nephron Loop, Vasa Recta, and Collecting Duct. These three structures work together to maintain a gradient of osmolarity in the renal medulla. The numbers in the tubule and vasa recta are in mOsm/L.

About 40% of the high osmolarity in the deep medullary tissue, however, is due not to NaCl and KCl, but to urea—which continually cycles from the collecting duct to the nephron loop and back **(fig. 23.21).** The lower end of the collecting duct is somewhat permeable to urea, permitting it to diffuse into the ECF. Some of it enters the descending limb of the loop and travels through the loop and DCT back to the collecting duct. Neither the thick segment nor the DCT is permeable to urea. Combined with new urea constantly added by glomerular filtration, urea remains concentrated in the collecting duct and some of it always diffuses out into the medulla, adding to its osmolarity.

23.5d The Countercurrent Exchange System

The large volume of water reabsorbed by the collecting duct must be returned to the bloodstream. It is picked up and carried away by the vasa recta, but this poses a problem: Why don't the vasa recta also carry away the urea and salt needed to maintain the high osmolarity of the medulla? The answer is that the vasa recta form a **countercurrent exchange** system that prevents this from happening. Blood flows in opposite directions in adjacent parallel capillaries. As it flows downward into the medulla, the vessels exchange water for salt—water diffuses out of the

capillaries and salt diffuses in. But as the blood flows back up to the cortex, the opposite occurs; the vasa recta give up salt and absorb water. Indeed, they absorb more water on the way out than they give up on the way in. Thus, they carry away water absorbed by the kidney but don't subtract from the osmolarity of the medulla.

To summarize what we have studied in this section, the collecting duct can adjust water reabsorption to produce urine as hypotonic (dilute) as 50 mOsm/L or as hypertonic (concentrated) as 1,200 mOsm/L, depending on the body's need for water conservation or removal. In a state of hydration, ADH is not secreted and the cortical part of the CD reabsorbs salt without reabsorbing water; the water remains to be excreted in the dilute urine. In a state of dehydration, ADH is secreted, the medullary part of the CD reabsorbs water, and the urine is more concentrated. The CD is able to do this because it passes through an osmotic gradient in the medulla from 300 mOsm/L near the cortex to 1,200 mOsm/L near the papilla. This gradient is maintained by the countercurrent multiplier of the nephron loop, which concentrates NaCl in the lower medulla, and by the diffusion of urea from the collecting duct into the medulla. The vasa recta are arranged as a countercurrent exchange system that enables them to remove water from the medulla without subtracting from its osmotic gradient.

TABLE 23.1	Hormones Affecting Renal Function	
Hormone	**Renal Targets**	**Effects**
Aldosterone	Nephron loop, DCT, CD	Promotes Na$^+$ reabsorption and K$^+$ secretion; indirectly promotes Cl$^-$ and H$_2$O reabsorption; maintains blood volume and reduces urine volume
Angiotensin II	Afferent and efferent arterioles, PCT	Reduces water loss, stimulates thirst and encourages water intake, and constricts blood vessels, thus raising blood pressure. Reduces GFR; stimulates PCT to reabsorb NaCl and H$_2$O; stimulates aldosterone and ADH secretion
Antidiuretic hormone	Collecting duct	Promotes H$_2$O reabsorption; reduces urine volume, increases concentration
Natriuretic peptides	Afferent and efferent arterioles, collecting duct	Dilate afferent arteriole, constrict efferent arteriole, increase GFR; inhibit secretion of renin, ADH, and aldosterone; inhibit NaCl reabsorption by collecting duct; increase urine volume and lower blood pressure
Calcitonin	DCT	Weak effects similar to those of parathyroid hormone
Calcitriol	DCT	Weak effects similar to those of parathyroid hormone
Epinephrine and norepinephrine	Juxtaglomerular apparatus, afferent arteriole	Induce renin secretion; constrict afferent arteriole; reduce GFR and urine volume
Parathyroid hormone	PCT, DCT, nephron loop	Promotes Ca^{2+} reabsorption by loop and DCT; increases phosphate excretion by PCT; promotes calcitriol synthesis

Figure 23.22 summarizes the major solutes reabsorbed and secreted in each part of the renal tubule. **Table 23.1** summarizes the hormones that affect renal function.

BEFORE YOU GO ON

Answer the following questions to test your understanding of the preceding section:

14. Predict how ADH hypersecretion would affect the sodium concentration of the urine, and explain why.

15. Concisely contrast the role of the countercurrent multiplier with that of the countercurrent exchanger.

16. How would the function of the collecting duct change if the nephron loop didn't exist?

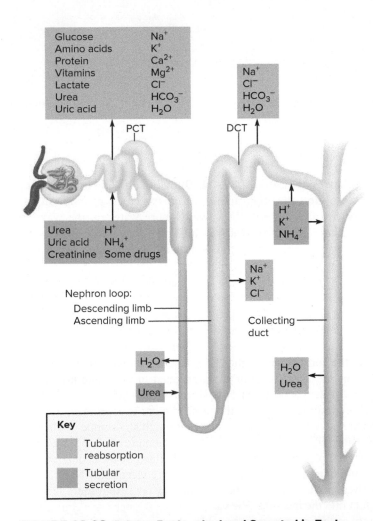

FIGURE 23.22 Solutes Reabsorbed and Secreted in Each Portion of the Renal Tubule.

23.6 Urine and Renal Function Tests

Expected Learning Outcomes

When you have completed this section, you should be able to

a. describe the composition and properties of urine; and

b. carry out some calculations to evaluate renal function.

Medical diagnosis often rests on determining the current and recent physiological state of the tissues. No two fluids are as valuable for this purpose as blood and urine. **Urinalysis,** the examination of the physical and chemical properties of urine, is therefore one of the most routine procedures in medical examinations. The principal characteristics of urine and certain tests used to evaluate renal function are described here.

23.6a Composition and Properties of Urine

The basic composition and properties of urine are as follows:

- **Appearance.** Urine varies from almost colorless to deep amber, depending on the body's state of hydration. The yellow color of urine is due to **urochrome,**[18] a pigment produced by the breakdown of hemoglobin from expired erythrocytes. Pink, green, brown, black, and other colors can result from certain foods, vitamins, drugs, and metabolic diseases. Urine is normally clear but turns cloudy upon standing because of bacterial growth. Pus in the urine (**pyuria**[19]) makes it cloudy and suggests kidney infection. Blood in the urine (**hematuria**) may be due to a urinary tract infection, trauma, or kidney stones. Cloudiness or blood in a urine specimen sometimes, however, simply indicates contamination with semen or menstrual fluid.

- **Odor.** Fresh urine has a distinctive but not necessarily repellent odor. As it stands, however, bacteria multiply, degrade urea to ammonia, and produce the pungent odor typical of stale wet diapers. Asparagus and other foods can impart distinctive aromas to the urine. Diabetes mellitus gives it a sweet, fruity odor of acetone. A mousy odor suggests phenylketonuria (PKU), and a rotten odor may indicate urinary tract infection.

- **Specific gravity.** This is a ratio of the density (g/mL) of a substance to the density of distilled water. Distilled water has a specific gravity of 1.000, and urine ranges from 1.001 when it is very dilute to 1.028 when it is very concentrated. Multiplying the last two digits of the specific gravity by a proportionality constant of 2.6 gives an estimate of the grams of solid matter per liter of urine. For example, a specific gravity of 1.025 indicates a solute concentration of $25 \times 2.6 = 65$ g/L.

- **Osmolarity.** Urine can have an osmolarity as low as 50 mOsm/L in a very hydrated person or as high as 1,200 mOsm/L in a dehydrated person. Compared with the osmolarity of blood (300 mOsm/L), then, urine can be either hypotonic or hypertonic.

- **pH.** The body constantly generates metabolic acids and gets rid of them by excreting mildly acidic urine, usually with a pH of about 6.0 (but ranging from 4.5 to 8.2). The next chapter (section 24.3) explains how the kidneys regulate urine pH.

- **Chemical composition.** Urine averages 95% water and 5% solutes by volume (**table 23.2**). Normally, the most abundant solute is urea, followed by sodium chloride, potassium chloride, and lesser amounts of creatinine, uric acid, phosphates, sulfates, and traces of calcium, magnesium, and sometimes bicarbonate. Urine contains urochrome

TABLE 23.2	Properties and Composition of Urine	
Physical Properties		
Specific gravity	1.001–1.028	
Osmolarity	50–1,200 mOsm/L	
pH	6.0 (range 4.5–8.2)	
Solute	**Concentration***	**Output****
Inorganic Ions		
Chloride	533 mg/dL	6.4 g/day
Sodium	333 mg/dL	4.0 g/day
Potassium	166 mg/dL	2.0 g/day
Phosphate	83 mg/dL	1 g/day
Ammonia	60 mg/dL	0.68 g/day
Calcium	17 mg/dL	0.2 g/day
Magnesium	13 mg/dL	0.16 g/day
Nitrogenous Wastes		
Urea	1.8 g/dL	21 g/day
Creatinine	150 mg/dL	1.8 g/day
Uric acid	40 mg/dL	0.5 g/day
Urobilin	125 µg/dL	1.52 mg/day
Bilirubin	20 µg/dL	0.24 mg/day
Other Organics		
Amino acids	288 µg/dL	3.5 mg/day
Ketones	17 µg/dL	0.21 mg/day
Carbohydrates	9 µg/dL	0.11 mg/day
Lipids	1.6 µg/dL	0.02 mg/day

*Typical values for a young adult male
**Assuming a urine output of 1.2 L/day

and a trace of bilirubin from the breakdown of hemoglobin and related products, and urobilin, a brown oxidized derivative of bilirubin. It is abnormal to find glucose, free hemoglobin, albumin, ketones, or bile pigments in the urine; their presence is an important indicator of disease.

23.6b Urine Volume

An average adult produces 1 to 2 L of urine per day. An output of >2 L/day is called **diuresis** or **polyuria**[20] (POL-ee-YOU-ree-uh). Fluid intake and some drugs can temporarily increase output to as much as 20 L/day. Chronic diseases such as diabetes (see next) can do so over a long term. **Oliguria**[21] (oll-ih-GURE-ee-uh)

---

is an output of <500 mL/day, and **anuria**[22] is an output of 0 to 100 mL/day. Low output can result from kidney disease, dehydration, circulatory shock, prostate enlargement, and other causes. If urine output drops to <400 mL/day, the body cannot maintain a safe, low concentration of wastes in the blood plasma. The result is azotemia.

Diabetes

Diabetes[23] is any metabolic disorder resulting in chronic polyuria. There are at least four forms of diabetes: *diabetes mellitus*[24] *type 1* and *type 2, gestational diabetes,* and *diabetes insipidus.*[25] In most cases, the polyuria results from a high concentration of glucose in the renal tubule. Glucose osmotically retains water in the tubule, so more water passes in the urine *(osmotic diuresis)* and a person may become severely dehydrated. In diabetes mellitus and gestational diabetes, the high glucose level in the tubular fluid is a result of hyperglycemia, a high level in the blood. About 1% to 3% of pregnant women experience gestational diabetes, in which pregnancy reduces the mother's insulin sensitivity, resulting in hyperglycemia and glycosuria. Diabetes insipidus results from ADH hyposecretion. Without ADH, the collecting duct doesn't reabsorb much water, so more water passes in the urine.

Diabetes mellitus and gestational diabetes are characterized by glycosuria. Before chemical tests for urine glucose were developed, physicians diagnosed diabetes mellitus by tasting the patient's urine for sweetness. Tests for glycosuria are now as simple as dipping a chemical test strip into the urine specimen—an advance in medical technology for which urologists are no doubt grateful. In diabetes insipidus, the urine contains no glucose and, by the old diagnostic method, would not taste sweet.

Diuretics

A **diuretic** is any chemical that increases urine volume. Some diuretics, such as caffeine, act by dilating the afferent arteriole and thus increasing glomerular filtration rate. Others act by reducing tubular reabsorption of water. Alcohol, for example, inhibits ADH secretion and thereby reduces reabsorption in the collecting duct. **Loop diuretics** such as furosemide (Lasix) act on the nephron loop to inhibit the Na^+–K^+–Cl^- symport. This impairs the countercurrent multiplier, thus reducing the osmotic gradient in the renal medulla and making the collecting duct unable to reabsorb as much water as usual. Diuretics are commonly administered to treat hypertension and congestive heart failure by reducing the body's fluid volume and blood pressure.

23.6c Renal Function Tests

There are several tests for diagnosing kidney diseases, evaluating their severity, and monitoring their progress. Here we examine two methods used to determine renal clearance and glomerular filtration rate.

Renal Clearance

Renal clearance is the volume of blood plasma from which a particular waste is completely removed in 1 minute. It represents the net effect of three processes:

Glomerular filtration of the waste

+ Amount added by tubular secretion

− Amount removed by tubular reabsorption

Renal clearance

In principle, we could determine renal clearance by sampling blood entering and leaving the kidney and comparing their waste concentrations. In practice, it isn't practical to draw blood samples from the renal artery and vein, but clearance can be assessed indirectly by collecting samples of blood and urine, measuring the waste concentration in each, and measuring the rate of urine output.

Suppose the following values were obtained for urea:

U (urea concentration in urine)   = 6.0 mg/mL

V (rate of urine output)   = 2 mL/min.

P (urea concentration in plasma)   = 0.2 mg/mL

The renal clearance (C) of urea would be:

$$C = UV/P$$

$$= (6.0 \text{ mg/mL})(2 \text{ mL/min.})/0.2 \text{ mg/mL}$$

$$= 60 \text{ mL/min.}$$

This means the equivalent of 60 mL of blood plasma is completely cleared of urea per minute. If this person has a normal GFR of 125 mL/min., then the kidneys will clear urea from 60/125 = 48% of the glomerular filtrate. This is a normal rate of urea clearance and is sufficient to maintain safe levels of urea in the blood.

▶▶▶APPLY WHAT YOU KNOW

What would you expect the value of renal clearance of glucose to be in a healthy individual? Why?

---

[22] *an* = without; *ur* = urine; *ia* = condition
[23] *diabetes* = passing through
[24] *melli* = honey, sweet
[25] *insipid* = tasteless

Glomerular Filtration Rate

Assessment of kidney disease often calls for a measurement of GFR. We cannot determine GFR from urea excretion for two reasons: (1) Some of the urea in the urine is secreted by the renal tubule, not filtered by the glomerulus; and (2) much of the urea filtered by the glomerulus is reabsorbed by the tubule. To measure GFR ideally requires a substance that isn't secreted or reabsorbed at all, so all of it in the urine gets there by glomerular filtration.

There doesn't appear to be a single urine solute produced by the body that isn't secreted or reabsorbed to some degree. However, several plants, including garlic and artichoke, produce a polysaccharide called inulin (IN-you-lin; not to be confused with insulin) that is useful for GFR measurement. All inulin filtered by the glomerulus remains in the renal tubule and appears in the urine; none is reabsorbed, nor does the tubule secrete it. GFR can be measured by injecting inulin and subsequently measuring the rate of urine output and the concentrations of inulin in the blood and urine.

For inulin, GFR is equal to the renal clearance. Suppose, for example, that a patient's plasma concentration of inulin is P = 0.5 mg/mL, the urine concentration is U = 30 mg/mL, and urine output is V = 2 mL/min. This person has a normal GFR:

$$GFR = UV/P$$

$$= (30 \text{ mg/mL})(2 \text{ mL/min.})/0.5 \text{ mg/mL}$$

$$= 120 \text{ mL/min.}$$

In clinical practice, GFR is more often estimated from creatinine excretion. This has a small but acceptable error of measurement, and is an easier procedure than injecting and measuring inulin.

A solute that is reabsorbed by the renal tubules will have a renal clearance *less* than the GFR (provided its tubular secretion is less than its rate of reabsorption). This is why the renal clearance of urea is about 60 mL/min. A solute that is secreted by the renal tubules will have a renal clearance *greater* than the GFR (provided its reabsorption does not exceed its secretion). Creatinine, for example, has a renal clearance of 140 mL/min.

BEFORE YOU GO ON

Answer the following questions to test your understanding of the preceding section:

17. Define *oliguria* and *polyuria*. Which of these is characteristic of diabetes?

18. Identify a cause of glycosuria other than diabetes mellitus.

19. How is the diuresis produced by furosemide like the diuresis produced by diabetes mellitus? How are they different?

20. Explain why GFR cannot be determined by measuring the amount of NaCl in the urine.

23.7 Urine Storage and Elimination

Expected Learning Outcomes
When you have completed this section, you should be able to

a. describe the functional anatomy of the ureters, urinary bladder, and male and female urethra; and

b. explain how the nervous system and urethral sphincters control the voiding of urine.

Urine is produced continually, but fortunately it doesn't drain continually from the body. Urination is episodic—occurring when we allow it. This is made possible by an apparatus for storing urine and neural controls for its timely release.

23.7a The Ureters

The renal pelvis funnels urine into the ureter, a retroperitoneal, muscular tube that extends to the urinary bladder. The ureter is about 25 cm long and reaches a maximum diameter of about 1.7 cm near the bladder. The ureters pass posterior to the bladder and enter it from below, passing obliquely through its muscular wall and opening onto its floor. A small flap of mucosa acts as a valve at the opening of each ureter into the bladder, preventing urine from backing up into the ureter when the bladder contracts.

The ureter has three layers: an adventitia, muscularis, and mucosa. The adventitia is a connective tissue layer that binds it to the surrounding tissues. The muscularis consists of two layers of smooth muscle over most of its length, but a third layer appears in the lower ureter. The mucosa has a urothelium (transitional epithelium) that begins in the minor calyces of the kidney and extends from there through the bladder.

When urine enters the ureter and stretches it, the muscularis contracts and initiates a peristaltic wave that milks the urine from the renal pelvis down to the bladder. These contractions occur every few seconds to few minutes, proportional to the rate at which urine enters the ureter. The lumen of the ureter is very narrow and is easily obstructed or injured by kidney stones (see Deeper Insight 23.2).

23.7b The Urinary Bladder

The urinary bladder (**fig. 23.23**) is a muscular sac on the floor of the pelvic cavity, inferior to the peritoneum and posterior to the pubic symphysis. It is covered by parietal peritoneum on its flattened superior surface and by a fibrous adventitia elsewhere.

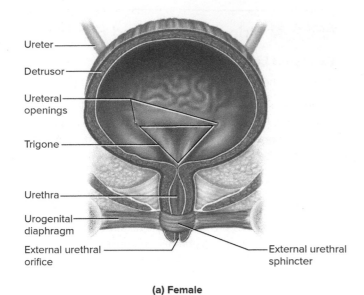

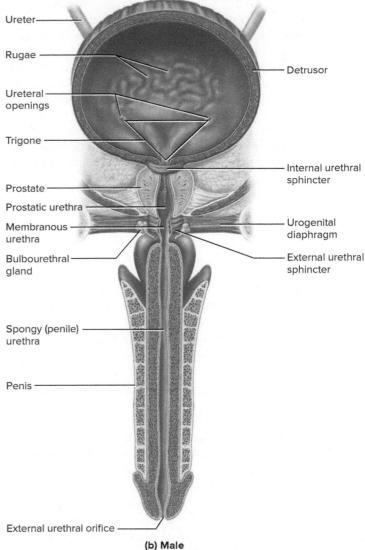

FIGURE 23.23 The Urinary Bladder and Urethra (Frontal Sections). (a) Female. (b) Male. **APR**

❓ *Why are women more susceptible than men to bladder infections?*

 DEEPER INSIGHT 23.2

CLINICAL APPLICATION

Kidney Stones

A *renal calculus*[26] (kidney stone) is a hard granule of calcium or phosphate salts and sometimes other components such as uric acid **(fig 23.24).** The presence of kidney stones is called *nephrolithiasis*. Renal calculi form in the renal pelvis and are usually small enough to pass unnoticed in the urine flow. Some, however, grow as large as a few centimeters and block the renal pelvis or ureter, which can lead to the destruction of nephrons as pressure builds in the kidney. A large, jagged calculus passing down the ureter stimulates strong contractions that can be excruciatingly painful. It can also tear the ureter and cause hematuria. Causes of renal calculi include hypercalcemia (excess calcium in the blood), dehydration, pH imbalances, frequent urinary tract infections, or an enlarged prostate gland causing urine retention. The most common treatment for renal calculi in the United States is called *shock wave lithotripsy*[27] *(SWL)*. The patient lies on an operating table under general anesthesia with a water-filled cushion on the abdomen or behind the kidney. One to two thousand underwater electrical sparks produce focused shock waves that pulverize the calculi into "stone dust" that the patient can subsequently pass in the urine. Very large stones (>2 cm) may require surgical removal, however, and SWL is not used for pregnant women, morbidly obese patients, and some others.

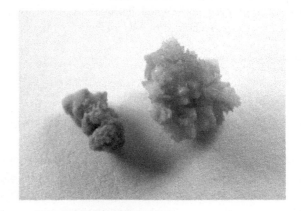

FIGURE 23.24 Kidney Stones.
remik44992/Shutterstock

[26]*calc* = calcium, stone; *ul* = little
[27]*litho* = stone; *tripsy* = crushing

Its muscularis, called the **detrusor**[28] (deh-TROO-zur), consists of three layers of smooth muscle. The openings of the two ureters and the urethra mark a smooth-surfaced triangular area called the **trigone**[29] (TRY-goan) on the bladder floor. This is a common site of bladder infection (see Deeper Insight 23.3).

The mucosa is lined with urothelium (transitional epithelium), whose unique surface *umbrella cells* protect it from the hypertonic and acidic urine as described in section 5.2b. The epithelium is thicker here than anywhere else in the urinary tract, since it is subject to the most prolonged exposure to stored urine. When the bladder is empty, the mucosa is typically five or six cells thick and exhibits wrinkles called **rugae**[30] (ROO-jee). As the bladder fills, the rugae flatten and the epithelium thins to two or three cells thick. A moderately full bladder contains about 500 mL of urine and extends about 12.5 cm from top to bottom. The maximum capacity is 700 to 800 mL.

23.7c The Urethra

The urethra conveys urine out of the body. In the female, it is a tube 3 to 4 cm long bound to the anterior wall of the vagina by fibrous connective tissue. Its opening, the **external urethral orifice,** lies between the vaginal orifice and clitoris. The male urethra is about 18 cm long and has three regions: (1) The **prostatic urethra** begins at the urinary bladder and passes for about 2.5 cm through the prostate. During orgasm, it receives semen from the reproductive glands. (2) The **membranous urethra** is a short (0.5 cm), thin-walled portion where the urethra passes through the muscular floor of the pelvic cavity. (3) The **spongy (penile) urethra** is about 15 cm long and passes through the penis to the external urethral orifice. It is named for the *corpus spongiosum* of the penis, through which it passes. The male urethra assumes an S shape: It passes downward from the bladder, turns anteriorly as it enters the root of

DEEPER INSIGHT 23.3
CLINICAL APPLICATION
Urinary Tract Infection (UTI)

Inflammation of the urinary bladder is called *cystitis.*[31] It is especially common in females because bacteria such as *Escherichia coli* can travel easily from the perineum up the short urethra. Because of this risk, young girls should be taught never to wipe the anus in a forward direction. Cystitis is frequently triggered in women by sexual intercourse ("honeymoon cystitis"). If cystitis is untreated, bacteria can spread up the ureters and cause *pyelitis,*[32] infection of the renal pelvis. If it reaches the renal cortex and nephrons, it is called *pyelonephritis.* Kidney infections can also result from invasion by blood-borne bacteria. Urine stagnation due to renal calculi or prostate enlargement increases the risk of infection.

---

[28]*de* = down; *trus* = push
[29]*tri* = three; *gon* = angle
[30]*rugae* = folds, wrinkles
[31]*cyst* = bladder; *itis* = inflammation
[32]*pyel* = pelvis; *itis* = inflammation

the penis, and then turns about 90° downward again as it enters the external, pendant part of the penis. The mucosa has a urothelium near the bladder, pseudostratified epithelium for most of its length, and finally stratified squamous epithelium near the external urethral orifice. There are mucous **urethral glands** in its wall.

In males, smooth muscle around the neck of the bladder and nearby urethra is of a different physiological type than the detrusor, richly innervated by the sympathetic nervous system and thickened into a collar of muscle called the **internal urethral sphincter.** It compresses the urethra when it contracts. Its function seems to be to prevent the reflux of semen into the bladder during ejaculation. There is no evidence of an internal urethral sphincter in females. In both sexes, however, there is an **external urethral sphincter** of skeletal muscle encircling the urethra where it passes through the pelvic floor. This provides voluntary control over the voiding of urine.

23.7d Voiding Urine

Between acts of urination, when the bladder is filling, it is important for the detrusor to relax and the urethral sphincters to remain closed. This is ensured by sympathetic pathways that originate in the upper lumbar spinal cord. Postganglionic fibers travel through the hypogastric nerve to the detrusor and the male internal urethral sphincter. The detrusor relaxes to allow the bladder to fill, but the sphincters contract to ensure that urine is retained in the bladder until voluntarily voided. The external urethral sphincter is held closed by somatic motor fibers that travel from the sacral spinal cord via the pudendal nerve to the sphincter.

To understand the act of urination, also called **micturition**[33] (MIC-too-RISH-un), let's begin with infants and very young children who haven't yet developed voluntary bladder control. Here, it is controlled by a relatively simple spinal **micturition reflex** depicted in steps ① through ④ of **figure 23.25.** Filling of the bladder to about 200 mL or more excites stretch receptors in the bladder wall. These issue signals by way of sensory fibers in the pelvic nerve to the sacral spinal cord (usually segments S2–S3). Efferent signals from the spinal cord travel back to the bladder muscles by way of motor fibers in the pelvic nerve and a parasympathetic ganglion in the bladder wall. Output from the ganglion stimulates the detrusor to contract. When there is no voluntary control over urination, this reflex alone releases urine from the bladder. This is the case, too, in people with spinal cord injuries that disconnect the brain from the lower spinal cord (see Deeper Insight 23.4). The inability to consciously control urination is called **urinary incontinence,** and can result not only from spinal cord injuries but from a number of disease conditions as well as simple aging (see table 23.3).

Normally, however, one also has voluntary control over urination. These mechanisms are shown in steps ⑤ through ⑧ of figure 23.25. There are still uncertainties in the scientific community, however, about some of the details. The figure depicts the male, with both internal and external urethral sphincters.

In both sexes, signals from the stretch receptors of the bladder ascend the spinal cord to a nucleus in the pons called the **micturition center.** This nucleus integrates information about bladder tension

---

[33]*mictur* = to urinate

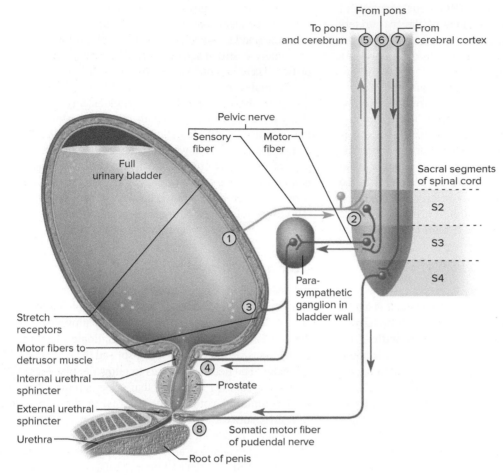

Pelvic nerve

From pons

To pons and cerebrum ⑤⑥⑦ From cerebral cortex

Sensory fiber   Motor fiber

Full urinary bladder

Sacral segments of spinal cord

S2

S3

S4

Para-sympathetic ganglion in bladder wall

Stretch receptors

Motor fibers to detrusor muscle

Internal urethral sphincter

Prostate

External urethral sphincter

Urethra

Somatic motor fiber of pudendal nerve

Root of penis

Involuntary micturition reflex

① Stretch receptors detect filling of bladder, transmit afferent signals to spinal cord.

② Signals return to bladder from spinal cord segments S2 and S3 via parasympathetic fibers in pelvic nerve.

③ Efferent signals excite detrusor muscle.

④ Efferent signals relax internal urethral sphincter. Urine is involuntarily voided if not inhibited by brain.

Voluntary control

⑤ For voluntary control, micturition center in pons receives signals from stretch receptors.

⑥ If it is timely to urinate, pons returns signals to spinal interneurons that excite detrusor and relax internal urethral sphincter. Urine is voided.

⑦ If it is untimely to urinate, signals from cerebrum excite spinal interneurons that keep external urethral sphincter contracted. Urine is retained in bladder.

⑧ If it is timely to urinate, signals from cerebrum inhibit sacral neurons that keep external sphincter closed. External urethral sphincter relaxes and urine is voided.

FIGURE 23.25 Neural Control of Micturition in the Male.
Control in the female differs slightly because of the lack of an internal urethral sphincter.

with information from other brain centers such as the amygdala and cerebrum. Thus, urination can be prompted by fear (via the amygdala) or inhibited by cerebral awareness that the circumstances are inappropriate for urination. Fibers from the micturition center descend the spinal cord through the reticulospinal tracts. Some of these fibers inhibit sympathetic neurons that innervate and constrict the male's internal urethral sphincter. Others descend farther to the sacral spinal cord and excite the parasympathetic neurons that relax the internal urethral sphincter and stimulate the detrusor. The initial contraction of the detrusor raises pressure in the bladder, further exciting the stretch receptors that started the process; thus, a positive feedback loop is established that intensifies bladder contraction as urination proceeds.

For the bladder to begin emptying, however, one final obstacle must be overcome—the external urethral sphincter. Nerve fibers from the cerebral cortex descend by way of the corticospinal tracts and inhibit sacral somatic motor neurons that normally keep that sphincter constricted. It is this voluntary component of micturition that gives a person conscious control of when to urinate and the ability to stop urination in midstream. Voluntary control develops as the nervous system

DEEPER INSIGHT 23.4

CLINICAL APPLICATION

Urination and Spinal Cord Injuries

Knowledge of the neural control of micturition is particularly important for understanding and treating persons with spinal cord injuries. Transection of the spinal cord, as in many cervical fractures, disconnects the *supraspinal* control centers (cerebrum and pons) from the spinal cord circuits that control urination. During the period of spinal shock (see Deeper Insight 13.5), a person is generally incontinent—lacking any control over urination. Bladder control returns as the spinal cord recovers, but is limited to the involuntary micturition reflex. The bladder often cannot empty completely, and there is consequently an increased incidence of cystitis.

matures in early childhood. Males expel the last few milliliters of urine by voluntarily contracting the bulbocavernosus muscle that ensheathes the root of the penis. This helps to reduce the retention of urine in the longer male urethra.

TABLE 23.3	Some Disorders of the Urinary System
Acute glomerulone-phritis	An autoimmune inflammation of the glomeruli, often following a streptococcus infection. Results in destruction of glomeruli leading to hematuria, proteinuria, edema, reduced glomerular filtration, and hypertension. Can progress to chronic glomerulonephritis and renal failure, but most individuals recover from acute glomerulonephritis without lasting effect.
Acute renal failure	An abrupt decline in renal function, often due to traumatic damage to the nephrons or a loss of blood flow stemming from hemorrhage or thrombosis.
Chronic renal failure	Long-term, progressive, irreversible loss of nephrons; see Deeper Insight 23.5 for a variety of causes. Requires a kidney transplant or hemodialysis.
Hydronephrosis[34]	Increase in fluid pressure in the renal pelvis and calyces owing to obstruction of the ureter by kidney stones, nephroptosis, or other causes. Can progress to complete cessation of glomerular filtration and atrophy of nephrons.
Nephroptosis[35] (NEFF-rop-TOE-sis) ("floating kidney")	Slippage of the kidney to an abnormally low position. Occurs in people with too little body fat to hold the kidney in place and in people who subject the kidneys to prolonged vibration, such as truck drivers, equestrians, and motorcyclists. Can twist or kink the ureter, which causes pain, obstructs urine flow, and potentially leads to hydronephrosis.
Nephrotic syndrome	Excretion of large amounts of protein in the urine (≥3.5 g/day) due to glomerular injury. Can result from trauma, drugs, infections, cancer, diabetes mellitus, lupus erythematosus, and other diseases. Loss of plasma protein leads to edema, ascites, hypotension, and susceptibility to infection (because of immunoglobulin loss).
Urinary incontinence	Inability to hold the urine; involuntary leakage from the bladder. Can result from aging; incompetence of the urinary sphincters; bladder irritation; pressure on the bladder in pregnancy; an obstructed urinary outlet so that the bladder is constantly full and dribbles urine (overflow incontinence); uncontrollable urination due to brief surges in bladder pressure, as in laughing or coughing (stress incontinence); and neurological disorders such as spinal cord injuries.

You can find other urinary system disorders described in the following places:

Uremia and *azotemia* in section 23.1b; *hematuria, proteinuria,* and *nephrosclerosis* in sections 23.3a, 23.3b; *pyuria, polyuria, oliguria,* and *anuria* in section 23.6b; *kidney stones* in Deeper Insight 23.2; *urinary tract infection* in Deeper Insight 23.3; and *renal insufficiency* in Deeper Insight 23.5.

In females, the external urethral sphincter may be the only mechanism for urine retention. Retention therefore depends on the strength of the voluntary pelvic floor muscles, which can be compromised by a history of pregnancy or obesity. Urinary incontinence is therefore more common in women than in men.

If the urge to urinate arises at an inconvenient time and one must suppress it, the stretch receptors fatigue and stop firing. As bladder tension increases, however, the signals return with increasing frequency and persistence. Conversely, there are times when the bladder isn't full enough to trigger the micturition reflex, but one wishes to "go" anyway because of a long drive or lecture coming up. In this case, the Valsalva maneuver (see section 22.2a) is used to compress the bladder and excite the stretch receptors early, thereby getting the reflex started. The Valsalva maneuver also aids in emptying the bladder.

The effects of aging on the urinary system are discussed in section 29.4a. Some disorders of this system are briefly described in **table 23.3.**

BEFORE YOU GO ON

Answer the following questions to test your understanding of the preceding section:

21. Describe the location and function of the detrusor.
22. Compare and contrast the functions of the internal and external urethral sphincters.
23. In males, the sympathetic nervous system triggers ejaculation and, at the same time, stimulates constriction of the internal urethral sphincter. What purpose is served by the latter action?

[34]*hydro* = water; *nephr* = kidney; *osis* = medical condition
[35]*nephro* = kidney; *ptosis* = sagging, falling

DEEPER INSIGHT 23.5

CLINICAL APPLICATION

Renal Insufficiency and Hemodialysis

Renal insufficiency is a state in which the kidneys cannot maintain homeostasis due to extensive destruction of their nephrons. Some causes of nephron destruction include

- hypertension;
- chronic or repetitive kidney infections;
- trauma from such causes as blows to the lower back or continual vibration from machinery;
- prolonged ischemia and hypoxia, as in long-distance runners and swimmers;
- poisoning by heavy metals such as mercury and lead and solvents such as carbon tetrachloride, acetone, and paint thinners. These are absorbed into the blood from inhaled fumes or by skin contact and then filtered by the glomeruli. They kill renal tubule cells.
- blockage of renal tubules with proteins small enough to be filtered by the glomerulus—for example, myoglobin released by skeletal muscle damage and hemoglobin released by a transfusion reaction;
- atherosclerosis, which reduces blood flow to the kidney; and
- glomerulonephritis, an autoimmune disease of the glomerular capillaries.

Nephrons can regenerate and restore kidney function after short-term injuries. Even when some of the nephrons are irreversibly destroyed, others hypertrophy and compensate for their lost function. Indeed, a person can survive on as little as one-third of one kidney. When 75% of the nephrons are lost, however, urine output may be as low as 30 mL/h

compared with the normal rate of 50 to 60 mL/h. This is insufficient to maintain homeostasis and is accompanied by azotemia and acidosis. Uremia develops when there is 90% loss of renal function. Renal insufficiency also tends to cause anemia because the diseased kidneys produce too little erythropoietin (EPO), the hormone that stimulates red blood cell formation.

Hemodialysis is a procedure for artificially clearing wastes from the blood when the kidneys aren't adequately doing so **(fig. 23.26)**. Blood is pumped from the radial artery to a *dialysis machine* (artificial kidney) and returned to the patient by way of a vein. In the dialysis machine, the blood flows through a semipermeable cellophane tube surrounded by dialysis fluid. Urea, potassium, and other solutes that are more concentrated in the blood than in the dialysis fluid diffuse through the membrane into the fluid, which is discarded. Glucose, electrolytes, and drugs can be administered by adding them to the dialysis fluid so they will diffuse through the membrane into the blood. People with renal insufficiency accumulate substantial amounts of excess body water between treatments, and dialysis serves also to remove it. Patients are typically given erythropoietin (EPO) to compensate for the lack of EPO from the failing kidneys.

Hemodialysis patients typically have three sessions per week for 4 to 8 hours per session. In addition to inconvenience, hemodialysis carries risks of infection and thrombosis. Blood tends to clot when exposed to foreign surfaces, so an anticoagulant such as heparin is added during dialysis. Unfortunately, this inhibits clotting in the patient's body as well, and dialysis patients sometimes suffer internal bleeding.

A procedure called *continuous ambulatory peritoneal dialysis (CAPD)* is more convenient. It can be carried out at home by the patient, who is provided with plastic bags of dialysis fluid. Fluid is introduced into the abdominal cavity through an indwelling catheter. Here, the peritoneum provides over 2 m^2 of blood-rich semipermeable membrane. The fluid is left in the body cavity for 15 to 60 minutes to allow the blood to equilibrate with it; then it is drained, discarded, and replaced with fresh dialysis fluid. The patient is not limited by a stationary dialysis machine and can go about most normal activities. CAPD is less expensive and promotes better morale than conventional hemodialysis, but it is less efficient in removing wastes and it is more often complicated by infection.

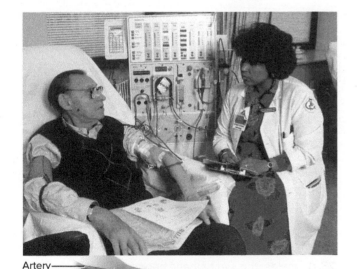

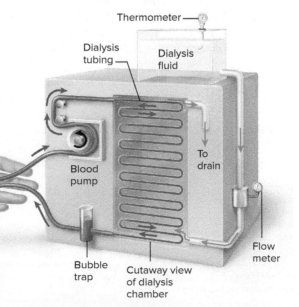

FIGURE 23.26 Hemodialysis. Blood is pumped into a dialysis chamber, where it flows through a selectively permeable membrane surrounded by dialysis fluid. Blood leaving the chamber passes through a bubble trap to remove air before it is returned to the patient's body. The fluid picks up excess water and metabolic wastes from the patient's blood and may contain medications that diffuse into the blood.

Photo: Hank Morgan/Science Source

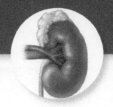

CONNECTIVE ISSUES

Effects of the **URINARY SYSTEM** on Other Organ Systems

ALL SYSTEMS
Excretes metabolic wastes to prevent poisoning of the tissues; maintains fluid, electrolyte, and acid–base balance necessary for homeostasis

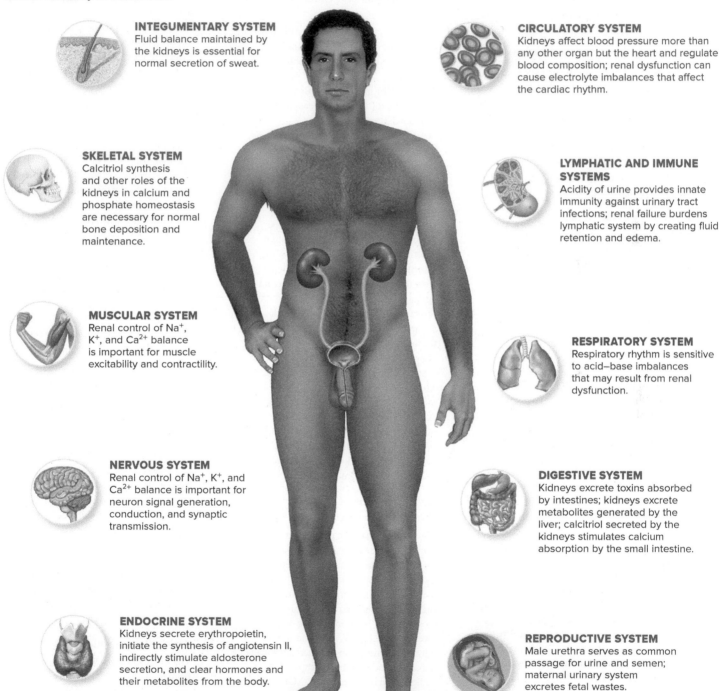

INTEGUMENTARY SYSTEM
Fluid balance maintained by the kidneys is essential for normal secretion of sweat.

SKELETAL SYSTEM
Calcitriol synthesis and other roles of the kidneys in calcium and phosphate homeostasis are necessary for normal bone deposition and maintenance.

MUSCULAR SYSTEM
Renal control of Na^+, K^+, and Ca^{2+} balance is important for muscle excitability and contractility.

NERVOUS SYSTEM
Renal control of Na^+, K^+, and Ca^{2+} balance is important for neuron signal generation, conduction, and synaptic transmission.

ENDOCRINE SYSTEM
Kidneys secrete erythropoietin, initiate the synthesis of angiotensin II, indirectly stimulate aldosterone secretion, and clear hormones and their metabolites from the body.

CIRCULATORY SYSTEM
Kidneys affect blood pressure more than any other organ but the heart and regulate blood composition; renal dysfunction can cause electrolyte imbalances that affect the cardiac rhythm.

LYMPHATIC AND IMMUNE SYSTEMS
Acidity of urine provides innate immunity against urinary tract infections; renal failure burdens lymphatic system by creating fluid retention and edema.

RESPIRATORY SYSTEM
Respiratory rhythm is sensitive to acid–base imbalances that may result from renal dysfunction.

DIGESTIVE SYSTEM
Kidneys excrete toxins absorbed by intestines; kidneys excrete metabolites generated by the liver; calcitriol secreted by the kidneys stimulates calcium absorption by the small intestine.

REPRODUCTIVE SYSTEM
Male urethra serves as common passage for urine and semen; maternal urinary system excretes fetal wastes.

STUDY GUIDE

▶ Assess Your Learning Outcomes

To test your knowledge, discuss the following topics with a study partner or in writing, ideally from memory.

23.1 Functions of the Urinary System

1. The six main organs of the urinary system
2. Six or more functions of the kidneys
3. Four main nitrogenous wastes and their metabolic sources; how metabolic wastes differ from other wastes
4. Blood urea nitrogen, azotemia, and uremia, and the pathological effects of uremia
5. The meaning of *excretion,* and four human organ systems that perform it

23.2 Anatomy of the Kidney

1. Location of the kidneys in relation to adjacent tissues and organs
2. Structures that enter and leave the kidney through the hilum
3. Three layers of tissue that surround and encapsulate the kidney
4. Arrangement of the renal parenchyma around the renal sinus; organization of the cortex, medulla, and renal pyramids
5. The relationship of a renal pyramid to a minor calyx, and of the minor calyces to the major calyces, renal pelvis, and ureter
6. The term for the microscopic functional units of the kidney, and their approximate number per kidney
7. Blood flow from the renal artery through the kidney to the renal vein, including circulation through both the cortex and the medulla
8. Structure of the renal corpuscle
9. Fluid flow from the point where it filters from the blood to the point where it leaves the kidney; those parts of the renal tubule that belong to a single nephron and the part that is shared by multiple nephrons
10. The distinction between glomerular filtrate, tubular fluid, and urine in relation to the progress of the fluid through the renal tubule
11. Differences in the structure and function of cortical nephrons and juxtamedullary nephrons
12. Innervation of the kidney and two effects of sympathetic stimulation on renal function

23.3 Urine Formation I: Glomerular Filtration

1. Four basic stages of urine formation
2. Structure of the glomerular filtration membrane; roles of the capillary fenestrations, basement membrane, and filtration slits in producing glomerular filtrate; the difference between the filtrate and blood plasma
3. Definitions of *proteinuria* and *hematuria,* and their causes
4. Forces of capillary filtration that account for the net filtration pressure (NFP) in the glomerulus; the magnitude of each and of the NFP
5. How glomerular filtration rate can be calculated from the NFP and filtration coefficient; typical GFR values
6. The meaning of *renal autoregulation*
7. How the myogenic mechanism of renal autoregulation works
8. Structure and function of the juxtaglomerular apparatus and how tubuloglomerular feedback works
9. How the sympathetic nervous system regulates GFR
10. The renin–angiotensin–aldosterone mechanism of regulating GFR; multiple effects of angiotensin II on the kidney and on the rest of the body
11. Effects of antidiuretic hormone and aldosterone on the kidney and how they reduce water loss from the body

23.4 Urine Formation II: Tubular Reabsorption and Secretion

1. The percentage of the glomerular filtrate that is eliminated as urine, and percentages of the water in the filtrate that are reabsorbed by PCT and nephron loop
2. Transcellular and paracellular routes of reabsorption, and the role of solvent drag
3. How the PCT reabsorbs NaCl, other electrolytes, glucose, urea, and water; why the reabsorption of water and solutes depends directly or indirectly on the sodium–glucose transporter (SGLT) and sodium reabsorption
4. How tubular reabsorption is limited by the transport maximum (T_m); how this relates to glycosuria in diabetes mellitus

5. Substances added to the tubular fluid by tubular secretion in the PCT
6. The primary functions of the nephron loop and DCT, and what they reabsorb
7. Effects of aldosterone, natriuretic peptides, parathyroid hormone, calcitonin, and calcitriol on nephron function

23.5 Urine Formation III: Water Conservation

1. Function of the collecting duct (CD) and the range of urine osmolarities it can produce
2. How the osmotic gradient of the renal medulla and selective permeability of the CD act to concentrate the urine
3. The effect of antidiuretic hormone (ADH) on the CD and the role of aquaporins in this effect
4. Function of the countercurrent multiplier and how it performs that role
5. Function of the countercurrent exchanger and how it performs that role

23.6 Urine and Renal Function Tests

1. Why urine is yellow; why the shade of yellow varies; and some causes of other, unusual colors
2. Normal ranges of urine specific gravity, osmolarity, and pH
3. Normal and abnormal odors of urine and some reasons for the latter
4. The three most abundant solutes in urine, and some causes of other, unusual solutes
5. Typical daily output of urine, and terms for abnormally low and high outputs
6. The defining sign of diabetes in general; four forms of diabetes and their causes
7. The general effect of diuretics; modes of diuretic action of caffeine, alcohol, and loop diuretics
8. Methods of measuring a person's GFR and renal clearance; ability to calculate these if given the necessary data

23.7 Urine Storage and Elimination

1. The route and mechanism of urine transport from the kidney to the urinary bladder; anatomy and histology of the ureters and their relationship to the bladder

STUDY GUIDE

2. Anatomy and histology of the urinary bladder; the detrusor, mucosal epithelium, rugae, and trigone
3. Anatomy of the female urethra and external urethral sphincter
4. Anatomy of the male urethra, its three segments, and the internal and external urethral sphincters
5. The mechanism of the spinal micturition reflex and the neural anatomy involved
6. Mechanisms of brainstem and cerebral control of micturition

▶ Testing Your Recall

Answers in Appendix A

1. Micturition occurs when the _____ contracts.
   a. detrusor
   b. internal urethral sphincter
   c. external urethral sphincter
   d. muscularis of the ureter
   e. all of the above

2. The compact ball of capillaries in a nephron is called
   a. the nephron loop.
   b. the peritubular plexus.
   c. the renal corpuscle.
   d. the glomerulus.
   e. the vasa recta.

3. Which of these is the most abundant nitrogenous waste in the blood?
   a. uric acid
   b. urea
   c. ammonia
   d. creatinine
   e. albumin

4. Which of these lies closest to the renal cortex?
   a. the parietal peritoneum
   b. the renal fascia
   c. the fibrous capsule
   d. the perirenal fat capsule
   e. the renal pelvis

5. Most sodium is reabsorbed from the glomerular filtrate by
   a. the vasa recta.
   b. the proximal convoluted tubule.
   c. the distal convoluted tubule.
   d. the nephron loop.
   e. the collecting duct.

6. A glomerulus and glomerular capsule make up one
   a. renal capsule.
   b. renal corpuscle.
   c. kidney lobule.
   d. kidney lobe.
   e. nephron.

7. The kidney has more _____ than any of the other structures listed.
   a. arcuate arteries
   b. minor calyces
   c. medullary pyramids
   d. afferent arterioles
   e. collecting ducts

8. The renal clearance of _____ is normally zero.
   a. sodium
   b. potassium
   c. uric acid
   d. urea
   e. amino acids

9. Beavers have relatively little need to conserve water and could therefore be expected to have _____ than humans do.
   a. fewer nephrons
   b. longer nephron loops
   c. shorter nephron loops
   d. longer collecting ducts
   e. longer convoluted tubules

10. Increased ADH secretion should cause the urine to have
    a. a higher specific gravity.
    b. a lighter color.
    c. a higher pH.
    d. a lower urea concentration.
    e. a lower potassium concentration.

11. The _____ reflex is an autonomic reflex activated by pressure in the urinary bladder.

12. _____ is the ability of a nephron to adjust its GFR independently of nervous or hormonal influences.

13. The two ureters and the urethra form the boundaries of a smooth area called the _____ on the floor of the urinary bladder.

14. The _____ is a group of epithelial cells of the nephron loop that monitors the composition of the tubular fluid.

15. To enter the capsular space, filtrate must pass between foot processes of the _____, cells that form the visceral layer of the glomerular capsule.

16. Glycosuria occurs if the rate of glomerular filtration of glucose exceeds the _____ of the proximal convoluted tubule.

17. _____ is a hormone that regulates the amount of water reabsorbed by the collecting duct.

18. The _____ sphincter of the male is under involuntary control and relaxes during the micturition reflex.

19. Very little _____ is found in the glomerular filtrate because it is negatively charged and is repelled by the basement membrane of the glomerulus.

20. Blood flows through the _____ arteries just before entering the cortical radiate arteries.

STUDY GUIDE

▶ Building Your Medical Vocabulary

Answers in Appendix A

State a meaning of each word element, and give a medical term from this chapter that uses it or a slight variation of it.

1. azoto-

2. cysto-

3. glomer-

4. juxta-

5. meso-

6. nephro-

7. podo-

8. -ptosis

9. pyelo-

10. recto-

▶ What's Wrong with These Statements?

Answers in Appendix A

Briefly explain why each of the following statements is false, or reword it to make it true.

1. The proximal convoluted tubule is not subject to hormonal influence.

2. Sodium is the most abundant solute in the urine.

3. The collecting ducts outnumber the renal corpuscles of the kidney.

4. Tight junctions prevent material from leaking between the epithelial cells of the renal tubule.

5. All forms of diabetes are characterized by glucose in the urine.

6. If all other conditions remain the same, dilation of the efferent arteriole raises the glomerular filtration rate.

7. Angiotensin II promotes urine output.

8. The minimum osmolarity of urine is 300 mOsm/L, equal to the osmolarity of the blood.

9. The amount of glucose in the urine is directly proportional to the amount of sodium.

10. Micturition depends on relaxation of the detrusor.

▶ Testing Your Comprehension

1. How would the glomerular filtration rate be affected by kwashiorkor (see Deeper Insight 18.1)?

2. A patient produces 55 mL of urine per hour. Urea concentration is 0.25 mg/mL in her blood plasma and 8.6 mg/mL in her urine. (a) What is her rate of renal clearance for urea? (b) About 95% of adults excrete urea at a rate of 12.6 to 28.6 g/day. Is this patient above, within, or below this range? Show how you calculated your answers.

3. A patient with poor renal perfusion is treated with an ACE inhibitor and goes into renal failure. Explain the reason for the renal failure.

4. Drugs called *renin inhibitors* are used to treat hypertension. Explain how they would have this effect.

5. Discuss how the unity of form and function is exemplified by each of the following comparisons: (a) the thin and thick segments of the nephron loop; (b) the proximal and distal convoluted tubules; and (c) the afferent and efferent arterioles.

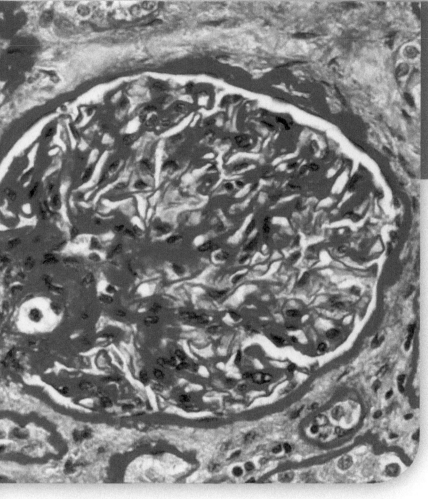

FLUID, ELECTROLYTE, AND ACID–BASE BALANCE

Water balance begins at the renal glomeruli like the one shown here

Michael Abbey/Science Source

Anatomy & Physiology
Revealed 4.0

Module 13: Urinary System

Cellular function requires a fluid medium with a carefully controlled composition. If the quantity, osmolarity, electrolyte concentration, or pH of this medium is altered, life-threatening disorders of cellular function may result. Consequently, the body has several mechanisms for keeping these variables within narrow limits and maintaining three types of homeostatic stability: fluid, electrolyte, and acid–base balance.

These balances are maintained by the collective action of the urinary, respiratory, digestive, integumentary, endocrine, nervous, cardiovascular, and lymphatic systems. This chapter describes the homeostatic regulation of fluid, electrolyte, and acid–base balance and shows the close relationship of these variables to each other. These balances are so crucial that fluid therapy, aimed at restoring one or more of these, is often a critical aspect of patient care. Problems of fluid and electrolyte balance also arise frequently in sports and recreational medicine, in situations ranging from summer football practice to backcountry hiking.

24.1   Fluid Balance

Expected Learning Outcomes

When you have completed this section, you should be able to

a. name the major fluid compartments and explain how water moves from one to another;

b. list the body's sources of water and routes of water loss;

c. describe the mechanisms of regulating water intake and output; and

d. describe some conditions in which the body has a deficiency or excess of water or an improper distribution of water among the fluid compartments.

We enter the world in rather soggy condition, having swallowed, excreted, and floated in amniotic fluid for months. At birth, a baby's weight is as much as 75% water; infants normally lose a little weight in the first day or two as they excrete the excess. Young adult men average 55% to 60% water; women average slightly less because they have more adipose tissue, which is nearly free of water. Obese and elderly people are as little as 45% water by weight. The **total body water (TBW)** content of a 70 kg (150 lb) young male is about 40 L.

24.1a Fluid Compartments

Body water is distributed among certain **fluid compartments,** areas separated by selectively permeable membranes and differing from each other in chemical composition. The major fluid compartments are

65% *intracellular fluid (ICF)* and

35% *extracellular fluid (ECF),* subdivided into

25% *tissue (interstitial) fluid,*

8% *blood plasma* and *lymph,* and

2% *transcellular fluid,* a catch-all category for cerebrospinal, synovial, peritoneal, pleural, and pericardial fluids; vitreous and aqueous humors of the eye; bile; and fluid in the digestive, urinary, and respiratory tracts.

Fluid is continually exchanged between compartments by way of capillary walls and plasma membranes **(fig. 24.1).** Water moves by osmosis from the digestive tract to the bloodstream and by capillary filtration from the blood to the tissue fluid. From the tissue fluid, it may be reabsorbed by the capillaries, osmotically absorbed into cells, or taken up by the lymphatic system, which returns it to the bloodstream.

Because water moves so easily through plasma membranes, osmotic gradients between the ICF and ECF never last for very long. If a local imbalance arises, osmosis usually restores the balance within seconds so that intracellular and extracellular osmolarity are equal. If the osmolarity of the tissue fluid rises, water moves out of the cells; if it falls, water moves into the cells.

Osmosis from one fluid compartment to another is determined by the relative concentration of solutes in each compartment. The most abundant solute particles by far are the electrolytes—especially sodium salts in the ECF and potassium salts in the ICF. Electrolytes play the principal role in governing the body's water distribution and total water content; the subjects of fluid and electrolyte balance are therefore inseparable.

24.1b Water Gain and Loss

A person is in a state of **fluid balance** when daily gains and losses are equal and fluids are properly distributed in the body. We typically gain and lose about 2,500 mL/day **(fig. 24.2).** The gains come from two sources. One of these is **metabolic water** (about 200 mL/day), which is produced as a by-product of dehydration synthesis reactions and aerobic respiration:

$$C_6H_{12}O_6 + 6\ O_2 \longrightarrow 6\ CO_2 + 6\ H_2O.$$

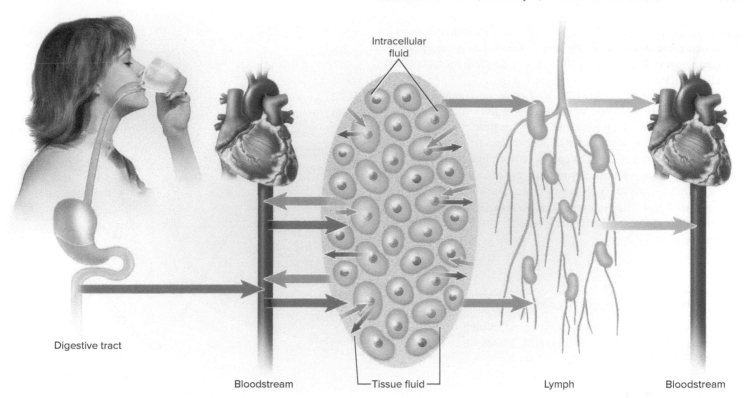

FIGURE 24.1 The Movement of Water Between the Major Fluid Compartments. Ingested water is absorbed by the bloodstream. There is a two-way exchange of water between the blood and tissue fluid and between the tissue fluid and intracellular fluids. Excess tissue fluid is picked up by the lymphatic system, which returns it to the bloodstream.

? *In which of these compartments would fluid accumulate in edema?*

The other source is **preformed water,** which is ingested in food (700 mL/day) and drink (1,600 mL/day).

The routes of water loss are more varied:

- 1,500 mL/day is excreted as urine.

- 200 mL/day is eliminated in the feces.

- 300 mL/day is lost in the expired breath. You can easily visualize this by breathing onto a cool surface such as a mirror.

- 100 mL/day of sweat is secreted by a resting adult at an ambient air temperature of 20°C (68°F).

- 400 mL/day is lost as **cutaneous transpiration,**[1] water that diffuses through the epidermis and evaporates. This is not the same as sweat; it's not a glandular secretion. A simple way to observe it is to cup the palm of your hand for a minute against a cool nonporous surface such as a laboratory benchtop or mirror. When you take your hand away, you will notice the water that transpired through the skin and condensed on that surface, even in places that were not in contact with your skin.

Water loss varies greatly with physical activity and environmental conditions. Respiratory loss increases in cold weather, for example, because cold air is drier and absorbs more body water from the respiratory tract. Hot, humid weather slightly reduces the respiratory loss but increases

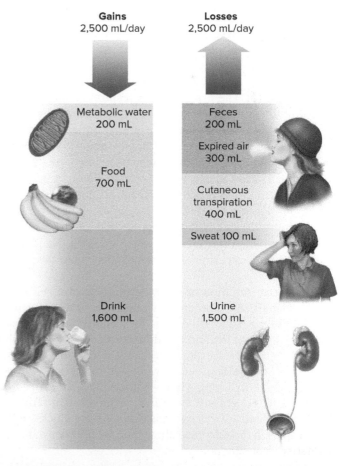

Gains 2,500 mL/day	Losses 2,500 mL/day
Metabolic water 200 mL	Feces 200 mL
	Expired air 300 mL
Food 700 mL	Cutaneous transpiration 400 mL
	Sweat 100 mL
Drink 1,600 mL	Urine 1,500 mL

FIGURE 24.2 Typical Daily Water Gains and Losses in a State of Fluid Balance.

---

[1]*trans* = through; *spiration* = breathing

perspiration to as much as 1,200 mL/day. Prolonged, heavy work can raise the respiratory loss to 650 mL/day and perspiration to as much as 5 L/day, though it reduces urine output by nearly two-thirds.

Output through the breath and cutaneous transpiration is called **insensible water loss** because we're not usually aware of it. **Sensible water loss** is noticeable output, particularly through the urine and in case of sufficient sweating to produce obvious wetness of the skin. **Obligatory water loss** is output that is relatively unavoidable: expired air, cutaneous transpiration, sweat, fecal moisture, and the minimum urine output, about 400 mL/day, needed to prevent azotemia. Even dehydrated individuals cannot prevent such losses; thus, they become further dehydrated.

24.1c Regulation of Intake

Fluid intake is governed mainly by thirst, which is controlled by the mechanisms shown in **figure 24.3**. Dehydration reduces blood volume and pressure and raises blood osmolarity. The hypothalamus has at least three groups of neurons called **osmoreceptors** that respond to angiotensin II and rising osmolarity of the ECF—both of which are signs that the body has a water deficit. The osmoreceptors communicate with other hypothalamic neurons that produce antidiuretic hormone (ADH), thus promoting water conservation; they apparently communicate also with the cerebral cortex to produce a conscious sense of thirst. A mere 2% to 3% increase in plasma osmolarity makes a person intensely thirsty, as does a 10% to 15% blood loss.

When we're thirsty, we salivate less. There are two reasons for this: (1) The osmoreceptor response leads to sympathetic output from the hypothalamus that inhibits the salivary glands. (2) Saliva is produced primarily by capillary filtration, but in a dehydrated person, this is opposed by the lower capillary blood pressure and higher osmolarity of the blood. Reduced salivation produces a dry, sticky-feeling mouth and a desire to drink, but it is by no means certain that this is the primary motivation to drink. Some people don't secrete saliva, yet they don't drink any more than normal individuals except when eating, when they need water to moisten the food. The same is true of experimental animals that have the salivary ducts tied off.

Long-term satiation of thirst depends on absorbing water from the small intestine and lowering the osmolarity of the blood. Reduced osmolarity stops the osmoreceptor response, promotes capillary filtration, and makes the saliva more abundant and watery. However, these changes require 30 minutes or longer to take effect, and it would be rather impractical if we had to drink that long while waiting to feel satisfied. Water intake would be grossly excessive, indeed potentially fatal. Fortunately, there are mechanisms that act more quickly to temporarily quench the thirst and allow time for the change in blood osmolarity to occur.

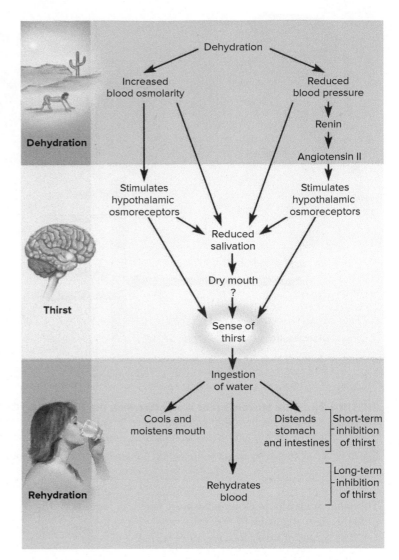

FIGURE 24.3 Dehydration, Thirst, and Rehydration. See the text concerning the uncertainty about a dry mouth contributing to the sense of thirst.

Experiments with rats and dogs have isolated the stimuli that quench the thirst. One of these is cooling and moistening the mouth; rats drink less if their water is cool than if it is warm, and simply moistening the mouth temporarily satisfies an animal even if the water is drained from its esophagus before it reaches the stomach. Distension of the stomach and small intestine is another inhibitor of thirst. If a dog is allowed to drink while the water is drained from its esophagus but its stomach is inflated with a balloon, its thirst is satisfied for a time. If the water is drained away but the stomach isn't inflated, satiation doesn't last as long. Such fast-acting stimuli as coolness, moisture, and filling of the stomach stop an animal (and presumably a human) from drinking an excessive amount of liquid, but they're effective for only 30 to 45 minutes. If they're not soon followed by absorption of water into the bloodstream, the thirst soon returns. Only a drop in blood osmolarity produces a lasting effect.

24.1d Regulation of Output

The only way to control water output significantly is through variations in urine volume. It must be realized, however, that the kidneys can't completely prevent water loss, nor can they replace lost water or electrolytes. Therefore, they never restore fluid volume or osmolarity, but in dehydration they can support existing fluid levels and slow down the rate of loss until water and electrolytes are ingested.

To understand the effect of the kidneys on fluid and electrolyte balance, it is also important to bear in mind that if a substance is reabsorbed by the kidneys, it is kept in the body and returned to the ECF, where it will affect fluid volume and composition. If a substance is filtered by the glomerulus or secreted by the renal tubules and not reabsorbed, then it is excreted in the urine and lost from the body fluids.

Changes in urine volume are usually linked to adjustments in sodium reabsorption. As sodium is reabsorbed or excreted, proportionate amounts of water accompany it. The total volume of fluid remaining in the body may change, but its osmolarity remains stable. Controlling fluid balance by controlling sodium excretion is best understood in the context of electrolyte balance, discussed later in the chapter.

Antidiuretic hormone (ADH), however, provides a means of controlling water output independently of sodium **(fig. 24.4).** In true dehydration (defined shortly), blood volume declines and sodium concentration rises. The increased osmolarity of the blood stimulates the hypothalamic osmoreceptors, which stimulate the posterior pituitary to release ADH. In response to ADH, cells of the collecting ducts of the kidneys synthesize the proteins called aquaporins. When installed in the plasma membrane, these serve as channels that allow water to diffuse out of the duct into the hypertonic tissue fluid of the renal medulla. The kidneys then reabsorb more water and produce less urine. Sodium continues to be excreted, so the *ratio* of sodium to water in the urine increases (the urine becomes more concentrated). By helping the kidneys retain water, ADH slows down the decline in blood volume and the rise in its osmolarity. Thus, the ADH mechanism forms a negative feedback loop.

Conversely, if blood volume and pressure are too high or blood osmolarity is too low, ADH release is inhibited. The renal tubules reabsorb less water, urine output increases, and total body water declines. This is an effective way of compensating for hypertension. Since the lack of ADH increases the ratio of water to sodium in the urine, it raises the sodium concentration and osmolarity of the blood.

24.1e Disorders of Fluid Balance

The body is in a state of fluid imbalance if there is an abnormality of total *volume, concentration,* or *distribution* of water among the compartments.

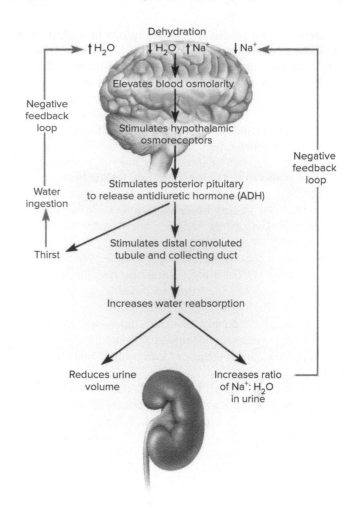

FIGURE 24.4 The Action of Antidiuretic Hormone. Pathways shown in red represent negative feedback.

Fluid Deficiency

Fluid deficiency arises when output exceeds intake over a long enough period of time. The two kinds of deficiency—volume depletion and dehydration—differ in the relative loss of water and electrolytes and the resulting osmolarity of the ECF. This important distinction calls for different strategies of fluid replacement therapy (see Deeper Insight 24.2 at the end of the chapter).

Volume depletion (hypovolemia[2]) occurs when proportionate amounts of water *and* sodium are lost without replacement. Total body water declines but osmolarity remains normal. Volume depletion occurs in cases of hemorrhage, severe burns, and chronic vomiting or diarrhea. A less common cause is aldosterone

---

[2]*hypo* = below normal; *vol* = volume; *emia* = blood condition

hyposecretion (Addison disease), which results in inadequate sodium and water reabsorption by the kidneys.

Dehydration (negative water balance) occurs when the body eliminates significantly more water than sodium, so the ECF osmolarity rises. The simplest cause of dehydration is lack of drinking water—for example, when stranded in a desert or at sea. It can be a serious problem for elderly and bedridden people who depend on others to provide them with water, especially for those who can't express their need or whose caretakers are insensitive to it. Diabetes mellitus, ADH hyposecretion (diabetes insipidus), profuse sweating, and overuse of diuretics are additional causes of dehydration. Cold weather can dehydrate a person just as much as hot weather (see Deeper Insight 24.1).

For three reasons, infants are more vulnerable to dehydration than adults: (1) Their high metabolic rate produces toxic metabolites faster, and they excrete more water to eliminate them. (2) Their kidneys are not fully mature and can't concentrate urine as effectively. (3) They have a greater ratio of body surface to volume; consequently, compared with adults, they lose twice as much water per kilogram of body weight by evaporation.

Dehydration affects all fluid compartments. Suppose, for example, that you play a strenuous tennis match on a hot summer day and lose a liter of sweat. Where does this fluid come from? Most of it filters out of the bloodstream through the capillaries of the sweat glands. In principle, 1 L of sweat

would amount to about one-third of the blood plasma. However, as the blood loses water, its osmolarity rises and water from the tissue fluid enters the bloodstream to balance the loss. This raises the osmolarity of the tissue fluid, so water moves out of the cells to balance that **(fig. 24.5)**. Ultimately, all three fluid compartments (the ICF, blood, and tissue fluid) lose water. To excrete 1 L of sweat, about 300 mL of water would come from the tissue fluid and 700 mL from the ICF. Immoderate exercise without fluid replacement can lead to losses greater than 1 L per hour.

The most serious effects of fluid deficiency are circulatory shock due to loss of blood volume and neurological dysfunction due to dehydration of brain cells. Volume depletion by diarrhea is a major cause of infant mortality, especially under unsanitary conditions that lead to intestinal infections such as cholera.

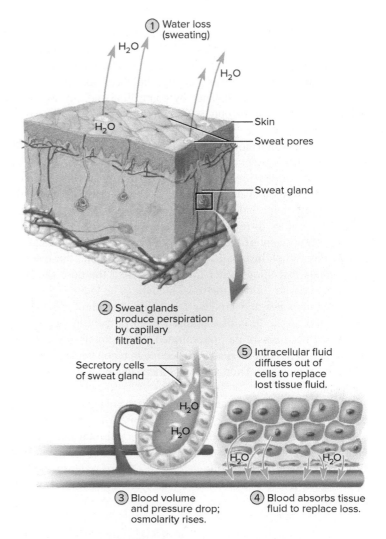

FIGURE 24.5 Effects of Profuse Sweating on the Fluid Compartments. In extreme dehydration, the loss of intracellular fluid can cause cellular shrinkage and dysfunction.

DEEPER INSIGHT 24.1

CLINICAL APPLICATION

Fluid Balance in Cold Weather

Hot weather and profuse sweating are obvious threats to fluid balance, but so is cold weather. The body conserves heat by constricting the blood vessels of the skin and subcutaneous tissue, thus forcing blood into the deeper circulation. This raises the blood pressure, which inhibits the secretion of antidiuretic hormone and increases the secretion of natriuretic peptides. These hormonal changes increase urine output and reduce blood volume. In addition, cold air is relatively dry and increases respiratory water loss. This is why exercise causes the respiratory tract to "burn" more in cold weather than in warm.

These cold-weather respiratory and urinary losses can cause significant hypovolemia. Furthermore, the onset of exercise stimulates vasodilation in the skeletal muscles. In a hypovolemic state, there may not be enough blood to supply them, and a person may experience weakness, fatigue, or fainting (hypovolemic shock). In winter sports and other activities such as snow shoveling, it is important to maintain fluid balance. Even if you don't feel thirsty, it is beneficial to take ample amounts of warm liquids such as soup or cider. Coffee, tea, and alcohol, however, have diuretic effects that defeat the purpose of fluid intake.

Fluid Excess

Fluid excess is less common than fluid deficiency because the kidneys are highly effective at compensating for excessive intake by excreting more urine **(fig. 24.6).** Renal failure and other causes, however, can lead to excess fluid retention.

Fluid excesses are of two types called volume excess and hypotonic hydration. In **volume excess,** both sodium and water are retained and the ECF remains isotonic. This can result from aldosterone hypersecretion or renal failure. In **hypotonic hydration** (also called **water intoxication** or **positive water balance**), more water than sodium is retained or ingested and the ECF becomes hypotonic. This can occur if you lose a large amount of water *and* salt through urine and sweat and you replace it by drinking plain water. Without a proportionate intake of electrolytes, water dilutes the ECF, makes it hypotonic, and causes cellular swelling. ADH hypersecretion can cause hypotonic hydration by stimulating excessive water retention as sodium continues to be excreted. Among the most serious effects of either type of fluid excess are pulmonary and cerebral edema and death.

The four preceding forms of fluid imbalance are summarized and compared in **table 24.1.**

▶▶▶ **APPLY WHAT YOU KNOW**

Some tumors of the brain, pancreas, and small intestine secrete ADH. What type of fluid imbalance would this produce? Explain why.

Fluid Sequestration

Fluid sequestration[3] (seh-ques-TRAY-shun) is a condition in which excess fluid accumulates in a particular location. Total body water and osmolarity may be normal, but the volume of circulating blood may drop to the point of causing circulatory shock. The most common form of sequestration is *edema,* the abnormal accumulation of fluid in the interstitial spaces, causing swelling of a tissue (see detailed discussion in section 20.3d). Hemorrhage can be another cause of fluid sequestration; blood that pools and clots in the tissues is lost to circulation. Yet another example is *pleural effusion,* caused by some lung infections, in which as much as several liters of fluid accumulate in the pleural cavity.

BEFORE YOU GO ON

Answer the following questions to test your understanding of the preceding section:

1. List five routes of water loss. Which one accounts for the greatest loss? Which one is most controllable?

2. Explain why even a severely dehydrated person inevitably experiences further fluid loss.

[3]*sequestr* = to isolate

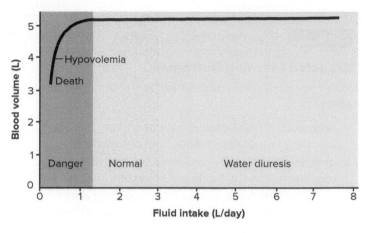

FIGURE 24.6 The Relationship of Blood Volume to Fluid Intake. The kidneys cannot compensate very well for inadequate fluid intake. Below an intake of about 1 L/day, blood volume drops significantly (left) and there may be a threat of death from hypovolemic shock. The kidneys compensate very well, on the other hand, for abnormally high fluid intake (right); they eliminate the excess by water diuresis and maintain a stable blood volume.

TABLE 24.1	Forms of Fluid Imbalance	
Form	Total Body Water	Osmolarity
Fluid Deficiency		
Volume depletion (hypovolemia)	Reduced	Isotonic (normal)
Dehydration (negative water balance)	Reduced	Hypertonic (elevated)
Fluid Excess		
Volume excess	Elevated	Isotonic (normal)
Hypotonic hydration (positive water balance, water intoxication)	Elevated	Hypotonic (reduced)

3. Suppose there were no mechanisms to stop the sense of thirst until the blood became sufficiently hydrated. Explain why we would routinely suffer hypotonic hydration.

4. Summarize the effect of ADH on total body water and blood osmolarity.

5. Name and define the four types of fluid imbalance, and give an example of a situation that could produce each type.

24.2 Electrolyte Balance

Expected Learning Outcomes

When you have completed this section, you should be able to

a. describe the physiological roles of sodium, potassium, calcium, magnesium, chloride, and phosphates;

b. describe the hormonal and renal mechanisms that regulate the concentrations of these electrolytes; and

c. state the term for an excess or deficiency of each electrolyte and describe the consequences of these imbalances.

Electrolyte balance is a state in which the amount of electrolytes absorbed by the small intestine balances the amount lost from the body, chiefly through the urine, and in which electrolyte concentrations in the body fluids are regulated within homeostatic limits. Electrolytes are physiologically important for multiple reasons: They are chemically reactive and participate in metabolism, they determine the electrical potential (charge difference) across cell membranes, and they strongly affect the osmolarity of the body fluids and the body's water content and distribution. Strictly speaking, electrolytes are salts such as sodium chloride, not just sodium or chloride ions. In common usage, however, the individual ions are often loosely referred to as electrolytes. The major cations of the electrolytes are sodium (Na^+), potassium (K^+), calcium (Ca^{2+}), magnesium (Mg^{2+}), and hydrogen (H^+); the major anions are chloride (Cl^-), bicarbonate (HCO_3^-), and phosphates (P_i). Hydrogen and bicarbonate regulation are discussed later under acid–base balance. Here we focus on the other six.

The typical concentrations of these ions in the blood plasma versus intracellular fluid are compared in **figure 24.7.** Notice that in spite of great differences in electrolyte concentrations, the two fluid compartments have the same osmolarity (300 mOsm/L). Blood plasma is the most accessible fluid for measurements of electrolyte concentration, so excesses and deficiencies are defined with reference to normal plasma concentrations. Concentrations in the tissue fluid differ only slightly from those in the plasma. The prefix *normo-* denotes a normal electrolyte concentration (for example, *normokalemia*), and *hyper-* and *hypo-* denote concentrations that are, respectively, sufficiently above or below normal to cause physiological disorders.

In the following sections, we'll examine the functions, homeostatic regulation, and imbalances of the principal electrolytes and then review the causes and effects of the cation imbalances in a summary table.

24.2a Sodium

Functions

Sodium is one of the principal ions responsible for the resting membrane potentials of cells, and the inflow of sodium through membrane channels is an essential event in the depolarization

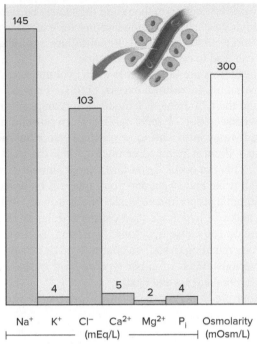

(a) Blood plasma

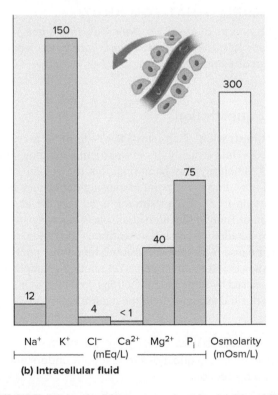

(b) Intracellular fluid

FIGURE 24.7 Electrolyte Concentrations in the Blood Plasma and Intracellular Fluid. Concentrations in the blood plasma (a) are shown directly above concentrations of the same ions in the intracellular fluid (b) for contrast. P_i collectively represents inorganic phosphates in the forms of PO_4^{3-}, HPO_4^{2-}, and $H_2PO_4^-$. Electrolyte concentrations (green bars) are given in mEq/L. Concentrations in mmol/L are the same for Na^+, K^+, and Cl^-; one-half of the illustrated values for Ca^{2+} and Mg^{2+}; and one-third for PO_4^{3-}. Osmolarity (yellow bars) is given in mOsm/L.

that underlies nerve and muscle function. Sodium is the principal cation of the ECF; sodium salts account for 90% to 95% of its osmolarity. Sodium is therefore the most significant solute in determining total body water and the distribution of water among fluid compartments. Sodium ions bound to the proteoglycans of cartilage retain water, ensuring that cartilages are well hydrated and able to act as effective cushions and shock absorbers. Sodium gradients across the plasma membrane provide the potential energy that is tapped to cotransport other solutes such as glucose, potassium, and calcium. The Na^+–K^+ pump is an important mechanism for generating body heat. Sodium bicarbonate ($NaHCO_3$) plays a major role in buffering the pH of the ECF.

Homeostasis

An adult needs about 0.5 g of sodium per day, whereas the typical American diet contains 3 to 7 g/day. Thus a dietary sodium deficiency is rare, and the primary concern is adequate excretion of the

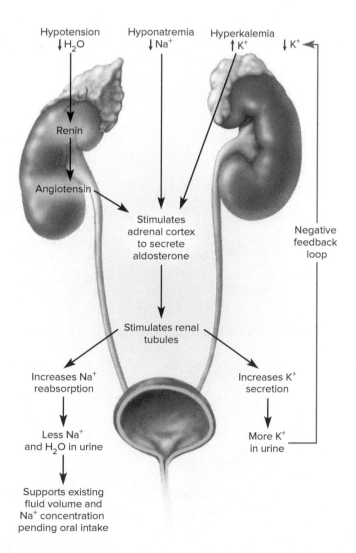

FIGURE 24.8 The Action of Aldosterone. The pathway shown in red represents negative feedback.

❓ *What is required, in addition to aldosterone, to increase blood volume?*

excess. This is one of the most important roles of the kidneys. There are multiple mechanisms for controlling sodium concentration, tied to its effects on blood pressure and osmolarity and coordinated by aldosterone, antidiuretic hormone, and the natriuretic peptides.

Aldosterone, the "salt-retaining hormone," plays the primary role in adjustment of sodium excretion. Hyponatremia and hyperkalemia directly stimulate the adrenal cortex to secrete aldosterone, and hypotension stimulates its secretion by way of the renin–angiotensin–aldosterone mechanism (**fig. 24.8**).

Only cells in the ascending limb of the nephron loop, the distal convoluted tubule, and the cortical part of the collecting duct have aldosterone receptors. Aldosterone, a steroid, binds to nuclear receptors and activates transcription of a gene for the Na^+–K^+ pump. In 10 to 30 minutes, enough Na^+–K^+ pumps are synthesized and installed in the plasma membrane to produce a noticeable effect—sodium concentration in the urine begins to fall and potassium concentration rises as the tubules reabsorb more sodium and secrete more hydrogen and potassium ions. Water and chloride passively follow sodium. Thus, the primary effects of aldosterone are that the urine contains less NaCl and more potassium and has a lower pH. An average adult male excretes 5 g of sodium per day, but the urine can be virtually sodium-free when aldosterone level is high. Although aldosterone strongly influences sodium reabsorption, it has little effect on plasma sodium *concentration* because reabsorbed sodium is accompanied by a proportionate amount of water.

Elevated blood pressure inhibits the renin–angiotensin–aldosterone mechanism. The kidneys then reabsorb almost no sodium beyond the proximal convoluted tubule (PCT), and the urine contains up to 30 g of sodium per day.

Aldosterone has only slight effects on urine volume, blood volume, and blood pressure in spite of the tendency of water to follow sodium osmotically. Even in aldosterone hypersecretion, blood volume is rarely more than 5% to 10% above normal. An increase in blood volume increases blood pressure and glomerular filtration rate (GFR). Even though aldosterone increases the tubular reabsorption of sodium and water, this is offset by the rise in GFR and there is only a small drop in urine output.

Antidiuretic hormone modifies water excretion independently of sodium excretion. Thus, unlike aldosterone, it can change sodium *concentration*. A high concentration of sodium in the blood stimulates the posterior lobe of the pituitary gland to release ADH. The kidneys then reabsorb more water, which slows down any further increase in blood sodium concentration. ADH alone cannot lower the concentration; this requires water ingestion to dilute the existing sodium. A drop in sodium concentration, by contrast, inhibits ADH release. More water is excreted, thereby raising the relative amount of sodium that remains in the blood.

The natriuretic peptides inhibit sodium and water reabsorption and the secretion of renin and ADH. The kidneys then eliminate more sodium and water and lower the blood pressure. Angiotensin II, by contrast, activates the Na^+–H^+ antiport in the PCT and thereby increases sodium reabsorption and reduces urinary sodium output.

Several other hormones also affect sodium homeostasis. Estrogen mimics the effect of aldosterone and causes women to retain water during pregnancy and part of the menstrual cycle. Progesterone reduces sodium reabsorption and has a diuretic effect. High levels of glucocorticoids promote sodium reabsorption and edema.

In some cases, sodium homeostasis is achieved by regulation of salt intake. A craving for salt occurs in people who are depleted of sodium—for example, by blood loss or Addison disease. Pregnant women sometimes develop a craving for salty foods. Salt craving is not limited to humans; many animals ranging from elephants to butterflies seek out wet salty soil where they can obtain this vital mineral.

Imbalances

True imbalances in sodium concentration are relatively rare because sodium excess or depletion is almost always accompanied by proportionate changes in water volume. **Hypernatremia**[4] is a plasma sodium concentration in excess of 145 mEq/L. It can result from the administration of intravenous saline (see Deeper Insight 24.2 at the end of this chapter). Its major consequences

are water retention, hypertension, and edema. Extreme hypertonicity shrinks cells, which damages their cytoskeleton, breaks DNA, and induces cell death by apoptosis. **Hyponatremia**[5] (less than 130 mEq/L) is usually the result of excess body water rather than excess sodium excretion, as in the case mentioned earlier of a person who loses large volumes of sweat or urine and replaces it by drinking plain water. Usually, hyponatremia is quickly corrected by excretion of the excess water, but if uncorrected it produces the symptoms of hypotonic hydration described earlier.

24.2b Potassium

Functions

Potassium is the most abundant cation of the ICF and is the greatest determinant of intracellular osmolarity and cell volume. Along with sodium, it produces the resting membrane potentials and action potentials of nerve and muscle cells **(fig. 24.9a).**

---

[4]*hyper* = excess, above normal; *natr* = sodium; *emia* = blood condition

[5]*hypo* = deficiency, below normal; *natr* = sodium; *emia* = blood condition

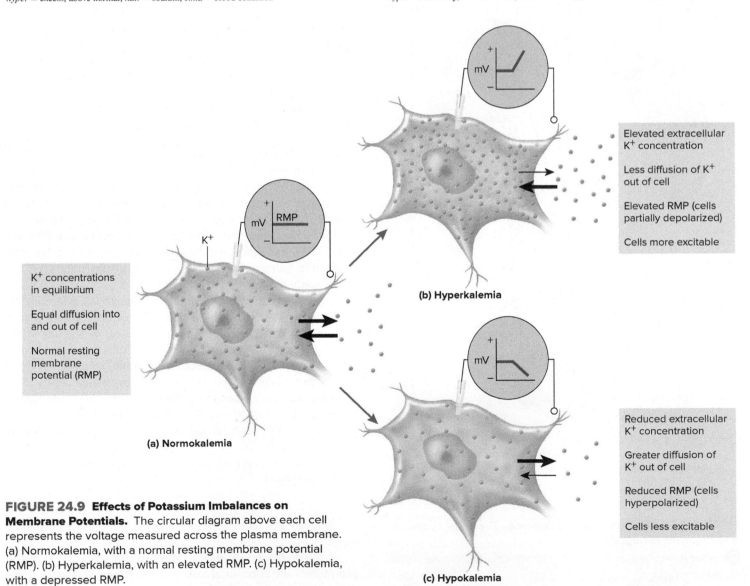

FIGURE 24.9 Effects of Potassium Imbalances on Membrane Potentials. The circular diagram above each cell represents the voltage measured across the plasma membrane. (a) Normokalemia, with a normal resting membrane potential (RMP). (b) Hyperkalemia, with an elevated RMP. (c) Hypokalemia, with a depressed RMP.

K+ concentrations in equilibrium

Equal diffusion into and out of cell

Normal resting membrane potential (RMP)

(a) Normokalemia

Elevated extracellular K+ concentration

Less diffusion of K+ out of cell

Elevated RMP (cells partially depolarized)

Cells more excitable

(b) Hyperkalemia

Reduced extracellular K+ concentration

Greater diffusion of K+ out of cell

Reduced RMP (cells hyperpolarized)

Cells less excitable

(c) Hypokalemia

Potassium is as important as sodium to the Na^+–K^+ pump and its functions of cotransport and thermogenesis (heat production). It is an essential cofactor for protein synthesis and some other metabolic processes.

Homeostasis

Potassium homeostasis is closely linked to that of sodium. Regardless of the body's state of potassium balance, about 90% of the potassium filtered by the glomerulus is reabsorbed by the PCT and the rest is excreted in the urine. Variations in potassium excretion are controlled later in the nephron by changing the amount of potassium returned to the tubular fluid by the distal convoluted tubule and cortical portion of the collecting duct (CD). When potassium concentration is high, these tubules secrete more potassium into the filtrate and the urine may contain more potassium than the glomerulus filters from the blood. When blood potassium level is low, the tubules secrete less. The distal convoluted tubule and collecting duct reabsorb potassium through their intercalated cells.

Aldosterone regulates potassium balance along with sodium (fig. 24.8). A rise in potassium concentration stimulates the adrenal cortex to secrete aldosterone. Aldosterone stimulates renal secretion of potassium at the same time that it stimulates reabsorption of sodium. The more sodium there is in the urine, the less potassium, and vice versa.

Imbalances

Potassium imbalances are the most dangerous of all electrolyte imbalances. **Hyperkalemia**[6] (>5.5 mEq/L) can have completely opposite effects depending on whether potassium concentration rises quickly or slowly. It can rise quickly when, for example, a crush injury or hemolytic anemia releases large amounts of potassium from ruptured cells. This can also result from a transfusion with outdated, stored blood because potassium leaks from erythrocytes into the plasma during storage. A sudden increase in extracellular potassium tends to make nerve and muscle cells abnormally excitable. Normally, potassium continually passes into and out of cells at equal rates—leaving by diffusion and reentering by the Na^+–K^+ pump. But in hyperkalemia, there is less concentration difference between the ICF and ECF, so the outward diffusion of potassium is reduced. More potassium remains in the cell than normal, and the plasma membrane therefore has a less negative resting potential and is closer to the threshold at which it will set off action potentials **(fig. 24.9b).** This is a very dangerous condition that can quickly produce cardiac arrest. High-potassium solutions are sometimes used by veterinarians to euthanize animals and are used in some states as a lethal injection for capital punishment.

Hyperkalemia can also have a slower onset stemming from such causes as aldosterone hyposecretion, renal failure, or acidosis. (The relationship of acid–base imbalances to potassium

imbalances is explained later.) Paradoxically, if the extracellular potassium concentration rises slowly, nerve and muscle become *less* excitable. *Slow* depolarization of a cell inactivates voltage-gated sodium channels, and the channels don't become excitable again until the membrane repolarizes. Inactivated sodium channels cannot produce action potentials.

Hypokalemia (<3.5 mEq/L) rarely results from a dietary deficiency, because most diets contain ample amounts of potassium; it can occur, however, in people with depressed appetites. Hypokalemia more often results from heavy sweating, chronic vomiting or diarrhea, excessive use of laxatives, aldosterone hypersecretion, or alkalosis. As ECF potassium concentration falls, more potassium moves from the ICF to the ECF. With the loss of these cations from the cytoplasm, cells become hyperpolarized and nerve and muscle cells are less excitable **(fig. 24.9c).** This is reflected in muscle weakness, loss of muscle tone, depressed reflexes, and irregular electrical activity of the heart.

▶▶▶APPLY WHAT YOU KNOW

Some tumors of the adrenal cortex secrete excess aldosterone and may cause paralysis. Explain this effect and identify the electrolyte and fluid imbalances you would expect to observe in such a case.

24.2c Calcium

Functions

Calcium lends strength to the skeleton, activates the sliding filament mechanism of muscle contraction, serves as a second messenger for some hormones and neurotransmitters, activates exocytosis of neurotransmitters and other cellular secretions, and is an essential factor in blood clotting. Cells maintain a very low intracellular calcium concentration because they require a high concentration of phosphate ions (for reasons discussed shortly). If calcium and phosphate were both very concentrated in a cell, calcium phosphate crystals would precipitate in the cytoplasm. To maintain a high phosphate concentration but avoid crystallization of calcium phosphate, cells pump out Ca^{2+} and keep it at a low intracellular concentration, or else sequester Ca^{2+} in the smooth ER and release it only when needed. Cells that store Ca^{2+} often have a protein called *calsequestrin,* which binds the stored Ca^{2+} and keeps it chemically unreactive.

Homeostasis

Calcium concentration is regulated chiefly by parathyroid hormone, calcitriol, and in children, calcitonin (see section 7.4b). These hormones work through their effects on bone deposition and resorption, intestinal absorption of calcium, and urinary excretion. Figure 7.17 presents two flowcharts that summarize calcium homeostasis.

---

[6]*hyper* = above normal; *kal* = potassium; *emia* = blood condition

Imbalances

Hypercalcemia (>5.8 mEq/L) can result from alkalosis, hyperparathyroidism, or hypothyroidism. It reduces the sodium permeability of plasma membranes and inhibits the depolarization of nerve and muscle cells. At concentrations ≥12 mEq/dL, hypercalcemia causes muscular weakness, depressed reflexes, and cardiac arrhythmia.

Hypocalcemia (<4.5 mEq/L) can result from vitamin D deficiency, diarrhea, pregnancy, lactation, acidosis, hypoparathyroidism, or hyperthyroidism. It increases the sodium permeability of plasma membranes, causing the nervous and muscular systems to be overly excitable. Tetany occurs when calcium concentration drops to 6 mg/dL and may be lethal at 4 mg/dL (2 mEq/L) due to laryngospasm and suffocation.

24.2d Magnesium

Functions

About 54% of the body's magnesium (Mg^{2+}) is in the bone tissue and 45% in the intracellular fluid, especially in the skeletal muscles. Magnesium is the second most abundant intracellular cation after potassium. Most ICF Mg^{2+} is complexed with ATP, but Mg^{2+} is also a necessary cofactor for many enzymes, membrane transport proteins, and nucleic acids. Magnesium imbalances can therefore have wide-ranging effects on membrane transport, membrane electrical potentials, cell metabolism, and DNA replication.

Homeostasis

Magnesium levels in the blood plasma normally range from 1.5 to 2.0 mEq/L, whereas intracellular concentrations are quite variable from one tissue to another, but range up to 40 mEq/L in skeletal muscle. Dietary intake of magnesium is typically 140 to 360 mg/day, but only 30% to 40% of it is absorbed by the small intestine and the rest passes through unused. Its intestinal absorption is regulated mainly by vitamin D.

About two-thirds of the body's Mg^{2+} loss is via the feces and one-third via the urine. Retention or loss of plasma Mg^{2+} is regulated mainly by the thick segment of the ascending limb of the nephron loop, where about 70% of the filtered Mg^{2+} is reabsorbed; smaller amounts are reabsorbed in other segments of the nephron. Reabsorption is mainly by the paracellular route (between tubule epithelial cells), driven by the positive electrical potential of the tubular fluid repelling the positive magnesium ions. Parathyroid hormone governs the rate of reabsorption and is the primary regulator of plasma Mg^{2+} level.

Imbalances

Magnesium imbalances are usually due to excessive loss from the body rather than dietary deficiency. **Hypermagnesemia,** an excess (>2.0 mEq/L), is rare except in renal insufficiency. It tends to have a sedative effect, with lethargy, muscle weakness, and weak reflexes; and it can cause respiratory depression or failure, hypotension due to lack of vasomotor tone, and flaccid, diastolic cardiac arrest.

Hypomagnesemia, a plasma Mg^{2+} deficiency (<1.5 mEq/L), can result from intestinal malabsorption, vomiting, diarrhea, or renal disease. It results in hyperirritability of the nervous and muscular systems; muscle tremors, spasms, or tetanus; hypertension resulting from excessive vasoconstriction; and tachycardia and ventricular arrhythmia.

24.2e Chloride

Functions

Chloride ions are the most abundant anions of the ECF and thus make a major contribution to its osmolarity. Chloride ions are required for the formation of stomach acid (HCl), and they are involved in the chloride shift that accompanies carbon dioxide loading and unloading by the erythrocytes (see figs. 22.24, 22.25). By a similar mechanism explained later, chloride ions play a major role in the regulation of body pH.

Homeostasis

Chloride ions are strongly attracted to Na^+, K^+, and Ca^{2+}. It would require great expenditure of energy to keep chloride ions separate from these cations, so chloride homeostasis is achieved primarily as a side effect of sodium homeostasis—as sodium is retained or excreted, chloride ions passively follow.

Imbalances

Hyperchloremia (>105 mEq/L) is usually the result of dietary excess or administration of intravenous saline. **Hypochloremia** (<95 mEq/L) is usually a side effect of hyponatremia but sometimes results from hyperkalemia or acidosis. In the latter case, the kidneys retain potassium by excreting more sodium, and sodium takes chloride with it. The primary effects of chloride imbalances are disturbances in acid–base balance, but this works both ways—a pH imbalance arising from some other cause can also produce a chloride imbalance. Chloride balance is therefore discussed further in connection with acid–base balance in section 24.3.

24.2f Phosphates

Functions

The inorganic phosphates (P_i) of the body fluids are an equilibrium mixture of phosphate (PO_4^{3-}), monohydrogen phosphate (HPO_4^{2-}), and dihydrogen phosphate ($H_2PO_4^-$) ions. Phosphates are relatively concentrated in the ICF, where they are generated by the hydrolysis of ATP and other phosphate compounds. They are a component of phospholipids, DNA, RNA, ATP, GTP, cAMP, creatine phosphate, and related compounds. Every process that depends on ATP depends on phosphate ions. Phosphates activate many metabolic pathways by phosphorylating enzymes and substrates such as glucose. They are also important as buffers that help stabilize the pH of the body fluids.

Homeostasis

The average diet provides ample amounts of phosphate, which is readily absorbed by the small intestine. Plasma phosphate concentration is usually maintained at about 4 mEq/L, with continual loss of excess phosphate by glomerular filtration. If plasma phosphate concentration drops much below this level, however, the renal tubules reabsorb all filtered phosphate.

Parathyroid hormone increases the excretion of phosphate as part of the mechanism for increasing the concentration of free calcium ions in the ECF. Lowering the ECF phosphate concentration minimizes the formation of calcium phosphate and thus helps support plasma calcium concentration. Rates of phosphate excretion are also strongly affected by the pH of the urine, as discussed in section 24.3.

Imbalances

Phosphate homeostasis is not as critical as that of other electrolytes. The body can tolerate broad variations several times above or below the normal concentration with little immediate effect on physiology.

24.2g Summary of Imbalances

Table 24.2 summarizes some causes and effects of sodium, potassium, calcium, and magnesium imbalances. Imbalances in the two anions previously discussed—chloride and phosphate—are important mainly in relation to acid–base balance, discussed in the next section.

The causes and effects of electrolyte balances are so complex and interconnected as to be almost bewildering. They sometimes appear even contradictory, such as vomiting and diarrhea being among the causes or effects of *both* excess and deficiency of the same electrolyte. To fully explain these would require a chapter in itself. Table 24.2 therefore presents only a few of the especially common causes and

TABLE 24.2	Causes and Effects of Some Key Electrolyte Imbalances	
Imbalance	**Causes**	**Clinical Manifestations**
Sodium		
Hypernatremia (Na^+ > 145 mEq/L)	Water loss from chronic vomiting or diarrhea; burns; diuretics; excessive sweating; diabetes insipidus. Dehydration from lack of access to water or inadequate thirst and water consumption. I.V. hypertonic saline infusion. Excess dietary sodium. Corticosterone hypersecretion.	Thirst and polyuria. Hypertension. Muscle spasms. CNS dysfunction due to brain cell shrinkage: confusion, lethargy or excitability, cerebral hemorrhage, seizures, coma.
Hyponatremia (Na^+ < 130 mEq/L)	Excess consumption of plain water. Vomiting, diarrhea, burns, diuretics, polydipsia. Hormone imbalances including cortisol, aldosterone, or thyroid hormone deficiency; diabetes mellitus (with hyperglycemia); ADH excess. Kidney disease.	Usually CNS dysfunction due to cerebral edema: headache, confusion, disorientation, personality changes, lethargy, stupor, seizures, coma. Pulmonary and cerebral edema. Tachycardia.
Potassium		
Hyperkalemia (K^+ > 5.5 mEq/L)	Kidney failure, burns, GI bleeding, crush injuries, rhabdomyolysis, hemolysis, transfusion with outdated blood, rapid I.V. KCl infusion, acidosis, hyperglycemia, aldosterone hyposecretion.	Usually begin with cardiotoxic effects: ventricular fibrillation, bradycardia, cardiac arrest. Irritability. Muscle weakness, flaccid paralysis. Nausea, vomiting, diarrhea.
Hypokalemia (K^+ < 3.5 mEq/L)	Laxative or diuretic overuse; chronic vomiting or diarrhea; heavy sweating. Glucocorticoid or aldosterone hypersecretion. Alkalosis.	Polyuria, polydipsia. Fatigue. Muscle pain, cramps, weakness, loss of muscle tone, depressed reflexes, tetanus, rhabdomyolysis. Cardiac hyperexcitability, arrhythmia. Nausea, vomiting, alkalosis, confusion. Respiratory arrest.
Calcium		
Hypercalcemia (Ca^{2+} > 5.8 mEq/L)	Usually excess bone resorption; metastatic bone cancer and some other cancers; Paget disease; parathyroid hormone or vitamin D excess; thyroid hormone deficiency; immobility. Excessive use of calcium carbonate antacids. Renal failure. Alkalosis.	Anorexia, nausea, vomiting, constipation. Polydipsia, polyuria, nocturia. Depression, personality changes. Muscle weakness, depressed reflexes. Bone pain. Kidney stones. Cardiac arrhythmia, arrest. Confusion, delirium, stupor, coma.
Hypocalcemia (Ca^{2+} < 4.5 mEq/L)	Dietary deficiency of calcium, magnesium, or vitamin D; vitamin D malabsorption; inadequate sunlight; parathyroid hormone deficiency or thyroid hormone excess. Chronic diarrhea. Pregnancy, lactation. Kidney disease. Acidosis.	Bone weakness, osteomalacia, fractures. Muscle cramps, tremors, tetanus, seizures; laryngospasm and asphyxiation. Paresthesia. Heart failure.
Magnesium		
Hypermagnesemia (Mg^{2+} > 2.0 mEq/L)	Excessive intake, as in magnesium-based antacids. Deficiency of aldosterone or thyroid hormone. Renal failure.	Muscle weakness, depressed reflexes, lethargy. Respiratory depression or failure. Hypotension, cardiac arrest.
Hypomagnesemia (Mg^{2+} < 1.5 mEq/L)	Alcoholism; intestinal malabsorption; malnutrition. Chronic vomiting or diarrhea. Some diuretics. Lactation. Renal failure.	Anorexia, lethargy, nausea, vomiting. Muscle weakness, tremor, spasms, fasciculations, tetanus. Hypertension, tachycardia, cardiac arrhythmia.

effects. It omits many drugs and clinical procedures (such as gastric suction and fluid therapy) that can trigger imbalances. (See Deeper Insight 24.2 for further discussion of fluid therapy.) With few exceptions, we focus on spontaneous illnesses and patient behaviors—for example, the common problem of surreptitious overuse of laxatives and diuretics by people obsessed with weight loss, often throwing themselves into dangerous fluid, electrolyte, and acid–base disturbances.

The clinical manifestations tabulated here include both **signs** (effects on a patient that can be observed by others, such as seizures and coma) and **symptoms** (effects that can be felt only by the patient, such as headache, nausea, and malaise). The tabulated manifestations don't occur in every case of imbalance, or even most. They vary greatly with the magnitude of imbalance and from one population to another—such as infants, healthy adults, and people who are elderly or disabled—and imbalances are often asymptomatic or produce signs discovered only in blood work or electrocardiograms.

For some of the terminology here, you may need to refer back to hormone imbalances (hyper- and hyposecretion, section 17.7), renal functions (section 23.6), or other earlier discussions in this book. *Acidosis* and *alkalosis,* associated with electrolyte imbalances as both cause and effect, are detailed in the next section (24.3).

Anorexia is lack of appetite. *Malaise* is a general sense of feeling uncomfortable or unwell, as if "coming down with something." *Polydipsia* means excessive thirst and drinking; *polyuria,* often associated with it, is excessive urine output. *Nocturia* is being awakened and having to urinate during the night and, sometimes, bed-wetting in children and incontinent adults.

Because electrolytes are so important in cell membrane potentials and nerve and muscle action, imbalances often have neuromuscular manifestations: *paresthesia,* abnormal sensation in the absence of external stimulation, such as numbness, burning, or tingling of the fingers; *muscle fasciculations,* involuntary twitching of individual fascicles of a muscle; or more extreme muscular reactions such as convulsions and *tetanus*—not the bacterial disease but the sustained contraction of a muscle, without relaxation. If it affects the respiratory muscles, tetanus can cause respiratory arrest; if it causes tightening of the laryngeal muscles, it can cause death by asphyxiation. Some electrolyte imbalances cause *rhabdomyolysis,* the death of muscle fibers, releasing their contents into the bloodstream, potentially clogging the kidneys with myoglobin and causing renal failure.

BEFORE YOU GO ON

Answer the following questions to test your understanding of the preceding section:

6. Which do you think would have the most serious effect, and why—a 5 mEq/L increase in the plasma concentration of sodium, potassium, chloride, or calcium?

7. Answer the same question for a 5 mEq/L decrease.

8. Explain why ADH is more likely than aldosterone to change the osmolarity of the blood plasma.

9. Explain why aldosterone hyposecretion could cause hypochloremia.

10. Magnesium sulfate, commonly sold as Epsom salt, can be used as a bath salt to relax tight, aching muscles. Explain this effect in view of what you have learned in this chapter section.

11. Why are more phosphate ions required in the ICF than in the ECF? How does this affect the distribution of calcium ions between these fluid compartments?

24.3 Acid–Base Balance

Expected Learning Outcomes

When you have completed this section, you should be able to

a. define *buffer* and write chemical equations for the bicarbonate, phosphate, and protein buffer systems;

b. discuss the relationship between pulmonary ventilation, pH of the extracellular fluids, and the bicarbonate buffer system;

c. explain how the kidneys secrete hydrogen ions and how these ions are buffered in the tubular fluid;

d. identify some types and causes of acidosis and alkalosis, and describe the effects of these pH imbalances; and

e. explain how the respiratory and urinary systems correct acidosis and alkalosis, and compare their effectiveness and limitations.

As we saw in section 2.4f, metabolism depends on the functioning of enzymes, and enzymes are very sensitive to pH. Slight deviations from the normal pH can shut down metabolic pathways as well as alter the structure and function of other macromolecules. Consequently, acid–base balance is one of the most important aspects of homeostasis.

The blood and tissue fluid normally have a pH of 7.35 to 7.45. **Acid–base balance** is a state in which the pH of the body fluids is homeostatically regulated within this range. Such a narrow range of variation is remarkable considering that our metabolism constantly produces acid: lactic acid from anaerobic fermentation, phosphoric acids from nucleic acid catabolism, fatty acids and ketones from fat catabolism, and carbonic acid from carbon dioxide. These acids are a constant challenge to our enzyme function, homeostasis, and survival. Here we examine *buffering* mechanisms for stabilizing internal pH and maintaining acid–base balance.

24.3a Acids, Bases, and Buffers

The pH of a solution is determined solely by its hydrogen ions (H^+). An acid is any chemical that releases H^+ in solution. A **strong acid** such as hydrochloric acid (HCl) ionizes freely, gives up most of its hydrogen ions, and can markedly lower the pH of a solution. A **weak acid** such as carbonic acid (H_2CO_3) ionizes only slightly and keeps most hydrogen in a chemically bound form that doesn't affect pH. A base is any chemical that accepts H^+. A **strong base** such as the hydroxide ion (OH^-) has a strong tendency to bind H^+ and raise the pH, whereas a **weak base** such as the bicarbonate ion (HCO_3^-) binds less of the available H^+ and has less effect on pH.

A **buffer,** broadly speaking, is any mechanism that resists pH changes by converting a strong acid or base to a weak one. The body has both physiological and chemical buffers. A **physiological buffer** is a system—namely, the respiratory or urinary system—that stabilizes pH by controlling the body's output of acids, bases, or CO_2. Of all buffer systems, the urinary system buffers the greatest quantity of acid or base, but it requires several hours to days to exert an effect. The respiratory system exerts an effect within a few minutes but cannot alter the pH as much as the urinary system can.

A **chemical buffer** is a substance that binds H^+ and removes it from solution as its concentration begins to rise, or releases H^+ into solution as its concentration falls. Chemical buffers can restore normal pH within a fraction of a second. They function as mixtures called **buffer systems** composed of a weak acid and a weak base. We have three major chemical buffer systems—the bicarbonate, phosphate, and protein systems.

The amount of acid or base that can be neutralized by a chemical buffer system depends on two factors: the concentration of the buffers and the pH of their working environment. Each system has an optimum pH at which it functions best; its effectiveness is greatly reduced if the pH of its environment deviates too far from this. The relevance of these factors will become apparent as you study the following buffer systems.

The Bicarbonate Buffer System

The **bicarbonate buffer system** is a solution of carbonic acid and bicarbonate ions. As we can see in the carbonic acid reaction, carbonic acid (H_2CO_3) forms by the reaction of carbon dioxide with water, then dissociates into bicarbonate (HCO_3^-) and H^+:

$$CO_2 + H_2O \rightleftharpoons H_2CO_3 \rightleftharpoons HCO_3^- + H^+.$$

This is a reversible reaction. When it proceeds to the right, carbonic acid acts as a weak acid by releasing H^+ and lowering pH. When the reaction proceeds to the left, bicarbonate acts as a weak base by binding H^+, removing the ions from solution, and raising pH.

At a pH of 7.4, the bicarbonate system wouldn't ordinarily have a particularly strong buffering capacity outside of the body. This is too far from its optimum pH of 6.1. If a strong acid was added to a beaker of carbonic acid–bicarbonate solution at pH 7.4, the preceding reaction would shift only slightly to the left. Much surplus H^+ would remain and the pH would be substantially lower. In the body, by contrast, the bicarbonate system works quite well because the lungs and kidneys constantly remove CO_2 and prevent an equilibrium from being reached. This keeps the reaction moving to the left, and more H^+ is neutralized. Conversely, if there is a need to lower the pH, the kidneys excrete HCO_3^- and keep this reaction moving to the right, which elevates the H^+ concentration of the ECF. Thus, you can see that the physiological and chemical buffers of the body function together in maintaining acid–base balance.

▶▶▶**APPLY WHAT YOU KNOW**

In the systemic circulation, arterial blood has a mean pH of 7.40 and venous blood has a mean of 7.35. What do you think causes this difference?

The Phosphate Buffer System

The **phosphate buffer system** is a solution of HPO_4^{2-} and $H_2PO_4^-$. It works in much the same way as the bicarbonate system. The following reaction can proceed to the right to liberate H^+ and lower pH, or it can proceed to the left to bind H^+ and raise pH:

$$H_2PO_4^- \rightleftharpoons HPO_4^{2-} + H^+.$$

The optimal pH for this system is 6.8, closer to the actual pH of the ECF (7.4). Thus, the phosphate buffer system has a stronger buffering effect than an equal amount of bicarbonate buffer. However, phosphates are much less concentrated in the ECF than bicarbonate, so they are less important in buffering the ECF. They are more important in the renal tubules and ICF, where not only are they more concentrated, but the pH is lower and closer to their functional optimum. In the ICF, the constant production of metabolic acids creates pH values ranging from 4.5 to 7.4, probably averaging 7.0. The reason for the low pH in the renal tubules is discussed later.

The Protein Buffer System

Proteins are more concentrated than either bicarbonate or phosphate buffers, especially in the ICF. The **protein buffer system** accounts for about three-quarters of all chemical buffering in the body fluids. The buffering ability of proteins is due to certain side groups of their amino acid residues. Some have carboxyl side groups (—COOH), which release H^+ when pH begins to rise and thus lower pH:

$$\text{—COOH} \longrightarrow \text{—COO}^- + H^+.$$

Others have amino side groups ($-NH_2$), which bind H^+ when pH falls too low, thus raising pH toward normal:

$$-NH_2 + H^+ \longrightarrow -NH_3^+.$$

▶▶▶**APPLY WHAT YOU KNOW**

What protein do you think is the most important buffer in blood plasma? In erythrocytes?

24.3b Respiratory Control of pH

The respiratory buffer system adjusts the pH of the body fluids by raising or lowering the rate and depth of breathing. The equation for the bicarbonate buffer system shows that the addition of CO_2 to the body fluids raises H^+ concentration and lowers pH, while the removal of CO_2 has the opposite effects. This is the basis for the strong buffering capacity of the respiratory system. Indeed, this system can neutralize two or three times as much acid as the chemical buffers can.

Carbon dioxide is constantly produced by aerobic metabolism and is normally eliminated by the lungs at an equivalent rate. As explained in section 22.3g, rising CO_2 concentration and falling pH stimulate peripheral and central chemoreceptors, which stimulate an increase in pulmonary ventilation. This expels excess CO_2 and thus reduces H^+ concentration. The free H^+ becomes part of the water molecules produced by this reaction:

$$HCO_3^- + H^+ \longrightarrow H_2CO_3 \longrightarrow CO_2 \text{ (expired)} + H_2O.$$

Conversely, a drop in H^+ concentration raises pH and reduces pulmonary ventilation. This allows metabolic CO_2 to accumulate in the ECF faster than it is expelled, thus lowering pH to normal.

These are classic negative feedback mechanisms that result in acid–base homeostasis. Respiratory control of pH has some limitations, however, that are discussed later under acid–base imbalances.

24.3c Renal Control of pH

The kidneys can neutralize more acid or base than either the respiratory system or the chemical buffers. They do so by varying the amount of acid eliminated in the urine. The essence of this mechanism is that the renal tubules secrete H^+ into the tubular fluid, where most of it binds to bicarbonate, ammonia, and phosphate buffers. Bound and free H^+ are then excreted in the urine. Thus the kidneys, in contrast to the lungs, actually expel H^+ itself from the body. The other buffer systems only reduce its concentration by binding it to another chemical.

Figure 24.10 shows how the renal tubules secrete and neutralize H^+. The hydrogen ions are colored so you can trace them from the blood (step ①) to the tubular fluid (step ⑥). Notice that it is not a simple matter of transporting free H^+ across the tubule cells; rather, the H^+ travels in the form of carbonic acid and water molecules.

The tubular secretion of H^+ takes place at step ⑥, where the ion is pumped out of the tubule cell into the tubular fluid. This can happen only if there is a steep enough concentration gradient between a high H^+ concentration within the cell and a lower concentration in the tubular fluid. If the pH of the tubular fluid drops any lower than 4.5, H^+ concentration in the fluid is so high that tubular secretion ceases. Thus, pH 4.5 is the **limiting pH** for tubular secretion. This has added significance later in our discussion.

In a person with normal acid–base balance, all bicarbonate ions (HCO_3^-) in the tubular fluid are consumed by neutralizing H^+; thus there is no HCO_3^- in the urine. Bicarbonate ions are filtered by the glomerulus, gradually disappear from the tubular fluid, and appear in the peritubular capillary blood. It *appears* as if HCO_3^- is reabsorbed by the renal tubules, but this is not the case; indeed, the renal tubules are incapable of reabsorbing HCO_3^- directly. The cells of the proximal convoluted tubule, however, have carbonic anhydrase (CAH) on their brush borders facing the lumen. This breaks down the H_2CO_3 in the tubular fluid to $CO_2 + H_2O$ (step ⑩). It is the CO_2 that is reabsorbed, not the bicarbonate. For every CO_2 reabsorbed, however, a *new* bicarbonate ion is formed in the tubule cell and released into the blood (step ⑤). The effect is the same as if the tubule cells had reabsorbed bicarbonate itself.

Note that for every bicarbonate ion that enters the peritubular capillaries, a sodium ion does too. Thus, Na^+ reabsorption by the renal tubules is part of the process of neutralizing acid. The more acid the kidneys excrete, the less sodium the urine contains.

The tubules secrete somewhat more H^+ than the available bicarbonate can neutralize. The urine therefore contains a slight excess of free H^+, which gives it a pH of about 5 to 6. Yet if all of the excess H^+ secreted by the tubules remained in this free ionic form, the pH of the tubular fluid would drop far below the limiting pH of 4.5, and H^+ secretion would stop. This must be prevented, and there are additional buffers in the tubular fluid to do so.

The glomerular filtrate contains Na_2HPO_4 (dibasic sodium phosphate), which reacts with some of the H^+ (**fig. 24.11**). A hydrogen ion replaces one of the sodium ions in the buffer, forming NaH_2PO_4 (monobasic sodium phosphate). This is passed in the urine, and the displaced Na^+ is transported into the tubule cell and from there to the bloodstream.

In addition, tubule cells catabolize certain amino acids and release ammonia (NH_3) as a product. Ammonia diffuses into the tubular fluid, where it acts as a base to neutralize acid. It reacts with H^+ and Cl^- (the most abundant anion in the glomerular filtrate) to form ammonium chloride (NH_4Cl), which is passed in the urine.

Since there is so much chloride in the tubular fluid, you may ask why H^+ isn't simply excreted as hydrochloric acid (HCl). Why involve ammonia? The reason is that HCl is a strong acid—it dissociates almost completely, so most of its hydrogen would

① H⁺ in blood reacts with HCO₃⁻ to form H₂CO₃.

② H₂CO₃ decomposes into H₂O and CO₂, which enter the tubule cell.

③ Tubule cells acquire CO₂ from blood, tubular fluid, and their own aerobic respiration.

④ Carbonic anhydrase (CAH) combines H₂O and CO₂ to re-form H₂CO₃.

⑤ H₂CO₃ ionizes to form HCO₃⁻ (which returns to the blood) and H⁺.

⑥ Na⁺–H⁺ antiport exchanges H⁺ for Na⁺.

⑦ NaHCO₃ from glomerular filtrate decomposes into Na⁺ and HCO₃⁻. Na⁺ is pumped into tubule cell.

⑧ Na⁺ is removed by Na⁺–K⁺ pump at the base of the cell.

⑨ HCO₃⁻ reacts with H⁺ from tubule cell to form H₂CO₃.

⑩ CAH on brush border decomposes H₂CO₃ to H₂O and CO₂ again.

⑪ CO₂ enters the tubular cell and H₂O passes in the urine (carrying the H⁺ that was originally in the blood).

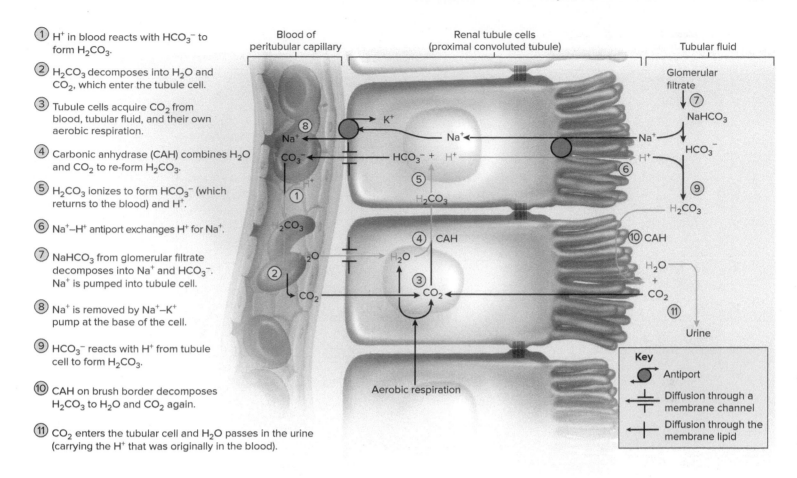

FIGURE 24.10 Secretion and Neutralization of Hydrogen Ions in the Kidneys. The colored hydrogen symbols allow you to trace hydrogen from H⁺ in the blood to H₂O in the urine.

❓ *If the pH of the tubular fluid went down, how would its Na⁺ concentration change?*

be in the form of free H⁺. The pH of the tubular fluid would drop below the limiting pH and prevent excretion of more acid. Ammonium chloride, by contrast, is a weak acid—most of its hydrogen remains bound to it and doesn't lower the pH of the tubular fluid.

24.3d Disorders of Acid–Base Balance

Figure 24.12 represents acid–base balance with an instructive metaphor to show its dependence on the bicarbonate buffer system. At a normal pH of 7.4, the ECF has a 20:1 ratio of HCO_3^- to H_2CO_3. Excess hydrogen ions convert HCO_3^- to H_2CO_3 and tip the balance to a lower pH. A pH below 7.35 is considered to be a state of **acidosis.** On the other hand, a H⁺ deficiency causes H_2CO_3 to dissociate into H⁺ and HCO_3^-, thus tipping the balance to a higher pH. A pH above 7.45 is a state of **alkalosis.** Either of these imbalances has potentially fatal effects. A person can't live more than a few hours if the blood pH is below 7.0 or above 7.7, and a pH below 6.8 or above 8.0 is quickly fatal.

In acidosis, H⁺ diffuses down its concentration gradient into cells, and to maintain electrical balance, K⁺ diffuses out

(fig. 24.13a). The H⁺ is buffered by intracellular proteins, so this exchange results in a net loss of cations from the cell. This makes the resting membrane potential more negative than usual (hyperpolarized) and makes nerve and muscle cells more difficult to stimulate. This is why acidosis depresses the central nervous system and causes such symptoms as confusion, disorientation, and coma.

In alkalosis, the extracellular H⁺ concentration is low. Hydrogen ions diffuse out of the cells and K⁺ diffuses in to replace them **(fig. 24.13b).** The net gain in positive intracellular charges shifts the membrane potential closer to firing level and makes the nervous system hyperexcitable. Neurons fire spontaneously and overstimulate skeletal muscles, causing muscle spasms, tetanus, convulsions, or respiratory paralysis.

Acid–base imbalances fall into two categories, respiratory and metabolic **(table 24.3). Respiratory acidosis** occurs when the rate of alveolar ventilation fails to keep pace with the body's rate of CO_2 production. Carbon dioxide accumulates in the ECF and lowers its pH. This occurs in such conditions as emphysema, in which there is a severe reduction in

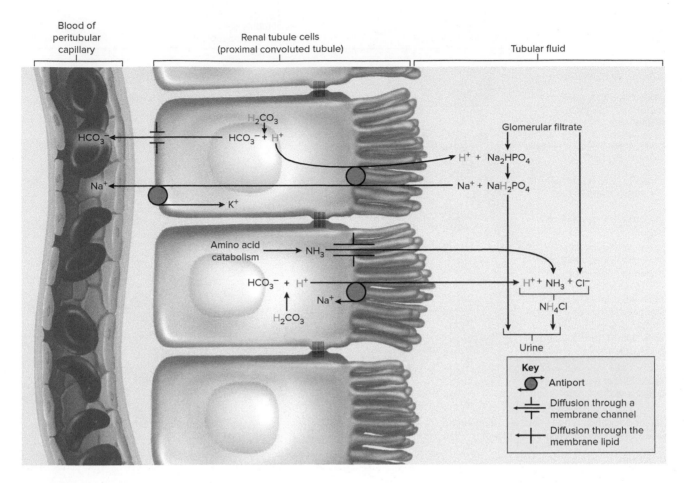

FIGURE 24.11 Acid Buffering in the Urine. Reactions in the tubule cells are the same as in figure 24.10 but are simplified in this diagram. The essential differences are the buffering mechanisms shown in the tubular fluid. Hydrogen symbols are colored to allow tracing them from carbonic acid to the urine.

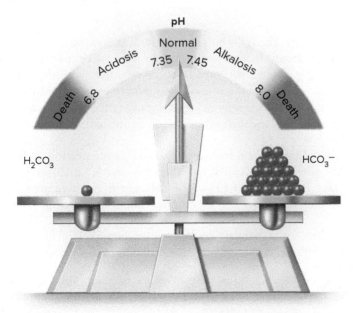

FIGURE 24.12 The Relationship of Bicarbonate–Carbonic Acid Ratio to pH. At a normal pH of 7.40, there is a 20:1 ratio of bicarbonate ions (HCO_3^-) to carbonic acid (H_2CO_3) in the blood plasma. An excess of HCO_3^- tips the balance toward alkalosis, whereas an excess of H_2CO_3 tips it toward acidosis.

the number of functional alveoli. **Respiratory alkalosis** results from hyperventilation, in which CO_2 is eliminated faster than it is produced.

Metabolic acidosis can result from increased production of organic acids, such as lactic acid in anaerobic fermentation and ketone bodies in alcoholism and diabetes mellitus. It can also result from the excessive ingestion of acidic drugs such as aspirin or from the loss of base due to chronic diarrhea or overuse of laxatives. Dying persons also typically exhibit acidosis. **Metabolic alkalosis** is rare but can result from overuse of bicarbonates (such as oral antacids and intravenous bicarbonate solutions) or from the loss of stomach acid by chronic vomiting.

24.3e Compensation for Acid–Base Imbalances

In **compensated** acidosis or alkalosis, either the kidneys compensate for pH imbalances of respiratory origin, or the respiratory system compensates for pH imbalances of metabolic origin. **Uncompensated** acidosis or alkalosis is a pH imbalance that the body cannot correct without clinical intervention.

In **respiratory compensation,** changes in pulmonary ventilation correct the pH of the body fluids by expelling or retaining

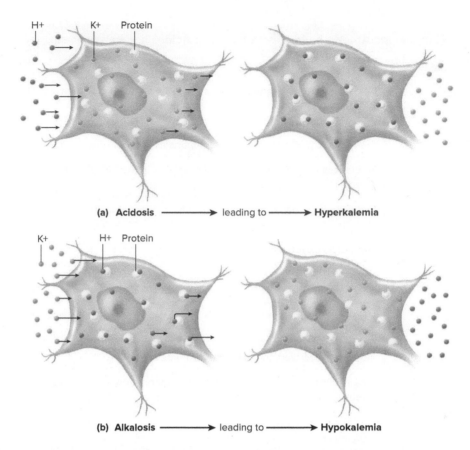

(a) **Acidosis** ⟶ leading to ⟶ **Hyperkalemia**

(b) **Alkalosis** ⟶ leading to ⟶ **Hypokalemia**

FIGURE 24.13 The Relationship Between Acid–Base Imbalances and Potassium Imbalances. (a) In acidosis, H⁺ diffuses into the cells and drives out K⁺, elevating the K⁺ concentration of the ECF. (b) In alkalosis, H⁺ diffuses out of the cells and K⁺ diffuses in to replace it, lowering the K⁺ concentration of the ECF.

? *How would you change part (a) to show the effect of hyperkalemia on the pH of the ECF?*

TABLE 24.3	Some Causes of Acidosis and Alkalosis	
	Acidosis	**Alkalosis**
Respiratory	Hypoventilation, apnea, or respiratory arrest; asthma; emphysema; cystic fibrosis; chronic bronchitis; narcotic overdose	Hyperventilation due to pain or emotions such as anxiety; oxygen deficiency (as at high elevation)
Metabolic	Excess production of organic acids as in diabetes mellitus and starvation; long-term anaerobic fermentation; hyperkalemia; chronic diarrhea; excessive alcohol consumption; drugs such as aspirin and laxatives	Rare but can result from chronic vomiting; overuse of bicarbonates (antacids); aldosterone hypersecretion

CO_2. If there is a CO_2 excess (hypercapnia), pulmonary ventilation increases to expel CO_2 and bring the blood pH back up to normal. If there is a CO_2 deficiency (hypocapnia), ventilation is reduced to allow CO_2 to accumulate in the blood and lower the pH to normal.

This is very effective in correcting pH imbalances due to abnormal P_{CO_2} but not very effective in correcting other causes of acidosis and alkalosis. In diabetic acidosis, for example, the lungs can't reduce the concentration of ketone bodies in the blood, although one can somewhat compensate for the H⁺ that ketones release by increasing pulmonary ventilation and exhausting extra CO_2. The respiratory system can adjust a blood pH of 7.0 back to 7.2 or 7.3 but not all the way back to the normal 7.4. Although the

respiratory system has a very powerful buffering effect, its ability to stabilize pH is therefore limited.

Renal compensation is an adjustment of pH by changing the rate of H⁺ secretion by the renal tubules. The kidneys are slower to respond to pH imbalances but better at restoring a fully normal pH. Urine usually has a pH of 5 to 6, but in acidosis it may fall as low as 4.5 because of excess H⁺, whereas in alkalosis it may rise as high as 8.2 because of excess HCO_3^-. The kidneys can't act quickly enough to compensate for short-term pH imbalances, such as the acidosis that could result from an asthmatic attack lasting an hour or two, or the alkalosis resulting from a brief episode of emotional hyperventilation. They are effective, however, at compensating for pH imbalances that last for a few days or longer.

TABLE 24.4		Some Relationships Among Fluid, Electrolyte, and Acid–Base Imbalances	
Cause		**Potential Effect**	**Reason**
Acidosis	→	Hyperkalemia	H^+ diffuses into cells and displaces K^+ (see fig. 24.13a). As K^+ leaves the ICF, K^+ concentration in the ECF rises.
Hyperkalemia	→	Acidosis	Opposite from the above; high K^+ concentration in the ECF causes less K^+ to diffuse out of the cells than normally. H^+ diffuses out to compensate, and this lowers the extracellular pH.
Alkalosis	→	Hypokalemia	H^+ diffuses from ICF to ECF. More K^+ remains in the ICF to compensate for the H^+ loss, causing a drop in ECF K^+ concentration (see fig. 24.13b).
Hypokalemia	→	Alkalosis	Opposite from the preceding line; low K^+ concentration in the ECF causes K^+ to diffuse out of cells. H^+ diffuses in to replace K^+, lowering the H^+ concentration of the ECF and raising its pH.
Acidosis	→	Hypochloremia	More Cl^- is excreted as NH_4Cl to buffer the excess acid in the renal tubules, leaving less Cl^- in the ECF.
Alkalosis	→	Hyperchloremia	More Cl^- is reabsorbed from the renal tubules, so ingested Cl^- accumulates in the ECF rather than being excreted.
Hyperchloremia	→	Acidosis	More H^+ is retained in the blood to balance the excess Cl^-, causing hyperchloremic acidosis.
Hypovolemia	→	Alkalosis	More Na^+ is reabsorbed by the kidney. Na^+ reabsorption is coupled to H^+ secretion (see fig. 24.10), so more H^+ is secreted and pH of the ECF rises.
Hypervolemia	→	Acidosis	Less Na^+ is reabsorbed, so less H^+ is secreted into the renal tubules. H^+ retained in the ECF causes acidosis.
Acidosis	→	Hypocalcemia	Acidosis causes more Ca^{2+} to bind to plasma protein and citrate ions, lowering the concentration of free, ionized Ca^{2+} and causing symptoms of hypocalcemia.
Alkalosis	→	Hypercalcemia	Alkalosis causes more Ca^{2+} to dissociate from plasma protein and citrate ions, raising the concentration of free Ca^{2+}.

In acidosis, the renal tubules increase the rate of H^+ secretion. The extra H^+ in the tubular fluid must be buffered; otherwise, the fluid pH could exceed the limiting pH and H^+ secretion would stop. Therefore, in acidosis, the renal tubules secrete more ammonia to buffer the added H^+, and the amount of ammonium chloride in the urine may rise to 7 to 10 times normal.

▶▶▶ **APPLY WHAT YOU KNOW**

Suppose you measured the pH and ammonium chloride concentration of urine from a person with emphysema and urine from a healthy individual. How would you expect the two to differ, and why?

In alkalosis, the bicarbonate concentration and pH of the urine are elevated. This is partly because there is more HCO_3^- in the blood and glomerular filtrate and partly because there isn't enough H^+ in the tubular fluid to neutralize all the HCO_3^- in the filtrate.

24.3f Acid–Base Imbalances in Relation to Electrolyte and Fluid Imbalances

The foregoing discussion once again underscores a point made early in this chapter—we can't understand or treat imbalances of fluid, electrolyte, or acid–base balance in isolation from each other,

because each of these frequently affects the other two. **Table 24.4** itemizes and explains some of these interactions. This is by no means a complete list of how fluid, electrolytes, and pH affect each other, but it does demonstrate their interdependence. Note that many of these relationships are reciprocal—for example, acidosis can cause hyperkalemia, and conversely, hyperkalemia can cause acidosis.

BEFORE YOU GO ON

Answer the following questions to test your understanding of the preceding section:

12. Write two chemical equations that show how the bicarbonate buffer system compensates for acidosis and alkalosis and two equations that show how the phosphate buffer system compensates for these imbalances.

13. Why are phosphate buffers more effective in the cytoplasm than in the blood plasma?

14. Renal tubules cannot reabsorb HCO_3^-; yet HCO_3^- concentration in the tubular fluid falls while in the blood plasma it rises. Explain this apparent contradiction.

15. In acidosis, the renal tubules secrete more ammonia. Why?

DEEPER INSIGHT 24.2

CLINICAL APPLICATION

Fluid Replacement Therapy

One of the most significant problems in the treatment of seriously ill patients is the restoration and maintenance of proper fluid volume, composition, and distribution among the fluid compartments. Fluids may be administered to replenish total body water, restore blood volume and pressure, shift water from one fluid compartment to another, or restore and maintain electrolyte and acid–base balance.

Drinking water is the simplest method of fluid replacement, but it doesn't replace electrolytes. Heat exhaustion can occur when you lose water and salt in the sweat and replace the fluid by drinking plain water. Broths, juices, and sports drinks replace water, carbohydrates, and electrolytes.

Patients who can't take fluids by mouth must be treated by alternative routes. Some fluids can be given by enema and absorbed through the colon. All routes of fluid administration other than the digestive tract are called *parenteral*[7] routes. The most common of these is the intravenous (I.V.) route, but for various reasons, including inability to find a suitable vein, fluids are sometimes given by subcutaneous (sub-Q), intramuscular (I.M.), or other parenteral routes. Many kinds of sterile solutions are available to meet the fluid replacement needs of different patients.

In cases of extensive blood loss, there may not be time to type and cross-match blood for a transfusion. The more urgent need is to replenish blood volume and pressure. *Normal saline* (isotonic, 0.9% NaCl) is a relatively quick and simple means of raising blood volume while maintaining normal osmolarity, but it has significant shortcomings. It takes three to five times as much saline as whole blood to rebuild normal volume because much of the saline escapes the circulation into the interstitial fluid compartment or is excreted by the kidneys. In addition, normal saline can induce hypernatremia and hyperchloremia, because the body excretes the water but retains much of the NaCl. Hyperchloremia can, in turn, produce acidosis. Normal saline also lacks potassium, magnesium, and calcium. Indeed, it dilutes those electrolytes that are already present and creates a risk of cardiac arrest from hypocalcemia. Saline also dilutes plasma albumin and RBCs, creating still greater risks for patients who have suffered extensive blood loss. Nevertheless, the emergency maintenance of blood volume sometimes takes temporary precedence over these other considerations.

Fluid therapy is also used to correct pH imbalances. Acidosis may be treated with *Ringer's lactate solution,* which includes sodium to rebuild ECF volume, potassium to rebuild ICF volume, lactate to balance the cations, and enough glucose to make the solution isotonic. Alkalosis can be treated with potassium chloride. This must be administered very carefully, because potassium ions can cause painful venous spasms, and

even a small potassium excess can cause cardiac arrest. High-potassium solutions should never be given to patients in renal failure or whose renal status is unknown, because in the absence of renal excretion of potassium, they can bring on lethal hyperkalemia. Ringer's lactate or potassium chloride also must be administered very cautiously, with close monitoring of blood pH, to avoid causing a pH imbalance opposite the one that was meant to be corrected. Too much Ringer's lactate causes alkalosis and too much KCl causes acidosis.

Plasma volume expanders are hypertonic solutions or colloids that are retained in the bloodstream and draw interstitial water into it by osmosis. They include albumin, sucrose, mannitol, and dextran. Plasma expanders are also used to combat hypotonic hydration by drawing water out of swollen cells, averting such problems as seizures and coma. A plasma expander can draw several liters of water out of the intracellular compartment within a few minutes.

Patients who can't eat are often given isotonic 5% dextrose (glucose). A fasting patient loses as much as 70 to 85 g of protein per day from the tissues as protein is broken down to fuel the metabolism. Giving 100 to 150 g of I.V. glucose per day reduces this by half and is said to have a *protein-sparing effect*. More than glucose is needed in some cases—for example, if a patient hasn't eaten for several days and can't be fed by nasogastric tube (due to lesions of the digestive tract, for example) or if large amounts of nutrients are needed for tissue repair following severe trauma, burns, or infections. In *total parenteral nutrition (TPN),* or *hyperalimentation,*[8] a patient is provided with complete I.V. nutritional support, including a protein hydrolysate (amino acid mixture), vitamins, electrolytes, 20% to 25% glucose, and on alternate days, a fat emulsion.

The water from parenteral solutions is normally excreted by the kidneys. If the patient has renal insufficiency, however, excretion may not keep pace with intake, and there is a risk of hypotonic hydration. Intravenous fluids are usually given slowly, by *I.V. drip,* to avoid abrupt changes or overcompensation for the patient's condition. In addition to pH, the patient's heart rate, blood pressure, hematocrit, and plasma electrolyte concentrations are monitored, and the patient is examined periodically for respiratory sounds indicating pulmonary edema.

The delicacy of fluid replacement therapy underscores the close relationships among fluids, electrolytes, and pH. It is dangerous to manipulate any one of these variables without close attention to the others. Parenteral fluid therapy is usually used for persons who are seriously ill. Their homeostatic mechanisms are already compromised and leave less room for error than in a healthy person.

---

[7]*para* = beside; *enter* = intestine

[8]*hyper* = above normal; *aliment* = nourishment

STUDY GUIDE

▶ Assess Your Learning Outcomes

To test your knowledge, discuss the following topics with a study partner or in writing, ideally from memory.

24.1 Fluid Balance

1. Fluid compartments; total body water content of a typical young adult; and what percentages of this are in the intracellular and extracellular fluid compartments
2. How water moves from one fluid compartment to another; which differs more from one compartment to another—osmolarity or chemical composition—and why
3. What it means to be in a state of fluid balance
4. The meanings of *sensible, insensible,* and *obligatory water loss*
5. Typical daily water gain and loss; sources of water gain and avenues of water loss, and the typical amounts of each
6. How the hypothalamus senses the body's state of hydration and how it promotes fluid intake and water conservation when necessary
7. Short- and long-term mechanisms by which thirst is satiated; why it is important to have the short-term mechanisms
8. The role of antidiuretic hormone in regulating the body's rate of fluid loss
9. The meaning of *fluid deficiency;* two forms of fluid deficiency and how they differ; and potential consequences of fluid deficiency
10. The meaning of *fluid excess;* two forms of fluid excess and how they differ; and potential consequences of fluid excess

11. The meaning of *fluid sequestration;* examples and potential consequences of fluid sequestration

24.2 Electrolyte Balance

1. Functions of electrolytes in general; the body's common electrolytes; and the relative ECF and ICF concentrations of Na^+, K^+, Cl^-, Ca^{2+}, Mg^{2+}, and phosphate ions
2. Physiological functions of sodium; how it is regulated by aldosterone, antidiuretic hormone, and natriuretic peptides; and causes and effects of hyper- and hyponatremia
3. Physiological functions of potassium; how it is regulated by the kidneys and aldosterone; and causes and effects of hyper- and hypokalemia
4. Physiological functions of calcium; why cells usually must maintain a low intracellular calcium level; how calcium homeostasis is regulated by parathyroid hormone, calcitriol, and calcitonin; and causes and effects of hyper- and hypocalcemia
5. Physiological functions of magnesium; how vitamin D and parathyroid hormone regulate magnesium level; and causes and effects of magnesium deficiency and excess
6. Physiological functions of chloride; why chloride levels are determined mainly by the sodium-regulating mechanisms; and causes and effects of hyper- and hypochloremia
7. Three forms of inorganic phosphate ions (P_i); the physiological functions of phosphate; and how phosphate homeostasis is regulated

24.3 Acid–Base Balance

1. The normal pH range of the blood and most other ECF, and why acid–base balance is so crucial to homeostasis
2. Strong and weak acids and bases, and examples
3. How a buffer resists pH changes; the body's principal physiological and chemical buffer systems
4. How the bicarbonate, phosphate, and protein buffer systems neutralize excess acid or base; their effectiveness relative to each other and to the physiological buffer systems
5. How the respiratory system buffers pH
6. How the renal tubule secretes acid; why urine is normally bicarbonate-free; why acid secretion is linked to sodium reabsorption; and the roles of Na_2HPO_4 and NH_3 in buffering urinary acid
7. The ratio of H_2CO_3 to HCO_3^- at normal blood pH, and how this ratio changes in acidosis and alkalosis; the pH levels at which acidosis and alkalosis are soon fatal
8. Mechanisms behind the neuromuscular effects of acidosis and alkalosis
9. Common causes of respiratory and metabolic acidosis and alkalosis
10. The difference between compensated and uncompensated acidosis and alkalosis, and how the respiratory and urinary systems compensate for pH imbalances
11. Examples of how fluid, electrolyte, and acid–base imbalances can each cause, or be caused by, imbalances in the other two categories

▶ Testing Your Recall

Answers in Appendix A

1. The greatest percentage of the body's water is in
   a. the blood plasma.
   b. the lymph.
   c. the intracellular fluid.
   d. the interstitial fluid.
   e. the extracellular fluid.

2. Hypertension is likely to increase the secretion of
   a. natriuretic peptide.
   b. antidiuretic hormone.
   c. bicarbonate ions.
   d. aldosterone.
   e. ammonia.

3. _____ increases water reabsorption without increasing sodium reabsorption.
   a. Antidiuretic hormone
   b. Aldosterone
   c. Natriuretic peptide
   d. Parathyroid hormone
   e. Calcitonin

4. Hypotonic hydration can result from
   a. ADH hypersecretion.
   b. ADH hyposecretion.
   c. aldosterone hypersecretion.
   d. aldosterone hyposecretion.
   e. *a* and *d* only.

5. Tetanus is most likely to result from
   a. hypernatremia.
   b. hypokalemia.
   c. hyperkalemia.
   d. hypocalcemia.
   e. *c* and *d* only.

STUDY GUIDE

6. The principal determinant of intracellular osmolarity and cellular volume is
   a. protein.
   b. phosphate.
   c. potassium.
   d. sodium.
   e. chloride.

7. Increased excretion of ammonium chloride in the urine most likely indicates
   a. hypercalcemia.
   b. hyponatremia.
   c. hypochloremia.
   d. alkalosis.
   e. acidosis.

8. The most effective buffer in the intracellular fluid is
   a. phosphate.
   b. protein.
   c. bicarbonate.
   d. carbonic acid.
   e. ammonia.

9. Tubular secretion of hydrogen is directly linked to
   a. tubular secretion of potassium.
   b. tubular secretion of sodium.
   c. tubular reabsorption of potassium.
   d. tubular reabsorption of sodium.
   e. tubular secretion of chloride.

10. Hyperchloremia is most likely to result in
    a. alkalosis.
    b. acidosis.
    c. hypernatremia.
    d. hyperkalemia.
    e. hypovolemia.

11. The most abundant cation in the ECF is _____.

12. The two most abundant cations in the ICF are _____ and _____.

13. Water produced by the body's chemical reactions is called _____.

14. The skin loses water by two processes, sweating and _____.

15. Any abnormal accumulation of fluid in a particular place in the body is called _____.

16. An excessive concentration of potassium ions in the blood is called _____.

17. A deficiency of sodium ions in the blood is called _____.

18. A blood pH of 7.2 caused by inadequate pulmonary ventilation would be classified as _____.

19. Tubular secretion of hydrogen ions ceases if the acidity of the tubular fluid falls below a value called the _____.

20. Long-term satiation of thirst depends on a reduction of the _____ of the blood.

▶ Building Your Medical Vocabulary

Answers in Appendix A

State a meaning of each word element, and give a medical term from this chapter that uses it or a slight variation of it.

1. aliment-

2. -emia

3. entero-

4. kali-

5. natri-

6. para-

7. sequestr-

8. spiro-

9. trans-

10. vol-

▶ What's Wrong with These Statements?

Answers in Appendix A

Briefly explain why each of the following statements is false, or reword it to make it true.

1. Hyperkalemia lowers the resting membrane potentials of nerve and muscle cells and makes them less excitable.

2. Aldosterone promotes sodium and water retention and can therefore greatly increase blood pressure.

3. Injuries that rupture a lot of cells, such as the mangling of an arm by farm or factory machinery, tend to elevate the Na$^+$ concentration of the ECF and can thereby cause cardiac arrest.

4. The phosphate level in the ECF is very crucial to survival and must be hormonally regulated within a narrow safe range.

5. Parathyroid hormone promotes calcium and phosphate reabsorption by the kidneys.

6. The bicarbonate system buffers more acid than any other chemical buffer.

7. The more sodium the renal tubules reabsorb, the less hydrogen ion appears in the urine and the higher the urine pH tends to be.

8. The body compensates for respiratory alkalosis by increasing the respiratory rate.

9. In true dehydration, the body fluids remain isotonic although total body water is reduced.

10. Long-term quenching of thirst results primarily from wetting and cooling of the mouth when one drinks.

STUDY GUIDE

▶ Testing Your Comprehension

1. A duck hunter is admitted to the hospital with a shotgun injury to the abdomen. He has suffered extensive blood loss but is conscious. He complains of being intensely thirsty. Explain the physiological mechanism connecting his injury to his thirst.

2. A woman living at poverty level finds bottled water at the grocery store next to the infant formula. The label on the water states that it is made especially for infants, and she construes this to mean that it can be used as a nutritional supplement. The water is much cheaper than formula, so she gives her baby several ounces of bottled water a day as a substitute for formula. After several days the baby has seizures and is taken to the hospital, where it is found to have edema, acidosis, and a plasma sodium concentration of 116 mEq/L. The baby is treated with anticonvulsants followed by normal saline and recovers. Explain each of the signs.

3. Explain why the respiratory and urinary systems are both necessary for the bicarbonate buffer system to work effectively in the blood plasma.

4. A 4-year-old child is caught up in tribal warfare in Africa. In a refugee camp, the only drinking water is from a sewage-contaminated pond. The child soon develops severe diarrhea from cholera and dies 10 days later of cardiac arrest. Explain the possible physiological cause(s) of his death.

5. The left column indicates some increases or decreases in blood plasma values. In the right column, replace the question mark with an up or down arrow to indicate the expected effect. Explain each effect.

Cause	Effect
a. ↑ H_2O	? Na^+
b. ↑ Na^+	? Cl^-
c. ↓ K^+	? H^+
d. ↑ H^+	? K^+
e. ↓ Ca^{2+}	? PO_4^{3-}

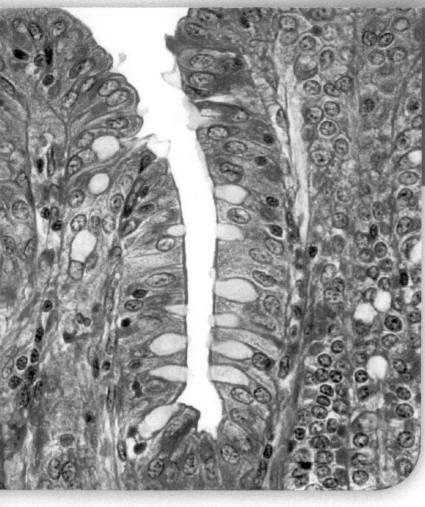

Mucosa of the small intestine
Steve Gschmeissner/Science Source

**Anatomy &
Physiology
Revealed® 4.0**

Module 12: Digestive System

- All chemical digestion consists of hydrolysis reactions, so you should understand this process and its bearing on the relationship between monomers and polymers (see section 2.4b).

- You must also know the basic structure of polysaccharides, disaccharides, triglycerides, and proteins to understand how these are digested (see section 2.4c).

- To best understand the activation and deactivation of various digestive enzymes in different regions of the digestive tract, refresh your memory on the effect of pH on enzyme action (see section 2.4f).

- The intestinal absorption of nutrients employs multiple modes of membrane transport discussed in section 3.3.

Most of the nutrients we eat cannot be used in the form found in our food. They must be broken down into smaller components, such as amino acids and monosaccharides, that are universal to all species. Consider what happens if you eat a piece of beef, for example. The myosin of beef differs very little from that of your own muscles, but the two are not identical, and even if they were, beef myosin could not be absorbed, transported in the blood, and properly installed in your muscle cells. Like any other dietary protein, it must be broken down into amino acids before it can be used. Since beef and human proteins are made of the same 20 amino acids, those of beef proteins could indeed become part of your own myosin but could equally well end up in your insulin, fibrinogen, collagen, or any other protein.

The digestive system is essentially a disassembly line—its primary purpose is to break nutrients down into forms that can be used by the body and to absorb them so they can be distributed to the tissues. The study of the digestive tract and the diagnosis and treatment of its disorders is called **gastroenterology.**[1]

25.1 General Anatomy and Digestive Processes

Expected Learning Outcomes

When you have completed this section, you should be able to

a. list the functions and major physiological processes of the digestive system;

b. distinguish between mechanical and chemical digestion;

c. identify the basic chemical process that underlies all chemical digestion, and name the major substrates and products of this process;

d. list the regions of the digestive tract and the accessory organs of the digestive system;

e. identify the layers of the digestive tract and describe its relationship to the peritoneum; and

f. describe the general nervous and chemical controls over digestive function.

25.1a Digestive Function APR

The **digestive system** is the organ system that processes food, extracts nutrients from it, and eliminates the residue. It does this in five stages:

1. **ingestion,** the selective intake of food;

2. **digestion,** the mechanical and chemical breakdown of food into a form usable by the body;

3. **absorption,** the uptake of nutrient molecules into the epithelial cells of the digestive tract and then into the blood or lymph;

4. **compaction,** absorbing water and consolidating the indigestible residue into feces; and finally,

5. **defecation,** the elimination of feces.

The digestion stage itself has two facets, mechanical and chemical. **Mechanical digestion** is the physical breakdown of food into smaller particles. It is achieved by the cutting and grinding action of the teeth and the churning contractions of the stomach. Mechanical digestion exposes more food surface to the action of digestive enzymes. **Chemical digestion** is a series of *hydrolysis* reactions that break dietary macromolecules into their monomers: polysaccharides into monosaccharides, proteins into amino acids, fats into monoglycerides and fatty acids, and nucleic acids into nucleotides. It is carried out by digestive enzymes produced by the salivary glands, stomach, pancreas, and small intestine. Some nutrients are already present in usable form in the ingested food and are absorbed without being digested: vitamins, free amino acids, minerals, cholesterol, and water.

25.1b General Anatomy

The digestive system has two anatomical subdivisions, the digestive tract and the accessory organs **(fig. 25.1).** The **digestive tract (alimentary**[2] **canal)** is a muscular tube extending from mouth to anus. It measures about 5 m (16 ft) long in a living person, but about 9 m (30 ft) in the cadaver due to the loss of muscle tone at death. It includes the mouth, pharynx, esophagus, stomach, small intestine, and large intestine. The stomach and intestines constitute the *gastrointestinal (GI) tract.* The teeth, tongue, salivary glands, liver, gallbladder, and pancreas are considered **accessory organs** of the digestive system.

The digestive tract is open to the environment at both ends. Most of the material in it hasn't entered any body tissues and is considered to be external to the body until it's absorbed by epithelial cells of the alimentary canal. In the strict sense, defecated food residue was never in the body.

---

[1]*gastro* = stomach; *entero* = intestines; *logy* = study of

[2]*aliment* = food

Most of the digestive tract follows the basic structural plan shown in **figure 25.2,** with a wall composed of the following tissue layers in order from the inner to the outer surface:

Mucosa

    Epithelium

    Lamina propria

    Muscularis mucosae

Submucosa

Muscularis externa

    Inner circular layer

    Outer longitudinal layer

Serosa

    Areolar tissue

    Mesothelium

Slight variations on this theme are found in different regions of the tract.

The inner lining of the tract, called the **mucosa** or **mucous membrane,** consists of an epithelium, a loose connective tissue layer called the **lamina propria,** and a thin layer of smooth muscle called the **muscularis mucosae** (MUSS-cue-LERR-is mew-CO-see). The epithelium is simple columnar in most of the digestive tract, but stratified squamous from the oral cavity through the esophagus and in the lower anal canal, where the tract is subject to more abrasion. The muscularis mucosae tenses the mucosa, creating grooves and ridges that enhance its surface area and contact with food. This improves the efficiency of digestion and nutrient absorption. The mucosa exhibits an abundance of lymphocytes and lymphatic nodules—the *mucosa-associated lymphatic tissue (MALT)* (see section 21.1c).

The **submucosa** is a thicker layer of loose connective tissue containing blood vessels and lymphatics, a nerve plexus, and in some places, glands that secrete lubricating mucus into the lumen. The MALT extends into the submucosa in some parts of the GI tract.

The **muscularis externa** consists of usually two layers of muscle near the outer surface. Cells of the inner layer encircle the tract while those of the outer layer run longitudinally. In some places, the circular layer is thickened to form valves (sphincters) that regulate the passage of material through the tract. The muscularis externa is responsible for the motility that propels food and residue through the digestive tract.

The **serosa** is composed of a thin layer of areolar tissue topped by a simple squamous mesothelium. The serosa begins in the lower 3 to 4 cm of the esophagus and ends just before the rectum. The pharynx, most of the esophagus, and the rectum have no serosa but are surrounded by a fibrous connective tissue layer called the **adventitia,** which blends into the adjacent connective tissue of other organs.

The esophagus, stomach, and intestines have a nervous network called the **enteric**[3] **nervous system,** which regulates

---

[3]*enter* = intestine

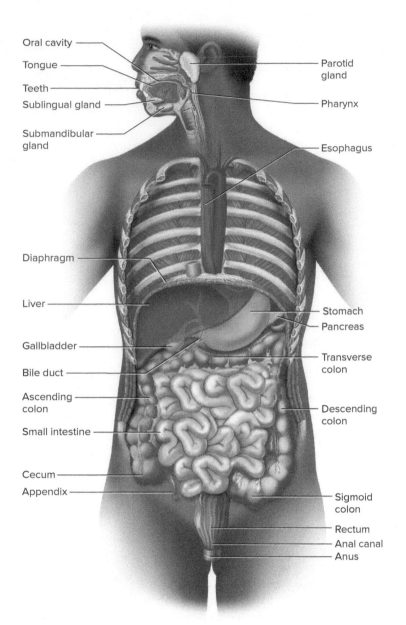

FIGURE 25.1 The Digestive System.

digestive tract motility, secretion, and blood flow. This system is thought to have over 100 million neurons—more than the spinal cord! It can function independently of the central nervous system, although the CNS usually exerts a significant influence on its action. It is usually regarded as part of the autonomic nervous system, but opinions on this vary.

The enteric nervous system is composed of two networks of neurons: the **submucosal plexus** in the submucosa and the **myenteric plexus** of parasympathetic ganglia and nerve fibers between layers of the muscularis externa. Parasympathetic preganglionic fibers of the vagus nerves terminate in the ganglia of the myenteric plexus. Postganglionic fibers arising in this plexus not only innervate the muscularis externa, but also pass through its inner circular layer and contribute to the submucosal plexus.

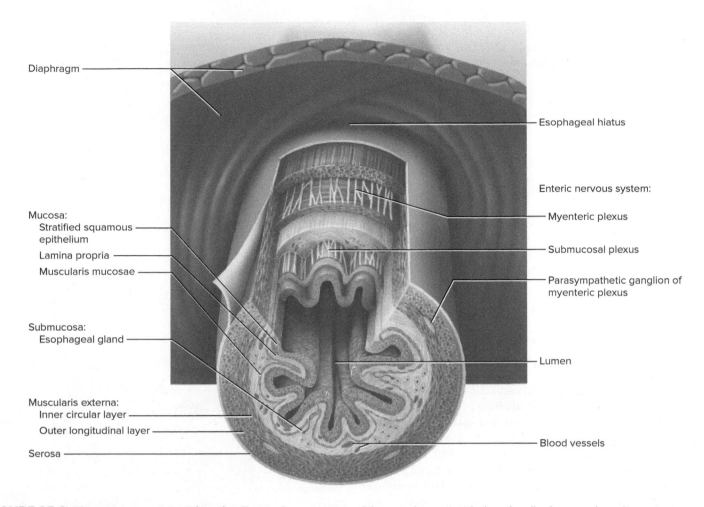

Diaphragm

Esophageal hiatus

Enteric nervous system:

Myenteric plexus

Mucosa:
  Stratified squamous
  epithelium
Lamina propria
Muscularis mucosae

Submucosal plexus

Parasympathetic ganglion of
myenteric plexus

Submucosa:
  Esophageal gland

Lumen

Muscularis externa:
  Inner circular layer
  Outer longitudinal layer

Serosa

Blood vessels

FIGURE 25.2 Tissue Layers of the Digestive Tract. Cross section of the esophagus just below the diaphragm where it meets the stomach.

The myenteric plexus controls peristalsis and other contractions of the muscularis externa, and the submucosal plexus controls movements of the muscularis mucosae and glandular secretion of the mucosa. The enteric nervous system also includes sensory neurons that monitor tension in the gut wall and conditions in the lumen.

25.1c Relationship to the Peritoneum

In processing food, the stomach and intestines undergo such strenuous contractions that they need freedom to move in the abdominal cavity. They're not tightly bound to the abdominal wall, but over most of their length, loosely suspended from it by connective tissue sheets called **mesenteries.** Mesenteries hold the abdominal viscera in their proper relationship to each other, provide passage for the blood vessels and nerves that supply the digestive tract, and contain many lymph nodes and lymphatic vessels. The small intestine is especially mobile, squirming and coiling during digestion. The mesentery prevents it from becoming twisted and tangled by its own contractions or changes in body position. Intestinal

movements are eased by the slippery peritoneal fluid that lubricates the mesenteries.

The parietal peritoneum is a serous membrane that lines the wall of the abdominal cavity. Along the posterior (dorsal) midline of the body, it turns inward and forms the **posterior mesentery,** a translucent two-layered membrane extending to the digestive tract. Upon reaching an organ such as the stomach or small intestine, the two layers of the mesentery separate and pass around opposite sides of the organ, forming the serosa. In some places, the two layers come together again on the far side of that organ and continue as another sheet of tissue, the **anterior mesentery.** This mesentery may hang freely in the abdominal cavity or attach to the anterior abdominal wall or other organs. The relationship between the mesenteries and the serosa is shown in atlas A, figures A.7 and A.8.

Two anterior mesenteries called *omenta* are associated with the stomach **(fig. 25.3).** The **lesser omentum** extends the short distance from the liver to the right superior margin *(lesser curvature)* of the stomach. The bile duct is embedded in the lesser omentum along its course between the liver and duodenum, as are

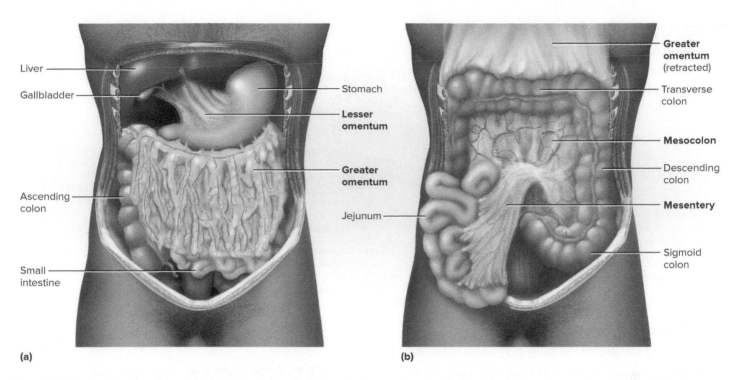

Liver

Gallbladder

Ascending colon

Small intestine

Stomach

Lesser omentum

Greater omentum

Jejunum

(a)

Greater omentum (retracted)

Transverse colon

Mesocolon

Descending colon

Mesentery

Sigmoid colon

(b)

FIGURE 25.3 Serous Membranes Associated with the Digestive Tract. (a) The greater and lesser omenta. (b) Greater omentum and small intestine retracted to show the mesocolon and mesentery. These membranes contain the mesenteric arteries and veins. **APR**

some major blood vessels leading to the liver. A much larger and fatty **greater omentum** hangs like an apron from the left inferior margin *(greater curvature)* of the stomach, loosely covering the small intestine. At its inferior margin, the greater omentum turns back on itself and passes upward, behind the superficial layer; the two layers adhere firmly to each other along most of their course. At the superior margin, the upturned layer continues as a serosa that encloses the spleen and transverse colon. From the transverse colon, it continues to the posterior abdominal wall and anchors the colon. This mesentery of the colon is called the **mesocolon.** The omenta have a loosely organized, lacy appearance due partly to their irregular distribution of adipose tissue. In obesity, much of the abdominal fat is in these mesenteries *(mesenteric fat; see* fig. 26.1).

The omenta adhere to perforations or inflamed areas of the stomach or intestines, contribute immune cells to the site, and isolate infections that might otherwise give rise to peritonitis. The greater omentum is part of the body's first line of defense against toxins and infections. Clusters of lymphatic tissue called *milky spots* in the omentum perform a "policing" function—collecting bacteria, other cells, and antigens from the peritoneal fluid and, if they detect a threat, initiating an immune response. Unfortunately, however, they fail to recognize metastatic cancer cells, which can aggregate in the omentum and turn it into a breeding ground for gastrointestinal, ovarian, and other cancers.

When an organ is enclosed by mesentery (serosa) on all sides, it is considered to be within the peritoneal cavity, or

intraperitoneal. When an organ lies against the posterior body wall and is covered by peritoneum on the anterior side only, it is said to be outside the peritoneal cavity, or **retroperitoneal.** The duodenum, most of the pancreas, and parts of the large intestine are retroperitoneal. The stomach, liver, and other parts of the small and large intestines are intraperitoneal.

25.1d Regulation of the Digestive Tract

The motility and secretion of the digestive tract are controlled by nervous, hormonal, and paracrine mechanisms. The neural controls include short and long autonomic reflexes. In **short (myenteric) reflexes,** stretching or chemical stimulation of the digestive tract acts through the myenteric plexus to stimulate contractions in nearby regions of the muscularis externa, such as the peristaltic contractions of swallowing. **Long (vagovagal) reflexes** act through autonomic nerve fibers that carry sensory signals from the digestive tract to the brainstem and motor commands back to the digestive tract. Parasympathetic fibers of the vagus nerves are especially important in stimulating digestive motility and secretion by way of these long reflexes.

The digestive tract also produces numerous hormones (such as *gastrin* and *secretin*) and paracrine secretions (such as *histamine* and *prostaglandins*) that stimulate digestive function. The hormones are secreted into the blood and stimulate relatively distant parts of the digestive tract. The paracrine secretions diffuse through the tissue fluids and stimulate nearby target cells.

BEFORE YOU GO ON

Answer the following questions to test your understanding of the preceding section:

1. What is the term for the serous membrane that suspends the intestines from the abdominal wall?

2. Which physiological process of the digestive system truly moves a nutrient from the outside to the inside of the body?

3. What one type of reaction is the basis of all chemical digestion?

4. Name some nutrients that are absorbed without being digested.

25.2 The Mouth Through Esophagus

Expected Learning Outcomes

When you have completed this section, you should be able to

a. describe the gross anatomy of the digestive tract from the mouth through the esophagus;

b. describe the composition and functions of saliva; and

c. describe the nervous control of salivation and swallowing.

25.2a The Mouth

The mouth is also known as the **oral,** or **buccal, cavity** (BUCK-ul). Its functions include ingestion (food intake), taste and other sensory responses to food, mastication (chewing), chemical digestion (starch is partially digested in the mouth), swallowing, speech, and respiration. The mouth is enclosed by the cheeks, lips, palate, and tongue **(fig. 25.4).** Its anterior opening between the lips is the **oral fissure** and its posterior opening into the throat is the **fauces**[4] (FAW-seez). The mouth is lined with stratified squamous epithelium. This epithelium is keratinized in areas subject to the greatest food abrasion, such as the gums and hard palate, and nonkeratinized in other areas such as the floor of the mouth, the soft palate, and the inside of the cheeks and lips.

The Cheeks and Lips

The cheeks and lips retain food and push it between the teeth for chewing. They are essential for articulate speech and for sucking and blowing actions, including suckling by infants. Their fleshiness is due mainly to subcutaneous fat, the buccinator muscles of the cheeks, and the orbicularis oris muscle of the lips. A median fold called the **labial frenulum**[5] attaches each lip

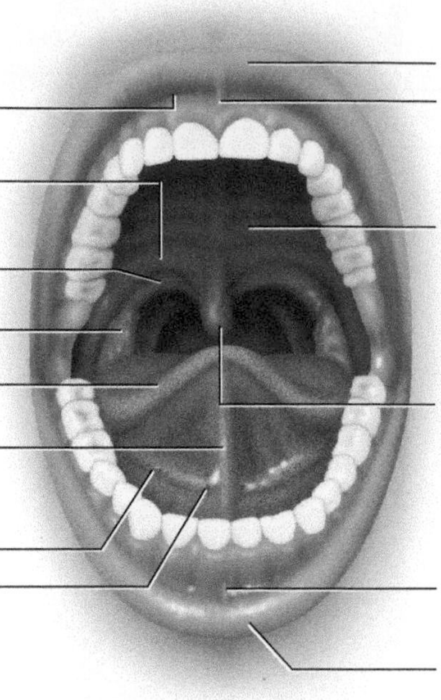

FIGURE 25.4 The Oral Cavity. For a photographic medial view, see figure B.2 in atlas B. **APR**

to the gum, anteriorly between the incisors. The **vestibule** is the space between the cheeks or lips and the teeth—the space where you insert your toothbrush when brushing the outer surfaces of your teeth.

The lips are divided into three areas: (1) The *cutaneous area* is colored like the rest of the face and has hair follicles and sebaceous glands; on the upper lip, this is where a mustache grows. (2) The *red area (vermilion)* is the hairless region where the lips meet (where one might apply lipstick). It has unusually tall dermal papillae, which allow blood capillaries and nerve endings to come closer to the epidermal surface. Thus, this area is redder and more sensitive than the cutaneous area. (3) The *labial mucosa* is the inner surface of the lip, facing the gums and teeth. It contains mucous *labial glands* that contribute to the saliva.

The Tongue

The tongue, although muscular and bulky, is a remarkably agile, sensitive, and versatile organ. It aids in food intake; it is sensitive enough to feel a stray hair or grain of sand in a bite of food and has sensory receptors for taste, texture, and temperature that are important in the acceptance or rejection of food; it compresses and breaks up food; it maneuvers food between the teeth for mastication while it avoids being bitten; it dislodges food particles from the teeth after a meal; it secretes mucus and enzymes; it compresses the chewed food into a soft mass, or *bolus,* that is easier to swallow; it initiates swallowing; and it is necessary for articulate speech. Its surface is covered with nonkeratinized

[4]*fauces* = throat
[5]*labi* = lip; *frenulum* = little bridle

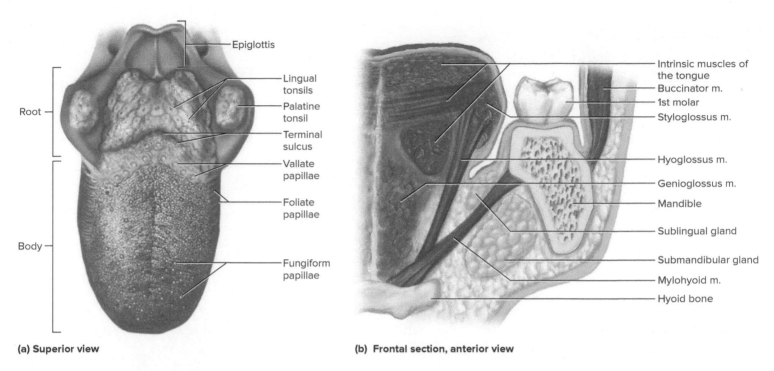

(a) Superior view

(b) Frontal section, anterior view

FIGURE 25.5 The Tongue. (a) Superior (dorsal) view. (b) Frontal section, anterior view. For a photographic sagittal section, see figure B.2 in atlas B.

stratified squamous epithelium and exhibits bumps and projections called **lingual papillae,** the site of most taste buds. The types of papillae and sense of taste are discussed in section 16.3a, and the general anatomy of the tongue is shown in **figure 25.5.**

▶▶▶**APPLY WHAT YOU KNOW**

How does proprioception protect the tongue from being bitten?

The anterior two-thirds of the tongue, called the **body,** occupies the oral cavity; and the posterior one-third, the **root,** occupies the oropharynx. The boundary between them is marked by a V-shaped row of **vallate papillae** and, behind these, a groove called the **terminal sulcus.** The body is attached to the floor of the mouth by a median fold called the **lingual frenulum.**

The muscles of the tongue, which compose most of its mass, are described in table 10.2. The **intrinsic muscles,** contained entirely within the tongue, produce the relatively subtle tongue movements of speech. The **extrinsic muscles** arise from attachments outside the tongue and produce most of the stronger tongue movements of food manipulation. The extrinsic muscles include the *genioglossus, hyoglossus, palatoglossus,* and *styloglossus* (fig. 25.5b; see also fig. 10.10). Within the tongue, amid the muscles, are serous and mucous **lingual glands,** which secrete a portion of the saliva. The **lingual tonsils** are contained in the root.

The Palate

The palate, separating the oral cavity from the nasal cavity, makes it possible to breathe while chewing food. Its anterior portion, the **hard (bony) palate,** is supported by the palatine processes of the maxillae and by the smaller palatine bones. It has transverse ridges called *palatine rugae* that aid the tongue in holding and manipulating food. Posterior to this is the **soft palate,** which has a more spongy texture and is composed mainly of skeletal muscle and glandular tissue, but no bone. It has a conical median projection, the **uvula,**[6] visible at the rear of the mouth. The uvula helps to retain food in the mouth until one is ready to swallow.

At the rear of the mouth, two muscular arches on each side begin at the roof near the uvula and descend to the floor. The anterior one is the **palatoglossal arch** and the posterior one is the **palatopharyngeal arch.** The latter arch marks the beginning of the pharynx. The palatine tonsils are located on the wall between the arches.

The Teeth

The teeth are collectively called the **dentition.** They serve to *masticate* the food, breaking it into smaller pieces. This not only makes the food easier to swallow, but also exposes more surface area to the action of digestive enzymes and thus speeds up chemical digestion. Adults normally have 16 teeth in the mandible (lower jaw) and 16 in the maxilla (upper jaw). From the midline to the rear

---

[6]*uvula* = little grape

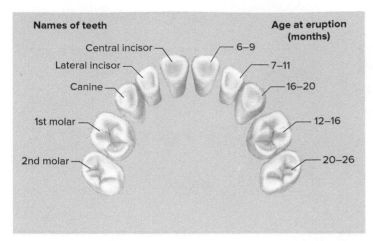

(a) Deciduous (baby) teeth

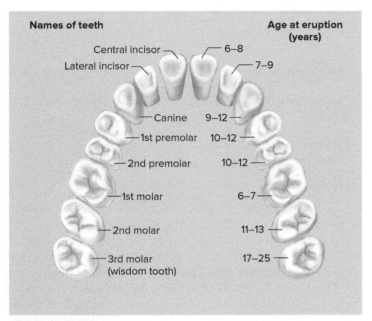

(b) Permanent teeth

FIGURE 25.6 The Dentition. (a) Deciduous (baby) teeth. (b) Permanent (adult) teeth. Each figure shows only the upper teeth. The ages at eruption are composite ages for the corresponding upper and lower teeth. Generally, the lower (mandibular) teeth erupt somewhat earlier than their upper (maxillary) counterparts. **APR**

? *Which teeth are absent from a 3-year-old child?*

of each jaw, there are two incisors, a canine, two premolars, and up to three molars on each side **(fig. 25.6).** The **incisors** are anterior, chisel-like cutting teeth used to bite off a piece of food. The **canines** are more pointed and act to puncture and shred it. They serve as weapons in many mammals but became reduced in the course of human evolution until they now project barely beyond the other teeth. The **premolars** and **molars** have relatively broad, lumpy surfaces adapted for crushing, shredding, and grinding; they are often informally called the *grinders.*

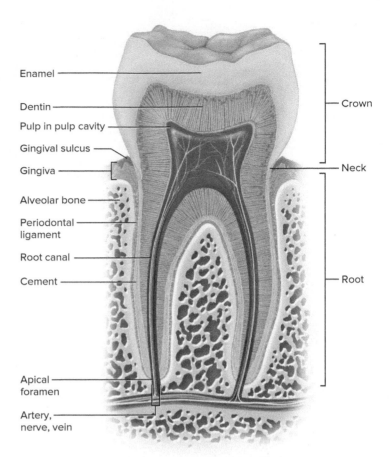

FIGURE 25.7 Structure of a Tooth and Its Alveolus. Shows typical anatomy of the tooth and periodontal tissues. This particular example is a molar.

? *Of all the components shown here, which is or are not living tissue(s)?*

Each tooth is embedded in a socket called an **alveolus,** forming a joint called a *gomphosis* between the tooth and bone **(fig. 25.7).** The alveolus is lined by a **periodontal ligament** (PERR-ee-oh-DON-tul), a modified periosteum whose collagen fibers penetrate into the bone on one side and into the tooth on the other. This anchors the tooth firmly in the alveolus but allows for slight movement under the stress of chewing. The ligament is innervated by proprioceptive nerve fibers that enable one to sense tooth movements and bite force. This sense is lost when a person has a tooth replaced by a dental implant. The gum, or **gingiva** (JIN-jih-vuh), covers the alveolar bone. Regions of a tooth are defined by their relationship to the gingiva: The **crown** is the portion above the gum attachment; the **root** is the portion below the gum, embedded in alveolar bone; and the **neck** is the point where the crown, root, and gum meet. The space between the tooth and gum is the **gingival sulcus.** The hygiene of this sulcus is especially important to dental health (see Deeper Insight 25.1). With some variation, the incisors and canines have a single root; the premolars have one or two roots; the first and second molars have two to three roots; and in the third molar, the roots are usually fused into one.

DEEPER INSIGHT 25.1

CLINICAL APPLICATION

Tooth and Gum Disease

The human mouth is home to more than 700 species of microorganisms, especially bacteria. Bacteria and sugars form a sticky residue on the teeth called *plaque.* If plaque isn't thoroughly removed by brushing and flossing, bacteria multiply, metabolize the sugars, and release lactic and other acids. These acids dissolve the minerals of enamel and dentin, and the bacteria enzymatically digest the collagen and other organic components. The eroded "cavities" of the tooth are known as *dental caries.*[7] If not repaired, caries may fully penetrate the dentin and spread to the pulp cavity. This requires either extraction of the tooth or *root canal therapy,* in which the pulp is removed and replaced with inert material.

When plaque calcifies on the tooth surface, it is called *calculus (tartar).* Calculus in the gingival sulcus wedges the tooth and gum apart and allows bacterial invasion of the sulcus. This leads to *gingivitis,* or gum inflammation. Nearly everyone has gingivitis at some time. In some cases, bacteria spread from the sulcus into the alveolar bone and begin to dissolve it, producing *periodontal disease.* About 86% of people over age 70 have some degree of periodontal disease and many suffer tooth loss as a result. This accounts for 80% to 90% of adult tooth loss.

Most of a tooth consists of hard yellowish tissue called **dentin,** covered with **enamel** in the crown and **cement** in the root. Dentin and cement are living connective tissues with cells or cell processes embedded in a calcified matrix. Cells of the cement *(cementocytes)* are scattered more or less randomly and occupy tiny cavities similar to the lacunae of bone. Cells of the dentin *(odontoblasts)* line the pulp cavity and have slender processes that travel through tiny parallel tunnels in the dentin. Enamel is not a tissue but a cell-free secretion produced before the tooth erupts above the gum. Damaged dentin and cement can regenerate, but damaged enamel cannot—it must be artificially repaired.

Internally, a tooth has a dilated **pulp cavity** in the crown and a narrow **root canal** in the lower root. These spaces are occupied by **pulp**—a mass of loose connective tissue, blood and lymphatic vessels, and nerves. These nerves and vessels enter the tooth through a pore, the **apical foramen,** at the basal end of each root canal.

The meeting of the teeth when the mouth closes is called **occlusion** and the surfaces where they meet are called the **occlusal surfaces** (ah-CLUE-zul). The occlusal surfaces of the premolars and molars have rounded bumps called **cusps**—two on each of the premolars and four to five on the molars. Cusps of the upper and lower premolars and molars mesh when the jaws are closed and slide over each other as the jaw makes lateral chewing motions. This grinds and tears food more effectively than if the occlusal surfaces were flat.

Teeth develop beneath the gums and **erupt** (emerge) in predictable order. Twenty **deciduous teeth** *(milk teeth* or *baby teeth)* erupt from the ages of 6 to 30 months, beginning with the incisors (fig. 25.6a). Between 6 and 25 years of age, these are replaced by the 32 **permanent teeth.** As a permanent tooth grows below a deciduous tooth **(fig. 25.8),** the root of the deciduous tooth dissolves and leaves little more than the crown by the time it falls out. The third molars *(wisdom teeth)* erupt around ages 17 to 25, if at all. Over the course of human evolution, the face became flatter and the jaws shorter, leaving little room for the third molars. Thus, they often remain below the gum and become *impacted*—so crowded against neighboring teeth and bone that they cannot erupt.

25.2b Mastication

Mastication (chewing) breaks food into pieces small enough to be swallowed and exposes more surface to the action of digestive enzymes. It is the first step in mechanical digestion. Mastication requires little thought because food stimulates oral receptors that trigger an automatic chewing reflex. The tongue, buccinator, and orbicularis oris muscles manipulate food and push it between the teeth. The masseter and temporalis muscles produce the up-and-down crushing action of the teeth, and the lateral and medial pterygoid muscles and masseters produce side-to-side grinding action (see fig. 10.11).

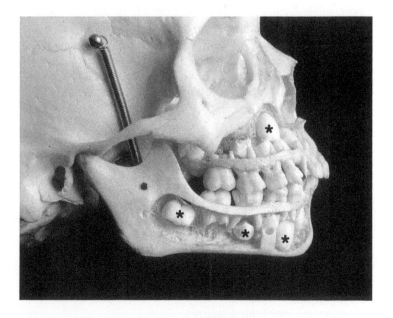

FIGURE 25.8 Permanent and Deciduous Teeth in a Child's Skull. This dissection shows erupted deciduous teeth and, deep to them and marked with asterisks, the permanent teeth waiting to erupt.

Rebecca Gray/Don Kincaid/McGraw-Hill Education

---

[7]*caries* = rottenness

25.2c Saliva and the Salivary Glands

Saliva moistens and cleanses the mouth, inhibits bacterial growth, dissolves molecules so they can stimulate the taste buds, digests a little starch and fat, and makes swallowing easier by binding the food particles into a soft mass (bolus) and lubricating it with mucus. It is a hypotonic solution of 97.0% to 99.5% water, a pH of 6.8 to 7.0, and the following solutes:

- **mucus,** which binds and lubricates the food bolus;
- **electrolytes,** salts of Na^+, K^+, Cl^-, phosphate, and bicarbonate;
- **lysozyme,** an enzyme that kills bacteria;
- **immunoglobulin A (IgA),** an antibacterial antibody;
- **salivary amylase,** an enzyme that begins starch digestion in the mouth; and
- **lingual lipase,** an enzyme that begins fat digestion in the mouth (but mainly after the food is swallowed).

The Salivary Glands

There are two kinds of salivary glands, intrinsic and extrinsic. The **intrinsic (minor) salivary glands** are an indefinite number of small glands dispersed amid the other oral tissues— *lingual glands* in the tongue, *labial glands* on the inside of the lips, *palatine glands* of the palate, and *buccal glands* on the inside of the cheeks. They secrete saliva at a fairly constant rate whether we're eating or not, but in relatively small amounts. This saliva contains lingual lipase and lysozyme and moistens the mouth when we're not eating.

The **extrinsic (major) salivary glands** are three pairs of larger, more discrete organs located outside of the oral mucosa. They are compound tubuloacinar glands (see fig. 5.31) with a tree-like duct system leading to the oral cavity **(fig. 25.9).** The secretory acini at the twig ends of the tree are in some cases purely mucous, in others purely serous, and in mixed acini, composed of both mucous and serous cells **(fig. 25.10).** Serous cells secrete a watery fluid rich in enzymes and electrolytes. The three pairs of extrinsic salivary glands are as follows:

1. The **parotid**[8] **glands** lie just beneath the skin anterior to the earlobes. The parotid duct passes superficially over the masseter muscle, pierces the buccinator muscle, and opens into the mouth opposite the second upper molar tooth. *Mumps* is a viral inflammation and swelling of the parotid glands.

2. The **submandibular glands** are located halfway along the body of the mandible, medial to its margin, just deep to the mylohyoid muscle. The submandibular duct empties into the mouth at a papilla on the side of the lingual frenulum, near the lower central incisors.

[8]*par* = next to; *ot* = ear

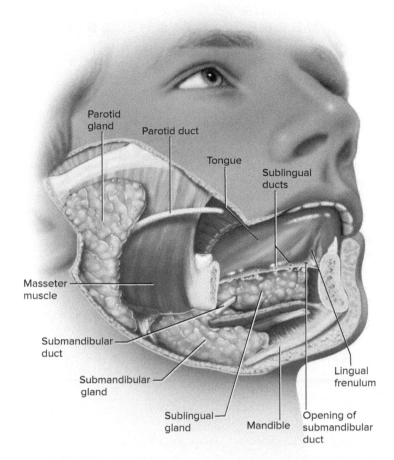

FIGURE 25.9 The Extrinsic Salivary Glands. Part of the mandible is omitted to expose the sublingual gland medial to it. **A&PR**

3. The **sublingual glands** are in the floor of the mouth. They have multiple ducts that empty into the mouth posterior to the papillae of the submandibular ducts.

Salivation

The extrinsic salivary glands secrete 1.0 to 1.5 L of saliva per day, mainly in response to food in the mouth. Salivation is controlled mainly by parasympathetic nerve fibers that originate in a group of **salivatory nuclei,** located in the brainstem near the junction of the pons and medulla oblongata. Preganglionic fibers travel from here by way of the facial and glossopharyngeal nerves to ganglia in and near the salivary glands; short postganglionic fibers then finish the path from there to the gland cells themselves (see fig. 15.7). Sympathetic nerve fibers also innervate the salivary glands, originating in the superior cervical ganglion of the sympathetic chain and following blood vessels to the glands (see fig. 15.4). Sympathetic stimulation, however, produces only slight increases in salivation, and may even inhibit it, as when fear or nervousness produces a dry mouth feeling.

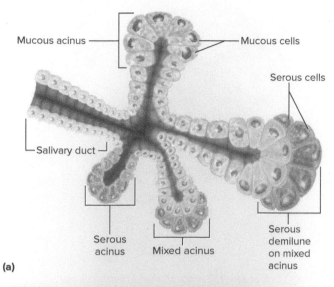

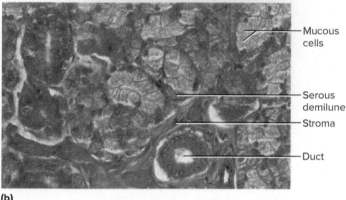

FIGURE 25.10 Microscopic Anatomy of the Salivary Glands.
(a) Duct and acini of a generalized salivary gland with a mixture of mucous and serous cells. Serous cells often form crescent-shaped caps called serous demilunes over the ends of mucous acini.
(b) Histology of the sublingual salivary gland.

b: Dennis Strete/McGraw-Hill Education

The salivatory nuclei respond to a wide variety of stimuli: the feel of food in the mouth; the flavor of food sensed by the taste buds, olfactory receptors, and free nerve endings in the oral mucosa; and the aroma, sight, or thought of food even when food isn't actually present in the mouth. Irritants in the pharynx, esophagus, stomach, and upper duodenum—spicy foods, stomach acid, and toxins, for example—also stimulate salivation. This helps to dilute and wash away irritating substances.

Parasympathetic stimulation dilates the blood vessels to the salivary glands and increases blood flow. Cells of the gland acini filter water and electrolytes from the blood and add their own secretory products to the filtrate—amylase, lingual lipase, lysozyme, and mucus. Cells of the ducts modify the electrolyte composition of the saliva. Salivary amylase begins to digest starch as the food

is chewed; lingual lipase begins fat digestion to a slight extent; and the mucus binds the masticated food particles into an easily swallowed bolus. Without mucus, one must drink much more liquid to swallow food.

25.2d The Pharynx

The pharynx, described in section 22.1b, is a muscular funnel that connects the oral cavity to the esophagus and the nasal cavity to the larynx; thus, it is a point where the digestive and respiratory tracts intersect. It has a deep layer of longitudinally oriented skeletal muscle and a superficial layer of circular skeletal muscle. The circular muscle is divided into superior, middle, and inferior **pharyngeal constrictors,** which force food downward during swallowing. When food is not being swallowed, the inferior constrictor remains contracted to exclude air from the esophagus. This constriction is regarded as the **upper esophageal sphincter,** although it isn't an anatomical feature of the esophagus. It disappears at the time of death when the muscle relaxes. Thus, it is regarded as a *physiological sphincter* rather than a constant anatomical structure.

25.2e The Esophagus

The **esophagus** is a straight muscular tube 25 to 30 cm long (see figs. 25.1, 25.2). It begins at a level between vertebra C6 and the cricoid cartilage, inferior to the larynx and posterior to the trachea. After passing downward through the mediastinum, it penetrates the diaphragm at an opening called the *esophageal hiatus,* continues another 3 to 4 cm, and meets the stomach at the level of vertebra T7. Its opening into the stomach is called the **cardial orifice** (named for its proximity to the heart). Food pauses briefly at this point before entering the stomach because of a constriction called the **lower esophageal sphincter (LES).** The LES prevents stomach contents from regurgitating into the esophagus, thus protecting the esophageal mucosa from the erosive effect of stomach acid. "Heartburn" has nothing to do with the heart, but is the burning sensation produced by acid reflux into the esophagus.

The wall of the esophagus is organized into the tissue layers described earlier, with some regional specializations. The mucosa has a nonkeratinized stratified squamous epithelium. The submucosa contains **esophageal glands** that secrete lubricating mucus into the lumen. When the esophagus is empty, the mucosa and submucosa are deeply folded into longitudinal ridges, giving the lumen a starlike shape in cross section.

The muscularis externa is composed of skeletal muscle in the upper one-third of the esophagus, a mixture of skeletal and smooth muscle in the middle one-third, and only smooth muscle in the lower one-third.

Most of the esophagus is in the mediastinum. Here, it is covered with a connective tissue adventitia that merges into the adventitias of the trachea and thoracic aorta. The short segment below the diaphragm is partially covered by a serosa.

25.2f Swallowing

Swallowing, or **deglutition** (DEE-glu-TISH-un), is a complex action involving over 22 muscles in the mouth, pharynx, and esophagus, coordinated by the **swallowing center,** a pair of nuclei in the medulla oblongata. This center communicates with muscles of the pharynx and esophagus by way of the trigeminal, facial, glossopharyngeal, and hypoglossal nerves (cranial nerves V, VII, IX, and XII). Swallowing occurs in three phases **(fig. 25.11).**

(1) The **oral phase** is under voluntary control. During chewing, the tongue collects food, presses it against the palate to form a bolus, and pushes it posteriorly. Food thus accumulates in the oropharynx in front of the blade of the epiglottis. When the bolus reaches a critical size, the epiglottis tips posteriorly and the bolus slides around it, through a space on each side, into the laryngopharynx.

(2) The **pharyngeal phase** is involuntary. The soft palate and root of the tongue block food and drink from entering the nasal cavity or reentering the mouth. To prevent choking, breathing is automatically suspended, the infrahyoid muscles pull the larynx up to meet the epiglottis and cover the laryngeal opening, and the vocal cords adduct to close the airway. These actions also widen the upper esophagus to receive the food. The pharyngeal constrictors contract in order from superior to middle to inferior, driving the bolus downward into the esophagus.

(3) The **esophageal phase** is a wave of involuntary contractions called **peristalsis,** controlled jointly by the brainstem swallowing center and the myenteric plexus in the esophageal wall. The bolus stimulates stretch receptors that feed into the plexus, which transmits signals to the muscularis externa above and below the bolus. The circular muscle layer above the bolus constricts and pushes the food downward. Below the bolus, the circular muscle relaxes while the longitudinal muscle contracts. The latter action pulls the wall of the esophagus slightly upward, making it a little shorter and dilating it to receive the descending food.

When one is standing or sitting upright, most food and liquid drop through the esophagus by gravity faster than the peristaltic wave can keep up with them. Peristalsis, however, propels more solid food pieces and ensures that you can swallow regardless of the body's position—even standing on your head! Liquid normally reaches the stomach in 1 to 2 seconds and a food bolus in 4 to 8 seconds. As a bolus reaches the lower end of the esophagus, the lower esophageal sphincter relaxes to let it pass into the stomach.

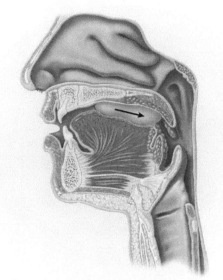

(1) **Oral phase.** The tongue forms a food bolus and pushes it into the laryngopharynx.

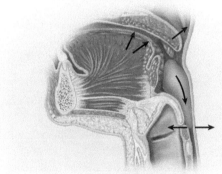

(2) **Pharyngeal phase.** The palate, tongue, vocal cords, and epiglottis block the oral and nasal cavities and airway while pharyngeal constrictors push the bolus into the esophagus.

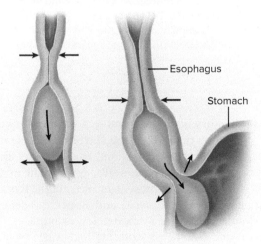

Esophagus

Stomach

(3) **Esophageal phase.** Peristalsis drives the bolus downward, and relaxation of the lower esophageal sphincter admits it into the stomach.

FIGURE 25.11 Swallowing. See numbered steps in the text for further explanation. **A&PR**

(?) *What actions prevent the pharynx from forcing food back into the mouth or nose?*

BEFORE YOU GO ON

Answer the following questions to test your understanding of the preceding section:

5. List as many functions of the tongue as you can.

6. Imagine a line from the root canal of a tooth to the adjacent bone of the mandible. Name the tissues, in order, through which this line would pass.

7. What is the difference in function and location between intrinsic and extrinsic salivary glands? Name the extrinsic salivary glands and describe their locations.

8. Identify at least two histological features of the esophagus that are especially tied to its role in swallowing.

9. Describe the mechanisms that prevent food from entering the nasal cavity and larynx during swallowing.

25.3 The Stomach APR

Expected Learning Outcomes

When you have completed this section, you should be able to

a. describe the gross and microscopic anatomy of the stomach;

b. state the function of each type of epithelial cell in the gastric mucosa;

c. identify the secretions of the stomach and state their functions;

d. explain how the stomach produces hydrochloric acid and pepsin;

e. describe the contractile responses of the stomach to food; and

f. describe the three phases of gastric function and how gastric activity is activated and inhibited.

The stomach is a muscular sac in the upper left abdominal cavity immediately inferior to the diaphragm. It functions primarily as a food storage organ, with an internal volume of about 50 mL when empty and 1.0 to 1.5 L after a typical meal. When extremely full, it may hold up to 4 L and extend nearly as far as the pelvis.

Well into the nineteenth century, authorities regarded the stomach as essentially a grinding chamber, fermentation vat, or cooking pot. Some even attributed digestion to a supernatural spirit in the stomach. We now know that it mechanically breaks up food particles, liquefies the food, and begins the chemical digestion of proteins and fat. This produces an acidic, soupy or pasty mixture of semidigested food called **chyme**[9] (pronounced

"kime"). Most digestion occurs after the chyme passes on to the small intestine.

25.3a Gross Anatomy

The stomach is J-shaped **(fig. 25.12),** relatively vertical in tall people and more nearly horizontal in short people. It is divided into four regions: (1) The **cardial part (cardia)** is a small area within about 3 cm of the cardial orifice. (2) The **fundic region (fundus)** is the dome superior to the esophageal attachment. (3) The **body** is the greatest part distal to the cardial orifice. (4) The **pyloric part** is a slightly narrower pouch at the inferior end; it is subdivided into a funnel-like **antrum**[10] and a narrower **pyloric canal.** The latter terminates at the **pylorus,**[11] a narrow passage into the duodenum. The pylorus is surrounded by a thick ring of smooth muscle, the **pyloric sphincter,** which regulates the passage of chyme into the duodenum.

Between the esophagus and duodenum, the stomach has two margins called the **greater** and **lesser curvatures.** The greater curvature is the long way around, about 40 cm, along the inferolateral surface. The greater omentum, overhanging the small intestine, is suspended from the greater curvature. The lesser curvature is the shorter distance from esophagus to duodenum, about 10 cm, along the superomedial margin facing the liver. The lesser omentum spans the space between the liver and lesser curvature (see fig. 25.3).

25.3b Innervation and Circulation

The stomach receives parasympathetic nerve fibers from the vagus nerves and sympathetic fibers from the celiac ganglia (see table 15.2). It is supplied with blood by branches of the celiac trunk (see section 20.7f, fig. 20.34c). All blood drained from the stomach and intestines enters the hepatic portal circulation and filters through the liver before returning to the heart.

25.3c Microscopic Anatomy

The stomach wall has tissue layers similar to those of the esophagus, with some variations. The mucosa is covered with a simple columnar glandular epithelium **(fig. 25.13).** The apical regions of its cells are filled with mucin; after it is secreted, mucin swells with water and becomes mucus. The mucosa and submucosa are flat and smooth when the stomach is full, but as it empties, these layers form conspicuous longitudinal wrinkles called **gastric rugae**[12] (ROO-jee). The lamina propria is almost entirely occupied by tubular glands, to be described shortly. The muscularis externa has three layers, rather than two: outer longitudinal, middle circular, and inner oblique layers (fig. 25.12).

---

[9]*chyme* = juice

[10]*antrum* = cavity
[11]*pylorus* = gatekeeper
[12]*rugae* = folds, creases

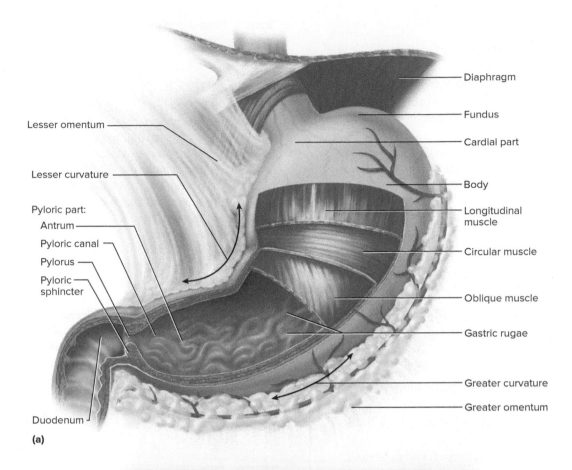

(a)

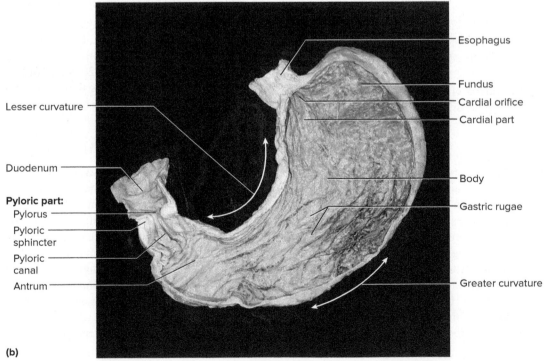

(b)

FIGURE 25.12 The Stomach. (a) Gross anatomy. (b) Photograph of the internal surface. **APR**

b: Rebecca Gray/McGraw-Hill Education

❓ *How does the muscularis externa of the stomach differ from that of the esophagus?*

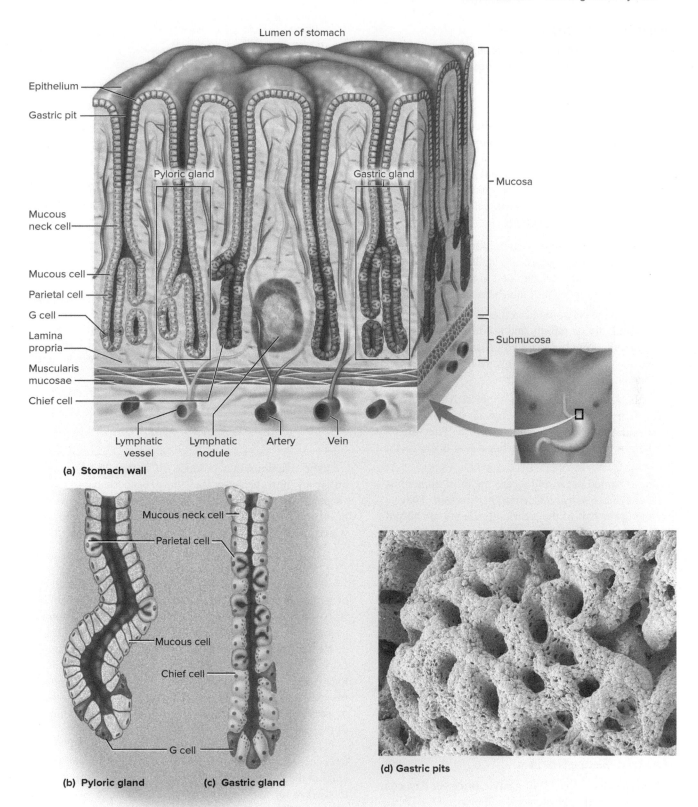

Lumen of stomach

Epithelium

Gastric pit

Pyloric gland

Gastric gland

Mucosa

Mucous neck cell

Mucous cell

Parietal cell

G cell

Lamina propria

Muscularis mucosae

Chief cell

Submucosa

Lymphatic vessel

Lymphatic nodule

Artery

Vein

(a) Stomach wall

Mucous neck cell

Parietal cell

Mucous cell

Chief cell

G cell

(b) Pyloric gland

(c) Gastric gland

(d) Gastric pits

FIGURE 25.13 Mucosa of the Stomach Wall. (a) Layers of the mucosa. (b) A pyloric gland from the inferior end of the stomach. Note the absence of chief cells and relatively few parietal cells. (c) A gastric gland, the most widespread type in the stomach. (d) Openings of the gastric pits into the stomach, surrounded by the rounded apical surfaces of the columnar epithelial cells of the mucosa (SEM). **APR**

d: Steve Gschmeissner/Science Source

Contrast the epithelium of the esophagus with that of the stomach. Why is each epithelial type best suited to the function of its respective organ?

The gastric mucosa is pocked with depressions called **gastric pits** lined with the same columnar epithelium as the surface (fig. 25.13). Two or three tubular glands open into the bottom of each gastric pit and span the rest of the lamina propria. In the cardial and pyloric regions, they are called **cardial glands** and **pyloric glands,** respectively. In the rest of the stomach, they are called **gastric glands.** These three glands differ in cellular composition, but collectively have the following cell types:

- **Mucous cells,** which secrete mucus, predominate in the cardial and pyloric glands. In gastric glands, they are called *mucous neck cells* and are concentrated in the narrow *neck* of the gland, where it opens into the gastric pit.

- **Regenerative (stem) cells,** found in the base of the pit and neck of the gland, divide rapidly and produce a continual supply of new cells. Newly generated cells migrate upward to the gastric surface as well as downward into the glands to replace cells that die.

- **Parietal cells,** found mostly in the upper half of the gland, secrete *hydrochloric acid, intrinsic factor,* and an appetite-stimulating hormone called *ghrelin.* They are found mostly in the gastric glands, but a few occur in the pyloric glands.

- **Chief cells,** so named because they are the most numerous, secrete the enzymes *gastric lipase* and *pepsinogen.* They dominate the lower half of the gastric glands but are absent from cardial and pyloric glands.

- **Enteroendocrine cells,** concentrated especially in the lower end of a gland, secrete hormones and paracrine messengers that regulate digestion. They occur in all regions of the stomach, but are most abundant in the gastric and pyloric glands. There are at least eight kinds of enteroendocrine cells in the stomach, each of which produces a different chemical messenger.

In general, the cardial and pyloric glands secrete mainly mucus; acid and enzyme secretion occur predominantly in the gastric glands; and hormones are secreted throughout the stomach.

25.3d Gastric Secretions

The gastric glands produce 2 to 3 L of **gastric juice** per day, composed mainly of water, hydrochloric acid, and pepsin.

Hydrochloric Acid

Gastric juice has a high concentration of hydrochloric acid (HCl) and a pH as low as 0.8. This is more acidic than the battery acid of a car and low enough to dissolve tooth enamel or cause a chemical burn on the skin. How, then, does the stomach produce and tolerate such acidity?

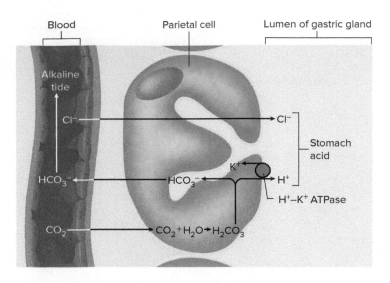

FIGURE 25.14 The Mechanism of Hydrochloric Acid Secretion. The parietal cell combines water with CO_2 from the blood to form carbonic acid (bottom line of figure). Carbonic acid breaks down into bicarbonate ion (HCO_3^-) and hydrogen ion (H^+). HCO_3^- returns to the blood. In exchange, Cl^- enters the lumen with H^+ and the two form hydrochloric acid.

❓ *What role does active transport play in this process?*

The reactions that produce HCl **(fig. 25.14)** may seem familiar by now because they have been discussed in previous chapters—most recently in connection with renal excretion of H^+ in section 24.3c. Parietal cells contain carbonic anhydrase (CAH), which catalyzes the first step in the following reaction:

$$CO_2 + H_2O \xrightarrow{\text{CAH}} H_2CO_3 \longrightarrow HCO_3^- + H^+.$$

Parietal cells pump the H^+ from this reaction into the lumen of a gastric gland by an active-transport protein similar to the Na^+–K^+ pump, called **H^+–K^+ ATPase.** This is an antiport that uses the energy of ATP to pump H^+ out of the cell and K^+ into it. HCl secretion doesn't affect the pH within the parietal cell because H^+ is pumped out as fast as it is generated. The bicarbonate ions (HCO_3^-) are exchanged for chloride ions (Cl^-) from the blood plasma—the same *chloride-shift* process that occurs in the renal tubules and red blood cells—and the Cl^- is pumped into the lumen of the gastric gland to join the H^+.

Thus, HCl accumulates in the stomach while bicarbonate ions accumulate in the blood. Because of the bicarbonate, blood leaving the stomach has a higher pH when digestion is occurring than when the stomach is empty. This high-pH blood is called the *alkaline tide.*

Stomach acid has several functions: (1) It activates the enzymes pepsin and lingual lipase, as discussed shortly. (2) It breaks up connective tissues and plant cell walls, helping to liquefy food and form chyme. (3) It converts ingested ferric ions (Fe^{3+}) to ferrous ions (Fe^{2+}), a form of iron that can be absorbed and used for hemoglobin synthesis. (4) It contributes to innate immunity by destroying most ingested pathogens.

Pepsin

Several digestive enzymes are secreted as inactive proteins called **zymogens** and then converted to active enzymes by the removal of some of their amino acids. In the stomach, chief cells secrete a zymogen called **pepsinogen.** Hydrochloric acid removes some of its amino acids and converts it to **pepsin.** Since pepsin digests protein, and pepsinogen itself is a protein, pepsin has an *autocatalytic* effect—as some pepsin is formed, it converts pepsinogen into more pepsin **(fig. 25.15).** The ultimate function of pepsin, however, is to digest dietary proteins to shorter peptide chains, which then pass to the small intestine, where their digestion is completed.

Gastric Lipase

The chief cells also secrete **gastric lipase.** This enzyme and lingual lipase, which plays a minor role, digest 10% to 15% of the dietary fat in the stomach. The remainder is digested in the small intestine.

Intrinsic Factor

Parietal cells secrete a glycoprotein called **intrinsic factor** that is essential for the absorption of vitamin B_{12} by the small intestine. Intrinsic factor binds vitamin B_{12} and the intestinal cells then absorb this complex by receptor-mediated endocytosis. Without vitamin B_{12}, hemoglobin cannot be synthesized and anemia develops. The secretion of intrinsic factor is the only indispensable function of the stomach. Digestion can continue following removal of the stomach *(gastrectomy),* but a person usually must then take vitamin B_{12} by injection, or vitamin B_{12} and intrinsic factor orally. As we age, the gastric mucosa atrophies and less intrinsic factor is secreted, increasing the risk of anemia. Some people, especially in old age, develop *pernicious anemia,* the result of an autoimmune disease that destroys gastric mucosa and reduces intrinsic factor secretion.

Chemical Messengers

The gastric and pyloric glands have various kinds of enteroendocrine cells that collectively produce as many as 20 hormones and paracrine signals. Several of them are peptides produced in both the digestive tract and the central nervous system; thus, they are called **gut–brain peptides.** These include substance P, vasoactive intestinal peptide (VIP), secretin, gastric inhibitory peptide (GIP), cholecystokinin, and neuropeptide Y (NPY). The functions of some of these peptides in digestion will be explained in the following sections, and their roles in appetite regulation are discussed in the next chapter (section 26.1b).

Several of the gastric secretions are summarized in **table 25.1.** Some of the functions listed there are explained later in the chapter.

25.3e Gastric Motility

As you begin to swallow, food stimulates mechanoreceptors in the pharynx and they transmit signals to the medulla oblongata. The medulla relays signals to the stomach by way of the vagus nerves. The stomach reacts with a **receptive-relaxation response,** in

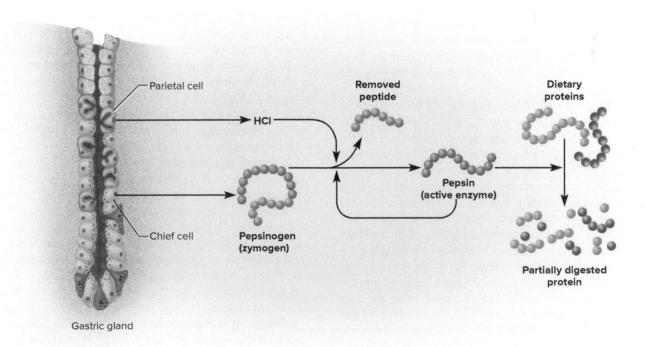

FIGURE 25.15 The Production and Action of Pepsin. The chief cells secrete pepsinogen and the parietal cells secrete HCl. HCl removes some of the amino acids from pepsinogen and converts it to pepsin. Pepsin catalyzes the production of more pepsin (an autocatalytic effect), as well as partially digesting dietary protein.

TABLE 25.1	Major Secretions of the Gastric Glands	
Secretory Cells	**Secretion**	**Function**
Mucous neck cells	Mucus	Protects mucosa from HCl and enzymes
Parietal cells	Hydrochloric acid	Activates pepsin and lingual lipase; helps liquefy food; reduces dietary iron to usable form (Fe^{2+}); destroys ingested pathogens
	Intrinsic factor	Enables small intestine to absorb vitamin B_{12}
Chief cells	Pepsinogen	Converted to pepsin, which digests protein
	Gastric lipase	Digests fat
Enteroendocrine cells	Gastrin	Stimulates gastric glands to secrete HCl and enzymes; stimulates intestinal motility; relaxes ileal papilla
	Serotonin	Stimulates gastric motility
	Histamine	Stimulates HCl secretion
	Somatostatin	Inhibits gastric secretion and motility; delays emptying of stomach; inhibits secretion by pancreas; inhibits gallbladder contraction and bile secretion; reduces blood circulation and nutrient absorption in small intestine
	Gut–brain peptides	Various roles in short- and long-term appetite regulation and energy balance

which it briefly resists stretching but then relaxes to accommodate the arriving food.

Soon, the stomach shows a rhythm of peristaltic contractions governed by a *basic electrical rhythm* set off by **enteric pacemaker cells** in the muscularis externa. The upper stomach (fundus) doesn't participate in these, but below the fundus, around midbody, a tight ring of constriction appears about every 20 seconds and progresses downward toward the antrum, becoming stronger as it goes. After food has been in the stomach for 30 minutes or so, these contractions become especially intense. They churn the food, mix it with gastric juice, and promote its physical breakup and chemical digestion.

The antrum holds about 30 mL of chyme at a time. The muscularis is thickest here, and acts as a strong *antral pump* that breaks up semidigested food into smaller particles and prepares it for the small intestine. A leading wave of antral contraction proceeds to the pyloric valve and closes it tightly. A trailing wave then comes along, churning and breaking up the chyme. Chyme jets backward through the trailing constriction into the gastric body, where it awaits the next wave of contraction to drive it down again. The repetitive downward propulsion and reverse jetting of chyme break the food into smaller and smaller particles. Food particles are not allowed to pass into the duodenum until they are reduced to 1 to 7 mm in size, and only about 3 mL of chyme is squirted into the duodenum at a time. Allowing only small amounts into the duodenum enables the duodenum to neutralize the stomach acid and digest nutrients little by little. If the duodenum becomes overfilled, it inhibits gastric motility and postpones receiving more chyme; the mechanism for this is discussed later. A typical meal is emptied from the stomach in about 4 hours, but it takes less time if the meal is more liquid, longer if the stomach contents are more acidic, and as long as 6 hours if the meal is high in fat.

25.3f Vomiting

Vomiting is the forceful ejection of stomach and intestinal contents (chyme) from the mouth. It involves multiple muscular actions integrated by the **emetic**[13] **center** of the medulla oblongata. Vomiting is commonly induced by overstretching of the stomach or duodenum; chemical irritants such as alcohol and bacterial toxins; visceral trauma (especially to the pelvic organs); intense pain; or psychological and sensory stimuli that activate the emetic center (thus, vomiting can be induced by repugnant sights, smells, and thoughts).

Vomiting is usually preceded by nausea and retching. In **retching,** thoracic expansion and abdominal contraction create a pressure difference that dilates the esophagus. The lower esophageal sphincter relaxes while the stomach and duodenum contract spasmodically. Chyme enters the esophagus but then drops back into the stomach as the muscles relax; it doesn't get past the upper esophageal sphincter. Retching is often accompanied by tachycardia, profuse salivation, and sweating. Vomiting occurs when abdominal contraction and rising thoracic pressure force the upper esophageal sphincter open, the esophagus and body of the stomach relax, and chyme is driven out of the stomach and mouth by strong abdominal contraction combined with reverse peristalsis of the gastric antrum and duodenum. **Projectile vomiting** is sudden vomiting with no prior nausea or retching. It may be caused by neurological lesions but is also common in infants after feeding.

Chronic vomiting can cause dangerous fluid, electrolyte, and acid–base imbalances. In cases of frequent vomiting, as in the eating disorder *bulimia,* the tooth enamel becomes severely eroded

---

[13]*emet* = vomiting

by the hydrochloric acid in the chyme. Aspiration (inhalation) of this acid is very destructive to the respiratory tract. Many have died from aspiration of vomit when they were unconscious or semiconscious. This is the reason that surgical anesthesia, which may induce nausea, must be preceded by fasting until the stomach and small intestine are empty.

25.3g Digestion and Absorption

Salivary and gastric enzymes partially digest protein and lesser amounts of starch and fat in the stomach, but most digestion and nearly all nutrient absorption occur after the chyme passes into the small intestine. The stomach doesn't absorb any significant amount of nutrients but does absorb aspirin and some lipid-soluble drugs. Alcohol is absorbed mainly by the small intestine, so its intoxicating effect depends partly on how rapidly the stomach is emptied.

25.3h Protection of the Stomach

One might think that the stomach would be its own worst enemy; it is, after all, made of meat. Some people enjoy haggis and tripe, dishes made from animal stomachs, and have no difficulty digesting those. Why, then, doesn't the human stomach digest itself? The answer is that the living stomach is protected

in three ways from the harsh acidic and enzymatic environment it creates:

1. **Mucous coat.** The thick, highly alkaline mucus resists the action of acid and enzymes.
2. **Tight junctions.** The epithelial cells are joined by tight junctions that prevent gastric juice from seeping between them and digesting the connective tissue below.
3. **Epithelial cell replacement.** In spite of these other protections, the stomach's epithelial cells live only 3 to 6 days and are then sloughed off into the chyme and digested with the food. They are replaced just as rapidly, however, by cell division in the gastric pits.

The breakdown of these protective mechanisms can result in inflammation and peptic ulcer (see Deeper Insight 25.2).

25.3i Regulation of Gastric Function

The nervous and endocrine systems collaborate to increase gastric secretion and motility when food is eaten and to suppress them as the stomach empties. Gastric activity is divided into three stages called the *cephalic, gastric,* and *intestinal phases,* based on whether the stomach is being controlled by the brain, by itself,

---

 DEEPER INSIGHT 25.2

CLINICAL APPLICATION

Peptic Ulcer

Inflammation of the stomach, called *gastritis,* can lead to a *peptic ulcer* as pepsin and hydrochloric acid erode the stomach wall **(fig. 25.16).** Peptic ulcers occur even more commonly in the duodenum and occasionally in the esophagus. If untreated, they can perforate the organ and cause fatal hemorrhaging, or perforate the organ and cause peritonitis—both potentially fatal. Most such fatalities occur in people over age 65.

There is no evidence to support the popular belief that peptic ulcers result from psychological stress. Hypersecretion of acid and pepsin is sometimes involved, but even normal secretion can cause ulceration if the mucosal defense is compromised by other causes. Most ulcers involve an acid-resistant bacterium, *Helicobacter pylori,* that invades the mucosa of the stomach and duodenum and opens the way to chemical damage to the tissue. Other risk factors include smoking and the use of aspirin and other nonsteroidal anti-inflammatory drugs (NSAIDs). NSAIDs suppress the synthesis of prostaglandins, which normally stimulate the secretion of protective mucus and acid-neutralizing bicarbonate.

At one time, the most widely prescribed drug in the United States was cimetidine (Tagamet), which was designed to treat peptic ulcers by reducing acid secretion. Histamine stimulates acid secretion by binding to sites on the parietal cells called H_2 *receptors;* cimetidine, an H_2 *blocker,* prevents this binding. Lately, however, ulcers have been treated more successfully with antibiotics against *Helicobacter* combined with bismuth suspensions such as Pepto-Bismol. This is a much shorter and less expensive course of treatment and permanently cures about 90% of peptic ulcers, as compared with a cure rate of only 20% to 30% for H_2 blockers.

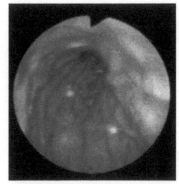 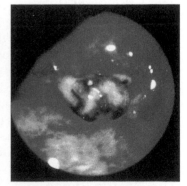

(a) Normal   **(b) Peptic ulcer**

FIGURE 25.16 Endoscopic Views of the Gastroesophageal Junction. The esophagus can be seen opening into the cardial stomach. (a) A view of the cardial orifice from above, showing a healthy esophageal mucosa. The small white spots are reflections of light from the endoscope. (b) A bleeding peptic ulcer. A peptic ulcer typically has an oval shape and yellow-white color. Here the yellowish floor of the ulcer is partially obscured by black blood clots, and fresh blood is visible around the margin of the ulcer.

a, b: CNRI/Science Source

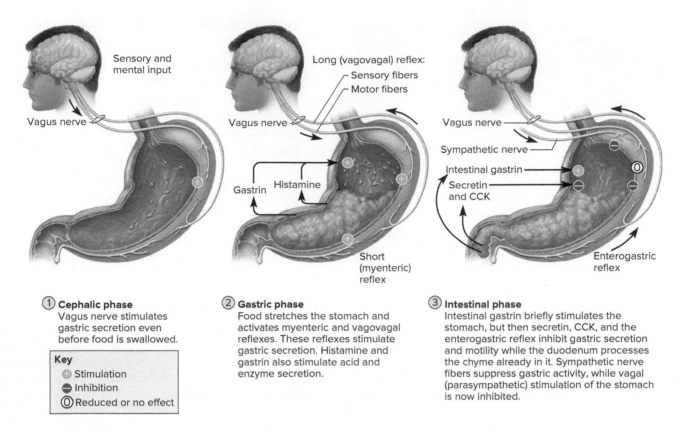

FIGURE 25.17 Neural and Hormonal Control of the Stomach.

① **Cephalic phase**
Vagus nerve stimulates gastric secretion even before food is swallowed.

Key
⊕ Stimulation
⊖ Inhibition
Ⓞ Reduced or no effect

② **Gastric phase**
Food stretches the stomach and activates myenteric and vagovagal reflexes. These reflexes stimulate gastric secretion. Histamine and gastrin also stimulate acid and enzyme secretion.

③ **Intestinal phase**
Intestinal gastrin briefly stimulates the stomach, but then secretin, CCK, and the enterogastric reflex inhibit gastric secretion and motility while the duodenum processes the chyme already in it. Sympathetic nerve fibers suppress gastric activity, while vagal (parasympathetic) stimulation of the stomach is now inhibited.

or by the small intestine, respectively **(fig. 25.17).** These phases overlap and all three can occur simultaneously.

The Cephalic Phase

The **cephalic phase** is the stage in which the stomach responds to the mere sight, smell, taste, or thought of food, even before food enters the stomach. These sensory and mental inputs converge on the hypothalamus, which relays signals to the medulla oblongata. Vagus nerve fibers from the medulla stimulate the enteric nervous system of the stomach, which, in turn, stimulates secretion by the parietal cells (acid) and G cells (gastrin). About 40% of the stomach's acid secretion occurs in the cephalic phase. This prepares the stomach to receive and process food.

The Gastric Phase

The **gastric phase** is a period in which swallowed food and semidigested protein (peptides and amino acids) activate gastric activity. About one-half of acid secretion and two-thirds of total gastric secretion occur during this phase. Ingested food stimulates gastric activity in two ways: by stretching the stomach and by raising the pH of its contents. Stretch activates two reflexes: a short reflex mediated through the myenteric plexus and a long reflex mediated through the vagus nerves and brainstem.

Gastric secretion is stimulated chiefly by three chemicals: acetylcholine (ACh), histamine, and gastrin. ACh is secreted by

parasympathetic nerve fibers of both the short and long reflex pathways. Histamine is a paracrine secretion from enteroendocrine cells in the gastric glands. **Gastrin** is a hormone produced by enteroendocrine **G cells** in the pyloric glands. All three of these signals stimulate parietal cells to secrete hydrochloric acid and intrinsic factor. The chief cells secrete pepsinogen in response to gastrin and especially ACh, and ACh also stimulates mucus secretion.

As dietary protein is digested, it breaks down into smaller peptides and amino acids, which directly stimulate the G cells to secrete even more gastrin—a positive feedback loop that accelerates protein digestion **(fig. 25.18).** Small peptides also buffer stomach acid so the pH doesn't fall excessively low. But as digestion continues and these peptides are emptied from the stomach, the pH drops lower and lower. Below pH of 2, stomach acid inhibits the parietal cells and G cells—a negative feedback loop that winds down the gastric phase as the need for pepsin and HCl declines.

The Intestinal Phase

The **intestinal phase** begins when chyme starts arriving in the duodenum; it enables the duodenum to control the rate of gastric emptying so the duodenum has time to process the chyme and is not overwhelmed by a sudden overload. This phase is mediated by both hormonal and nervous reflexes.

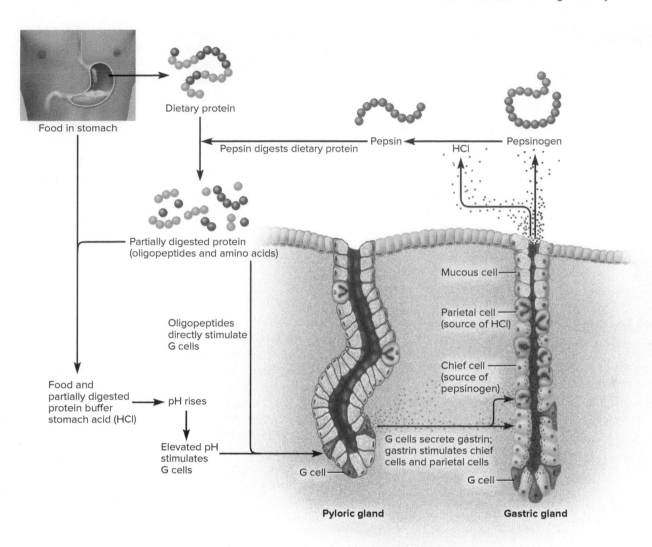

Dietary protein

Food in stomach

Pepsin digests dietary protein

Pepsin ← HCl ← Pepsinogen

Partially digested protein
(oligopeptides and amino acids)

Oligopeptides
directly stimulate
G cells

Food and
partially digested
protein buffer
stomach acid (HCl) → pH rises

Elevated pH
stimulates
G cells

G cell

Pyloric gland

Mucous cell

Parietal cell
(source of HCl)

Chief cell
(source of
pepsinogen)

G cells secrete gastrin;
gastrin stimulates chief
cells and parietal cells

G cell

Gastric gland

FIGURE 25.18 Feedback Control of Gastric Secretion. Note the positive feedback loop: Pepsin digests dietary protein; partially digested protein and ingested food raise the pH in the stomach; the elevated pH stimulates G cells to secrete gastrin; gastrin stimulates the gastric glands to secrete more pepsinogen and hydrochloric acid (HCl); pepsin production increases; and food digestion is accelerated. In addition to the feedback mechanism shown here, acetylcholine from parasympathetic fibers of the vagus nerves and histamine from the G cells of the gastric glands also powerfully stimulate pepsinogen and HCl secretion.

Initially, the duodenum enhances gastric secretion. Stretching of the duodenum accentuates vagovagal reflexes that stimulate the stomach, and peptides and amino acids in the chyme stimulate G cells of the duodenum to secrete **intestinal gastrin,** which further stimulates the stomach.

Soon, however, the acid and semidigested fats in the duodenum trigger the **enterogastric reflex**—the duodenum sends inhibitory signals to the stomach by way of the enteric nervous system, and sends signals to the medulla that (1) inhibit the vagal nuclei, thus reducing vagal stimulation of the stomach; and (2) stimulate sympathetic neurons, which send inhibitory signals to the stomach. Chyme also stimulates duodenal enteroendocrine cells to release **secretin** and **cholecystokinin (CCK)**

(CO-leh-SIS-toe-KY-nin). They primarily stimulate the pancreas and gallbladder, but also suppress gastric secretion and motility. The effect of this is that gastrin secretion declines and the pyloric sphincter contracts tightly to limit the admission of more chyme into the duodenum. This gives the duodenum time to work on the chyme it has already received before being loaded with more.

The enteroendocrine cells also secrete **glucose-dependent insulinotropic peptide (GIP).** Originally called *gastric-inhibitory peptide* (the original source of the GIP abbreviation), it is no longer thought to have a significant effect on the stomach, but seems more concerned with stimulating insulin secretion in preparation for processing the nutrients about to be absorbed by the small intestine.

Answer the following questions to test your understanding of the preceding section:

10. Name four types of epithelial cells of the gastric and pyloric glands and state what each one secretes.

11. Explain how the gastric glands produce hydrochloric acid and why this produces an alkaline tide.

12. What positive feedback cycle can you identify in the formation and action of pepsin?

13. How does food in the duodenum inhibit motility and secretion in the stomach?

25.4 The Liver, Gallbladder, and Pancreas

Expected Learning Outcomes

When you have completed this section, you should be able to

a. describe the gross and microscopic anatomy of the liver, gallbladder, bile duct system, and pancreas;

b. describe the digestive secretions and functions of the liver, gallbladder, and pancreas; and

c. explain how hormones regulate secretion by the liver and pancreas.

The small intestine receives not only chyme from the stomach but also secretions from the liver and pancreas, which enter the digestive tract near the junction of the stomach and small intestine. These secretions are so important to the digestive processes of the small intestine that it is necessary to understand them before we move on to intestinal physiology.

25.4a The Liver **APR**

The liver (**fig. 25.19**) is a reddish brown gland located immediately inferior to the diaphragm, filling most of the right hypochondriac and epigastric regions. It is the body's largest gland, weighing about 1.4 kg (3 lb). It has a tremendous variety of functions, but only one of them, the secretion of bile, contributes to digestion. Others are discussed in the following chapter (see table 26.6), which provides a more thorough physiological basis for understanding nondigestive liver functions.

Gross Anatomy

The liver has four lobes called the right, left, quadrate, and caudate lobes. From an anterior view, we see only a large **right lobe** and smaller **left lobe.** They are separated from each other by the **falciform**[14] **ligament,** a sheet of mesentery that suspends the liver from the diaphragm and anterior abdominal wall. The **round ligament (ligamentum teres),** also visible anteriorly, is a fibrous remnant of the umbilical vein, which carries blood from the umbilical cord to the liver of a fetus.

From the inferior view, we also see a squarish **quadrate lobe** next to the gallbladder and a tail-like **caudate**[15] **lobe** posterior to that. An irregular opening between these lobes, the **porta hepatis,**[16] is a point of entry for the hepatic portal vein and proper hepatic artery and a point of exit for the bile passages, all of which travel in the lesser omentum. The gallbladder adheres to a depression on the inferior surface of the liver between the right and quadrate lobes. The posterior aspect of the liver has a deep sulcus that accommodates the inferior vena cava. The superior surface has a *bare area* where it is attached to the diaphragm. The rest of the liver is covered by a serosa.

Microscopic Anatomy

The interior of the liver is filled with innumerable cylinders called **hepatic lobules,** about 2 mm long by 1 mm in diameter. A lobule consists of a **central vein** passing down its core, surrounded by radiating plates of cuboidal cells called **hepatocytes (fig. 25.20).** Imagine spreading a book wide open until its front and back covers touch. The pages of the book would fan out around the spine somewhat like the plates of hepatocytes fan out from the central vein of a liver lobule.

Each plate of hepatocytes is an epithelium one or two cells thick. The spaces between the plates are blood-filled channels called **hepatic sinusoids.** These are lined by a fenestrated endothelium that separates the hepatocytes from the blood cells, but allows blood plasma into the space between the hepatocytes and endothelium. The hepatocytes have a brush border of microvilli that project into this space. Blood filtering through the sinusoids comes directly from the stomach and intestines. After a meal, the hepatocytes absorb glucose, amino acids, iron, vitamins, and other nutrients from it for metabolism or storage. They also remove and degrade hormones, toxins, bile pigments, and drugs. At the same time, they secrete albumin, lipoproteins, clotting factors, angiotensinogen, and other products into the blood. Between meals, they break down stored glycogen and release glucose into the circulation. The sinusoids also contain phagocytic cells called **stellate macrophages,** which remove bacteria and debris from the blood.

The liver secretes bile into narrow channels, the **bile canaliculi,** between the back-to-back layers of hepatocytes within each plate. Bile passes from there into small **bile ductules** between the lobules, and these converge to ultimately form **right** and **left hepatic ducts.** They converge on the inferior side of the liver to form the **common hepatic duct.** A short distance farther on, this is joined by the **cystic duct** coming from the gallbladder (**fig. 25.21**). Their union forms the **bile duct,** which descends through the lesser omentum toward the duodenum. Near the duodenum, the bile duct joins the duct of the pancreas

---

[14]*falci* = sickle; *form* = shape

[15]*caud* = tail

[16]*porta* = gateway, entrance; *hepatis* = of the liver

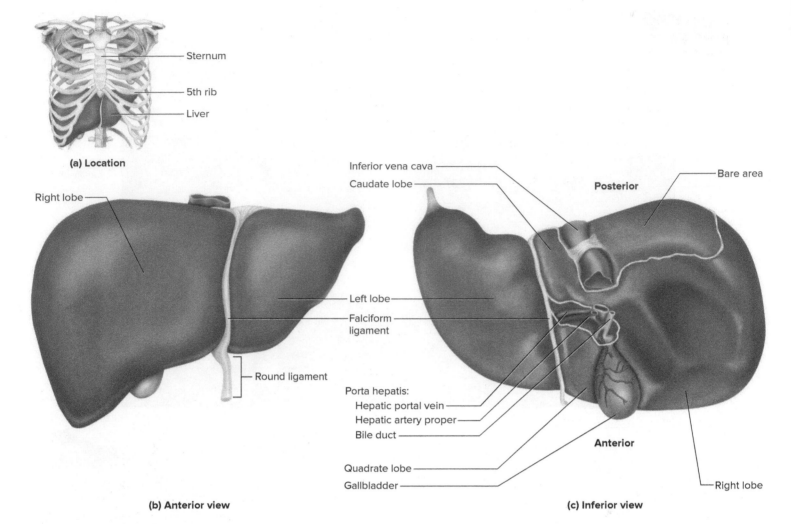

(a) Location

Sternum

5th rib

Liver

Right lobe

Inferior vena cava

Caudate lobe

Posterior

Bare area

Left lobe

Falciform ligament

Round ligament

Porta hepatis:
Hepatic portal vein
Hepatic artery proper
Bile duct

Anterior

Quadrate lobe

Gallbladder

Right lobe

(b) Anterior view

(c) Inferior view

FIGURE 25.19 Gross Anatomy of the Liver. (a) Location relative to thoracic cage. (b) Anterior view, showing right and left lobes. (c) Inferior view, showing all four lobes. **A&PR**

and forms an expanded chamber called the **hepatopancreatic ampulla.** The ampulla terminates at a fold of tissue, the **major duodenal papilla,** on the duodenal wall. This papilla contains a muscular **hepatopancreatic sphincter,** which regulates the passage of bile and pancreatic juice into the duodenum. Between meals, this sphincter is closed and prevents the release of bile into the intestine.

The hepatic lobules are separated by a sparse connective tissue stroma. In cross sections, the stroma is especially visible in the triangular areas where three or more lobules meet. Here there is often a **hepatic triad** consisting of a bile ductule and two blood vessels—branches of the hepatic artery proper and the hepatic portal vein.

Circulation

The liver receives blood from two sources: about 70% from the **hepatic portal vein** and 30% from the **hepatic arteries.** The hepatic portal vein receives blood from the stomach, intestines,

pancreas, and spleen, and carries it into the liver at the porta hepatis; see the *hepatic portal system* in section 20.7g. All nutrients absorbed by the small intestine reach the liver by this route except for lipids (transported in the lymphatic system). Arterial blood bound for the liver exits the aorta at the celiac trunk and follows the route shown in figure 20.34: celiac trunk → common hepatic artery → hepatic artery proper → right and left hepatic arteries, which enter the liver at the porta hepatis. These arteries deliver oxygen and other materials to the liver.

Both the hepatic portal vein and hepatic arteries travel to the liver through the lesser omentum. Within the liver, their finer branches meet each other in the spaces between the liver lobules, and both drain into the liver sinusoids. Hence, there is an unusual mixing of venous and arterial blood in the sinusoids. After processing by the hepatocytes, the blood collects in the central vein at the core of the lobule. Blood from the central veins ultimately converges on a few hepatic veins that exit the superior surface of the liver and empty into the nearby inferior vena cava.

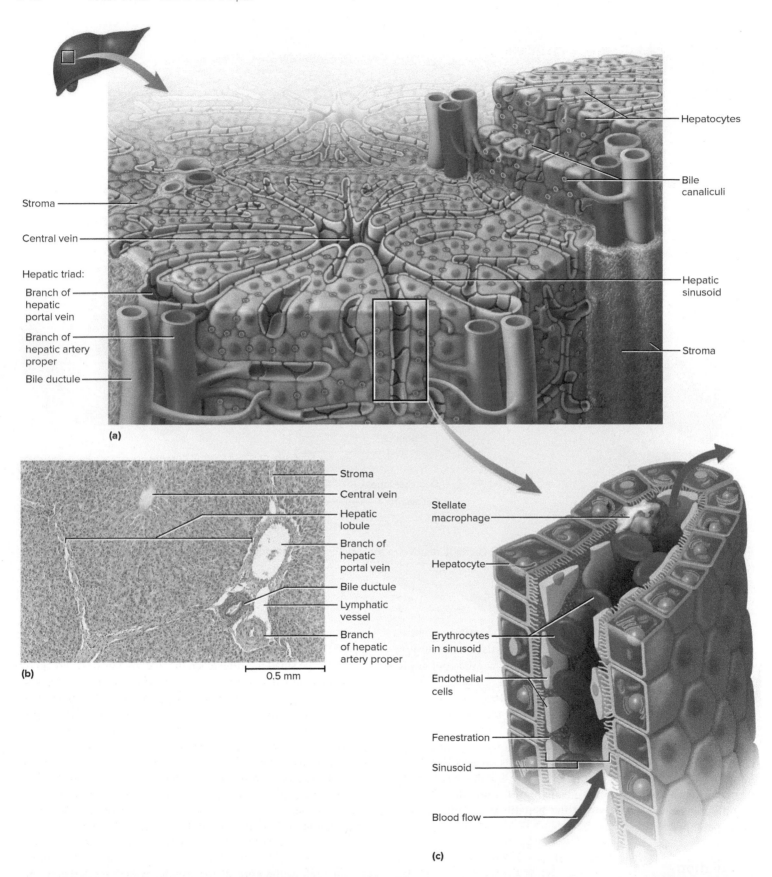

Hepatocytes

Bile canaliculi

Hepatic sinusoid

Stroma

Stroma

Central vein

Hepatic triad:

Branch of hepatic portal vein

Branch of hepatic artery proper

Bile ductule

(a)

(b)

0.5 mm

Stroma

Central vein

Hepatic lobule

Branch of hepatic portal vein

Bile ductule

Lymphatic vessel

Branch of hepatic artery proper

Stellate macrophage

Hepatocyte

Erythrocytes in sinusoid

Endothelial cells

Fenestration

Sinusoid

Blood flow

(c)

FIGURE 25.20 Microscopic Anatomy of the Liver. (a) The hepatic lobules and their relationship to the blood vessels and bile tributaries. (b) Histological section of the liver. (c) A hepatic sinusoid.

b: Dennis Strete/McGraw-Hill Education

❓ *Identify two blood vessels in tables 20.7 and 20.8 that supply blood to the hepatic sinusoids.* **APR**

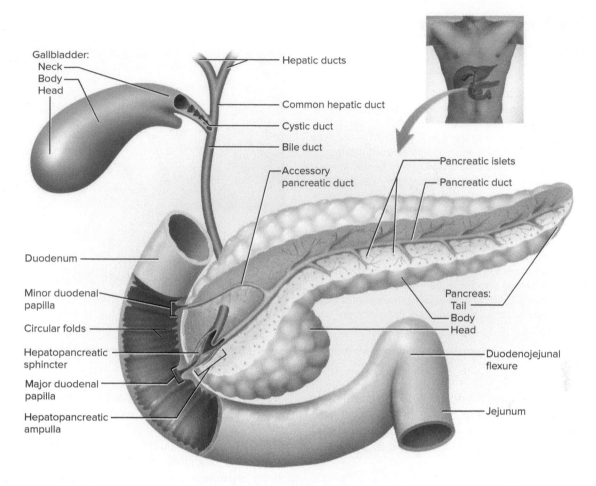

FIGURE 25.21 Gross Anatomy of the Gallbladder, Pancreas, and Bile Passages. The liver is omitted to show more clearly the gallbladder, which adheres to its inferior surface, and the hepatic ducts, which emerge from the liver tissue. **APR**

25.4b The Gallbladder and Bile

The **gallbladder** is a pear-shaped sac on the underside of the liver that serves to store and concentrate bile. It is about 10 cm long and internally lined by a highly folded mucosa with a simple columnar epithelium. Its head *(fundus)* usually projects slightly beyond the inferior margin of the liver. Its neck *(cervix)* leads into the cystic duct, which leads in turn to the bile duct.

The gallbladder doesn't secrete anything of its own except for a little mucus. It only receives, stores, and concentrates the bile produced by the liver. **Bile** is a light yellow-green color when secreted by the liver, but becomes a deep, intense green when concentrated in the gallbladder. It is a watery solution of minerals, cholesterol, neutral fats, phospholipids, bile pigments, bile acids, and lipid-transport vesicles called *micelles* (explained in section 25.6c). The principal bile pigment is **bilirubin,** derived from the decomposition of hemoglobin. Bacteria of the intestine metabolize bilirubin to a colorless product called **urobilinogen.** About half of this is reabsorbed in the small intestine and excreted by the kidneys. It is

converted to **urobilin,** which gives urine its yellow color. Urobilinogen remaining in the intestine is converted to **stercobilin,** from which feces get their brown color. In the absence of bile secretion, the feces are grayish white and marked with streaks of undigested fat *(acholic feces).* **Bile acids (bile salts)** are steroids synthesized from cholesterol. Bile acids, micelles, and **lecithin,** a phospholipid, aid in fat digestion and absorption, as discussed later. All other components of the bile are wastes destined for excretion in the feces. When these waste products become excessively concentrated, they may form gallstones (see Deeper Insight 25.3).

Bile gets into the gallbladder by first filling the bile duct, then overflowing into the gallbladder. Between meals, the gallbladder absorbs water and electrolytes from the bile and concentrates it by a factor of 5 to 20 times. The liver secretes about 500 to 1,000 mL of bile per day.

About 80% of the bile acids are reabsorbed in the ileum, the last portion of the small intestine, and returned to the liver, where the hepatocytes absorb and resecrete them. This route of secretion, reabsorption, and resecretion, called the *enterohepatic circulation,*

DEEPER INSIGHT 25.3

CLINICAL APPLICATION

Gallstones

Gallstones (biliary calculi) **(fig. 25.22)** are hard masses in the gallbladder or bile ducts, usually composed of cholesterol, calcium carbonate, and bilirubin. *Cholelithiasis,*[17] the formation or presence of gallstones, is most common in obese women over the age of 40, but certainly not limited to them; it occurs also in men and sometimes even children. It can occur when cholesterol becomes too concentrated to stay in solution and begins to precipitate out as crystals that steadily grow in size. The gallbladder may contain dozens of gallstones or even more, some over 1 cm in diameter. Gallstones can cause excruciating pain when they obstruct the bile ducts or when the gallbladder or bile ducts contract. When they block the flow of bile into the duodenum, they cause jaundice (yellowing of the skin due to bile pigment accumulation), poor fat digestion, inflammation of the pancreas *(pancreatitis)*, and impaired absorption of fat-soluble vitamins. Gallstones are now usually removed by minimally invasive laparoscopic surgery. Only the gallbladder can concentrate bile enough to cause gallstones, so it is often removed along with the gallstones to prevent recurrence.

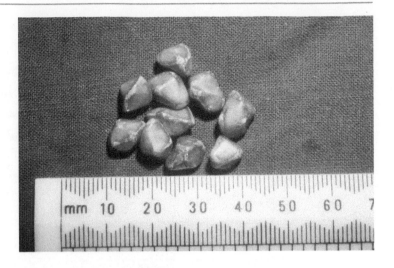

FIGURE 25.22 Gallstones.
Biophoto Associates/Science Source

---

reuses the bile acids two or more times during the digestion of an average meal. The 20% of the bile that isn't reabsorbed is excreted in the feces. This is the body's only way of eliminating excess cholesterol. The liver synthesizes new bile acids from cholesterol to replace the quantity lost in the feces.

▶▶▶ APPLY WHAT YOU KNOW

Certain drugs designed to reduce blood cholesterol work by blocking the reabsorption of bile acids in the ileum. Explain why they would have this cholesterol-lowering effect.

25.4c The Pancreas

The pancreas (fig. 25.21) is a flattened, spongy, retroperitoneal gland pressed between the body wall and the greater curvature of the stomach. It measures 12 to 15 cm long and about 2.5 cm thick. It has a globose *head* encircled by the duodenum, a midportion called the *body,* and a blunt, tapered *tail* on the left. The pancreas is both an endocrine and exocrine gland. Its endocrine part is the pancreatic islets, which secrete insulin and glucagon (see section 17.3f). About 99% of the pancreas is exocrine tissue, which secretes 1,200 to 1,500 mL of **pancreatic juice** per day. Pancreatic islets are relatively concentrated in the tail of the pancreas, whereas the head is more exocrine. Over 90% of pancreatic cancers arise from the ducts of the exocrine portion *(ductal carcinomas),* so cancer is most common in the head of the gland.

The cells of the secretory acini exhibit a high density of rough endoplasmic reticulum and secretory vesicles *(zymogen granules)* **(fig. 25.23).** The acini open into a system of branched ducts that eventually converge on the main **pancreatic duct.** This duct runs lengthwise through the middle of the gland and joins the bile duct at the hepatopancreatic ampulla. The hepatopancreatic sphincter thus controls the release of both bile and pancreatic juice into the duodenum. Most people, however, also have a smaller **accessory pancreatic duct** that branches from the main pancreatic duct and opens independently into the duodenum at the **minor duodenal papilla,** proximal to the major papilla. The accessory duct bypasses the sphincter and allows pancreatic juice to be released into the duodenum even when bile is held back.

Pancreatic juice is an alkaline mixture of water, enzymes, zymogens, sodium bicarbonate, and other electrolytes. The acini secrete the enzymes and zymogens, whereas the ducts secrete the sodium bicarbonate. The bicarbonate buffers HCl arriving from the stomach.

The pancreatic zymogens are **trypsinogen** (trip-SIN-oh-jen), **chymotrypsinogen** (KY-mo-trip-SIN-o-jen), and **procarboxypeptidase** (PRO-car-BOC-see-PEP-tih-dase). When trypsinogen is secreted into the intestinal lumen, it is converted to **trypsin** by **enteropeptidase,** an enzyme on the brush border of the duodenum **(fig. 25.24).** Trypsin is autocatalytic—it converts trypsinogen into still more trypsin. It also converts the other two zymogens into **chymotrypsin** and **carboxypeptidase,** in addition to its primary role of digesting dietary protein.

Other pancreatic enzymes include **pancreatic amylase,** which digests starch; **pancreatic lipase,** which digests fat; and **ribonuclease** and **deoxyribonuclease,** which digest RNA and DNA, respectively. Unlike the zymogens, these enzymes are not altered after secretion. They become fully active, however, only upon exposure to bile or ions in the intestinal lumen.

---

[17]*chole* = bile, gall; *lith* = stone; *iasis* = medical condition

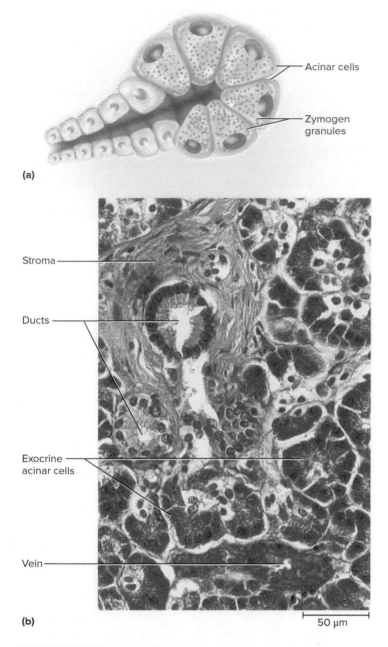

(a)

(b)

FIGURE 25.23 Microscopic Anatomy of the Pancreas. (a) An acinus. (b) Histological section of the exocrine tissue and some of the connective tissue stroma.

b: Dennis Strete/McGraw-Hill Education

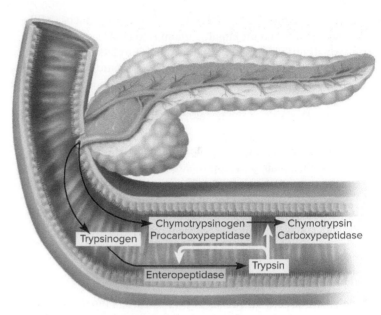

FIGURE 25.24 The Activation of Pancreatic Enzymes in the Small Intestine. The pancreas secretes trypsinogen, and enteropeptidase on the duodenal brush border converts it to trypsin. Trypsin not only digests dietary protein but also catalyzes the production of more trypsin and activates two other pancreatic zymogens—chymotrypsinogen and procarboxypeptidase.

TABLE 25.2	Exocrine Secretions of the Pancreas
Secretion	**Function**
Sodium Bicarbonate	Neutralizes HCl
Zymogens	Converted to active digestive enzymes after secretion
Trypsinogen	Becomes trypsin, which digests protein
Chymotrypsinogen	Becomes chymotrypsin, which digests protein
Procarboxypeptidase	Becomes carboxypeptidase, which hydrolyzes the terminal amino acid from the carboxyl (—COOH) end of small peptides
Enzymes	
Pancreatic amylase	Digests starch
Pancreatic lipase	Digests fat
Ribonuclease	Digests RNA
Deoxyribonuclease	Digests DNA

The exocrine secretions of the pancreas are summarized in **table 25.2.** Their specific digestive functions are explained later in more detail.

25.4d Regulation of Secretion

Three stimuli are chiefly responsible for the release of pancreatic juice and bile.

1. **Acetylcholine (ACh)** comes from the vagus nerves and enteric neurons. ACh stimulates the pancreatic acini to

secrete their enzymes even during the cephalic phase of gastric control, before food is swallowed. The enzymes remain stored in the pancreatic acini and ducts, however, in preparation for release later when chyme enters the duodenum.

2. **Cholecystokinin**[18] **(CCK)** is secreted by the mucosa of the duodenum and proximal jejunum (the next segment of the small intestine), primarily in response to fats in the small intestine. CCK also stimulates the pancreatic acini to secrete enzymes, but it is named for its strongly stimulatory effect on the gallbladder. It induces contractions of the gallbladder and relaxation of the hepatopancreatic sphincter, discharging bile into the duodenum.

3. **Secretin** is produced by the same regions of the small intestine, mainly in response to the acidity of chyme from the stomach. Secretin stimulates the ducts of both the liver and pancreas to secrete an abundant sodium bicarbonate solution. In the pancreas, this flushes the enzymes into the duodenum. Sodium bicarbonate buffers the hydrochloric acid arriving from the stomach, with the reaction

$$HCl + NaHCO_3 \longrightarrow NaCl + H_2CO_3 \text{ (carbonic acid).}$$

The carbonic acid then breaks down to carbon dioxide and water. CO_2 is absorbed into the blood and ultimately exhaled. What is left in the small intestine, therefore, is salt water—NaCl and H_2O. Sodium bicarbonate is therefore important in protecting the intestinal mucosa from HCl as well as raising the intestinal pH to the level needed for activity of the pancreatic and intestinal digestive enzymes.

▶▶▶APPLY WHAT YOU KNOW

Draw a negative feedback loop showing how secretin influences duodenal pH.

BEFORE YOU GO ON

Answer the following questions to test your understanding of the preceding section:

14. What does the liver contribute to digestion?

15. Trace the pathway taken by bile acids from the liver and back. What is this pathway called?

16. Name two hormones, four enzymes, and one buffer secreted by the pancreas, and state the function of each.

17. What stimulates cholecystokinin (CCK) secretion, and how does CCK affect other parts of the digestive system?

25.5 The Small Intestine

Expected Learning Outcomes

When you have completed this section, you should be able to

a. describe the gross and microscopic anatomy of the small intestine;

b. state how the mucosa of the small intestine differs from that of the stomach, and explain the functional significance of the differences;

c. define *contact digestion* and describe where it occurs; and

d. describe the types of movement that occur in the small intestine.

Nearly all chemical digestion and nutrient absorption occur in the small intestine. To perform these roles efficiently and thoroughly, the small intestine is the longest part of the digestive tract—about 5 m long (range 3–7 m) in a living person; in the cadaver, where there is no muscle tone, it is up to 8 m long. The term *small* intestine refers not to its length but to its diameter—about 2.5 cm (1 in.).

25.5a Gross Anatomy

The small intestine is a coiled tube filling most of the abdominal cavity inferior to the stomach and liver. It is divided into three regions (**fig. 25.25**): the *duodenum, jejunum,* and *ileum.*

The **duodenum** (dew-ODD-eh-num, DEW-oh-DEE-num) constitutes the first 25 cm (10 in.). Its name refers to its length, about equal to the width of 12 fingers.[19] It begins at the pyloric valve, arcs around the head of the pancreas and passes to the left, and ends at a sharp bend called the **duodenojejunal flexure.**

---

[19]*duoden* = 12

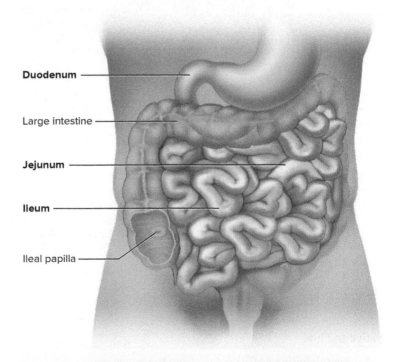

FIGURE 25.25 Gross Anatomy of the Small Intestine. APR

---

[18]*chole* = bile; *cysto* = bladder (gallbladder); *kin* = action

Slightly distal to the pyloric valve, it exhibits the previously described wrinkles called the major and minor duodenal papillae, where it receives the pancreatic duct and accessory pancreatic duct, respectively. Along with the pancreas, most of the duodenum is retroperitoneal. It receives the stomach contents, pancreatic juice, and bile. Stomach acid is neutralized here, fats are physically broken up (emulsified) by the bile acids, pepsin is inactivated by the elevated pH, and pancreatic enzymes take over the job of chemical digestion.

The **jejunum** (jeh-JOO-num), by definition, is the first 40% of the small intestine beyond the duodenum—about 1.0 to 1.7 m in a living person. Its name refers to the fact that early anatomists typically found it to be empty.[20] The jejunum begins in the upper left quadrant of the abdomen but lies mostly within the umbilical region (defined in atlas A, fig. A.4). Its wall is thick and muscular, and it has an especially rich blood supply, which gives it a relatively red color. Most digestion and nutrient absorption occur here.

The **ileum**[21] forms the last 60% of the postduodenal small intestine (about 1.6 to 2.7 m). It occupies mainly the hypogastric region and part of the pelvic cavity. Compared with the jejunum, its wall is thinner, less muscular, less vascular, and has a paler pink color. On the side opposite from its mesenteric attachment, the ileum has prominent lymphatic nodules in clusters called **aggregated lymphoid nodules** *(Peyer[22] patches),* which are readily visible to the naked eye and become progressively larger approaching the large intestine.

The end of the small intestine is the **ileocecal junction** (ILL-ee-oh-SEE-cul), where the ileum joins the *cecum* of the large intestine. The muscularis of the ileum is thickened at this point to form a valve called the **ileal papilla,** which protrudes into the cecum. The papilla consists of a pair of lips with an opening, the **ileal orifice,** between them. The ileal papilla regulates the passage of food residue into the large intestine and prevents feces from backing up into the ileum.

25.5b Circulation

The small intestine receives nearly all of its blood supply from the *superior mesenteric artery,* which fans out through the mesentery to give rise to 12 to 15 *jejunal* and *ileal arteries* leading to the intestinal wall (see fig. 20.35a). Branches of these arteries travel through the submucosa and give rise to capillary beds in the villi (described shortly), where the blood picks up all absorbed nutrients except lipids. Blood from here converges on another fanlike array of mesenteric veins, which leave by way of the *superior mesenteric vein* (see fig. 20.37a). This joins the splenic vein and then flows into the hepatic portal system, headed for the liver with its load of nutrients (see section 20.7g).

25.5c Microscopic Anatomy

The tissue layers of the small intestine are reminiscent of those in the esophagus and stomach with modifications appropriate for nutrient digestion and absorption. The lumen is lined with simple columnar epithelium. The muscularis externa is notable for a thick inner circular layer and a thinner outer longitudinal layer. The jejunum and ileum are intraperitoneal and thus covered on all sides with a serosa, which is continuous with the complex, folded mesentery that suspends the small intestine from the posterior abdominal wall. Most of the duodenum is retroperitoneal and has a serosa only on its anterior surface; its other surfaces are covered by adventitia.

Effective digestion and absorption require the small intestine to have a large internal surface area. This is provided by its relatively great length and by three kinds of internal folds or projections: the *circular folds, villi,* and *microvilli.* If the mucosa were smooth, like the inside of a hose, it would have a surface area of about 0.3 to 0.5 m², but with these surface elaborations, its actual surface area is about 200 m²—clearly a great advantage for nutrient absorption. The circular folds increase the surface area by a factor of 2 to 3, the villi by a factor of 10, and the microvilli by a factor of 20.

▶▶▶ APPLY WHAT YOU KNOW

The small intestine exhibits some of the same structural adaptations as the proximal convoluted tubule of the kidney (section 23.2d), and for the same reasons. Discuss what they have in common, the reasons for it, and how this relates to this book's theme of the unity of form and function.

Circular folds, the largest of these elaborations, are transverse to spiral ridges up to 1 cm high (see fig. 25.21). These involve only the mucosa and submucosa; they are not visible on the external surface, which is smooth. They slow the progress of the chyme and make it flow on a somewhat spiral path, which increases its contact with the mucosa and promotes more thorough mixing and nutrient absorption. Circular folds begin in the duodenum. In the jejunum, they are especially large, tall, and closely spaced. They become smaller and more sparse in the ileum. These changes are correlated with the relative amount of nutrient absorption occurring in each region. Circular folds are absent from the distal half of the ileum, but most nutrient absorption is completed by that point.

Villi (VIL-eye; singular, *villus*) are projections that give the inner lining of the intestine a fuzzy texture, like a terry cloth towel. They are about 0.5 to 1.0 mm high, with tongue- to fingerlike shapes **(fig. 25.26).** Villi are largest in the duodenum and become progressively smaller in more distal regions of the intestine. Villi are covered with two kinds of epithelial cells: columnar **enterocytes (absorptive cells)** and mucus-secreting **goblet cells.** Like epithelial cells of the stomach, those of the small intestine are joined by tight junctions that prevent digestive enzymes from seeping between them and eroding the underlying tissue.

The core of a villus is filled with areolar tissue of the lamina propria and contains an arteriole, blood capillaries, a venule, and a lymphatic capillary called a **lacteal** (LAC-tee-ul). The blood capillaries absorb most nutrients, but the lacteal absorbs most lipids.

---

[20]*jejun* = empty, dry
[21]from *eilos* = twisted
[22]Johann K. Peyer (1653–1712), Swiss anatomist

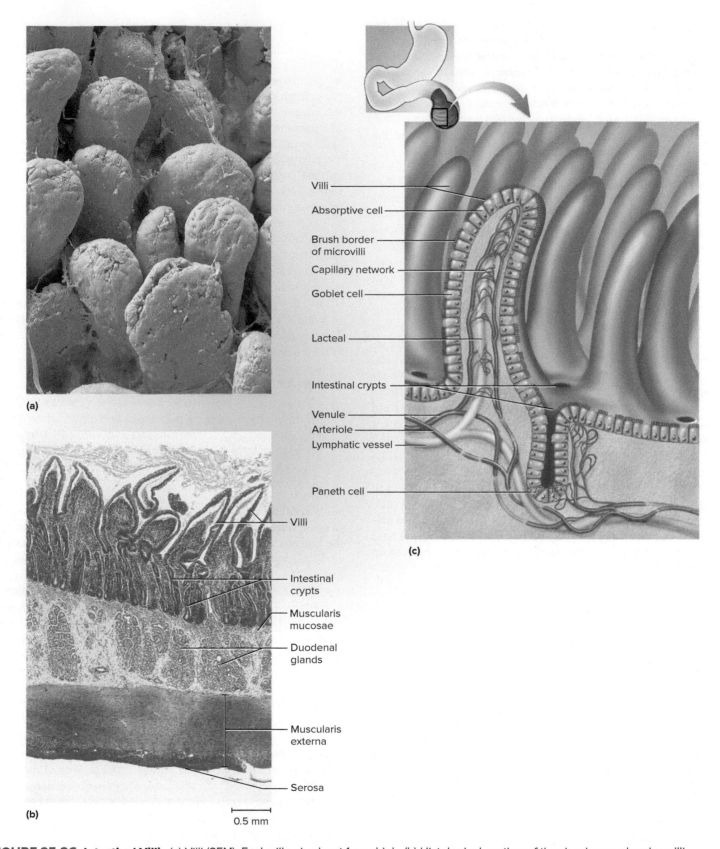

(a)

(b)

0.5 mm

Villi

Intestinal
crypts

Muscularis
mucosae

Duodenal
glands

Muscularis
externa

Serosa

(c)

Villi

Absorptive cell

Brush border
of microvilli

Capillary network

Goblet cell

Lacteal

Intestinal crypts

Venule
Arteriole
Lymphatic vessel

Paneth cell

FIGURE 25.26 Intestinal Villi. (a) Villi (SEM). Each villus is about 1 mm high. (b) Histological section of the duodenum showing villi, intestinal crypts, and duodenal glands. (c) Structure of a villus.

a: Meckes/Ottawa/Science Source; b: Dennis Strete/McGraw-Hill Education

Lipids give its contents a milky appearance for which the lacteal is named.[23] The core of the villus also has a few smooth muscle cells that contract periodically. This enhances mixing of the chyme in the intestinal lumen and milks lymph down the lacteal to larger lymphatics in the submucosa.

Microvilli are much smaller plasma membrane extensions, about 1 μm high, that form a fuzzy **brush border** on the surface of each enterocyte. In addition to increasing surface area, they contain **brush border enzymes** in the plasma membrane. These enzymes carry out some of the final stages of chemical digestion. They're not secreted into the lumen; instead, the chyme must contact the brush border for digestion to occur. This process, called **contact digestion,** is one reason why it is so important that intestinal contractions churn the chyme and ensure that it all contacts the mucosa.

On the floor of the small intestine, between the bases of the villi, there are numerous pores that open into tubular glands called **intestinal crypts.** These crypts, similar to the gastric glands, extend as far as the muscularis mucosae. In the upper half, they consist of enterocytes and goblet cells like those of the villi. The lower half is dominated by dividing stem cells. In its life span of 3 to 6 days, an epithelial cell migrates up the crypt to the tip of the villus, where it is sloughed off and digested. A few **Paneth**[24] **cells** are clustered at the base of each crypt. They secrete lysozyme, phospholipase, and defensins—defensive proteins that resist bacterial invasion of the mucosa.

The duodenum has prominent **duodenal glands** in the submucosa. They secrete an abundance of bicarbonate-rich mucus, which neutralizes stomach acid and shields the mucosa from its erosive effects. The mucus also contains signaling molecules that

influence immune cells of the GI tract (dendritic cells) to tolerate food antigens and beneficial bacteria. Throughout the small intestine, the lamina propria and submucosa have a large population of lymphocytes that intercept pathogens before they can invade the bloodstream. In some places, such as the ileum, these are aggregated into conspicuous lymphatic nodules.

25.5d Intestinal Secretion

The intestinal crypts secrete 1 to 2 L of **intestinal juice** per day, especially in response to acid, hypertonic chyme, and distension of the intestine. This fluid has a pH of 7.4 to 7.8. It contains water and mucus but relatively little enzyme. Most enzymes that function in the small intestine are found in the brush border and pancreatic juice.

25.5e Intestinal Motility

Contractions of the small intestine serve three functions: (1) to mix chyme with intestinal juice, bile, and pancreatic juice, allowing these fluids to neutralize acid and digest nutrients more effectively; (2) to churn chyme and bring it into contact with the mucosa for contact digestion and nutrient absorption; and (3) to move residue toward the large intestine.

Segmentation is a movement in which stationary ringlike constrictions appear at several places along the intestine and then relax as new constrictions form elsewhere (**fig. 25.27a**). This is the most common type of intestinal contraction. Its effect is to knead or churn the contents. Pacemaker cells of the muscularis externa set the rhythm of segmentation, with contractions about 12 times per minute in the duodenum and 8 to 9 times per minute in the ileum. Since the contractions are less frequent distally, segmentation causes slow progression of the chyme toward the colon. The intensity (but not frequency) of contractions is modified by nervous and hormonal influences.

---

[23]*lact* = milk
[24]Josef Paneth (1857–90), Austrian physician

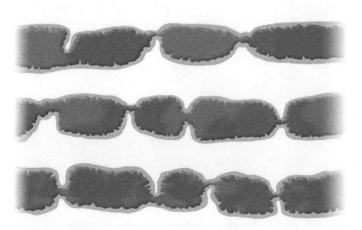

(a) Segmentation

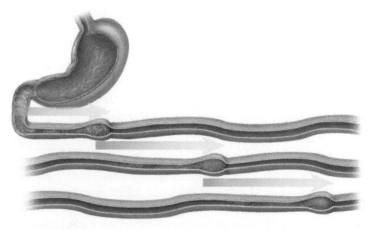

(b) Peristalsis

FIGURE 25.27 Types of Intestinal Motility. (a) Segmentation, showing progressive stages from top to bottom. Circular constrictions of the intestine cut into the contents, churning and mixing them as represented by the progressive blending of the two colors. (b) The migrating motor complex of peristalsis, in which successive waves of peristalsis overlap each other. Each wave travels partway down the intestine and milks the contents toward the colon.

When most nutrients have been absorbed and little remains but undigested residue, segmentation declines and peristalsis begins. The duodenum secretes a hormone called **motilin** that triggers a peristaltic wave beginning in the duodenum. The wave travels 10 to 70 cm and dies out, only to be followed by another wave that begins a little farther down the tract than the first one (**fig. 25.27b**). These successive, overlapping waves of contraction are called a **migrating motor complex.** They milk the chyme toward the colon over a period of about 2 hours. A second complex then expels residue and bacteria from the small intestine, thereby helping to limit bacterial colonization. Refilling of the stomach at the next meal suppresses peristalsis and reactivates segmentation as new chyme enters the small intestine.

The ileal papilla is usually closed. Food in the stomach, however, triggers both the release of gastrin and the **gastroileal reflex,** both of which enhance segmentation in the ileum and relax the papilla. As the cecum fills with residue, the pressure pinches the papilla shut and prevents the reflux of cecal contents into the ileum.

BEFORE YOU GO ON

Answer the following questions to test your understanding of the preceding section:

18. What three structures increase the absorptive surface area of the small intestine?

19. Sketch a villus and label its epithelium, brush border, lamina propria, blood capillaries, and lacteal.

20. Distinguish between segmentation and the migrating motor complex of the small intestine. How do these differ in function?

25.6 | Chemical Digestion and Absorption

Expected Learning Outcomes

When you have completed this section, you should be able to

a. describe how each major class of nutrients is chemically digested, name the enzymes involved, and discuss the functional differences among these enzymes; and

b. describe how each type of nutrient is absorbed by the small intestine.

Chemical digestion and nutrient absorption are essentially finished by the time food residue leaves the small intestine and enters the cecum. But before going on to the functions of the large intestine, we trace each major class of nutrients—especially carbohydrates, proteins, and fats—from the mouth through the small intestine to see how it is chemically degraded and absorbed. The illustration series in this section depicts the details of the digestion and absorption of each major class of organic nutrients.

25.6a Carbohydrates

Most digestible dietary carbohydrate is starch. Cellulose is indigestible and is not considered here, although its importance as dietary fiber is discussed in section 26.1f. The amount of glycogen in the diet is negligible, but it is digested in the same manner as starch.

Starch is digested first to oligosaccharides up to eight glucose residues long, then into the disaccharide maltose, and finally to glucose, which is absorbed by the small intestine. The process begins in the mouth, where salivary amylase breaks starch down into shorter segments (oligosaccharides). Salivary amylase functions best at pH 6.8 to 7.0, typical of the oral cavity. It is quickly denatured upon contact with stomach acid, but it can digest starch for as long as 1 to 2 hours in the stomach as long as it is in the middle of a food mass and escapes contact with the acid. Amylase therefore works longer when the meal is larger, especially in the fundus, where gastric motility is weakest and a food bolus takes longer to break up. As acid, pepsin, and the churning contractions of the stomach break up the bolus, amylase is denatured; it doesn't function at a pH any lower than 4.5. Being a protein, amylase is then digested by pepsin along with the dietary proteins.

About 50% of the dietary starch is digested before it reaches the small intestine. Its digestion resumes in the small intestine when the chyme mixes with pancreatic amylase (**fig. 25.28**). Starch is entirely converted to oligosaccharides and maltose within 10 minutes. Its digestion is completed as the chyme contacts the brush border of the enterocytes. Two brush border enzymes, **dextrinase** and **glucoamylase,** hydrolyze oligosaccharides that are

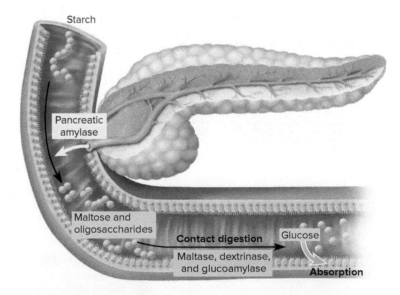

FIGURE 25.28 Starch Digestion in the Small Intestine. Pancreatic amylase digests starch into maltose and small oligosaccharides. Brush border enzymes (maltase, dextrinase, and glucoamylase) digest these to glucose, which is absorbed by the epithelial cells.

three or more residues long, while **maltase** hydrolyzes maltose. The end product of all of these is glucose, which is then absorbed.

Maltose is also present in some foods, but the major dietary disaccharides are sucrose (cane sugar) and lactose (milk sugar). They are digested by the brush border enzymes **sucrase** and **lactase,** respectively, and the resulting monosaccharides are immediately absorbed (glucose and fructose from the former; glucose and galactose from the latter). In most of the world population, however, lactase production ceases or declines to a low level after age 4 and lactose becomes indigestible (see Deeper Insight 25.4).

DEEPER INSIGHT 25.4

CLINICAL APPLICATION

Lactose Intolerance

Homo sapiens is a strange species indeed—the only mammal that continues drinking milk after infancy, and even odder, drinks the milk of other species! To digest milk sugar (lactose) requires the enzyme lactase. Understandably, lactase production normally ceases after weaning in mammals, including most humans worldwide. Its cessation results in *lactose intolerance,* the inability to digest lactose. This occurs in about 90% of American blacks, who are predominantly descended from African tribes that historically didn't raise livestock for milk; 15% of American whites; 70% or more of Mediterraneans; and nearly all people of Asian descent, including those of us descended from the native migrants into the Americas.

If a person with lactose intolerance consumes milk, lactose passes undigested into the large intestine, increases the osmolarity of the intestinal contents, and causes colonic water retention and diarrhea. In addition, lactose fermentation by colonic bacteria produces gas, resulting in painful cramps and flatulence. People with lactose intolerance can, however, consume products such as yogurt and cheese, in which bacteria have broken down the lactose, and they can digest milk and ice cream with the aid of lactase tablets.

Lactase is encoded by a gene named *LCT* on chromosome 2. In most people, after the age of weaning, another gene on that chromosome, *MCM6,* shuts down *LCT.* Lactase production wanes and finally ceases, rendering the individual no longer able to digest lactose. Many people who *can* freely consume dairy products have a mutation in the *MCM6* gene that makes it unable to turn off *LCT.* This confers on them a state of *lactase persistence,* the continued production of lactase in adulthood, with a lasting ability to digest lactose. A DNA analysis of ancient European skeletons suggests that the *MCM6* mutation appeared about 4,300 years ago. Other mutations resulting in lactase persistence occurred independently in at least three populations of Africa. Today, lactase persistence is found only in people of western and northern Europe, Mongolia, a few pastoral tribes of Africa, and their descendants in the Americas and elsewhere. They have an ancestral history of milking domestic animals that goes back as much as 10,000 years.

The causes of lactase persistence are more complex than simple genetics, however. There are various degrees of lactose tolerance and intolerance, and environmental factors seem to play a role. Some people, such as immigrant populations, acquire tolerance over time through exposure to dairy products.

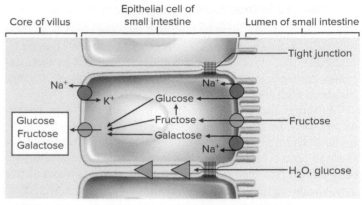

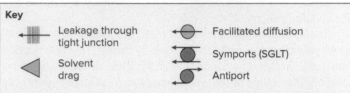

FIGURE 25.29 Monosaccharide Absorption by the Small Intestine. Glucose and galactose are absorbed by SGLT symports (violet) in the apical membranes of the absorptive cells (right). Glucose is also absorbed along with water through the paracellular route (between cells) by solvent drag. Fructose is absorbed separately by facilitated diffusion. Most fructose is converted to glucose within the epithelial cell. The monosaccharides pass through the basal membrane of the cell by facilitated diffusion (left) and are then absorbed by the blood capillaries of the villus.

The plasma membrane of the enterocytes has transport proteins that absorb monosaccharides as fast as they are produced by the foregoing enzymes **(fig. 25.29).** About 80% of the absorbed sugar is glucose, which is taken up by a sodium–glucose transporter (SGLT) like that of the kidney tubules (see section 23.4a). The glucose is subsequently transported out the base of the cell into the extracellular fluid (ECF). Sugar entering the ECF increases its osmolarity, and this draws water osmotically from the lumen of the intestine, through the now-leaky tight junctions between the epithelial cells. Water carries more glucose and other nutrients with it by *solvent drag,* much as it does in the kidney. After a high-carbohydrate meal, solvent drag absorbs two to three times as much glucose as the SGLT.

The SGLT also absorbs galactose, whereas fructose is absorbed by facilitated diffusion using a separate carrier that doesn't depend on Na^+. Inside the enterocyte, most fructose is converted to glucose. Glucose, galactose, and the small amount of remaining fructose are then transported out the base of the cell by facilitated diffusion and absorbed by the blood capillaries of the villus. The hepatic portal system delivers them to the liver; the next chapter (section 26.2) follows the fate of these sugars from there.

25.6b Proteins

The amino acids absorbed by the small intestine come from three sources: (1) dietary proteins, (2) digestive enzymes digested by each other, and (3) sloughed epithelial cells digested by these enzymes. Amino acids from the last two sources total about 30 g/day, compared with about 44 to 60 g/day from the diet.

Enzymes that digest proteins are called **proteases (peptidases).** They are absent from the saliva but first encountered in the stomach. Here, pepsin hydrolyzes any peptide bond between tyrosine and phenylalanine, thereby digesting 10% to 15% of the dietary protein into shorter polypeptides and a small amount of free amino acids **(fig. 25.30).** Pepsin has an optimal pH of 1.5 to 3.5, so it is inactivated when it passes into the duodenum and mixes with the alkaline pancreatic juice (pH 8).

In the small intestine, the pancreatic enzymes trypsin and chymotrypsin take over protein digestion by hydrolyzing polypeptides into even shorter oligopeptides. Finally, these are taken apart one amino acid at a time by three more enzymes: (1) **Carboxypeptidase** removes amino acids from the —COOH end of the chain; (2) **aminopeptidase** removes them from the —NH$_2$ end; and (3) **dipeptidase** splits dipeptides in the middle and releases the last two free amino acids. The last two of these are brush border enzymes, whereas carboxypeptidase is a pancreatic secretion.

Amino acid absorption is similar to that of monosaccharides. Enterocytes have several sodium-dependent amino acid cotransporters for different classes of amino acids. Dipeptides and tripeptides can also be absorbed, but they are hydrolyzed within the enterocytes before their amino acids are released to the bloodstream. At the basal surfaces of the cells, amino acids behave like the monosaccharides discussed previously—they leave the cell by facilitated diffusion, enter the capillaries of the villus, and are carried away in the hepatic portal circulation.

The absorptive cells of infants can take up intact proteins by pinocytosis and release them to the blood by exocytosis. This allows IgA from breast milk to pass into an infant's bloodstream and confer passive immunity from mother to infant. It has the disadvantage, however, that intact proteins entering the infant's blood are detected as foreign antigens and sometimes trigger food allergies. As the intestine matures, its ability to pinocytose protein declines but never completely ceases.

25.6c Lipids

The hydrophobic quality of lipids makes their digestion and absorption more complicated than that of carbohydrates and proteins **(fig. 25.31).** Fats are digested by enzymes called **lipases.** *Lingual lipase,* secreted by the intrinsic salivary glands of the tongue, digests a small amount of fat while food is still in the mouth, but becomes more active at the acidic pH of the stomach. Here it is joined by *gastric lipase,* which makes a much larger contribution to preduodenal fat digestion. About 10% to 15% of dietary fat is digested before the chyme passes on to the duodenum.

Being hydrophobic, ingested fat takes the form of large globules that, without further physical processing, could be attacked by these lipases only at their surface. This would result in rather slow, inefficient digestion. The stomach's vigorous *antral pumping*

described earlier, however, breaks the fat up into small droplets dispersed through the watery chyme—that is, it *emulsifies* the fat, exposing much more of its surface to enzymatic action. The resulting **emulsification droplets** are promptly passed on to the duodenum and coated by certain components of the bile—lecithin and bile acids. These agents have hydrophobic regions attracted to the surface of a fat droplet and hydrophilic regions attracted to the surrounding water. The agitation produced by intestinal segmentation breaks the fat up further into droplets as small as 1 μm, and the coating of lecithin and bile acids keeps it broken up, preventing the droplets from coalescing into larger globules.

There is enough *pancreatic lipase* in the small intestine after a meal to digest the average daily fat intake in as little as 1 or 2 minutes. When lipase acts on a triglyceride, it removes the first and third fatty acids from the glycerol backbone and usually leaves the middle one. The products of lipase action are therefore two free fatty acids (FFAs) and a monoglyceride. Being smaller than triglycerides, these are more soluble in the enterocyte plasma membrane and thus easier to absorb.

The absorption of lipids depends on minute droplets in the bile called **micelles**[25] (my-SELLS). Micelles, made in the liver, consist of 20 to 40 bile acid molecules aggregated with their hydrophilic side groups facing outward and their hydrophobic steroid rings facing inward. Bile phospholipids and cholesterol diffuse into the center of the micelle to form its core. The micelles pass down the bile duct into the duodenum, where they absorb fat-soluble vitamins, more cholesterol, and the fatty acids and monoglycerides produced by fat digestion. Because of their charged, hydrophilic surfaces, micelles remain suspended in water more easily than free lipids do. When they contact the enterocytes, they release their lipid cargo. Some of the lipids simply diffuse through the plasma membrane into the enterocytes, but these cells also have specific carrier proteins that facilitate their uptake. The micelles are reused, picking up another cargo of lipids and ferrying them to the enterocytes. Without micelles, the small intestine absorbs only about 40% to 50% of the dietary fat and almost no cholesterol.

Within the enterocytes, fatty acids and monoglycerides are transported into the smooth endoplasmic reticulum and resynthesized into triglycerides. The Golgi complex combines these with a small amount of cholesterol and coats the complex with a film of phospholipid and protein, forming droplets 75 to 1,200 nm in diameter called **chylomicrons**[26] (KY-lo-MY-crons). It packages chylomicrons into secretory vesicles that migrate to the basal surface of the cell and release their contents into the core of the villus. Although some free fatty acids enter the blood capillaries, chylomicrons are too large to penetrate the endothelium. They are taken up instead by the more porous lacteals into the lymph. This fatty, milk-white intestinal lymph, called *chyle* (pronounced "kile"), flows through larger and larger lymphatic vessels of the mesenteries, eventually passing through the cisterna chyli (see fig. 21.1) to the thoracic duct, then entering the bloodstream at the left subclavian vein. The further fate of dietary fat is described in the next chapter (section 26.3a).

---

[25]*mic* = grain, crumb; *elle* = little
[26]*chyl* = juice; *micr* = small

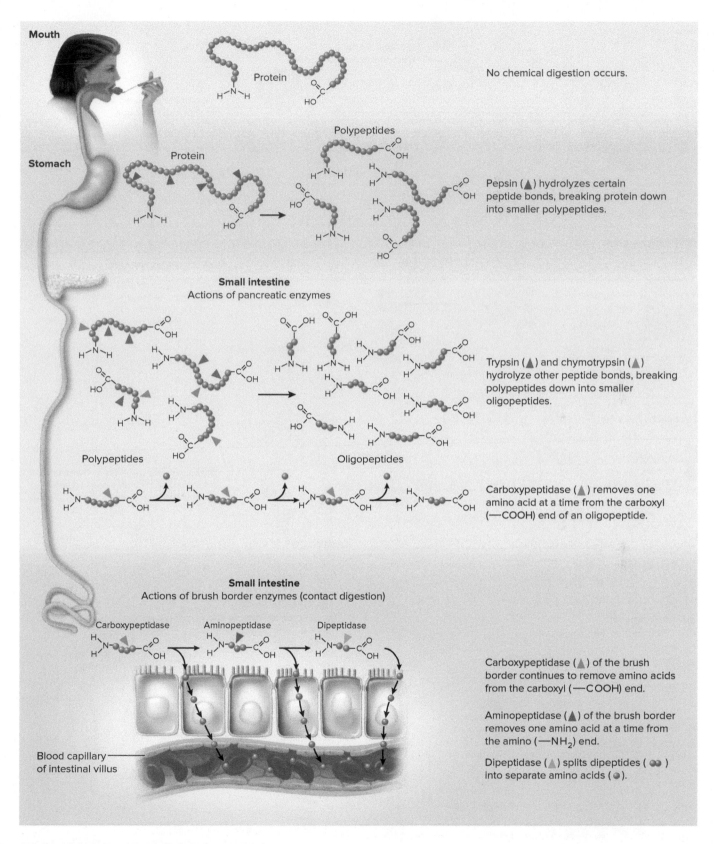

Mouth

Protein

No chemical digestion occurs.

Stomach

Protein

Polypeptides

Pepsin (▲) hydrolyzes certain peptide bonds, breaking protein down into smaller polypeptides.

Small intestine
Actions of pancreatic enzymes

Polypeptides

Oligopeptides

Trypsin (▲) and chymotrypsin (▲) hydrolyze other peptide bonds, breaking polypeptides down into smaller oligopeptides.

Carboxypeptidase (▲) removes one amino acid at a time from the carboxyl (—COOH) end of an oligopeptide.

Small intestine
Actions of brush border enzymes (contact digestion)

Carboxypeptidase   Aminopeptidase   Dipeptidase

Blood capillary
of intestinal villus

Carboxypeptidase (▲) of the brush border continues to remove amino acids from the carboxyl (—COOH) end.

Aminopeptidase (▲) of the brush border removes one amino acid at a time from the amino (—NH₂) end.

Dipeptidase (▲) splits dipeptides (●●) into separate amino acids (●).

FIGURE 25.30 Protein Digestion and Absorption.

Emulsification

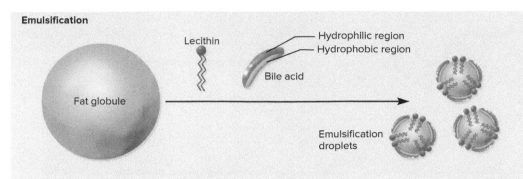

Fat globule is broken up and coated by lecithin and bile acids.

Fat hydrolysis

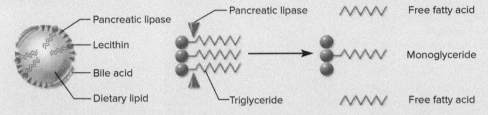

Emulsification droplets are acted upon by pancreatic lipase, which hydrolyzes the first and third fatty acids from triglycerides, usually leaving the middle fatty acid.

Lipid uptake by micelles

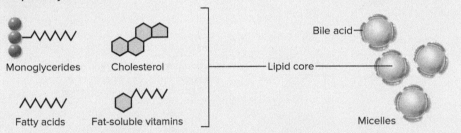

Micelles in the bile pass to the small intestine and pick up several types of dietary and semidigested lipids.

Chylomicron formation

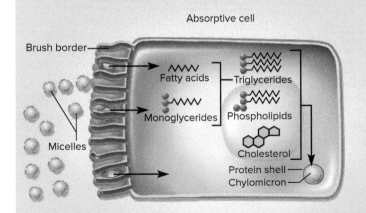

Intestinal cells absorb lipids from micelles, resynthesize triglycerides, and package triglycerides, cholesterol, and phospholipids into protein-coated chylomicrons.

Chylomicron exocytosis and lymphatic uptake

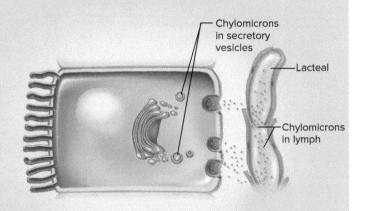

Golgi complex packages chylomicrons into secretory vesicles; chylomicrons are released from basal cell membrane by exocytosis and enter the lacteal (lymphatic capillary) of the villus.

FIGURE 25.31 Fat Digestion and Absorption.

▶▶▶**APPLY WHAT YOU KNOW**

Explain why the right lymphatic duct does not contribute any dietary fat to the bloodstream.

Figure 25.32 summarizes the major aspects of carbohydrate, protein, and fat digestion and absorption.

25.6d Nucleic Acids

The nucleic acids, DNA and RNA, are present in much smaller quantities than the polymers discussed previously. The **nucleases** (ribonuclease and deoxyribonuclease) of pancreatic juice hydrolyze these to their constituent nucleotides. **Nucleosidases** and **phosphatases** of the brush border then decompose the nucleotides into phosphate ions, nitrogenous bases, and simple sugars (ribose from RNA and deoxyribose from DNA). These products are transported across the intestinal epithelium by membrane carriers and enter the capillary blood of the villus.

25.6e Vitamins

Vitamins are not digested, but absorbed unchanged. The fat-soluble vitamins A, D, E, and K are absorbed with other lipids as just described. Therefore, if they are ingested without fat-containing food, such as by simply popping vitamin tablets with a glass of water, they're not absorbed at all but passed in the feces and wasted. Water-soluble vitamins (the B complex and vitamin C) are absorbed by simple diffusion. An exception is vitamin B_{12}, an unusually large molecule that is absorbed poorly unless bound to the intrinsic factor (IF) secreted by the stomach's parietal cells. Then as it passes down the small intestine, the B_{12}–IF complex binds to receptors on absorptive cells of the distal ileum, where it is taken up by receptor-mediated endocytosis.

25.6f Minerals

Minerals (electrolytes) are absorbed along the entire length of the small intestine. Sodium ions are cotransported with sugars and amino acids. Chloride ions are actively transported in the distal ileum by a pump that exchanges them for bicarbonate ions, reversing the chloride–bicarbonate exchange that occurs in the stomach. Potassium ions are absorbed by simple diffusion. The K^+ concentration of chyme rises as water is absorbed, creating a gradient favorable to K^+ absorption. In diarrhea, when water absorption is hindered, potassium ions remain in the intestine and pass with the feces; therefore, chronic diarrhea can lead to hypokalemia.

Most minerals are absorbed at fairly constant rates regardless of need, leaving it to the kidneys to excrete any excess. Iron is one exception; its absorption is hormonally regulated. Intestinal enterocytes bind ferrous ions (Fe^{2+}) and take them in by active transport; they cannot absorb ferric ions (Fe^{3+}), but stomach acid (HCl) reduces most Fe^{3+} to absorbable Fe^{2+}. Fe^{2+} is transported to the basal surface of the cell and there taken up by the extracellular protein *transferrin*. The transferrin–iron complex diffuses into the blood and is carried to such places as the bone marrow for hemoglobin synthesis, muscular tissue for myoglobin synthesis, and the liver for storage (see fig. 18.7). Excess dietary iron, if absorbed, binds irreversibly to ferritin in the enterocyte and is

held there until that cell sloughs off and passes in the feces. Iron absorption and mobilization are regulated by the liver hormone **hepcidin.** An iron overload is dangerously toxic (indeed, a leading cause of death in young children who get into a parent's iron supplement pills), but hepcidin normally prevents overload. It *inhibits* intestinal iron absorption and the mobilization of iron from the liver, thus preventing the blood iron level from rising too high. Anemia and hypoxia reduce hepcidin synthesis, removing its inhibitory effect and thus allowing increased absorption of dietary iron and mobilization of stored iron so it becomes available for hemoglobin synthesis.

▶▶▶**APPLY WHAT YOU KNOW**

Young adult women have four times as many iron transport proteins in the intestinal mucosa as men have. Can you explain this in terms of functional significance?

The small intestine absorbs nearly all dietary phosphate, predominantly by active transport. By contrast, it absorbs only about 40% of the dietary calcium, leaving the rest to pass in the feces. In the duodenum, calcium is absorbed by the transcellular route. It enters the enterocytes through calcium channels in the apical plasma membrane and binds to a cytoplasmic protein called *calbindin.* This keeps the intracellular concentration of free calcium low, maintaining a gradient that favors uptake. What free calcium exists in the cytoplasm is then pumped out the basal side of the cell by active transport, using a protein called *calcium–ATPase* as well as a *sodium–calcium antiport.* From there, it enters the blood capillaries of the villus.

Transcellular calcium uptake is under hormonal influence. Parathyroid hormone is secreted in response to a drop in blood calcium level. It stimulates the kidneys to synthesize vitamin D from the precursors made by the epidermis and liver (see fig. 7.16). Vitamin D then affects the absorptive cells of the duodenum in three ways: It increases the number of calcium channels in the apical membrane, the amount of calbindin in the cytoplasm, and the number of calcium–ATPase pumps in the basal membrane. Thus, it increases absorption of dietary calcium and raises the level of calcium in the blood.

Because of their much greater length, the jejunum and ileum absorb much more calcium than the duodenum does, but here it is by the paracellular route (passing between cells) and is independent of hormones. Most absorbed calcium is from meat and dairy products. Although green leafy vegetables are high in calcium, little of this is absorbed because they also contain an agent, *oxalate,* that binds calcium and makes it unavailable for absorption. Dietary fat retards calcium absorption by reacting with it to form poorly absorbed calcium soaps.

25.6g Water

The digestive system is one of several systems involved in fluid balance. The digestive tract receives about 9 L of water per day—0.7 L in food, 1.6 L in drink, and 6.7 L in the gastrointestinal secretions: saliva, gastric juice, bile, pancreatic juice, and intestinal juice. About 8 L of this is absorbed by the small intestine and 0.8 L by the large intestine, leaving 0.2 L voided in the daily fecal

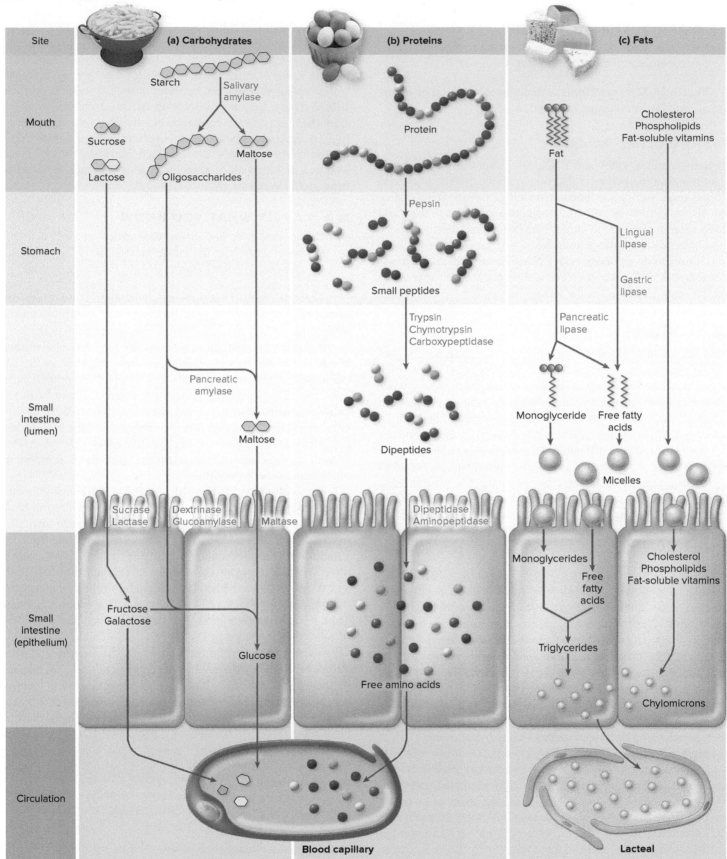

FIGURE 25.32 Summary of the Digestion and Absorption of the Major Organic Nutrients. Enzyme names are indicated in red.

(pasta): John A. Rizzo/Getty Images; **(eggs, cheeses):** Pixtal/agefotostock

❓ *As they leave the small intestine, sugars and amino acids arrive at the liver before any other organ, but lipids do not. Why not? Trace the route that a dietary fat would have to take to reach the liver, using information from section 21.1a and table 20.7.*

output. Water is absorbed by osmosis, following the absorption of salts and organic nutrients that create an osmotic gradient from the intestinal lumen to the ECF.

Diarrhea occurs when the large intestine absorbs too little water. This occurs when the intestine is irritated by bacteria and feces pass through too quickly for adequate reabsorption, or when the feces contain abnormally high concentrations of a solute such as lactose that opposes osmotic absorption of water. *Constipation* occurs when fecal movement is slow, too much water is reabsorbed, and the feces become hardened. This can result from lack of dietary fiber, lack of exercise, emotional upset, or long-term laxative abuse.

▶▶▶**APPLY WHAT YOU KNOW**

Magnesium sulfate (Epsom salt) is poorly absorbed by the intestines. In light of this, explain why it has a laxative effect.

BEFORE YOU GO ON

Answer the following questions to test your understanding of the preceding section:

21. What three classes of nutrients are most abundant? What are the end products of enzymatic digestion of each?

22. What two digestive enzymes occur in the saliva? Why is one of these more active in the stomach than in the mouth?

23. Name as many enzymes of the intestinal brush border as you can, and identify the substrate or function of each.

24. Explain the distinctions between an emulsification droplet, a micelle, and a chylomicron.

25. What happens to digestive enzymes after they have done their job? What happens to dead epithelial cells that slough off the gastrointestinal mucosa? Explain.

25.7 The Large Intestine

Expected Learning Outcomes

When you have completed this section, you should be able to

a. describe the gross anatomy of the large intestine;

b. summarize the functions of the large intestine;

c. contrast the mucosa of the colon with that of the small intestine;

d. state the physiological significance of intestinal bacteria;

e. discuss the types of contractions that occur in the colon; and

f. explain the neurological control of defecation.

The large intestine receives about 500 mL of indigestible food residue per day, reduces it to about 150 mL of feces by absorbing water and salts, and eliminates the feces by defecation.

25.7a Gross Anatomy

The large intestine measures about 1.5 m (5 ft) long and 6.5 cm (2.5 in.) in diameter in the cadaver. It is named for its relatively large diameter, not its length. It consists of four regions: the cecum, colon, rectum, and anal canal (**fig. 25.33**).

The **cecum**[27] is a blind pouch in the lower right abdominal quadrant inferior to the ileal papilla. Attached to its lower end is the **appendix,** a blind tube 2 to 7 cm long. The appendix is densely populated with lymphocytes and is a significant source of immune cells.

The **colon** is that part of the large intestine between the ileocecal junction and rectum (not including the cecum, rectum, or anal canal). It is divided into the ascending, transverse, descending, and sigmoid regions. The **ascending colon** begins at the ileal papilla and passes up the right side of the abdominal cavity. It makes a 90° turn at the **right colic (hepatic) flexure,** near the right lobe of the liver, and becomes the **transverse colon.** This passes horizontally across the upper abdominal cavity and turns 90° downward at the **left colic (splenic) flexure** near the spleen. Here it becomes the **descending colon,** which passes down the left side of the abdominal cavity. Ascending, transverse, and descending colons thus form a squarish, three-sided frame around the small intestine; this, however, is highly variable from person to person and between ethnic groups.

The pelvic cavity is narrower than the abdominal cavity, so at the hip bone, the colon turns medially and travels along the iliac fossa before turning downward at the pelvic inlet into the pelvic cavity. (See fig. 8.35 for review of the skeletal landmarks.) The resulting S-shaped portion of the tract is called the **sigmoid**[28] **colon.** (Visual examination of this region is performed with an instrument called a *sigmoidoscope.*) In the pelvic cavity, the large intestine continues as the **rectum,**[29] about 15 cm long. Despite its name, the rectum is not quite straight but has three lateral curves as well as an anteroposterior curve. It has three infoldings called **transverse rectal folds (rectal valves),** which enable it to retain feces while passing gas.

The final 3 cm of the large intestine is the **anal canal** (fig. 25.33b), which passes through the levator ani muscle of the pelvic floor and terminates at the anus. Here, the mucosa forms longitudinal ridges called **anal columns** with depressions between them called **anal sinuses.** As feces pass through the canal, they press the sinuses and cause them to exude extra mucus and lubricate the canal during defecation. Prominent **hemorrhoidal veins** form superficial plexuses in the anal columns and around the orifice. Unlike veins in the limbs, they lack valves and are particularly subject to distension and venous pooling. *Hemorrhoids* are permanently distended veins that protrude into the anal canal or form bulges external to the anus. They can result from the impaired venous return that occurs in obesity and pregnancy.

The muscularis externa of the colon is unusual. Although it completely encircles the colon just as it does the small intestine, its

---

[27]*cec* = blind
[28]*sigm* = sigma or S; *oid* = resembling
[29]*rect* = straight

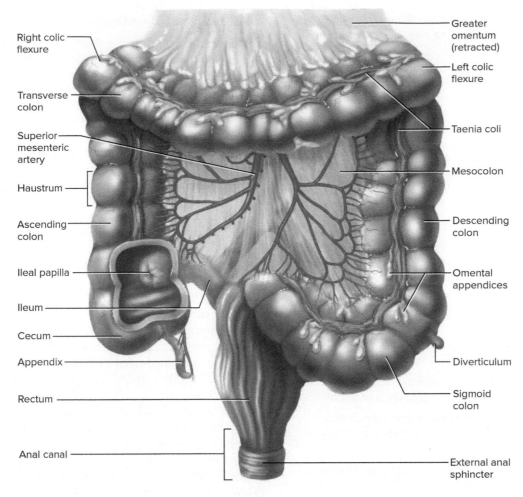

Right colic flexure

Transverse colon

Superior mesenteric artery

Haustrum

Ascending colon

Ileal papilla

Ileum

Cecum

Appendix

Rectum

Anal canal

Greater omentum (retracted)

Left colic flexure

Taenia coli

Mesocolon

Descending colon

Omental appendices

Diverticulum

Sigmoid colon

External anal sphincter

(a) Gross anatomy

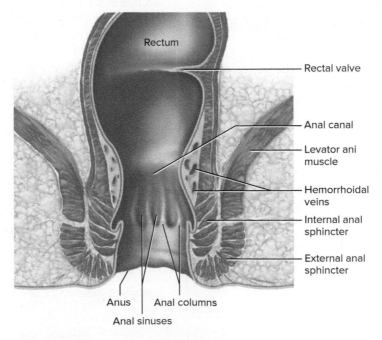

Rectum

Rectal valve

Anal canal

Levator ani muscle

Hemorrhoidal veins

Internal anal sphincter

External anal sphincter

Anus

Anal columns

Anal sinuses

(b) Anal canal

FIGURE 25.33
The Large Intestine.
(a) Gross anatomy.
(b) Anatomy of the anal canal. **APR**

? *Which anal sphincter is controlled by the autonomic nervous system? Which is controlled by the somatic nervous system? Explain the basis for your answers.*

longitudinal fibers are especially concentrated in three thickened, ribbonlike strips. Each strip is called a **taenia coli**[30] (TEE-nee-ah CO-lye) (plural, *taeniae coli*). The muscle tone of the taeniae coli contracts the colon lengthwise and causes its wall to bulge, forming pouches called **haustra**[31] (HAW-stra; singular, *haustrum*). Haustra are conspicuous in colonic X-rays of living patients; they are not evident in a cadaver, however, because they disappear when muscle tone is lost at death. In the rectum and anal canal, the longitudinal muscle forms a continuous sheet and haustra are absent. The anus is regulated by two sphincters: an **internal anal sphincter** composed of smooth muscle of the muscularis externa and an **external anal sphincter** composed of skeletal muscle of the pelvic diaphragm.

The ascending and descending colon are retroperitoneal and have a serosa only on the anterior surface, whereas the transverse and sigmoid colon are entirely enclosed in serosa and anchored to the posterior abdominal wall by the mesocolon. The serosa of the transverse through sigmoid colon often has **omental (fatty) appendices,** clublike fatty pouches of peritoneum of unknown function. In older people, the serosal surface of the colon often shows outpocketings called *diverticula* (see Deeper Insight 25.5).

DEEPER INSIGHT 25.5
CLINICAL APPLICATION

Diverticulosis and Diverticulitis

Older people often exhibit a condition called *diverticulosis,* the presence of pouches *(diverticula)* on the wall of the colon (see fig. 25.33a). This occurs in about one-half of Americans and Canadians over 60 years old. It is often attributed to a low-fiber diet; when the stool is lacking in bulk, contractions of the colon are thought to put more pressure on the wall and cause it to balloon out, especially in the sigmoid region. This is an unproven hypothesis, however, and other factors are known or suspected. The wall of the colon weakens with age, for one thing, and there is also a hereditary component. In a pair of identical twins, if one gets diverticulosis, there is a 40% chance that the other will too, regardless of diet.

Diverticulosis can cause dull pain, mild cramps, constipation, and blood in the stool, but it is often asymptomatic and discovered only when a person has a colonoscopy or CT scan. Symptoms can be relieved by increasing dietary fiber intake. The most serious consequences of diverticulosis are that it increases the risk of colon cancer and that about one in five cases progresses to diverticulitis.

Diverticulitis is inflammation of diverticula, possibly caused by impacted feces in the pouches. This causes more intense abdominal pain, tenderness in the lower left quadrant (but on the right in Asians), and sometimes nausea, vomiting, and fever. Diverticula can perforate and leak feces into the pelvic cavity, causing life-threatening peritonitis. Diverticulitis is treated with antibiotics and pain relievers, but sometimes requires surgical resection of the colon (removal of the affected region).

---

[30]*taenia* = ribbon; *coli* = of the colon
[31]*haustr* = to draw, like a purse string

25.7b Circulation

The large intestine is served by mesenteric arteries and veins much like the small intestine. Branches of the superior mesenteric artery fan out to supply the ascending colon and most of the transverse colon; the inferior mesenteric artery supplies the rest of the transverse colon as well as the descending and sigmoid colon and the rectum (see section 20.7f). The superior and inferior mesenteric veins drain the same parts of the large intestine as the correspondingly named arteries and drain into the hepatic portal system (see section 20.7g).

25.7c Microscopic Anatomy

The mucosa of the large intestine **(fig. 25.34)** has a simple columnar epithelium in all regions except the lower half of the anal canal, where it has a nonkeratinized stratified squamous epithelium. The latter resists abrasion by the passage of feces. There are no circular folds or villi in the large intestine, but there are intestinal crypts. They are deeper than in the small intestine and have a greater density of goblet cells; mucus is their only significant secretion. The lamina propria and submucosa have an abundance of lymphatic tissue, providing protection from the bacteria that densely populate the large intestine.

25.7d Intestinal Microbes and Gas

The large intestine harbors about 800 species of bacteria collectively called the **gut microbiome.** We have a mutually beneficial relationship with many of these. We provide them with room and board while they provide us with nutrients from our food that we're not equipped to extract on our own. For example, they digest cellulose, pectin, and other plant polysaccharides for which we have no digestive enzymes, and we absorb the resulting sugars. Thus, we get more nutrition from our food because of these bacteria than we would get without them. Indeed, one person may get more calories than another from the same amount of food because of differences in their bacterial populations. Some bacteria also synthesize B vitamins and vitamin K, which are absorbed by the colon. This vitamin K is especially important because the diet alone usually doesn't provide enough to ensure adequate blood clotting.

One of the less desirable and sometimes embarrassing products of these bacteria is intestinal gas. The large intestine contains about 7 to 10 L of gas, expelling about 500 mL/day as **flatus** and reabsorbing the rest. Much of this is swallowed air that has worked its way through the digestive tract, but the gut microbes add to it. Painful cramping can result when undigested nutrients pass into the colon and furnish an abnormal substrate for bacterial action, so the bacteria produce excess gas—for example, in lactose intolerance. Flatus is composed mostly of nitrogen (N_2), carbon dioxide (CO_2), hydrogen (H_2), methane (CH_4), hydrogen sulfide (H_2S), and two amines: indole and skatole. Indole, skatole, and H_2S produce most of the odor of flatus and feces, whereas the others are odorless. The hydrogen gas is combustible and has been known to explode during the use of electrical cauterization in surgery.

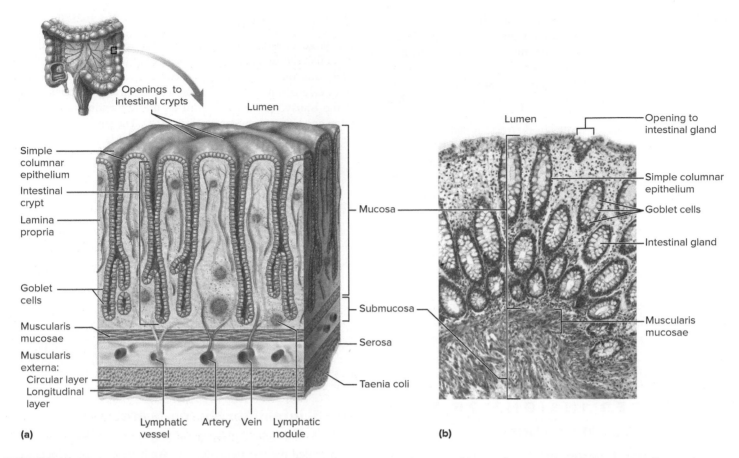

FIGURE 25.34 Microscopic Anatomy of the Colon. (a) A block of tissue showing all layers from mucosa (top) to serosa (bottom). (b) Light micrograph of the mucosa.

b: Jose Luis Calvo/Shutterstock

25.7e Absorption and Motility

The large intestine takes 36 to 48 hours to reduce the residue of a meal to feces, with the residue spending the greatest time (about 24 h) in the transverse colon. The colon doesn't chemically change the residue, but reabsorbs water and electrolytes (especially NaCl) from it. Feces usually consist of about 75% water and 25% solids. The solids are about 30% bacteria, 30% undigested dietary fiber, 10% to 20% fat, and smaller amounts of protein, sloughed epithelial cells, salts, mucus, and other digestive secretions. The fat is not from the diet but from bacteria and broken-down epithelial cells.

The most common type of colonic motility is a type of segmentation called **haustral contractions,** which occur about every 30 minutes. Distension of a haustrum with feces stimulates it to contract. This churns and mixes the residue, promotes water and salt absorption, and passes the residue distally to another haustrum. Stronger contractions called **mass movements** occur one to three times a day. They last about 15 minutes and move residue several centimeters at a time. They are often triggered by the **gastrocolic** and **duodenocolic reflexes,** in which filling of the stomach and duodenum stimulates motility of the colon. Mass movements occur especially in the transverse to sigmoid colon, often within an hour after breakfast, moving the feces that accumulated and stretched the colon overnight.

25.7f Defecation

Stretching of the rectum stimulates the defecation reflexes, which account for the urge to defecate that is often felt soon after a meal. You may find it enlightening to compare the following discussion of the defecation reflexes with the similar mechanisms controlling urination (see fig. 23.25). The predictability of the defecation reflexes is useful in house training pets and toilet training children. The overall process involves two reflexes:

1. The **intrinsic defecation reflex.** This reflex is mediated entirely by the myenteric plexus. Stretch signals travel through the plexus to the muscularis of the descending and sigmoid colon and the rectum. This activates a peristaltic wave that drives feces downward, and it relaxes the internal anal sphincter. This reflex is relatively weak, however, and usually requires the cooperative action of the following reflex.

2. The **parasympathetic defecation reflex.** This is a spinal reflex. Its principal events **(fig. 25.35)** are that stretch signals are transmitted to the spinal cord; motor signals return by way of the pelvic nerves; and these signals intensify peristalsis in the descending and sigmoid colon and rectum while they relax the internal anal sphincter.

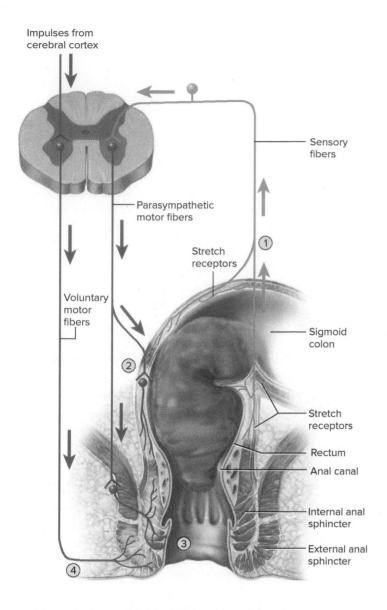

① Feces stretch the rectum and stimulate stretch receptors, which transmit signals to the spinal cord.

② A spinal reflex stimulates contraction of the rectum.

③ The spinal reflex also relaxes the internal anal sphincter.

④ Impulses from the brain prevent untimely defecation by keeping the external anal sphincter contracted. Defecation occurs only if this sphincter also relaxes.

FIGURE 25.35 Neural Control of Defecation.

These reflexes are involuntary and are the sole means of controlling defecation in infants and some people with transecting spinal cord injuries. However, the external anal sphincter, like the external urethral sphincter controlling urination, is under voluntary control, enabling one to limit defecation to appropriate circumstances. Voluntary retention of feces is also aided by the **puborectalis muscle,** which loops around the rectum like a sling and creates a sharp anorectal angle that blocks the passage of feces. Defecation normally occurs only when the external anal sphincter and puborectalis muscle are voluntarily relaxed. The kink in the rectum then straightens out and the sphincter opens to allow the feces to fall away. Defecation is also aided by the voluntary Valsalva maneuver, in which a breath hold and contraction of the abdominal muscles increase abdominal pressure, compress the rectum, and squeeze the feces from it. This maneuver can also initiate the defecation reflex by forcing feces from the descending colon into the rectum. The external anal sphincter and external urethral sphincter are controlled together by inhibitory signals from the brainstem, so as this inhibition is released, defecation is usually accompanied by urination. Some spinal cord injuries and diseases abolish the voluntary control of the external anal sphincter. The resulting inability to voluntarily retain the feces is called *fecal incontinence.*

If the defecation urge is suppressed, contractions cease in a few minutes and the rectum relaxes. The defecation reflexes recur a few hours later or when another mass movement propels more feces into the rectum.

The effects of aging on the digestive system are discussed in section 29.4a. The most life-threatening digestive disorder in older age is colorectal cancer (see Deeper Insight 25.6). Other disorders of this system are described in **table 25.3.**

BEFORE YOU GO ON

Answer the following questions to test your understanding of the preceding section:

26. How does the mucosa of the large intestine differ from that of the small intestine? How does the muscularis externa differ?

27. Name and briefly describe two types of contractions that occur in the colon and nowhere else in the alimentary canal.

28. Describe the reflexes that cause defecation in an infant. Describe the additional neural controls that function following toilet training.

DEEPER INSIGHT 25.6

CLINICAL APPLICATION

Colorectal Cancer

Cancer of the colon and rectum *(colorectal cancer)* is the second most common cause of cancer deaths in the United States. It usually arises from mucus-secreting goblet cells in a colon polyp and, if neglected, readily metastasizes to distant organs including the liver, lungs, and brain. Early signs of colorectal cancer include persistent diarrhea, constipation, and abdominal pain; blood in the stool; and weakness, fatigue, and weight loss.

Some risk factors for colorectal cancer are avoidable: smoking, heavy alcohol use, physical inactivity, and obesity. The connection with diet is uncertain, but diets low in fruit and vegetable fiber and high in red meats, char-grilled meat, and processed meats such as hot dogs and sandwich meats, have been implicated as possible risk factors. Other factors are unavoidable. Persons of African and Ashkenazi Jewish ancestry and persons with a family history of colorectal cancer are at greater than average risk. It is associated also with a history of colorectal polyps, inflammatory bowel disease (IBS), and diverticulosis (see Deeper Insight 25.5). It is more common among prosperous than poorer people, perhaps because of dietary and other lifestyle choices.

All colorectal cancer is genetic, but only a small percentage of cases are hereditary—in other words, it is seldom passed from parent to offspring, but almost always arises by new mutations during one's lifetime. About 85% of cases involve mutation of tumor suppressor gene *p53* on chromosome 17 (see Deeper Insight 4.3), but additional mutations on other chromosomes are also needed for progression to malignancy. For this reason, colorectal cancer is slow to develop and usually appears after age 50, but it can occur at any age. Colorectal cancer mortality is declining worldwide because of improved awareness, better screening, and better treatment; yet it is rising among younger people for unknown reasons.

The best safeguards against colorectal cancer are regular screening and early detection. The most common screening methods are fecal exams for traces of nonvisible (occult) blood; *sigmoidoscopy* (endoscopic examination of the rectum and sigmoid colon); *and colonoscopy* (endoscopy of the entire colon). Polyps observed in endoscopy are removed before they can turn malignant. The frequency and starting age of such screenings vary with medical opinion, but a common recommendation is to have fecal exams annually (mail-in kits for at-home sampling are available for this), sigmoidoscopy every 5 years, and colonoscopy every 10 years, starting at age 50.

TABLE 25.3	Some Digestive System Diseases
Acute pancreatitis	Severe pancreatic inflammation perhaps caused by trauma leading to leakage of pancreatic enzymes into parenchyma, where they digest tissue and cause inflammation and hemorrhage.
Appendicitis	Inflammation of the appendix, with swelling, pain, and sometimes gangrene, perforation, and peritonitis.
Cancers	Malignant tumors especially of the esophagus, stomach, colon, liver, and pancreas, with colorectal and pancreatic cancer being among the leading causes of cancer death in the United States.
Crohn disease	Inflammation of small and large intestines, similar to ulcerative colitis. Produces granular lesions and fibrosis of intestine, diarrhea, and lower abdominal pain. Often hereditary.
Dysphagia	Difficulty swallowing. Can result from esophageal obstructions (tumors, constrictions) or impaired peristalsis (due to neuromuscular disorders).
Gluten-sensitive enteropathy	Formerly called *sprue* or *celiac disease.* Atrophy of intestinal villi triggered in genetically susceptible individuals by *gluten,* the protein component of cereal grains. Onset is usually in infancy or early childhood. Results in severe malabsorption of most nutrients, causing watery or fatty diarrhea, abdominal pain, diminished growth, and multiple problems tied to nutritional deficiencies. Treatable with intensive dietary management.
Hiatal hernia	Protrusion of part of the stomach into the thoracic cavity, where the negative thoracic pressure may cause it to balloon. Often causes gastroesophageal reflux (especially when a person is supine) and esophagitis (inflammation of the esophagus).
Ulcerative colitis	Chronic inflammation resulting in ulceration of the large intestine, especially the sigmoid colon and rectum. Tends to be hereditary but exact causes are not well known.
You can find other digestive system disorders described in the following places:	

Portal hypertension and *ascites* in Deeper Insight 20.4; *dental caries, gingivitis,* and other *periodontal disease* in Deeper Insight 25.1; *impacted molars* in section 25.2a; *heartburn* in section 25.2e; *peptic ulcer* in Deeper Insight 25.2; *gallstones* in Deeper Insight 25.3; *lactose intolerance* in Deeper Insight 25.4; *diverticulosis* and *diverticulitis* in Deeper Insight 25.5; *colorectal cancer* in Deeper Insight 25.6; *constipation* and *diarrhea* in section 25.6g; *hemorrhoids* in section 25.7a; and *hepatitis* and *hepatic cirrhosis* in Deeper Insight 26.3.

DEEPER INSIGHT 25.7

MEDICAL HISTORY

The Man with a Hole in His Stomach

Perhaps the most famous episode in the history of digestive physiology began with a grave accident in 1822 on Mackinac Island in northern Michigan. Alexis St. Martin, a 28-year-old Canadian voyageur **(fig. 25.36),** was standing outside a trading post when he was accidentally hit by a shotgun blast from 3 feet away. A frontier Army doctor stationed at Fort Mackinac, William Beaumont, was summoned to examine St. Martin. As Beaumont later wrote, "a portion of the lung as large as a turkey's egg" protruded through St. Martin's lacerated and burnt flesh. Below that was a portion of the stomach with a puncture in it "large enough to receive my forefinger." Beaumont did his best to pick out bone fragments and dress the wound, though he did not expect St. Martin to survive.

Surprisingly, he lived. Over a period of months, the wound extruded pieces of bone, cartilage, gunshot, and gun wadding. As the wound healed, a fistula (hole) remained in the stomach, so large that Beaumont had to cover it with a compress to prevent food from coming out. The opening remained, covered only by a loose flap of skin, for the rest of St. Martin's life. A fold of tissue later grew over the fistula, but it was easily opened. A year later, St. Martin was still feeble. Town authorities decided they could no longer support him on public funds and wanted to ship him 1,500 miles to his home. Beaumont, however, was imbued with a passionate sense of destiny. Very little was known about digestion, and he saw the accident as a unique opportunity to learn. He took St. Martin in at his personal expense and performed 238 experiments on him over several years. Beaumont had never attended medical school and had little idea how scientists work, yet he proved to be an astute experimenter. Under crude frontier conditions and with almost no equipment, he discovered many of the basic facts of gastric physiology discussed in this chapter.

"I can look directly into the cavity of the stomach, observe its motion, and almost see the process of digestion," Beaumont wrote. "I can pour in water with a funnel and put in food with a spoon, and draw them out again with a siphon." He put pieces of meat on a string into the stomach and removed them hourly for examination. He sent vials of gastric juice to the leading chemists of America and Europe, who could do little but report that it contained hydrochloric acid. He proved that digestion required HCl and could even occur outside the stomach, but he found that HCl alone didn't digest meat; gastric juice must contain some other digestive ingredient. Theodor Schwann, one of the founders of the cell theory, identified that ingredient as pepsin. Beaumont also demonstrated that gastric juice is secreted only in response to food; it didn't accumulate between meals as previously thought. He disproved the idea that hunger is caused by the walls of the empty stomach rubbing against each other.

Now disabled from wilderness travel, St. Martin agreed to participate in Beaumont's experiments in exchange for room and board—though he felt helpless and humiliated by it all. The fur trappers taunted him as "the man with a hole in his stomach," and he longed to return to his work in the wilderness. He had a wife and daughter in Canada whom he rarely got to see, and he ran away repeatedly to join them. He was once gone

for 4 years before poverty made him yield to Beaumont's financial enticement to come back. Beaumont despised St. Martin's drunkenness and profanity and was quite insensitive to his embarrassment and discomfort over the experiments. Yet St. Martin's temper enabled Beaumont to make the first direct observations of the relationship between emotion and digestion. During St. Martin's emotional outbursts, Beaumont noted that little digestion occurred—as we now know, the sympathetic nervous system inhibits digestive activity.

Beaumont published a book in 1833 that laid the foundation for modern gastric physiology and dietetics. It was enthusiastically received by the medical community and had no equal until Russian physiologist Ivan Pavlov (1849–1936) performed his celebrated experiments on digestion in animals. Building on the methods pioneered by Beaumont, Pavlov received the 1904 Nobel Prize for Physiology or Medicine.

In 1853, Beaumont slipped on some ice, suffered a blow to the base of his skull, and died a few weeks later. St. Martin continued to tour medical schools and submit to experiments by other physiologists, whose conclusions were often less correct than Beaumont's. Some, for example, attributed chemical digestion to lactic acid instead of hydrochloric acid. St. Martin lived in wretched poverty in a tiny shack with his wife and several children, and died 28 years after Beaumont. By then he was senile and believed he had been to Paris, where Beaumont had often promised to take him.

William Beaumont (1785–1853)   **Alexis St. Martin (1794–1880)**

FIGURE 25.36 Doctor and Patient in a Pioneering Study of Digestion. Today's standards of scientific ethics would prohibit Beaumont's experiments on St. Martin.

(both): Source: National Library of Medicine

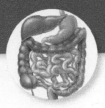

CONNECTIVE ISSUES

Effects of the DIGESTIVE SYSTEM on Other Organ Systems

ALL SYSTEMS
Digestion provides all systems with nutrients in a form usable for cellular metabolism and tissue growth and maintenance.

INTEGUMENTARY SYSTEM
Liver disease can cause the skin discoloration of jaundice; excess dietary fat is deposited in dermal and subcutaneous adipose tissue.

SKELETAL SYSTEM
Bone deposition and maintenance depend on calcium and phosphate absorption by the small intestine.

MUSCULAR SYSTEM
The liver promotes recovery from muscle fatigue by metabolizing lactic acid generated by the muscles; the liver and intestinal epithelium store iron and release it as needed for myoglobin synthesis.

NERVOUS SYSTEM
Gut–brain peptides produced in the stomach and small intestine stimulate appetite-controlling centers in the brain; chronic vomiting or diarrhea can cause electrolyte and pH imbalances that lead to nervous system dysfunction.

ENDOCRINE SYSTEM
The liver degrades hormones and limits their action; many hormones are produced by endocrine cells of the stomach, intestines, pancreas, and liver.

CIRCULATORY SYSTEM
Intestinal fluid absorption supports blood volume; the liver degrades the heme from dead erythrocytes; the liver synthesizes the albumin, most blood-clotting factors, and other plasma proteins; the liver stabilizes blood glucose level; the liver and intestinal epithelium store iron and release it as needed for hemoglobin synthesis; the liver secretes erythropoietin, which stimulates RBC production.

LYMPHATIC AND IMMUNE SYSTEMS
The small intestine is the source of lipids transported by lymphatic vessels; the intestinal mucosa is a major source of lymphocytes; acid, enzymes, and lysozyme provide innate immunity against ingested pathogens; infants acquire passive immunity by intestinal absorption of IgA from breast milk.

RESPIRATORY SYSTEM
Contraction of the abdominal muscles pushes the stomach against the diaphragm and aids in forced expiration.

URINARY SYSTEM
The liver synthesizes the urea excreted by the kidneys; this urea also contributes to the osmotic gradient that enables the kidneys to concentrate urine; intestines complement the kidneys in water and electrolyte reabsorption.

REPRODUCTIVE SYSTEM
Digestion provides nutrients for fetal growth; certain aspects of egg fertilization depend on calcium absorbed by the small intestine.

▶ Assess Your Learning Outcomes

To test your knowledge, discuss the following topics with a study partner or in writing, ideally from memory.

25.1 General Anatomy and Digestive Processes

1. Three functions of the digestive system and the five stages in which it carries these out
2. The difference between the digestive tract and the accessory organs of the digestive system; the organs that belong in each category
3. Tissue layers typical of most regions of the digestive tract
4. Functions of the enteric nervous system; its two subdivisions, their locations, and their respective functions
5. Functions of the mesenteries and their relationship to the abdominal digestive organs
6. Hormones, paracrines, and visceral reflexes that regulate motility and secretion in the digestive tract

25.2 The Mouth Through Esophagus

1. Seven functions of the oral cavity
2. Anatomical boundaries of the mouth; variations in its mucosal epithelium; and all digestive system organs contained in it
3. Anatomy of the cheeks and lips; the three regions of the lip
4. Anatomy and functions of the tongue; what forms the border between the body and root of the tongue; its intrinsic and extrinsic muscles; the lingual glands and lingual tonsils
5. Anatomy of the hard and soft palates; the two arches that mark the border between the oral cavity and pharynx
6. The structure of a typical tooth and periodontal tissues; the four kinds of teeth and number and position of each; the mode of replacement of deciduous teeth by permanent teeth; and the functions of mastication
7. Six functions of saliva; its composition and pH; general histology of salivary glands; names and function of the intrinsic salivary glands; the three pairs of extrinsic salivary glands; and how the nervous system regulates salivation

8. Anatomy of the pharynx; the pharyngeal constrictor muscles and upper esophageal sphincter, and the functions of these muscles
9. Gross anatomy and histology of the esophagus; the distribution of skeletal and smooth muscle in the esophageal wall; the location and function of the esophageal glands; the cardial orifice and lower esophageal sphincter
10. The physiology of swallowing; the swallowing center and the cranial nerves involved in the process; what occurs in the buccal and pharyngoesophageal phases of swallowing; how peristalsis is controlled; and to what extent swallowing depends on peristalsis or occurs independently of it

25.3 The Stomach

1. Anatomy and functions of the stomach; features that mark its beginning and end; and the volume of the empty stomach and its full capacity
2. Innervation of the stomach; its blood supply and relation to the hepatic portal system
3. Structure of the gastric mucosa including the gastric pits; the glands that open into them; and differences in the spatial distribution and functions of gastric, cardial, and pyloric glands; and five cell types of these glands and their respective functions
4. The composition of gastric juice
5. The cells that secrete hydrochloric acid, how they do so, and the functions of the acid
6. The difference between a zymogen and an active enzyme
7. The source of pepsinogen; how it is converted to pepsin; and the function of pepsin
8. The source and function of gastric lipase
9. The source and function of intrinsic factor; the effect of hyposecretion of intrinsic factor; and how a deficiency of intrinsic factor is treated
10. Hormones and paracrine secretions that regulate gastrointestinal function; why some of these are called gut–brain peptides
11. The nature and functions of the receptive-relaxation response and peristalsis in the stomach; the reason very little chyme is passed into the duodenum at a time

12. The degree of digestion that occurs in the stomach; what is absorbed by the stomach and what is not
13. How the stomach is protected from its own acid and enzymes
14. How gastric activity is controlled; the regulatory mechanisms of the cephalic, gastric, and intestinal phases

25.4 The Liver, Gallbladder, and Pancreas

1. The location, gross anatomy, and digestive function of the liver
2. Structure and spatial arrangement of the hepatic lobules
3. The route of blood flow through the liver
4. Composition and functions of the bile, the route of bile flow from the hepatocytes to the duodenum; and the recycling of bile acids and its relationship to the elimination of cholesterol from the body
5. Structure and function of the gallbladder, and its connection to the bile duct
6. Location, gross anatomy, and digestive functions of the pancreas
7. Structure of the pancreatic acini, the duct system, and its connection to the duodenum
8. Composition and digestive functions of pancreatic juice; the names and functions of its digestive zymogens and enzymes
9. Hormones that regulate the secretion of bile and pancreatic juice

25.5 The Small Intestine

1. Structures that mark the beginning and end of the small intestine; the three regions of the small intestine and their respective lengths and histological differences
2. How the small intestine is protected from the erosive effect of stomach acid
3. The importance of surface area for the function of the small intestine, and four features that give it a large surface area
4. Histology of the intestinal villi and crypts; the cell types found in each, and their respective functions; the relationship of the lacteal to the lymphatic system, and its function
5. Brush border enzymes of the small intestine and their functions
6. Two types of intestinal motility and their functional difference

25.6 Chemical Digestion and Absorption

1. Steps in carbohydrate digestion from the mouth to small intestine; the enzymes involved at each step and their respective contributions to carbohydrate hydrolysis
2. Mechanisms of monosaccharide absorption by the intestinal mucosa
3. Steps in protein digestion from the stomach to small intestine; the enzymes involved at each step and their respective contributions to peptide hydrolysis
4. Mechanisms of amino acid absorption by the intestinal mucosa
5. Steps in fat digestion from the stomach to small intestine; the enzymes involved at each step and their respective contributions to peptide hydrolysis
6. The necessity of emulsification for efficient fat digestion; the role of bile acids and lecithin in this process

7. Mechanisms of lipid absorption by the intestinal mucosa; the role of the lacteals; and how and why lipid absorption and transport differ from the absorption and transport of sugars and amino acids
8. Differences between emulsification droplets, micelles, and chylomicrons in lipid processing
9. Digestion of DNA and RNA in the small intestine, and the mode of absorption of their decomposition products
10. Nutrients that are not digested but simply absorbed; special aspects of the absorption of fat-soluble vitamins and vitamin B_{12}
11. Modes of absorption of water and minerals, particularly Na^+, K^+, Cl^-, Fe^{2+}, and Ca^{2+}; the roles of hepcidin, calcitriol, and parathyroid hormone in iron and calcium absorption

25.7 The Large Intestine

1. Gross anatomy, histology, and functions of the large intestine, including its six segments and total length
2. The gut microbiome of the colon; the composition and sources of flatus
3. Control of colonic motility; differences between its haustral contractions and mass movements; and the role of gastrocolic and duodenocolic reflexes
4. Mechanisms of the intrinsic and parasympathetic defecation reflexes, and of voluntary control over defecation; the neuroanatomy involved in these control mechanisms; and how the Valsalva maneuver can trigger and aid defecation

▶ Testing Your Recall

Answers in Appendix A

1. Which of the following enzymes acts in the stomach?
   a. chymotrypsin
   b. lingual lipase
   c. carboxypeptidase
   d. enteropeptidase
   e. dextrinase

2. Which of the following enzymes does *not* digest any nutrients?
   a. chymotrypsin
   b. lingual lipase
   c. carboxypeptidase
   d. enteropeptidase
   e. dextrinase

3. Which of the following is *not* an enzyme?
   a. chymotrypsin
   b. enteropeptidase
   c. secretin
   d. pepsin
   e. nucleosidase

4. The substance in question 3 that is *not* an enzyme is
   a. a zymogen.
   b. a nutrient.
   c. an emulsifier.
   d. a neurotransmitter.
   e. a hormone.

5. The lacteals absorb
   a. chylomicrons.
   b. micelles.
   c. emulsification droplets.
   d. amino acids.
   e. monosaccharides.

6. All of the following contribute to the absorptive surface area of the small intestine *except*
   a. its length.
   b. the brush border.
   c. haustra.
   d. circular folds.
   e. villi.

7. Which of the following is a periodontal tissue?
   a. the gingiva
   b. the enamel
   c. the cement
   d. the pulp
   e. the dentin

8. Anatomically, the _____ of the stomach most closely resemble the _____ of the small intestine.
   a. gastric pits, intestinal crypts
   b. pyloric glands, intestinal crypts
   c. rugae, aggregated lymphoid nodules
   d. parietal cells, goblet cells
   e. gastric glands, duodenal glands

9. Which of the following cells secrete digestive enzymes?
   a. chief cells
   b. mucous neck cells
   c. parietal cells
   d. goblet cells
   e. enteroendocrine cells

10. What phase of gastric regulation includes inhibition by the enterogastric reflex?
   a. the intestinal phase
   b. the gastric phase
   c. the buccal phase
   d. the cephalic phase
   e. the pharyngoesophageal phase

11. Cusps are a feature of the _____ surfaces of the molars and premolars.

12. The acidity of the stomach halts the action of _____ but promotes the action of _____, both of which are salivary enzymes.

13. The _____ salivary gland is named for its proximity to the ear.

14. The submucosal and myenteric plexuses collectively constitute the _____ nervous system.

15. Nervous stimulation of gastrointestinal activity is mediated mainly through the parasympathetic fibers of the _____ nerves.

STUDY GUIDE

16. Food in the stomach causes G cells to secrete _____, which in turn stimulates the secretion of HCl and pepsinogen.

17. Stellate macrophages occur in blood-filled spaces of the liver called _____.

18. The brush border enzyme that finishes the job of protein digestion, splitting the last two amino acids apart, is called _____.

19. Fats entering the duodenum are coated with lecithin and _____ to keep them emulsified and enhance the efficiency of their digestion.

20. Within the absorptive cells of the small intestine, ferritin binds the nutrient _____.

▶ Building Your Medical Vocabulary

Answers in Appendix A

State a meaning of each word element, and give a medical term from this chapter that uses it or a slight variation of it.

1. antro-

2. chylo-

3. -elle

4. emet-

5. freno-

6. hepato-

7. jejuno-

8. porto-

9. pyloro-

10. sigmo-

▶ What's Wrong with These Statements?

Answers in Appendix A

Briefly explain why each of the following statements is false, or reword it to make it true.

1. Fat is not digested until it reaches the duodenum.

2. A tooth is composed mostly of enamel.

3. Hepatocytes secrete bile into the hepatic sinusoids.

4. The ileal papilla regulates the passage of chyme from the stomach into the duodenum.

5. Lipids enter the circulation when the intestinal lacteals take up the micelles formed by the small intestine.

6. Hepcidin increases iron availability by promoting its intestinal absorption.

7. The only monosaccharide absorbed by the small intestine is glucose.

8. Most of the water in the digestive tract is reabsorbed in the large intestine.

9. Secretin is a hormone that stimulates the stomach to secrete digestive enzymes.

10. Tight junctions of the small intestine prevent anything from leaking between the epithelial cells.

▶ Testing Your Comprehension

1. On Monday, David has a waffle with syrup for breakfast at 7:00, and by 10:30 he feels hungry again. On Tuesday, he has bacon and eggs and feels satisfied until his noon lunch hour approaches. Assuming an equal quantity of food on both days and all other factors to be equal, explain this difference.

2. Which of these do you think would have the most severe effect on digestion: surgical removal of the stomach, gallbladder, or pancreas? Explain.

3. What do carboxypeptidase and aminopeptidase have in common? Identify as many differences between them as you can.

4. What do micelles and chylomicrons have in common? Identify as many differences between them as you can.

5. Explain why most dietary lipids must be absorbed by the lacteals rather than by the blood capillaries of a villus.

NUTRITION AND METABOLISM

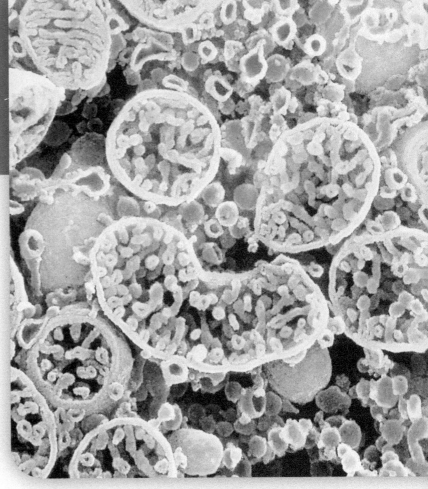

Mitochondria (green) and smooth endoplasmic reticulum in a cell of the ovary (SEM)

P.M. Motta/S. Makabe & T. Nagur/SPL/Science Source

Anatomy & Physiology *Revealed® 4.0*

Module 12: Digestive System

BRUSHING UP

- Understanding metabolism requires prior familiarity with the basic concepts of metabolism in section 2.3d and metabolic pathways in section 2.4f.

- You should be familiar with the chemistry of cholesterol and saturated and unsaturated fats before reading on LDLs, HDLs, and other blood lipoproteins in this chapter (see section 2.4d).

- Lipoprotein processing involves receptor-mediated endocytosis, introduced in section 3.3f.

- The catabolic reactions discussed in this chapter are predominantly ways of making ATP. You must understand the structure and functions of ATP (see fig. 2.29 and the associated text).

- Insulin and glucagon are particularly important in regulating metabolism; brush up on these hormones in section 17.3f if necessary.

- In the regulation of body temperature, heat transfer follows the principle of flow down thermal gradients introduced in section 1.6e.

Nutrition is the starting point and basis for all human form and function. From the time a single-celled, fertilized egg divides in two, nutrition provides the matter needed for cell division, growth, and development. It is the source of fuel that provides the energy for all biological work, and of the raw materials for replacement of worn-out biomolecules and cells. The fact that nutrients are only the raw materials means, further, that chemical change—metabolism—lies at the foundation of form and function. In chapter 25, we saw how the digestive system breaks nutrients down into usable form and absorbs them into the blood and lymph. We now consider these nutrients in more depth, follow their fate after absorption, and explore related issues of metabolism and body heat.

26.1 Nutrition

Expected Learning Outcomes

When you have completed this section, you should be able to

a. describe some factors that regulate hunger and satiety;

b. define *nutrient* and list the six major categories of nutrients;

c. state the function of each class of macronutrients, the approximate amounts required in the diet, and some major dietary sources of each;

d. name the blood lipoproteins, state their functions, and describe how they differ from each other; and

e. name the major vitamins and minerals required by the body and the general functions they serve.

26.1a Body Weight and Energy Balance

The subject of nutrition quickly brings to mind the subject of body weight and the popular desire to control it. Weight is determined by one's energy balance—if energy intake and output are equal, body weight is stable. We gain weight if intake exceeds output and lose weight if output exceeds intake. Body weight usually remains quite stable over many years' time and seems to have a homeostatic set point. This has been experimentally demonstrated in animals. If an animal is force-fed until it becomes obese and then allowed to feed at will, it voluntarily reduces intake and soon stabilizes at its former weight. Similarly, if an animal is undernourished until it loses much of its weight and then allowed to feed at will, it increases its intake and again quickly stabilizes at its former weight.

In humans, the set point varies greatly from person to person, and body weight results from a combination of hereditary and environmental influences. From studies of identical twins and other people, it appears that about 30% to 50% of the variation in human weight is due to heredity, and the rest to factors such as eating and exercise habits.

26.1b Appetite

The struggle for weight control often seems to be a struggle against the appetite. Since the early 1990s, physiologists have discovered a still-growing list of peptide hormones and regulatory pathways that control short- and long-term appetite and body weight. Some of the hormones have been called *gut–brain peptides* because they act as two-way chemical signals between the gastrointestinal tract and brain. A few will be described here to give some idea of regulatory mechanisms known to date and where a great deal of research is currently focused.

Short-Term Regulators of Appetite

The following peptides work over periods of minutes to hours, making one feel hungry and begin eating, then feel satiated and end a meal:

- **Ghrelin.**[1] This is secreted by parietal cells in the gastric fundus, especially when the stomach is empty. It produces the sensation of hunger and stimulates the hypothalamus to secrete growth hormone–releasing hormone, priming the body to take advantage of the nutrients about to be absorbed. Within an hour after eating, ghrelin secretion ceases.

- **Peptide YY (PYY).** This hormone is secreted by enteroendocrine cells in the ileum and colon, which sense that food has arrived even as it enters the stomach. They secrete PYY long before the chyme reaches the ileum, and in quantities proportional to the calories consumed. The primary effect of PYY is to signal satiety and terminate eating. Thus, ghrelin is one of the signals that begins a meal, and PYY is one of the signals that ends it. PYY remains elevated well after a meal. It acts as an *ileal brake* that prevents the stomach from emptying too quickly, and therefore prolongs the sense of satiety.

---

[1]named partly from *ghre* = growth, and partly as an acronym derived from growth hormone–releasing hormone

- **Cholecystokinin (CCK).** CCK is secreted by enteroendocrine cells in the duodenum and jejunum. It stimulates the secretion of bile and pancreatic enzymes, but also stimulates the brain and sensory fibers of the vagus nerves, producing an appetite-suppressing effect. Thus, it joins PYY as a signal to stop eating.

- **Amylin.** This hormone from the beta cells of the pancreatic islets also produces a feeling of satiety and winds down the digestive activities of the stomach.

Long-Term Regulators of Appetite

Other peptides regulate appetite, metabolic rate, and body weight over the longer term, thus governing one's average rate of caloric intake and energy expenditure over periods of weeks to years. The following two members of this group work as "adiposity signals," informing the brain of how much adipose tissue the body has and activating mechanisms for adding or reducing fat.

- **Leptin.**[2] Leptin is secreted by adipocytes throughout the body. Its level is proportional to one's fat stores, so this is the brain's primary way of knowing how much body fat we have. Adipose tissue is innervated by thick bundles of

---

[2]*lept* = thin

DEEPER INSIGHT 26.1

CLINICAL APPLICATION

Obesity

Obesity is clinically defined as a weight more than 20% above the recommended norm for one's age, sex, and height. In the United States, about 30% of the population is obese and another 35% is overweight; there has lately been an alarming increase in the number of children who are morbidly obese by the age of 10. You can judge whether you are overweight or obese by calculating your *body mass index (BMI)*. If W is your weight in kilograms and H is your height in meters, $BMI = W/H^2$. (Or if using weight in pounds and height in inches, $BMI = 703W/H^2$.) A BMI of 20 to 25 kg/m^2 is considered to be optimal for most people. A BMI over 27 kg/m^2 is considered overweight, and above 30 kg/m^2 is considered obese **(fig. 26.1).**

Excess weight shortens life expectancy and increases a person's risk of atherosclerosis, hypertension, diabetes mellitus, joint pain and degeneration, kidney stones, and gallstones; cancer of the breast, uterus, and liver in women; and cancer of the colon, rectum, and prostate in men. Excess thoracic fat impairs breathing and results in increased blood P_{CO_2}, sleepiness, and reduced vitality. Obesity is also a significant impediment to some surgeries.

Heredity plays as much a role in obesity as in height, and even more than in many other disorders generally acknowledged to be hereditary. However, a predisposition to obesity is often greatly worsened by overfeeding in infancy and childhood. Consumption of excess calories in childhood causes adipocytes to increase in size and number. In adulthood, adipocytes don't multiply except in some extreme weight gains; their number remains constant while weight gains and losses result from changes in cell size (cellular hypertrophy).

As so many dieters learn, it is very difficult to substantially reduce one's adult weight. Most diets are unsuccessful over the long run as dieters lose and regain the same weight over and over. From an evolutionary standpoint, this is not surprising. The body's appetite- and weight-regulating mechanisms have evolved more to limit weight loss than weight gain, for a scarcity of food was surely a more common problem than a food surplus for our prehistoric ancestors. Were it not for the mechanisms that thwart weight loss, our ancestors might not have made it through the lean eons and we might not be here; but now that we're surrounded with a glut of tempting food, these survival mechanisms have become mechanisms of pathology.

Understandably, pharmaceutical companies are keenly interested in developing effective weight-control drugs. There could be an enormous profit, for example, in a drug that inhibits ghrelin signaling or enhances or mimics leptin or melanocortin signaling. Such efforts have so far met with little success, but clearly a prerequisite to drug development is a better understanding of appetite-regulating peptides and their receptors.

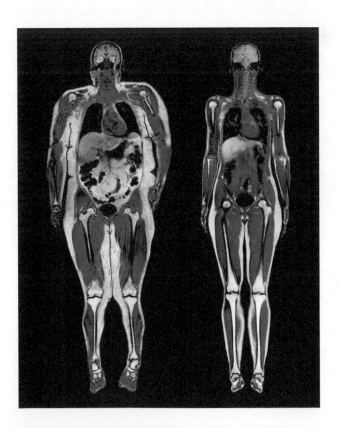

FIGURE 26.1 MRI Images of Persons with Obesity and Normal Weight. The individual on the left is a 40-year-old female 168 cm (5 ft 6 in.) tall, weighing 113 kg (250 lb), with a BMI of 40.3 kg/m^2. The adipose tissue is yellowish-white. Note the large amount of *subcutaneous fat* between the skin and muscle and *mesenteric fat* in the abdominal cavity.

Marty Chobot/National Geographic Creative

sympathetic nerve fibers. Leptin stimulates these fibers to secrete norepinephrine, which, in turn, stimulates fat breakdown *(lipolysis)*. Animals with a leptin deficiency or a defect in leptin receptors exhibit *hyperphagia* (overeating) and extreme obesity. With few exceptions, however, obese humans are not leptin-deficient or aided by leptin injections. *Leptin insensitivity* is a more common factor in obesity—a receptor defect rather than a hormone deficiency. Adipose tissue is increasingly seen as an important source of multiple hormones that influence the body's energy balance.

- **Insulin.** Insulin is secreted by the pancreatic beta cells. It stimulates glucose and amino acid uptake and promotes glycogen and fat synthesis. But it also has receptors in the brain and functions, like leptin, as an index of the body's fat stores. It has a weaker effect on appetite than leptin does, however.

An important brain center for appetite regulation is the **arcuate nucleus** of the hypothalamus. The aforementioned peptides have receptors in the arcuate nucleus, although they act on other target cells in the body as well. The arcuate nucleus has two neural networks involved in hunger. One group secretes **neuropeptide Y (NPY),** itself a potent appetite stimulant. The other secretes **melanocortin,** which inhibits eating. Ghrelin stimulates NPY secretion, whereas insulin, PYY, and leptin inhibit it. Leptin also stimulates melanocortin secretion **(fig. 26.2)** and inhibits the secretion of appetite stimulants called *endocannabinoids,* named for their resemblance to the tetrahydrocannabinol (THC) of marijuana.

▶▶▶ APPLY WHAT YOU KNOW

A friend encourages you to invest in a company that proposes to produce tablets of leptin and CCK to be taken as oral diet pills. Would you consider this a wise investment? Why or why not?

Gut–brain peptides certainly aren't the whole story behind appetite regulation. Hunger is also stimulated partly by gastric peristalsis. Mild **hunger contractions** begin soon after the stomach is emptied and increase in intensity over a period of hours. They can become quite a painful and powerful incentive to eat, yet they don't affect the amount of food consumed—this remains much the same even when nervous connections to the stomach and intestines are severed to cut off all conscious perception of hunger contractions. Food intake is terminated not only by PYY and CCK, but also in ways similar to the way water intake slakes the thirst (see section 24.1c). Merely chewing and swallowing food briefly satisfy the appetite, even if the food is removed through an esophageal fistula (opening) before reaching the stomach. Inflating the stomach with a balloon inhibits hunger even in an animal that hasn't actually swallowed any food. Satiety produced by these mechanisms, however, is very short-lived. Lasting satiety depends on the absorption of nutrients into the blood.

Appetite isn't merely a question of *how much* but also *what kind* of food is consumed. Even animals shift their diets from one kind of food to another, apparently because some foods provide nutrients that others do not. In humans, different neurotransmitters also seem to govern the appetite for different classes of nutrients.

For example, *norepinephrine* stimulates the appetite for carbohydrates, *galanin* for fatty foods, and *endorphins* for protein.

26.1c Calories

One calorie is the amount of heat that will raise the temperature of 1 g of water 1°C. One thousand calories is called a Calorie (capital *C*) in dietetics and a **kilocalorie (kcal)** in biochemistry and physiology. The relevance of calories to physiology is that they are a measure of the capacity to do biological work.

Nearly all dietary calories come from carbohydrates, proteins, and fats. Carbohydrates and proteins yield about 4 kcal/g when completely oxidized, and fats yield about 9 kcal/g. Alcohol (7.1 kcal/g) and sugary foods promote malnutrition by providing "empty calories"—they suppress the appetite but fail to provide other nutrients the body requires (see Deeper Insight 26.4). In sound nutrition, the body's energy needs are met by more complex foods that simultaneously meet the need for proteins, lipids, vitamins, and other nutrients.

When a chemical is described as **fuel** in this chapter, we mean it is oxidized solely or primarily to extract energy from it. The extracted energy is usually used to make ATP, which then transfers the energy to other physiological processes (see fig. 2.30).

26.1d Nutrients

A **nutrient** is any ingested chemical that is absorbed into the tissues and used for growth, repair, or maintenance of the body. Nutrients fall into six major classes: water, carbohydrates, lipids, proteins, minerals, and vitamins. Water, carbohydrates, lipids, and proteins are considered **macronutrients** because they must be consumed in relatively large quantities. Minerals and vitamins are called **micronutrients** because only small quantities are required. We measure dietary requirements in terms of grams per day for macronutrients but only milligrams to micrograms per day for micronutrients.

Many nutrients can be synthesized by the body when they are unavailable from the diet. The body is incapable, however, of synthesizing minerals, most vitamins, eight of the amino acids, and one to three of the fatty acids. These are called **essential nutrients** because it is essential that they be included in the diet.

Table 26.1 summarizes the functions and recommended daily intake of the macronutrient classes. (Micronutrients are discussed and tabulated later in this section.) The tabulated data are daily intakes recommended by the U.S. National Academy of Medicine for persons 19 to 50 years old. The Academy uses the term **recommended dietary allowance (RDA)** when there are enough sound data to say what intake should meet the needs of 97% or more of men and women in a given age group. In cases of less certainty, owing to less data, the Academy gives values called **adequate intake (AI),** the daily consumption thought to meet the needs of persons in a given age range. RDA and AI are components of a broader system of nutritional recommendations called *dietary reference intakes (DRIs),* which also include recommendations for special classes of individuals such as infants, children, and pregnant or lactating women, and tolerable upper

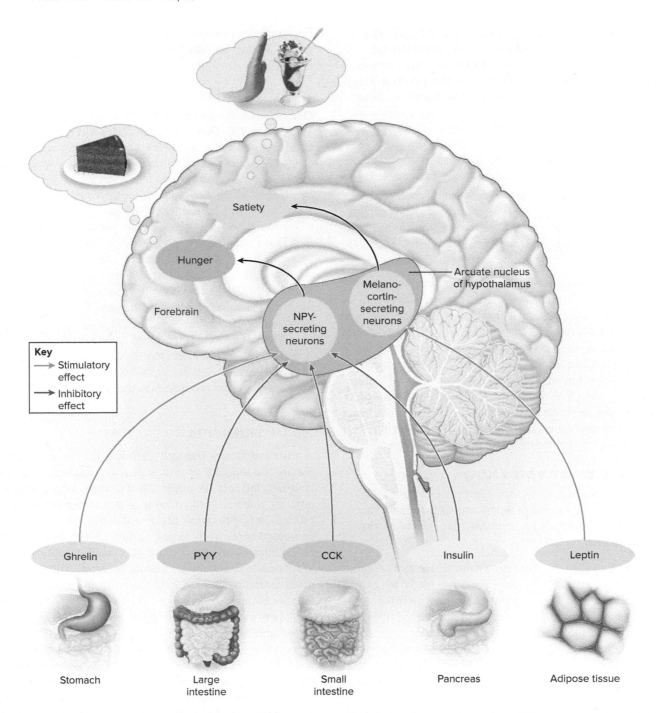

FIGURE 26.2 Principal Pathways of Appetite Regulation by Gut–Brain Peptides. Tissues and organs at the bottom of the figure are sources of peptides that stimulate or inhibit appetite-regulating neurons in the arcuate nucleus of the hypothalamus. Depending on the balance of stimulation and inhibition, those neurons secrete NPY or melanocortin to create a conscious sensation of hunger or satiety, respectively. (The arcuate nucleus is shown far larger than its real size.) (PYY = peptide YY; CCK = cholecystokinin; NPY = neuropeptide Y)

limits on intake to avoid toxic excesses such as iron overload and hypervitaminosis (explained shortly).

26.1e Carbohydrates

A well-nourished average adult has about 440 g of carbohydrate in the body, most of it in three places: 325 g of muscle glycogen, 90 to 100 g of liver glycogen, and 15 to 20 g of blood glucose.

Sugars function as a structural component of other molecules including glycoproteins, glycolipids, ATP and related nucleotides (GTP, cAMP, etc.), and nucleic acids; they can also be converted to amino acids and fats. Most of the body's carbohydrate, however, serves as fuel—an easily oxidized source of chemical energy. Most cells meet their energy needs from a combination of carbohydrates and fats, but some cells, such as neurons and erythrocytes, depend almost exclusively on carbohydrates. Even a brief period

TABLE 26.1	Macronutrient Requirements and Functions		
Nutrient	RDA/AI, Males	RDA/AI, Females	Representative Functions
Water	3.7 L	2.7 L	Solvent; coolant; reactant or product in many metabolic reactions (especially hydrolysis and condensation); dilutes and eliminates metabolic wastes; supports blood volume and pressure
Carbohydrate	130 g	130 g	Fuel; a component of nucleic acids, ATP and other nucleotides, glycoproteins, and glycolipids
Protein	56 g	46 g	Muscle contraction; ciliary and flagellar motility; structure of cellular membranes and extracellular material; enzymes; major component of connective tissues; transport of plasma lipids; some hormones; oxygen-binding and -transport pigments; blood-clotting factors; blood viscosity and osmolarity; antibodies; immune recognition; neuromodulators; buffers; emergency fuel
Fat	20% to 35% of total calories		Fuel; plasma membrane structure; myelin sheaths of nerve fibers; hormones; eicosanoids; bile acids; insulation; protective padding around organs; absorption of fat-soluble vitamins; vitamin D synthesis; some blood-clotting factors

of **hypoglycemia**[3] (deficiency of blood glucose) causes nervous system disturbances felt as weakness or dizziness.

Blood glucose concentration is therefore carefully regulated, mainly through the interplay of insulin and glucagon. Among other effects, these hormones regulate the balance between glycogen and free blood glucose. If blood glucose concentration drops too low, the body draws on its stores of glycogen to meet its energy needs. If glycogen stores are depleted, physical endurance is greatly reduced. Thus, it is important to consume enough carbohydrate to ensure that the body maintains adequate stores of glycogen for periods of exercise and fasting (including sleep).

Carbohydrate intake also influences the metabolism of other nutrients. When glucose and glycogen levels are too low to meet our energy needs, we oxidize fat as fuel; conversely, excess carbohydrate is converted to fat. This is why the consumption of starchy and sugary foods has a pronounced effect on body weight. It is unwise, however, to try to "burn off fat" by excessively reducing carbohydrate intake. The complete and efficient oxidation of fats depends on adequate carbohydrate intake and the presence of certain intermediates of carbohydrate metabolism. If these are lacking, fats are incompletely oxidized to ketone bodies, which may cause metabolic acidosis.

Requirements

Because carbohydrates are rapidly oxidized, they are required in greater amounts than any other nutrient except water. The RDA for both sexes is about 130 g. The brain alone consumes about 120 g of glucose per day. Most Americans get about 40% to 50% of their calories from carbohydrates, but highly active people should get up to 60%.

The National Academy of Medicine recommends that no more than 25% of one's daily calories come from added sugars beyond those that occur naturally in food. Carbohydrate consumption in the United States has become excessive over the past century, however, because of a combination of fondness for sweets,

DEEPER INSIGHT 26.2
EVOLUTIONARY MEDICINE

Evolution of the Sweet Tooth

Our craving for sugar doubtlessly originated in our prehistoric ancestors. Not only did they have to work much harder to survive than we do, but high-calorie foods were scarce and people were at constant risk of starvation. Those who were highly motivated to seek and consume sugary, high-calorie foods passed their "sweet tooth" on to us, their descendants—along with a similarly adaptive appetite for other rare but vital nutrients, namely fat and salt. The tastes that were essential to our ancestors' survival can now be a disadvantage in a culture in which salty, fatty, and sugary foods are all too easy to obtain; the food industry eagerly capitalizes on these tastes.

increased use of sugar in processed foods, and reduced physical activity (see Deeper Insight 26.2). A century ago, Americans consumed an average of 1.8 kg (4 lb) of sugar per year. Now, with sucrose and high-fructose corn syrup so widely used in processed foods and beverages, the average American ingests 200 to 300 g of carbohydrate per day and the equivalent of 27 kg (60 lb) of table sugar and 21 kg (46 lb) of corn syrup per year. A single 355 mL (12 oz) serving of nondiet soft drink contains 38 to 43 g of sugar (about 8 teaspoons).

Dietary carbohydrates come in three principal forms: monosaccharides, disaccharides, and polysaccharides (complex carbohydrates). The only nutritionally significant polysaccharide is starch. Although glycogen is a polysaccharide, only trivial amounts of it are present in meat. Cellulose, another polysaccharide, isn't considered a nutrient because it is not digested and never enters the human tissues. Its importance as dietary fiber, however, is discussed shortly.

The three major dietary disaccharides are sucrose, lactose, and maltose. The major monosaccharides are glucose, galactose, and fructose, which arise mainly from the digestion of starch and disaccharides. The small intestine and liver convert fructose and

---

[3]*hypo* = below normal; *glyc* = sugar; *emia* = blood condition

galactose to glucose, so ultimately all carbohydrate digestion generates glucose. Outside of the hepatic portal system, glucose is the only monosaccharide present in the blood in significant quantity; thus, it is known as *blood sugar*. Its concentration is normally maintained at 70 to 110 mg/dL in peripheral venous blood.

▶▶▶ APPLY WHAT YOU KNOW

Glucose concentration is about 15 to 30 mg/dL higher in arterial blood than in most venous blood. Explain why.

The effect of a dietary carbohydrate on one's blood glucose level can be expressed as the **glycemic index (GI).** The effect of ingesting 50 g of glucose on blood glucose level over the next 2 hours is set at 100, and the effects of other carbohydrates are expressed in relation to this. A carbohydrate with a GI of 50, for example, would produce half the effect of pure glucose. Carbohydrates with a high GI ($\geq$70) are quickly digested and absorbed and rapidly raise blood glucose. Such carbohydrates are found, for example, in white bread, white rice, baked white potatoes, and many processed breakfast cereals. High-GI carbohydrates stimulate a high insulin demand and raise the risk of obesity and type 2 diabetes mellitus. Carbohydrates with a low GI ($\leq$55) are digested more slowly and raise blood glucose more gradually. These include the carbohydrates found in most fruits and vegetables, legumes, milk, and grainy bread and pasta. The glycemic index of a given food varies, however, from person to person and even in the same person from day to day, and depends as well on how the food is cooked.

Ideally, most carbohydrate intake should be in the form of starch. This is partly because foods that provide starch also usually provide other nutrients. Simple sugars not only provide empty calories but also promote tooth decay. A typical American, however, now obtains only 50% of his or her carbohydrates from starch and the other 50% from sucrose and corn syrup.

Dietary Sources

Nearly all dietary carbohydrates come from plants—particularly grains, legumes, fruits, and root vegetables. Sucrose is refined from sugarcane and sugar beets. Fructose is present in fruits, honey, and corn syrup. Maltose is present in some foods such as germinating cereal grains. Lactose is the most abundant solute in cow's milk (about 4.6% lactose by weight).

26.1f Fiber

Dietary fiber refers to all fibrous materials of plant and animal origin that resist digestion. Most is plant matter—the carbohydrates cellulose and pectin and such noncarbohydrates as gums and lignin. Although it's not a nutrient, fiber is an essential component of the diet. The RDA of fiber is about 25 g for females and 38 g for males, but average intake varies greatly from country to country— from 40 to 150 g/day in India and Africa to only 12 g/day in the United States.

Water-soluble fiber includes pectin and certain other carbohydrates found in oats, beans, peas, carrots, brown rice, and fruits. It reduces blood cholesterol and low-density lipoprotein (LDL) levels (see Deeper Insight 19.4). **Water-insoluble fiber**

includes cellulose, hemicellulose, and lignin. It apparently has no effect on cholesterol or LDL levels, but it absorbs water and swells, thereby softening the stool and increasing its bulk by 40% to 100%. This effect stretches the colon and stimulates peristalsis, thereby quickening the passage of feces. In doing so, water-insoluble fiber reduces the risk of constipation and diverticulitis (see table 25.3).

Studies are contradictory as to whether dietary fiber has a clear effect on the incidence of colorectal cancer. Excess fiber can actually have a deleterious effect on health by interfering with the absorption of iron, calcium, magnesium, phosphorus, and some trace elements.

26.1g Lipids

Healthy young men and women average, respectively, about 15% and 25% fat by weight. Fat accounts for most of the body's stored energy. Lesser amounts of phospholipid, cholesterol, and other lipids also play vital structural and physiological roles.

A well-nourished adult meets 80% to 90% of his or her resting energy needs from fat. Fat is superior to carbohydrates for energy storage for two reasons: (1) Carbohydrates are hydrophilic, absorb water, and thus expand and occupy more space in the tissues. Fat, however, is hydrophobic, contains almost no water, and is a more compact energy storage substance. (2) Fat is less oxidized than carbohydrate and contains over twice as much energy (9 kcal/g of fat compared with 4 kcal/g of carbohydrate). A man's typical fat reserves contain enough energy for 119 hours of running, whereas his carbohydrate stores would last for only 1.6 hours.

Fat has **glucose-sparing** and **protein-sparing effects**—as long as enough fat is available to meet the energy needs of the tissues, protein isn't catabolized for fuel and glucose is spared for consumption by cells that can't use fat, such as neurons.

Vitamins A, D, E, and K are fat-soluble vitamins, which depend on dietary fat for their absorption by the intestine. People who ingest less than 20 g of fat per day are at risk of vitamin deficiency because there isn't enough fat in the intestine to transport these vitamins into the tissues.

Phospholipids and cholesterol are major structural components of plasma membranes and myelin. Cholesterol is also important as a precursor of steroid hormones, bile acids, and vitamin D. Thromboplastin, an essential blood-clotting factor, is a lipoprotein. Two fatty acids—arachidonic acid and linoleic acid—are precursors of prostaglandins and other eicosanoids.

In addition to its metabolic and structural roles, fat has important protective and insulating functions described in section 5.3c.

Requirements

Fat should account for no more than 35% of one's daily caloric intake, and no more than 10% of fat intake should be saturated fat. A typical American consumes 30 to 150 g of fat per day and obtains 40% to 50% of his or her calories from fat. It is important that the diet include certain **essential fatty acids**—so named because the body cannot synthesize these from other precursors and therefore must obtain them from food. These include linoleic acid

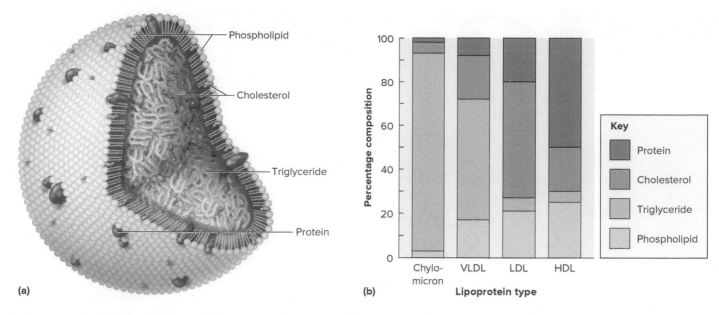

FIGURE 26.3 Serum Lipoproteins. (a) Structure of a lipoprotein. (b) Lipid and protein composition of the lipoprotein classes.

and possibly linolenic and arachidonic acids; there are differences of opinion about the body's ability to synthesize the last two. As long as 1% to 2% of the total energy intake comes from linoleic acid, people show no signs of essential fatty acid deficiency. In the typical Western diet, linoleic acid provides about 6% of the calories. Other fatty acids can be synthesized in the body if lacking from the diet.

Sources

Saturated fats are predominantly of animal origin. They occur in meat, egg yolks, and dairy products but also in some plant products such as coconut and palm oils (common in nondairy coffee creamers and other products). Processed foods such as hydrogenated oils and vegetable shortening are also high in saturated fat, which is therefore abundant in many baked goods. Unsaturated fats predominate in nuts, seeds, and most vegetable oils. The essential fatty acids are amply provided by the vegetable oils in mayonnaise, salad dressings, and margarine and by whole grains and vegetables. Excessive consumption of saturated and unsaturated fats is a risk factor for diabetes mellitus, cardiovascular disease, and breast and colon cancer.

The richest source of cholesterol is egg yolks, but it is also prevalent in milk products; shellfish (especially shrimp); organ meats such as kidneys, liver, and brains; and other mammalian meat. Foods of plant origin contain only insignificant traces of cholesterol. The serum cholesterol level is strongly influenced by the types and quantity of fatty acids in the diet.

Cholesterol and Serum Lipoproteins

Lipids are an important part of the diet and must be transported to all cells of the body, yet they are hydrophobic and don't dissolve in the aqueous blood plasma. This problem is overcome by complexes called **lipoproteins**—tiny droplets with a core of cholesterol and triglycerides and a coating of proteins and phospholipids **(fig. 26.3a).** The coating not only enables the lipids to remain suspended in the blood, but also serves as a recognition marker for cells that absorb them. The complexes are often referred to as *serum lipoproteins* because their concentrations are expressed in terms of a volume of blood serum, not whole blood.

Lipoproteins are classified into four major categories (and some lesser ones) by their density: **chylomicrons, high-density lipoproteins (HDLs), low-density lipoproteins (LDLs),** and **very-low-density lipoproteins (VLDLs) (fig. 26.3b).** The higher the proportion of lipid to protein, the lower the density; this is easy to remember if you bear in mind that oil and fat float in water because of their relatively low density. These particles also differ considerably in size: Chylomicrons range widely from 75 to 1,200 nm in diameter, but the others diminish in size from VLDLs (30–80 nm), to LDLs (18–25 nm), to HDLs (5–12 nm). Their most important differences, however, are in composition and function.

Figure 26.4 shows the three primary pathways by which blood lipoproteins are made and processed. Chylomicrons form in the absorptive cells of the small intestine and then pass into the lymphatic system and ultimately the bloodstream. Endothelial cells of the blood capillaries have a surface enzyme called **lipoprotein lipase** that hydrolyzes chylomicron triglycerides into monoglycerides and free fatty acids (FFAs). These products can then pass through the capillary walls into adipocytes, where they are resynthesized into storage triglycerides. Some FFAs, however, remain in the blood plasma bound to albumin. The remainder of a chylomicron after the triglycerides have been extracted, called a *chylomicron remnant,* is removed and degraded by the liver.

VLDLs, produced by the liver, transport lipids to the adipose tissue for storage. When their triglycerides are removed in the adipose tissue, the VLDLs become LDLs and contain mostly cholesterol. Cells that need cholesterol (usually for membrane structure or steroid hormone synthesis) absorb LDLs by receptor-mediated

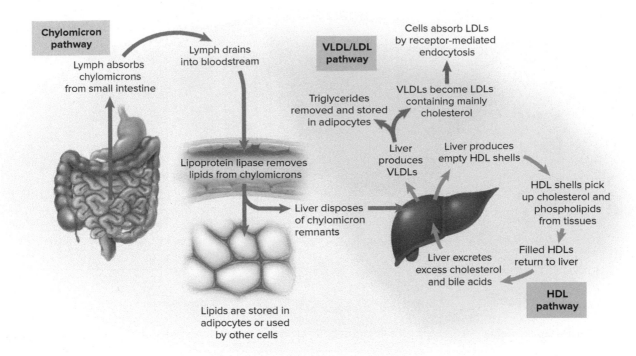

FIGURE 26.4 Lipoprotein Processing. Pathways of processing chylomicrons, VLDL/LDLs, and HDLs.

❓ *Why is a high HDL:LDL ratio healthier than a high LDL:HDL ratio?*

endocytosis, digest them with lysosomal enzymes, and release the cholesterol for cellular use.

HDL production begins in the liver, which produces an empty, collapsed protein shell. This shell travels in the blood and picks up cholesterol and phospholipids from other organs. The next time it circulates through the liver, the liver removes the cholesterol and eliminates it in the bile as either cholesterol or bile acids. HDLs are therefore a vehicle for removing excess cholesterol from the body.

It is desirable to maintain a total cholesterol concentration of 200 mg/dL or less in the blood plasma. From 200 to 239 mg/dL is considered borderline high, and levels over 240 mg/dL are pathological. Most of the body's cholesterol is endogenous (internally synthesized) rather than dietary, and the body compensates for variations in dietary intake. High intake steps down cholesterol synthesis by the liver, whereas a low dietary intake steps it up. Thus, lowering dietary cholesterol has little effect on blood cholesterol levels. The Academy of Medicine recommends consuming no more than 300 mg of cholesterol per day, which is only a little more than the amount in one egg yolk (240 mg). However, recent studies have found no correlation between dietary cholesterol intake and levels of serum cholesterol, and dietary cholesterol has lately been dismissed as no longer a concern for public health.

More important is the fact that certain saturated fatty acids (SFAs) raise serum cholesterol level. For example, palmitic acid, a 16-carbon SFA, raises serum cholesterol by blocking its uptake by the tissues (yet stearic acid, an 18-carbon SFA, doesn't raise it). Some food advertising is deceptive on this point. It may truthfully advertise a food as being cholesterol-free, but neglect to mention

that it contains SFAs that may raise the consumer's cholesterol level anyway. A moderate reduction of saturated fatty acid intake can lower blood cholesterol by 15% to 20%—considerably more effective than reducing dietary cholesterol itself. An unsaturated fatty acid, linoleic acid, has a cholesterol-lowering effect.

Vigorous exercise also lowers blood cholesterol levels. The mechanism is somewhat roundabout: Exercise reduces the sensitivity of the right atrium of the heart to blood pressure, so the heart secretes less natriuretic peptide. Consequently, the kidneys excrete less sodium and water, and the blood volume rises. This dilutes the lipoproteins in the blood, and the adipocytes compensate by producing more lipoprotein lipase. The adipocytes therefore consume more blood triglycerides. This shrinks VLDL particles, which shed some of their cholesterol in the process, and HDLs pick up this free cholesterol for removal by the liver.

Blood cholesterol isn't the only important measure of healthy lipid concentrations. A high LDL concentration is a warning sign because, as you can see from the function of LDLs described previously, it signifies a high rate of cholesterol deposition in the arteries. In the popular media, LDLs are often called "bad cholesterol"—a misleading expression, since these lipoproteins are made of more than just cholesterol, and there is only one kind of cholesterol, which does more overall good than harm. LDLs are elevated not only by saturated fats but also by cigarette smoking, coffee, and stress. A high proportion of HDL—so-called "good cholesterol"—is beneficial because it indicates that cholesterol is being removed from the arteries and transported to the liver for disposal. Thus it is desirable to increase your ratio of HDL to LDL. This is best done with a diet low in calories and saturated fats and is promoted by regular aerobic exercise.

26.1h Proteins

Protein constitutes about 12% to 15% of the body mass; 65% of it is in the skeletal muscles. Proteins are responsible for muscle contraction and the motility of cilia and flagella. They are a major structural component of all cellular membranes, with multiple roles such as membrane receptors, pumps, ion channels, and cell-identity markers. Fibrous proteins such as collagen, elastin, and keratin make up much of the structure of bone, cartilage, tendons, ligaments, skin, hair, and nails. Globular proteins include antibodies, hormones, neuromodulators, hemoglobin, myoglobin, and about 2,000 enzymes that control nearly every aspect of cellular metabolism. They also include the albumin and other plasma proteins that maintain blood viscosity and osmolarity and transport lipids and some other plasma solutes. Proteins buffer the pH of body fluids and contribute to the resting membrane potentials of all cells. No other class of biomolecules has such a broad variety of functions.

Requirements

For persons of average weight, the RDA of protein is 46 to 56 g, depending on age and sex. Multiplying your weight in pounds by 0.37 or your weight in kilograms by 0.8 gives an estimate of your protein RDA in grams. A higher intake is recommended, however, under conditions of stress, infection, injury, and pregnancy. Infants and children require more protein than adults relative to body weight. Excessive protein intake, however, overloads the kidneys with nitrogenous waste and can cause renal damage. This is a risk in certain high-protein fad diets.

Total protein intake isn't the only significant measure of dietary adequacy. The nutritional value of a protein depends on whether it supplies the right amino acids in the proportions needed for building human proteins. Adults can synthesize 12 of the 20 amino acids from other organic compounds when they're not available from the diet, but there are 8 **essential amino acids** that we can't synthesize: isoleucine, leucine, lysine, methionine, phenylalanine, threonine, tryptophan, and valine. (Infants also require histidine.) In addition, 2 amino acids can be synthesized only from essential amino acids: cysteine from methionine and tyrosine from phenylalanine. The other 10 (9 in infants) are called **inessential amino acids**—not because the body doesn't need them but because it can synthesize its own when the diet doesn't supply them.

When a protein is to be synthesized, all of the necessary amino acids must be present at once; if even one is missing, the protein cannot be made. High-quality **complete proteins** are those that provide all essential amino acids in the necessary proportions for human tissue growth, maintenance, and nitrogen balance. Lower-quality **incomplete proteins** lack one or more essential amino acids. For example, cereals are low in lysine and legumes are low in methionine.

Protein quality is also determined by **net protein utilization**—the percentage of the amino acids in a protein that the human body uses. We typically use 70% to 90% of animal protein but only 40% to 70% of plant protein. It therefore takes a larger serving of plant protein than animal protein to meet our needs—for example, we need 400 g (about 14 oz) of rice and beans to provide as much usable protein as 115 g (about 4 oz) of lean hamburger. However, reducing meat intake and increasing plant intake have advantages. Among other considerations, plant foods provide more vitamins, minerals, and fiber; less saturated fat; no cholesterol; and less pesticide. In an increasingly crowded world, it must also be borne in mind that it requires far more land (and often habitat destruction) to produce meat than to produce food crops.

Dietary Sources

The animal proteins of meat, eggs, and dairy products closely match human proteins in amino acid composition. Thus, animal products provide high-quality complete protein, whereas plant proteins are incomplete. Nevertheless, this doesn't mean that your dietary protein *must* come from meat; indeed, about two-thirds of the world's population receives adequate protein nutrition from diets containing very little meat. We can combine plant foods so that one provides what another lacks—beans and rice, for example, are a complementary combination of legume and cereal. Beans provide the isoleucine and lysine lacking in grains, while rice provides the tryptophan and cysteine lacking in beans.

Nitrogen Balance

Proteins are our chief dietary source of nitrogen. **Nitrogen balance** is a state in which the rate of nitrogen ingestion equals the rate of excretion (chiefly as nitrogenous wastes in the urine). Growing children exhibit a state of **positive nitrogen balance** because they ingest more than they excrete, thus retaining protein for tissue growth. Pregnant women and athletes in resistance training also show positive nitrogen balance. When excretion exceeds ingestion, a person is in a state of **negative nitrogen balance.** This indicates that body proteins are being broken down and used as fuel. Proteins of the muscles and liver are more easily broken down than others; therefore, negative nitrogen balance tends to be associated with muscle atrophy. Negative nitrogen balance may occur if carbohydrate and fat intake are insufficient to meet the need for energy. Carbohydrates and fats are said to have a protein-sparing effect because they prevent protein catabolism when present in sufficient amounts to meet one's energy needs.

Nitrogen balance is affected by some hormones. Growth hormone and sex steroids promote protein synthesis and positive nitrogen balance during childhood, adolescence, and pregnancy. Glucocorticoids, on the other hand, promote protein catabolism and negative nitrogen balance in states of stress.

▶▶▶ APPLY WHAT YOU KNOW

Would you expect a person recovering from a long infectious disease to be in a state of positive or negative nitrogen balance? Why?

26.1i Minerals and Vitamins

Minerals are inorganic elements that plants extract from soil or water and introduce into the food web. Vitamins are small dietary organic compounds that are necessary to metabolism. Neither is used as fuel, but both are essential to our ability to use other nutrients. With the exception of a few vitamins, these nutrients can't be synthesized by the body and must be included in the diet. They are required in relatively small quantities, and thus classified as micronutrients. Nevertheless, they have very potent effects on physiology. Indeed, excessive amounts are toxic and potentially lethal.

RDAs have not been firmly established for all vitamins and minerals. Values in the following tables are RDAs where known, but where an RDA isn't firmly established, they are measures of adequate intake (AI) as explained earlier. The tabulated values are for average healthy adults from 19 to 50 years old.

Minerals

Minerals constitute about 4% of the body mass, with three-quarters of this being the calcium and phosphorus in the bones and teeth. Phosphorus is also a key structural component of phospholipids, DNA, RNA, ATP, cAMP, GTP, and creatine phosphate, and is the basis of the phosphate buffer system (see section 24.3a). Calcium, iron, magnesium, and manganese function as cofactors for enzymes. Iron is essential to the oxygen-carrying capacity of hemoglobin and myoglobin. Chlorine is a component of stomach acid (HCl). Many mineral salts function as electrolytes and govern the function of nerve and muscle cells, osmotically regulate the content and distribution of water in the body, and maintain blood volume (see chapter 24).

Table 26.2 summarizes adult mineral requirements and dietary sources. Broadly speaking, the best sources of minerals are vegetables, legumes, milk, eggs, fish, shellfish, and some other meats. Cereal grains are a relatively poor source, but processed cereals are often mineral-fortified.

Throughout history, sodium chloride has been both a prized commodity and a curse. Animal tissues contain relatively large amounts of salt, and carnivores rarely lack ample salt in their diets. Plants, however, are relatively poor in salt, so herbivores often must supplement their diet by ingesting salt from the soil. As humans developed agriculture and became more dependent on plants, they also became increasingly dependent on supplemental salt. Salt was once used as a common form of payment for goods and services—the word *salary* comes from *sal* (salt). Our fondness for salt and high sensitivity to it undoubtedly stem from its physiological importance and its scarcity in a largely vegetarian diet.

Whether salt intake is significantly correlated with hypertension and heart disease has been a subject of great controversy for decades. The kidneys are remarkably capable of excreting excess salt, and multiple studies have found no elevated risk of hypertension in healthy people on high-salt diets. Other investigators, however, dispute this. The greatest concern about salt intake arises for patients with renal insufficiency, diabetes, hypertension, and people with a hereditary elevated sensitivity to salt. Hypertension is a leading cause of death among black Americans, for example, who have twice the risk of hypertension and 10 times the risk of dying from it that white Americans have. An evolutionary theory for this is that people of West African ancestry, which includes the majority of black Americans, have kidneys with an especially strong tendency to retain salt. For adults in good health with no hypersensitivity to salt, the Academy of Medicine recommends a daily sodium intake of 1.5 g/day and an upper limit of 2.3 g/day

TABLE 26.2	Mineral Requirements and Some Dietary Sources		
Mineral	RDA/AI, Males	RDA/AI, Females	Some Dietary Sources*
Major Minerals			
Potassium	4,700 mg	4,700 mg	Red meat, poultry, fish, cereals, spinach, squash, bananas, apricots, tomatoes, orange juice, beans, peas, nuts
Chloride	2,300 mg	2,300 mg	Table salt, some vegetables; usually present in excess
Sodium	1,500 mg	1,500 mg	Table salt, processed foods, egg whites, miso; usually present in excess
Calcium	1,000 mg	1,000 mg	Milk, cheese, fish, shellfish, greens, tofu, orange juice, fortified cereals
Phosphorus	700 mg	700 mg	Red meat, poultry, fish, eggs, milk, legumes, whole grains, nuts
Magnesium	400–420 mg	310–320 mg	Milk, greens, whole grains, nuts, legumes, dark chocolate
Trace Minerals			
Zinc	11 mg	8 mg	Red meat, seafood, nuts, wheat germ, legumes, cereals, yeast
Iron	8 mg	15 mg	Red meat, liver, shellfish, eggs, dried fruits, nuts, legumes, molasses
Fluoride	4 mg	3 mg	Fluoridated water and toothpaste, tea, seafood, seaweed
Manganese	2.3 mg	1.8 mg	Greens, fruits, legumes, whole grains, nuts
Copper	900 µg	900 µg	Red meat, liver, shellfish, legumes, whole grains, nuts, cocoa
Iodine	150 µg	150 µg	Marine fish, fish oils, shellfish, iodized salt
Selenium	55 µg	55 µg	Red meats, organ meats, fish, shellfish, eggs, cereals
Molybdenum	45 µg	45 µg	Beans, whole grains, nuts
Chromium	35 µg	25 µg	Meats, liver, cheese, eggs, whole grains, yeast, wine

*"Red meat" refers to mammalian muscle such as beef and pork. "Organ meat" refers to brain, pancreas, heart, kidney, etc. Liver is specified separately and refers to beef, pork, and chicken livers, which are similar for most nutrients.

(sodium only; this is 5.8 g of NaCl); the average American intake is about 3.4 g/day (8.5 g NaCl), about 77% of which comes from presalted packaged and restaurant foods.

Vitamins

Vitamins were originally named with letters in the order of their discovery, but they also have chemically descriptive names such as ascorbic acid (vitamin C) and riboflavin (vitamin B_2). Most vitamins must be obtained from the diet **(table 26.3)**, but the body synthesizes some of them from precursors called *provitamins*—niacin from the amino acid tryptophan; vitamin D from cholesterol; and vitamin A from carotene, which is abundantly present in carrots, squash, and other yellow vegetables and fruits. Vitamin K, pantothenic acid, biotin, and folic acid are produced by the bacteria of the large intestine. Indeed, the feces contain more biotin than food does.

Vitamins are classified as water-soluble or fat-soluble. **Water-soluble vitamins** are absorbed with water from the small intestine, dissolve freely in the body fluids, and are quickly excreted by the kidneys. They can't be stored in the body and therefore seldom accumulate to excess. The water-soluble vitamins are ascorbic acid and the B vitamins. Ascorbic acid promotes hemoglobin synthesis, collagen synthesis, and sound connective tissue structure; it also is an antioxidant that scavenges free radicals and possibly reduces the risk of cancer. The B vitamins function as coenzymes or parts of coenzyme molecules; they assist enzymes by transferring electrons from one metabolic reaction to another, making it possible for enzymes to catalyze these reactions. Some of their functions arise later in this chapter as we consider carbohydrate metabolism.

Fat-soluble vitamins are incorporated into lipid micelles in the small intestine and absorbed with dietary lipids. They vary in function more than water-soluble vitamins. Vitamin A is a component of the visual pigments and promotes proteoglycan synthesis and epithelial maintenance. Vitamin D promotes calcium absorption and bone mineralization. Vitamin K is essential to prothrombin synthesis and blood clotting. Vitamins A and E are antioxidants, like ascorbic acid.

It is common knowledge that various diseases result from vitamin deficiencies, but it is less commonly known that **hypervitaminosis** (vitamin excess) also causes disease. A *deficiency* of vitamin A, for example, can result in night blindness, dry skin and hair, a dry conjunctiva and cloudy cornea, and increased incidence of urinary, digestive, and respiratory infections. This is the world's most common vitamin deficiency. An *excess* of vitamin A, however, may cause anorexia, nausea and vomiting, headache, pain and fragility of the bones, hair loss, an enlarged liver and spleen, and birth defects. Vitamins B_6, C, D, and E have also been implicated in toxic hypervitaminosis.

Some people take *megavitamins*—doses 10 to 1,000 times the RDA—thinking that they will improve athletic performance. Since vitamins are not burned as fuel, and small amounts fully meet the body's metabolic needs, there is no evidence that vitamin supplements improve performance except when used to correct a dietary deficiency. Megadoses of fat-soluble vitamins can be especially harmful because they are the most likely to accumulate in the body to toxic levels.

TABLE 26.3	Vitamin Requirements and Some Dietary Sources		
Vitamin	**RDA/AI, Males**	**RDA/AI, Females**	**Some Dietary Sources***
Water-Soluble Vitamins			
Ascorbic acid (C)	90 mg	75 mg	Citrus fruits, strawberries, tomatoes, greens, cabbage, cauliflower, broccoli, brussels sprouts
Niacin (nicotinic acid, B_3)	16 mg	14 mg	Readily synthesized from tryptophan, which is present in any diet with adequate protein; red meat, liver, other organ meats, poultry, fish, apricots, legumes, whole grains, mushrooms
Panthothenic acid (B_5)	5 mg	5 mg	Widely distributed, and deficiencies are rare; red meat, liver, other organ meats, eggs, green and yellow vegetables, legumes, whole grains, mushrooms, yeast
Riboflavin (B_2)	1.3 mg	1.1 mg	Widely distributed, and deficiencies are rare; all types of meat, milk, eggs, greens, whole grains, apricots, legumes, mushrooms, yeast
Pyridoxine (B_6)	1.3 mg	1.3 mg	Red meat, fish, liver, other organ meats, greens, apricots, legumes, whole grains, seeds
Thiamin (B_1)	1.2 mg	1.1 mg	Red meat, liver, other organ meats, eggs, greens, asparagus, legumes, whole grains, seeds, yeast
Folic acid (folacin, B_9)	400 μg	400 μg	Eggs, liver, greens, citrus fruits, legumes, whole grains, seeds
Biotin (B_7)	30 μg	30 μg	Red meat, liver, other organ meats, eggs, cheese, cabbage, cauliflower, bananas, legumes, nuts
Cobalamin (B_{12})	2.4 μg	2.4 μg	Red meat, liver, other organ meats, shellfish, eggs, milk; absent from food plants
Fat-Soluble Vitamins			
α-tocopherol (E)	15 mg	15 mg	Fish oils, greens, seeds, wheat germ, vegetable oils, margarine, nuts
Retinol (A)	900 μg	700 μg	Fish oils, eggs, cheese, milk, greens, other green and yellow vegetables and fruits, margarine
Phylloquinone (K)	120 μg	90 μg	Liver, greens, cabbage, cauliflower; most of requirement is supplied by intestinal bacteria
Calcitriol (D)	5 μg	5 μg	Fish, fish oils, fortified milk; formed by exposure of skin to sunlight

*See footnote in table 26.2.

Answer the following questions to test your understanding of the preceding section:

1. Name two hormones that regulate short-term hunger and satiety. How does leptin differ from these in its effects?

2. Explain the following statement: Cellulose is an important part of a healthy diet but it is not a nutrient.

3. What class of nutrients provides most of the calories in the diet? What class of nutrients provides the body's major reserves of stored energy?

4. Contrast the functions of VLDLs, LDLs, and HDLs. Explain how this is related to the fact that a high blood HDL level is desirable, but a high VLDL–LDL level is undesirable.

5. Why do some proteins have more nutritional value than others?

26.2   Carbohydrate Metabolism

Expected Learning Outcomes

When you have completed this section, you should be able to

a. describe the principal reactants and products of each major step of glucose oxidation;

b. contrast the functions and products of anaerobic fermentation and aerobic respiration;

c. explain where and how cells produce ATP; and

d. describe the production, function, and use of glycogen.

Most dietary carbohydrate is burned as fuel within a few hours of absorption. Although three monosaccharides are absorbed from digested food—glucose, galactose, and fructose—the last two are quickly converted to glucose, and all oxidative carbohydrate metabolism is essentially a matter of glucose catabolism. The overall reaction for this is

$$C_6H_{12}O_6 + 6\ O_2 \longrightarrow 6\ CO_2 + 6\ H_2O.$$

The function of this reaction is not to produce carbon dioxide and water but to transfer energy from glucose to ATP.

Along the pathway of glucose oxidation are several links through which other nutrients—especially fats and amino acids—can also be oxidized as fuel. Carbohydrate catabolism therefore provides a central vantage point from which we can view the catabolism of all fuels and the generation of ATP.

26.2a   Glucose Catabolism

If the preceding reaction were carried out in a single step, it would generate a short, intense burst of heat—like the burning of paper, which has the same chemical equation. Not only would this be useless to the body's metabolism, it would kill the cells. In the body, however, the process is carried out in a series of small steps, each controlled by a separate enzyme. Energy is released in small

manageable amounts, and as much as possible is transferred to ATP. The rest is released as heat.

There are three major pathways of glucose catabolism:

1. **glycolysis,**[4] which splits a glucose molecule into two molecules of pyruvate;

2. **anaerobic fermentation,** which reduces pyruvate to lactate without using oxygen; and

3. **aerobic respiration,** which requires oxygen and oxidizes pyruvate to carbon dioxide and water.

You may find it helpful to review figure 2.31 for a broad overview of these processes and their relationship to ATP production. The next four figures examine these processes in closer detail.

Coenzymes are vitally important to these reactions. Enzymes remove electrons (as hydrogen atoms) from the intermediate compounds of these pathways, but they don't bind them. Instead, they transfer the hydrogen atoms to coenzymes, and the coenzymes donate them to other compounds later in one of the reaction pathways. Thus, the enzymes of glucose catabolism can't function without their coenzymes.

The two coenzymes of special importance to glucose catabolism are **NAD+** (nicotinamide adenine dinucleotide) and **FAD** (flavin adenine dinucleotide). Both are derived from B vitamins—NAD+ from niacin and FAD from riboflavin. Hydrogen atoms are removed from metabolic intermediates in pairs—that is, two protons and two electrons ($2\ H^+$ and $2\ e^-$) at a time—and transferred to a coenzyme. This produces a reduced coenzyme with a higher free energy content than it had before the reaction. Coenzymes thus become the temporary carriers of the energy extracted from glucose metabolites. The reactions for this are

$$FAD + 2\ H \longrightarrow FADH_2$$

and

$$NAD^+ + 2\ H \longrightarrow NADH + H^+.$$

FAD binds two protons and two electrons to become $FADH_2$. NAD+, however, binds the two electrons but only one of the protons to become NADH. The other proton remains a free hydrogen ion, H^+ (or H_3O^+ when it combines with water, but it is represented in this chapter as H^+).

26.2b   Glycolysis

Upon entering a cell, glucose begins a series of conversions called glycolysis **(fig. 26.5).** The numbered steps in this figure correspond to the numbered explanations in the following text.

1. **Phosphorylation.** The enzyme *hexokinase* transfers an inorganic phosphate (P_i) group from ATP to glucose, producing glucose 6-phosphate (G6P). This has two effects:

   • It keeps the intracellular concentration of glucose low, maintaining a concentration gradient that favors the continued diffusion of more glucose into the cell.

---

[4]*glyco* = sugar; *lysis* = splitting

- Phosphorylated compounds can't pass through the plasma membrane, so this prevents the sugar from leaving the cell. In most cells, step 1 is irreversible because the cells lack the enzyme to convert G6P back to glucose. The few exceptions are cells that must be able to release free glucose to the blood: absorptive cells of the small intestine, proximal convoluted tubule cells in the kidney, and liver cells.

G6P is a versatile molecule that can be converted to fat or amino acids, polymerized to form glycogen for storage, or further oxidized to extract its energy. For now, we are mainly concerned with its further oxidation (glycolysis), the general effect of which is to split G6P (a six-carbon sugar, C_6) into two three-carbon (C_3) molecules of **pyruvate.** Continue tracing these steps in figure 26.5 as you read.

2. **Priming.** G6P is rearranged (isomerized) to form fructose 6-phosphate, which is phosphorylated again to form fructose 1,6-diphosphate. This "primes" the process by providing activation energy, somewhat like the heat of a match used to light a fireplace. Two molecules of ATP have already been consumed, but just as a fire gives back more heat than it takes to start it, aerobic respiration eventually gives back far more ATP than it takes to prime glycolysis.

3. **Cleavage.** The "lysis" part of glycolysis occurs when fructose 1,6-diphosphate splits into two three-carbon (C_3) molecules. Through a slight rearrangement of one of them (not shown in the figure), this generates two molecules of **PGAL (phosphoglyceraldehyde,** also called **glyceraldehyde 3-phosphate).**

4. **Oxidation.** Each PGAL is then oxidized by removing a pair of hydrogen atoms. The electrons and one proton are picked up by NAD^+ and the other proton is released into the cytosol, yielding $NADH + H^+$. At this step, a phosphate (P_i) group is also added to each of the C_3 fragments. Unlike the earlier steps, this P_i isn't supplied by ATP but comes from the cell's pool of free phosphate ions.

5. **Dephosphorylation.** In the next two steps, phosphate groups are taken from the glycolysis intermediates and transferred to ADP, converting it to ATP. The C_3 compound becomes pyruvate.

The net end products of glycolysis are therefore

$$2 \text{ pyruvate} + 2\ NADH + 2\ H^+ + 2\ ATP.$$

Note that 4 ATP are actually produced (step 5), but 2 ATP were consumed to initiate glycolysis (steps 1 and 2), so the net gain is 2 ATP per glucose. Some of the energy originally in the glucose is contained in this ATP, some is in the NADH, and some is lost as heat. Most of the energy, however, remains in the pyruvate.

26.2c Anaerobic Fermentation

The fate of pyruvate depends on whether or not oxygen is available. In an exercising muscle, the demand for ATP may exceed the supply of oxygen. The only ATP the cells can make under these circumstances is the 2 ATP produced by glycolysis. Cells without

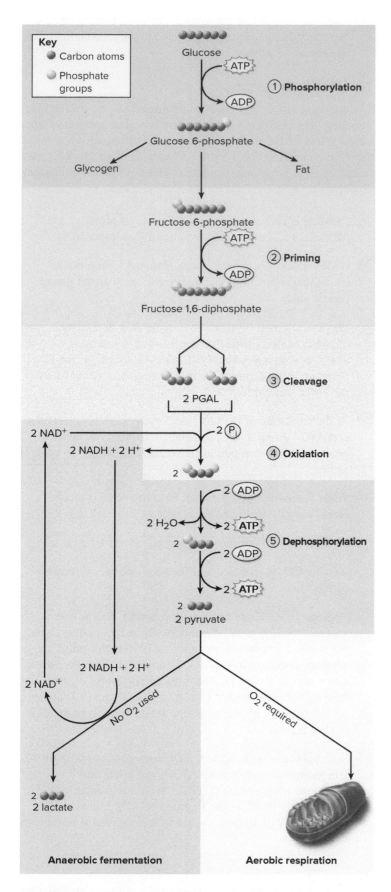

FIGURE 26.5 Glycolysis and Anaerobic Fermentation. Numbered reaction steps are explained in the text.

mitochondria, such as erythrocytes, are restricted to making ATP by this method.

But glycolysis would quickly come to a halt if the reaction stopped at pyruvate. Why? Because it would use up the supply of NAD^+, which is needed to accept electrons at step 4 and keep glycolysis going. NAD^+ must be replenished. To achieve that in the absence of oxygen, a cell resorts to a one-step reaction called anaerobic fermentation. (This is often inaccurately called *anaerobic respiration,* but strictly speaking, human cells don't carry out anaerobic respiration; that is a process found only in certain bacteria.) In this pathway, NADH donates a pair of electrons to pyruvate, thus reducing it to **lactate** and regenerating NAD^+.

▶▶▶ **APPLY WHAT YOU KNOW**

Does lactate have more free energy than pyruvate or less? Explain.

Lactate leaves the cells that generate it and travels by way of the bloodstream to the liver. When oxygen becomes available again, the liver oxidizes lactate back to pyruvate, which can then enter the aerobic pathway described shortly. The oxygen required to do this is part of the excess postexercise oxygen consumption (EPOC) created by exercising skeletal muscles (see section 11.6c). The liver can also convert lactate back to G6P and can do either of two things with that: (1) Polymerize it to form glycogen for storage, or (2) remove the phosphate group and release free glucose into the blood.

Although anaerobic fermentation keeps glycolysis running a little longer, it has some drawbacks. One is that it is wasteful, because most of the energy of glucose is still in the lactate and has contributed no useful work. The other is that excess lactate is toxic.

Skeletal muscle is relatively tolerant of anaerobic fermentation, and cardiac muscle is less so. The brain employs almost no anaerobic fermentation. During birth, when the infant's blood supply is cut off, almost all of its organs switch to anaerobic fermentation so they don't compete with the brain for the limited supply of oxygen.

▶▶▶ **APPLY WHAT YOU KNOW**

At what point in figure 26.5 would the reaction stop, and what reaction intermediate would accumulate, if NAD^+ was unavailable to the cell? What process replenishes the NAD^+ supply?

26.2d Aerobic Respiration

Most ATP is generated in the mitochondria, which require oxygen as the final electron acceptor. In the presence of oxygen, pyruvate enters the mitochondria and is oxidized by aerobic respiration. This occurs in two principal steps:

- a group of reactions we will call the **matrix reactions,** because their controlling enzymes are in the fluid of the mitochondrial matrix; and

- reactions we will call the **membrane reactions,** because their controlling enzymes are bound to the membranes of the mitochondrial cristae.

The Matrix Reactions

The matrix reactions are shown in **figure 26.6,** where the reaction steps are numbered to resume where the previous figure ended. Most of the matrix reactions constitute a series called the **citric acid (Krebs[5]) cycle.** Preceding this, however, are three steps that prepare pyruvate to enter the cycle and thus link glycolysis to it.

⑥ Pyruvate is *decarboxylated;* that is, CO_2 is removed and pyruvate, a C_3 compound, becomes a C_2 compound.

⑦ NAD^+ removes hydrogen atoms from the C_2 compound (an oxidation reaction) and converts it to an **acetyl group (acetic acid).**

⑧ The acetyl group binds to coenzyme A, a derivative of pantothenic acid (a B vitamin). The result is **acetyl-coenzyme A (acetyl-CoA).** At this stage, the C_2 remnant of the original glucose molecule is ready to enter the citric acid cycle.

⑨ At the beginning of the citric acid cycle, CoA hands off the acetyl (C_2) group to a C_4 compound, **oxaloacetic acid.** This produces the C_6 compound **citric acid,** for which the cycle is named.

⑩ Water is removed and the citric acid molecule is reorganized, but still retains its six carbon atoms.

⑪ Hydrogen atoms are removed and accepted by NAD^+.

⑫ Another CO_2 is removed and the substrate becomes a five-carbon chain.

⑬–⑭ Steps 11 and 12 are essentially repeated, generating another free CO_2 molecule and leaving a four-carbon chain. No more carbon atoms are removed beyond this point; the substrate remains a series of C_4 compounds from here back to the start of the cycle. The three carbon atoms of pyruvate have all been removed as CO_2 at steps 6, 12, and 14. These *decarboxylation reactions* are the source of most of the CO_2 in your breath.

⑮ Some of the energy in the C_4 substrate goes to phosphorylate guanosine diphosphate (GDP) and to convert it to guanosine triphosphate (GTP), a molecule similar to ATP. GTP quickly transfers the P_i group to ADP to make ATP. Coenzyme A participates again in this step but is not shown in the figure.

---

[5]Sir Hans Krebs (1900–1981), German biochemist

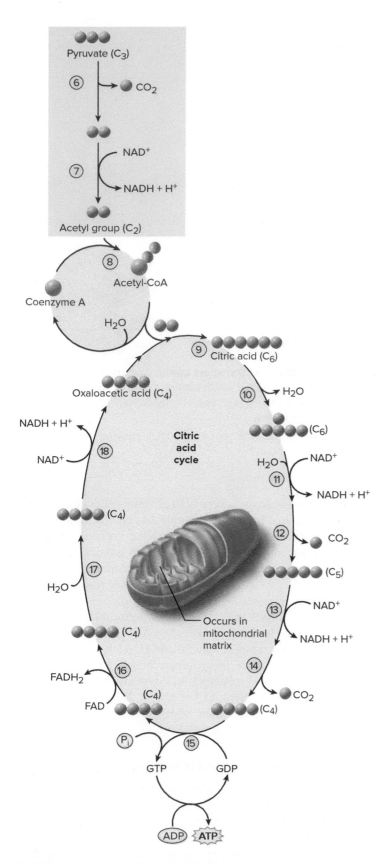

FIGURE 26.6 The Mitochondrial Matrix Reactions. Numbered reaction steps begin where figure 26.5 left off and are explained in the text.

(16) Two hydrogen atoms are removed and accepted by the coenzyme FAD.

(17) Water is added.

(18) Two final hydrogen atoms are removed and transferred to NAD^+. This reaction generates oxaloacetic acid, which is available to start the cycle all over again.

It is important to remember that for every glucose molecule that entered glycolysis, all of these matrix reactions occur twice (once for each pyruvate). The matrix reactions can be summrized in four equations.

$$2 \text{ pyruvate} + 6\ H_2O \longrightarrow 6\ CO_2$$

$$+\ 2\ ADP + 2\ P_i \longrightarrow 2\ ATP$$

$$+\ 8\ NAD^+ + 8\ H_2 \longrightarrow 8\ NADH + 8\ H^+$$

$$+\ 2\ FAD + 2\ H_2 \longrightarrow 2\ FADH_2$$

There is nothing left of the organic matter of the glucose; its carbon atoms have all been carried away as CO_2. Although still more of its energy is lost as heat along the way, some is stored in the additional 2 ATP, and most of it, by far, is in the reduced coenzymes: 8 NADH and 2 $FADH_2$ molecules generated by the matrix reactions and 2 NADH generated by glycolysis. These must be oxidized to extract the energy from them.

The citric acid cycle not only oxidizes glucose metabolites but is also a pathway and source of intermediates for the synthesis of fats and nonessential amino acids. The connections between the citric acid cycle and the metabolism of other nutrients are discussed later.

The Membrane Reactions

The membrane reactions have two purposes: (1) to further oxidize NADH and $FADH_2$ and transfer their energy to ATP and (2) to regenerate NAD^+ and FAD and make them available again to earlier reaction steps. The membrane reactions are carried out by a series of compounds called the **mitochondrial electron-transport chain (fig. 26.7).** Most members of the chain are bound to the inner mitochondrial membrane. They are arranged in a precise order that enables each one to receive a pair of electrons from the member on one side of it (or, in two cases, from NADH and $FADH_2$) and pass these electrons along to the member on the other side—like a row of people passing along a hot potato. By the time the "potato" reaches the last member in the chain, it is relatively "cool"—its energy has been used to make ATP.

The members of this transport chain are as follows:

- **Flavin mononucleotide (FMN),** a derivative of riboflavin similar to FAD, bound to a membrane protein. FMN accepts electrons from NADH.

- **Iron–sulfur (Fe–S) centers,** complexes of iron and sulfur atoms bound to membrane proteins.

- **Coenzyme Q (CoQ),** which accepts electrons from $FADH_2$. Unlike the other members, this is a relatively small, mobile molecule that moves about in the membrane.
- **Copper (Cu) ions** bound to two membrane proteins.
- **Cytochromes,**[6] five enzymes with iron cofactors, so named because they are brightly colored in pure form. In order of participation in the chain, they are cytochromes b, c_1, c, a, and a_3.

Electron Transport   Figure 26.7 shows the order in which electrons are passed along the chain. Hydrogen atoms are split apart as they transfer from coenzymes to the chain. The protons are pumped into the intermembrane space **(fig. 26.8),** and the electrons travel in pairs ($2\ e^-$) along the transport chain. Each electron carrier in the chain becomes reduced when it receives an electron pair and oxidized again when it passes the electrons along to the next carrier. Energy is liberated at each transfer.

The final electron acceptor in the chain is oxygen. Each oxygen atom (half of an O_2 molecule) accepts two electrons ($2\ e^-$) from cytochrome a_3 and two protons ($2\ H^+$) from the mitochondrial matrix. The result is a molecule of water:

$$1/2\ O_2 + 2\ e^- + 2\ H^+ \longrightarrow H_2O$$

This is the body's primary source of the *metabolic water* mentioned in section 24.1b—water synthesized in the body rather than ingested in food and drink. This reaction also explains why the body requires oxygen. Without it, this reaction stops and, like a traffic jam, stops all the other processes leading to it. As a result, a cell produces too little ATP to sustain life, and death ensues within a few minutes.

The Chemiosmotic Mechanism   Of primary importance is what happens to the energy liberated by the electrons as they pass along the chain. Some of it is unavoidably lost as heat, but some of it drives the **respiratory enzyme complexes.** The first complex includes FMN and five or more Fe–S centers; the second complex includes cytochromes b and c_1 and an Fe–S center; and the third complex includes two copper centers and cytochromes a and a_3. Each complex collectively acts as a **proton pump** that removes H^+ from the mitochondrial matrix and pumps it into the space between the inner and outer mitochondrial membranes. Coenzyme Q is a shuttle that transfers electrons from the first pump to the second, and cytochrome c shuttles electrons from the second pump to the third.

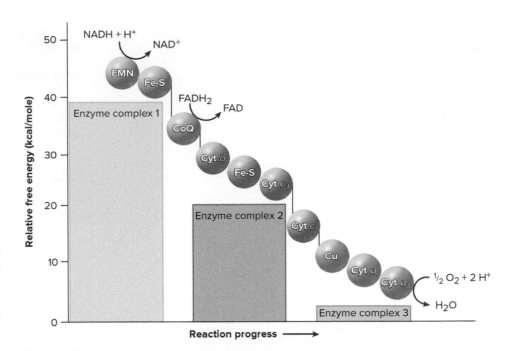

FIGURE 26.7 The Mitochondrial Electron-Transport Chain. Transport molecules are grouped into three enzyme complexes, each of which acts as a proton pump. Molecules at the upper left of the figure have a relatively high free energy content, and molecules at the lower right are relatively low in energy.

❓ *What two molecules import energy into this reaction chain, supplying the energy that becomes stored in ATP?*

These pumps create a very high H^+ concentration (low pH) and positive charge between the membranes compared with a low H^+ concentration and negative charge in the mitochondrial matrix. That is, they create a steep electrochemical gradient across the inner mitochondrial membrane. If the inner membrane were freely permeable to H^+, these ions would have a strong tendency to diffuse down this gradient and back into the matrix.

The inner membrane, however, is permeable to H^+ only through specific channel proteins called **ATP synthase** (separate from the electron-transport system). As H^+ flows through these channels, it creates an electrical current (which, you may recall, is simply moving charged particles). ATP synthase harnesses the energy of this current to drive ATP synthesis. This process is called the **chemiosmotic**[7] **mechanism,** which suggests the "push" created by the electrochemical H^+ gradient.

26.2e Overview of ATP Production

NADH releases its electron pairs (as hydrogen atoms) to FMN in the first proton pump of the electron-transport system. From there to the end of the chain, this generates enough energy to synthesize 2.5 ATP molecules per electron pair. $FADH_2$ releases its electron pairs to coenzyme Q, the shuttle between the first and second proton pumps. Therefore, it enters the chain at a point beyond the first pump and doesn't contribute energy to

---

[6]*cyto* = cell; *chrom* = color

[7]*chemi* = chemical; *osmo* = push

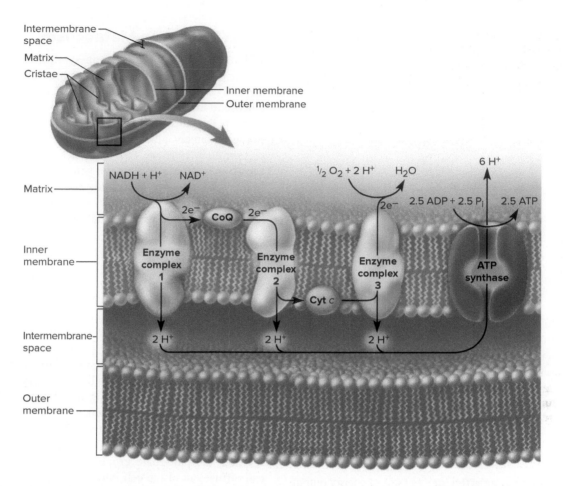

FIGURE 26.8 The Chemiosmotic Mechanism of ATP Synthesis. Each enzyme complex pumps hydrogen ions into the space between the mitochondrial membranes. These hydrogen ions diffuse back into the matrix by way of ATP synthase, which taps their energy to synthesize ATP.

that pump. Each $FADH_2$ contributes enough energy to synthesize 1.5 ATP.

With that in mind, we can draw up an energy balance sheet to see how much ATP is produced by the complete aerobic oxidation of glucose to CO_2 and H_2O and where the ATP comes from; see also **figure 26.9.** This summary refers back to the reaction steps 1 to 18 in figures 26.5 and 26.6. For each glucose molecule, there are

	10	NADH produced at steps 4, 7, 11, 13, and 18
	× 2.5	ATP per NADH produced by the electron-transport chain
	= **25**	**ATP** generated by NADH
Plus:	2	$FADH_2$ produced at step 16
	× 1.5	ATP per $FADH_2$ produced by the electron-transport chain
	= **3**	**ATP** generated by $FADH_2$
Plus:	**2**	**ATP** net amount generated by glycolysis (step 5 offset by step 2)
	2	**ATP** generated by the matrix reactions (step 15)
Total:	**32**	**ATP** per glucose.

This should be viewed as a theoretical maximum. There is some uncertainty about how much H^+ must be pumped between the mitochondrial membranes to generate each ATP, and some of the energy from the H^+ current is consumed by pumping ATP from the mitochondrial matrix into the cytosol and exchanging it for more raw materials (ADP and P_i) pumped from the cytosol into the mitochondria.

Furthermore, the NADH generated by glycolysis can't enter the mitochondria and donate its electrons directly to the electron-transport chain. In liver, kidney, and heart cells, NADH passes its electrons to *malate,* a shuttle molecule that delivers the electrons to the beginning of the electron-transport chain and generates the maximum amount of ATP. In skeletal muscle and brain cells, however, the glycolytic NADH transfers its electrons to *glycerol phosphate,* a different shuttle that donates the electrons farther down the electron-transport chain and generates less ATP. Therefore, the amount of ATP produced per NADH differs from one cell type to another and is still unknown for others.

But if we assume the maximum ATP yield, every mole (180 g) of glucose releases enough energy to synthesize up to 32 moles of ATP. Glucose has an energy content of 686 kcal/mole and ATP has 7.3 kcal/mole (233.6 kcal in 32 moles). This means

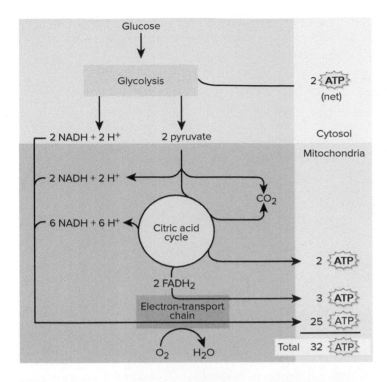

FIGURE 26.9 Summary of the Sources of ATP Generated by the Complete Oxidation of Glucose.

that aerobic respiration has an **efficiency** (a ratio of energy output to input) of up to 233.6/686 kcal = 34%. The other 66% is lost as body heat.

The pathways of glucose catabolism are summarized in **table 26.4.** The aerobic respiration of glucose can be represented in the summary equation:

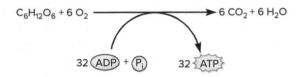

26.2f Glycogen Metabolism

ATP is quickly used after it is synthesized—it is an *energy-transfer* molecule, not an *energy-storage* molecule. Therefore, if the body has an ample amount of ATP and there is still more glucose in the blood, it doesn't produce and store excess ATP but converts the glucose to other compounds better suited for energy storage—namely, glycogen and fat. Fat synthesis is considered in section 26.3. Here we consider the synthesis and use of glycogen (**fig. 26.10**), as well as the generation of glucose from other sources. The average adult body contains about 400 to 450 g of glycogen: nearly one-quarter of it in the liver, three-quarters of it in the skeletal muscles, and small amounts in cardiac muscle and other tissues.

Glycogenesis, the synthesis of glycogen, is stimulated by insulin. Glucose 6-phosphate (G6P) is isomerized to glucose 1-phosphate (G1P). The enzyme *glycogen synthase* then cleaves off the phosphate group and attaches the glucose to a growing polysaccharide chain, thus assembling glycogen one glucose at a time.

Glycogenolysis, the hydrolysis of glycogen, releases glucose between meals when new glucose is not being ingested. The process is stimulated by glucagon and epinephrine. The enzyme *glycogen phosphorylase* begins by phosphorylating a glucose residue and splitting it off the glycogen molecule as G1P. This is isomerized to G6P, which can then enter the pathway of glycolysis.

G6P usually cannot leave the cells that produce it. Liver cells, however, have an enzyme called *glucose 6-phosphatase,* which removes the phosphate group and produces free glucose. This can diffuse out of the cell into the blood, where it is available to any cells in the body. Although muscle cells can't directly release glucose into the blood, they contribute indirectly to blood glucose concentration because they release pyruvate and lactate, which are converted to glucose by the liver.

Gluconeogenesis[8] is the synthesis of glucose from noncarbohydrates such as glycerol and amino acids. It occurs chiefly in the liver, but after several weeks of fasting, the kidneys also undertake

[8]*gluco* = sugar, glucose; *neo* = new; *genesis* = production of

TABLE 26.4	Pathways of Glucose Catabolism		
Stage	**Principal Reactants**	**Principal Products**	**Purpose**
Glycolysis	Glucose, 2 ADP, 2 P_i, 2 NAD^+	2 pyruvate, 2 ATP, 2 NADH, 2 H_2O	Reorganizes glucose and splits it in two in preparation for further oxidation by the mitochondria; sole source of ATP in anaerobic conditions
Anaerobic fermentation	2 pyruvate, 2 NADH	2 lactate, 2 NAD^+	Regenerates NAD^+ so glycolysis can continue to function (and generate ATP) in the absence of oxygen
Aerobic respiration			
Matrix reactions	2 pyruvate, 8 NAD^+, 2 FAD, 2 ADP, 2 P_i, 8 H_2O	6 CO_2, 8 NADH, 2 $FADH_2$, 2 ATP, 2 H_2O	Remove electrons from pyruvate and transfer them to coenzymes NAD^+ and FAD; produce some ATP
Membrane reactions	10 NADH, 2 $FADH_2$, 6 O_2	Up to 28 ATP, 12 H_2O	Finish oxidation and produce most of the ATP of cellular respiration

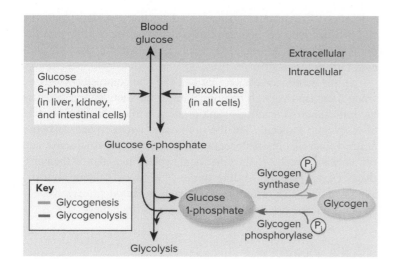

FIGURE 26.10 Major Pathways of Glucose Storage and Use. In most cells, the glucose 1-phosphate generated by glycogenolysis can undergo only glycolysis. In liver, kidney, and intestinal cells, it can be converted back to free glucose and released into circulation.

TABLE 26.5	Some Terminology Related to Glucose and Glycogen Metabolism
Anabolic (Synthesis) Reactions	
Glycogenesis	The synthesis of glycogen by polymerizing glucose
Gluconeogenesis	The synthesis of glucose from noncarbohydrates such as glycerol and amino acids
Catabolic (Breakdown) Reactions	
Glycolysis	The splitting of glucose into two molecules of pyruvate in preparation for anaerobic fermentation or aerobic respiration
Glycogenolysis	The hydrolysis of glycogen to release free glucose or glucose 1-phosphate

this process and eventually produce just as much glucose as the liver does.

Table 26.5 summarizes the distinctions among those similar terms.

BEFORE YOU GO ON

Answer the following questions to test your understanding of the preceding section:

6. Identify the reaction steps in figures 26.5 and 26.6 at which vitamins are needed for glucose catabolism.

7. In the laboratory, glucose can be oxidized in a single step to CO_2 and H_2O. Why do living cells do it in so many little steps?

8. Explain the origin of the word *glycolysis* and why this is an appropriate name for the function of that reaction pathway.

9. What are two advantages of aerobic respiration over anaerobic fermentation?

10. What important enzyme is found in the inner mitochondrial membrane other than those of the electron-transport chain? Explain how its function depends on the electron-transport chain.

11. Describe how the liver responds to (a) an excess and (b) a deficiency of blood glucose.

26.3 Lipid and Protein Metabolism

Expected Learning Outcomes
When you have completed this section, you should be able to

a. describe the processes of lipid catabolism and anabolism;

b. describe the processes of protein catabolism and anabolism;

c. explain the metabolic source of ammonia and how the body disposes of it; and

d. describe the many functions of the liver and explain why liver failure is so serious.

In the foregoing discussion, glycolysis and the mitochondrial reactions were treated from the standpoint of carbohydrate oxidation. These pathways also serve for the oxidation of proteins and lipids as fuel and as a source of metabolic intermediates that can be used for protein and lipid synthesis. Here we examine these related metabolic pathways.

26.3a Lipids

Triglycerides are stored primarily in the body's adipocytes, where the average fat molecule remains for about 2 to 3 weeks. Although the total amount of stored fat remains quite constant, there is a continual turnover as lipids are released, transported in the blood, and either oxidized for energy or redeposited in other adipocytes. Synthesizing fats from other types of molecules is called **lipogenesis,** and breaking down fat for fuel is called **lipolysis** (lih-POL-ih-sis).

Lipogenesis

It's common knowledge that a diet high in sugars causes us to put on fat. Lipogenesis employs compounds such as sugars and amino acids to synthesize glycerol and fatty acids, the triglyceride precursors. PGAL, one of the intermediates of glycolysis, can be converted to glycerol. As glucose and amino acids enter the citric acid cycle by way of acetyl-CoA, the acetyl-CoA can also be diverted to make fatty acids. The glycerol and fatty acids can then be condensed to form a triglyceride, which can be stored in the adipose tissue or converted to other lipids. These pathways are summarized in **figure 26.11.**

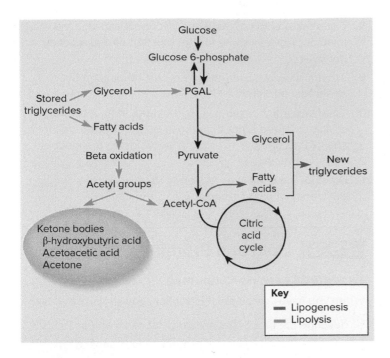

FIGURE 26.11 Pathways of Lipolysis and Lipogenesis in Relation to Glycolysis and the Citric Acid Cycle.

❓ *Name the acid–base imbalance that results from the accumulation of the ketone bodies shown in the oval.*

Lipolysis

Lipolysis, also shown in figure 26.11, begins with the hydrolysis of a triglyceride into glycerol and fatty acids—a process stimulated by epinephrine, norepinephrine, glucocorticoids, thyroid hormone, and growth hormone. The glycerol and fatty acids are further oxidized by separate pathways. Glycerol is easily converted to PGAL and thus enters the pathway of glycolysis. It generates only half as much ATP as glucose, however, because it is a C_3 compound compared with glucose (C_6); thus, it leads to the production of only half as much pyruvate.

The fatty acid component is catabolized in the mitochondrial matrix by a process called **beta oxidation,** which removes 2 carbon atoms at a time. The resulting acetyl (C_2) groups are bonded to coenzyme A to make acetyl-CoA—the entry point into the citric acid cycle. A fatty acid of 16 carbon atoms can yield 129 molecules of ATP—obviously a much richer source of energy than a glucose molecule; remember, too, that each fat molecule generates 3 fatty acids.

Excess acetyl groups can be metabolized by the liver in a process called **ketogenesis.** Two acetyl groups are condensed to form acetoacetic acid, and some of this is further converted to β-hydroxybutyric acid and acetone. These three products are the **ketone bodies.** Some cells convert acetoacetic acid back to acetyl-CoA and thus feed the C_2 fragments into the citric acid cycle to extract their energy. When the body is rapidly oxidizing fats, however, excess ketone bodies accumulate. This causes the ketoacidosis typical of type 1 diabetes mellitus, in which cells must oxidize fats because they can't absorb glucose.

Acetyl-CoA cannot go backward up the glycolytic pathway and produce glucose, because this pathway is irreversible past the point of pyruvate. Although glycerol can be used for gluconeogenesis, fatty acids cannot.

It was mentioned earlier that fats can't be completely oxidized when there isn't enough carbohydrate in the diet. This is because the mitochondrial reactions can't proceed without oxaloacetic acid as a "pickup molecule" in the citric acid cycle. When carbohydrate is unavailable, oxaloacetic acid is converted to glucose and becomes unavailable to the citric acid cycle. Fat oxidation then produces excess ketones, leading to elevated blood ketones *(ketosis)* and potentially to a resulting pH imbalance *(ketoacidosis).* Ketosis can be a serious risk in extreme low-carbohydrate diets.

26.3b Proteins

About 100 g of tissue protein breaks down each day into free amino acids. These combine with the amino acids from the diet to form an **amino acid pool** that cells can draw upon to make new proteins. The fastest rate of tissue protein turnover is in the intestinal mucosa, where epithelial cells are replaced at a very high rate. Dead cells are digested along with the food and thus contribute to the amino acid pool. Of all the amino acid absorbed by the small intestine, about 50% is from the diet, 25% from dead epithelial cells, and 25% from enzymes that have digested each other.

Some amino acids in the pool can be converted to others. Free amino acids also can be converted to glucose and fat or directly used as fuel. Such conversions involve three processes: (1) **deamination,** the removal of an amino group ($-NH_2$); (2) **amination,** the addition of $-NH_2$; or (3) **transamination,** the transfer of $-NH_2$ from one molecule to another. The following discussion shows how these processes are involved in amino acid metabolism.

Use as Fuel

The first step in using amino acids as fuel is to deaminate them. After the $-NH_2$ group is removed, the remainder of the molecule is called a *keto acid.* Depending on which amino acid is involved, the resulting keto acid may be converted to pyruvate, acetyl-CoA, or one of the acids of the citric acid cycle **(fig. 26.12).** It is important to note that some of these reactions are reversible. When there is a deficiency of amino acids in the body, citric acid cycle intermediates can be aminated and converted to amino acids, which are then available for protein synthesis. In gluconeogenesis, keto acids are used to synthesize glucose, essentially through a reversal of the glycolysis reactions.

Transamination, Ammonia, and Urea

When an amino acid is deaminated, its amino group is transferred to a citric acid cycle intermediate, α-ketoglutaric acid, converting it to glutamic acid. Such transamination reactions are the route by which several amino acids enter the citric acid cycle.

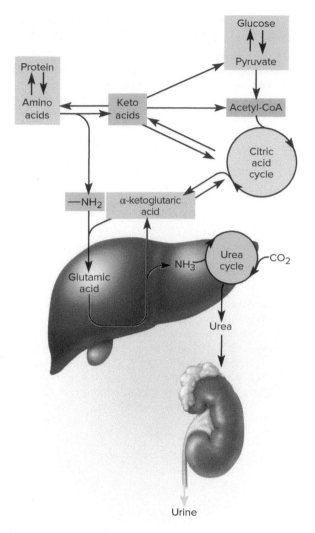

FIGURE 26.12 Pathways of Amino Acid Metabolism in Relation to Glycolysis and the Citric Acid Cycle.

? *Find a pathway for gluconeogenesis in this diagram.*

Glutamic acid can travel from any of the body's cells to the liver. Here, its —NH$_2$ group is removed, converting it back to α-ketoglutaric acid. The —NH$_2$ becomes ammonia (NH$_3$), which is extremely toxic to cells and cannot be allowed to accumulate. In a pathway called the **urea cycle,** the liver quickly combines ammonia with carbon dioxide to produce a less toxic waste, urea. Urea is then excreted in the urine as one of the body's nitrogenous wastes. Other nitrogenous wastes and their sources are described in section 23.1b. When a diseased liver can't carry out the urea cycle, NH$_3$ accumulates in the blood and death from *hepatic coma* may ensue within a few days.

Protein Synthesis

Protein synthesis, described in detail in section 4.2c, is a complex process involving DNA, mRNA, tRNA, ribosomes, and often the rough ER. It is stimulated by growth hormone, thyroid hormones, and insulin. It requires a supply of all the amino acids necessary for a particular protein. The liver can make many of these amino acids from other amino acids or from citric acid cycle intermediates by transamination reactions. The essential amino acids, however, must be obtained from the diet.

26.3c Liver Functions in Metabolism

You may notice that the liver plays a wide variety of roles in the processes discussed in this chapter—especially carbohydrate, lipid, and protein metabolism. Although it is connected to the digestive tract and regarded as a digestive gland, most of its functions are nondigestive **(table 26.6).** Except for phagocytosis, all of them are performed by the hepatocytes described in section 25.4a. Such functional diversity is remarkable in light of the uniform structure of these cells. Because of the numerous critical functions performed by the liver, degenerative liver diseases such as hepatitis, cirrhosis, and liver cancer are especially life-threatening (see Deeper Insight 26.3).

TABLE 26.6	Functions of the Liver

Carbohydrate Metabolism
Converts dietary fructose and galactose to glucose. Stabilizes blood glucose concentration by storing excess glucose as glycogen (glycogenesis), releasing glucose from glycogen when needed (glycogenolysis), and synthesizing glucose from fats and amino acids (gluconeogenesis) when glucose demand exceeds glycogen reserves. Receives lactate generated by anaerobic fermentation in skeletal muscle and other tissues and converts it back to pyruvate or glucose 6-phosphate.

Lipid Metabolism
Degrades chylomicron remnants. Carries out most of the body's lipogenesis (fat synthesis) and synthesizes cholesterol and phospholipids; produces VLDLs to transport lipids to adipose tissue and other tissues for storage or use; and stores fat in its own cells.

Carries out most beta oxidation of fatty acids; produces ketone bodies from excess acetyl-CoA. Produces HDL shells, which pick up excess cholesterol from other tissues and return it to the liver; excretes the excess cholesterol in bile.

Protein and Amino Acid Metabolism
Carries out most deamination and transamination of amino acids. Removes —NH$_2$ from glutamic acid and converts the resulting ammonia to urea by means of the urea cycle. Synthesizes nonessential amino acids by transamination reactions.

Synthesis of Plasma Proteins
Synthesizes nearly all the proteins of blood plasma, including albumin, alpha and beta globulins, fibrinogen, prothrombin, and several other clotting factors. (Does not synthesize plasma enzymes or gamma globulins.)

(continued)

TABLE 26.6	Functions of the Liver (continued)

Vitamin and Mineral Metabolism

Converts vitamin D_3 to calcidiol, a step in the synthesis of calcitriol; stores a 3- to 4-month supply of vitamin D. Stores a 10-month supply of vitamin A and enough vitamin B_{12} to last from one to several years. Secretes hepcidin to regulate iron absorption; stores iron in ferritin and releases it as needed. Excretes excess calcium by way of the bile.

Digestion

Synthesizes bile acids and lecithin, which emulsify fat and promote its digestion; produces micelles, which aid in absorption of dietary lipids.

Disposal of Drugs, Toxins, and Hormones

Detoxifies alcohol, antibiotics, and many other drugs. Metabolizes bilirubin from RBC breakdown and excretes it as bile pigments. Deactivates thyroxine and steroid hormones and excretes them or converts them to a form more easily excreted by the kidneys.

Phagocytosis

Macrophages cleanse blood of bacteria and other foreign matter.

DEEPER INSIGHT 26.3

CLINICAL APPLICATION

Hepatitis and Cirrhosis

Hepatitis, inflammation of the liver, is usually caused by one of the six strains of hepatitis viruses (HVA to HVF). They differ in mode of transmission, severity of the resulting illness, affected age groups, and the best strategies for prevention. Hepatitis A *(infectious hepatitis)* is common and mild. Over 45% of people in urban areas of the United States have had it. It spreads rapidly in such settings as day-care centers and residential institutions for psychiatric patients, and it can be acquired by eating uncooked seafood such as oysters, as well as by sewage contamination of food and water and by hand-to-mouth fecal transmission. Hepatitis A can cause up to 6 months of illness, but most people recover and then have permanent immunity to it. Hepatitis E, with a similar mode of transmission, is uncommon in the United States but a significant cause of water-borne epidemics and mortality in less economically developed countries.

Hepatitis B and C are far more serious in the United States. Both are transmitted sexually and through blood and other body fluids; the incidence of hepatitis C has surpassed AIDS as a sexually transmitted disease. Initial signs and symptoms of hepatitis include fatigue, malaise, nausea, vomiting, and weight loss. The liver becomes enlarged and tender. Jaundice, or yellowing of the skin (see fig. 6.6b), tends to follow as hepatocytes are destroyed, bile passages are blocked, and bile pigments accumulate in the blood. Hepatitis B and C often lead to chronic hepatitis, which can progress to cirrhosis or liver cancer. More liver transplants are necessitated by hepatitis C than by any other cause.

Cirrhosis is an irreversible inflammatory liver disease. Most cases result from alcohol abuse, but hepatitis, gallstones, pancreatic inflammation, and other conditions can also bring it about. It develops slowly over a period of years, but has a high mortality rate and is one of the leading causes of death in the United States. It is characterized by a disorganized liver histology in which regions of scar tissue alternate with nodules of regenerating cells, giving the liver a lumpy or knobby appearance and hardened texture **(fig. 26.13).** As in hepatitis, blockage of the bile passages results in jaundice. Protein synthesis declines as the liver deteriorates, leading to ascites, impaired blood clotting, and other cardiovascular effects (see Deeper Insight 26.4). Obstruction of the hepatic circulation by scar tissue leads to *angiogenesis,* the growth of new blood vessels to bypass the liver. Deprived of blood, the condition of the liver worsens, with increasing necrosis and, often, liver failure. The prognosis for recovery is often poor.

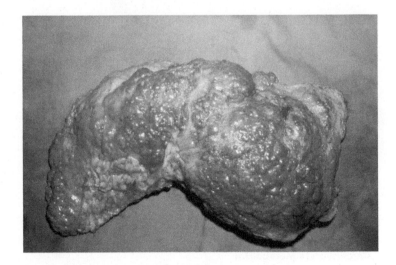

FIGURE 26.13 Liver with Cirrhosis.

Biophoto Associates/Getty Images

BEFORE YOU GO ON

Answer the following questions to test your understanding of the preceding section:

12. Which of the processes in table 26.5 is most comparable to lipogenesis? Which is most comparable to lipolysis? Explain.

13. When fats are converted to glucose, only the glycerol component is used in this way, not the fatty acid. Explain why, and state what happens to the fatty acids.

14. What metabolic process produces ammonia? How does the body dispose of ammonia?

26.4 Metabolic States and Metabolic Rate

Expected Learning Outcomes
When you have completed this section, you should be able to

a. define the *absorptive* and *postabsorptive states;*

b. explain what happens to carbohydrates, fats, and proteins in each of these states;

c. describe the hormonal and nervous regulation of each state;

d. define *metabolic rate* and *basal metabolic rate;* and

e. describe some factors that alter the metabolic rate.

One's metabolism changes from hour to hour depending on how long it has been since the last meal. The **absorptive (fed) state** prevails for about 4 hours during and after a meal. This is a time in which nutrients are being absorbed and may be stored or used immediately to meet energy and other needs. The **postabsorptive (fasting) state** prevails in the late morning, late afternoon, and overnight. During this time, the stomach and small intestine are empty and the body's energy needs are met from stored fuels. The two states are compared in **table 26.7** and explained in the following discussion.

26.4a The Absorptive State

In the absorptive state, blood glucose is readily available for ATP synthesis. It serves as the primary fuel and spares the body from having to draw on stored fuels. The status of major nutrient classes during this phase is as follows:

- **Carbohydrates.** Absorbed sugars are transported by the hepatic portal system to the liver. Most glucose passes through the liver and becomes available to cells everywhere in the body. Glucose in excess of immediate need, however, is absorbed by the liver and may be converted to glycogen

or fat. Most fat synthesized in the liver is released into the circulation; its further fate is comparable to that of dietary fats, discussed next.

- **Fats.** Fats enter the lymphatic system as chylomicrons and initially bypass the liver on their way to the subclavian veins, where they are dumped into the bloodstream. As described earlier, lipoprotein lipase removes fats from the blood-borne chylomicrons for uptake by the tissues, especially adipose and muscular tissue. The liver disposes of the chylomicron remnants. Fats are the primary energy substrate for hepatocytes, adipocytes, the heart, and the muscles.

- **Amino acids.** Amino acids, like sugars, circulate first to the liver. Most pass through and become available to other cells for protein synthesis. Some, however, are removed by the liver and have one of the following fates: (1) to be used for protein synthesis; (2) to be deaminated and used as fuel for ATP synthesis; or (3) to be deaminated and used for fatty acid synthesis.

Regulation of the Absorptive State

The absorptive state is regulated largely by insulin, which is secreted in response to elevated blood glucose and amino acid levels and to the intestinal hormones gastrin, secretin, cholecystokinin, and glucose-dependent insulinotropic peptide (GIP). Insulin regulates the rate of glucose uptake by nearly all cells except neurons, kidney cells, and erythrocytes, which have independent rates of uptake. With those exceptions, insulin has the following effects on its target cells:

- Within minutes, it increases the cellular uptake of glucose by as much as 20-fold. As cells absorb glucose, the blood glucose concentration falls.

- It stimulates glucose oxidation, glycogenesis, and lipogenesis.

- It inhibits gluconeogenesis, which makes sense because blood glucose concentration is already high and there is no immediate need for more.

TABLE 26.7	Major Aspects of the Absorptive and Postabsorptive States	
	Absorptive	**Postabsorptive**
Regulatory hormones	Principally insulin Also gastrin, secretin, CCK, and GIP	Principally glucagon Also epinephrine, growth hormone
Carbohydrate metabolism	Blood glucose rising Glucose uptake Glucose stored by glycogenesis Gluconeogenesis suppressed	Blood glucose falling Glucose released by glycogenolysis Gluconeogenesis stimulated
Lipid metabolism	Lipogenesis occurring Lipid uptake from chylomicrons Lipid storage in fat and muscle	Lipolysis occurring Fatty acids oxidized as fuel Glycerol used for gluconeogenesis
Protein metabolism	Amino acid uptake, protein synthesis Excess amino acids oxidized as fuel	Proteins oxidized as fuel if glycogen and fat stores are inadequate for energy needs

- It stimulates the active transport of amino acids into cells and promotes protein synthesis.
- It acts on the brain as an adiposity signal, an index of the body's fat stores.

Following a high-protein, low-carbohydrate meal, it may seem that the amino acids would stimulate insulin secretion; insulin would accelerate both amino acid and glucose uptake; and since there was relatively little glucose in the ingested food, this would create a risk of hypoglycemia. In actuality, this is prevented by the fact that a high amino acid level stimulates the secretion of *both* insulin and glucagon. Glucagon, you may recall, is an insulin antagonist. It supports an adequate level of blood glucose to meet the needs of the brain.

26.4b The Postabsorptive State

The essence of the postabsorptive state is to homeostatically regulate plasma glucose concentration within about 90 to 100 mg/dL. This is especially critical to the brain, which cannot use alternative energy substrates except in cases of prolonged fasting. The postabsorptive status of major nutrients is as follows:

- **Carbohydrates.** Glucose is drawn from the body's glycogen reserves (glycogenolysis) or synthesized from other compounds (gluconeogenesis). The liver usually stores enough glycogen after a meal to support 4 hours of postabsorptive metabolism before significant gluconeogenesis occurs.
- **Fats.** Adipocytes and hepatocytes hydrolyze fats and convert the glycerol to glucose. Free fatty acids (FFAs) can't be converted to glucose, but they can favorably affect blood glucose concentration. As the liver oxidizes them to ketone bodies, other cells absorb and use these, or use FFAs directly, as their source of energy. By switching from glucose to fatty acid catabolism, they leave glucose for use by the brain (the glucose-sparing effect). After 4 to 5 days of fasting, the brain begins to use ketone bodies as supplemental fuel.
- **Proteins.** If glycogen and fat reserves are depleted, the body begins to use proteins as fuel. Some proteins are more resistant to catabolism than others. Collagen is almost never broken down for fuel, but muscle protein goes quickly. People with cancer and certain other chronic diseases sometimes exhibit **cachexia**[9] (ka-KEX-ee-ah), an extreme wasting away due to altered metabolism and loss of appetite (anorexia).

Regulation of the Postabsorptive State

Postabsorptive metabolism is more complex than the absorptive state. It is regulated mainly by the sympathetic nervous system

and glucagon, but several other hormones are involved. As blood glucose level drops, insulin secretion declines and the pancreatic alpha cells secrete glucagon. Glucagon promotes glycogenolysis and gluconeogenesis, raising the blood glucose level, and it promotes lipolysis and a rise in FFA levels. Thus, it makes both glucose and lipids available for fuel.

The sympathoadrenal system also promotes glycogenolysis and lipolysis, especially under conditions of injury, fear, anger, and other forms of stress. Adipose tissue is richly innervated by the sympathetic nervous system, while adipocytes, hepatocytes, and muscle cells also respond to epinephrine from the adrenal medulla. In circumstances in which there is likely to be tissue injury and a need for repair, the sympathoadrenal system therefore mobilizes stored energy reserves and makes them available to meet the demands of tissue repair. Stress also stimulates the release of cortisol, which promotes fat and protein catabolism and gluconeogenesis.

Growth hormone is secreted in response to a rapid drop in blood glucose level and in states of prolonged fasting. It opposes insulin and raises the blood glucose concentration.

26.4c Metabolic Rate

Metabolic rate means the amount of energy liberated in the body per unit of time, expressed in such terms as kcal/h or kcal/day. Metabolic rate can be measured directly by putting a person in a **calorimeter,** a closed chamber with water-filled walls that absorb the heat given off by the body. The rate of energy release is measured from the temperature change of the water. Metabolic rate can also be measured indirectly with a spirometer (see fig. 22.17), which measures the amount of oxygen a person consumes. For every liter of oxygen, approximately 4.82 kcal of energy is released from organic nutrients. This is only an estimate, because the number of kilocalories per liter of oxygen varies slightly with the type of nutrients the person is oxidizing at the time of measurement.

Metabolic rate depends on physical activity, mental state, absorptive or postabsorptive status, thyroid hormone and other hormones, and other factors. The **basal metabolic rate (BMR)** is a baseline or standard of comparison that minimizes the effects of such variables. It is the metabolic rate when one is awake but relaxed, in a room at comfortable temperature, in a postabsorptive state 12 to 14 hours after the last meal. It isn't the minimum metabolic rate needed to sustain life. When one is asleep, the metabolic rate is slightly lower than the BMR. **Total metabolic rate (TMR)** is the sum of BMR and energy expenditure for voluntary activities, especially muscular contractions.

The BMR of an average adult is about 2,000 kcal/day for a male and slightly less for a female. Roughly speaking, one must therefore consume at least 2,000 kcal/day to fuel essential metabolic tasks—active transport, muscle tone, brain activity, cardiac and respiratory rhythms, renal function, and other essential processes. Even a relatively sedentary lifestyle requires another 500 kcal/day to support a low level of physical activity, and someone who does hard physical labor may require as much as 5,000 kcal/day.

---

[9]*cac* = bad; *exia* = body condition

Aside from physical activity, some factors that raise the TMR and caloric requirements include pregnancy, anxiety (which stimulates epinephrine release and muscle tension), fever (TMR rises about 14% for each 1°C of body temperature), eating (TMR rises after a meal), and the catecholamine and thyroid hormones. TMR is relatively high in children and declines with age. Therefore, as we reach middle age we often find ourselves gaining weight with no apparent change in food intake.

Some factors that lower TMR include apathy, depression, and prolonged starvation. In weight-loss diets, loss is often rapid at first and then goes more slowly. This is partly because the initial loss is largely water and partly because the TMR drops over time, fewer dietary calories are "burned off," and there is more lipogenesis even with the same caloric intake. As one reduces food intake, the body reduces its metabolic rate to conserve body mass—thus making weight loss all the more difficult.

BEFORE YOU GO ON

Answer the following questions to test your understanding of the preceding section:

15. Define *absorptive* and *postabsorptive states.* In which state is the body storing excess fuel? In which state is it drawing from these stored fuel reserves?

16. What hormone primarily regulates the absorptive state, and what are the major effects of this hormone?

17. Explain why triglycerides have a glucose-sparing effect.

18. List a variety of factors and conditions that raise a person's total metabolic rate above basal metabolic rate.

26.5 Body Heat and Thermoregulation

Expected Learning Outcomes

When you have completed this section, you should be able to

a. identify the principal sources of body heat;

b. describe some factors that cause variations in body temperature;

c. define and contrast the different forms of heat loss;

d. describe how the hypothalamus monitors and controls body temperature; and

e. describe conditions in which the body temperature is excessively high or low.

The enzymes that control our metabolism depend on an optimal, stable working temperature. In order to maintain this, the rates of metabolic heat generation and heat loss from the body must match. An excessively low body temperature, called **hypothermia,** can slow down the metabolism to the point that it can't sustain life. Conversely, an excessively high body temperature, called **hyperthermia,** can make some metabolic pathways race ahead of others and disrupt their coordination to the point that this, too, can lead to death. **Thermoregulation,** the balance between heat production and loss, is therefore a critically important aspect of homeostasis.

26.5a Body Temperature

"Normal" body temperature depends on when, where, and in whom it is measured. Body temperature fluctuates about 1°C (1.8°F) in a 24-hour cycle. It tends to be lowest in the early morning and highest in the late afternoon. Temperature also varies from place to place in one body. The body is warmest in its deep *core* and cooler near the surface, the *shell.*

The most important body temperature is the **core temperature**—the temperature of organs in the cranial, thoracic, and abdominal cavities. The best estimate of core temperature obtainable with ease is rectal temperature: usually 37.2° to 37.6°C (99.0° to 99.7°F), but as high as 38.5°C (101°F) in active children and some adults. **Shell temperature** is the temperature closer to the surface, especially skin and oral temperature. Here, heat is lost from the body and temperatures are slightly lower than rectal temperature. Adult oral temperature is typically 36.6° to 37.0°C (97.9° to 98.6°F) but may be as high as 40°C (104°F) during hard exercise. Shell temperature fluctuates as a result of processes that serve to maintain a stable core temperature.

Blood circulation is crucial to thermoregulation. We depend on blood flow to carry metabolic heat from the body core to the shell, where it can be dissipated into the environment. Without this "radiator effect," we would soon die of hyperthermia as metabolic heat raised the core temperature beyond survivable range.

26.5b Heat Production and Loss

Most body heat comes from exergonic (energy-releasing) chemical reactions such as nutrient oxidation and ATP use. A little heat is generated by joint friction, blood flow, and other movements. At rest, most heat is generated by the brain, heart, liver, and endocrine glands; the skeletal muscles contribute about 20% to 30% of the total resting heat. Increased muscle tone or exercise greatly increases heat generation in the muscles, however; in vigorous exercise, they produce 30 to 40 times as much heat as all the rest of the body.

The body loses heat in four ways: radiation, conduction, convection, and evaporation:

1. **Radiation** is the emission of infrared (IR) rays by moving molecules. In essence, *heat* means molecular motion, and all molecular motion produces IR radiation. When an object absorbs IR rays, its molecular motion and temperature increase. Therefore, IR radiation removes heat from its source and adds heat to anything that absorbs it. The heat lamps in bathrooms and restaurants work on this principle. Our bodies continually receive IR from the objects around us and give off IR to our surroundings. Since we're usually warmer than the objects around us, we usually lose more heat this way than we gain.

2. **Conduction** is the transfer of kinetic energy from molecule to molecule as they collide with one another. Heat generated in the body core is conducted to the surface through the tissues, then lost from the body by conduction from the skin to any cooler objects or medium in contact with it. The warmth of your body adds to the molecular motion of your clothes, the chair you sit in, the air around you, or water if you go swimming or sit in a cool bath. With this transfer of kinetic energy to your surroundings, you lose body heat. You can also gain heat by conduction, as on a very hot day when the air temperature is greater than your shell temperature, or when you use a heating pad for sore muscles, bask in a hot tub, or lie on hot sand at the beach.

3. **Convection** is the transfer of heat to a moving fluid—blood, air, or water. Most of the heat generated by metabolism in the body core is carried by convection in the bloodstream to the body surface. At the skin surface, body heat warms the adjacent air. Warm air is less dense than cool air, so it rises from the body and is replaced by cooler air from below. This can be visualized by a technique called *schlieren photography* **(fig. 26.14).** Water does this as well if one stands still enough in a cool lake. Such movement of a fluid caused entirely by its change in temperature and density is called **natural convection.** When air movement is forced by a fan or the wind, even if the air itself is no cooler, it carries heat away from the body more rapidly. This effect, called **forced convection,** is the reason why, even at the same temperature, we feel cooler on a windy day than on a day when the air is still. It is the basis for the *windchill factor* of a cold, windy day. Forced convection increases heat loss by both conduction and evaporation (discussed next), but has no effect on radiation.

4. **Evaporation** is the change from a liquid to a gaseous state. The cohesion of water molecules hampers their vibrations in response to heat input. If the temperature of water is raised sufficiently, however, its molecular motion becomes great enough for molecules to break free and evaporate. Evaporation of water thus carries a substantial amount of heat with it (0.58 kcal per gram of water). This is the significance of perspiration. Sweat wets the skin surface and its evaporation carries heat away. In extreme conditions, the body can lose 2 L or more of sweat and dissipate up to 600 kcal of heat per hour by evaporative loss. Evaporative heat loss is increased by forced convection, as you can readily feel when you are sweaty and stand in front of a fan or a refreshing breeze begins to blow.

The relative amounts of heat lost by different methods depend on prevailing conditions. A nude body in still air at 21°C (70°F) loses about 60% of its heat by radiation, 18% by conduction and convection, and 22% by evaporation. If air temperature is higher than skin temperature, evaporation becomes the only means of heat loss because radiation and conduction add more heat to the body than they remove from it. Hot, humid weather hinders even

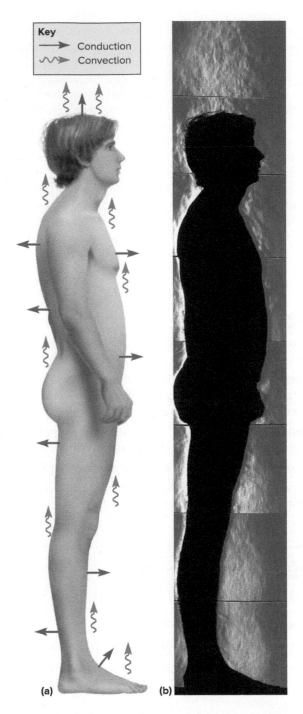

(a)   **(b)**

FIGURE 26.14 Heat Loss by Conduction and Convection.
(a) Heat transfers from the body to surrounding air molecules by conduction. Warm air then rises from the body by convection, carrying heat away. Cool air replaces this warm air from below. (b) Schlieren photograph of the column of warm air rising from the body.
b: Dr. Ray Clark FRPS/Science Source

evaporative cooling because there is less of a humidity gradient from skin to air. Such conditions increase the risk of heatstroke (discussed shortly).

26.5c Thermoregulation

Thermoregulation is achieved through several negative feedback loops that govern cutaneous blood flow and other mechanisms for raising or lowering body temperature. The preoptic area of the hypothalamus (anterior to the optic chiasm) functions as a **hypothalamic thermostat.** It monitors blood temperature and receives signals also from **peripheral thermoreceptors** located mainly in the skin. In turn, it sends signals either to the **heat-loss center,** a nucleus still farther anterior in the hypothalamus, or to the **heat-promoting center,** a more posterior nucleus near the mammillary bodies.

When the heat-loss center senses that the blood temperature is too high, it activates heat-losing mechanisms. The first and simplest of these is cutaneous vasodilation, which increases blood flow to the body shell (skin and subcutaneous tissue) and thus promotes heat loss. In warm conditions, the shell, or zone of relatively cool tissue, may be less than 1 cm thick **(fig. 26.15a).** If cutaneous vasodilation fails to restore normal temperature, the heat-loss center triggers sweating. It also inhibits the heat-promoting center.

When the blood temperature is too low, the heat-promoting center activates mechanisms to conserve body heat or generate more. By way of the sympathetic nervous system, it causes cutaneous vasoconstriction. This diverts warm blood from the shell and retains it deeper in the body so less heat is lost through the skin. The cooler shell may then be several centimeters thick **(fig. 26.15b).** In other mammals, the sympathetic nervous system also stimulates the arrector muscles, which make the hair stand on end. This traps an insulating blanket of still air near the skin. The human sympathetic nervous system attempts to do this as well, but since our body hair is so slight, usually the only noticeable effect of this is goose bumps.

If dermal vasoconstriction can't restore or maintain normal core temperature, the body resorts to **shivering thermogenesis.** If you leave a warm house on a very cold day, you may notice that your muscles become tense, sometimes even painfully taut, and you begin to shiver. Shivering involves a spinal reflex that causes tiny alternating contractions in antagonistic muscle pairs. Every muscle contraction releases heat from ATP, and shivering can increase the body's heat production as much as fourfold.

Nonshivering thermogenesis is a longer-term mechanism for generating heat, occurring especially in the colder seasons of the year. The sympathetic

nervous system raises the metabolic rate as much as 30% after several weeks of cold weather. More nutrients are burned as fuel; we consume more calories to "stoke the furnace"; and consequently, we have more appetite in the winter than in the summer. Infants generate heat by breaking down *brown fat,* a tissue in

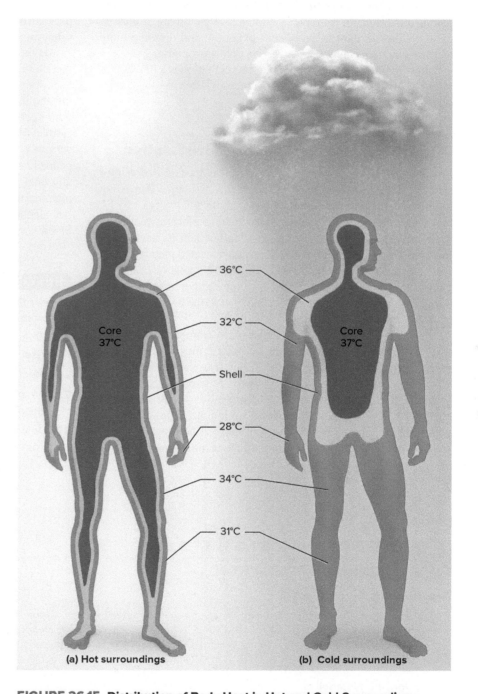

FIGURE 26.15 Distribution of Body Heat in Hot and Cold Surroundings. (a) In a hot environment, cutaneous vasodilation carries heat close to the body surface and the shell is relatively thin. (b) In a cold environment, cutaneous vasoconstriction retains heat deeper in the body and the insulating shell is significantly thicker. It is easy to see from this why frostbite so often affects extremities such as fingers and toes.

which lipolysis is not linked to ATP synthesis, so all the energy released from the fat is in the form of heat.

In addition to these physiological mechanisms, and of even greater importance, humans and other animals practice **behavioral thermoregulation**—behaviors that raise or lower the body's heat gains and losses. Just getting out of the sun greatly cuts down heat gain by radiation, for example; shedding heavy clothing or kicking off a blanket at night helps to cool the body; and dressing more warmly maintains body temperature in cold surroundings.

In summary, you can see that thermoregulation is a function of multiple organs: the brain, autonomic nerves, thyroid gland, skin, blood vessels, and skeletal muscles.

26.5d Disturbances of Thermoregulation

Fever is a normal protective mechanism against infection (see section 21.2e); it should be allowed to run its course if it is not too high. A body temperature above 42° to 43°C (108° to 110°F), however, is dangerous. The high temperature elevates the metabolic rate and the body generates heat faster than its heat-losing mechanisms can disperse it. Therefore, the elevated metabolic rate increases the fever and the fever increases the metabolic rate in a dangerous positive feedback loop. A core temperature of 44° to 45°C (111° to 113°F) can produce fatal metabolic dysfunction and neurological damage.

Exposure to excessive heat causes heat cramps, heat exhaustion, and heatstroke. **Heat cramps** are painful muscle spasms that result from electrolyte loss in the sweat. They occur especially when one begins to relax after strenuous exertion and heavy sweating. **Heat exhaustion** results from more severe water and electrolyte loss and is characterized by hypotension, dizziness, vomiting, and sometimes fainting. Prolonged heat waves, especially if accompanied by high humidity, bring on many deaths from **heatstroke (sunstroke).** The body gains heat by radiation and conduction, but the humidity retards evaporative cooling. Heatstroke is clinically defined as a state in which the core body temperature is over 40°C (104°F); the skin is hot and dry; and the subject exhibits nervous system dysfunctions such as delirium, convulsions, or coma. It is also accompanied by tachycardia, hyperventilation, inflammation, and multiorgan dysfunction; it is often fatal.

Hypothermia can result from exposure to cold weather or immersion in icy water. It, too, entails life-threatening positive feedback loops. If the core temperature falls below 33°C (91°F), the metabolic rate drops so low that heat production can't keep pace with heat loss, and the temperature falls even more. Death from cardiac fibrillation may occur below 32°C (90°F), but some people survive body temperatures as low as 29°C (84°F) in a state of suspended animation. A body temperature below 24°C (75°F) is usually fatal. It is dangerous to give alcohol to someone in a state of hypothermia; the chemical "burn" produces an illusion of warmth, but alcohol actually accelerates heat loss by dilating cutaneous blood vessels.

BEFORE YOU GO ON

Answer the following questions to test your understanding of the preceding section:

19. What is the primary source of body heat? What are some lesser sources?

20. What mechanisms of heat loss are aided by convection?

21. Describe the major heat-promoting and heat-losing mechanisms of the body.

22. Describe the positive feedback loops that can cause death from hyper- and hypothermia.

DEEPER INSIGHT 26.4

CLINICAL APPLICATION

Alcohol and Alcoholism

Alcohol not only is a popular mind-altering drug but also is regarded in many cultures as a food staple. As a source of empty calories, an addictive drug, and a toxin, it can have a broad spectrum of adverse effects on the body when it is abused.

Absorption and Metabolism

Alcohol is rapidly absorbed from the digestive tract—about 10% of it from the stomach and 90% from the proximal small intestine. Carbonation, as in beer and sparkling wines, increases its rate of absorption by moving it more quickly to the small intestine, whereas food reduces its absorption by delaying gastric emptying. Alcohol is soluble in both water and fat, so it is rapidly distributed to all body tissues and easily crosses the blood–brain barrier to exert its intoxicating effects on the brain.

Alcohol is detoxified by the hepatic enzyme *alcohol dehydrogenase,* which oxidizes it to acetaldehyde. This enters the citric acid cycle and is oxidized to CO_2 and H_2O. The average adult male can clear the blood of about 10 mL of 100% (200 proof) alcohol per hour—the amount in about 30 mL (1 oz) of whiskey or 355 mL (12 oz) of beer. Women have less alcohol dehydrogenase and clear alcohol from the bloodstream more slowly. They are also more vulnerable to alcohol-related illnesses such as cirrhosis of the liver.

Tolerance to alcohol, the ability to "hold your liquor," results from two factors: behavioral modification, such as giving in less readily to lowered inhibitions, and increased levels of alcohol dehydrogenase in response to routine alcohol consumption. Alcohol dehydrogenase also deactivates other drugs, and drug dosages must be adjusted to compensate for this when treating alcoholics for other diseases.

Physiological Effects

Nervous System Alcohol is a depressant that inhibits the release of norepinephrine and disrupts the function of GABA receptors. In low doses, it depresses inhibitory synapses and creates sensations of confidence, euphoria, and giddiness. As the dosage rises, however, the breakdown products of ethanol enhance the diffusion of K^+ out of neurons, hyperpolarizing them and making them less responsive to neurotransmitters. Thus, the timing and coordination of communication between neurons are impaired, resulting in such symptoms of intoxication as slurred speech, poor coordination, and slower reaction time. These symptoms begin to become significant at a blood alcohol level of 80 to 100 mg/dL—the legal criterion of intoxication in many states. Above 400 mg/dL, alcohol can so disrupt the electrophysiology of neurons as to induce coma and death.

Liver The liver's role in metabolizing alcohol makes it especially susceptible to long-term toxic effects. Heavy drinking stresses the liver with a high load of acetaldehyde and acetate; this depletes its oxidizing agents and reduces its ability to catabolize these intermediates as well as fatty acids. Alcoholism often produces a greatly enlarged and fatty liver for multiple reasons: The calories provided by alcohol make it unnecessary to burn fat as fuel, fatty acids are poorly oxidized, and acetaldehyde is converted to new fatty acids. Acetaldehyde also causes inflammation of the liver and pancreas *(hepatitis* and *pancreatitis),* leading to disruption of digestive function. Acetaldehyde and other toxic intermediates destroy hepatocytes faster than they can be regenerated, leading to cirrhosis (see Deeper Insight 26.3). Many symptoms of alcoholism stem from deterioration of liver functions. Hepatic coma may occur as the liver becomes unable to produce urea, thus allowing ammonia to accumulate in the blood. Jaundice is a sign of the liver's inability to excrete bilirubin.

Circulatory System Deteriorating liver functions exert several effects on the blood and cardiovascular system. Blood clotting is impaired because the liver cannot synthesize clotting factors adequately. Edema results from inadequate synthesis of blood albumin. Cirrhosis obstructs the hepatic portal blood circulation. Portal hypertension results, and combined with hypoproteinemia, this causes the liver and other organs to "weep" serous fluid into the peritoneal cavity. This leads to *ascites—* swelling of the abdomen with as much as several liters of serous fluid (see Deeper Insight 20.4). The combination of hypertension and impaired clotting often leads to hemorrhaging. *Hematemesis,*[10] the vomiting of blood, may occur as enlarged veins of the esophagus hemorrhage. Alcohol abuse also destroys myocardial tissue, reduces contractility of the heart, and causes cardiac arrhythmia.

Digestive System and Nutrition Alcohol breaks down the protective mucous barrier of the stomach and the tight junctions between its epithelial cells. Thus, it may cause gastritis and bleeding. Heavy drinking, especially in combination with smoking, increases the incidence of esophageal cancer. Malnutrition is a typical complication of alcoholism, partly because the empty calories of alcohol suppress the appetite for more nutritious foods. The average American gets about 4.5% of his or her calories from alcohol (more when nondrinkers are excluded), but heavy drinkers may obtain half or more of their calories from alcohol and have less appetite for foods that would meet their other nutritional requirements. In addition, acetaldehyde interferes with vitamin absorption and use. Thiamine deficiency is common in alcoholism, and thiamine is routinely given to alcoholics in treatment.

Addiction

Alcohol is the most widely available addictive drug in America. In many respects it is almost identical to barbiturates in its toxic effects, its potential for tolerance and dependence, and the risk of overdose. The difference is that obtaining barbiturates usually requires a prescription, while obtaining alcohol requires, at most, proof of age.

Alcoholism is defined by a combination of criteria, including the pathological changes just described; physiological tolerance of high concentrations; impaired physiological, psychological, and social functionality; and withdrawal symptoms occurring when intake is reduced or stopped. Heavy drinking followed by a period of abstinence—for example, when a patient is admitted to the hospital and cannot get access to alcohol—may trigger *delirium tremens (DT),* characterized by restlessness, insomnia, confusion, irritability, tremors, incoherent speech, hallucinations, convulsions, and coma. DT has a 5% to 15% mortality rate.

Most alcoholism (type I) sets in after age 25 and is usually associated with stress or peer pressure. These influences lead to increased drinking, which can start a vicious cycle of illness, reduced job performance, family and social problems, arrest, and other stresses leading to still more drinking. A smaller number of alcoholics have type II alcoholism, which is at least partially hereditary. Most people with type II alcoholism are men who become addicted before age 25, especially the sons of other type II alcoholics. Type II alcoholics show abnormally rapid increases in blood acetaldehyde levels when they drink, and they have unusual brain waves (EEGs) even when not drinking. Children of alcoholics have a higher than average incidence of becoming alcoholic even when raised by nonalcoholic foster parents. It is by no means inevitable that such people will become alcoholic, but stress or peer pressure can trigger alcoholism more easily in those who are genetically predisposed to it.

Alcoholism is treated primarily through behavior modification—abstinence, peer support, avoidance or correction of the stresses that encourage drinking, and sometimes psychotherapy. Drugs such as disulfiram (Antabuse) have been used to support behavior modification programs by producing unpleasant effects from alcohol consumption, but drug treatment has been fraught with potentially dangerous side effects and little evidence of effectiveness.

---

[10]*hemat* = blood; *emesis* = vomiting

STUDY GUIDE

▶ Assess Your Learning Outcomes

To test your knowledge, discuss the following topics with a study partner or in writing, ideally from memory.

26.1 Nutrition

1. Evidence of a homeostatic set point for body weight; relative contributions of heredity and behavior to differences in body weight
2. The meaning of *gut–brain peptides*
3. Sources and actions of ghrelin, peptide YY, cholecystokinin, and amylin as short-term regulators of appetite
4. Sources and actions of leptin and insulin as adiposity signals and long-term regulators of appetite
5. Roles of the arcuate nucleus, neuropeptide YY, and melanocortin in appetite regulation
6. The role of hunger contractions in the onset of feeding; factors that satiate hunger over the short and long terms, and how these resemble the satiation of thirst
7. Hormones that stimulate an appetite for specific classes of nutrients such as carbohydrates, fats, and proteins
8. The definition of *calorie* and how this relates to dietary Calories (kilocalories)
9. Principal dietary sources of calories; the relative yield from fats as compared to carbohydrates and proteins; and the meaning of *empty calories*
10. The definition of *nutrient;* why some nutrients are not digested and yield no calories; and why some things are not considered nutrients even though they are important components of a healthy diet
11. The difference between macronutrients and micronutrients; the nutrients in each category
12. Why some substances are considered to be essential nutrients
13. Forms and amounts of stored and mobile carbohydrates in the body; how the body uses carbohydrates; how dietary carbohydrates influence the metabolism of fats
14. Hormones that regulate the balance between blood glucose and stored glycogen; the normal range of blood glucose concentration
15. The recommended daily intake of carbohydrates; the percentage of calories that come from carbohydrates in a typical U.S. diet; the forms in which carbohydrates exist in the diet, and their relative amounts; dietary sources of carbohydrates

16. The meaning of *dietary fiber;* the recommended daily intake of fiber and how actual consumption varies around the world; the forms of dietary fiber; which forms are classified as soluble and insoluble fiber, and differences in the health benefits of these two classes; the detrimental effects of too much dietary fiber
17. Two reasons why the body stores more energy as fat than as carbohydrate; the caloric yield from fat compared to carbohydrate; the typical percentages of body fat in normal males and females
18. Why fat is said to have glucose-sparing and protein-sparing effects
19. Metabolically important lipids other than fat, and their uses in the body
20. The recommended daily intake of fat, and how the typical U.S. diet compares to this.
21. Why linoleic acid is called an essential fatty acid; two other fatty acids that might be essential
22. Dietary sources of saturated and unsaturated fats, essential fatty acids, and cholesterol; the health risks of excessive saturated and unsaturated fats
23. Types of lipoproteins found in the bloodstream—chylomicrons, VLDLs, LDLs, and HDLs—and the differences in their source, composition, and functions; the relevance of LDLs and HDLs to cardiovascular health and how these relate to the colloquial expressions "good cholesterol" and "bad cholesterol"
24. Functions of proteins in the body, and a typical percentage of the body mass composed of protein
25. The recommended daily intake of protein; how that can be estimated from body weight; good dietary sources of protein; conditions that call for a protein intake greater than normal; and the risks from excessive dietary protein
26. Why nutritional value of a protein depends on its amino acid composition; the eight essential amino acids; the difference between complete and incomplete proteins; the meaning of net protein utilization and why it is different for dietary proteins of plant and animal origin; and some dietary and ecological advantages of plant protein
27. The meanings of *positive* and *negative nitrogen balance* and the conditions under which each of them occurs

28. The definition and ultimate source of *dietary minerals;* the functions of minerals in the body; the most abundant minerals in the body; and, in general, good and poor dietary sources of minerals
29. The general history of human salt consumption; the recommended daily intake of sodium and some reasons why most U.S. diets greatly exceed this; and the consequences of excessive sodium intake
30. The definition of *vitamins;* dietary and nondietary sources; the functions of vitamins in the body; the difference between water-soluble and fat-soluble vitamins

26.2 Carbohydrate Metabolism

1. The summary equation for the complete aerobic oxidation of glucose
2. Function of the coenzymes NAD^+ and FAD in glucose oxidation
3. The general process and outcome of glycolysis, and its net ATP yield
4. Anaerobic fermentation and its primary purpose
5. The cellular site of aerobic respiration, its end products, and its advantages
6. The citric acid cycle, where it occurs, the fate of the carbon atoms that originated in the glucose, and the cycle's yield of ATP, NADH, and $FADH_2$
7. Mitochondrial membrane reactions; where they occur in the organelle; the components of the mitochondrial electron-transport chain; how mitochondria transport electrons from NADH and $FADH_2$ to oxygen; and how the reactions produce metabolic water
8. Mitochondrial proton pumps, the chemiosmotic mechanism, and ATP synthase in producing ATP
9. The net ATP yield of glycolysis and aerobic respiration; the amount of ATP produced at each step from glucose to H_2O; and why the yield varies slightly between different cell types
10. The efficiency of aerobic respiration and how to calculate this
11. How excess glucose is converted to glycogen; the body's typical glycogen store and where these reserves are located; and the processes and purposes of glycogenesis, glycogenolysis, and gluconeogenesis

STUDY GUIDE

26.3 Lipid and Protein Metabolism

1. What cells are primarily responsible for storing and releasing triglycerides; the essence of the lipogenesis and lipolysis carried out by these and other cells

2. The process of lipolysis including the hydrolysis of triglycerides and the beta oxidation of fatty acids; the ATP yield from complete oxidation of a typical fatty acid

3. The meaning of *ketogenesis;* the metabolic use of ketone bodies and the pathological effects of excessive ketone levels; common circumstances in which excessive ketogenesis occurs

4. A typical daily rate of protein turnover in the body; where and why the fastest rate of protein turnover occurs; and the dietary and nondietary sources of the amino acids absorbed by the small intestine

5. The uses of free amino acids in the amino acid pool

6. What occurs in the deamination, amination, and transamination processes in amino acid metabolism; the body's uses of deaminated amino acids

7. How amino acids are shuttled into the citric acid cycle for oxidation as fuel

8. How the liver produces urea

9. Other nondigestive functions of the liver

26.4 Metabolic States and Metabolic Rate

1. When the body is in its absorptive state; what things occur in this state with respect to carbohydrate, fat, and protein metabolism

2. The main hormone that regulates the absorptive state; its primary metabolic effects in this state; and what antagonist modulates its effects

3. When the body is in its postabsorptive state; what things occur in this state with respect to carbohydrate, fat, and sometimes protein metabolism

4. Hormones that regulate the postabsorptive state, their effects, and the role of the sympathetic nervous system in its regulation

5. The meaning of *metabolic rate;* how it is measured and in what units of measurement it is expressed; what factors cause it to vary; and how the basal metabolic rate (BMR) differs from total metabolic rate (TMR)

6. Typical values for the BMR and TMR under different conditions of physical exertion

26.5 Body Heat and Thermoregulation

1. The meaning of *thermoregulation;* terms for abnormally low and high body temperatures; and reasons why those two conditions can be fatal

2. Typical core and shell body temperatures and how the two are measured

3. How most body heat is produced, and which organs are the most important sources of body heat at rest and in exercise

4. Four mechanisms by which body heat is lost, and the percentages of total heat loss attributable to each of them at rest and at a comfortable ambient temperature (21°C)

5. How the hypothalamic thermostat monitors core and shell body temperature

6. Two mechanisms for lowering body temperature and two mechanisms of raising it; regions of the hypothalamus involved in each

7. The meanings of *nonshivering thermogenesis* and *behavioral thermoregulation,* and examples of the latter

8. Differences between heat cramps, heat exhaustion, and heatstroke; the role of positive feedback loops in hyperthermia; and how and at what temperature range heatstroke can lead to death

9. The role of positive feedback loops in hypothermia, and how and at what temperature range hypothermia can lead to death

▶ Testing Your Recall

Answers in Appendix A

1. _____ are not used as fuel and are required in relatively small quantities.
   a. Micronutrients
   b. Macronutrients
   c. Essential nutrients
   d. Proteins
   e. Lipids

2. The only significant digestible polysaccharide in the diet is
   a. glycogen.
   b. cellulose.
   c. starch.
   d. maltose.
   e. fiber.

3. Which of the following store(s) the greatest amount of energy for the smallest amount of space in the body?
   a. glucose
   b. triglycerides
   c. glycogen
   d. proteins
   e. vitamins

4. The lipoproteins that remove cholesterol from the tissues are
   a. chylomicrons.
   b. lipoprotein lipases.
   c. VLDLs.
   d. LDLs.
   e. HDLs.

5. Which of the following is most likely to make you hungry?
   a. leptin
   b. ghrelin
   c. cholecystokinin
   d. peptide YY
   e. melanocortin

6. The primary function of B-complex vitamins is to act as
   a. structural components of cells.
   b. sources of energy.
   c. components of pigments.
   d. antioxidants.
   e. coenzymes.

7. FAD is reduced to $FADH_2$ in
   a. glycolysis.
   b. anaerobic fermentation.
   c. the citric acid cycle.
   d. the electron-transport chain.
   e. beta oxidation of lipids.

8. The primary, direct benefit of anaerobic fermentation is to
   a. regenerate NAD^+.
   b. produce $FADH_2$.
   c. produce lactate.
   d. dispose of pyruvate.
   e. produce more ATP than glycolysis does.

9. Which of these occurs in the mitochondrial matrix?
   a. glycolysis
   b. chemiosmosis
   c. the cytochrome reactions
   d. the citric acid cycle
   e. anaerobic fermentation

STUDY GUIDE

10. When the body emits more infrared energy than it absorbs, it is losing heat by
    a. convection.
    b. forced convection.
    c. conduction.
    d. radiation.
    e. evaporation.

11. A/an _____ protein lacks one or more essential amino acids.

12. In the postabsorptive state, glycogen is hydrolyzed to liberate glucose. This process is called _____.

13. Synthesis of glucose from amino acids or triglycerides is called _____.

14. The major nitrogenous waste resulting from protein catabolism is _____.

15. The organ that synthesizes the nitrogenous waste in question 14 is the _____.

16. The absorptive state is regulated mainly by the hormone _____.

17. The temperature of organs in the body cavities is called _____.

18. The appetite hormones ghrelin, leptin, CCK, and others act on part of the hypothalamus called the _____ nucleus.

19. The brightly colored, iron-containing, electron-transfer molecules of the inner mitochondrial membrane are called _____.

20. The flow of H^+ from the intermembrane space to the mitochondrial matrix creates an electrical current used by the enzyme _____ to make _____.

▶ Building Your Medical Vocabulary

Answers in Appendix A

State a meaning of each word element, and give a medical term from this chapter that uses it or a slight variation of it.

1. asco-

2. cac-

3. chromo-

4. -genesis

5. glyco-

6. -ites

7. lepto-

8. -lysis

9. neo-

10. osmo-

▶ What's Wrong with These Statements?

Answers in Appendix A

Briefly explain why each of the following statements is false, or reword it to make it true.

1. Ghrelin and leptin are two hormones that stimulate the appetite.

2. Water is not considered a nutrient because we don't digest it and it contains no calories.

3. A gram of carbohydrates contains twice as much energy as a gram of fat.

4. Most of the body's cholesterol comes from the diet.

5. There is no harm in maximizing one's daily protein intake.

6. Extremely low-fat fad diets tend to produce potentially dangerous high levels of blood ketones.

7. Reactions occurring in the mitochondrial matrix produce more ATP than glycolysis and the mitochondrial membrane reactions combined.

8. Gluconeogenesis occurs especially in the absorptive state during and shortly after a meal.

9. Brown fat generates more ATP than white fat and is therefore especially important for thermoregulation.

10. At an air temperature of 21°C (70°F), the body loses more heat as conduction to the surrounding air than by any other means.

▶ Testing Your Comprehension

1. Cyanide blocks the transfer of electrons from cytochrome a_3 to oxygen. In light of this, explain why it is so lethal. Also explain whether cyanide poisoning could be treated by giving a patient supplemental oxygen, and justify your answer.

2. Chapter 17 defines and describes some hormone actions that are synergistic and antagonistic. Identify some synergistic and antagonistic hormone interactions in the postabsorptive state of metabolism.

3. Ms. Jones, a 42-year-old woman, complains, "Everything I eat goes to fat. But my husband and my son eat twice as much as I do, and they're both as skinny as can be." How would you explain this to her?

4. A television advertisement proclaims, "Feeling tired? Need more energy? Order your supply of Zippy Megavitamins and feel better fast!" Your friend Cathy is about to send in her order, and you try to talk her out of wasting her money. Summarize the argument you would use.

5. Explain why a patient whose liver has been extensively damaged by hepatitis could show elevated concentrations of thyroid hormone and bilirubin in the blood.

CHAPTER

27

THE MALE REPRODUCTIVE SYSTEM

Seminiferous tubules, where sperm are produced. Sperm tails are seen as hairlike masses in the center of the tubules (SEM).

CNRI/SPL/Science Source

Anatomy & Physiology Revealed 4.0

Module 14: Reproductive System

BRUSHING UP

- The flow of heat down thermal gradients is important in the temperature control of the testes (see section 1.6e).
- Your understanding of male reproductive anatomy may benefit if you refresh your memory of the pelvic girdle (see section 8.5a) and muscles of the pelvic floor (see fig. 10.21).
- Chromosome structure (see fig. 4.5), the human karyotype (see fig. 4.16), and mitosis (see fig. 4.15) are important for understanding sperm production.
- Sexual development and adult function depend on the gonadotropins and sex steroids introduced in sections 17.2c and 17.3g. You should know the anatomy of the pituitary gland (see fig. 17.4) and the mechanism of negative feedback inhibition (see section 17.2e).

From all we have learned of the structural and functional complexity of the human body, it seems a wonder that it works at all! The fact is, however, that even with modern medicine we can't keep it working forever. The body suffers various degenerative changes as we age, and eventually our time is up and we must say good-bye. Yet our genes live on in new containers—our offspring. The production of offspring is the subject of these last three chapters. In this chapter, we examine some general aspects of human reproductive biology and then focus on the role of the male in reproduction. The next two chapters deal, respectively, with female reproductive function and on the embryonic development of humans and changes at the other end of the life span—the changes of old age.

27.1 Sexual Reproduction and Development

Expected Learning Outcomes

When you have completed this section, you should be able to

a. identify the most fundamental biological distinction between male and female;

b. define *primary sex organs, secondary sex organs,* and *secondary sex characteristics;*

c. explain the role of the sex chromosomes in determining sex;

d. explain how the Y chromosome determines the response of the fetal gonad to prenatal hormones;

e. identify which of the male and female external genitalia are homologous to each other; and

f. describe the descent of the gonads and explain why it is important.

27.1a The Two Sexes

The essence of sexual reproduction is that it is biparental—the offspring receive genes from two parents, so they are not genetically identical to either one. To achieve this, the parents must produce

gametes[1] (sex cells) that meet and combine their genes in a **zygote**[2] (fertilized egg). Two things are necessary for reproduction to be successful: (1) gamete motility so they can achieve contact, and (2) enough cytoplasm to divide up into the first cells of a developing embryo, with intracellular nutrients to sustain it until it begins to receive external nutrition. A single cell cannot perform both of these roles optimally, because to contain ample cytoplasm means to be relatively large and heavy, and this is inconsistent with the need for motility. Therefore, these tasks are usually apportioned to two kinds of gametes. The small motile one—little more than DNA with a propeller—is the **sperm (spermatozoon),** and the large nutrient-laden one is the **egg (ovum).**

In any sexually reproducing species, by definition, an individual that produces eggs is female and one that produces sperm is male. These criteria are not always that simple, as we see in certain abnormalities in sexual development. Genetically, however, any human with a Y sex chromosome is classified as male and anyone lacking a Y is classified as female. In contrast to these chromosomally determined sexes, *gender* is a person's psychological sense of feminine, masculine, or other sexual identity. One's gender can be different from one's biological sex.

In mammals, the female is also the parent that provides a sheltered internal environment for the development and nutrition of the embryo. For fertilization and development to occur in the female, the male must have a copulatory organ, the penis, for introducing his gametes into the female reproductive tract, and the female must have a copulatory organ, the vagina, for receiving the sperm. This is the most obvious difference between the sexes, but appearances can be deceiving (see fig. 17.28 and Deeper Insight 27.1).

27.1b Overview of the Reproductive System

The **reproductive system** in the male serves to produce sperm and introduce them into the female body. The female reproductive system produces eggs, receives the sperm, provides a place for the union of these gametes, harbors the fetus, gives birth, and nourishes the offspring.

The reproductive system consists of primary and secondary sex organs. The **primary sex organs,** or **gonads,**[3] are organs that produce the gametes—**testes** of the male and **ovaries** of the female. The **secondary sex organs** are organs other than gonads that are necessary for reproduction. In the male, they constitute a system of ducts, glands, and the penis, concerned with sperm storage, survival, and delivery. In the female, they include the uterine tubes, uterus, and vagina, concerned with uniting the sperm and egg and harboring the fetus.

According to location, the reproductive organs are classified as **external** and **internal genitalia (table 27.1).** The external genitalia are located in the perineum (see fig. 27.6). Most of them are externally visible, except for the subcutaneous accessory glands of the female perineum. The internal genitalia are located mainly in the pelvic cavity, except for the male testes and some associated ducts contained in the scrotum.

---

[1] *gam* = marriage, union
[2] *zygo* = yoke, union
[3] *gon* = seed

DEEPER INSIGHT 27.1

CLINICAL APPLICATION

Androgen Insensitivity Syndrome

Occasionally, a child who was always assumed to be a girl shows the usual changes of puberty except that she fails to menstruate. Medical examination reveals testes in the abdomen and the XY karyotype of a male. The testes produce a normal male level of testosterone, but the target cells lack receptors for it and the testosterone therefore has no effect. This condition is called *androgen insensitivity syndrome (AIS)* or *testicular feminization.*

Figure 27.1 shows three siblings with XY chromosomes, but feminized by AIS. In such individuals, the external genitals exhibit female anatomy from birth, as if no testosterone was present. At puberty, feminine breasts and other secondary sex characteristics develop because testosterone can't override the effect of the small amounts of estrogen that testes normally secrete. Despite external appearances, there are no ovaries, vagina, or uterus. If the abdominal testes are not removed, an AIS person has an elevated risk of testicular cancer.

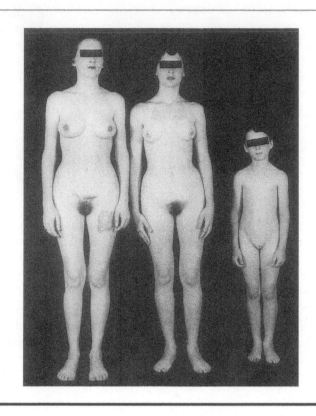

FIGURE 27.1 Androgen Insensitivity Syndrome.

Courtesy Mihaly Bartalos, from M. Bartalos and T.A. Baramki

 In what way is androgen insensitivity syndrome similar to type 2 diabetes mellitus?

TABLE 27.1	The External and Internal Genitalia
External Genitalia	**Internal Genitalia**
Male	
Penis	Testes (singular, *testis*)
Scrotum	Epididymides (singular, *epididymis*)
	Ductus deferentes (singular, *ductus deferens*)
	Seminal vesicles
	Prostate
	Bulbourethral glands
Female	
Mons pubis	Ovaries
Labia majora (singular, *labium majus*)	Uterine tubes
	Uterus
Labia minora (singular, *labium minus*)	Vagina
Clitoris	
Vaginal orifice	
Vestibular bulbs	
Vestibular glands	
Paraurethral glands	

Secondary sex characteristics are features that further distinguish the sexes and play a role in mate attraction. They typically appear only as an animal approaches sexual maturity (during adolescence in humans). From the call of a bullfrog to the tail of a peacock, these are well known in the animal kingdom. In humans, the physical attributes that contribute to sexual attraction are so culturally conditioned that it's harder to identify what secondary sex characteristics are biologically fundamental. Generally accepted as such in both sexes are the pubic and axillary hair and their associated scent glands, and the pitch of the voice. Other traits commonly regarded as male secondary sex characteristics are the facial hair, relatively coarse and visible hair on the torso and limbs, and the relatively muscular physique. In females, they include the distribution of body fat, enlargement of the breasts (independently of lactation), and relatively hairless appearance of the skin.

27.1c Chromosomal Sex Determination

What determines whether a zygote develops into a male or female? The distinction begins with the combination of sex chromosomes bequeathed to the zygote. Most of our cells have 23 pairs of chromosomes: 22 pairs of *autosomes* and 1 pair of *sex chromosomes* (see fig. 4.16). A sex chromosome can be either a large X chromosome or a small Y chromosome. Every egg contains an X chromosome, but half of the sperm carry an X and the other half carry a Y. If an egg is fertilized with an X-bearing sperm, it produces

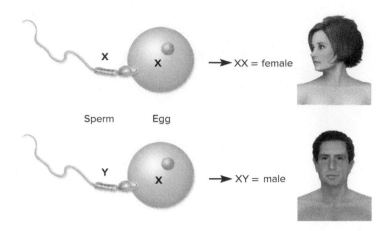

FIGURE 27.2 Chromosomal Sex Determination. All eggs carry the X chromosome. The sex of a child is determined by whether the egg is fertilized by an X-bearing sperm or a Y-bearing sperm.

an XX zygote that is destined to become a female. If it is fertilized with a Y-bearing sperm, it produces an XY zygote destined to become a male. Thus, the sex of a child is determined at conception (fertilization), and not by the mother's egg but by the sperm that fertilizes it **(fig. 27.2).**

27.1d Prenatal Hormones and Sexual Differentiation

Sex determination doesn't end with fertilization, however. It requires an interaction between genes and hormones produced by the mother and fetus. Just as we have seen with other hormones, those involved here require specific receptors on their target cells to exert an effect.

Up to a point, a fetus is sexually undifferentiated, or "noncommittal" as to which sex it will become. Its gonads begin to develop at 5 to 6 weeks as *gonadal ridges,* each lying alongside a primitive kidney, the *mesonephros,* which later degenerates. Adjacent to each gonadal ridge are two ducts: the **mesonephric**[4] **duct** (MEZ-oh-NEF-ric), which originally serves the mesonephros, and the **paramesonephric**[5] **duct.** In males, the mesonephric ducts develop into the reproductive tract and the paramesonephric ducts degenerate. In females, the opposite occurs **(fig. 27.3).**

But why? The Y chromosome has a gene called *SRY* (sex-determining region of the Y) that codes for a protein called **testis-determining factor (TDF).** TDF then interacts with genes on some of the other chromosomes, including a gene on the X chromosome for androgen receptors and genes that initiate the development of male anatomy. By 8 to 9 weeks, the male gonadal ridge has become a rudimentary testis that begins to secrete testosterone. Testosterone stimulates the mesonephric duct on its own side to develop into the system of male reproductive

ducts. By this time, the testis also secretes a hormone called **müllerian-inhibiting factor (MIF)** that causes atrophy of the paramesonephric duct (formerly called the *müllerian duct*) on that side. Even an adult male, however, retains a tiny Y-shaped vestige of the paramesonephric ducts, like a vestigial uterus and uterine tubes, in the area of the prostatic urethra.

It may seem as if androgens should induce the formation of a male reproductive tract and estrogens induce a female reproductive tract. However, the estrogen level is always high during pregnancy, so if this mechanism were the case, it would feminize all fetuses. Thus, the development of a female results from the absence of androgens, not the presence of estrogens.

27.1e Development of the External Genitalia

You perhaps regard the external genitals as the most definitive characteristics of a male or female, yet there is more similarity between the sexes than most people realize. In the embryo, the genitals begin developing from identical structures in both sexes. By 6 weeks, the embryo has the following:

- the **genital tubercle,** an anterior median bud;
- **urogenital folds,** a pair of medial tissue folds slightly posterior to the genital tubercle; and
- **labioscrotal folds,** a larger pair of tissue folds lateral to the urogenital folds.

By the end of week 9, the fetus begins to show sexual differentiation, and either male or female genitalia are distinctly formed by the end of week 12 **(fig. 27.4).** In the female, the three structures just listed become the clitoral glans, labia minora, and labia majora, respectively; all of these are more fully described in the next chapter. In the male, the genital tubercle elongates to form the *phallus;* the urogenital folds fuse to enclose the urethra, joining the phallus to form the penis; and the labioscrotal folds fuse to form the scrotum, a sac that will later contain the testes.

Male and female organs that develop from the same embryonic structure are said to be **homologous.** Thus, the penis is homologous to the clitoris and the scrotum is homologous to the labia majora. This becomes strikingly evident in some abnormalities of sexual development. In the presence of excess androgen, the clitoris may become greatly enlarged and resemble a small penis. In other cases, the ovaries descend into the labia majora as if they were testes descending into a scrotum. Such abnormalities sometimes result in mistaken identification of the sex of an infant at birth.

27.1f Descent of the Gonads

Both male and female gonads initially develop high in the abdominal cavity, near the kidneys, and migrate into the pelvic cavity (ovaries) or scrotum (testes). In the embryo, a connective tissue cord called the *gubernaculum*[6] (GOO-bur-NACK-you-lum)

---

[4]*meso* = middle; *nephr* = kidney
[5]*para* = next to; *meso* = middle; *nephr* = kidney

[6]*gubern* = rudder, to guide

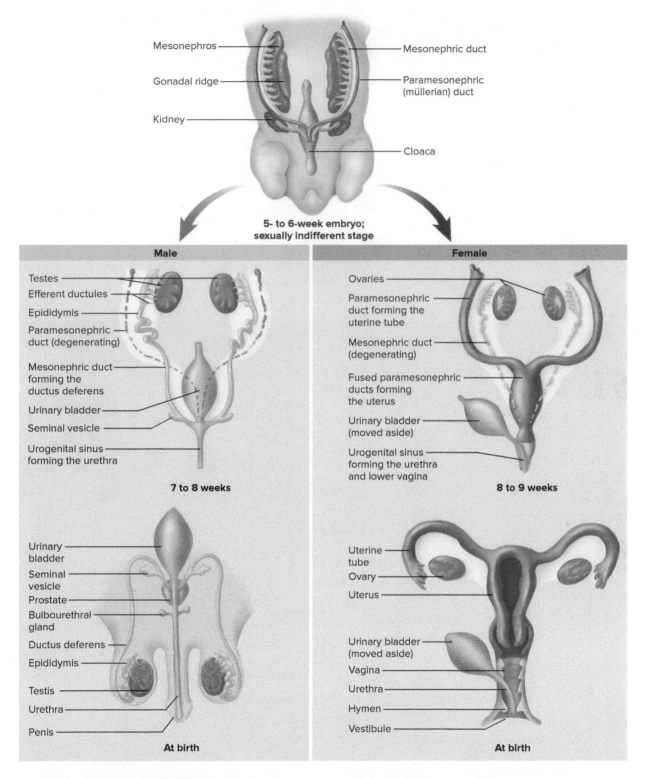

**5- to 6-week embryo;
sexually indifferent stage**

FIGURE 27.3 Embryonic Development of the Male and Female Reproductive Tracts. Note that the male tract develops from the mesonephric duct and the female tract from the paramesonephric duct; the other duct in each sex degenerates.

anchors the gonad to the floor of the abdominopelvic cavity. As the male gubernaculum continues to grow, it passes between the internal and external oblique muscles and into the scrotal swelling. Independently of migration of the testis, the peritoneum also develops a fold that extends into the scrotum as the

vaginal[7] *process.* The gubernaculum and vaginal process create a path of low resistance through the groin, anterior to the pubic symphysis, called the **inguinal canal**—the most common site

---

[7]*vagin* = sheath

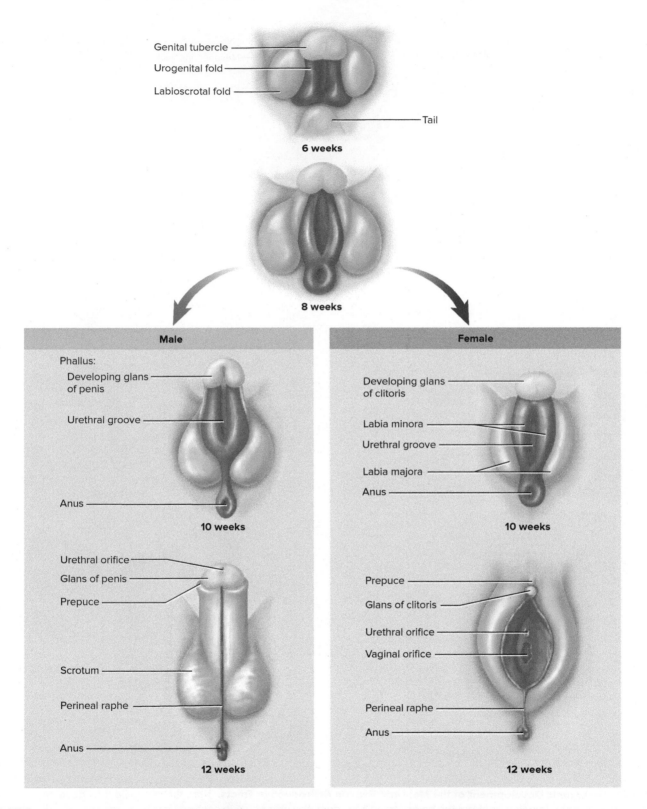

FIGURE 27.4 Development of the External Genitalia. By 6 weeks, the embryo has three primordial structures—the genital tubercle, urogenital folds, and labioscrotal folds—which will become the male or female genitalia. At 8 weeks, these structures have grown but the sexes are still indistinguishable. Slight sexual differentiation is noticeable at 10 weeks, and the sexes are fully distinguishable by 12 weeks. Matching colors identify homologous structures of the male and female.

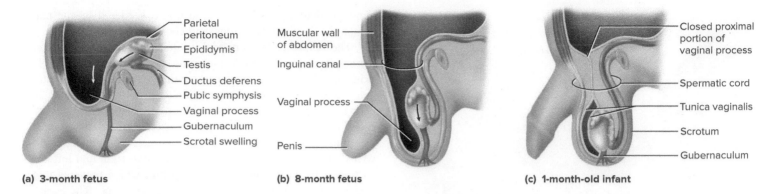

(a) 3-month fetus   **(b)** 8-month fetus   **(c)** 1-month-old infant

FIGURE 27.5 Descent of the Testis. (a) Abdominal position of the testes in a 3-month fetus. (b) Descending testes in an 8-month fetus. (c) Scrotal position of the testes in a 1-month-old infant. Note that the testis and spermatic ducts are retroperitoneal. An extension of the peritoneum called the *vaginal process* passes through the inguinal canal and becomes the tunica vaginalis.

? *Why is this structure of male anatomy called the* tunica vaginalis?

of herniation in boys and men (*inguinal hernia;* see Deeper Insight 10.3).

The **descent of the testes (fig. 27.5)** begins as early as week 6. The superior part of the embryonic gonad degenerates and its inferior part migrates downward, guided by the gubernaculum. In the seventh month, the testes abruptly pass through the inguinal canals into the scrotum. As they descend, they are accompanied by ever-elongating testicular arteries and veins and by lymphatic vessels, nerves, spermatic ducts, and extensions of the internal oblique muscle. The vaginal process becomes separated from the peritoneal cavity and persists as a sac, the *tunica vaginalis,* enfolding the anterior and lateral sides of the testis and protecting the testis from abrasion against the scrotum with movements of the body.

The actual mechanism of descent remains obscure, although multiple hypotheses have been offered. Testosterone stimulates descent, but it is unknown how. The reason this descent is necessary, however, will be explained in the next section.

About 3% of boys are born with undescended testes, or **cryptorchidism.**[8] In most such cases, the testes descend within the first year of infancy, but if they don't, the condition can usually be corrected with a testosterone injection or a fairly simple surgery to dilate the inguinal canals and draw the testes into the scrotum. Uncorrected cryptorchidism, however, leads inevitably to sterility and sometimes to testicular cancer.

The ovaries also descend, but to a much lesser extent. The female gubernaculum extends from the inferior pole of the ovary to the labioscrotal fold. The ovaries eventually lodge just inferior to the brim of the lesser pelvis. Each gubernaculum becomes a pair of ligaments that support the ovary and uterus.

BEFORE YOU GO ON

Answer the following questions to test your understanding of the preceding section:

1. Define *gonad* and *gamete.* Explain the relationship between the terms.

2. Define *male, female, sperm,* and *egg.*

3. What are mesonephric and paramesonephric ducts? What factors determine which one develops and which one regresses in the fetus?

4. What male structure develops from the genital tubercle and urogenital folds? What develops from the labioscrotal folds?

5. Describe the pathway taken during descent of the male gonad.

27.2 Male Reproductive Anatomy APR

Expected Learning Outcomes

When you have completed this section, you should be able to

a. describe the anatomy of the scrotum, testes, and penis;

b. describe the pathway taken by a sperm cell from its formation to its ejaculation, naming all the passages it travels; and

c. state the names, locations, and functions of the male accessory reproductive glands.

We will survey the male reproductive system in order according to the sites of sperm formation, transport, and emission—therefore beginning with the scrotum and testes, continuing through the spermatic ducts and accessory glands associated with them, and ending with the penis.

27.2a The Scrotum

The scrotum and penis constitute the external genitalia of the male and occupy the **perineum**[9] (PERR-ih-NEE-um). This is a

---

[8]*crypto* = hidden; *orchid* = testis; *ism* = condition

[9]*peri* = around; *neum,* from *inan* = to empty out

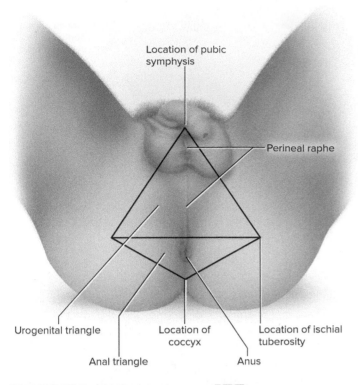

Location of pubic symphysis

Perineal raphe

Urogenital triangle

Location of coccyx

Location of ischial tuberosity

Anal triangle

Anus

FIGURE 27.6 The Male Perineum. APR

diamond-shaped area between the thighs bordered by the pubic symphysis, ischial tuberosities, and coccyx (**fig. 27.6**).

The **scrotum**[10] is a pendulous pouch of skin, muscle, and fibrous connective tissue, containing the testes (**fig. 27.7**). The skin has sebaceous glands, sparse hair, rich sensory innervation, and somewhat darker pigmentation than skin elsewhere. Just deep to the skin is a layer of smooth muscle and connective tissue called the **dartos**[11] **fascia;** its muscle is called the **dartos muscle.** The muscle is normally somewhat contracted, giving the skin a wrinkled texture. The scrotum is divided into right and left compartments by an internal **median septum,** which prevents infections of one testis from spreading to the other one. The location of the septum is externally marked by a seam called the **perineal raphe** (RAY-fee), which also extends anteriorly along the ventral side of the penis and posteriorly as far as the margin of the anus. The left testis is usually suspended lower than the right so the two aren't compressed against each other between the thighs.

Posteriorly, the scrotum contains the **spermatic cord,** a bundle of fibrous connective tissue containing the *ductus deferens* (a sperm duct), lymphatic vessels, testicular nerves, the testicular artery, and a complex of veins called the **pampiniform**[12] **plexus** closely surrounding the artery. It passes upward behind and superior to the testis, where it is easily palpated through the skin of the

[10]*scrotum* = bag
[11]*dartos* = skinned
[12]*pampin* = tendril; *form* = shape

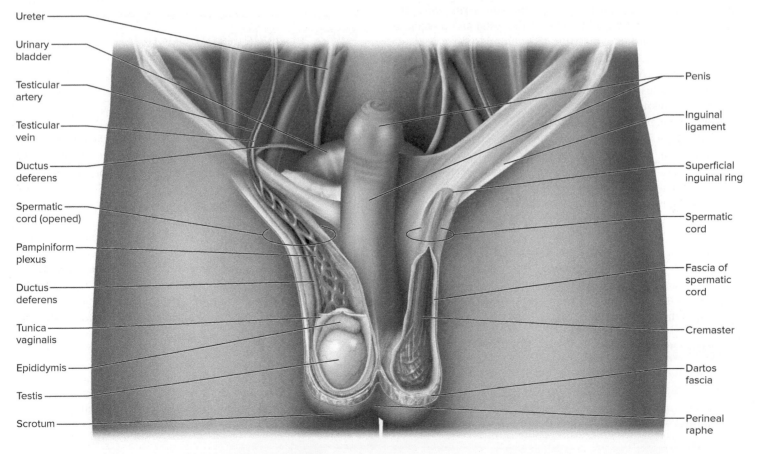

Ureter

Urinary bladder

Testicular artery

Testicular vein

Ductus deferens

Spermatic cord (opened)

Pampiniform plexus

Ductus deferens

Tunica vaginalis

Epididymis

Testis

Scrotum

Penis

Inguinal ligament

Superficial inguinal ring

Spermatic cord

Fascia of spermatic cord

Cremaster

Dartos fascia

Perineal raphe

FIGURE 27.7 The Scrotum and Spermatic Cord. APR

scrotum. It continues across the anterior side of the pubis and into a 4 cm **inguinal canal,** which leads through the muscles of the groin and emerges into the pelvic cavity. The inferior entrance into the inguinal canal is called the *superficial inguinal ring,* and its superior exit into the pelvic cavity is the *deep inguinal ring.* Within the scrotum, the spermatic cord is enmeshed in strips of internal oblique muscle called the **cremaster.**[13]

The original reason that a scrotum evolved is a subject of debate among reproductive biologists; it is absent from some mammals, such as elephants, sea cows, and whales, so it isn't universally necessary for mammalian sperm production. For whatever reason human testes reside in the scrotum, however, they are now adapted to this cooler environment and can't produce sperm at the core body temperature of 37°C; they must be held at about 35°C. The scrotum has three mechanisms for regulating the temperature of the testes:

1. **The cremaster.** When it is cold, the cremaster contracts and draws the testes closer to the body to keep them warm. When it is warm, the cremaster relaxes and the testes are suspended farther from the body.

2. **The dartos muscle.** This, too, contracts when it is cold, and the scrotum becomes taut and even more wrinkled. The tautness of the scrotum helps to hold the testes snugly against the warm body and it reduces the surface area of the scrotum, thus reducing heat loss.

3. **The pampiniform plexus.** Without this venous plexus, warm arterial blood would heat the testis and inhibit sperm production. The pampiniform plexus, however, prevents this by acting as a *countercurrent heat exchanger* **(fig. 27.8).** The relatively cool venous blood ascending the spermatic cord toward the pelvic cavity draws heat out of the descending arterial blood headed for the testis, so by the time it reaches the testis the blood is 1.5° to 2.5°C cooler than the core body temperature.

27.2b The Testes

The testes (testicles) **(fig. 27.9)** are combined endocrine and exocrine glands that produce sex hormones and sperm. The testis is oval and slightly flattened, about 4 cm long, 3 cm from anterior to posterior, and 2.5 cm wide. Its anterior and lateral surfaces are covered by the tunica vaginalis. The testis itself has a white fibrous capsule called the **tunica albuginea**[14] (TOO-nih-ca AL-byu-JIN-ee-uh). Connective tissue septa extend from the capsule into the parenchyma, dividing it into 250 to 300 wedge-shaped lobules. Each lobule contains one to three **seminiferous**[15] **tubules** (SEM-ih-NIF-er-us)—slender ducts up to 70 cm long in which the sperm are produced. Between the seminiferous tubules are clusters of **interstitial**[16] **endocrine cells,** the source of testosterone.

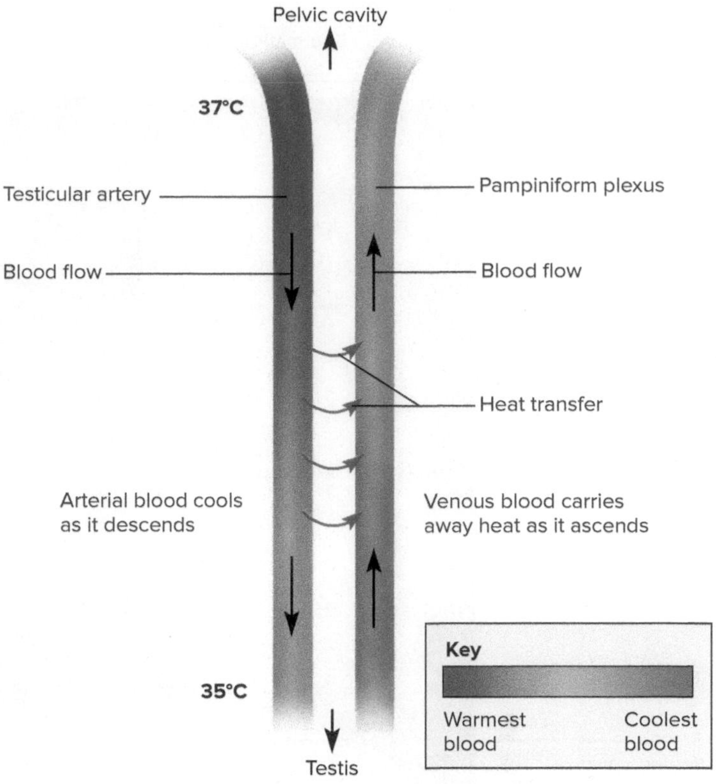

FIGURE 27.8 The Countercurrent Heat Exchanger. Although illustrated as one vessel, the pampiniform plexus is a network of veins surrounding the testicular artery (see fig. 27.7). Note the cooling of the arterial blood as it descends the artery and its heat transfers to the adjacent, ascending venous blood.

A seminiferous tubule has a narrow lumen lined by a thick **germinal epithelium.** The epithelium consists of several layers of germ cells in the process of becoming sperm, and a much smaller number of tall **nurse cells (supporting cells, sustentocytes**[17]**),** which protect the germ cells and promote their development. The germ cells depend on the nurse cells for nutrients, waste removal, growth factors, and other needs. The nurse cells also secrete two proteins called *androgen-binding protein* and *inhibin,* both of which regulate sperm production in ways described later.

A nurse cell is shaped a little like a tree trunk whose roots spread out over the basement membrane, forming the boundary of the tubule, and whose thick trunk reaches to the tubule lumen. Tight junctions between adjacent nurse cells form a **blood–testis barrier (BTB),** which prevents antibodies and other large molecules in the blood and intercellular fluid from getting to the germ cells. This is important because the germ cells, being genetically different from other cells of the body, would otherwise be attacked by the immune system. Some cases of sterility occur when the BTB fails to form adequately in adolescence and the immune system produces autoantibodies against the germ cells.

---

[13]*cremast* = to suspend
[14]*tunica* = coat; *alb* = white
[15]*semin* = seed, sperm; *fer* = to carry
[16]*inter* = between; *stit* = placed

[17]*sustent* = support

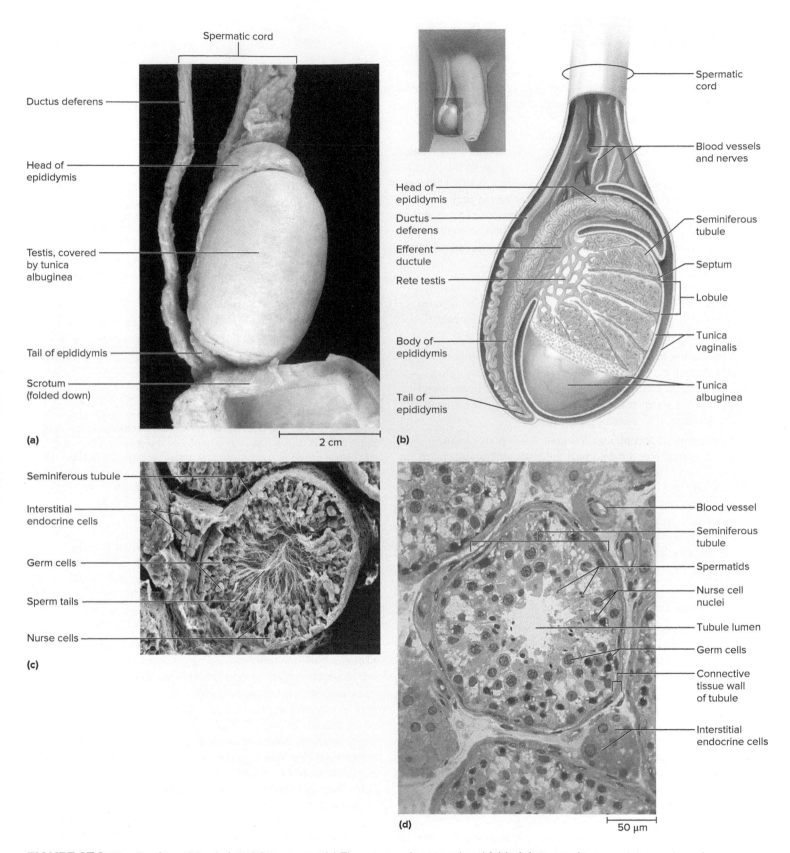

FIGURE 27.9 The Testis and Associated Structures. (a) The scrotum is opened and folded downward to reveal the testis and associated organs. (b) Anatomy of the testis, epididymis, and spermatic cord. (c) Scanning electron micrograph of the seminiferous tubules. (d) Light micrograph. This region of the tubule did not have mature sperm in it at the time. **APR**

a: Dennis Strete/McGraw-Hill Education; c: Steve Gschmeissner/Science Source; d: Ed Reschke/Getty Images

▶▶▶ **APPLY WHAT YOU KNOW**

Would you expect to find blood capillaries in the walls of the seminiferous tubules? Why or why not?

The seminiferous tubules lead into a network called the **rete**[18] **testis** (REE-tee), embedded in the capsule on the posterior side of the testis. Sperm partially mature in the rete. They are moved along by the flow of fluid secreted by the nurse cells and by the cilia on some rete cells. Sperm don't swim while they're in the male reproductive tract.

Each testis is supplied by a **testicular artery** that arises from the abdominal aorta just below the renal artery. This is a very long, slender artery that winds its way down the posterior abdominal wall before passing through the inguinal canal into the scrotum (see fig. 27.7). Its blood pressure is very low, and indeed this is one of the few arteries to have no pulse. Consequently, blood flow to the testes is quite meager and the testes receive a poor oxygen supply. In response to this, the sperm develop unusually large mitochondria, which may precondition them for survival in the hypoxic environment of the female reproductive tract.

Blood leaves the testis by way of the pampiniform plexus of veins. As these veins pass through the inguinal canal, they converge and form the **testicular vein.** The right testicular vein drains into the inferior vena cava and the left one drains into the left renal vein. Lymphatic vessels also drain each testis. They travel through the inguinal canal with the veins and lead to lymph nodes adjacent to the lower aorta. Lymph from the penis and scrotum, however, travels to lymph nodes adjacent to the iliac arteries and veins and in the inguinal region.

Testicular nerves lead to the gonads from spinal cord segments T10 and T11. They are mixed sensory and motor nerves containing predominantly sympathetic but also some parasympathetic fibers. The sensory fibers are concerned primarily with pain and the autonomic fibers are predominantly vasomotor, for regulation of blood flow.

27.2c The Spermatic Ducts

After leaving the testis, the sperm travel through a series of *spermatic ducts* to reach the urethra **(fig. 27.10).** These include the following:

- **Efferent ductules.** About 12 small efferent ductules arise from the posterior side of the testis and carry sperm to the epididymis. They have clusters of ciliated cells that help drive the sperm along.
- **Duct of the epididymis.** The **epididymis**[19] (EP-ih-DID-ih-miss; plural, *epididymides*) is a site of sperm maturation and storage. It adheres to the posterior side of the testis (fig. 27.9). The superior clublike portion where it receives the efferent ductules is called the *head;* the long middle portion below the last efferent ductule is the *body;* and the slender inferior end is the *tail.* It contains a single coiled

duct embedded in connective tissue. The duct is about 6 m (20 ft) long, but it is so slender and highly coiled that it is packed into an epididymis only 7.5 cm long. The duct reabsorbs about 90% of the fluid secreted by the testis. Sperm are physiologically immature when they leave the testis but mature as they travel through the head and body of the epididymis. In 20 days or so, they reach the tail. They are stored here and in the adjacent portion of the ductus deferens pending ejaculation, and remain viable for 40 to 60 days. If they become too old without being ejaculated, they disintegrate and the epididymis reabsorbs them.

- **Ductus deferens.**[20] The duct of the epididymis straightens out at the tail, turns 180°, and becomes the ductus deferens, also called the *vas deferens* (from which comes the term *vasectomy*). This is a muscular tube about 45 cm long and 2.5 mm in diameter. It passes upward through the spermatic cord and inguinal canal and enters the pelvic cavity. There, it turns medially and approaches the urinary bladder. After passing between the bladder and ureter, the duct turns downward behind the bladder and widens into a terminal **ampulla.** The ductus deferens ends by uniting with the duct of an accessory gland, the seminal vesicle. The duct has a very narrow lumen and a thick wall of smooth muscle well innervated by sympathetic nerve fibers. Vasectomy, the surgical method of male contraception, consists of cutting out a short portion of the ductus (vas) deferens to interrupt the passage of sperm.
- **Ejaculatory duct.** Where the ductus deferens and duct of the seminal vesicle meet, they form a short (2 cm) ejaculatory duct, which passes through the prostate and empties into the urethra. The ejaculatory duct is the last of the spermatic ducts.

The male urethra is shared by the reproductive and urinary systems. It is about 18 cm long and consists of three regions: the *prostatic, membranous,* and *spongy (penile) urethra.* Although it serves both urinary and reproductive roles, it cannot pass urine and semen simultaneously for reasons explained in section 27.5c.

27.2d The Accessory Glands

There are three sets of *accessory glands* in the male reproductive system—the seminal vesicles, prostate, and bulbourethral glands:

1. The **seminal vesicles (seminal glands)** are a pair of glands posterior to the urinary bladder; one is associated with each ductus deferens. A seminal vesicle is about 5 cm long, with approximately the dimensions of one's little finger. It has a connective tissue capsule and underlying layer of smooth muscle. The secretory portion is a very convoluted duct with numerous branches that form a complex labyrinth. It empties into the ejaculatory duct. The yellowish secretion of the seminal vesicles constitutes about 65% to 75% of the semen.

---

[18]*rete* = network
[19]*epi* = upon; *didym* = twins, testes

[20]*de* = away from; *fer* = to carry

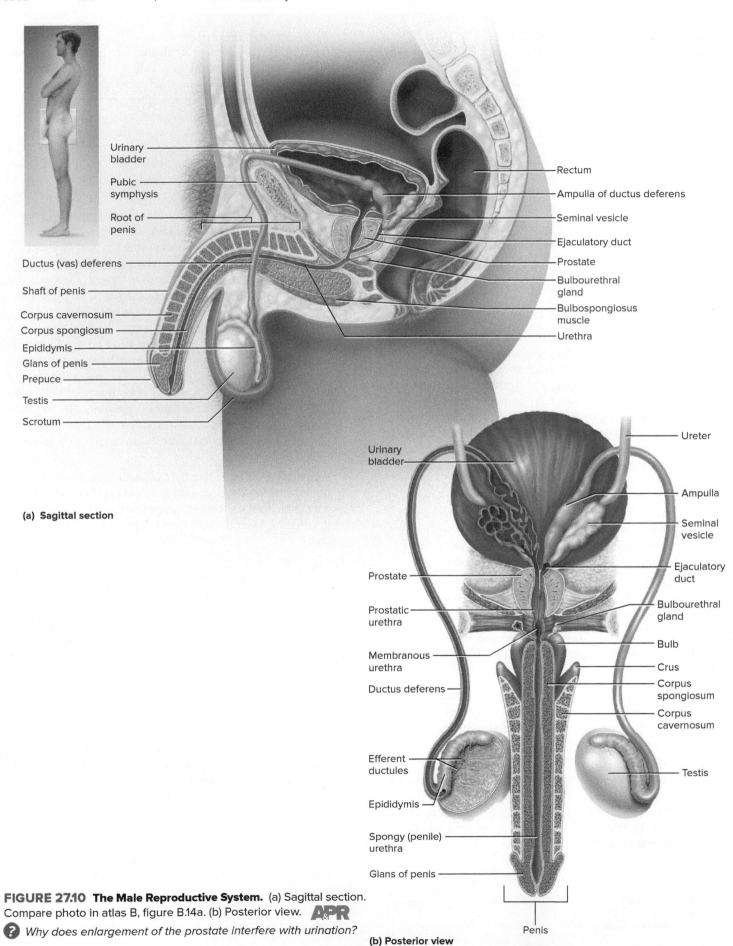

Urinary bladder

Pubic symphysis

Root of penis

Ductus (vas) deferens

Shaft of penis

Corpus cavernosum

Corpus spongiosum

Epididymis

Glans of penis

Prepuce

Testis

Scrotum

Rectum

Ampulla of ductus deferens

Seminal vesicle

Ejaculatory duct

Prostate

Bulbourethral gland

Bulbospongiosus muscle

Urethra

(a) Sagittal section

Urinary bladder

Prostate

Prostatic urethra

Membranous urethra

Ductus deferens

Efferent ductules

Epididymis

Spongy (penile) urethra

Glans of penis

Ureter

Ampulla

Seminal vesicle

Ejaculatory duct

Bulbourethral gland

Bulb

Crus

Corpus spongiosum

Corpus cavernosum

Testis

Penis

(b) Posterior view

FIGURE 27.10   The Male Reproductive System. (a) Sagittal section.
Compare photo in atlas B, figure B.14a. (b) Posterior view. **A&PR**

❓ *Why does enlargement of the prostate interfere with urination?*

2. The **prostate**[21] (PROSS-tate) surrounds the urethra and ejaculatory ducts immediately inferior to the urinary bladder (see Deeper Insight 27.2). It measures about 2 × 4 × 3 cm and is an aggregate of 30 to 50 compound tubuloacinar glands enclosed in a single fibrous capsule. These glands empty through about 20 pores in the urethral wall. The stroma of the prostate consists of connective tissue and smooth muscle, like that of the seminal vesicles. The milky secretion of the prostate constitutes about 25% to 30% of the semen.

3. The **bulbourethral glands** are named for their position near a dilated bulb at the inner end of the penis and their association with the urethra. They are brownish, spherical glands about 1 cm in diameter, with a 2.5 cm duct to the urethra. During sexual arousal, they produce *preejaculate,* a clear slippery fluid that lubricates the head of the penis in preparation for intercourse. More importantly, though, it protects the sperm by neutralizing the acidity of the male's urethra and female's vagina, and it creates a relatively low-viscosity pathway for sperm to migrate from the vagina, through the cervical canal, into the uterus.

DEEPER INSIGHT 27.2
CLINICAL APPLICATION
Prostate Diseases

The prostate weighs about 20 g by age 20, remains at that weight until age 45 or so, and then begins to grow slowly again. By age 70, over 80% of men show some degree of *benign prostatic hyperplasia (BPH)*—noncancerous enlargement of the gland. The major complication of this is that it compresses the urethra, obstructs the flow of urine, makes it harder to completely empty the bladder, and sometimes promotes bladder and kidney infections. BPH is more common in men who are obese, physically inactive, and consume alcohol to excess.

Prostate cancer is the second most common cancer in men (after lung cancer); it affects about 9% of men over the age of 50. Prostate tumors tend to form near the periphery of the gland, where they don't obstruct urine flow; therefore, they often go unnoticed until they cause pain. Prostate cancer often metastasizes to nearby lymph nodes and then to the lungs and other organs. It is more common among black Americans than among white Americans and uncommon among people of Japanese descent.

The position of the prostate immediately anterior to the rectum allows it to be palpated through the rectal wall to check for tumors. This procedure is called *digital rectal examination (DRE).* Prostate cancer can also be diagnosed from elevated levels of *serine protease* (also known as *prostate-specific antigen, PSA*) and *acid phosphatase* (another prostatic enzyme) in the blood. Up to 80% of men with prostate cancer survive when it is detected and treated early, but only 10% to 50% survive if it spreads beyond the prostatic capsule. It is such a slow-growing cancer, however, that if discovered late in life, the risks of surgery may outweigh the benefits and the doctor and patient may reasonably elect not to treat it. It can often be managed until the elderly patient dies normally of some other cause.

27.2e The Penis

The **penis**[22] serves to deposit semen in the vagina. Half of it is an internal **root** and half is the externally visible **shaft** and **glans**[23] (**fig. 27.11,** fig. 27.10). The glans is the expanded head at the distal end of the penis with the external urethral orifice at its tip. The external portion of the penis is about 8 to 10 cm (3–4 in.) long and 3 cm in diameter when flaccid (nonerect); the typical dimensions of an erect penis are 13 to 18 cm (5–7 in.) long and 4 cm in diameter.

Directional terminology may be a little confusing in the penis, because the *dorsal* side is the one that faces anteriorly, at least when the penis is flaccid, whereas the *ventral* side of the penis faces posteriorly. This is because in most mammals, the penis is horizontal, held against the abdomen by skin, and it points anteriorly. The urethra passes through its lower, more obviously ventral, half. Directional terminology in the human penis follows the same convention as for other mammals, even though our bipedal posture and more pendulous penis change these anatomical relationships.

The skin is loosely attached to the penile shaft, allowing for movement and expansion during erection. It continues over the glans as the **prepuce (foreskin).** The inner surface of the prepuce and facing surface of the glans are covered with a thin mucous membrane similar to the inner surface of the eyelid. At birth and for at least a few years after, these two membranes are firmly fused to each other; attempts to retract the foreskin of an infant or child can therefore be injurious. The membranes separate gradually over a period of several years; this is usually complete by age 17. The adult prepuce remains anchored to the proximal margin of the glans by a ventral fold of tissue called the **frenulum.**[24] Contrary to some sources, there are no glands in the prepuce; in some males, however, exfoliated epithelial cells and fluid accumulate beneath the prepuce as a creamy secretion called *smegma.*[25] The mucosa of the adult prepuce contains dendritic cells, a component of the immune system (see section 21.1b), thus providing protection from infection at this body orifice. However, these dendritic cells and those of the vagina afford a potential route of entry for HIV, the AIDS virus. The prepuce is the most densely innervated and sensitive region of the penis, with an abundance of tactile corpuscles and nerves concentrated in ridges on its proximal inner surface. Circumcision thus removes the most sensitive part of the penis. The exposed mucous membrane of the glans then transforms to a thin, drier, and less sensitive epidermis.

The shaft of the penis consists mainly of three cylindrical bodies called **erectile tissues,** which fill with blood during sexual arousal and account for its enlargement and erection. A single erectile body, the **corpus spongiosum,** passes along the ventral side of the penis and encloses the penile urethra. It expands at the distal end to fill the entire glans. Proximal to the glans, the dorsal side of the penis has a **corpus cavernosum** (plural, *corpora*

---

[21]*pro* = before; *stat* = to stand; commonly misspelled and mispronounced "prostrate"

[22]*penis* = tail
[23]*glans* = acorn
[24]*fren* = bridle; *ulum* = little
[25]*smegma* = unguent, ointment, soap

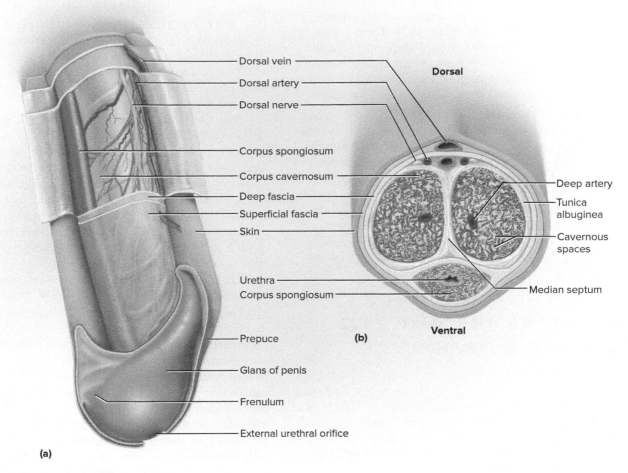

FIGURE 27.11 Anatomy of the Penis. (a) Superficial dissection of shaft, lateral view. (b) Cross section at midshaft. **APR**

❓ *What is the functional benefit of the corpus spongiosum not having a tunica albuginea?*

cavernosa) on each side. Each is ensheathed in a fibrous **tunica albuginea,** and they are separated from each other by a **median septum.** (Be careful not to confuse these with the tunica albuginea of the testis and median septum of the scrotum.)

All three cylinders of erectile tissue are spongy in appearance and contain numerous tiny blood sinuses called **cavernous spaces (lacunae).** The partitions between these spaces, called **trabeculae,** are composed of connective tissue and smooth **trabecular muscle.** In the flaccid penis, muscle tone in the trabeculae collapses the cavernous spaces, which appear as tiny slits in the tissue.

At the body surface, the penis turns 90° and continues inward as the root. The corpus spongiosum terminates internally as a dilated **bulb,** which is ensheathed in the bulbospongiosus muscle and attached to the lower surface of the muscular pelvic floor within the urogenital triangle (see fig. 10.21). The corpora cavernosa diverge like the arms of a Y. Each arm, called a *crus* (pronounced "cruss"; plural, *crura*), attaches the penis to the pubic arch (ischiopubic ramus) and perineal membrane on its respective

side. Each crus is enveloped by an ischiocavernosus muscle. The innervation and blood supply to the penis are discussed later in connection with the mechanism of erection.

> **BEFORE YOU GO ON**
>
> Answer the following questions to test your understanding of the preceding section:
>
> **6.** State the names and locations of two muscles that help regulate the temperature of the testes.
>
> **7.** Name three types of cells in the testes, and describe their locations and functions.
>
> **8.** Name all the ducts that the sperm follow, in order, from the time they form in the testis to the time of ejaculation.
>
> **9.** Describe the locations and functions of the seminal vesicles, prostate, and bulbourethral glands.
>
> **10.** Name the erectile tissues of the penis, and describe their locations relative to each other.

27.3 Puberty, Hormonal Control, and Climacteric

Expected Learning Outcomes

When you have completed this section, you should be able to

a. describe the hormonal control of puberty;

b. describe the resulting changes in the male body; and

c. define and describe *male climacteric* and the effect of aging on male reproductive function.

Unlike any other organ system, the reproductive system remains dormant for several years after birth. At puberty, however, a hormonal surge awakens the reproductive system and begins preparing it for adult reproductive function.

27.3a Puberty and Adolescence

Definitions of *puberty* and *adolescence* vary. This book regards **puberty**[26] in boys to be the period from the onset of pituitary gonadotropin secretion (usually around age 10 to 12) until the first ejaculation of viable sperm (typically around age 14). The following chapter describes the criteria and age span for girls. **Adolescence**[27] is the broader period of time including puberty and extending until a person attains full adult height. Hormonal mechanisms explained in the next section—especially the rising levels of *testosterone* and *dihydrotestosterone (DHT)*, the two **androgens**—bring about the many bodily changes familiar to all who have endured adolescence:

- They stimulate growth of the sex organs. The first visible sign of puberty is usually enlargement of the testes and scrotum around age 13. The penis continues to grow for about 2 more years after the testes attain their mature size. Internally, the ducts and accessory glands also enlarge.

- Testosterone stimulates sperm production. If testosterone secretion ceases, the sperm count and semen volume decline rapidly and a male becomes sterile.

- Testosterone stimulates a burst of generalized body growth—the limb bones elongate rapidly, a boy grows taller, and he develops more muscle mass. The larynx enlarges, deepening the voice and making the thyroid cartilage more prominent on the front of the neck. Even erythropoiesis is accelerated, resulting in a higher RBC count and hematocrit in males than in females. Along with all this growth, the basal metabolic rate increases, accompanied by an increase in appetite.

- Testosterone also stimulates the brain and awakens the **libido** (sex drive)—although, perhaps surprisingly, the neurons convert it to estrogen, which is what directly affects the behavior. With increasing libido and sensitivity to stimulation, erections occur frequently and ejaculation often occurs during sleep (nocturnal emissions, or "wet dreams").

- DHT stimulates development of the pubic hair, axillary hair, and later the facial hair. The skin becomes darker and thicker and secretes more sebum, which often leads to acne; acne patients have 2 to 20 times the normal level of DHT in their skin. The apocrine scent glands of the perineal, axillary, and beard areas develop in conjunction with the hair in those regions.

27.3b Hormonal Control of Male Reproductive Function

The testes secrete substantial amounts of testosterone in the first trimester (3 months) of fetal development. Even in the first few months of infancy, testosterone levels are about as high as they are in midpuberty, but then the testes become dormant for the rest of infancy and childhood.

It is still unknown why puberty begins at age 10 to 12 and not earlier. There seems to be a childhood brake on the secretion of **gonadotropin-releasing hormone (GnRH).** Release from this restraint in late childhood brings on GnRH secretion. GnRH travels to the anterior pituitary and stimulates cells called *gonadotropic cells.* These cells secrete the two pituitary *gonadotropins:* **follicle-stimulating hormone (FSH)** and **luteinizing hormone (LH)** (see section 17.2c). From now through adulthood, reproductive function is regulated by hormonal interactions between the hypothalamus, pituitary gland, and gonads—the *hypothalamo–pituitary–gonadal axis.*

Luteinizing hormone (LH) is also sometimes called *interstitial cell–stimulating hormone (ICSH)* because it stimulates the interstitial endocrine cells of the testes to secrete androgens, mainly testosterone. Among the many effects of testosterone previously itemized, it promotes sperm production. That effect, however, requires that the testes concentrate testosterone in the sites where the sperm develop. This is where the other gonadotropin comes into play: follicle-stimulating hormone (FSH, named for its female function). FSH stimulates the nurse cells of the testes to secrete **androgen-binding protein (ABP),** which binds and accumulates testosterone in the seminiferous tubules and epididymis. Testosterone has no effect on the testes if FSH and ABP are absent. Developing sperm have no androgen receptors and don't respond directly to it.

Thus, we can see that testicular development and sperm production depend on signals from the pituitary and ultimately the hypothalamus, but this isn't the whole story. The testes also send feedback signals to those sites and regulate gonadotropin output **(fig. 27.12).** Nurse cells secrete not only ABP but also a hormone called **inhibin,** which selectively suppresses the secretion of FSH by the pituitary. A lower FSH level results in a reduced rate of sperm production. If, however, sperm production is too slow (reflected by a sperm count below 20 million sperm per milliliter of semen), inhibin levels drop, FSH level rises, and sperm production increases. Inhibin thus provides a means for the pituitary

---

[26]*puber* = grown up
[27]*adolesc* = to grow up

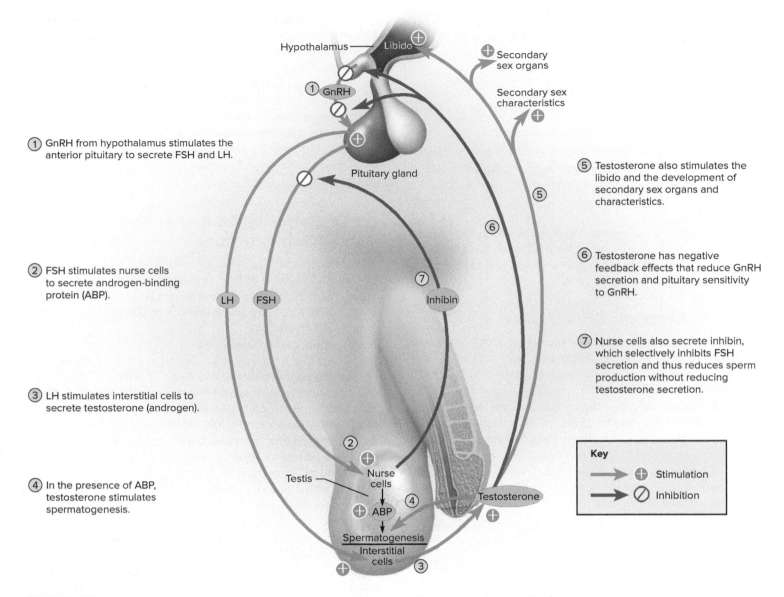

① GnRH from hypothalamus stimulates the anterior pituitary to secrete FSH and LH.

② FSH stimulates nurse cells to secrete androgen-binding protein (ABP).

③ LH stimulates interstitial cells to secrete testosterone (androgen).

④ In the presence of ABP, testosterone stimulates spermatogenesis.

⑤ Testosterone also stimulates the libido and the development of secondary sex organs and characteristics.

⑥ Testosterone has negative feedback effects that reduce GnRH secretion and pituitary sensitivity to GnRH.

⑦ Nurse cells also secrete inhibin, which selectively inhibits FSH secretion and thus reduces sperm production without reducing testosterone secretion.

Key
⟶ ⊕ Stimulation
⟶ ⊘ Inhibition

FIGURE 27.12 Hormonal Relationships Between the Hypothalamus, Pituitary Gland, and Testis.

to monitor and adjust the rate of sperm production, but without reducing the production of testosterone (which depends on LH output, not FSH). Testosterone, however, also has negative feedback effects on the hypothalamus, reducing the output of GnRH and the pituitary's sensitivity to it. This enables the hypothalamo–pituitary system to monitor and regulate testosterone secretion.

▶▶▶ APPLY WHAT YOU KNOW

If a male animal is castrated, would you expect FSH and LH levels to rise, fall, or be unaffected. Why?

27.3c Aging and Sexual Function

Menopause is a well-known period of declining reproductive function in women, but whether men experience any such decline—sometimes called **andropause** or **male climacteric**—is a controversial concept not accepted by all authorities. Testosterone

secretion peaks around age 20 at about 7 mg/day, then steadily declines to as little as one-fifth of this level by age 80. There is a corresponding decline in the number and secretory activity of the interstitial endocrine cells and nurse cells. Along with the declining testosterone level, the sperm count and libido diminish, as do the volume and force of ejaculation. By age 65, sperm count is typically about one-third of what it was in a man's 20s. Older men may become less interested in sex, but nevertheless remain capable of fathering a child throughout old age.

As testosterone and inhibin levels decline, so does feedback inhibition of the pituitary. The less-inhibited pituitary secretes elevated levels of FSH and LH. These gonadotropins may cause mood changes, hot flashes, or even illusions of suffocation—symptoms similar to those in perimenopausal women. Most men, however, notice few or no such effects as they pass through this age. Despite comedic or sardonic references to "male menopause," the term *menopause* refers to the cessation of menstruation and therefore makes no sense in the context of male physiology.

About 20% of men in their 60s and 50% of men in their 80s experience *erectile dysfunction (impotence),* the frequent inability to produce or maintain an erection sufficient for intercourse (see table 27.3). Erectile dysfunction (ED) and declining sexual activity can have a major impact on older people's perception of the quality of life. Over 90% of men with ED, however, remain able to ejaculate.

BEFORE YOU GO ON

Answer the following questions to test your understanding of the preceding section:

11. State the source, target organ, and effect of GnRH.
12. Identify the target cells and effects of FSH and LH.
13. Explain how testicular hormones affect the secretion of FSH and LH.
14. Describe the major effects of androgens on the body.
15. Define *male climacteric.*

27.4 Sperm and Semen

Expected Learning Outcomes
When you have completed this section, you should be able to

a. describe the stages of meiosis and contrast meiosis with mitosis;
b. describe the sequence of cell types in spermatogenesis, and relate these to the stages of meiosis;
c. describe the role of nurse cells in spermatogenesis;
d. describe or draw and label a sperm cell; and
e. describe the composition of semen and functions of its components.

Spermatogenesis is the process of sperm production. It occurs in the seminiferous tubules and involves three principal events: (1) division and remodeling of a relatively large germ cell into four small, mobile cells with flagella; (2) reduction of the chromosome number by one-half; and (3) a shuffling of the genes so that each chromosome of the sperm carries new gene combinations that didn't exist in the chromosomes of the parents. This ensures genetic variety in the offspring, further accentuated by the independent assortment of chromosomes into different sperm, and the randomness of fertilization. The genetic recombination and reduction in chromosome number are achieved through a form of cell division called **meiosis,** which produces four daughter cells that subsequently differentiate into sperm.

27.4a Meiosis

In nearly all living organisms except bacteria, there are two forms of cell division: mitosis and meiosis. Mitosis, described in section 4.3d, is the basis for division of the single-celled fertilized egg,

growth of an embryo, and all postnatal growth and tissue repair. It is essentially the splitting of a cell with a distribution of chromosomes that results in two genetically identical daughter cells. It consists of four stages: prophase, metaphase, anaphase, and telophase.

You may find it beneficial to review figure 4.15 because of the important similarities and differences between mitosis and meiosis. There are three important differences:

1. In mitosis, each double-stranded chromosome divides into two single-stranded ones, but each daughter cell still has 46 chromosomes (23 pairs). Meiosis, by contrast, reduces the chromosome number by half. The parent cell is **diploid (2n),** meaning it has 46 chromosomes in 23 homologous pairs, whereas the daughter cells are **haploid (n),** with 23 unpaired chromosomes.

2. In mitosis, the chromosomes don't change their genetic makeup. In an early stage of meiosis, however, the chromosomes of each homologous pair join and exchange portions of their DNA. This creates new combinations of genes, so the chromosomes we pass to our offspring aren't the same ones that we inherited from our parents.

3. In mitosis, each parent cell produces only two daughter cells. In meiosis, it produces four. In the male, four sperm therefore develop from each original germ cell. The situation is somewhat different in the female (see section 28.3a).

Why use such a relatively complicated process for gametogenesis? Why not use mitosis, as we do for all other cell replication in the body? The answer is that sexual reproduction is, by definition, biparental. If we're going to combine gametes from two parents to make a child, there must be a mechanism for keeping the chromosome number constant from generation to generation. Mitosis would produce eggs and sperm with 46 chromosomes each. If these gametes combined, the zygote and the next generation would have 92 chromosomes per cell, the generation after that would have 184, and so forth. To prevent the chromosome number from doubling in every generation, the number is reduced by half during gametogenesis. Meiosis[28] is sometimes called *reduction division* for this reason.

The stages of meiosis are fundamentally the same in both sexes. Briefly, it consists of two cell divisions in succession and occurs in the following phases: prophase I, metaphase I, anaphase I, telophase I, interkinesis, prophase II, metaphase II, anaphase II, and telophase II. These events are detailed in **figure 27.13,** but let us note some of the unique and important aspects of meiosis.

In prophase I, pairs of homologous chromosomes line up side by side and form **tetrads** (*tetra* denoting the four chromatids). One chromosome of each tetrad is from the individual's father (the paternal chromosome) and the other is from the mother (the maternal chromosome). The paternal and maternal chromosomes

---

[28]*meio* = less, fewer

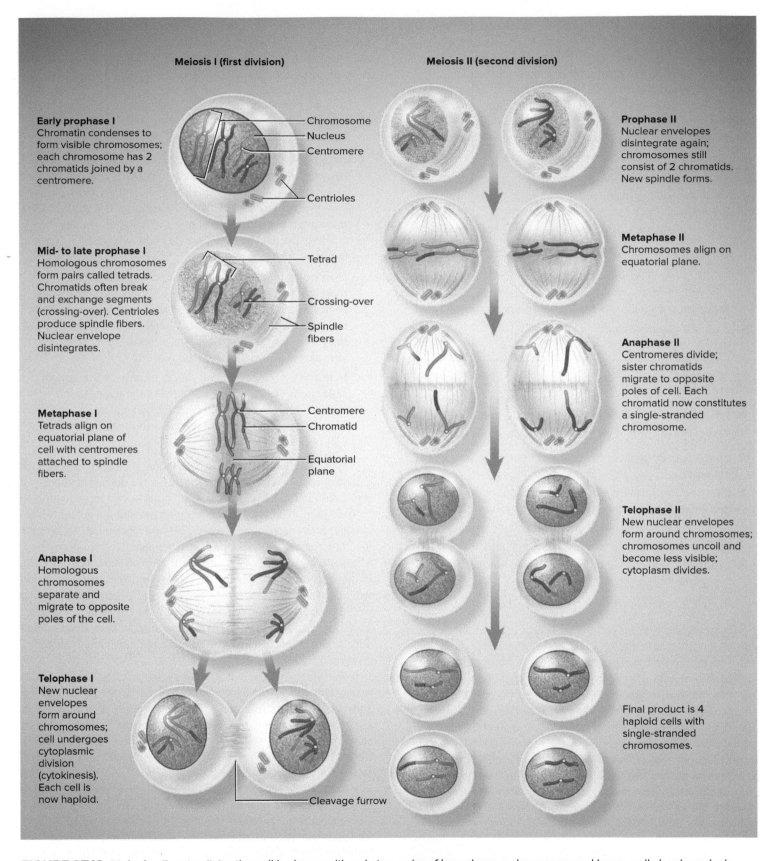

Meiosis I (first division)

Early prophase I
Chromatin condenses to form visible chromosomes; each chromosome has 2 chromatids joined by a centromere.

- Chromosome
- Nucleus
- Centromere
- Centrioles

Mid- to late prophase I
Homologous chromosomes form pairs called tetrads. Chromatids often break and exchange segments (crossing-over). Centrioles produce spindle fibers. Nuclear envelope disintegrates.

- Tetrad
- Crossing-over
- Spindle fibers

Metaphase I
Tetrads align on equatorial plane of cell with centromeres attached to spindle fibers.

- Centromere
- Chromatid
- Equatorial plane

Anaphase I
Homologous chromosomes separate and migrate to opposite poles of the cell.

Telophase I
New nuclear envelopes form around chromosomes; cell undergoes cytoplasmic division (cytokinesis). Each cell is now haploid.

- Cleavage furrow

Meiosis II (second division)

Prophase II
Nuclear envelopes disintegrate again; chromosomes still consist of 2 chromatids. New spindle forms.

Metaphase II
Chromosomes align on equatorial plane.

Anaphase II
Centromeres divide; sister chromatids migrate to opposite poles of cell. Each chromatid now constitutes a single-stranded chromosome.

Telophase II
New nuclear envelopes form around chromosomes; chromosomes uncoil and become less visible; cytoplasm divides.

Final product is 4 haploid cells with single-stranded chromosomes.

FIGURE 27.13 Meiosis. For simplicity, the cell is shown with only two pairs of homologous chromosomes. Human cells begin meiosis with 23 pairs.

❓ *Although we pass the same genes to our offspring as we inherit from our parents, we do not pass on the same chromosomes. What process in this figure accounts for the latter fact?*

exchange segments of DNA in a process called **crossing-over.** This creates new combinations of genes and thus contributes to genetic variety in the offspring.

After crossing-over, the chromosomes line up at the midline of the cell in metaphase I, they separate at anaphase I, and the cell divides in two at telophase I. This looks superficially like mitosis, but there is an important difference: The centromeres don't divide and the chromatids don't separate from each other at anaphase I; rather, each homologous chromosome parts company with its twin. Therefore, at the conclusion of meiosis I, each chromosome is still double-stranded, but each daughter cell has only 23 chromosomes—it has become haploid.

Meiosis II is more like mitosis—the chromosomes line up on the cell equator again at metaphase II, the centromeres divide, and each chromosome separates into two chromatids. These chromatids are drawn to opposite poles of the cell at anaphase II. At the end of meiosis II, there are four haploid cells, each containing 23 single-stranded chromosomes. Fertilization combines 23 chromosomes from the father with 23 chromosomes from the mother and reestablishes the diploid number of 46 in the zygote.

27.4b Sperm Production

Now we will relate meiosis to spermatogenesis **(fig. 27.14).** The first stem cells specifically destined to become sperm are **primordial germ cells.** Like the first blood cells, these form in the yolk sac, a membrane associated with the developing embryo. In the fifth to sixth week of development, they crawl into the embryo itself and colonize the gonadal ridges. Here they become stem cells called **spermatogonia.** They remain dormant through childhood, lying along the periphery of the seminiferous tubule near the basement membrane, outside the blood–testis barrier (BTB).

At puberty, testosterone secretion rises, reactivates the spermatogonia, and brings on spermatogenesis. The essential steps of spermatogenesis are as follows, numbered to match figure 27.14.

1. Spermatogonia divide by mitosis. One daughter cell from each division remains near the tubule wall as a stem cell called a *type A spermatogonium.* Type A spermatogonia serve as a lifetime supply of stem cells, so men normally remain fertile even in old age. The other daughter cell, called a *type B spermatogonium,* migrates slightly away from the wall on its way to producing sperm.

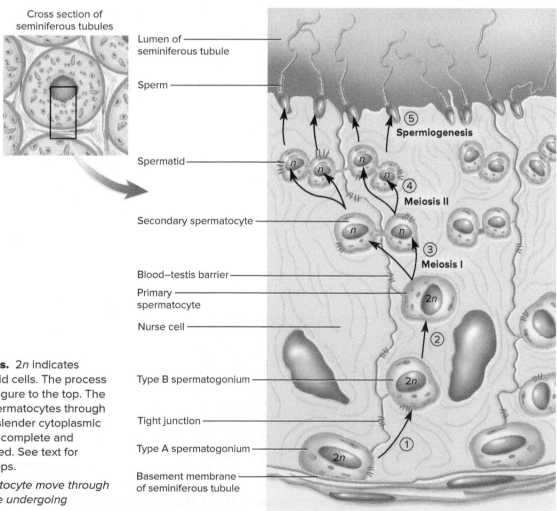

Cross section of seminiferous tubules

Lumen of seminiferous tubule

Sperm

⑤ Spermiogenesis

Spermatid

④ Meiosis II

Secondary spermatocyte

③ Meiosis I

Blood–testis barrier

Primary spermatocyte

Nurse cell

②

Type B spermatogonium

Tight junction

Type A spermatogonium

①

Basement membrane of seminiferous tubule

FIGURE 27.14 Spermatogenesis. 2*n* indicates diploid cells and *n* indicates haploid cells. The process proceeds from the bottom of the figure to the top. The daughter cells from secondary spermatocytes through spermatids remain connected by slender cytoplasmic processes until spermiogenesis is complete and individual spermatozoa are released. See text for explanation of the five process steps.

❓ *Why must the primary spermatocyte move through the blood–testis barrier before undergoing meiosis?*

② The type B spermatogonium enlarges and becomes a **primary spermatocyte.** Since this cell is about to undergo meiosis and become genetically different from other cells of the body, it must be protected from the immune system. Ahead of the primary spermatocyte, the tight junction between two nurse cells is dismantled, opening a door for the movement of the spermatocyte toward the lumen. Behind it, a new tight junction forms like a door closing between the spermatocyte and the blood supply in the periphery of the tubule. The spermatocyte moves forward, like an astronaut passing through the double-door airlock of a spaceship, and is now protected by the BTB closing behind it.

③ Now safely isolated from blood-borne antibodies, the primary spermatocyte undergoes meiosis I, which gives rise to two equal-size, haploid, and genetically unique **secondary spermatocytes.**

④ Each secondary spermatocyte undergoes meiosis II, dividing into two **spermatids**—a total of four for each spermatogonium.

⑤ A spermatid divides no further, but undergoes a transformation called **spermiogenesis,** in which it differentiates into a single spermatozoon **(fig. 27.15).** The spermatid sprouts a tail (flagellum) and discards most of its cytoplasm, making the sperm a lightweight, self-propelled cell. It won't move under its own power, however, until ejaculation.

Each stage of this process is a little closer to the lumen than the earlier stages. All stages on the lumenal side of the BTB are bound to the nurse cells by tight junctions and gap junctions, and are closely enveloped in tendrils of the nurse cells. Throughout their meiotic divisions, the daughter cells never completely separate, but remain connected to each other by cytoplasmic bridges. Eventually, however, the mature sperm separate from each other, depart from their supportive nurse cells, and are washed down the tubule by a slow flow of fluid. Spermatogenesis occurs in cycles, progressing down the tubule in *spermatogenic waves.* At any particular time, therefore, cells in a given portion of the tubule are at about the same stage of spermatogenesis, not evenly distributed among all stages.

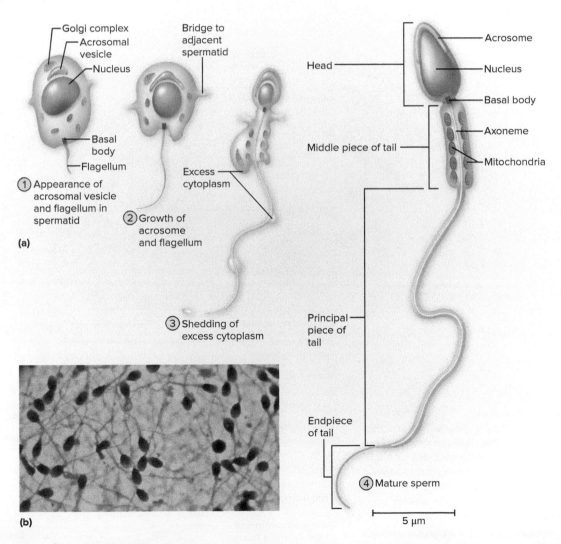

FIGURE 27.15 Spermiogenesis and Sperm Structure. (a) Stages of spermiogenesis, with mature sperm structure at stage 4. (b) Light micrograph of human sperm (1,000×).

b: Alicia Gonzalez/Alamy

It takes about 70 days for a type B spermatogonium to become mature spermatozoa. A young man produces about 300,000 sperm per minute, or 400 million per day.

27.4c The Spermatozoon

The spermatozoon is an example, par excellence, of the unity of form and function—shaped by evolution for lightness, streamlining, motility, and the effective delivery of its cargo of DNA. It has two parts: a pear-shaped head and a long tail (fig. 27.15, stage 4). The **head,** about 4 to 5 μm long and 3 μm wide at its broadest part, contains three structures: a nucleus, acrosome, and flagellar basal body. The most important of these is the nucleus, which fills most of the head and contains a haploid set of condensed, genetically inactive chromosomes. The **acrosome**[29] is a lysosome in the form of a thin cap covering the apical half of the nucleus. It contains enzymes that are later used to penetrate the egg if the sperm is successful. The basal body of the tail flagellum is nestled in an indentation at the basal end of the nucleus. This is essentially a solitary centriole surrounded by a centrosome, like the centrioles of other cells. It plays an important role in fertilization (see section 29.1b).

The **tail** is divided into three regions called the middle piece, principal piece, and endpiece. The **middle piece,** a cylinder about 5 to 9 μm long and half as wide as the head, is the thickest part. It contains numerous large mitochondria that coil tightly around the axoneme of the flagellum. They produce the ATP needed for the beating of the tail when the sperm migrates up the female reproductive tract. The **principal piece,** 40 to 45 μm long, constitutes most of the tail and consists of the axoneme surrounded by a sheath of supportive fibers. The **endpiece,** 4 to 5 μm long, consists of the axoneme only and is the narrowest part of the sperm.

27.4d Semen

The fluid expelled during orgasm is called **semen**[30] (seminal fluid). A typical ejaculation discharges 2 to 5 mL of semen, composed of about 2% to 5% sperm and spermatic duct secretions, 25% to 30% prostatic fluid, 65% to 70% seminal vesicle fluid, and a trace of bulbourethral fluid. Most of the sperm emerge in the first one or two jets of semen. The semen usually has a **sperm count** of 50 to 120 million sperm/mL. A sperm count any lower than 20 to 25 million sperm/mL is usually associated with **infertility** (sterility), the inability to fertilize an egg (see table 27.3).

Table 27.2 lists the major constituents of semen with their glandular sources and functions. This isn't an exhaustive list; other components with still-unknown functions are not tabulated.

A well-known property of semen is its stickiness, an adaptation that promotes fertilization. It arises when the clotting enzyme from the prostate activates *prosemenogelin,* converting it to a sticky fibrinlike protein, **semenogelin.** This process is very similar to blood clotting. Semenogelin entangles the sperm, sticks to the walls of the inner vagina and cervix, and ensures that the semen doesn't simply drain back out of the vagina. It may also promote the uptake of sperm-laden clots of semen into the uterus. Twenty to 30 minutes after ejaculation, the **serine protease** of the prostatic fluid breaks down semenogelin and liquifies the semen. Serine protease is also known clinically as **prostate-specific antigen (PSA);** an elevated blood PSA level is an indicator of possible prostate cancer (see Deeper Insight 27.2).

Fructose and **citrate** are the two most significant nutrients in semen, metabolized by the sperm mitochondria to generate ATP for flagellar motility. **Calcium** is also needed for flagellar beating, and plays an additional role in releasing enzymes from the acrosome when the sperm penetrates an egg. **Zinc** in the semen

---

[29]*acro* = tip, peak; *some* = body

[30]*semen* = seed

TABLE 27.2	Composition of Semen		
Source	**Fraction of Semen Volume**	**Constituents**	**Functions**
Testes	2% to 5%	50–120 million sperm per mL	Fertilization of egg
Seminal vesicles	65% to 75%	Fructose, citrate, ascorbic acid	Nutrients for sperm
		Prostaglandins	Stimulate peristalsis of ductus deferens and uterus; inhibit sperm rejection by female immune system
		Prosemenogelin	Fibrinogen-like clotting protein; coagulates semen
		Calcium	Activates sperm motility; triggers release of enzymes from acrosome for penetration of egg
Prostate	25% to 30%	Clotting enzyme	Acts on prosemenogelin, coagulates semen
		Serine protease	Liquifies coagulated semen after delay
		Citrate	Nutrient for sperm
		Bicarbonate and phosphate buffers	Neutralize acidity of urethra and vagina
		Zinc	Stabilizes sperm chromatin; deficiency causes sperm fragility
Bulbourethral glands	<1%	Mucus	Lubricates urethra; forms low-viscosity channel for sperm migration through vagina and cervix
		Buffers	Neutralize acidity of urethra and vagina

stabilizes the chromatin in the sperm head; a dietary deficiency of zinc can result in fragile sperm and infertility.

Sperm encounter hostile conditions as soon as they leave the safety of the spermatic ducts. Residual urine makes the male urethra acidic, and the vagina has a film of lactic acid to protect it from microbial overgrowth. The prostate and bulbourethral glands secrete bicarbonate and phosphate buffers to neutralize this acidity and protect the sperm. Yet another jeopardy to the sperm is attack by the female's immune system, which recognizes the sperm as foreign. **Prostaglandins** from the seminal vesicles inhibit this immune response and minimizes sperm loss. (Prostaglandins are named for the fact that they were first discovered in the fluid

DEEPER INSIGHT 27.3

CLINICAL APPLICATION

Reproductive Effects of Pollution

In recent decades, there has been a great deal of interest within the scientific community and popular media concerning *endocrine disrupting chemicals (EDCs)*—environmental agents that interfere with our natural hormones and may disrupt reproduction, development, and homeostasis.

Proven or suspected EDCs occur in industrial solvents and lubricants, pesticides, plastics (including the plastic lining of food cans), prescription drugs and medical devices, and even infant soy milk formulas. We're exposed to EDCs through food, drinking water, contaminated air and soil, and household chemicals, and in certain occupations such as farming and manufacturing that use such chemicals. Some EDCs may affect not only the exposed person, but also that person's descendants through the DNA methylation and epigenetic effects (see section 4.4h). Your grandchildren could be genetically affected by your chemical exposures today.

EDCs act by several mechanisms. They or their metabolites can mimic the effects of estrogen by activating its receptors; antagonize the effects of androgens; alter gene expression; or disrupt positive and negative feedback loops that regulate the body's secretion of its own estrogens and androgens.

EDCs are suspected or implicated, at least tentatively, in a broad spectrum of reproductive abnormalities—in males, cryptorchidism, hypospadias (a urethra opening ventrally on the penis instead of at the tip), low sperm count and reduced motility, and testicular cancer; in females, premature breast development, premature menopause, breast cancer, uterine fibroids, endometriosis, and disrupted ovulation and lactation.

But in many such cases, the data are contradictory, weak, or in dispute. The evidence, however disturbing, is often vague and indirect. It is enormously difficult to prove a link between a particular reproductive disorder and a suspected EDC. For one thing, we can't experiment on this with humans, and the results of animal experiments often don't translate to humans. For another, the effects may be delayed by years, decades, or perhaps even generations; and there are so many variables in human life that they cover up the trail of causation—prenatal or infant exposure with no effects visible until adulthood; changes in occupation, residence, and environmental exposure; migration and international adoption; and exposure to complex mixtures of environmental chemicals—making it impossible to single out any one cause or to know how they interact to produce effects that no one of them would produce alone. Despite such difficulties, EDCs pose a compelling problem under continuing investigation.

from the bovine prostate.) Prostaglandins also stimulate peristalsis in both sexes—in the ductus deferens of the male, driving sperm toward the penis; and in the uterus of the female, possibly serving to draw up semen from the vagina. Peristaltic waves in the uterus and uterine tubes may also help spread sperm through the female reproductive tract.

Two requirements must be met for sperm motility: an elevated pH and an energy source. The pH of the vagina is about 3.5 to 4.0, and the male spermatic ducts are also quite acidic. The sperm remain motionless at such low pHs. But as the prostatic fluid buffers the vaginal and seminal acidity, the pH rises to about 7.5 and the sperm become active at the time of ejaculation. The activated sperm now thrash with their tails and crawl up the mucosa of the vagina and uterus.

BEFORE YOU GO ON

Answer the following questions to test your understanding of the preceding section:

16. Name the stages of spermatogenesis from spermatogonium to spermatozoa. How do they differ in the number of chromosomes per cell and chromatids per chromosome?

17. Describe the two major parts of a spermatozoon and state what organelles or cytoskeletal components are contained in each.

18. List the major contributions of the seminal vesicles and prostate to the semen, and state the functions of these components.

27.5 Male Sexual Response

Expected Learning Outcomes

When you have completed this section, you should be able to

a. describe the blood and nerve supply to the penis; and

b. explain how these govern erection and ejaculation.

Sexual intercourse is also known as **coitus, coition,**[31] or **copulation.**[32] The physiology of sexual intercourse was unexplored territory before the 1950s because of repressive attitudes toward the subject. British psychologist Havelock Ellis published the groundbreaking six-volume *Studies in the Psychology of Sex* (1897–1910), only to have it banned for several years as too controversial for victorian tastes. In the 1950s, William Masters and Virginia Johnson daringly launched the first physiological studies of sexual response in the laboratory. In 1966, they published *Human Sexual Response,* which detailed measurements and observations on more than 10,000 sexual acts by nearly 700 volunteer men and women. Masters and Johnson then turned their attention to disorders of sexual function and pioneered modern therapy for sexual dysfunctions. They divided intercourse into

---

[31]*coit* = to come together
[32]*copul* = to link, bond

four recognizable phases, which they called *excitement, plateau, orgasm,* and *resolution.* The following discussion is organized around this model, although other authorities have modified it or proposed alternatives.

27.5a Anatomical Foundations

To understand male sexual function, we must give closer attention to the blood circulation and nerve supply to the penis.

Each internal iliac artery gives rise to an **internal pudendal (penile) artery,** which enters the root of the penis and divides in two. One branch, the **dorsal artery,** travels dorsally along the penis not far beneath the skin (see fig. 27.11), supplying blood to the skin, fascia, and corpus spongiosum. The other branch, the **deep artery,** travels through the core of the corpus cavernosum and gives off smaller **helicine**[33] **arteries,** which penetrate the trabeculae and empty into the cavernous spaces. When the penis is flaccid, most of its blood supply comes from the dorsal arteries. When the deep artery dilates, the cavernous spaces fill with blood and the penis becomes erect. There are numerous anastomoses between the dorsal and deep arteries, so neither of them is the exclusive source of blood to any one erectile tissue. A median **deep dorsal vein** drains blood from the penis. It runs between the two dorsal arteries beneath the deep fascia and empties into a plexus of prostatic veins.

The penis is richly innervated by sensory and motor nerve fibers. The glans and foreskin have an abundance of tactile, pressure, and temperature receptors, especially on the frenulum and proximal margin of the glans. The receptors lead by way of a pair of prominent **dorsal nerves** to the **internal pudendal nerves,** then via the sacral plexus to segments S2 to S4 of the spinal cord. Sensory fibers of the shaft, scrotum, perineum, and elsewhere are also highly important to sexual stimulation.

Both autonomic and somatic motor fibers carry impulses from integrating centers in the spinal cord to the penis and other pelvic organs. Sympathetic fibers arise from levels T12 to L2, pass through the hypogastric and pelvic plexuses, and innervate the penile arteries, trabecular muscle, spermatic ducts, and accessory glands. They dilate the penile arteries and can induce erection even when the sacral region of the spinal cord is damaged. They also initiate erection in response to input to the special senses and to sexual thoughts.

Parasympathetic fibers extend from segments S2 to S4 of the spinal cord through the pudendal nerves to the arteries of the penis. They are involved in an autonomic reflex arc that causes erection in response to direct stimulation of the penis and perineal region.

27.5b Excitement and Plateau

The **excitement phase** is characterized by **vasocongestion** (swelling of the genitals with blood); **myotonia** (muscle tension); and increases in heart rate, blood pressure, and pulmonary ventilation **(fig. 27.16).** The bulbourethral glands secrete their fluid during this phase. The excitement phase can be initiated by a broad spectrum of erotic stimuli—sights, sounds, aromas, touch—and even by dreams or thoughts. Conversely, emotions can inhibit sexual response and make it difficult to function when a person is anxious, stressed, or preoccupied with other thoughts.

The most obvious manifestation of male sexual arousal is **erection** of the penis, which makes entry of the vagina possible. Erection is an autonomic reflex mediated predominantly by parasympathetic nerve fibers that travel alongside the deep and helicine arteries of the penis. These fibers trigger the secretion of nitric oxide (NO), which leads to the relaxation of the deep arteries and cavernous spaces (see Deeper Insight 27.4). Whether this is enough to cause erection, or whether it is also necessary to block the outflow of blood from the penis, is still debated. According to one hypothesis, as cavernous spaces near the deep arteries fill with blood, they compress the spaces closer to the periphery of the erectile tissue. This is where blood leaves the erectile tissues, so the compression of the peripheral spaces helps retain blood in the penis. Their compression is aided by the fact that each corpus cavernosum is wrapped in a tunica albuginea, which fits over the erectile tissue like a tight fibrous sleeve and contributes to its tension and firmness. In addition, the bulbospongiosus and ischiocavernosus muscles aid in erection by compressing the root of the penis and forcing blood forward into the shaft.

As the corpora cavernosa expand, the penis becomes enlarged, rigid, and elevated to an angle conducive to entry of the vagina. Longitudinal expansion of the penis retracts the foreskin, exposing the glans. Once **intromission** (entry) is achieved, the tactile and pressure sensations produced by vaginal massaging of the penis further accentuate the erection reflex.

The corpus spongiosum has neither a central artery nor a tunica albuginea. It swells and becomes more visible as a cordlike ridge along the ventral surface of the penis, but it doesn't become nearly as engorged and hardened as the corpora cavernosa. Vasocongestion isn't limited to the penis; the testes also become as much as 50% larger during excitement.

In the **plateau phase,** variables such as respiratory rate, heart rate, and blood pressure are sustained at a high level, or rise slightly, for a few seconds to a few minutes before orgasm. This phase may be marked by increased vasocongestion and myotonia.

▶▶▶APPLY WHAT YOU KNOW

Why is it important that the corpus spongiosum not become as engorged and rigid as the corpora cavernosa?

27.5c Orgasm and Ejaculation

The **orgasm,**[34] or **climax,** is a short but intense reaction that lasts 3 to 15 seconds and usually is marked by the discharge of semen. The heart rate increases to as high as 180 beats/min., blood pressure rises proportionately, and the respiratory rate becomes as high as 40 breaths/min. From the standpoint of producing offspring, the most significant aspect of male orgasm is the **ejaculation**[35] of semen into the vagina.

---

[33]*helic* = coil, helix

[34]*orgasm* = swelling

[35]*e* = *ex* = out; *jacul* = to throw

FIGURE 27.16 Neural Control of Male Sexual Response.

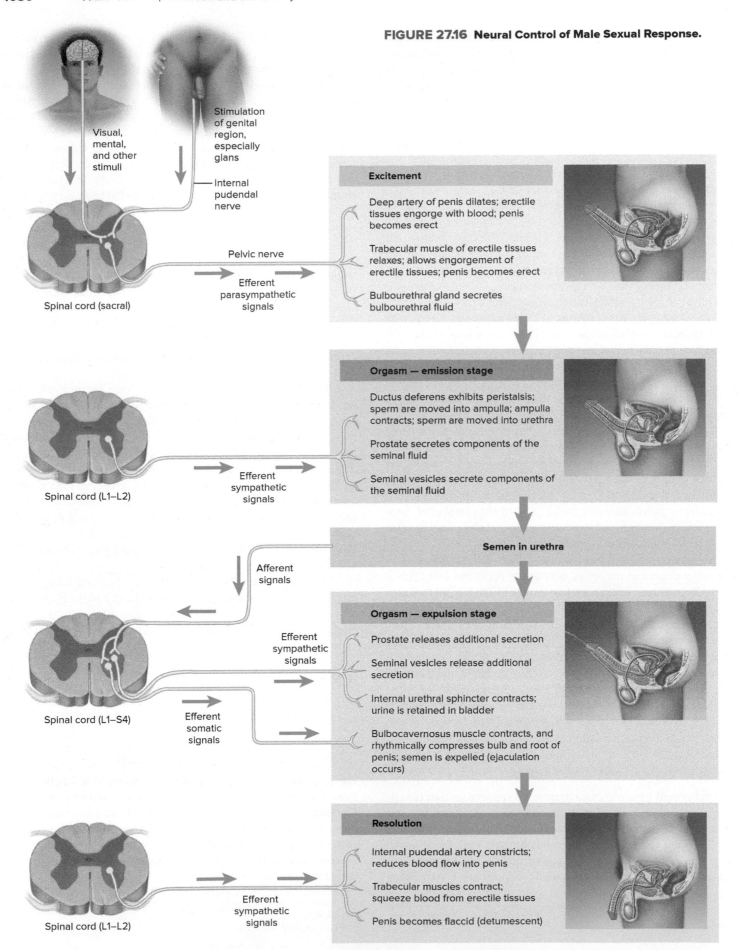

Visual, mental, and other stimuli

Stimulation of genital region, especially glans

Internal pudendal nerve

Spinal cord (sacral)

Pelvic nerve

Efferent parasympathetic signals

Excitement

Deep artery of penis dilates; erectile tissues engorge with blood; penis becomes erect

Trabecular muscle of erectile tissues relaxes; allows engorgement of erectile tissues; penis becomes erect

Bulbourethral gland secretes bulbourethral fluid

Spinal cord (L1–L2)

Efferent sympathetic signals

Orgasm — emission stage

Ductus deferens exhibits peristalsis; sperm are moved into ampulla; ampulla contracts; sperm are moved into urethra

Prostate secretes components of the seminal fluid

Seminal vesicles secrete components of the seminal fluid

Semen in urethra

Afferent signals

Efferent sympathetic signals

Efferent somatic signals

Spinal cord (L1–S4)

Orgasm — expulsion stage

Prostate releases additional secretion

Seminal vesicles release additional secretion

Internal urethral sphincter contracts; urine is retained in bladder

Bulbocavernosus muscle contracts, and rhythmically compresses bulb and root of penis; semen is expelled (ejaculation occurs)

Spinal cord (L1–L2)

Efferent sympathetic signals

Resolution

Internal pudendal artery constricts; reduces blood flow into penis

Trabecular muscles contract; squeeze blood from erectile tissues

Penis becomes flaccid (detumescent)

DEEPER INSIGHT 27.4

CLINICAL APPLICATION

Treating Erectile Dysfunction

Among the most lucrative drugs developed in the 1990s were the popular treatments for erectile dysfunction: sildenafil (Viagra), vardenafil (Levitra), and tadalafil (Cialis). The basis for developing them was a seemingly unrelated discovery: the role of nitric oxide in cell signaling. When sexual stimulation triggers NO secretion, NO activates the enzyme guanylate cyclase. Guanylate cyclase produces cyclic guanosine monophosphate (cGMP). cGMP then relaxes the smooth muscle of the deep arteries and cavernous spaces of the corpora cavernosa, increasing blood flow into these erectile tissues and bringing about an erection **(fig. 27.17).**

The erection subsides when cGMP is broken down by the enzyme *phosphodiesterase type 5 (PDE5).* The problem for many men and their partners is that it subsides too soon, and the solution is to prevent cGMP from breaking down so fast. The aforementioned drugs are in a family called *phosphodiesterase inhibitors.* By slowing down the action of PDE5, they prolong the life of cGMP and the duration of the erection.

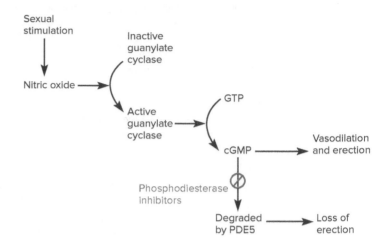

FIGURE 27.17 The Action of Viagra and Other Phosphodiesterase Inhibitors.

Ejaculation occurs in two stages called emission and expulsion. In **emission,** the sympathetic nervous system stimulates peristalsis in the smooth muscle of the ductus deferens, which propels sperm from the tail of the epididymis, along the ductus, and into the ampulla. Contractions of the ampulla propel the sperm into the prostatic urethra, and contractions of smooth muscle in the prostate force prostatic fluid into the urethra. Secretions of the seminal vesicles join the semen soon after the prostatic secretion. The contractions and seminal flow of this phase create an urgent sensation that ejaculation is inevitable.

Semen in the urethra activates somatic and sympathetic reflexes that result in its **expulsion.** Sensory signals travel to the spinal cord via the internal pudendal nerve and reach an integrating center in the upper lumbar region. Sympathetic nerve fibers carry motor signals from here out to the prostate and seminal vesicles, causing the smooth muscle in their walls to express more fluid into the urethra. The sympathetic reflex also constricts the internal urethral sphincter so urine can't enter the urethra and semen can't enter the bladder.

Somatic motor signals leave the third and fourth sacral segments of the cord and travel to the bulbospongiosus, ischiocavernosus, and levator ani muscles. The bulbospongiosus, which envelops the root of the penis (see fig. 10.20a), undergoes five or six strong, spasmodic contractions that compress the urethra and forcibly expel the semen. Most sperm are ejected in the first milliliter of semen, mixed primarily with prostatic fluid. The seminal vesicle secretion follows and flushes most remaining sperm from the ejaculatory ducts and urethra. Some sperm may seep from the penis prior to ejaculation, and pregnancy can therefore result from genital contact even without orgasm.

Orgasm is accompanied by an intense feeling of release from tension. Ejaculation and orgasm are not the same. Although they usually occur together, it is possible to have all of the sensations of orgasm without ejaculating, and ejaculation occasionally occurs with little or no sensation of orgasm.

27.5d Resolution

Immediately following orgasm comes the **resolution** phase. Discharge of the sympathetic nervous system constricts the internal pudendal artery and reduces the flow of blood into the penis. It also causes contraction of the trabecular muscles, which squeeze blood from the erectile tissues. The penis may remain semierect long enough to continue intercourse, which may be important to the female's attainment of climax, but gradually the penis undergoes **detumescence**—it becomes soft and flaccid again. The resolution phase is also a time in which cardiovascular and respiratory functions return to normal. Many people break out in sweat during the resolution phase. In men, resolution is followed by a **refractory period,** lasting anywhere from 10 minutes to a few hours, in which it is usually impossible to attain another erection and orgasm.

Men and women have many similarities and a few significant differences in sexual response. The response cycle of women is described in section 28.4.

Two of the most common concerns related to sex are sexually transmitted diseases (STDs) and contraception. Understanding most contraceptive methods requires a prior understanding of female anatomy and physiology, so contraceptive techniques for both sexes are discussed at the end of the next chapter, while STDs are discussed in this chapter (see Deeper Insight 27.5). This is not to imply, of course, that STDs are only a male concern and contraception only a female concern.

Reproductive disorders specific to males and females are briefly summarized in **table 27.3** and table 28.5, respectively. The effects of aging on the reproductive system are described in section 29.4a.

TABLE 27.3	Some Male Reproductive Disorders
Breast cancer	Accounts for 0.2% of male cancers in the United States; usually seen after age 60 but sometimes in children and adolescents. (For every male who gets breast cancer, about 175 females do so.) Usually felt as a lump near the nipple, often with crusting and discharge from nipple. Often quite advanced by the time of diagnosis, with poor prospects for recovery, because of denial and delay in seeking treatment.
Erectile dysfunction (impotence)	Inability to maintain an erection adequate for vaginal entry in half or more of one's attempts. Can stem from aging and declining testosterone level as well as cardiovascular and neurological diseases, diabetes mellitus, medications, fear of failure, depression, and other causes.
Hypospadias[36] (HY-po-SPAY-dee-us)	A congenital defect in which the urethra opens on the ventral side or base of the penis rather than at the tip; usually corrected surgically at about 1 year of age.
Infertility	Inability to fertilize an egg because of a low sperm count (lower than 20 to 25 million/mL), poor sperm motility, or a high percentage of deformed sperm (two heads, defective tails, etc.). May result from malnutrition, gonorrhea and other infections, toxins, or testosterone or zinc deficiency.
Penile cancer	Accounts for 1% of male cancers in the United States; most common in black males ages 50 to 70 and of low income. Most often seen in men with nonretractable foreskins (phimosis) combined with poor penile hygiene; least common in men circumcised at birth.
Testicular cancer	The most common solid tumor in men 15 to 34 years old, especially white males of middle to upper economic classes. Typically begins as a painless lump or enlargement of the testis. Highly curable if detected early. Men should routinely palpate the testes for normal size and smooth texture.
Varicocele (VAIR-ih-co-seal)	Abnormal dilation of veins of the spermatic cord, so that they resemble a "bag of worms." Occurs in 10% of males in the United States. Caused by absence or incompetence of venous valves. Reduces testicular blood flow and often causes infertility.
You can find other male reproductive disorders described in the following places:	
Androgen insensitivity syndrome in Deeper Insight 27.1; *benign prostatic hyperplasia* and *prostate cancer* in Deeper Insight 27.2; and *sexually transmitted diseases (gonorrhea, chlamydia, syphilis, genital herpes,* and *genital warts)* in Deeper Insight 27.5.	

BEFORE YOU GO ON

Answer the following questions to test your understanding of the preceding section:

19. Explain how penile blood circulation changes during sexual arousal and why the penis becomes enlarged and stiffened.

20. State the roles of the sympathetic, parasympathetic, and somatic nervous systems in male sexual response.

[36]*hypo* = below; *spad* = to draw off (the urine)

DEEPER INSIGHT 27.5

CLINICAL APPLICATION

Sexually Transmitted Diseases

Sexually transmitted diseases (STDs) have been well known since the writings of Hippocrates. Here we discuss three bacterial STDs—gonorrhea, chlamydia, and syphilis—and three viral STDs—genital herpes, genital warts, and hepatitis. AIDS is discussed in section 21.6.

All of these STDs have an *incubation period* in which the pathogen multiplies without symptoms, and a *communicable period* in which one can transmit the disease to others, even in the absence of symptoms. STDs often cause fetal deformity, stillbirth, and neonatal death.

Gonorrhea (GON-oh-REE-uh) is caused by the bacterium *Neisseria gonorrhoeae.* Galen, thinking the pus discharged from the penis was semen, named the disease *gonorrhea* ("flow of seed"). Gonorrhea causes abdominal discomfort, genital pain and discharge, painful urination, and abnormal uterine bleeding, but most infected women are asymptomatic. It can cause scarring of the uterine tubes, resulting in infertility. Gonorrhea is treated with antibiotics.

Nongonococcal urethritis (NGU) is any urethral inflammation caused by agents other than the gonorrhea bacterium. NGU often produces pain or discomfort on urination. The most common bacterial NGU is *chlamydia,* caused by *Chlamydia trachomatis.* Most chlamydia infections are asymptomatic, but they may cause urethral discharge and pain in the testes or pelvic region. Gonorrhea and chlamydia frequently occur together.

Pelvic inflammatory disease (PID) is acute, painful inflammation of the female pelvic organs, usually due to infection with *Chlamydia* or *Neisseria.* It often causes irregular menstrual bleeding or pain on urination. It can result in sterility and may require surgical removal of infected uterine tubes or other organs. PID is responsible for many cases of ectopic pregnancy (see Deeper Insight 29.2).

Syphilis (SIFF-ih-liss) is caused by a spiral bacterium named *Treponema pallidum.* After an incubation period of 2 to 6 weeks, a small, hard lesion called a *chancre* (SHAN-kur) appears at the site of infection—in males, usually on the penis, but in females, sometimes out of sight in the vagina. It disappears in 4 to 6 weeks, ending the first stage of syphilis and often creating an illusion of recovery. A second stage ensues, however, with a widespread pink rash, other skin eruptions, fever, joint pain, and hair loss. This subsides in 3 to 12 weeks, but symptoms can come and go for up to 5 years. A person is contagious even when symptoms are not present. The disease may progress to a third stage, *tertiary syphilis (neurosyphilis),* with cardiovascular damage and brain lesions that can cause paralysis and dementia. Syphilis is treatable with antibiotics.

Genital herpes is the most common STD in the United States, with 20 to 40 million infected people. It is usually caused by the *herpes simplex virus type 2 (HSV-2).* After an incubation period of 4 to 10 days, the virus causes blisters on the penis of the male; on the labia, vagina, or cervix of the female; and sometimes on the thighs and buttocks of either sex. Over 2 to 10 days, these blisters rupture, seep fluid, and begin to form scabs. The initial infection may be painless or may cause intense pain, urethritis, and watery discharge from the penis or vagina. The lesions heal in 2 to 3 weeks and leave no scars.

During this time, however, HSV colonizes sensory nerves and ganglia. Here it can lie dormant for years, later migrating along the nerves and causing epithelial lesions anywhere on the body. The movement from place to place is the basis of the name *herpes.*[37] Most patients have five to seven recurrences, ranging from several years apart to several times a year. An infected person is contagious to a sexual partner when the lesions are present and sometimes even when they are not. HSV may increase the risk of cervical cancer and AIDS.

Genital warts (condylomas) are caused by various strains of *human papillomavirus (HPV).* In most cases, HPV infection goes away on its own and does not cause any health problems. If it persists, however, it can cause genital warts or worse. In the male, warts usually appear on the penis, perineum, or anus; and in the female, they are usually on the cervix, vaginal wall, perineum, or anus. Lesions are sometimes small and almost invisible. Genital warts can be treated with cryosurgery (freezing and excision), laser surgery, or interferon. An HPV vaccine became available in 2006 and infection rates in young people seem to be declining as a result of vaccination. Certain strains of HPV different from those that usually cause genital warts cause cancer of the penis, vagina, cervix, anus, and throat; nearly all cervical cancer and about 70% of throat cancer is caused by HPV. There are about 14 million new cases of HPV infection in the United States per year. Given the alarming incidence of sexual activity and HPV among young adolescents, the U.S. Food and Drug Administration recommends vaccination of girls and boys at the age of puberty in hopes of immunizing most before the onset of sexual activity.

Hepatitis B and *C* are inflammatory liver diseases caused by the hepatitis B and C viruses (HBV, HCV), introduced in Deeper Insight 26.3. Although they can be transmitted by means other than sex, they are becoming increasingly common as STDs. Hepatitis C threatens to become a major epidemic of the twenty-first century. It already far surpasses the prevalence of AIDS and is the leading reason for liver transplants in the United States.

---

[37]*herp* = to creep

▶ Assess Your Learning Outcomes

To test your knowledge, discuss the following topics with a study partner or in writing, ideally from memory.

27.1 Sexual Reproduction and Development

1. Essential characteristics of sexual reproduction; what defines *male* and *female* in any sexual species; and the names and defining characteristics of their respective gametes and gonads
2. Multiple functions of the male and female reproductive systems
3. Which organs of each sex are considered to be primary and secondary sex organs; which are considered to be internal and external genitalia; and how secondary sex characteristics differ from secondary sex organs
4. The difference between sex chromosomes and autosomes; the number of each; names of the sex chromosomes; and how males and females differ chromosomally
5. The male-determining gene on the Y chromosome; the name of the protein encoded by it; and the effect of that protein on embryonic development
6. Fates of the mesonephric and paramesonephric ducts in the male and female embryos, and why this is indirectly determined by the *SRY* gene
7. Structures of the embryonic genital tubercle, urogenital folds, and labioscrotal folds; and mature structures of the male and female that arise from each
8. Descent of the gonads; similarities and differences in this process in the male and female fetus; and consequences for the male if it fails to occur to completion

27.2 Male Reproductive Anatomy

1. Anatomy and functions of the scrotum and spermatic cord
2. Why the testes must be kept cooler than the core body temperature, and three mechanisms for achieving this
3. Anatomy of the testis and functions of its seminiferous tubules and interstitial endocrine cells
4. The germinal epithelium of the seminiferous tubule; its cell types and their functions; the necessity and structure of the blood–testis barrier

5. The arterial supply and venous drainage of the testis; testicular nerves and lymphatic vessels
6. Gross anatomy of the epididymis; the series of spermatic ducts from the efferent ductules to the ejaculatory duct; and differences in their anatomy and relationships to adjacent organs
7. Three sets of male accessory glands; their anatomy, functions, and relationships to adjacent organs
8. The root, shaft, and glans of the penis; the prepuce and frenulum distally; the bulb and the crura proximally
9. Erectile tissues of the penis; their histological structure; the cavernous spaces, trabeculae, and trabecular muscle, differences between the corpus spongiosum and the corpora cavernosa

27.3 Puberty, Hormonal Control, and Climacteric

1. Definitions of *puberty* and *adolescence;* the typical age range of each
2. The hormonal trigger for the onset of puberty; the roles of GnRH, FSH, LH, androgens, and androgen-binding protein in male adolescence
3. Bodily changes of male adolescence, onset of the libido, and their respective hormonal causes
4. The source of inhibin and its role in male sexual physiology
5. Changes in the levels of testosterone, inhibin, FSH, and LH over the male life span; how these relate to negative feedback inhibition of the pituitary; and the effects experienced by some men in male climacteric
6. Effects of old age on male sexual function

27.4 Sperm and Semen

1. The meaning of *spermatogenesis* and distinction between spermatogenesis and spermiogenesis
2. Why meiosis is necessary in sexually reproducing species, how it affects the chromosome number of gametes, and why chromosome number remains constant from one generation to the next
3. The nine stages of meiosis—four in meiosis I, interkinesis, and four in meiosis II; events

of each stage; the final number of functional daughter cells, their chromosome number, and final chromosome structure in the male
4. Multiple reasons that meiosis results in genetic diversity of the gametes
5. The origin of primordial germ cells, their migration to the embryonic gonads, and the stage they have reached by the time of birth
6. The mode and location of production of type A and type B spermatogonia and the difference between them
7. Stages in the transformation of spermatogonia to sperm; how the germ cells migrate through the germinal epithelium as this is occurring; when they must pass through the blood–testis barrier, why, and how they do so
8. The process and effects of spermiogenesis
9. Morphology of a mature sperm and the functions of its parts
10. Composition of semen and percentages of it that come from its three main sources; functions of the fructose, semenogelin, clotting enzyme, prostaglandins, and serine protease; and the identity and clinical relevance of prostate-specific antigen (PSA)
11. The typical sperm count and the minimum necessary for fertility

27.5 Male Sexual Response

1. Blood vessels of the penis and how they function in the flaccid penis and in erection
2. The nerve supply of the penis and its relationship to the sacral plexus and spinal cord; three types of nerve fibers that the penis receives
3. Physiological changes that the male undergoes during the excitement phase of the sexual response
4. The mechanism of erection including the roles of parasympathetic stimulation, nitric oxide, and vasodilation; why the corpora cavernosa become more engorged than the corpus spongiosum
5. The physiological state of the male in the plateau phase of sexual response
6. The mechanism of male orgasm, including the stages of ejaculation
7. Characteristics of the male resolution phase; the mechanism of penile detumescence; and the refractory period

STUDY GUIDE

▶ Testing Your Recall

Answers in Appendix A

1. The ductus deferens develops from the
   _____ of the embryo.
   a. mesonephric duct
   b. paramesonephric duct
   c. phallus
   d. labioscrotal folds
   e. urogenital folds

2. The protein that clots and causes the stickiness of the semen is
   a. semenogelin.
   b. prostaglandin.
   c. fibrin.
   d. phosphodiesterase.
   e. serine protease.

3. The expulsion of semen occurs when the
   bulbospongiosus muscle is stimulated by
   a. somatic efferent neurons.
   b. somatic afferent neurons.
   c. sympathetic efferent neurons.
   d. parasympathetic efferent neurons.
   e. prostaglandins.

4. Prior to ejaculation, sperm are stored
   primarily in
   a. the seminiferous tubules.
   b. the cavernous spaces.
   c. the epididymis.
   d. the seminal vesicles.
   e. the ejaculatory ducts.

5. The penis is attached to the pubic arch by
   crura of
   a. the corpora cavernosa.
   b. the corpus spongiosum.
   c. the perineal membrane.
   d. the bulbospongiosus.
   e. the ischiocavernosus.

6. The first hormone secreted at the onset of
   puberty is
   a. follicle-stimulating hormone.
   b. interstitial cell–stimulating hormone.
   c. human chorionic gonadotropin.
   d. gonadotropin-releasing hormone.
   e. testosterone.

7. When it is necessary to reduce sperm
   production without reducing testosterone
   secretion, the nurse cells secrete
   a. dihydrotestosterone.
   b. androgen-binding protein.
   c. LH.
   d. FSH.
   e. inhibin.

8. Four spermatozoa arise from each
   a. primordial germ cell.
   b. type A spermatogonium.
   c. type B spermatogonium.
   d. secondary spermatocyte.
   e. spermatid.

9. The point in meiosis at which sister chromatids separate from each other is
   a. prophase I.
   b. metaphase I.
   c. anaphase I.
   d. anaphase II.
   e. telophase II.

10. Blood is forced out of the cavernous spaces
    of the penis by contraction of the _____
    a. bulbospongiosus muscle.
    b. ischiocavernosus muscle.
    c. cremaster.
    d. trabecular muscles.
    e. dartos muscle.

11. Under the influence of androgens, the
    embryonic _____ duct develops into the
    male reproductive tract.

12. A deficiency of _____ can cause fragile
    sperm and male infertility.

13. The _____, a network of veins in the spermatic cord, helps keep the testes cooler than
    the core body temperature.

14. All germ cells beginning with the _____
    are genetically different from the rest of the
    body cells and therefore must be protected
    by the blood–testis barrier.

15. The corpora cavernosa, as well as the testes,
    have a fibrous capsule called the _____.

16. Over half of the semen consists of secretions from a pair of glands called the
    _____.

17. The blood–testis barrier is formed by tight
    junctions between the _____ cells.

18. The earliest haploid stage of spermatogenesis is the _____.

19. Erection of the penis occurs when nitric
    oxide causes the _____ arteries to dilate.

20. A sperm penetrates the egg by means of
    enzymes in its _____.

▶ Building Your Medical Vocabulary

Answers in Appendix A

*State a meaning of each word element, and give
a medical term from this chapter that uses it or a
slight variation of it.*

1. crypto-

2. didymo-

3. e-

4. gamo-

5. -ism

6. meio-

7. orchido-

8. rete

9. -some

10. vagino-

▶ What's Wrong with These Statements?

Answers in Appendix A

Briefly explain why each of the following statements is false, or reword it to make it true.

1. Testosterone is secreted by the nurse cells of the testis.

2. Sperm carry most of their DNA in the thick middle piece just behind the head of the cell.

3. Spermiogenesis is a stage in which the male sex cells complete meiosis II and become mature sperm cells.

4. The testes and penis are the primary sex organs of the male.

5. A high testosterone level makes a fetus develop a male reproductive system, and a high estrogen level makes it develop a female reproductive system.

6. Most of the volume of the semen is produced by the testes.

7. The pampiniform plexus serves to keep the testes warm enough for sperm to develop.

8. Developing sperm must bind testosterone in order to complete their development.

9. Male menopause is the cessation of sperm production around the age of 55.

10. Erection is caused by sympathetic stimulation of the erectile tissues.

▶ Testing Your Comprehension

1. Explain why testosterone may be considered both an endocrine and a paracrine secretion of the testes. (Review paracrines in section 17.6 if necessary.)

2. A young man is in a motorcycle accident that severs his spinal cord at the neck and leaves him paralyzed from the neck down. When informed of the situation, his wife asks the physician if her husband will be able to have erections and father any children. What should the doctor tell her? Explain your answer.

3. Considering the temperature in the scrotum, would you expect hemoglobin to unload more or less oxygen to the testes than it unloads in the warmer internal organs? Why? (*Hint:* See fig. 22.26.) How would you expect this fact to influence sperm development?

4. Why is it possible for spermatogonia to be outside the blood–testis barrier, yet necessary for primary spermatocytes and later stages to be within the barrier, isolated from the blood?

5. A 68-year-old man taking medication for hypertension complains to his physician that it has made him impotent. Explain why this could be an effect of antihypertension drugs.

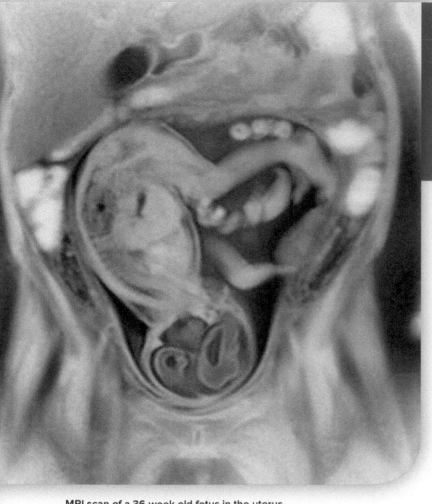

MRI scan of a 36-week-old fetus in the uterus

Simon Fraser/Science Source

THE FEMALE REPRODUCTIVE SYSTEM

Anatomy & Physiology Revealed® 4.0

Module 14: Reproductive System

The female reproductive system is more complex than the male's because it serves more purposes. Whereas the male needs only to produce and deliver gametes, the female must do this as well as provide nutrition and safe harbor for fetal development, then give birth and nourish the infant. Furthermore, female reproductive physiology is more conspicuously cyclic, and female hormones are secreted in a more complex sequence compared with the relatively steady, simultaneous secretion of regulatory hormones in the male.

This chapter discusses the anatomy of the female reproductive system; the production of gametes and how it relates to the ovarian and menstrual cycles; the female sexual response; and the physiology of pregnancy, birth, and lactation. Embryonic and fetal development are treated in the next chapter.

28.1 Female Reproductive Anatomy APR

Expected Learning Outcomes

When you have completed this section, you should be able to

a. describe the structure of the ovary;

b. trace the female reproductive tract and describe the gross anatomy and histology of each organ;

c. identify the ligaments that support the female reproductive organs;

d. describe the blood supply to the female reproductive tract;

e. identify the external genitalia of the female; and

f. describe the structure of the breast.

28.1a Sexual Differentiation

The female reproductive system (**fig. 28.1**) is obviously different from that of the male, but as we saw earlier, the two sexes are indistinguishable for the first 8 to 10 weeks of development (see fig. 27.4). The female reproductive tract develops from the paramesonephric duct not because of the positive action of any hormone, but because of the absence of testosterone and müllerian-inhibiting factor (MIF). Without testosterone, the mesonephric duct degenerates while the genital tubercle becomes the glans of the clitoris, the urogenital folds develop into labia minora, and the labioscrotal folds develop into labia majora. Without MIF, the paramesonephric ducts develop into the uterine tubes, uterus, and vagina (see fig. 27.3). This developmental pattern can be disrupted, however, by abnormal hormonal exposure before birth, as happens in adrenogenital syndrome (see fig. 17.28).

28.1b The Genitalia

The **internal genitalia** include the ovaries and a duct system that runs from the vicinity of each ovary to the outside of the body—the uterine tubes, uterus, and vagina. The **external genitalia** include principally the clitoris, labia minora, labia majora, and associated subcutaneous glands and erectile tissues. These occupy the perineum, which is defined by the same skeletal landmarks as in the male (see fig. 27.6). The ovaries are the primary sex organs, and the other internal and external genitalia are the secondary sex organs.

The Ovaries

The female gonads are the **ovaries,**[1] which produce egg cells (ova) and sex hormones. The ovary is an almond-shaped organ nestled in the *ovarian fossa,* a depression in the posterior pelvic wall. It measures about 3 cm long, 1.5 cm wide, and 1 cm thick. Its capsule, like that of the testis, is called the **tunica albuginea.** The interior of the ovary is divided into a central **medulla** and an outer **cortex (fig. 28.2),** with no sharp boundary between them. The medulla is a core of fibrous connective tissue occupied by the largest arteries and veins within the ovary. The cortex is the site of the many thousands of ovarian **follicles.** A follicle consists of a spheroidal mass of small *follicular cells* surrounding one ovum. As a follicle matures, a capsule develops around it, the follicular cells become multilayered, and a fluid cavity forms at the center. The ovary has no system of tubules like the testis; eggs are released one at a time by the bursting of the follicles *(ovulation).* In childhood, the ovaries are smooth-surfaced. During the reproductive years, they become more corrugated because growing follicles of various ages produce bulges in the surface. After menopause, the ovaries are shrunken and composed mostly of scar tissue.

---

[1]*ov* = egg; *ary* = place for

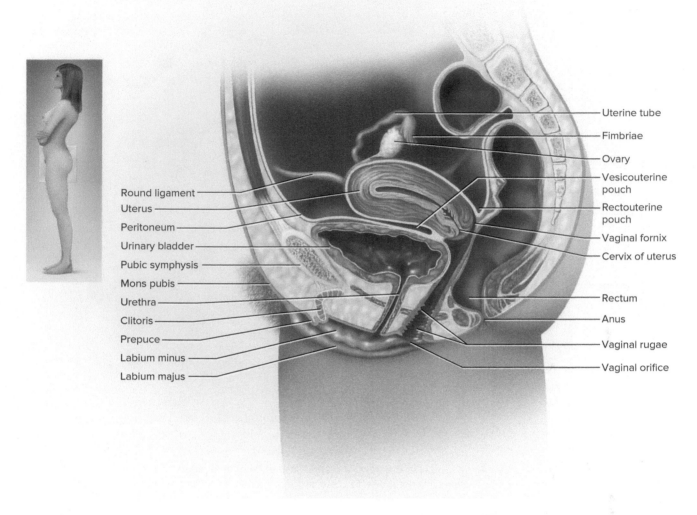

Round ligament
Uterus
Peritoneum
Urinary bladder
Pubic symphysis
Mons pubis
Urethra
Clitoris
Prepuce
Labium minus
Labium majus

Uterine tube
Fimbriae
Ovary
Vesicouterine pouch
Rectouterine pouch
Vaginal fornix
Cervix of uterus
Rectum
Anus
Vaginal rugae
Vaginal orifice

FIGURE 28.1 The Female Reproductive System. Compare photo in atlas B, figure B.14b. **A&PR**

Several connective tissue ligaments hold the ovaries and other internal genitalia in place **(fig. 28.3).** The medial pole of the ovary is attached to the uterus by the **ovarian ligament** and its lateral pole is attached to the pelvic wall by the **suspensory ligament.** The anterior margin of the ovary is anchored by a peritoneal fold called the **mesovarium.**[2] This ligament extends to a sheet of peritoneum called the *broad ligament,* which flanks the uterus and encloses the uterine tube in its superior margin. If you picture these ligaments as a sideways T, the vertical bar would represent the broad ligament, flanking the uterus and enfolding the uterine tube at its superior end, and the horizontal bar would represent the mesovarium enfolding the ovary at its free end.

The ovary receives blood from two arteries: the **ovarian artery,** which passes through the suspensory ligament and approaches the lateral pole of the ovary, and the **ovarian branch**

of the uterine artery, which passes through the mesovarium and approaches the medial pole. The ovarian artery is the female equivalent of the male testicular artery, arising high on the aorta and traveling down the posterior body wall to the gonad. The ovarian and uterine arteries anastomose along the margin of the ovary and give off multiple small arteries that enter the ovary on that side. Ovarian veins, lymphatics, and nerves also travel through the suspensory ligament. The veins and lymphatics follow courses similar to those described for the testes (see section 27.2b).

The Uterine Tubes

The **uterine tubes,** also called **oviducts** or **fallopian**[3] **tubes,** are canals about 10 cm long leading from each ovary to the uterus. At the distal (ovarian) end, the tube flares into a trumpet-shaped

---

[2]*mes* = middle; *ovari* = ovary

[3]Gabriele Fallopio (1523–62), Italian anatomist and physician

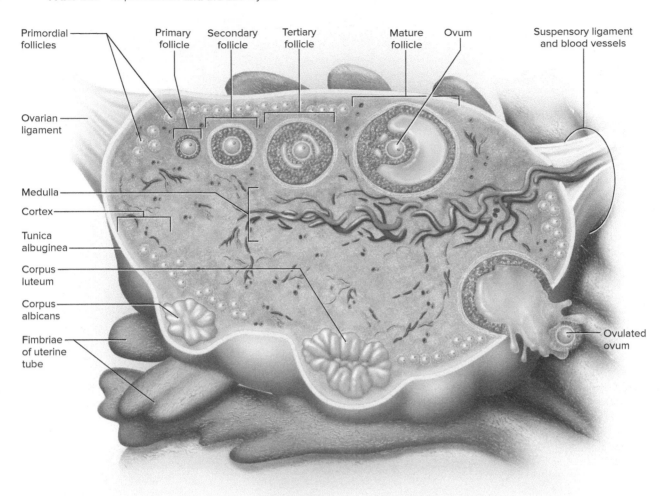

FIGURE 28.2 Structure of the Ovary. Arrows indicate the developmental sequence of an ovarian follicle; they are not meant to imply that follicles migrate around the ovary. The follicles are not drawn to scale; indeed the mature follicle at the top and ovulating follicle at the lower right have diameters about equal to the entire 3 cm length of the ovary, from ovarian ligament to suspensory ligament, and bulge from the ovarian surface like enormous blisters. **A&PR**

infundibulum[4] with feathery projections called **fimbriae**[5] (FIM-bree-ee); the middle and longest part of the tube is the **ampulla;** and near the uterus it forms a narrower **isthmus.** The uterine tube is enfolded in the **mesosalpinx**[6] (MEZ-oh-SAL-pinks), which is the superior margin of the broad ligament.

The wall of the uterine tube is well endowed with smooth muscle. Its mucosa is highly folded into longitudinal ridges and has an epithelium of ciliated cells and a smaller number of secretory cells **(fig. 28.4).** The cilia beat toward the uterus and, with the help of muscular contractions of the tube, convey the egg in that direction.

The Uterus

The **uterus**[7] is a thick muscular chamber that opens into the roof of the vagina and usually tilts forward over the urinary bladder (see fig. 28.1). Its function is to harbor the fetus, nourish it, and expel the fetus at the end of its development. It is somewhat pear-shaped, with a broad superior curvature called the **fundus,** a midportion called the **body,** and a cylindrical inferior end called the **cervix** (fig. 28.3). The uterus measures about 7 cm from cervix to fundus, 4 cm wide at its broadest point on the fundus, and 2.5 cm thick, but it is somewhat larger in women who have been pregnant.

The lumen of the uterus is roughly triangular, with its two upper corners opening into the uterine tubes. In the nonpregnant uterus, the lumen isn't a hollow cavity but rather a *potential space;* the mucous membranes of the opposite walls are pressed against each other with little room between them. The lumen communicates with the vagina by way of a narrow passage through the cervix called the **cervical canal.** The superior opening of this canal into the body of the uterus is the *internal os*[8]

---

[4]*infundibulum* = funnel
[5]*fimbria* = fringe
[6]*meso* = mesentery; *salpin* = trumpet
[7]*uterus* = womb

[8]*os* = mouth

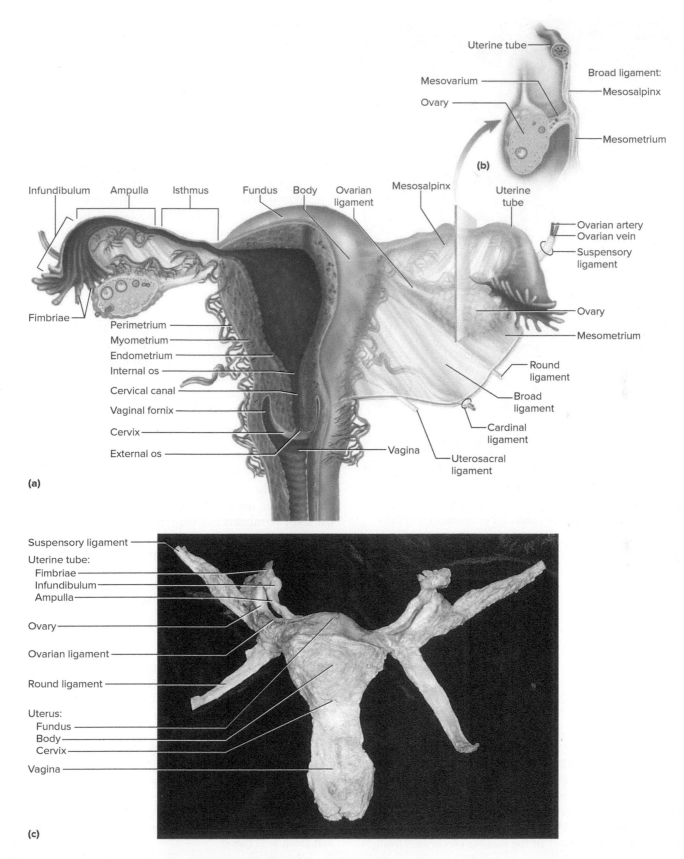

FIGURE 28.3 The Female Reproductive Tract and Supportive Ligaments. (a) Posterior view of the reproductive tract. (b) Relationship of the uterine tube and ovary to the supporting ligaments. (c) Anterior view of the major female reproductive organs from a cadaver.

c: Rebecca Gray/McGraw-Hill Education

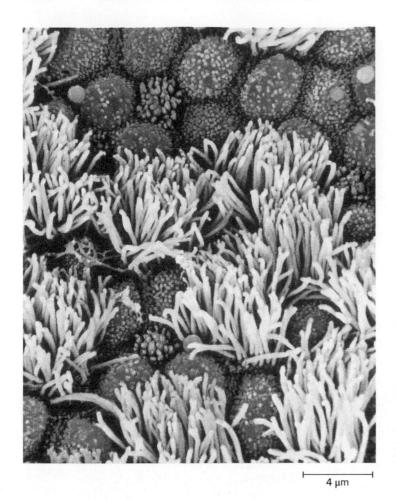

4 µm

FIGURE 28.4 Epithelial Lining of the Uterine Tube. Secretory cells are shown in red and green, and cilia of the ciliated cells in yellow (SEM). **APR**

SPL/Science Source

? *What purpose do these cilia serve?*

(pronounced "oz" or "ose") and its opening into the vagina is the *external os.* The canal contains **cervical glands** that secrete mucus, thought to prevent the spread of microorganisms from the vagina into the uterus. Near the time of ovulation, the mucus becomes thinner than usual and allows easier passage for sperm.

Uterine Wall   The uterine wall consists of three layers. The outermost layer, the **perimetrium,** is a thin serosa of simple squamous epithelium and loose connective tissue.

The middle and thickest layer is the **myometrium,**[9] about 1.25 cm thick in the nonpregnant uterus. It is composed mainly of bundles of smooth muscle that sweep downward from the fundus and spiral around the body of the uterus. The myometrium is less muscular and more fibrous near the cervix; the cervix itself is almost entirely collagenous. The muscle cells of the myometrium are about 40 µm long immediately after menstruation, but they are twice this long at the middle of the menstrual cycle (near the time of ovulation) and 10 times as long in pregnancy. The function of the myometrium is to produce the labor contractions that help to expel the fetus.

The innermost layer is a mucosa called the **endometrium.**[10] It has a simple columnar epithelium, compound (branching) tubular glands, and a lamina propria populated by leukocytes, macrophages, and other cells **(fig. 28.6).** The superficial half to two-thirds of it, called the **functional layer (stratum functionalis),** is shed in each menstrual period. The deeper layer, called the **basal layer (stratum basalis),** stays behind and regenerates a new functional layer in the next cycle (see fig. 28.16). When pregnancy occurs, the endometrium is the site of attachment of the embryo and forms the maternal part of the *placenta* from which the fetus is nourished.

Uterine Ligaments and Peritoneum   The uterus is supported by the muscular floor of the pelvis and folds of peritoneum that form supportive ligaments around the organ, as they do for the ovary and uterine tube (see fig. 28.3a). The **broad ligament** has two parts: the *mesosalpinx* mentioned earlier and the *mesometrium* on each side of the uterus. The cervix and superior part of the vagina are supported by **cardinal (lateral cervical) ligaments** extending to the pelvic wall. A pair of **uterosacral ligaments** attaches the posterior side of the uterus to the sacrum, and a pair of **round ligaments** arises from the anterior surface of the uterus, passes through the inguinal canals, and terminates in the labia majora, much like the gubernaculum of the testis terminating in the scrotum.

As the peritoneum folds around the various pelvic organs, it creates several dead-end recesses and pouches (extensions of the peritoneal cavity). Two major ones are the *vesicouterine*[11] *pouch,* which forms the space between the uterus and urinary bladder, and *rectouterine pouch* between the uterus and rectum (see fig. 28.1).

Blood Supply   The uterine blood supply is particularly important to the menstrual cycle and pregnancy. A **uterine artery** arises from each internal iliac artery and travels through the broad ligament to the uterus **(fig. 28.7).** It gives off several branches that penetrate into the myometrium and lead to **arcuate arteries.** Each arcuate artery travels in a circle around the uterus and anastomoses with the arcuate artery on the other side. Along its course, it gives rise to smaller arteries that penetrate the rest of the way through the myometrium, into the endometrium, and give off **spiral arteries.** The spiral arteries wind tortuously between the endometrial glands toward the surface of the mucosa (see fig. 28.16). They rhythmically constrict and dilate, making the mucosa alternately blanch and flush with blood.

[9]*myo* = muscle; *metr* = uterus

[10]*endo* = inside; *metr* = uterus
[11]*vesico* = bladder

DEEPER INSIGHT 28.1

CLINICAL APPLICATION

Pap Smears and Cervical Cancer

Cervical cancer usually occurs between the ages of 30 and 50, especially in women who smoke, who began sexual activity at an early age, and who have histories of frequent sexually transmitted diseases or cervical inflammation. It is almost always caused by the human papillomavirus (HPV), a sexually transmitted pathogen (see Deeper Insight 27.5). Cervical cancer typically begins in the epithelial cells of the lower cervix, develops slowly, and remains a local, easily removed lesion for several years. If the cancerous cells spread to the subepithelial connective tissue, however, the cancer is said to be *invasive* and potentially life-threatening.

Next to condoms, the best protection against cervical cancer is early detection by means of a *Pap*[12] *smear*—a procedure in which loose cells are removed from the cervix and vagina with a small flat stick and cervical brush, then microscopically examined. The pathologist looks for cells with signs of *dysplasia* (abnormal development) or carcinoma **(fig. 28.5)**. One system of staging Pap smears classifies abnormal results into three grades of *cervical intraepithelial neoplasia (CIN)*. Findings are rated on the following scale, and further vigilance or treatment is planned accordingly:

CIN I—mild dysplasia with cellular changes typically associated with HPV
CIN II—moderate dysplasia with precancerous lesions
CIN III—severe dysplasia, *carcinoma in situ* (preinvasive carcinoma of surface cells)

A rating of ASCUS or CIN I calls for a repeat Pap smear and visual examination of the cervix *(colposcopy)* in 3 to 6 months. CIN II calls for a biopsy, often done with an "electric scalpel" in a procedure called LEEP (loop electrosurgical excision procedure). A cone of tissue is removed to evaluate the depth of invasion by the malignant or premalignant cells. This in itself may be curative if all margins of the specimen are normal, indicating all abnormal cells were removed. CIN III may be cause for radiation therapy or *hysterectomy*[13] (removal of the uterus).

From age 21 to 65, women are advised to have a Pap smear every 3 years. Pap smears are not recommended before age 21 or after 65.

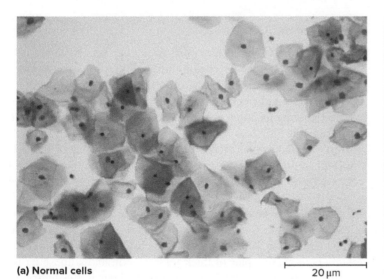

(a) Normal cells   20 μm

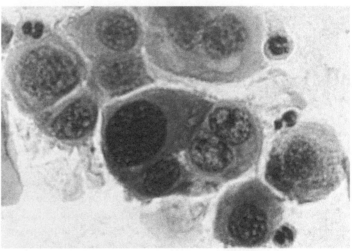

(b) Malignant (CIN III) cells

FIGURE 28.5 Pap Smears. These are smears of squamous epithelial cells scraped from the cervix. (a) Normal cells. Note the small nuclei and large volume of cytoplasm. (b) Malignant (CIN III) cells. Note the greatly enlarged nuclei and proportionately less cytoplasm.
a: Komsan Loonprom/Shutterstrock; **b:** Parviz M. Pour/Science Source

The Vagina

The **vagina**[14] is a tube about 8 to 10 cm long that allows for the discharge of menstrual fluid, receipt of the penis and semen, and birth of a baby. The vaginal wall is thin but stretches easily. It consists of an outer adventitia, a middle muscularis, and an inner mucosa. The vagina tilts posteriorly between the urethra and rectum; the urethra is bound to its anterior wall. The vagina has no glands, but it is lubricated by the seepage of serous fluid through its walls *(transudation)* and by mucus from the cervical glands above it. The vagina extends slightly beyond the cervix as a blind pouch called the *fornix*[15] (see figs. 28.1, 28.3a).

---

[12]George N. Papanicolaou (1883–1962), Greek–American physician and cytologist
[13]*hyster* = uterus; *ectomy* = cutting out
[14]*vagina* = sheath

[15]*fornix* = arch, vault

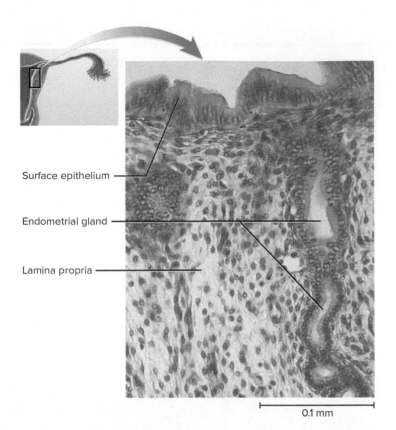

Surface epithelium

Endometrial gland

Lamina propria

0.1 mm

FIGURE 28.6 Functional Layer of the Endometrium. APR
Ed Reschke

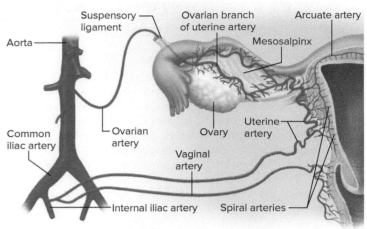

FIGURE 28.7 Blood Supply to the Female Reproductive Tract.
The vaginal, uterine, and ovarian arteries are exaggerated in length
by the perspective of the drawing, moving the aorta away from the
uterus for clarity.

The lower end of the vagina has transverse friction ridges, or
vaginal rugae, which contribute to both male and female stimulation during intercourse. At the vaginal orifice, the mucosa folds
inward and forms a membrane, the **hymen,** which stretches across
the opening. The hymen has one or more openings to allow for
discharge of menstrual fluid. It is often torn during childhood or
adolescence by ordinary physical activity, the use of tampons, or
medical examination with a speculum, or it may tear at the first act
of sexual intercourse.

The vaginal epithelium is simple cuboidal in childhood, but
the estrogens of puberty transform it into a stratified squamous epithelium. This is an example of *metaplasia,* the transformation of
one tissue type to another. The epithelial cells are rich in glycogen.
Bacteria ferment this to lactic acid, which produces a low vaginal pH (about 3.5–4.0) that inhibits the growth of pathogens. This
acidity is neutralized by the semen so it doesn't harm the sperm.
The mucosa also has antigen-presenting **dendritic cells,** which aid
in immunity at this body orifice, but unfortunately are also a route
by which HIV can invade the female body.

▶▶▶APPLY WHAT YOU KNOW

*For what functional reason do you think the vaginal
epithelium changes type at puberty? Of all types of
epithelium it might become, why stratified squamous?*

The External Genitalia

The external genitalia occupy most of the perineum and are collectively called the **vulva**[16] or **pudendum;**[17] they include the mons
pubis, labia majora and minora, clitoris, vaginal orifice, and accessory glands and erectile tissues **(fig. 28.8).** These structures lie
within the same anatomical boundaries as described for the male
perineum (see fig. 27.6): the pubic symphysis anteriorly, coccyx
posteriorly, and ischial tuberosities laterally. Muscles of the pelvic floor in this region are especially important in pregnancy and
obstetrics and in supporting the internal reproductive organs (see
section 10.3d and fig. 10.21).

The **mons**[18] **pubis** consists mainly of an anterior mound of
adipose tissue overlying the pubic symphysis, bearing most of the
pubic hair (see fig. A.3a in atlas A). The **labia majora**[19] (singular,
labium majus) are a pair of thick folds of skin and adipose tissue
inferior to the mons; the fissure between them is the *pudendal
cleft.* Pubic hair grows on the lateral surfaces of the labia majora
at puberty, but the medial surfaces remain hairless. Medial to
the labia majora are the much thinner, entirely hairless **labia
minora**[20] (singular, *labium minus*). The area enclosed by them,
called the **vestibule,**[21] contains the urinary and vaginal orifices.

The **clitoris**[22] (CLIT-er-is, cli-TOR-is) is structured like
the penis in many respects, but has no urinary role. Its function
is entirely sensory, serving as the primary center of sexual
stimulation. Unlike the penis, it is almost entirely internal, it
has no corpus spongiosum, and it doesn't enclose the urethra.
Essentially, it is a pair of corpora cavernosa enclosed in connective
tissue. Its head, the **glans,** is the only externally visible portion.

---

[16]*vulva* = covering
[17]*pudend* = shameful

[18]*mons* = mountain
[19]*labi* = lip; *major* = larger, greater
[20]*minor* = smaller, lesser
[21]*vestibule* = entryway
[22]origin uncertain; possibly from *kleis* = door key, or *klei* + *ein* = to close

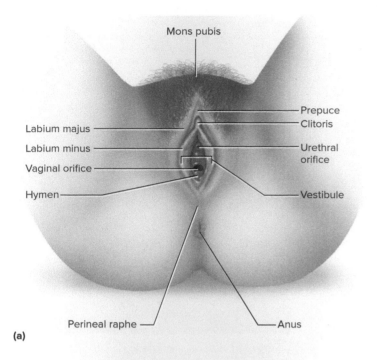

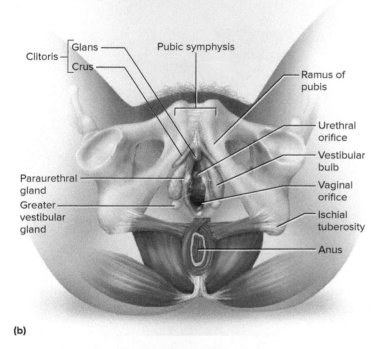

FIGURE 28.8 The Female Perineum. (a) Surface anatomy. (b) Subcutaneous structures. **APR**

❓ *The male prostate is homologous with what gland(s) of the female?*

It is partially covered by a hoodlike **prepuce** where the labia minora meet. The **body** passes internally, inferior to the pubic symphysis (see fig. 28.1). At its internal end, the corpora cavernosa diverge like a Y as a pair of **crura,** which, like those of the penis, attach the clitoris to each side of the pubic arch. The circulation and innervation of the clitoris are much like those of the penis (see section 27.5a).

Just deep to the labia majora, a pair of subcutaneous erectile tissues called the **vestibular bulbs** bracket the vagina like parentheses. On each side of the vagina is a pea-size **greater vestibular (Bartholin[23]) gland** with a short duct opening into the vestibule or lower vagina (fig. 28.8b). These glands are homologous to the bulbourethral glands of the male. They keep the vulva moist, and during sexual excitement they provide most of the lubrication for intercourse. The vestibule is also lubricated by a number of **lesser vestibular glands.** A pair of mucous **paraurethral glands** opens into the vestibule near the external urethral orifice. These are homologous to the male prostate and are also called the **female prostate** or, formerly, the Skene[24] glands. A discussion of the physiology of intercourse later in this chapter details the functions of these organs.

28.1c The Breasts and Mammary Glands

The **breast (fig. 28.9)** is a mound of tissue overlying the pectoralis major muscle. It enlarges at puberty and remains so for life, but most of this time it contains very little mammary gland. The **mammary gland** develops within the breast during pregnancy, remains active in the lactating breast, and atrophies when a woman ceases to nurse.

The breast has two principal regions: the conical to pendulous **body,** with the nipple at its apex, and an extension toward the armpit called the **axillary tail.** Lymphatics of the axillary tail are especially important as a route of breast cancer metastasis.

The nipple is surrounded by a circular zone, the **areola,** usually darker than the rest of the breast. Dermal blood capillaries and nerves come closer to the surface here than in the surrounding skin, accentuating the color and sensitivity of the areola. Pregnancy increases melanin deposition in the areola and nipple, making them a more visible "target" to the indistinct vision of a nursing infant. Sensory nerve fibers of the areola are important in triggering a *milk ejection reflex* when an infant nurses. The areola has sparse hairs and **areolar glands,** visible as small bumps on the surface. These glands are intermediate between sweat glands and mammary glands in their degree of development. When a woman is nursing, secretions of the areolar glands and sebaceous glands protect the areola and nipple from chapping and cracking. The dermis of the areola has smooth muscle fibers that contract in response to cold, touch, and sexual arousal, wrinkling the skin and erecting the nipple.

Internally, the nonlactating breast consists mostly of adipose and collagenous tissue (fig. 28.9b). Breast size is determined by the amount of adipose tissue and has no relationship to the amount of milk the mammary gland can produce. **Suspensory ligaments** attach the breast to the dermis of the overlying skin and to the fascia of the underlying muscle (pectoralis major). Although the nonlactating breast contains little glandular tissue, it does have a system of ducts branching through its fibrous stroma and converging on the nipple.

When the mammary gland develops during pregnancy, it exhibits 15 to 20 lobes arranged radially around the nipple, separated

---

[23]Caspar Bartholin (1655–1738), Danish anatomist
[24]Alexander Skene (1837–1900), American gynecologist

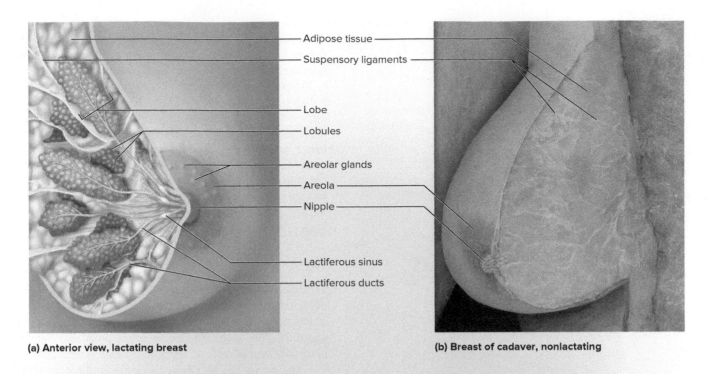

Adipose tissue

Suspensory ligaments

Lobe

Lobules

Areolar glands

Areola

Nipple

Lactiferous sinus

Lactiferous ducts

(a) Anterior view, lactating breast

(b) Breast of cadaver, nonlactating

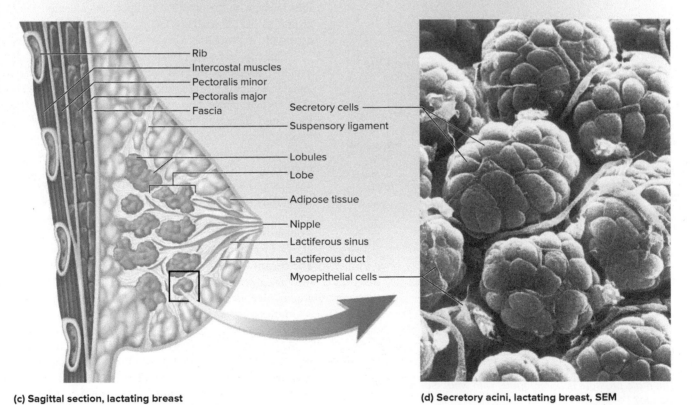

Rib

Intercostal muscles

Pectoralis minor

Pectoralis major

Fascia

Secretory cells

Suspensory ligament

Lobules

Lobe

Adipose tissue

Nipple

Lactiferous sinus

Lactiferous duct

Myoepithelial cells

(c) Sagittal section, lactating breast

(d) Secretory acini, lactating breast, SEM

FIGURE 28.9 The Breast. Parts (a), (c), and (d) depict the breast in a lactating state. Some of the features in parts (a) and (c) are absent from the nonlactating breast in part (b). The cluster of lobules boxed in part (c) would contain numerous microscopic acini like the ones in part (d). **APR**

b: The University of Toledo,/McGraw-Hill Education; d: Dr. Donald Fawcett/Science Source

What is the function of the myoepithelial cells in part (d)?

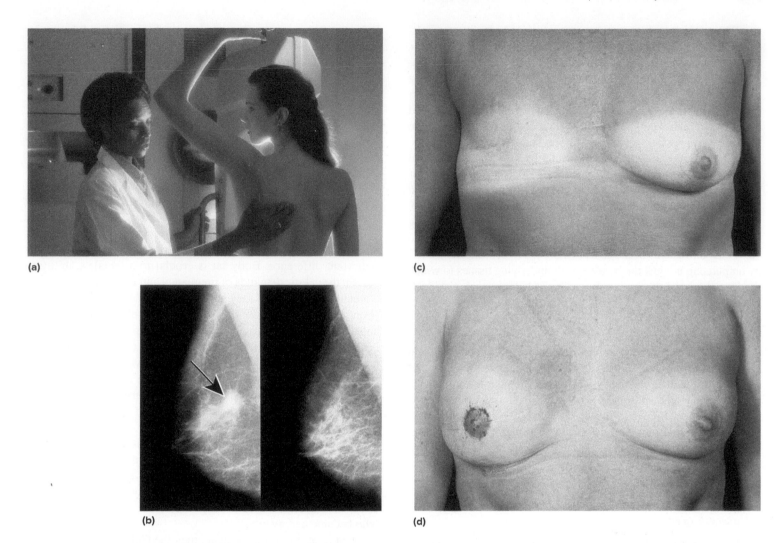

FIGURE 28.10 Breast Cancer Screening and Treatment. (a) Radiologic technologist assisting a patient in mammography. (b) Mammogram of a breast with a tumor visible at the arrow (left), compared with the appearance of normal fibrous connective tissue of the breast (right). (c) Patient following mastectomy of the right breast. (d) The same patient following surgical breast reconstruction. **APR**

a: Tony Stone Images/Getty Images; b: The Image Bank/Getty Images; c, d: Biophoto Associates/Science Source

❓ *What is the diagnostic benefit of compressing the breast for a mammogram?*

from each other by stroma (fig. 28.9a). Each lobe is drained by a **lactiferous**[25] **duct,** which dilates to form a **lactiferous sinus** opening onto the nipple. Distally, each duct branches repeatedly with the finest branches ending in sacs called acini. The acini are organized into grapelike clusters (lobules) within each lobe of the breast. Each acinus consists of a sac of conical secretory cells arranged around a central lumen (see fig. 5.30). Like an orange in a mesh bag, the acinus is surrounded by a network of contractile **myoepithelial cells** (fig. 28.9d). Their role in milk release and other aspects of the lactating breast are described later in this chapter.

Breast Cancer

Breast cancer **(fig. 28.10)** occurs in one out of every eight or nine American women and is the most common and deadly cancer of women worldwide. Breast tumors begin with cells of the mammary

ducts and may metastasize to other organs by way of the mammary and axillary lymphatics. Signs of breast cancer include a palpable lump (the tumor), puckering of the skin, changes in skin texture, and discharge from the nipple.

Two genes called *BRCA1* and *BRCA2* have been implicated in some breast cancers, as have some rarer genes that code for mechanisms of DNA repair, but most breast cancer is nonhereditary. Some breast tumors are stimulated by estrogen. Consequently, breast cancer is more common among women who begin menstruating early in life and who reach menopause relatively late—that is, women who have a long period of fertility and estrogen exposure. Its incidence is declining in the United States and many other western countries, but rising in Latin America, Russia, and East Asia owing to changes in diet, excessive alcohol and fat intake, obesity, smoking, exposure to carcinogenic chemicals, delayed childbearing, longer life expectancy, and denial—delaying medical consultation and treatment. Over 70% of cases, however, lack any identifiable risk factors.

[25]*lact* = milk; *fer* = to carry

The majority of tumors are discovered during breast self-examination (BSE), which should be a monthly routine for all women. Instructions for this are widely available on the Internet. *Mammograms* (breast X-rays), however, can detect tumors too small to be noticed by BSE. Although opinions vary, a schedule commonly recommended is to have a baseline mammogram at age 40 or 50 and then biennially through the mid-70s. Annual screening is deemed to produce too many false positive results and unnecessary biopsies.

Treatment of breast cancer is usually by *lumpectomy* (removal of the tumor only) or *simple mastectomy* (removal of the breast tissue only or breast tissue and some axillary lymph nodes). *Radical mastectomy,* invented in the late 1800s and rarely done since 1985, involved the removal of not only the breast but also the underlying muscle, fascia, and lymph nodes. The concept behind this was to "root out" all vestiges of the cancer (the word *radical* means "root") by amputating not just the breast but all underlying tissues to which the cancer might have spread. But this was before oncologists realized that cancer doesn't simply radiate out from the primary tumor, but spreads (metastasizes) through the lymphatic system or blood. By the time a radical mastectomy was performed, the breast cancer usually had already spread to far-distant parts of the body. Radical mastectomy terribly disfigured and disabled countless women, yet proved no more effective than simple mastectomy or lumpectomy.

Surgery is generally followed by radiation or chemotherapy, and estrogen-sensitive tumors may also be treated with an estrogen blocker such as tamoxifen. A natural-looking breast can often be reconstructed from skin, fat, and muscle from other parts of the body.

BEFORE YOU GO ON

Answer the following questions to test your understanding of the preceding section:

1. How do the site of female gamete production and mode of release from the gonad differ from those in the male?

2. How is the structure of the uterine tube mucosa related to its function?

3. Contrast the function of the endometrium with that of the myometrium.

4. List the subcutaneous erectile tissues and glands of the female perineum and state the function of each.

28.2 Puberty and Menopause

Expected Learning Outcomes

When you have completed this section, you should be able to

a. name the hormones that regulate female reproductive function, and state their roles;

b. describe the principal signs of puberty;

c. describe the hormonal changes of female climacteric and their effects; and

d. define and describe *menopause,* and distinguish menopause from climacteric.

Puberty and menopause are physiological transitions at the beginning and end of a female's reproductive years.

28.2a Puberty

Puberty begins at ages 8 to 10 for most well-nourished girls in affluent countries, but significantly later in many countries. Yet, a 1997 study of more than 17,000 girls in the United States showed 3% of black girls and 1% of white girls beginning puberty by age 3, and 27% and 7%, respectively, by age 7. The youngest mother known to history was Lina Medina of Peru, who began menstruating at 8 months of age, was impregnated at age 4, and gave birth at age 5, in 1939. You can find her story online.

Puberty is triggered by the same hypothalamic and pituitary hormones in girls as in boys (see section 27.3b), but with one important difference. Body fat is crucial to a female's ability to sustain the caloric demands of pregnancy and lactation, so girls and women don't ovulate if they have too little of it. A girl must attain about 17% body fat before she can begin to ovulate and menstruate, and adult women commonly cease if they drop below 22% fat. This is an evolutionary adaptation stemming from times when adequate nutrition was by no means a sure thing, serving to spare females from pregnancies that likely couldn't lead to successful birth and lactation. How does the brain know if fat reserves are adequate for reproduction? **Leptin,** the hormone secreted by fat cells, acts as an adiposity signal to the brain. If the leptin level is too low, the hypothalamus doesn't secrete **gonadotropin-releasing hormone (GnRH).** Puberty is therefore delayed in undernourished girls, unusually thin girls, and in other girls with low body fat due to such vigorous and habitual physical activity as gymnastics and ballet. Ovulation and menstruation may cease even in adult women who become underweight.

But if fat stores are adequate, then the GnRH level rises in late childhood and stimulates the anterior pituitary to secrete follicle stimulating hormone (FSH) and luteinizing hormone (LH). FSH, especially, stimulates development of the ovarian follicles, which, in turn, secrete estrogens, progesterone, inhibin, and a small amount of androgens. These hormone levels rise gradually from ages 8 to 12 and then more sharply in the early teens. The **estrogens**[26] are feminizing hormones with widespread effects on the body. They include *estradiol* (the most abundant), *estriol,* and *estrone.* Most of the visible changes at puberty result from estradiol and androgens.

The earliest noticeable sign of puberty in girls is **thelarche**[27] (theel-AR-kee), the onset of breast development. Estrogen, progesterone, and prolactin initially induce the formation of lobules and ducts in the breast. Duct development is completed under the influence of glucocorticoids and growth hormone, while adipose and fibrous tissue enlarge the breast. Breast development is complete around age 20, but they undergo minor changes in each menstrual cycle and major changes in pregnancy.

Thelarche is soon followed by **pubarche** (pyu-BAR-kee), the appearance of pubic and axillary hair, sebaceous glands, and axillary glands. Androgens from the ovaries and adrenal cortex stimulate

---

[26]*estro* = desire, frenzy; *gen* = to produce
[27]*thel* = breast, nipple; *arche* = beginning

pubarche as well as the libido (sex drive). Women secrete about 0.5 mg of androgens per day, compared with 6 to 8 mg/day in men.

Next comes **menarche**[28] (men-AR-kee), the first menstrual period. In Europe and America, the average age at menarche declined from age 16.5 in 1860 to age 12.5 today, probably due mostly to improved nutrition, although many other genetic, geographic, and ethnic variables enter into this.

Menarche doesn't necessarily signify fertility. A girl's first few menstrual cycles are typically *anovulatory* (no egg is ovulated). Most girls don't ovulate regularly until a year or more after they begin menstruating. This probably reflects the fact, detailed later in this chapter, that it takes about 290 days for ovarian follicles to mature and ovulate.

Estradiol stimulates many other changes of puberty. It causes the vaginal metaplasia described earlier. It stimulates growth of the ovaries and secondary sex organs. It stimulates growth hormone secretion and causes a rapid increase in height and widening of the pelvis. Estradiol is largely responsible for the feminine physique because it stimulates fat deposition in the mons pubis, labia majora, hips, thighs, buttocks, and breasts. It makes a girl's skin thicken, but the skin remains thinner, softer, and warmer than in males of corresponding age.

Progesterone[29] acts primarily on the uterus, preparing it for possible pregnancy in the second half of each menstrual cycle and playing roles in pregnancy discussed later. Estrogens and progesterone also regulate FSH and LH secretion through negative feedback inhibition of the anterior pituitary. **Inhibin** selectively regulates FSH secretion.

Thus, we see many hormonal similarities in males and females from puberty onward. The sexes differ less in the identity of the hormones present than in their relative amounts—high androgen levels and low estrogen levels in males and the opposite in females. Another difference is that these hormones are secreted more or less continually and simultaneously in males, whereas in females, secretion is distinctly cyclic and the hormones are secreted in sequence. This will be very apparent as you read about the ovarian and menstrual cycles later in this chapter.

28.2b Climacteric and Menopause

Women, like men, go through a midlife change in hormone secretion called the **climacteric.** In women, it is accompanied by **menopause,** the cessation of menstruation (see Deeper Insight 28.2).

A female is born with up to 2 million eggs in her ovaries, each in its own follicle. The older she gets, the fewer follicles remain. Climacteric begins not at any specific age, but when she has only about 1,000 follicles left. Even the remaining ones are less responsive to gonadotropins, so they secrete less estrogen and progesterone. Without these steroids, the uterus, vagina, and breasts atrophy. Intercourse may become uncomfortable, and vaginal infections more common, as the vagina becomes thinner, less distensible, and drier. The skin becomes thinner, cholesterol levels rise (increasing the risk of cardiovascular disease), and bone mass declines (increasing the risk of osteoporosis). Blood vessels constrict and dilate in response to shifting hormone balances, and the sudden dilation of cutaneous

arteries often causes **hot flashes**—a spreading sense of heat from the abdomen to the thorax, neck, and face, accompanied by sweating. Hot flashes may occur several times a day, sometimes accompanied by headaches resulting from the sudden vasodilation of arteries in the head. In some people, the changing hormonal profile also causes mood changes. Many physicians prescribe hormone replacement therapy (HRT)—low doses of estrogen and progesterone usually taken orally or by a skin patch—to relieve some of these symptoms. The risks and benefits of HRT are under debate.

▶▶▶ APPLY WHAT YOU KNOW

FSH and LH secretions rise at climacteric and these hormones attain high concentrations in the blood. Explain this using the preceding information and what you know about the pituitary–gonadal relationship.

Menopause is the cessation of menstrual cycles, usually occurring between the ages of 45 and 55. The average age has increased steadily in the last century and is now about 52. It is difficult to precisely establish the time of menopause because the menstrual periods can stop for several months and then begin again. Menopause is generally considered to have occurred when there has been no menstruation for a year or more.

BEFORE YOU GO ON

Answer the following questions to test your understanding of the preceding section:

5. Describe the similarities and differences between male and female puberty.

6. Describe the major changes that occur in female climacteric and the principal cause of these changes.

7. What is the difference between climacteric and menopause?

DEEPER INSIGHT 28.2

EVOLUTIONARY MEDICINE

The Evolution of Menopause

There has been considerable speculation about why women don't remain fertile to the end of their lives, as men do. Some theorists argue that menopause served a biological purpose for our prehistoric foremothers. Human offspring take a long time to rear. Beyond a certain point, the frailties of age make it unlikely that a woman could rear another infant to maturity or even survive the stress of pregnancy. She might do better in the long run to become infertile and finish rearing her last child, or help to rear her grandchildren, instead of having more. In this view, menopause was biologically advantageous for our ancestors—in other words, an evolutionary adaptation.

Others argue against this "grandmother hypothesis" on the grounds that Pleistocene (Ice Age) skeletons indicate that early hominids rarely lived past age 40. If this is true, menopause setting in at 45 to 55 years of age could have served little purpose. In this view, Pleistocene women may indeed have been fertile to the end of their lives; menopause now may be just an artifact of modern nutrition and medicine, which have made it possible for us to live much longer than our ancestors did.

---

[28]*men* = monthly; *arche* = beginning
[29]*pro* = favoring; *gest* = pregnancy; *sterone* = steroid hormone

28.3 Oogenesis and the Sexual Cycle APR

Expected Learning Outcomes

When you have completed this section, you should be able to

a. describe the process of egg production (oogenesis);

b. describe changes in the ovarian follicles (folliculogenesis) in relation to oogenesis;

c. describe the hormonal events that regulate the ovarian cycle;

d. describe how the uterus changes during the menstrual cycle; and

e. construct a chart of the phases of the monthly sexual cycle showing the hormonal, ovarian, and uterine events of each phase.

The reproductive lives of women are conspicuously cyclic. They include the **reproductive cycle,** which encompasses the sequence of events from fertilization to giving birth and returning to a state of fertility, and the **sexual cycle,** which encompasses the events that recur every month when pregnancy doesn't intervene. The sexual cycle, in turn, consists of two interrelated cycles controlled by shifting patterns of hormone secretion: the **ovarian cycle,** consisting of events in the ovaries, and the **menstrual cycle,** consisting of parallel changes in the uterus.

Before we delve into the familiar 28-day sexual cycle, let us look at the developmental stages that the eggs and their follicles go through. Then we can integrate that with the controlling hormones and the monthly rhythm of ovulation and menstruation.

28.3a Oogenesis

Egg production is called **oogenesis**[30] (OH-oh-JEN-eh-sis) **(fig. 28.11).** Like spermatogenesis, it produces a haploid gamete by means of meiosis. There are, however, numerous differences between the two. The most obvious, perhaps, is that males produce sperm continually at a rate of about 400 million/day, whereas oogenesis is a distinctly cyclic event that usually releases only one egg per month. Oogenesis is accompanied by cyclic changes in hormone secretion and in the histological structure of the ovaries and uterus; the uterine changes result in the monthly menstrual flow.

Oogenesis begins before a girl is born. The first germ cells arise, like those of the male, from the embryonic yolk sac. They migrate into the embryo and colonize the gonadal ridges in the first 5 to 6 weeks of development and then differentiate into **oogonia** (OH-oh-GO-nee-uh). Oogonia multiply until the fifth month, reach 6 to 7 million in number, then go into a state of arrested development until shortly before birth. At that time, they differentiate into **primary oocytes** and go as far as early meiosis I. All of them reach this stage by birth; no oogonia remain after that.

Any stage from the primary oocyte to the time of fertilization can be called an **egg,** or **ovum.**

Most primary oocytes undergo a process of degeneration called **atresia** (ah-TREE-zhee-uh) before a girl is born. As many as 2 million oocytes remain at the time of birth; 90% of those undergo atresia during childhood, and by puberty, only about 200,000 remain. This is the female's lifetime supply of gametes, but it's more than ample; even if she ovulated one egg every 28 days from the age of 14 to 50, she would ovulate only 480 eggs. All of the other oocytes undergo atresia between puberty and menopause.

Egg development resumes in adolescence. Each month for about 30 years, except during pregnancy, a cohort (developmental group) of about 2 dozen arrested follicles is recruited to resume development. (After 30 years of ovulation, the process becomes more irregular, and at menopause, it ceases.) The 28-day menstrual cycle creates a common misconception that eggs and ovarian follicles take 28 days to develop from one ovulation to the next. In reality, though, from the time a cohort of follicles is activated, it takes about 290 days for one of them to fully mature and ovulate. The reason for the 28-day cycle is that one cohort follows behind another, in overlapping waves, with one cohort reaching maturity each month.

Meiosis I is completed on the day of ovulation and produces two daughter cells—a large one called the **secondary oocyte** and a much smaller one called the **first polar body.** The polar body may pointlessly complete meiosis II, but ultimately it or its daughter cells degenerate. It is merely a means of discarding the extra haploid set of chromosomes. The secondary oocyte proceeds as far as metaphase II, then stops. If it isn't fertilized, it dies and never finishes meiosis. If fertilized, it completes meiosis II and casts off a second polar body, which disposes of one chromatid from each chromosome. The chromosomes of the large remaining egg then unite with those of the sperm. Further development of the fertilized egg is discussed in the next chapter.

Note the contrast between spermatogenesis and oogenesis. In spermatogenesis, a primary spermatocyte gives rise to four equal-size sperm. But in oogenesis, a primary oocyte gives rise to only one mature egg; the other three daughter cells (at most) are tiny polar bodies that die. In oogenesis it is important to produce an egg with as much cytoplasm as possible, because if fertilized it must divide repeatedly and produce numerous daughter cells. Splitting each oocyte into four equal but small parts would run counter to this purpose of providing enough "raw material" for early embryonic development.

28.3b Folliculogenesis

As an egg undergoes oogenesis, the follicle around it undergoes **folliculogenesis,** passing through the following stages.

1. **Primordial follicles.** A primordial follicle is about 40 μm in diameter. It consists of a primary oocyte in early meiosis, surrounded by a single layer of squamous follicular cells and a basement membrane separating the follicle from the surrounding stroma of the ovary **(fig. 28.12a).** Primordial follicles are concentrated in the ovarian cortex, close to the capsule. All of them form in the sixth through ninth month of gestation, but they persist into adulthood. In the adult

---

[30]*oo* = egg; *genesis* = production

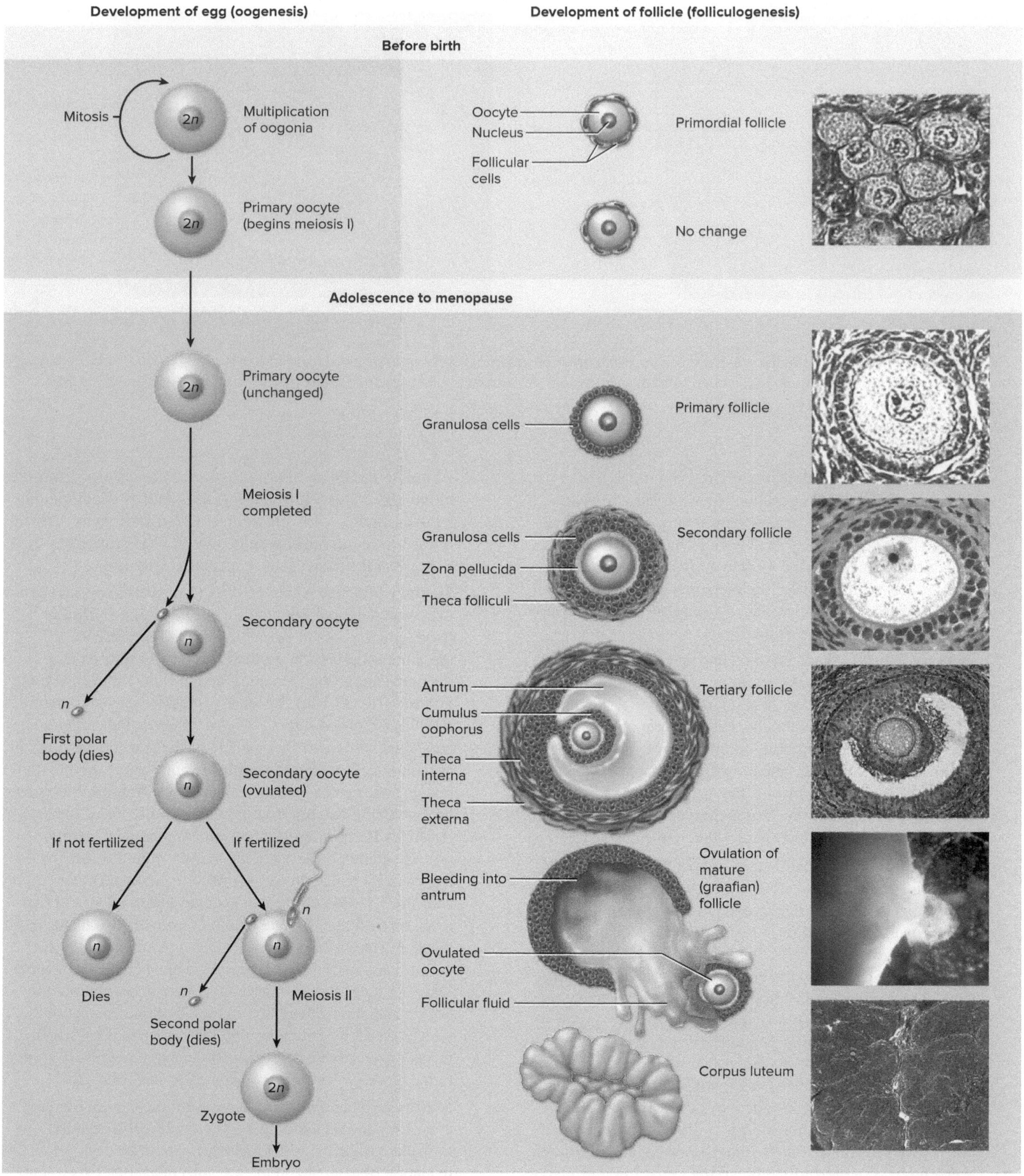

Development of egg (oogenesis)   **Development of follicle (folliculogenesis)**

Before birth

Mitosis — 2n — Multiplication of oogonia

2n — Primary oocyte (begins meiosis I)

Oocyte / Nucleus / Follicular cells — Primordial follicle

No change

Adolescence to menopause

2n — Primary oocyte (unchanged)

Granulosa cells — Primary follicle

Meiosis I completed

n — Secondary oocyte

Granulosa cells / Zona pellucida / Theca folliculi — Secondary follicle

n — First polar body (dies)

n — Secondary oocyte (ovulated)

Antrum / Cumulus oophorus / Theca interna / Theca externa — Tertiary follicle

If not fertilized   If fertilized

n — Dies

n — n

n — Second polar body (dies)

Meiosis II

Bleeding into antrum — Ovulation of mature (graafian) follicle

Ovulated oocyte / Follicular fluid

2n — Zygote

Corpus luteum

Embryo

FIGURE 28.11 Oogenesis (Left) and Corresponding Development of the Follicle (Right). APR

(1, 2): Ed Reschke/Getty Images; (3): Alvin Telser/McGraw-Hill Education; (4): Ed Reschke/Getty Images; (5): Petit Format/Science Source; (6): Alvin Telser/McGraw-Hill Education

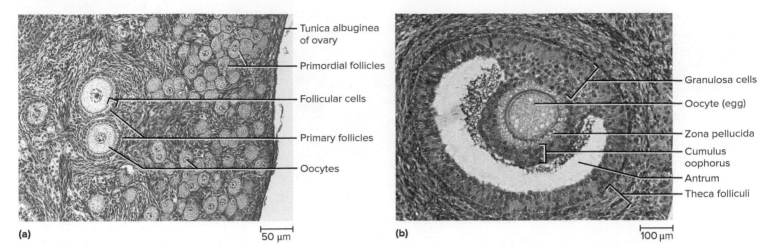

FIGURE 28.12 Ovarian Follicles. (a) Note the very thin layer of squamous cells around the oocyte in a primordial follicle, and the single layer of cuboidal cells in a primary follicle. (b) A mature (graafian) follicle. Just before ovulation, this follicle will grow to as much as 25 to 30 mm in diameter. **APR**

a: Ed Reschke; b: Ed Reschke/Getty Images

ovary, 90% to 95% of the follicles are primordial. Those that survive childhood atresia must wait at least 13 years—and some as long as 50 years—before they are reactivated, resume their development, and have a chance to ovulate. **Recruitment (primordial follicle activation)** awakens about 2 dozen primordial follicles each month to begin a 290-day march to maturity; usually, only one of these eventually ovulates and the rest die.

2. **Primary follicles.** About 140 days into the cycle, the recruited primordial follicles have become primary follicles about 100 μm in diameter. These have a larger oocyte and their follicular cells are now cuboidal, but still form only a single layer. Development from primordial to primary follicle is controlled by local **paracrine** growth factors, not by gonadotropins (FSH or LH), for which they still have no receptors. The follicular cells, however, soon develop FSH receptors and the follicle depends on FSH to progress to the next stage.

3. **Secondary follicles.** These appear about 170 days into the cycle, still about six menstrual cycles before ovulation. They are distinguished by follicular cells that have multiplied and piled atop each other to form two or more layers; they are now called **granulosa cells.** Secondary follicles are about 200 μm in diameter and the oocyte alone is about 120 μm—five times its original size in preparation for development of the early embryo. The oocyte is surrounded by a layer of glycoprotein gel, the **zona pellucida.**[31]

The follicle is now enclosed in a tough husk called the **theca**[32] **folliculi** (THEE-ca fol-IC-you-lye). The theca is richly supplied with blood vessels, which deliver nutrients, hormones, and cholesterol. It divides into an outer *theca externa* of innervated smooth muscle and an inner *theca interna* of steroid-synthesizing cells. LH and insulin

stimulate the theca interna to absorb cholesterol from the blood and convert it to androgens—androstenedione and a lesser amount of testosterone. These androgens diffuse inward to the granulosa cells, where FSH stimulates them to convert it to estrogens, especially estradiol.

4. **Tertiary follicles.** About 60 days (2 menstrual cycles) before ovulation, the granulosa cells begin secreting **follicular fluid,** which pools in the follicle wall. The presence of these pools defines the tertiary follicle. As they enlarge, the pools merge and become a single fluid-filled cavity, the **antrum (fig. 28.12b).** Because of this, tertiary and mature follicles are called *antral follicles,* whereas the earlier stages are called *preantral.* On one side of the antrum, a mound of granulosa cells called the **cumulus oophorus**[33] covers the oocyte and secures it to the follicle wall. Antral follicles are big enough to be seen even in ultrasound scans of the ovaries. This is one approach to evaluating female fertility.

The innermost layer of cells of the cumulus, surrounding the zona pellucida and oocyte, is called the **corona radiata.**[34] These cells and the oocyte sprout microvilli that reach out and interdigitate like the fingers of two hands laced together. Gap junctions form between them, enabling the cells to pass nutrients, wastes, and chemical signals to each other. Some granulosa microvilli penetrate deeply into the oocyte and almost reach its nucleus. Nothing can get to the oocyte except by going through the corona radiata, which forms a protective barrier around the egg functionally similar to the blood–testis barrier described in section 27.2b.

5. **Mature follicles.** Normally only one follicle in each month's cohort becomes a mature follicle (fig. 28.12b), destined to ovulate while the rest degenerate. About 20 days before ovulation (that is, late in the previous menstrual cycle), one

---

[31]*zona* = zone; *pellucid* = clear, transparent
[32]*theca* = box, case

[33]*cumulus* = little mound; *oo* = egg; *phor* = to carry
[34]*corona* = crown; *radiata* = radiating

follicle in the cohort is selected to be the dominant follicle, the one destined to ovulate. It captures and sequesters FSH, while other follicles fail to accumulate FSH and their development slows down. By the time a woman's menstrual period begins—day 1 of the cycle in which this follicle will ovulate—the dominant follicle is about 5 mm in diameter and 2 weeks away from ovulation. By 5 days before ovulation, it grows to 20 mm in diameter and is considered a **preovulatory (graafian[35]) follicle;** it attains an astonishing size up to 30 mm by the time of ovulation, about as wide as the whole ovary is long. The preovulatory follicle bulges from the ovary like a huge fluid-filled blister. As ovulation approaches, the cumulus oophorus swells and its attachment to the follicle wall constricts until the oocyte is attached to the wall by only a narrow stalk. In the last day or so, the oocyte and cumulus break away and float freely in the antrum, ready for that momentous event in its life—ovulation.

28.3c The Sexual Cycle

We can now correlate these changes in the egg cell and follicle with the rhythms of the ovaries and uterus—the sexual cycle. The cycle averages 28 days in length, so we will use that as the basis for the timetable described in the following discussion. It commonly varies from 20 to 45 days, however, so be aware that the timetable given in this discussion may differ from person to person and month to month. As you study this cycle, bear in mind that it is regulated by the **hypothalamo–pituitary–ovarian axis:** Hormones of the hypothalamus regulate the pituitary gland; pituitary hormones regulate the ovaries; and the ovaries, in turn, secrete hormones that regulate the uterus. That is, the basic hierarchy of control can be represented: hypothalamus → pituitary → ovaries → uterus. However, the ovaries also exert positive and negative feedback controls over the hypothalamus and pituitary, so these hormonal relationships are more like a communication loop than a straight-line chain of command.

Let us start with a brief preview of the sexual cycle as a whole **(fig. 28.13).** It begins with a 2-week *follicular phase.* The first 3 to 5 days of this are marked by menstruation, the vaginal discharge of blood and endometrial tissue. The uterus then replaces the lost tissue by mitosis. During this endometrial reconstruction, a cohort of tertiary follicles grows until the dominant follicle ovulates around day 14. After ovulation, the remainder of that follicle becomes a body called the *corpus luteum.* Over the next 2 weeks, called the *luteal phase,* the corpus luteum stimulates endometrial secretion, making the endometrium thicken still more, up to about day 26. If pregnancy doesn't occur, the endometrium breaks down again in the last 2 days. As loose tissue and blood accumulate, menstruation begins and the cycle starts over.

The Ovarian Cycle

We'll now see, in three principal steps, what happens in the ovaries and in their relationship to the hypothalamus and pituitary gland. This is the ovarian cycle, depicted in the top half of figure 28.13.

[35]Reijnier de Graaf (1641–73), Dutch physiologist and histologist

1. **Follicular phase.** The follicular phase of the cycle extends from the beginning of menstruation until ovulation—that is, from day 1 to day 14 in an average cycle. The portion from the *end* of menstruation until ovulation is also called the *preovulatory phase.* The follicular phase is the most variable part of the cycle, so unfortunately for family planning or pregnancy avoidance, it is seldom possible to reliably predict the date of ovulation.

   During the follicular phase, FSH stimulates continued growth of all follicles in the cohort, but of the dominant follicle above all. FSH stimulates the granulosa cells of the antral follicles to secrete estradiol. In response to estradiol, the dominant follicle up-regulates its receptors for FSH, LH, and estradiol itself, thereby becoming increasingly sensitive to these hormones. At the same time, estradiol inhibits the secretion of gonadotropin-releasing hormone (GnRH) by the hypothalamus. The anterior pituitary gland secretes less and less FSH, but an increasing amount of LH. Most antral follicles suffer from the reduced FSH level and degenerate (undergo atresia). The dominant follicle, however, has the richest blood supply and the greatest density of FSH receptors, so it becomes the mature, preovulatory follicle. The ovary, at this stage, also exhibits follicles in many other stages, belonging to other cohorts trailing behind the lead cohort like freshmen to juniors trailing behind the senior class.

   Dramatic changes occur in the last day or so preceding ovulation. Estradiol from the ovary stimulates the hypothalamus and anterior pituitary **(fig. 28.14).** Responding to GnRH from the hypothalamus and to the estradiol directly, the anterior pituitary produces a surge of LH and a lesser spike in FSH (see the midpoint of fig. 28.13a). LH induces several momentous events. The primary oocyte completes meiosis I, producing a haploid secondary oocyte and the first polar body. Follicular fluid builds rapidly; the follicle swells to as much as 25 or 30 mm in diameter, contains up to 7 mL of fluid, and bulges from the ovary like a blister. Macrophages and leukocytes are attracted to the area and secrete enzymes that weaken the follicular wall and adjacent ovarian tissue. A nipplelike **stigma** appears on the ovarian surface over the follicle. With mounting internal pressure and a weakening wall, the mature follicle approaches rupture.

   Meanwhile, the uterine tube prepares to catch the oocyte when it emerges. It swells with edema; its fimbriae envelop and caress the ovary in synchrony with the woman's heartbeat; and its cilia create a gentle current in the nearby peritoneal fluid.

2. **Ovulation.** Ovulation itself takes only 2 or 3 min. The stigma seeps follicular fluid for 1 or 2 min., and then the follicle bursts. The remaining fluid oozes out, carrying the oocyte and cumulus oophorus **(fig. 28.15).** These are normally swept up by the ciliary current and taken into the uterine tube, although many oocytes fall into the pelvic cavity and die.

3. **Luteal phase.** Days 15 to 28, from just after ovulation to the onset of menstruation, are called the **luteal (postovulatory) phase.** Assuming pregnancy doesn't occur, the major events of this phase are as follows.

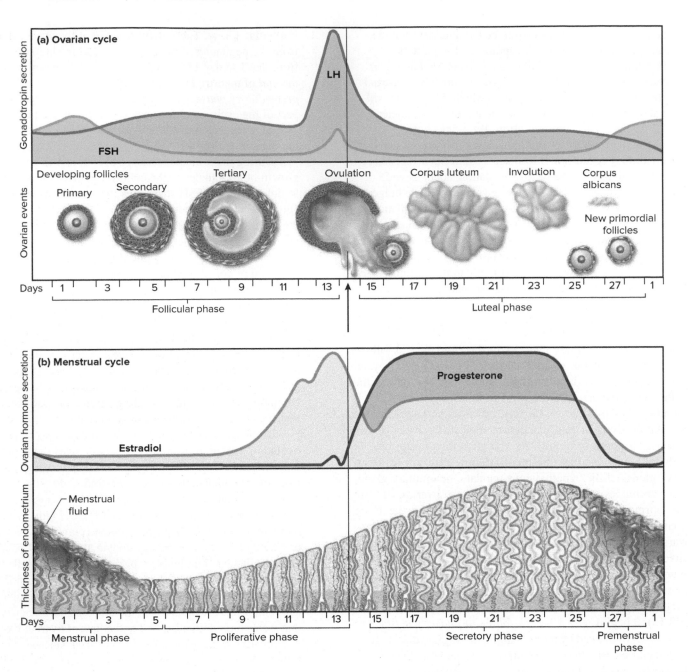

FIGURE 28.13 The Female Sexual Cycle. (a) The ovarian cycle (events in the ovary). (b) The menstrual cycle (events in the uterus). The two hormone levels in part (a) are drawn to the same scale, but those in part (b) are not. The peak progesterone concentration is about 17 times as high as the peak estradiol concentration. **APR**

When the follicle ruptures, it collapses and bleeds into the antrum. As the clotted blood is slowly absorbed, granulosa and theca interna cells multiply and fill the antrum, and a dense bed of blood capillaries grows amid them. The ovulated follicle has now become a structure called the **corpus luteum,**[36] named for a yellow lipid that accumulates in the theca interna cells. These cells are now called **lutein cells.** The transformation from ruptured follicle to corpus luteum is regulated by LH; hence, LH is also called *luteotropic hormone.*

LH stimulates the corpus luteum to continue growing and to secrete rising levels of estradiol and progesterone. There is a 10-fold increase in progesterone level (fig. 28.14), which has a crucial role in preparing the uterus for the possibility of pregnancy. Notwithstanding its luteinizing role, however, LH secretion declines steadily over the rest of the cycle, as does FSH. This is because the high levels of estradiol and progesterone, along with inhibin from the corpus luteum, have a negative feedback effect on the pituitary. (This is the basis for hormonal birth control; see Deeper Insight 28.5.)

If pregnancy doesn't occur, the corpus luteum begins a process of **involution,** or shrinkage, beginning around

[36]*corpus* = body; *lute* = yellow

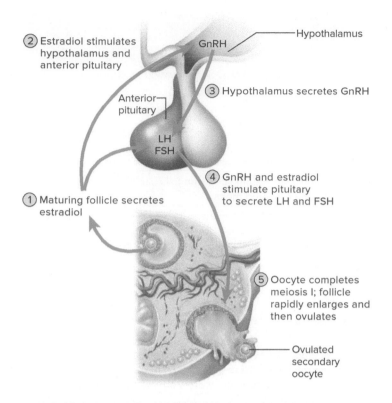

FIGURE 28.14 Hormonal Control of Ovulation.

① Maturing follicle secretes estradiol

② Estradiol stimulates hypothalamus and anterior pituitary

③ Hypothalamus secretes GnRH

④ GnRH and estradiol stimulate pituitary to secrete LH and FSH

⑤ Oocyte completes meiosis I; follicle rapidly enlarges and then ovulates

Hypothalamus

GnRH

Anterior pituitary

LH FSH

Ovulated secondary oocyte

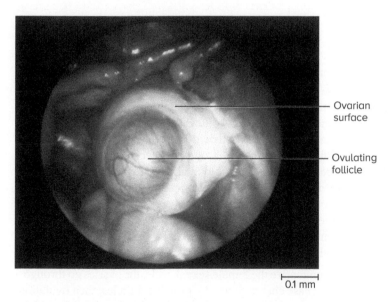

Ovarian surface

Ovulating follicle

0.1 mm

FIGURE 28.15 Endoscopic Photo of Human Ovulation.
Dr Patrice Langlois/CNRI/Science Source

day 22 (8 days after ovulation). By day 26, involution is complete and the corpus luteum has become an inactive bit of scar tissue called the **corpus albicans.**[37] With the waning of ovarian steroid secretion, the pituitary is no longer inhibited and FSH levels begin to rise again, stimulating a new cohort of follicles.

[37]*corpus* = body; *alb* = white

All of these events repeat themselves every month, but bear in mind that the follicles engaged in each monthly cycle began their development prenatally, as much as 50 years earlier, then lay dormant through childhood; the oocyte that ovulates each month began ripening 290 days earlier, not in the cycle when it ovulates. Ovulation normally occurs in only one ovary per cycle, and the ovaries usually alternate from month to month. **Table 28.1** summarizes the main events of the ovarian cycle and correlates them with events of the menstrual cycle, which we examine next.

The Menstrual Cycle

The menstrual cycle runs concurrently with the ovarian cycle. It consists of a buildup of the endometrium through most of the sexual cycle, followed by its breakdown and vaginal discharge. It is divided into a *proliferative phase, secretory phase, premenstrual phase,* and *menstrual phase* (see fig. 28.13b). The menstrual phase averages 5 days long, and the first day of noticeable vaginal discharge is defined as day 1 of the sexual cycle. But even though it begins our artificial timetable for the cycle, menstruation is best understood after you become acquainted with the buildup of endometrial tissue that precedes it. Thus, we begin our survey of the cycle with the proliferative phase.

1. **Proliferative phase.** The functional layer of endometrial tissue lost in the last menstruation is rebuilt during the proliferative phase. At the end of menstruation, around day 5, the endometrium is about 0.5 mm thick and consists only of the basal layer. But as a new cohort of follicles develops, they secrete more and more estrogen. Estrogen stimulates mitosis in the basal layer and the prolific regrowth of blood vessels, thus regenerating the functional layer **(fig. 28.16a).** By day 14, the endometrium is 2 to 3 mm thick. Estrogen also stimulates endometrial cells to produce progesterone receptors, priming them for the progesterone-dominated secretory phase to follow.

[38]*mittel* = in the middle; *schmerz* = pain

TABLE 28.1	Phases of the Ovarian Cycle	
Days	Phase	Major Features
1–14	**Follicular Phase**	Development of ovarian follicles and secretion primarily of estradiol. Coincides with menstrual and proliferative phases of the menstrual cycle.
	Primordial follicle	Formed prenatally and many persist into adulthood. Consists of an oocyte surrounded by a single layer of squamous follicular cells.
	Primary follicle	Consists of an oocyte surrounded by one layer of cuboidal follicular cells.
	Secondary follicle	Follicular cells stratify, become granulosa cells, and secrete a zona pellucida. Theca folliculi forms around follicle.
	Tertiary follicle	Develops from a secondary follicle in each cycle. Forms an antrum filled with follicular fluid and exhibits a cumulus oophorus, corona radiata, zona pellucida, and bilayered theca.
	Dominant follicle	The tertiary follicle that is destined to ovulate. Present by the end of the menstrual phase. Hormonally dominates the rest of the cycle, while other follicles in the cohort undergo atresia. Secretes mainly estradiol. Coincides with the proliferative phase of the menstrual cycle, in which the uterine endometrium thickens by mitosis.
	Mature follicle	The dominant follicle just prior to ovulation. Attains a diameter of 20 to 30 mm and builds to high internal fluid pressure as adjacent ovarian wall weakens.
14	**Ovulation**	Rupture of mature follicle and release of oocyte.
15–28	**Luteal (Postovulatory) Phase**	Dominated by corpus luteum. Coincides with secretory and premenstrual phases of the menstrual cycle.
	Corpus luteum	Develops from ovulated follicle by proliferation of granulosa and theca interna cells. Progesterone stimulates thickening of endometrium by secretion (secretory phase of the menstrual cycle). Begins to involute by day 22 in the absence of pregnancy; involution complete by day 26.
	Corpus albicans	Scar tissue left by involution of corpus luteum; not hormonally active. In the absence of progesterone, endometrium exhibits ischemia, necrosis, and sloughing of tissue. Necrotic endometrial tissue mixes with blood and forms menstrual fluid.

2. **Secretory phase.** The endometrium thickens still more during the **secretory phase,** but as a result of secretion and fluid accumulation rather than mitosis. This phase extends from day 15 (after ovulation) to day 26 of a typical cycle. After ovulation, the corpus luteum secretes mainly progesterone. This hormone stimulates the endometrial glands to secrete glycogen. The glands grow wider, longer, and more coiled, and the lamina propria swells with tissue fluid **(fig. 28.16b).** By the end of this phase, the endometrium is 5 to 6 mm thick—a soft, wet, nutritious bed available for embryonic development in the event of pregnancy.

3. **Premenstrual phase.** The last 2 days or so of the cycle are the **premenstrual phase,** a period of endometrial degeneration. As we have already seen, when there is no pregnancy, the corpus luteum atrophies and the progesterone level falls sharply. The drop in progesterone triggers spasmodic contractions of the spiral arteries of the endometrium, causing endometrial ischemia (interrupted blood flow). The premenstrual phase is therefore also called the **ischemic phase** (iss-KEE-mic). The lack of blood flow brings on death of endometrial tissue in the functional layer. Arterial spasms in the deeper myometrium are responsible for menstrual cramps, as any muscle deprived of blood flow hurts, and the uterus is mostly muscle. As the endometrial glands, stroma, and blood vessels degenerate, pools of blood accumulate in the functional layer. Necrotic endometrium falls away from the uterine wall, mixes with blood and

serous fluid in the lumen, and forms the **menstrual fluid (fig. 28.16c).**

4. **Menstrual phase.** When enough menstrual fluid accumulates in the uterus, it begins to be discharged from the vagina for a period called the **menstrual phase (menses).** The first day of discharge marks day 1 of a new cycle. The average woman expels about 40 mL of blood and 35 mL of serous fluid over a 5-day period. Menstrual fluid contains fibrinolysin, so it doesn't clot. The vaginal discharge of clotted blood may indicate uterine pathology rather than normal menstruation. Menstruation sheds the functional layer of endometrium, leaving once again only the basal layer.

To summarize the female sexual cycle, the ovaries go through a follicular phase characterized by growing follicles, then ovulation, and then a postovulatory (mostly luteal) phase dominated by the corpus luteum. The uterus, in the meantime, goes through a menstrual phase in which it discharges its functional layer; then a proliferative phase in which it replaces that tissue by mitosis; then a secretory phase in which the endometrium thickens by the accumulation of secretions; and finally, a premenstrual (ischemic) phase in which the functional layer breaks down again. The first half of the cycle is governed largely by follicle-stimulating hormone (FSH) from the pituitary gland and estrogen from the ovaries. Ovulation is triggered by luteinizing hormone (LH) from the pituitary, and the second half of the cycle is governed mainly by LH and progesterone, the latter secreted by the corpus luteum of the ovary.

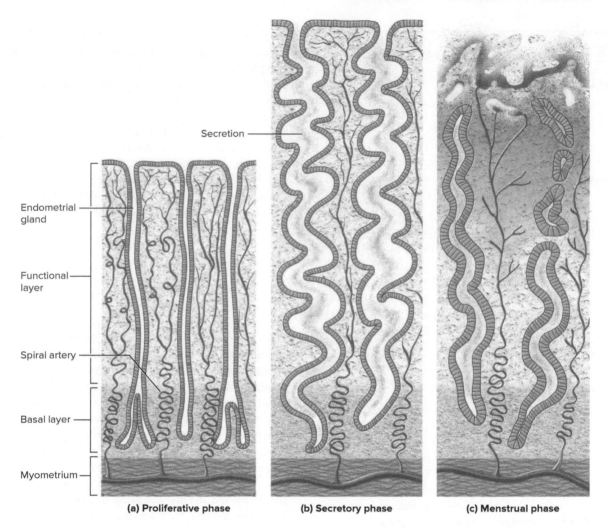

Secretion

Endometrial
gland

Functional
layer

Spiral artery

Basal layer

Myometrium

(a) Proliferative phase   **(b) Secretory phase**   **(c) Menstrual phase**

FIGURE 28.16 Endometrial Changes Through the Menstrual Cycle. (a) Late proliferative phase. The endometrium is 2 to 3 mm thick and has relatively straight, narrow endometrial glands. Spiral arteries penetrate upward between the endometrial glands. (b) Secretory phase. The endometrium has thickened to 5 to 6 mm by accumulating glycogen and mucus. The endometrial glands are much wider and more distinctly coiled, showing a zigzag or "sawtooth" appearance in histological sections. (c) Menstrual phase. Ischemic tissue has begun to die and fall away from the uterine wall, with bleeding from broken blood vessels and pooling of blood in the tissue and uterine lumen.

BEFORE YOU GO ON

Answer the following questions to test your understanding of the preceding section:

8. Name the sequence of cell types in oogenesis and identify the ways in which oogenesis differs from spermatogenesis.

9. Distinguish between primordial, primary, secondary, and tertiary follicles. Describe the major structures of a mature follicle.

10. Describe what happens in the ovary during the follicular and postovulatory phases.

11. Describe what happens in the uterus during the menstrual, proliferative, secretory, and premenstrual phases.

12. Describe the effects of FSH and LH on the ovary.

13. Describe the effects of estrogen and progesterone on the uterus, hypothalamus, and anterior pituitary.

 DEEPER INSIGHT 28.4

CLINICAL APPLICATION

Endometriosis

Any growth of endometrium in a site other than the uterus is called *endometriosis*. Endometrial tissue may lodge and grow in the uterine tubes, surface of the ovaries, urinary bladder, vagina, pelvic cavity, peritoneum, small or large intestine, or even as far away as the lungs and pleural cavity. Endometrium in these ectopic locations acts the same as in the uterus, thickening with each premenstrual phase and being shed in synchrony with menstruation. The shed tissue has nowhere to go, and causes irritation and formation of scar tissue and adhesions in the body cavities.

Endometriosis affects 6% to 10% of women, often causing pelvic pain; dysmenorrhea (painful menstruation); pain associated with intercourse, urination, or defecation; abnormal vaginal bleeding; and sometimes infertility. The most widely accepted theory of endometriosis is *retrograde menstruation*—menstrual fluid flowing backward and exiting through the uterine tube instead of the vagina. Management options include hormone therapy and surgery; in severe cases, hysterectomy may be required as a last resort. No cure is known at present.

28.4   Female Sexual Response

Expected Learning Outcomes

When you have completed this section, you should be able to

a. describe the female sexual response at each phase of intercourse; and

b. compare and contrast the female and male sexual responses.

Female sexual response, the physiological changes that occur during intercourse, may be viewed in terms of the four phases identified by Masters and Johnson and discussed in section 27.5: excitement, plateau, orgasm, and resolution **(fig. 28.17).** The neurological and vascular controls of the female response are essentially the same as in the male and need not be repeated here. The emphasis here is on ways the female response differs from that of the male.

28.4a   Excitement and Plateau

Excitement is marked by myotonia; vasocongestion; and increased heart rate, blood pressure, and respiratory rate. Although vasocongestion works by the same mechanism in both sexes, its effects are quite different in females. The labia minora become congested and often protrude beyond the labia majora. The labia majora redden and enlarge, then flatten and spread away from the vaginal orifice. The lower one-third of the vagina constricts to form a narrow passage called the **orgasmic platform,** owing partly to vasocongestion of the vestibular bulbs that bracket the vaginal orifice (see fig. 28.8b). The narrower canal and the vaginal rugae (friction ridges) enhance stimulation and help induce orgasm in both partners. The upper end of the vagina, in contrast, dilates and becomes cavernous.

Increased blood flow in the vaginal wall turns it purple and produces a serous fluid, the **vaginal transudate,** that seeps through the wall into the canal. Along with secretions of the greater vestibular glands, this moistens the vestibule and provides lubrication.

The uterus, which normally tilts forward over the urinary bladder, stands more erect during excitement and the cervix withdraws from the vagina. In plateau, the uterus is nearly vertical and extends into the greater pelvis. This is called the **tenting effect.**

Although the vagina is the female copulatory organ, the clitoris is more comparable to the penis in structure, physiology, and importance as the primary focus of sexual stimulation. It has a high concentration of sensory nerve endings, which, by contrast, are relatively scanty in the vagina. Recall that the penis and clitoris are homologous structures. Both have a pair of corpora cavernosa with *deep arteries* and become engorged by the same mechanism. The glans and shaft of the clitoris swell to two or three times their unstimulated size, but since the clitoris cannot swing upward away from the body like the penis, it tends to withdraw beneath the prepuce. Thrusting of the penis in the vagina tugs on the labia minora and, by extension, pulls on the prepuce and stimulates the clitoris. The clitoris may also be stimulated by pressure between the pubic symphyses of the partners.

The breasts also become congested and swollen during the excitement phase, and the nipples become erect. Stimulation of the breasts also enhances sexual arousal.

28.4b   Orgasm and Resolution

Late in plateau, many women experience involuntary pelvic thrusting, followed by 1 to 2 seconds of "suspension" or "stillness" preceding orgasm. Orgasm is commonly described as an intense sensation spreading from the clitoris through the pelvis, sometimes with pelvic throbbing and a spreading sense of warmth. The orgasmic platform gives three to five strong contractions about 0.8 second apart, while the cervix plunges spasmodically into the vagina and pool of semen, should this be present. The uterus exhibits peristaltic waves of contraction, which may help to draw semen from the vagina. The anal and urethral sphincters constrict, and the paraurethral glands, homologous to the prostate, sometimes expel fluid similar to prostatic fluid. Tachycardia and hyperventilation occur; the breasts enlarge still more and the areolae often become engorged; and in many women, a reddish, rashlike flush appears on the lower abdomen, chest, neck, and face.

During resolution, the uterus drops forward to its resting position. The orgasmic platform quickly relaxes, while the inner end of the vagina returns more slowly to its normal dimensions. The flush disappears quickly and the areolae and nipples undergo rapid detumescence (loss of vascular congestion), but it may take 5 to 10 minutes for the breasts to return to their normal size. In many women (and men), there is a postorgasmic outbreak of perspiration. Unlike men, women do not have a refractory period and may quickly experience additional orgasms.

BEFORE YOU GO ON

Answer the following questions to test your understanding of the preceding section:

14. What are the female sources of lubrication in coitus?

15. What female tissues and organs become vasocongested?

16. Describe the actions of the uterus throughout the sexual response cycle.

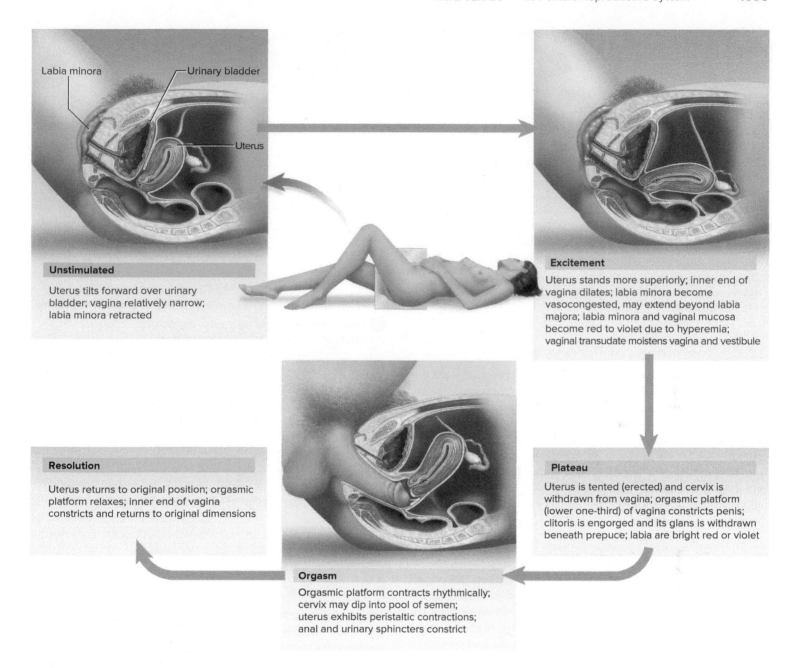

FIGURE 28.17 Stages of the Female Sexual Response. Anatomy is shown in the supine position.

28.5 Pregnancy and Childbirth

Expected Learning Outcomes

When you have completed this section, you should be able to

a. list the major hormones that regulate pregnancy and explain their roles;

b. describe a woman's bodily adaptations to pregnancy;

c. identify the physical and chemical stimuli that increase uterine contractility in late pregnancy;

d. describe the mechanism of labor contractions;

e. name and describe the three stages of labor; and

f. describe the physiological changes that occur in a woman during the weeks following childbirth.

This section treats pregnancy from the maternal standpoint—that is, adjustments of the woman's body to pregnancy and the mechanism of childbirth. Development of the fetus is described in the next chapter.

Gestation (pregnancy) lasts an average of 266 days from conception to childbirth, but the gestational calendar is usually measured from the first day of the woman's last menstrual period (LMP). Thus, the birth is predicted to occur 280 days (40 weeks) from the LMP. The duration of pregnancy, called its *term,* is commonly described in 3-month intervals called **trimesters.**

28.5a Prenatal Development

A few fundamental facts of fetal development must be introduced as a foundation for understanding maternal physiology. All the products of conception—the embryo or fetus as well as the placenta and membranes associated with it—are collectively called the **conceptus.** The developing individual is a hollow ball called a *blastocyst* for much of the first 2 weeks, an *embryo* from day 16 through week 8, and a *fetus* from the beginning of week 9 until birth. The fetus is attached by way of an *umbilical cord* to a disc-shaped *placenta* on the uterine wall. The placenta provides fetal nutrition and waste disposal, and secretes hormones that regulate pregnancy, mammary development, and fetal development. For the first 4 weeks after birth, the infant is called a *neonate.*[39]

28.5b Hormones of Pregnancy

The hormones with the strongest influences on pregnancy are estrogens, progesterone, human chorionic gonadotropin, and human chorionic somatomammotropin. The levels of these hormones in the maternal blood over the course of the pregnancy provide a good indicator of the well-being of the fetus. They are secreted primarily by the placenta, but the corpus luteum is an important source of hormones in the first several weeks. If the corpus luteum is removed before week 7, the pregnancy almost always miscarries (aborts). From weeks 7 to 17, the corpus luteum degenerates and the placenta takes over its endocrine functions.

Human Chorionic Gonadotropin

Human chorionic gonadotropin (HCG) (CORE-ee-ON-ic go-NAD-oh-TRO-pin) is secreted by the blastocyst and placenta. Its presence in the urine is the basis of pregnancy tests and can be detected with home testing kits as early as 8 or 9 days after conception. HCG secretion peaks around 10 to 12 weeks and then falls to a relatively low level for the rest of gestation **(fig. 28.18).** Like LH, it stimulates growth of the corpus luteum, which doubles in size and secretes increasing amounts of progesterone and estrogen. Without HCG, the corpus luteum would atrophy and the uterus would expel the conceptus.

Estrogens

Estrogen secretion increases to about 30 times the usual amount by the end of gestation. The corpus luteum is an important source of estrogen for the first 12 weeks; after that, it comes mainly from the placenta. The adrenal glands of the mother and fetus secrete androgens, which the placenta converts to

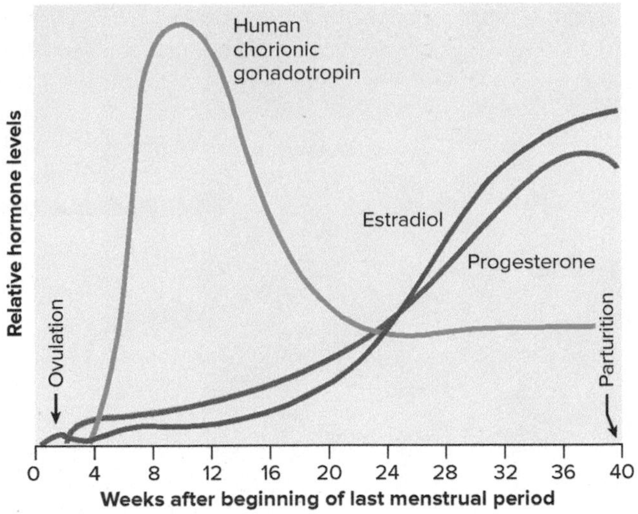

[39]*neo* = new; *nate* = born, birth

FIGURE 28.18 Hormone Levels over the Course of Pregnancy.

? *How does the changing ratio of estradiol to progesterone relate to the onset of labor contractions?*

estrogens. The most abundant estrogen of pregnancy is estriol, but its effects are relatively weak; estradiol is less abundant but 100 times as potent.

Estrogen stimulates tissue growth in the fetus and mother. It causes the mother's uterus and external genitalia to enlarge, the mammary ducts to grow, and the breasts to increase to nearly twice their former size. It makes the pubic symphysis more elastic and the sacroiliac joints more limber, so the pelvis widens during pregnancy and the pelvic outlet expands during childbirth.

Progesterone

The placenta secretes a great deal of progesterone, and early in the pregnancy, so does the corpus luteum. Progesterone and estrogen suppress pituitary secretion of FSH and LH, thereby preventing more follicles from developing during pregnancy. Progesterone also suppresses uterine contractions so the conceptus isn't prematurely expelled. It prevents menstruation and promotes the proliferation of *decidual cells* of the endometrium, on which the blastocyst feeds. Once estrogen has stimulated growth of the mammary ducts, progesterone stimulates development of the secretory acini—another step toward lactation.

Human Chorionic Somatomammotropin

Human chorionic somatomammotropin (HCS) (so-MAT-oh-MAM-oh-TRO-pin) is secreted in amounts several times that of all the other hormones combined, yet its function is the least understood. The placenta begins secreting HCS around the fifth week and output increases steadily from then until term, in proportion to the size of the placenta.

HCS is sometimes called *human placental lactogen* because, in other mammals, it causes mammary development and lactation; however, it doesn't induce lactation in humans. Its effects seem similar to those of growth hormone, but weaker. It also seems to reduce the mother's insulin sensitivity and glucose usage such that the mother consumes less glucose and leaves more of it for use by the fetus. HCS promotes the release of free fatty acids from the mother's adipose tissue, providing an alternative energy substrate for her cells to use in lieu of glucose.

Other Hormones

Many other hormones induce additional bodily changes in pregnancy **(table 28.2).** A pregnant woman's pituitary gland grows about 50% larger and produces markedly elevated levels of thyrotropin, prolactin, and ACTH. The thyroid gland also enlarges about 50% under the influence of HCG, pituitary thyrotropin, and *human chorionic thyrotropin* from the placenta. Elevated thyroid hormone secretion increases the metabolic rate of the mother and fetus. The parathyroid glands enlarge and stimulate osteoclast activity, liberating calcium from the mother's bones for fetal use. ACTH stimulates glucocorticoid secretion, which may serve primarily to mobilize amino acids for fetal protein synthesis. Aldosterone secretion rises and promotes fluid retention, contributing to the mother's increased blood volume. The corpus luteum and placenta secrete *relaxin,* which relaxes the pubic symphysis in other animals but doesn't seem to have this effect in humans. In humans, it synergizes progesterone in stimulating the multiplication of decidual cells in early pregnancy and promotes the growth of blood vessels in the pregnant uterus.

28.5c Adjustments to Pregnancy

Pregnancy places considerable stress on a woman's body and requires adjustments in nearly all the organ systems. A few of the major adjustments and effects of pregnancy are described here.

Digestive System, Nutrition, and Metabolism

For many women, one of the first signs of pregnancy is **morning sickness**—nausea, especially after rising from bed—in the first few months of gestation. The cause is unknown. One hypothesis is that it stems from the reduced intestinal motility caused by the steroids of pregnancy. Another is that it is an evolutionary adaptation to protect the fetus. The fetus is most vulnerable to toxins at the same time that morning sickness peaks. Women with morning sickness tend to prefer bland foods and avoid spicy and pungent foods, which are highest in compounds that could be toxic to the fetus. Women who experience morning sickness have fewer infants with birth defects than women who don't have it. In some women, the nausea progresses to vomiting. Occasionally, this is severe enough to require hospitalization (see *hyperemesis gravidarum* in table 28.5).

Constipation and heartburn are common in pregnancy. The former is another result of reduced intestinal motility. The latter is due to the enlarging uterus pressing upward on the stomach, causing the reflux of gastric contents into the esophagus.

The basal metabolic rate rises about 15% in the second half of gestation. Pregnant women often feel overheated because of this and the effort of carrying the extra weight. The appetite may be

TABLE 28.2	The Hormones of Pregnancy
Hormone	Effects
Human chorionic gonadotropin (HCG)	Prevents involution of corpus luteum and stimulates its growth and secretory activity; basis of pregnancy tests
Estrogens	Stimulate maternal and fetal tissue growth, including enlargement of uterus and maternal genitalia; stimulate development of mammary ducts; soften pubic symphysis and sacroiliac joints, facilitating pelvic expansion in pregnancy and childbirth; suppress FSH and LH secretion
Progesterone	Suppresses premature uterine contractions; prevents menstruation; stimulates proliferation of decidual cells, which nourish embryo; stimulates development of mammary acini; suppresses FSH and LH secretion
Human chorionic somatomammotropin (HCS)	Has weak growth-stimulating effects similar to growth hormone, and a glucose-sparing effect on mother, making glucose more available to fetus; mobilizes fatty acids for use as maternal fuel
Pituitary thyrotropin	Stimulates thyroid activity and metabolic rate
Human chorionic thyrotropin	Same effect as pituitary thyrotropin
Parathyroid hormone	Stimulates osteoclasts and mobilizes maternal calcium for fetal use
Adrenocorticotropic hormone	Stimulates glucocorticoid secretion; thought to mobilize amino acids for fetal protein synthesis
Aldosterone	Causes fluid retention, contributing to increased maternal blood volume
Relaxin	Promotes development of decidual cells and blood vessels in the pregnant uterus

strongly stimulated, but a pregnant woman needs only 300 extra kcal/day even in the last trimester. Some women overeat, however, and gain as much as 34 kg (75 lb) of weight compared with a healthy average of 11 kg (24 lb). Maternal nutrition should emphasize the quality of food eaten, not quantity.

During the last trimester, the fetus needs more nutrients than the mother's digestive tract can absorb. In preparation for this, the placenta stores nutrients early in gestation and releases them in the final trimester. The demand is especially high for protein, iron, calcium, and phosphates. A pregnant woman needs an extra 600 mg/day of iron for her own added hematopoiesis and 375 mg/day for the fetus. She is likely to become anemic if she doesn't ingest enough iron during late pregnancy. Supplemental vitamin K is often given late in pregnancy to promote prothrombin synthesis in the fetus. In the United States, newborns are routinely given an injection of vitamin K to minimize the risk of neonatal hemorrhage, especially in the brain, caused by the stresses of birth. A vitamin D supplement helps to ensure adequate calcium absorption to meet fetal demands. Supplemental folic acid reduces the risk of neurological disorders in the fetus, such as spina bifida and anencephaly (failure of the cerebrum, cerebellum, and calvaria to develop), but it is effective only if taken habitually prior to conception.

Circulatory System

By full term, the placenta receives about 625 mL/min. of blood from the mother. The mother's blood volume rises about 30% during pregnancy because of fluid retention and hematopoiesis; she eventually has about 1 to 2 L of extra blood. Cardiac output rises about 30% to 40% above normal by 27 weeks, but for unknown reasons, it falls almost to the nonpregnant level in the last 8 weeks. As the pregnant uterus puts pressure on the large pelvic blood vessels, it interferes with venous return from the legs and pelvic region. This can cause blood pressure to back up into the pelvic region and lower limbs, resulting in hemorrhoids, varicose veins, and edema of the ankles and feet.

Respiratory System

Over the course of pregnancy, respiratory rate remains constant but the tidal volume and minute ventilation increase about 40%. There are two reasons for this: (1) The oxygen demand rises in proportion to the woman's increased metabolic rate and the increasing needs of the fetus. (2) Progesterone increases the sensitivity of the woman's respiratory chemoreceptors to carbon dioxide, and ventilation is adjusted to keep her arterial P_{CO_2} lower than normal. Low maternal P_{CO_2} promotes the diffusion of CO_2 from the fetal bloodstream through the placenta into the maternal blood. As pregnancy progresses, many women feel an increasing "air hunger" (dyspnea) and make more conscious efforts to breathe. This sensation apparently stems from increased CO_2 sensitivity and, late in pregnancy, pressure on the diaphragm from the growing uterus. In the last month, however, the pelvis usually expands enough for the fetus to drop lower in the abdominopelvic

cavity, taking some pressure off the diaphragm and allowing one to breathe more easily.

Urinary System

Aldosterone and the steroids of pregnancy promote water and salt retention by the kidneys. Nevertheless, the glomerular filtration rate increases by 50% and urine output is slightly elevated. This enables a woman to dispose of both her own and the fetus's metabolic wastes. As the pregnant uterus compresses the bladder and reduces its capacity, urination becomes more frequent and some women experience uncontrollable leakage of urine (incontinence).

Integumentary System

The skin grows to accommodate expansion of the abdomen and breasts and the added fat deposition in the hips and thighs. Stretching of the dermis often tears the connective tissue and causes **striae** (stretch marks) (STRY-ee). These appear reddish at first but fade after pregnancy. Melanocyte activity increases in some areas and darkens the areolae and linea alba. The latter often becomes a dark line, the **linea nigra**[40] (LIN-ee-uh NY-gruh), from the umbilical to the pubic region. Some women also acquire a temporary blotchy darkening of the skin over the nose and cheeks called the "mask of pregnancy," or **chloasma**[41] (clo-AZ-muh), which usually disappears when the pregnancy is over.

Uterine Growth and Weight Gain

The uterus weighs about 50 g when a woman is not pregnant and about 900 g by the end of pregnancy. Its growth is monitored by palpating the fundus, which eventually reaches almost to the xiphoid process **(fig. 28.19)**. **Table 28.3** shows the distribution of weight gain in a typical healthy pregnancy.

28.5d Childbirth

In the seventh month of gestation, the fetus normally turns into a head-down *vertex position*. Consequently, most babies are born head first, the head acting as a wedge that widens the mother's cervix, vagina, and vulva during birth. The ancients thought that the fetus kicked against the uterus and pushed itself out head first. The fetus, however, is a rather passive player in its own birth; its expulsion is achieved only by the contractions of the mother's uterine and abdominal muscles. Yet there is evidence that the fetus may play some role in its birth by chemically stimulating labor contractions and perhaps even sending chemical signals that signify when it is developed enough to be born.

---

[40]*linea* = line; *nigra* = black
[41]*chlo* = green; *asma* = to be

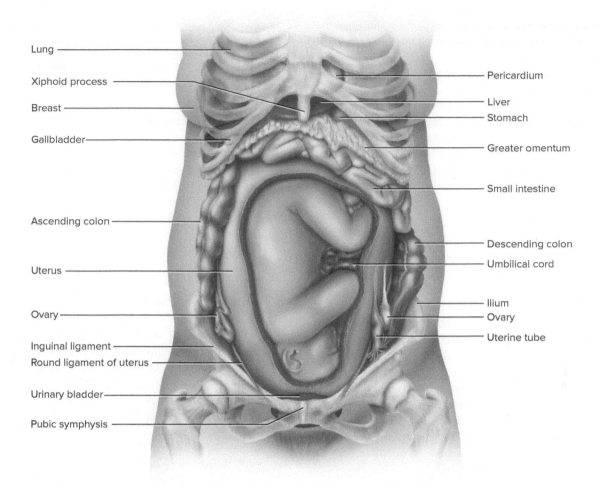

Lung

Xiphoid process

Breast

Gallbladder

Ascending colon

Uterus

Ovary

Inguinal ligament

Round ligament of uterus

Urinary bladder

Pubic symphysis

Pericardium

Liver

Stomach

Greater omentum

Small intestine

Descending colon

Umbilical cord

Ilium

Ovary

Uterine tube

FIGURE 28.19 The Full-Term Fetus in Vertex Position. Note the displacement and compression of the abdominal viscera.

TABLE 28.3	Typical Distribution of Weight Gain in Pregnancy
Fetus	3 kg (7 lb)
Placenta, fetal membranes, and amniotic fluid	1.8 kg (4 lb)
Blood and tissue fluid	2.7 kg (6 lb)
Fat	1.4 kg (3 lb)
Uterus	0.9 kg (2 lb)
Breasts	0.9 kg (2 lb)
Total	**11 kg (24 lb)**

Uterine Contractility

Over the course of gestation, the uterus exhibits relatively weak **Braxton Hicks**[42] **contractions.** These become stronger in late pregnancy and often send women rushing to the hospital with "false labor." At term, however, these contractions transform

suddenly into the more powerful **labor contractions.** True labor contractions mark the onset of **parturition** (PAR-too-RISH-un), the process of giving birth.

Progesterone and estrogen (estradiol) balance may be one factor in this pattern of increasing contractility. Both hormone levels increase over the course of gestation. Progesterone inhibits uterine contractions, but its secretion levels off or declines slightly after 6 months, while estradiol secretion continues to rise (fig. 28.18). Estradiol stimulates uterine contractions and may be a factor in the irritability of the uterus in late pregnancy.

Also, as the pregnancy nears full term, the posterior pituitary releases more oxytocin (OT) and the uterine muscle equips itself with more OT receptors by up-regulation. Oxytocin promotes labor in two ways: (1) It directly stimulates muscle of the myometrium; and (2) it stimulates the fetal membranes to secrete prostaglandins, which are synergists of OT in producing labor contractions. Labor is prolonged if OT or prostaglandins are lacking, and it may be induced or accelerated by giving intravenous OT or a vaginal prostaglandin suppository.

The conceptus itself may produce chemical stimuli promoting its own birth. Fetal cortisol secretion rises in late pregnancy and may enhance estrogen secretion by the placenta. The fetal

---

[42]John Braxton Hicks (1823–97), British gynecologist

pituitary gland also produces oxytocin, which doesn't enter the maternal circulation but may promote prostaglandin secretion as noted earlier.

Uterine stretching is also thought to play a role in initiating labor. Stretching any smooth muscle increases its contractility, and movements of the fetus produce the sort of intermittent stretch that is especially stimulatory to the myometrium. Twins are born an average of 19 days earlier than solitary infants, probably because of the greater stretching of the uterus. When a fetus is in the vertex position, its head pushes against the cervix, which is especially sensitive to stretch.

Labor Contractions

Labor contractions begin about 30 minutes apart. As labor progresses, they become more intense and eventually occur every 1 to 3 minutes. It is important that they be intermittent rather than one long, continual contraction. Each contraction compresses the arteries in the uterine wall and sharply reduces maternal blood flow to the placenta, so the uterus must periodically relax to restore flow and oxygen delivery to the fetus. Contractions are strongest in the fundus and body of the uterus and weaker near the cervix, thus pushing the fetus downward.

According to the **positive feedback theory of labor,** labor contractions are induced by stretching of the cervix. This triggers a reflex contraction of the uterine body that pushes the fetus downward and stretches the cervix still more. Thus, there is a self-amplifying cycle of stretch and contraction. In addition, cervical stretching induces a neuroendocrine reflex through the spinal cord, hypothalamus, and posterior pituitary. The posterior pituitary releases oxytocin, which is carried in the blood and stimulates the uterine muscle both directly and through the action of prostaglandins. This, too, is a positive feedback cycle: cervical stretching → oxytocin secretion → uterine contraction → cervical stretching (see fig. 1.9).

As labor progresses, a woman feels a growing urge to "bear down." A reflex arc extends from the uterus to the spinal cord and back to the skeletal muscles of the abdomen. Contraction of these muscles—partly reflexive and partly voluntary—aids in expelling the fetus, especially when combined with the Valsalva maneuver for increasing intra-abdominal pressure.

The pain of labor is due at first mainly to ischemia of the myometrium—muscle hurts when deprived of blood, and each labor contraction temporarily restricts uterine circulation. As the fetus enters the vaginal canal, the pain becomes stronger because of stretching of the cervix, vagina, and perineum and sometimes the tearing of tissue. At this stage, the obstetrician may perform an *episiotomy*—an incision in the vulva to widen the vaginal orifice and prevent random tearing. The pain of human childbirth, compared with the relative ease with which other mammals give birth, is an evolutionary product of two factors: the unusually large brain and head of the human infant, and the narrowing of the pelvic outlet, which helped to adapt hominids to bipedal locomotion.

Stages of Labor

Labor occurs in three stages **(fig. 28.20).** The duration of each tends to be longer in a **primipara**[43] (a woman giving birth for the first time) than in a **multipara**[44] (a woman who has previously given birth).

1. **Dilation (first) stage.** This is the longest stage, lasting 8 to 24 hours in a primipara but as little as a few minutes in a multipara. It is marked by the **dilation** (widening) of the cervical canal and **effacement** (thinning) of the cervix. The cervix reaches a maximum diameter of about 10 cm (the diameter of the baby's head). During dilation, the fetal membranes usually rupture and the *amniotic fluid* is discharged (the "breaking of the waters"). Dilation in labor is often called *dilatation* (DIL-a-TAY-shun), meaning dilation of an organ beyond the normal limits seen in other circumstances.

2. **Expulsion (second) stage.** This stage typically lasts about 30 to 60 minutes in a primipara and as little as 1 minute in a multipara. It begins when the baby's head enters the vagina and lasts until the baby is entirely expelled. The baby is said to be **crowning** when the top of its head is visible, stretching the vulva. Delivery of the head is the most difficult part, with the rest of the body following more easily. An episiotomy may be performed during this stage. An attendant often uses a suction bulb to remove mucus from the baby's mouth and nose even before it is fully delivered. When the baby is fully expelled, an attendant drains the blood of the umbilical vein into the baby, clamps the umbilical cord in two places, and cuts the cord between the clamps.

3. **Placental (third) stage.** The uterus continues to contract after expulsion of the baby. The placenta, however, is a nonmuscular organ that can't contract, so it buckles away from the uterine wall. About 350 mL of blood is typically lost at this stage, but contractions of the myometrium compress the blood vessels and prevent more extensive bleeding. The placenta, amnion, and other fetal membranes are expelled by uterine contractions, which may be aided by a gentle pull on the umbilical cord. The membranes *(afterbirth)* must be carefully inspected to be sure everything has been expelled. If any of these structures remain in the uterus, they can cause postpartum hemorrhaging. The umbilical blood vessels are counted because an abnormal number in the cord may indicate cardiovascular abnormalities in the infant.

---

[43]*primi* = first; *para* = birth
[44]*multi* = many; *para* = births

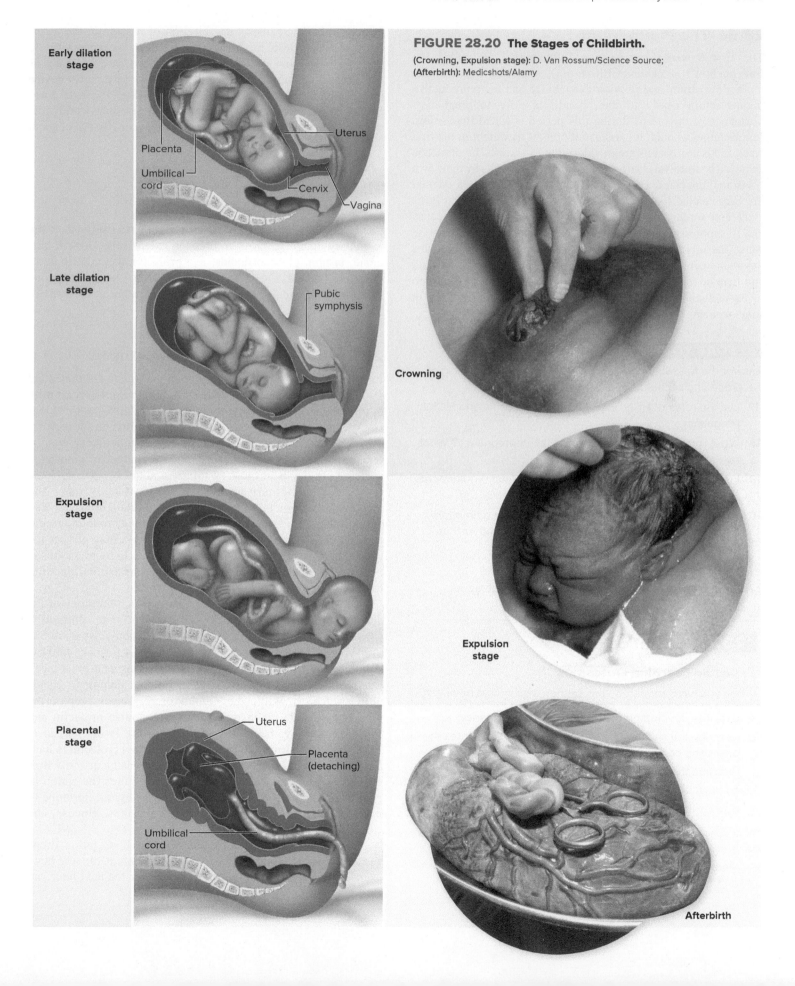

Early dilation stage

Placenta
Umbilical cord
Uterus
Cervix
Vagina

Late dilation stage

Pubic symphysis

Expulsion stage

Placental stage

Uterus
Placenta (detaching)
Umbilical cord

FIGURE 28.20 The Stages of Childbirth.
(Crowning, Expulsion stage): D. Van Rossum/Science Source;
(Afterbirth): Medicshots/Alamy

Crowning

Expulsion stage

Afterbirth

28.5e The Puerperium

The first 6 weeks **postpartum** (after birth) are called the **puerperium**[45] (PYU-er-PEER-ee-um), a period in which the mother's anatomy and physiology stabilize and the reproductive organs return nearly to their condition prior to pregnancy. Shrinkage of the uterus during this period is called **involution.** In a lactating woman, it loses about 50% of its weight in the first week and is nearly at its pregravid weight in 4 weeks. Involution is achieved by **autolysis** (self-digestion) of uterine cells by their own lysosomal enzymes. For about 10 days, this produces a vaginal discharge called **lochia,** which is bloody at first and then turns clear and serous. Breast-feeding promotes involution because (1) it suppresses estrogen secretion, which would otherwise cause the uterus to remain more flaccid; and (2) it stimulates oxytocin secretion, which causes the myometrium to contract and firm up the uterus sooner. It is important for the puerperium to be undisturbed, as emotional upset can inhibit lactation in some women.

BEFORE YOU GO ON

Answer the following questions to test your understanding of the preceding section:

17. List the roles of HCG, estrogen, progesterone, and HCS in pregnancy.

18. What is the role of the corpus luteum in pregnancy? What eventually takes over this role?

19. List and briefly explain the special nutritional requirements of pregnancy.

20. How much weight does the average woman gain in pregnancy? What contributes to this weight gain other than the fetus?

21. Describe the positive feedback theory of labor.

22. What major events define the three stages of labor?

28.6 Lactation

Expected Learning Outcomes

When you have completed this section, you should be able to

a. describe development of the breasts in pregnancy;

b. describe the shifting hormonal balance that regulates the onset and continuation of lactation;

c. describe the mechanism of milk ejection;

d. contrast colostrum with breast milk; and

e. discuss the benefits of breast-feeding.

---

[45]*puer* = child; *per* (from *par*) = birth

Lactation is the synthesis and ejection of milk from the mammary glands. It lasts for as little as 1 week in women who do not breast-feed, but it can continue for many years as long as the breast is stimulated by a nursing infant or mechanical device (breast pump). Numerous studies conducted before the widespread marketing of artificial infant formulas suggest that worldwide, women traditionally nursed their infants until a median age of about 2.8 years.

28.6a Development of the Mammary Glands

The high estrogen level in pregnancy stimulates the ducts of the mammary glands to grow and branch extensively. Growth hormone, insulin, glucocorticoids, and prolactin also contribute to this development. Once the ducts are complete, progesterone stimulates the budding and development of acini at the ends of the ducts (see fig. 28.9).

28.6b Colostrum and Milk Synthesis

In late pregnancy, the mammary acini and ducts are distended with a secretion called **colostrum.** This is similar to breast milk in protein and lactose content but contains about one-third less fat. It is the infant's only natural source of nutrition for the first 1 to 3 days postpartum. Colostrum has a thin watery consistency and a cloudy yellowish color. The amount of colostrum secreted per day is at most 1% of the amount of milk secreted later, but since infants are born with excess body water and ample fat, they don't require high calorie or fluid intake at first. A major benefit of colostrum is that it contains immunoglobulins, especially IgA. IgA resists digestion and may protect the infant from gastroenteritis. It is also thought to be pinocytosed by the small intestine and to confer wider, systemic immunity to the neonate.

Milk synthesis is promoted by **prolactin,** a hormone of the anterior pituitary gland. In the nonpregnant state, **dopamine (prolactin-inhibiting hormone)** from the hypothalamus inhibits prolactin secretion. Prolactin secretion begins 5 weeks into the pregnancy, and by full term it is 10 to 20 times its normal level. Even so, prolactin has little effect on the mammary glands until after birth. While the steroids of pregnancy prepare the mammary glands for lactation, they antagonize prolactin and suppress milk synthesis. When the placenta is discharged at birth, the steroid levels abruptly drop and allow prolactin to have a stronger effect. Milk is synthesized in increasing quantity over the following week. Milk synthesis also requires the action of growth hormone, cortisol, insulin, and parathyroid hormone to mobilize the necessary amino acids, fatty acids, glucose, and calcium.

At the time of birth, baseline prolactin secretion drops to the nonpregnant level. Every time the infant nurses, however, it jumps to 10 to 20 times this level for the next hour and

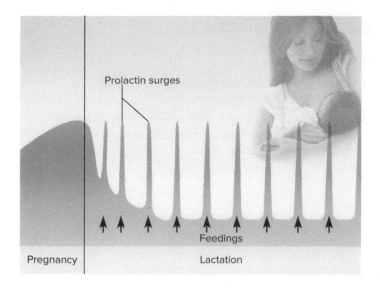

FIGURE 28.21 Prolactin Secretion in the Lactating Female.
Each time the infant nurses, maternal prolactin secretion surges.
This stimulates synthesis of the milk that will be available at the
next feeding.

stimulates the synthesis of milk for the next feeding **(fig. 28.21).**
These prolactin surges are accompanied by smaller increases in
estrogen and progesterone secretion. If the mother doesn't nurse
or these hormone surges are absent (due to pituitary damage, for
example), the mammary glands stop producing milk in about
a week. Even if she does nurse, milk production declines after
7 to 9 months.

Only 5% to 10% of women become pregnant again while
breast-feeding. Apparently, either prolactin or nerve signals from
the breast inhibit GnRH secretion, which, in turn, results in reduced
gonadotropin secretion and ovarian cycling. This mechanism may
have evolved as a natural means of spacing births, but breast-
feeding isn't a reliable means of contraception. Even in women
who breast-feed, the ovarian cycle sometimes resumes several
months postpartum. In those who don't breast-feed, the cycles
resume in a few weeks, but for the first 6 months they are usually
anovulatory.

28.6c Milk Ejection

Milk is continually secreted into the mammary acini, but it
doesn't flow easily into the ducts. Its flow, called **milk ejection
(letdown),** is controlled by a neuroendocrine reflex. The infant's
suckling stimulates nerve endings of the nipple and areola,
which in turn signal the hypothalamus and posterior pituitary
to release oxytocin. Oxytocin stimulates the myoepithelial
cells that enmesh each gland acinus (see fig. 28.9d). These cells
are of epithelial origin, but are packed with actin and contract
like smooth muscle to squeeze milk from the acinus into the
duct. The infant doesn't get any milk for the first 30 to 60 seconds

of suckling, but milk soon fills the ducts and lactiferous sinuses
and is then easily sucked out.

▶▶▶ **APPLY WHAT YOU KNOW**

*When a woman is nursing her baby at one breast, would
you expect only that breast, or both breasts, to eject
milk? Explain why.*

28.6d Breast Milk

Table 28.4 compares the composition of colostrum, human milk,
and cow's milk. Breast milk changes composition over the first
2 weeks, varies from one time of day to another, and changes even
during the course of a single feeding. For example, at the end of a
feeding there is less lactose and protein in the milk, but six times
as much fat, as there is at the beginning.

Cow's milk is not a good substitute for human milk. It has
one-third less lactose but three to five times as much protein and
minerals. The excess protein forms a harder curd in the infant's
stomach, so cow's milk isn't digested and absorbed as efficiently as
mother's milk. It also increases the infant's nitrogenous waste excretion, which increases the incidence and severity of diaper rash,
particularly as bacteria in the diaper break urea down to ammonia,
a skin irritant.

Colostrum and milk have a laxative effect that helps to clear
the neonatal intestine of *meconium,* a greenish black, sticky
fecal matter composed of bile, epithelial cells, and other wastes
that accumulated during fetal development. By clearing bile and
bilirubin from the body, breast-feeding also reduces the incidence
and degree of jaundice in neonates. Breast milk promotes
colonization of the neonatal intestine with beneficial bacteria
and supplies antibodies that lend protection against infection by
pathogenic bacteria. Breast-feeding also tends to promote a closer
bond between mother and infant.

TABLE 28.4	A Comparison of Colostrum, Human Milk, and Cow's Milk*		
Nutrient	Human Colostrum	Human Milk	Cow's Milk
Total protein (g/L)	22.9	10.6	30.9
Lactalbumin (g/L)	—	3.7	25.0
Casein (g/L)	—	3.6	2.3
Immunoglobulins (g/L)	19.4	0.09	0.8
Fat (g/L)	29.5	45.4	38.0
Lactose (g/L)	57	71	47
Calcium (mg/L)	481	344	1,370
Phosphorus (mg/L)	157	141	910

*Colostrum data are for the first day postpartum, and human milk data are for "mature
milk" at about 15 days postpartum.

A woman nursing one baby eventually produces about 1.5 L of milk per day; women with twins produce more. Lactation places a great metabolic demand on the mother. It is equivalent to losing 50 g of fat, 100 g of lactose (made from her blood glucose), and 2 to 3 g of calcium phosphate per day. A woman is at greater risk of bone loss when breast-feeding than when she is pregnant, because much of the infant's skeleton is still cartilage at birth and becomes mineralized at her expense in the first year postpartum. If a nursing mother doesn't have enough calcium and vitamin D in her own diet, lactation stimulates parathyroid hormone secretion and osteoclast activity, taking calcium from her bones to supply her baby.

To conclude this chapter, **table 28.5** briefly describes some common female reproductive disorders.

BEFORE YOU GO ON

Answer the following questions to test your understanding of the preceding section:

23. Why is little or no milk secreted while a woman is pregnant?

24. How does a lactating breast differ from a nonlactating breast in structure? What stimulates these differences to develop during pregnancy?

25. What is colostrum and what is its significance?

26. How does suckling stimulate milk ejection?

27. Why is breast milk superior to cow's milk for an infant?

TABLE 28.5	Some Female Reproductive Disorders
Amenorrhea	Absence of menstruation. Normal in pregnancy, lactation, early adolescence, and perimenopausal years, but can also result from gonadotropin hyposecretion, genetic disorders, CNS disorders, or insufficient body fat.
Dysmenorrhea	Painful menstruation in the absence of pelvic disease, caused by excessive endometrial prostaglandin secretion. Prostaglandins stimulate painful contractions of myometrium and uterine blood vessels. Usually begins around age 15 or 16 and affects up to 75% of women from 15 to 25 years old at times. May accompany leiomyoma.
Leiomyoma (uterine fibroids)	Benign tumor of the uterine smooth muscle. Usually small and asymptomatic, but can become very large and may cause abnormal uterine bleeding, heavy menstruation, and dysmenorrhea.
Disorders of Pregnancy	
Abruptio placentae[46]	Premature separation of the placenta from the uterine wall, often associated with preeclampsia or cocaine use. May require birth by cesarean section.
Ectopic[47] pregnancy	Implantation of the conceptus anywhere other than the uterus; usually in the uterine tube (tubal pregnancy) but occasionally in the abdominopelvic cavity. See Deeper Insight 29.2 for further details.
Gestational diabetes	A form of diabetes mellitus that develops in about 1% to 3% of pregnant women, characterized by insulin insensitivity, hyperglycemia, glycosuria, and a risk of excessive fetal size and birth trauma. Glucose metabolism often returns to normal after delivery of the infant, but 40% to 60% of women with gestational diabetes develop diabetes mellitus within 15 years after the pregnancy.
Hyperemesis gravidarum[48]	Severe vomiting, dehydration, alkalosis, and weight loss in early pregnancy, often requiring hospitalization to stabilize fluid, electrolyte, and acid–base balance; sometimes associated with liver damage.
Placenta previa[49]	Blockage of the cervical canal by the placenta, preventing birth of the infant before the placenta separates from the uterus. Requires birth by cesarean section.
Preeclampsia[50]	Gestational hypertension and proteinuria, often with edema of the face and hands, occurring especially in the third trimester in primiparas. Correlated with abnormal development of placental arteries, potentially leading to widespread thrombosis and organ dysfunction in the mother. Occurs in 5% to 8% of pregnancies. Sometimes progresses to *eclampsia* (seizures), which can be fatal to the mother, fetus, or both. Eclampsia may occur postpartum.
Spontaneous abortion	Occurs in 10% to 15% of pregnancies, usually because of fetal deformities or chromosomal abnormalities incompatible with survival, but may also result from maternal abnormalities, infectious disease, and drug abuse.

You can find other female reproductive disorders described in the following places:

Sexually transmitted diseases in Deeper Insight 27.5; *breast cancer* in section 28.1c; *cervical cancer* in Deeper Insight 28.1; and *endometriosis* in Deeper Insight 28.4.

---

[46]*ab* = away; *rupt* = to tear; *placentae* = of the placenta
[47]*ec* = out of; *top* = place
[48]*hyper* = excessive; *emesis* = vomiting; *gravida* = pregnant woman
[49]*pre* = before; *via* = the way (obstructing the way)
[50]*ec* = forth; *lampsia* = shining

DEEPER INSIGHT 28.5

CLINICAL APPLICATION

Methods of Contraception

The term *contraception* is used here to mean any procedure or device intended to prevent pregnancy (the presence of an implanted conceptus in the uterus). This essay describes the most common methods of contraception, some issues involved in choosing among them, and their relative reliability. Several options are shown in **figure 28.22.**

Behavioral Methods

Abstinence (refraining from intercourse) is obviously a completely reliable method if used consistently. The *fertility awareness-based method* (formerly called the *rhythm method*) is based on avoiding intercourse near the time of expected ovulation. Among typical users, it has a 25% failure rate, partly due to lack of restraint and partly because it is difficult to predict the exact date of ovulation. Intercourse must be avoided for at least 7 days before ovulation so there will be no surviving sperm in the reproductive tract when the egg is ovulated, and for at least 2 days after ovulation so there will be no fertile egg present when sperm are introduced. This method is valuable, however, for couples who are trying to conceive a child by having intercourse at the time of apparent ovulation.

Withdrawal (coitus interruptus) requires the male to withdraw the penis before ejaculation. This often fails because of lack of willpower, because sperm are occasionally present in the preejaculatory fluid, and because sperm ejaculated anywhere in the vulva can potentially get into the reproductive tract.

Barrier and Spermicidal Methods

Barrier methods are designed to prevent sperm from getting into or beyond the vagina. They are most effective when used with chemical *spermicides,* available as nonprescription foams, creams, and jellies.

The *male condom* is a sheath of latex, rubber, or animal membrane (lamb intestine) that is unrolled over the erect penis and collects the semen. It is inexpensive, convenient, and very reliable when used carefully. About 25% of American couples who use contraceptives use only condoms, which rank second to birth-control pills in popularity.

The *female condom* is less used. It is a polyurethane sheath with a flexible ring at each end. The inner ring fits over the cervix and the outer ring covers the external genitalia. Male and female condoms are the only contraceptives that also protect against disease transmission. Animal membrane condoms, however, are porous to HIV and hepatitis B viruses and do not afford dependable protection from disease.

The *diaphragm* is a latex or rubber dome that is placed over the cervix to block sperm migration. It requires a physical examination and prescription to ensure proper fit, but is otherwise comparable to the condom in convenience and reliability, provided it is used with a spermicide. Without a spermicide, it isn't very effective.

The *sponge* is a foam disc inserted before intercourse to cover the cervix. It is impregnated with a spermicide and acts by trapping and killing the sperm. It requires no prescription or fitting. The sponge provides

Male condom

Female condom

Diaphragm with contraceptive jelly

Contraceptive foam with vaginal applicator

Birth-control pills

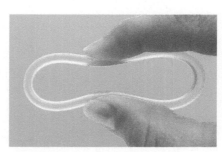
Vaginal ring

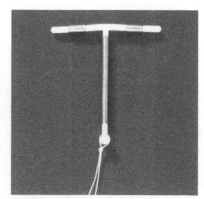
Copper IUD

FIGURE 28.22 Contraceptive Devices.

(Male, Female Condom, Diaphragm, Contraceptive foam, Birth Control Pills, & IUD): Bob Coyle/McGraw-Hill Education; (Vaginal ring): vario images GmbH & Co.KG/Alamy

(continued)

protection for up to 24 hours, and must be left in place for at least 6 hours after the last act of intercourse.

Contraceptive sponges and other barrier methods date to antiquity. Ancient Egyptians and Greeks used vaginal sponges soaked in lemon juice, which had a mild spermicidal effect. Some Egyptian women used vaginal pessaries made of crocodile dung and honey, but crocodile dung is difficult to find in pharmacies these days, limiting the modern usefulness of this idea.

Hormonal Methods

Most hormonal methods of contraception are aimed at preventing ovulation. Efforts to develop a hormonal contraceptive for men have so far been unsuccessful, but are continuing. In women, hormonal contraceptives mimic the negative feedback effect of ovarian hormones, inhibiting FSH and LH secretion so follicles do not mature. For most women, they are highly effective. Their differences lie in convenience, method of application, and to some extent, reliability and risk of complications.

The oldest and most widely used hormonal method is the *combined oral contraceptive,* or *birth-control pill.* "The pill" is composed of estrogen and progestin (a synthetic progesterone-like hormone). It must be taken daily, at the same time of day, for 21 days each cycle. It comes in 28-day packets, marked day by day, with the last 7 pills being plain sugar just to keep the user in the habit of taking one every day. The 7-day withdrawal from hormones allows for menstruation. Side effects include an elevated risk of heart attack or stroke in smokers and in women with a history of diabetes, hypertension, or clotting disorders.

Other hormonal methods avoid the need to remember a daily pill. One option is a skin patch that releases estrogen and progestin transdermally. It is changed at 7-day intervals (3 patches per month and 1 week without). Also available is a soft, flexible vaginal ring that releases estrogen and progestin for absorption through the vaginal mucosa. It must be worn continually for 3 weeks and removed for the fourth week of each cycle. *Medroxyprogesterone* is a progestin administered by injection every 3 months. It provides highly reliable, long-term contraception, although in some women it causes headaches, nausea, or weight gain, and fertility may not return immediately when its use is discontinued.

Some drugs can be taken orally after intercourse to prevent implantation of a conceptus. These are called emergency contraceptive pills (ECPs), or "morning-after pills." An ECP is a high dose of estrogen and progestin or a progestin alone. It can be taken up to 120 hours after intercourse and induces menstruation within 2 weeks. ECPs work on several fronts: inhibiting ovulation; inhibiting sperm or egg transport in the uterine tube; and preventing implantation. They don't work if a blastocyst is already implanted. ECPs are available without a prescription in most places.

Mifepristone (RU-486) is a progesterone antagonist. It is used less as a contraceptive than as an *abortifacient;* in high doses, it induces abortion up to 2 months into pregnancy. But at a dose of 2 mg/day, it prevents ovulation like other steroidal contraceptives, and a single 10 mg dose can also be used as an emergency "morning-after" contraceptive if taken after intercourse but before ovulation.

The Intrauterine Device

Intrauterine devices (IUDs) are springy, often T-shaped devices inserted through the cervical canal into the uterus. Some IUDs act by releasing a synthetic progesterone, but most have a copper wire wrapping or copper sleeve. IUDs act by irritating the uterine lining and interfering with blastocyst implantation, and copper IUDs also inhibit sperm motility. A copper IUD is the most effective after-sex contraceptive even when installed up to 10 days after intercourse. IUDs, however, have relatively high up-front cost. An IUD can be left in place for 5 to 12 years.

Surgical Sterilization

People who are confident that they don't want more children (or any) often elect to be surgically sterilized. This entails the cutting and tying or clamping of the genital ducts, thus blocking the passage of sperm or eggs. Surgical sterilization has the advantage of convenience, since it requires no further attention. Its initial cost is higher, however, and for people who later change their minds, surgical reversal is much more expensive than the original procedure and is often unsuccessful. *Vasectomy* is the severing of the ductus (vas) deferens, done through a small incision in the scrotum. In *tubal ligation,*[51] the uterine tubes are cut. This can be done through small abdominal incisions to admit a cutting instrument and laparoscope (viewing device).

Issues in Choosing a Contraceptive

Many issues enter into the appropriate choice of a contraceptive, including personal preference, pattern of sexual activity, medical history, religious views, convenience, initial and ongoing costs, and disease prevention. For most people, however, the two primary issues are safety and reliability.

Table 28.6 shows the expected rates of failure for several types of contraception as reported by the World Health Organization (WHO). Each column shows the number of sexually active women who typically become pregnant within 1 year while they or their partners are using the indicated contraceptives. The lowest rate (perfect use) is for those who use the method correctly and consistently, whereas the higher rate (typical use) is based on random surveys of users and takes human error (lapses and incorrect usage) into account.

We have not considered all the currently available methods of contraception or all the issues important to the choice of a contraceptive. No one contraceptive method can be recommended as best for all people. Further information necessary to a sound choice and proper use of contraceptives should be sought from a health department, college health service, physician, Planned Parenthood, or other such sources.

TABLE 28.6	Failure Rates of Contraceptive Methods	
	Rate of Failure (Pregnancies per 100 Users)	
Method	**Perfect Use**	**Typical Use**
No protection	85	85
Rhythm method	3–5	25
Withdrawal	4	27
Spermicide alone	18	26
Condom alone (male or female)	2–5	15–21
Diaphragm with spermicide	6	16
Vaginal sponge	9–20	16–32
Birth-control pill, patch, or vaginal ring	0.3–0.5	8
Medroxyprogesterone	0.3	3
Intrauterine device	0.2–0.6	0.2–0.8
Vasectomy	0.10	0.15
Tubal ligation	0.5	0.5

[51]*ligat* = to tie

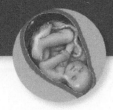

CONNECTIVE ISSUES

Effects of the **REPRODUCTIVE SYSTEM** on Other Organ Systems

INTEGUMENTARY SYSTEM
At puberty, androgens stimulate development of body hair and apocrine glands and increased sebaceous secretion; estrogens stimulate fat deposition and breast development; pregnancy necessitates growth of skin, especially in abdominal and mammary regions, and may cause pigmentation changes and stretch marks.

SKELETAL SYSTEM
Androgens and estrogens stimulate bone deposition and adolescent skeletal growth and maintain adult bone mass.

MUSCULAR SYSTEM
Androgens stimulate muscle growth; sexual climax and childbirth involve contractions of specific skeletal muscles.

NERVOUS SYSTEM
Sex steroids stimulate the brain and libido; gonadal and placental hormones exert negative feedback control on the hypothalamus.

ENDOCRINE SYSTEM
The gonads and placenta secrete androgens, estrogens, progesterone, and hormones of pregnancy.

CIRCULATORY SYSTEM
Androgens stimulate erythropoiesis; estrogens inhibit atherosclerosis in females; pregnancy increases blood volume and cardiac output and may cause varicose veins.

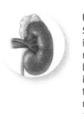

LYMPHATIC AND IMMUNE SYSTEMS
Barriers in the testis and ovary protect germ cells from antibodies; androgens somewhat inhibit immunity and increase susceptibility to infectious diseases.

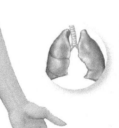

RESPIRATORY SYSTEM
Sexual arousal increases pulmonary ventilation; pregnancy increases CO_2 sensitivity of respiratory chemoreceptors and increases tidal volume and minute ventilation.

URINARY SYSTEM
Sexual arousal constricts the male internal urinary sphincter, which prevents reflux of semen into the male urinary bladder; prostatic hyperplasia can impede urine flow; pregnancy crowds the bladder, reduces its capacity, and may cause incontinence; pregnancy promotes salt and water reabsorption by the kidneys and increases glomerular filtration rate and urine output.

DIGESTIVE SYSTEM
A growing fetus crowds the stomach and intestines and may cause heartburn; pregnancy is often associated with constipation and nausea.

STUDY GUIDE

▶ Assess Your Learning Outcomes

To test your knowledge, discuss the following topics with a study partner or in writing, ideally from memory.

28.1 Female Reproductive Anatomy

1. Why the female paramesonephric duct develops into a reproductive tract whereas the male's paramesonephric duct does not; what mature female structures arise from the duct
2. What mature female structures arise from the embryonic genital tubercle, urogenital folds, and labioscrotal folds
3. Internal structure of the ovary; its supportive ligaments; and its blood and nerve supplies
4. General structure of ovarian follicles; their function and how they compare and contrast with the male's seminiferous tubules; and their location in the ovary
5. Gross anatomy of the uterine (fallopian) tube; its three segments; its supportive ligament; and the structure of its mucosa and relationship of that structure to its function
6. Gross anatomy of the uterus; its supportive ligaments; its relationship to the vesicouterine and rectouterine pouches; its blood supply; and function of the cervical glands
7. Tissue layers of the uterine wall; histology of the endometrium; functions of the endometrial sublayers
8. The tilt of the vagina and its relationship to adjacent organs; histology of its mucosa in childhood and adulthood; significance of its dendritic cells; sources of its lubrication; and anatomy of the hymen
9. Anatomy of the vulva including the mons pubis, labia majora and minora, clitoris and prepuce, vaginal and urethral orifices, accessory glands, and erectile tissues
10. Anatomy of the mature breast in the resting and lactating states
11. The prevalence of breast cancer; its diagnostic signs; genetic and other risk factors for breast cancer; preventive breast care; and treatment options

28.2 Puberty and Menopause

1. The typical age of onset of female puberty in the United States and Europe
2. The hormonal trigger for the onset of female puberty; roles of GnRH, FSH, LH, inhibin, androgens, and estrogens; and three types of estrogen

3. Thelarche, pubarche, and menarche as signs of female puberty; their hormonal causes; and the hormonal basis of the libido
4. The typical age of menarche and its relationship to the onset of ovulation
5. Bodily effects of estradiol, progesterone, and inhibin in female puberty
6. Ovarian and hormonal changes that bring on female climacteric and menopause; effects commonly experienced by perimenopausal women; and differences between female and male climacteric
7. The criterion for determining that a woman has passed through menopause, and the reason one cannot identify the exact time of menopause

28.3 Oogenesis and the Sexual Cycle

1. Meanings of and distinctions between the female *sexual cycle, ovarian cycle,* and *menstrual cycle*
2. The meaning of *oogenesis* and ways in which it differs from spermatogenesis
3. Prenatal development of oogonia and primary oocytes; the peak number of oogonia typically attained in the fetus; why this number is so much less at the time of birth and again by the onset of puberty; and the name for the prenatal and childhood degeneration of female germ cells
4. Ways in which meiosis in the female differs from that in the male; why male gametogenesis produces four functional gametes per stem cell and female gametogenesis produces only one; what happens to the other three meiotic daughter cells in the female
5. How far meiosis has progressed by the time the egg is ovulated, and what must happen thereafter for meiosis to be completed
6. Development of a follicle from primary to mature (graafian) types; the structural differences between the stages; and how folliculogenesis is correlated with oogenesis
7. Structural details of a mature follicle
8. The timetable of oogenesis and folliculogenesis; why the ovarian cycle is considered to average 28 days long whereas any given egg and follicle take much longer to mature; and what event marks day 1 of a cycle
9. How many follicles begin to develop in each cycle of folliculogenesis; how many of them normally ovulate; what happens to the rest, and what that fate is called

10. Roles of FSH and LH in regulating the ovarian cycle
11. The process of ovulation, the day on which it occurs in a typical cycle, and how the egg gets into the uterine tube
12. Production, structure, function, and eventual involution of the corpus luteum; why days 15 through 28 of a typical cycle are called the luteal phase; what remains after a corpus luteum has fully involuted
13. Four phases of the menstrual cycle; what happens histologically to the endometrium in each phase; what days of the cycle are spanned by each phase; and what hormones regulate these changes

28.4 Female Sexual Response

1. Ways in which the female sexual response differs from the male's in the excitement phase; vasocongestion of the labia, clitoris, and breasts; sources of lubrication of the vagina and vulva; anatomical changes in the vagina and uterus during sexual arousal
2. Physiological responses of orgasm and resolution in the female and how they differ from those of the male; absence of a refractory period and potential for multiple orgasms

28.5 Pregnancy and Childbirth

1. The timetable of gestation and how the date of birth is predicted
2. What is included in the conceptus
3. Human chorionic gonadotropin (HCG), its source and effects, the time course of its rising and falling secretion during pregnancy, and its usefulness in pregnancy tests
4. Sources and effects of estrogen, progesterone, and human chorionic gonadotropin in pregnancy
5. Effects of thyroid hormone, parathyroid hormone, glucocorticoids, aldosterone, and relaxin in pregnancy
6. Causes of morning sickness, constipation, and heartburn in pregnancy; the change in basal metabolic rate and the related nutritional needs of pregnancy
7. Effects of pregnancy on blood volume and cardiac output; how pregnancy can cause edema, hemorrhoids, and varicose veins
8. Effects of pregnancy on respiratory function; the mechanism for enhancing diffusion of carbon dioxide from the fetal blood into the maternal blood of the placenta

STUDY GUIDE

9. Effects of pregnancy on glomerular filtration, urine output, and the capacity of the bladder
10. Effects of pregnancy on the skin; causes of striae (stretch marks), the linea nigra, and chloasma
11. The vertex position and the developmental age at which the fetus typically assumes it
12. The nature and possible cause of Braxton Hicks contractions, when they occur, and how they differ from true labor contractions
13. Factors that stimulate the onset of labor contractions; the roles of oxytocin, positive feedback, and the voluntary abdominal muscles in labor

14. Events that mark each stage of labor, and the names of the stages
15. The puerperium, its time course, the postpartum changes in a woman's body during this time

28.6 Lactation

1. Influences of estrogen, growth hormone, insulin, glucocorticoids, and prolactin on mammary gland development during pregnancy
2. The fluid secreted by the mammary glands for the first few days postpartum, how it differs from breast milk, and its benefits to the neonate

3. Why prolactin stimulates milk synthesis after birth but not during pregnancy
4. The neuroendocrine reflex stimulated by the suckling of an infant, and the roles of oxytocin and prolactin in breast-feeding
5. Composition of breast milk in comparison to colostrum and cow's milk; reasons why cow's milk is less healthy than breast milk for an infant
6. How breast milk varies in composition from one time to another; which components of the milk are released early, and which are released nearer the end, of a single feeding
7. The daily quantity of breast milk typically produced (eventually) and its nutritional demands on the mother

▶ Testing Your Recall

Answers in Appendix A

1. Of the following organs, the one(s) most comparable to the penis in structure is/are
   a. the clitoris.
   b. the vagina.
   c. the vestibular bulbs.
   d. the labia minora.
   e. the prepuce.

2. The ovaries secrete all of the following *except*
   a. estrogens.
   b. progesterone.
   c. androgens.
   d. follicle-stimulating hormone.
   e. inhibin.

3. The first haploid stage in oogenesis is
   a. the oogonium.
   b. the primary oocyte.
   c. the secondary oocyte.
   d. the second polar body.
   e. the zygote.

4. The secondary oocyte is shielded from immune attack by
   a. the zona pellucida.
   b. the theca folliculi.
   c. the cumulus oophorus.
   d. follicular fluid.
   e. inhibin.

5. The hormone that most directly influences the secretory phase of the menstrual cycle is
   a. HCG.
   b. FSH.
   c. LH.
   d. estrogen.
   e. progesterone.

6. The ischemic phase of the uterus results from
   a. rising progesterone levels.
   b. falling progesterone levels.
   c. stimulation by oxytocin.
   d. stimulation by prostaglandins.
   e. stimulation by estrogens.

7. Before secreting milk, the mammary glands secrete
   a. prolactin.
   b. colostrum.
   c. lochia.
   d. meconium.
   e. chloasma.

8. One is less likely to become pregnant while nursing than at other times because _____ inhibits GnRH secretion.
   a. FSH
   b. prolactin
   c. prostaglandin
   d. oxytocin
   e. HCG

9. Smooth muscle cells of the myometrium and myoepithelial cells of the mammary glands are the target cells for
   a. prostaglandins.
   b. LH.
   c. oxytocin.
   d. progesterone.
   e. FSH.

10. Which of these is *not* true of the luteal phase of the sexual cycle?
    a. Progesterone level is high.
    b. The endometrium stores glycogen.

    c. Ovulation occurs.
    d. Fertilization may occur.
    e. The endometrial glands enlarge.

11. Each egg cell develops in its own fluid-filled space called a/an _____.

12. The mucosa of the uterus is called the _____.

13. A girl's first menstrual period is called _____.

14. A yellowish structure called the _____ secretes progesterone during the secretory phase of the menstrual cycle.

15. The layer of cells closest to a mature secondary oocyte is the _____.

16. A tertiary follicle differs from a primary follicle in having a cavity called the _____.

17. Menopause occurs during a midlife period of changing hormone secretion called _____.

18. All the products of fertilization, including the embryo or fetus, the placenta, and the embryonic membranes, are collectively called the _____.

19. The funnel-like distal end of the uterine tube is called the _____ and has feathery processes called _____.

20. Postpartum uterine involution produces a vaginal discharge called _____.

STUDY GUIDE

▶ Building Your Medical Vocabulary

Answers in Appendix A

State a meaning of each word element, and give a medical term from this chapter that uses it or a slight variation of it.

1. -arche

2. -arum

3. cumulo-

4. gesto-

5. hystero-

6. lacto-

7. ligat-

8. metri-

9. oo-

10. primi-

▶ What's Wrong with These Statements?

Answers in Appendix A

Briefly explain why each of the following statements is false, or reword it to make it true.

1. After ovulation, a follicle begins to move down the uterine tube to the uterus.

2. Human chorionic gonadotropin is secreted by the granulosa cells of the follicle.

3. A follicle ovulates shortly after its oocyte completes meiosis II.

4. A slim girl who is active in dance and gymnastics is likely to begin menstruating at a younger age than an overweight inactive girl.

5. There are more future egg cells in the ovary at puberty than there are at birth.

6. Women do not lactate while they are pregnant because prolactin is not secreted until after birth.

7. Colostrum contains more fat than mature milk, ensuring the neonate of adequate caloric intake in its first month of separation from placental nutrition.

8. Normally, only one primary follicle develops to the secondary follicle stage in each month's ovarian cycle.

9. Progesterone promotes the uterine contractions of childbirth.

10. The entire endometrium is shed in each menstrual period.

▶ Testing Your Comprehension

1. Would you expect puberty to create a state of positive or negative nitrogen balance? Explain. (See "Nitrogen Balance" in section 26.1h for background.)

2. Aspirin and ibuprofen can inhibit the onset of labor and are sometimes used to prevent premature birth. Review your knowledge of these drugs and the mechanism of labor, and explain this effect.

3. At 6 months postpartum, a nursing mother is in an automobile accident that fractures her skull and severs the hypophysial portal vessels. How would you expect this to affect her milk production? How would you expect it to affect her future ovarian cycles? Explain the difference.

4. If the ovaries are removed in the first 6 weeks of pregnancy, the embryo will be aborted. If they are removed later in pregnancy, the pregnancy can go to a normal full term. Explain the difference.

5. A breast-feeding woman leaves her baby at home and goes shopping. There, she hears another woman's baby crying and notices her blouse becoming wet with a little exuded milk. Explain the physiological link between hearing that sound and the ejection of milk.

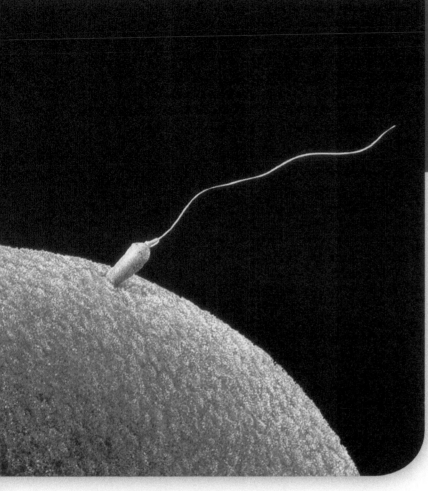

Boy meets girl: the union of sperm and egg (SEM)
Francis Leroy, Biocosmos/Science Source

Anatomy & Physiology
Revealed 4.0

Module 14: Reproductive System

P erhaps the most dramatic, miraculous-seeming aspect of human life is the transformation of a one-celled fertilized egg into an independent, fully developed individual. From the beginning of recorded thought, people have pondered how a baby forms in the mother's body and how two parents can produce another human being who, although unique, possesses characteristics of each. Aristotle, in his quest to understand prenatal development, dissected bird embryos and established the sequence in which their organs appeared and took shape. He also speculated that the hereditary traits of a child resulted from the mixing of the male's semen with the female's menstrual blood. Such misconceptions about human development persisted for many centuries. In the seventeenth century, scientists thought that the features of the infant existed in a preformed state in the egg or sperm, and simply unfolded and expanded as the embryo developed. Some thought that the head of the sperm had a miniature human curled up in it, while others thought that the miniature person existed in the egg and the sperm were parasites in the semen.

The modern science of **embryology**—the study of prenatal development—wasn't born until the nineteenth century, largely because darwinism at last gave biologists a systematic framework for asking the right questions and discovering unifying themes in the development of diverse species of animals, including humans. It was in that era, too, that the human egg was first observed. Embryology is now a part of **developmental biology,** a broader science that embraces changes in form and function from fertilized egg through old age. A rapidly expanding area of developmental biology today is the genetic regulation of development.

In this book's closing chapter, it is fitting that we reflect on the closing chapter of life as well. Why do our bodies wear out? Isn't there something we can do about that? Is there any cure for old age on the horizon? Our scope of discussion here embraces the human life span from conception to death.

29.1 Fertilization and the Preembryonic Stage

Expected Learning Outcomes
When you have completed this section, you should be able to

a. describe the processes of sperm migration and fertilization;
b. explain how an egg prevents fertilization by more than one sperm;
c. describe the major events that transform a fertilized egg into an embryo; and
d. describe the implantation of the preembryo in the uterine wall.

Authorities attach different meanings to the word **embryo.** Some use it to denote stages beginning with the fertilized egg or at least with the two-celled stage produced by its first division. Others first apply the word *embryo* to an individual 16 days old, when it consists of three **primary germ layers** called the *ectoderm, mesoderm,* and *endoderm.* The events leading up to that stage are called *embryogenesis,* so the first 16 days after fertilization are called the *preembryonic stage.* This is the sense in which we will use such terms in this book. We begin with the process in which a sperm locates and fertilizes the egg.

29.1a Sperm Migration and Capacitation

If it is to survive, an egg must be fertilized within 12 to 24 hours of ovulation; yet it takes about 72 hours for an egg to reach the uterus. Therefore, in order to fertilize an egg before it dies, sperm must encounter it somewhere in the distal one-third of the uterine tube. The vast majority of sperm never make it that far. Many are destroyed by vaginal acid or drain out of the vagina. Others fail to penetrate the mucus of the cervical canal, and those that do are often destroyed by leukocytes in the uterus. Of those that get past the uterus, probably half go up the wrong uterine tube. Finally, about 200 spermatozoa reach the vicinity of the egg—not many of the 300 million that were ejaculated.

Sperm migrate mainly by means of the snakelike lashing of their tails as they crawl along the female mucosa, but they are assisted by certain aspects of female physiology. Strands of mucus guide them through the cervical canal. Although female orgasm isn't required for fertilization, orgasm does involve uterine contractions that may suck semen from the vagina and spread it throughout the uterus, like hand lotion pressed between your palms. The egg itself may release a chemical that attracts sperm from a short distance; this has been demonstrated for some animals but remains unproven for humans.

Sperm can reach the distal uterine tube in half an hour or less after ejaculation, but they can't fertilize an egg for about 10 hours. While migrating, they must undergo a process called **capacitation** that makes them capable of penetrating an egg. In fresh sperm, the plasma membrane is toughened by cholesterol. This prevents the premature release of acrosomal enzymes while sperm are still in the male, and thus avoids both wastage of sperm and enzymatic damage to the spermatic ducts. After ejaculation, however, fluids of the female reproductive tract leach cholesterol from the plasma membrane and dilute other inhibitory factors in the semen. The membrane of the sperm head becomes more fragile and more permeable to calcium ions, which diffuse into the sperm and stimulate more powerful lashing of the tail.

Sperm remain viable for up to 6 days after ejaculation, so there is little chance of pregnancy from intercourse occurring more than a week before ovulation. Fertilization also is unlikely if intercourse takes place more than 14 hours after ovulation, because the egg would no longer be viable by the time

the sperm became capacitated. For those wishing to conceive a child, the optimal window of opportunity is therefore from a few days before ovulation to 14 hours after. Those wishing to avoid pregnancy, however, should allow a wider margin of safety for variations in sperm and egg longevity, capacitation time, and time of ovulation—variations that make the fertility-awareness based (rhythm) method of contraception so unreliable.

29.1b Fertilization

When the sperm encounters an egg, it undergoes an **acrosomal reaction**—exocytosis of the acrosome, releasing the penetration enzymes. But the first sperm to reach an egg isn't the one to fertilize it. Sperm must first penetrate the granulosa cells and zona pellucida that surround it **(fig. 29.1).** It may require numerous sperm to clear a path for the one that penetrates the egg proper.

Two of the acrosomal enzymes are **hyaluronidase,** which digests the hyaluronic acid that binds granulosa cells together, and **acrosin,** a protease similar to the trypsin of pancreatic juice. When a path has been cleared through the granulosa cells, a sperm

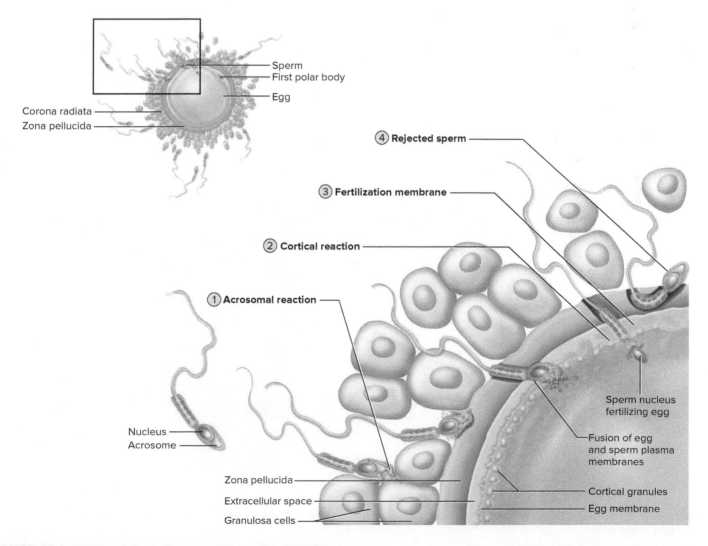

FIGURE 29.1 Fertilization and the Slow Block to Polyspermy.

binds to the zona pellucida and releases its enzymes, digesting a pathway through the zona until it contacts the egg itself. The sperm head and middle piece enter the egg, but the egg destroys the sperm mitochondria and passes only maternal mitochondria on to the offspring.

Fertilization combines the haploid (*n*) set of sperm chromosomes with the haploid set of egg chromosomes, producing a diploid (*2n*) set. Fertilization by two or more sperm, called **polyspermy,** would produce a triploid (*3n*) or larger set of chromosomes and the egg would die of a "gene overdose." Thus it is important for the egg to prevent this, and it has two mechanisms for doing so: a fast block and slow block to polyspermy. In the **fast block,** binding of the sperm to the egg opens Na^+ channels in the egg membrane. The rapid inflow of Na^+ depolarizes the membrane and inhibits the attachment of any more sperm. The **slow block** involves secretory vesicles called **cortical granules** just beneath the membrane. Sperm penetration releases an inflow of Ca^{2+}; this, in turn, stimulates a **cortical reaction** in which the cortical granules release their secretion beneath the zona pellucida. The secretion swells with water, pushes any remaining sperm away from the egg, and creates an impenetrable **fertilization membrane** between the egg and zona pellucida.

▶▶▶ **APPLY WHAT YOU KNOW**

What similarity can you see between the slow block to polyspermy and the release of acetylcholine from the synaptic vesicles of a neuron? (Compare "Synaptic Transmission," section 12.5d.)

A secondary oocyte begins meiosis II before ovulation and completes it only if fertilized. Through the formation of a second polar body, the fertilized egg discards one chromatid from each chromosome. The sperm and egg nuclei then swell and become **pronuclei.** The sperm centrosome sprouts microtubules and pushes the sperm pronucleus toward the center of the egg, aiding in the union of the male and female pronuclei. A mitotic spindle forms between the pronuclei, each of them ruptures, and the chromosomes of the two gametes mix into a single diploid set **(fig. 29.2).** The fertilized egg, now called a **zygote,** is ready for its first mitotic division.

As in section 28.5a, we will use the term *conceptus* for everything that arises from this zygote—not only the developing individual but also the placenta, umbilical cord, and membranes associated with the embryo and fetus.

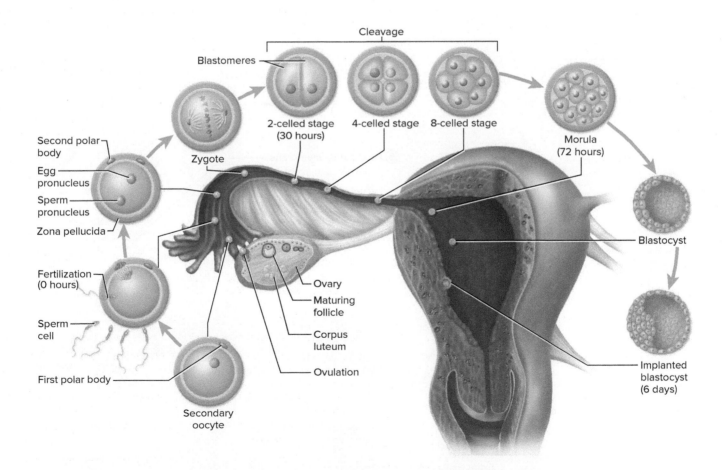

FIGURE 29.2 Migration of the Conceptus. The egg is fertilized in the distal end of the uterine tube, and the preembryo begins cleavage as it migrates to the uterus.

❓ *Why can't the egg be fertilized in the uterus?*

29.1c Major Stages of Prenatal Development

Clinically, the course of a pregnancy is divided into 3-month intervals called **trimesters:**

1. The **first trimester** extends from fertilization through the first 12 weeks. This is the most precarious stage, for more than half of all embryos die then. The conceptus is most vulnerable to stress, drugs, and nutritional deficiencies during this time, but may also die early because of chromosomal defects or other factors.

2. The **second trimester** (weeks 13 through 24) is a period in which the organs complete most of their development. It becomes possible with sonography to see good anatomical detail in the fetus. By the end of this trimester, the fetus looks distinctly human, and with intensive care, infants born at the end of the second trimester have a chance of survival.

3. In the **third trimester** (week 25 to birth), the fetus grows rapidly and the organs achieve enough cellular differentiation to support life outside the womb. Some organs, such as the brain, liver, and kidneys, however, require further differentiation after birth to become fully functional. At 35 weeks from fertilization, the fetus typically weighs about 2.5 kg (5.5 lb). It is considered mature at this weight, and usually survives if born early. Most twins are born at about 35 weeks and solitary infants at 40 weeks.

From a more biological than clinical standpoint, human development is divided into three stages called the *preembryonic, embryonic,* and *fetal stages.* The timetable and landmark events that distinguish them are outlined in **table 29.1** and described in the following pages.

29.1d The Preembryonic Stage

The **preembryonic stage** comprises the first 16 days of development, culminating in the existence of an embryo. This is a period in which the zygote divides into hundreds of cells, the cells organize themselves into the primary germ layers, and the conceptus becomes firmly attached to the uterine wall. It can be summarized in three words: *cleavage, implantation,* and *embryogenesis.*

Cleavage

Cleavage refers to mitotic divisions that occur in the first 3 days, while the conceptus migrates down the uterine tube (fig. 29.2). The first cleavage occurs about 30 hours after fertilization and produces the first two daughter cells, or **blastomeres.**[1] These divide simultaneously at shorter and shorter time intervals, doubling the number of blastomeres each time. By the time the conceptus arrives in the uterus, about 72 hours after ovulation, it consists of 16 or more cells and somewhat resembles a mulberry—hence, it is called a **morula.**[2] The morula is no larger than the zygote; cleavage merely produces smaller and smaller blastomeres and a larger number of cells from which to form different embryonic tissues. At times, the morula splits into two cell masses and produces identical twins (see Deeper Insight 29.1).

The morula lies free in the uterine cavity for 4 to 5 days and divides into 100 cells or so. Meanwhile, the zona pellucida disintegrates and releases the conceptus, which is now at a stage called the **blastocyst**—a hollow sphere with an outer layer of squamous cells called the **trophoblast,**[3] an inner cell mass called the **embryoblast,** and an internal cavity called the **blastocoel**

---

[1]*blast* = bud, precursor; *mer* = segment, part
[2]*mor* = mulberry; *ula* = little
[3]*troph* = food, nourishment

TABLE 29.1	The Stages of Prenatal Development	
Stage	**Age from Time of Fertilization**	**Major Developments and Defining Characteristics**
Preembryonic Stage		
Zygote	0–30 hours	A single diploid cell formed by the union of egg and sperm
Cleavage	30–72 hours	Mitotic division of the zygote into smaller, identical blastomeres
Morula	3–4 days	A spheroidal stage consisting of 16 or more blastomeres
Blastocyst	4–16 days	A fluid-filled, spheroidal stage with an outer mass of trophoblast cells and inner mass of embryoblast cells; becomes implanted in the endometrium; the inner cell mass forms an embryonic disc and differentiates into the three primary germ layers
Embryonic Stage	16 days–8 weeks	A stage in which the primary germ layers differentiate into organs and organ systems; ends when all organ systems are present
Fetal Stage	8–38 weeks	A stage in which organs grow and mature at a cellular level to the point of being capable of supporting life independently of the mother

DEEPER INSIGHT 29.1

CLINICAL APPLICATION

Twins

There are two ways in which twins are produced (and, by extension, other multiple births). About two-thirds of twins are *dizygotic (DZ)*—produced when two eggs are ovulated and fertilized by separate sperm. They are no more or less genetically similar than any other siblings and may be of different sexes. Multiple ovulation can also result in triplets, quadruplets, or even greater numbers of offspring. DZ twins implant separately on the uterine wall and each forms its own placenta **(fig. 29.3),** although their placentas may fuse if they implant close together.

Monozygotic (MZ) twins are produced when a single egg is fertilized and, up to 14 days later, the cell mass divides into two at the morula or embryoblast stage. When the split is early in gestation, each twin usually forms its own amnion and placenta. If it comes late, they may share a single amnion and placenta. Such twins have a high mortality rate because they become entangled in each other's umbilical cords. MZ twins that split still later are at risk of developing as conjoined twins (fused at the head, chest, abdomen, or pelvis). MZ twins are genetically identical, or nearly so, and are therefore of the same sex and nearly identical appearance. Identical triplets and quadruplets occasionally result from the splitting of a single embryoblast.

Reproductive biologists are beginning to question whether MZ twins are truly genetically identical. They have suggested that blastomeres may undergo mutation in the course of DNA replication, and the splitting of the embryoblast may represent an attempt of each cell mass to reject the other one as genetically different and seemingly foreign.

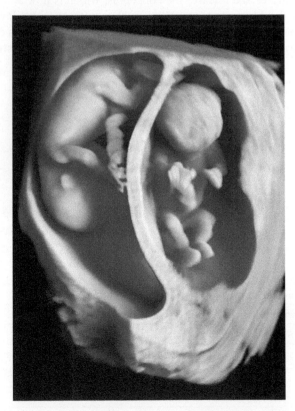

FIGURE 29.3 Dizygotic Twins with Separate Placentas.
A three-dimensional sonogram.

Bernard Benoit/GE Healthcare/Science Source

(BLAST-oh-seal) **(fig. 29.4a).** The trophoblast is destined to form part of the placenta and play an important role in nourishment of the embryo, whereas the embryoblast is destined to become the embryo itself.

Implantation

About 6 days after ovulation, the blastocyst attaches to the endometrium, usually on the fundus or posterior wall of the uterus. The process of attachment, called **implantation,** begins when the blastocyst adheres to the endometrium. The trophoblast cells on this side separate into two layers. In the superficial layer, in contact with the endometrium, the plasma membranes break down and the trophoblast cells fuse into a multinucleate mass called the **syncytiotrophoblast**[4] (sin-SISH-ee-oh-TRO-fo-blast). (A *syncytium* is any body of cytoplasm containing multiple nuclei.) The deep layer, close to the embryoblast, is called the **cytotrophoblast** because it retains individual cells divided by membranes **(fig. 29.4b).**

The syncytiotrophoblast grows into the uterus like little roots, digesting endometrial cells along the way. The endometrium reacts to this injury by growing over the blastocyst and eventually covering it, so the conceptus becomes completely buried in endometrial tissue **(fig. 29.4c).** Implantation takes about a week and is completed about the time the next menstrual period would have occurred if the woman had not become pregnant.

Another role of the trophoblast is to secrete human chorionic gonadotropin (HCG). HCG stimulates the corpus luteum to secrete estrogen and progesterone, and progesterone suppresses menstruation. The level of HCG in the mother's blood rises until the end of the second month. During this time, the trophoblast develops into a membrane called the *chorion,* which takes over the role of the corpus luteum and makes HCG unnecessary. The ovaries then become inactive for the rest of the pregnancy, but estrogen and progesterone levels rise dramatically as they are secreted by the ever-growing chorion (see fig. 28.18).

Embryogenesis

During implantation, the embryoblast undergoes **embryogenesis**—arrangement of the blastomeres into the three primary germ layers: *ectoderm, mesoderm,* and *endoderm.* At the beginning of this phase, the embryoblast separates slightly from the trophoblast, creating a narrow space between them called the **amniotic cavity.** The embryoblast flattens into an **embryonic disc** composed initially of two layers: the *epiblast* facing the amniotic cavity and the *hypoblast* facing away. Some hypoblast cells multiply and form a membrane called the *yolk sac* enclosing the blastocoel. Now the embryonic disc is flanked by two spaces: the amniotic cavity on one side and the yolk sac on the other (fig. 29.4c).

Meanwhile, the embryonic disc elongates and, around day 15, a thickened cell layer called the **primitive streak** forms along the midline of the epiblast, with a **primitive groove** running down its middle **(fig. 29.5).** These events make the embryo bilaterally symmetric and define its future right and left sides, dorsal and ventral surfaces, and cephalic and caudal (head and tail) ends.

[4]*syn* = together; *cyt* = cell

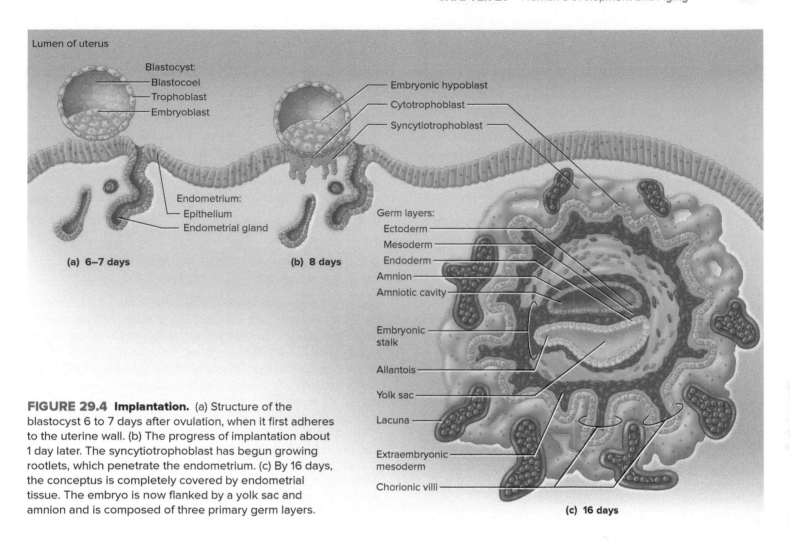

Lumen of uterus

Blastocyst:
- Blastocoel
- Trophoblast
- Embryoblast

Embryonic hypoblast
Cytotrophoblast
Syncytiotrophoblast

Endometrium:
- Epithelium
- Endometrial gland

Germ layers:
- Ectoderm
- Mesoderm
- Endoderm

Amnion
Amniotic cavity

Embryonic stalk

Allantois

Yolk sac

Lacuna

Extraembryonic mesoderm

Chorionic villi

(a) 6–7 days

(b) 8 days

(c) 16 days

FIGURE 29.4 Implantation. (a) Structure of the blastocyst 6 to 7 days after ovulation, when it first adheres to the uterine wall. (b) The progress of implantation about 1 day later. The syncytiotrophoblast has begun growing rootlets, which penetrate the endometrium. (c) By 16 days, the conceptus is completely covered by endometrial tissue. The embryo is now flanked by a yolk sac and amnion and is composed of three primary germ layers.

DEEPER INSIGHT 29.2

CLINICAL APPLICATION

Ectopic Pregnancy

In about 1 out of 300 pregnancies, the blastocyst implants somewhere other than the uterus, producing an *ectopic*[5] *pregnancy.* Most cases are *tubal pregnancies,* implantation in the uterine tube. This usually occurs because the conceptus encounters a constriction resulting from such causes as earlier pelvic inflammatory disease, tubal surgery, previous ectopic pregnancies, or repeated miscarriages. The uterine tube can't expand enough to accommodate the growing conceptus for long; if the situation isn't detected and treated early, the tube usually ruptures within 12 weeks, potentially with fatal hemorrhaging. Occasionally, a conceptus implants in the abdominopelvic cavity, producing an *abdominal pregnancy.* It can grow anywhere it finds an adequate blood supply—for example, on the broad ligament or the outside of the uterus, colon, or bladder. About 1 pregnancy in 7,000 is abdominal. This is a serious threat to the mother's life and usually requires therapeutic abortion, but about 9% of abdominal pregnancies result in live birth by cesarean section.

[5]*ec* = outside; *top* = place

The next step is **gastrulation**—multiplying epiblast cells migrate medially toward the primitive groove and down into it. They replace the original hypoblast with a layer now called **endoderm,** which will become the inner lining of the digestive tract among other things. A day later, migrating epiblast cells form a third layer between the first two, called **mesoderm.** Once this is formed, the remaining epiblast is called **ectoderm.** Thus, all three primary germ layers arise from the original epiblast. Some mesoderm overflows the embryonic disc and becomes an extensive *extraembryonic mesoderm,* which contributes to formation of the placenta (fig. 29.4c).

The ectoderm and endoderm are epithelia composed of tightly joined cells, but the mesoderm is a more loosely organized tissue. It later differentiates into skeletal muscle and a fetal connective tissue called **mesenchyme**—a loose network of wispy *mesenchymal cells* embedded in a gelatinous ground substance. Mesenchyme, in turn, differentiates into such tissues as smooth and cardiac muscle, cartilage, bone, and blood.

Once the three primary germ layers are formed, embryogenesis is complete and the individual is considered an embryo. It is about 2 mm long and 16 days old at this point.

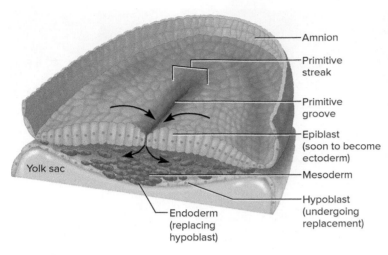

FIGURE 29.5 Formation of the Primary Germ Layers (Gastrulation). Composite view of the embryosnic disc at 15 to 16 days. Epiblast cells migrate over the surface and down into the primitive groove, first replacing the hypoblast cells with endoderm, then filling the space with mesoderm. Upon completion of this process, the uppermost layer is considered ectoderm.

BEFORE YOU GO ON

Answer the following questions to test your understanding of the preceding section:

1. How soon can a sperm reach an egg after ejaculation? How soon can it fertilize an egg? What accounts for the difference?

2. Describe two ways a fertilized egg prevents the entry of excess sperm.

3. In the blastocyst, what are the cells called that eventually give rise to the embryo? What are the cells that carry out implantation?

4. What major characteristic distinguishes an embryo from a preembryo?

29.2 The Embryonic and Fetal Stages

Expected Learning Outcomes

When you have completed this section, you should be able to

a. describe the formation and functions of the placenta;

b. explain how the conceptus is nourished before the placenta takes over this function;

c. describe the embryonic membranes and their functions;

d. identify the major tissues derived from the primary germ layers;

e. describe the major events of fetal development; and

f. describe the fetal circulatory system.

Sixteen days after conception, the germ layers are present and the **embryonic stage** of development begins. Over the next 6 weeks, a placenta forms on the uterine wall and becomes the embryo's primary means of nutrition, while the germ layers differentiate into organs and organ systems—a process called **organogenesis (table 29.2).** Although these organs are still far from functional, it is their presence at 8 weeks that marks the transition from the embryonic stage to the fetal stage. In the following pages, we will examine the transformation from embryo to fetus, how the membranes collectively known as the "afterbirth" develop around the fetus, and how the conceptus is nourished throughout its gestation.

29.2a Embryonic Folding and Organogenesis

One of the major transformations to occur in the embryonic stage is conversion of the flat embryonic disc of figure 29.5 into a somewhat cylindrical form. This occurs during week 4 as the embryo rapidly grows and folds around the yolk sac **(fig. 29.6).** As the cephalic and caudal ends curve around the ends of the yolk sac, the embryo becomes C-shaped, with the head and tail almost touching. At the same time, the lateral margins of the disc fold around the sides of the yolk sac to form the ventral surface of the embryo. This lateral folding encloses a longitudinal channel, the *primitive gut,* which later becomes the digestive tract.

As a result of embryonic folding, the entire surface is covered with ectoderm, which later produces the epidermis of the skin. In the meantime, the mesoderm splits into two layers. One of them adheres to the ectoderm and the other to the endoderm, opening a body cavity between them called the **coelom** (SEE-loam) (fig. 29.6c). The coelom divides into the thoracic cavity and peritoneal cavity separated by a wall, the diaphragm. By the end of week 5, the thoracic cavity further subdivides into pleural and pericardial cavities.

Two more especially significant events in organogenesis are the appearance of a **neural tube** (fig. 29.6b), which will later become the brain and spinal cord, and segmentation of the mesoderm into blocks of tissue called **somites** (fig. 29.7a, b). These will give rise to the vertebral column, trunk muscles, and dermis of the skin.

We cannot delve at greater length into development of all the organ systems, but this description is at least enough to see how some of them begin to form. Some have also been described in earlier chapters. Some highlights of prenatal development through the end of gestation are summarized in **table 29.3.** Prenatal growth is charted by weight and body length. Body length is customarily measured from the crown of the head to the curve of the buttocks *(crown-to-rump length, CRL),* thus excluding the lower limbs. **Figure 29.7** illustrates some key features of embryonic and fetal development. In the following discussion, we will see how these features unfold.

▶▶▶ **APPLY WHAT YOU KNOW**

List the four primary tissue types of the adult body (see section 5.1) and identify which of the three primary germ layers of the embryo predominantly gives rise to each.

TABLE 29.2	Derivatives of the Three Primary Germ Layers
Germ Layer	**Major Derivatives**
Ectoderm	Epidermis; hair follicles and arrector muscles; cutaneous glands; nervous system; adrenal medulla; pineal and pituitary glands; lens, cornea, and intrinsic muscles of the eye; internal and external ear; salivary glands; epithelia of nasal cavity, oral cavity, and anal canal
Mesoderm	Bones; bone marrow; cartilage; skeletal, cardiac, and most smooth muscle; adrenal cortex; middle ear; dermis; blood; blood and lymphatic vessels; lymphatic tissue; epithelium of kidneys, ureters, gonads, and genital ducts; mesothelium of abdominal and thoracic cavities
Endoderm	Most mucosal epithelium of digestive and respiratory tracts; mucosal epithelium of urinary bladder and parts of urethra; epithelial components of accessory reproductive and digestive glands (except salivary glands); thyroid and parathyroid glands; thymus

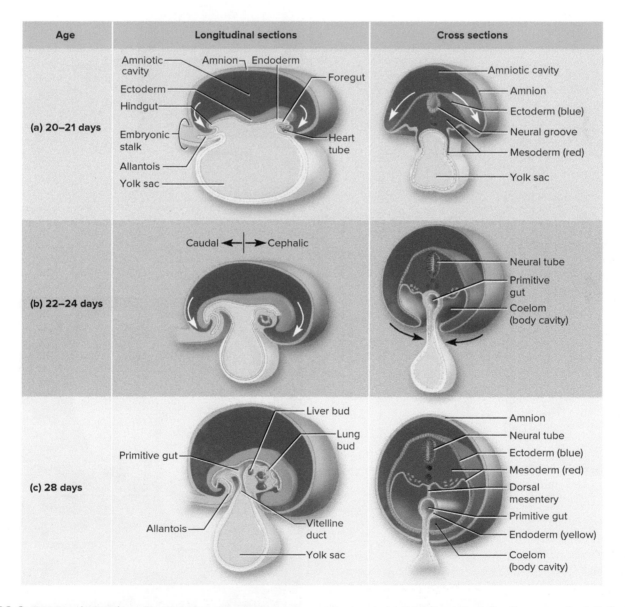

FIGURE 29.6 Embryonic Folding. The right-hand figures are cross sections cut about midway along the figures on the left. Part (a) corresponds to figure 29.4c at a slightly later stage of development. Note the general trend for the cephalic and caudal (head and tail) ends of the embryo to curl toward each other (left-hand figures) until the embryo assumes a C shape, and for the flanks of the embryo to fold laterally (right-hand figures), converting the flat embryonic disc into a more cylindrical body and eventually enclosing a body cavity (c).

FIGURE 29.7 The Developing Human. Parts (a) through (d) show development through the end of the embryonic stage. Parts (e) and (f) represent the fetal stage of development.

a: Source: Human Developmental Anatomy Center, National Museum of Health and Medicine, Silver Spring, MD, USA; **b:** Anatomical Travelogue/Science Source; **c:** ISM/Medical Images; **d:** Dr G. Moscoso/Science Source; **e:** John Watney/Science Source; **f:** Biophoto Associates/Science Source

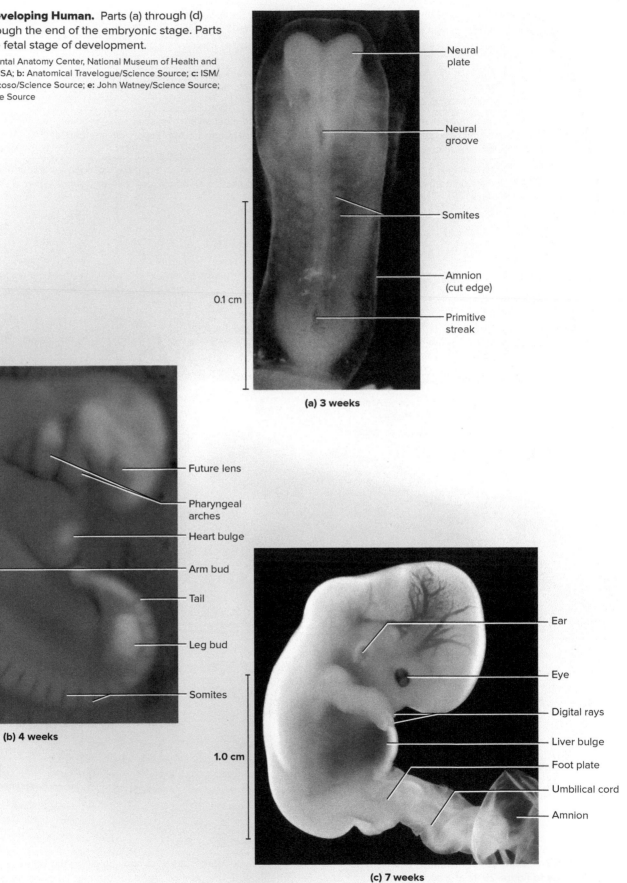

(a) 3 weeks

(b) 4 weeks

(c) 7 weeks

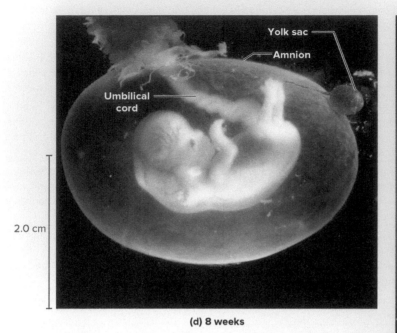

(d) 8 weeks

Yolk sac

Amnion

Umbilical cord

2.0 cm

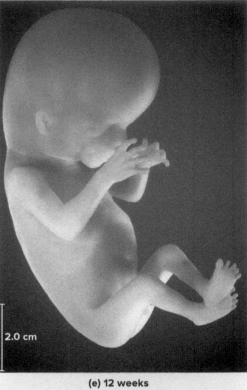

(e) 12 weeks

2.0 cm

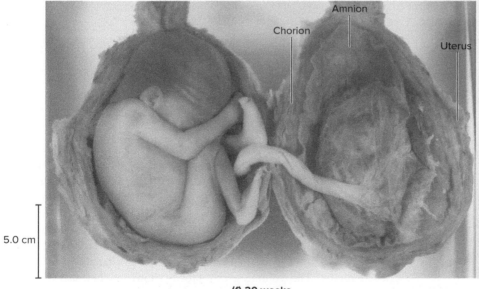

Amnion

Chorion

Uterus

(f) 20 weeks

5.0 cm

TABLE 29.3		Major Events of Prenatal Development, with Emphasis on the Fetal Stage
End of Week	**Crown-to-Rump Length; Weight**	**Developmental Events**
4	0.6 cm; <1 g	Vertebral column and central nervous system begin to form; limbs represented by small limb buds; heart begins beating around day 22; no visible eyes, nose, or ears
8	3 cm; 1 g	Eyes form, eyelids fused shut; nose flat, nostrils evident but plugged with mucus; head nearly as large as the rest of the body; brain waves detectable; bone calcification begins; limb buds form paddlelike hands and feet with ridges called **digital rays,** which then separate into distinct fingers and toes; blood cells and major blood vessels form; genitals present but sexes not yet distinguishable
12	9 cm; 45 g	Eyes well developed, facing laterally; eyelids still fused; nose develops bridge; external ears present; limbs well formed, digits exhibit nails; fetus swallows amniotic fluid and produces urine; fetus moves, but too weakly for mother to feel it; liver is prominent and produces bile; palate is fusing; sexes can be distinguished
16	14 cm; 200 g	Eyes face anteriorly, external ears stand out from head, face looks more distinctly human; body larger in proportion to head; skin is bright pink, scalp has hair; joints forming; lips exhibit sucking movements; kidneys well formed; digestive glands forming and **meconium**[6] (fetal feces) accumulating in intestine; heartbeat can be heard with a stethoscope
20	19 cm; 460 g	Body covered with fine **downy hair (lanugo**[7]**)** and cheeselike sebaceous secretion called **vernix caseosa,**[8] which protects it from amniotic fluid; skin bright pink; brown fat forms and will be used for postpartum heat production; fetus is now bent forward into "fetal position" because of crowding; **quickening** occurs—mother can feel fetal movements
24	23 cm; 820 g	Eyes partially open; skin wrinkled, pink, and translucent; lungs begin producing surfactant; rapid weight gain
28	27 cm; 1,300 g	Eyes fully open; skin wrinkled and red; full head of hair present; eyelashes formed; fetus turns into upside-down **vertex position;** testes begin to descend into scrotum; marginally viable if born at 28 weeks
32	30 cm; 2,100 g	Subcutaneous fat deposition gives fetus a more plump, babyish appearance, with lighter, less wrinkled skin; testes descending; twins usually born at this stage
36	34 cm; 2,900 g	More subcutaneous fat deposited, body plump; downy hair is shed; nails extend to fingertips; limbs flexed; firm hand grip
38	36 cm; 3,400 g	Prominent chest, protruding breasts; testes in inguinal canal or scrotum; fingernails extend beyond fingertips

29.2b Embryonic Membranes

Several accessory organs develop alongside the embryo: a *placenta; umbilical cord;* and four embryonic membranes called the *amnion, yolk sac, allantois,* and *chorion* (figs. 29.6, 29.7). To understand these membranes, it helps to realize that all mammals evolved from egg-laying reptiles. Within the shelled, self-contained egg of a reptile, the embryo rests atop a yolk, which is enclosed in the yolk sac; it floats in a little sea of liquid contained in the amnion; it stores its toxic wastes in the allantois; and to breathe, it has a chorion permeable to gases. All of these membranes persist in mammals, including humans, but are modified in their functions.

The **amnion** is a transparent sac that develops from cells of the epiblast (see figs. 29.4c, 29.5). It grows to completely enclose the embryo and is penetrated only by the umbilical cord. The amnion fills with **amniotic fluid** (fig. 29.7d), which protects the embryo

from trauma, infection, and temperature fluctuations; allows the freedom of movement important to muscle development; enables the embryo to develop symmetrically; prevents body parts from adhering to each other, such as an arm to the trunk; and stimulates lung development as the fetus "breathes" the fluid. At first, the amniotic fluid forms by filtration of the mother's blood plasma, but beginning at 8 to 9 weeks, the fetus urinates into the amniotic cavity about once an hour and contributes substantially to the fluid volume. The volume grows slowly, however, because the fetus swallows amniotic fluid at a comparable rate. At term, the amnion contains 700 to 1,000 mL of fluid.

The **yolk sac** arises from hypoblast cells opposite the amnion. It is a small sac suspended from the ventral side of the embryo. It contributes to the formation of the digestive tract and produces the first blood cells and forerunners of the future egg or sperm cells.

The **allantois** (ah-LON-toe-iss) begins as an outpocketing of the yolk sac (see fig. 29.4c), but eventually becomes an outgrowth of the caudal end of the gut. It forms the foundation for the umbilical cord and becomes part of the urinary bladder. It can be seen in cross sections of umbilical cord cut near the fetal end.

---

[6]*mecon* = poppy juice, opium; refers to an appearance similar to black tar opium
[7]*lan* = down, wool
[8]*vernix* = varnish; *caseo* = cheese

The **chorion** is the outermost membrane, enclosing all the rest of the membranes and the embryo (fig. 29.7f). Initially, it has shaggy outgrowths called **chorionic villi** around its entire surface, but as the pregnancy advances, the villi of the placental region grow and branch while the rest of them degenerate. At the placental attachment, the chorion is then called the *villous chorion,* and the rest is called the *smooth chorion.* The villous chorion forms the fetal portion of the placenta, discussed shortly.

29.2c Prenatal Nutrition

Over the course of gestation, the conceptus is nourished in three different, overlapping ways: by *uterine milk, trophoblastic nutrition,* and *placental nutrition.*

Uterine milk is a glycogen-rich secretion of the uterine tubes and endometrial glands. The conceptus absorbs this fluid as it travels down the tube and lies free in the uterine cavity before implantation. The accumulating fluid forms the blastocoel in figure 29.4a.

As it implants, the conceptus makes a transition to **trophoblastic nutrition,** in which it consumes so-called **decidual**[9] **cells** of the endometrium. Progesterone from the corpus luteum stimulates these cells to proliferate and accumulate a store of glycogen, proteins, and lipids. As the conceptus burrows into the endometrium, the syncytiotrophoblast digests the decidual cells and supplies the nutrients to the embryoblast. Trophoblastic nutrition is the only mode of nutrition for the first week after implantation. It remains the dominant source of nutrients through the end of week 8; the period from implantation through week 8 is therefore called the **trophoblastic phase** of the pregnancy. Trophoblastic nutrition wanes as placental nutrition takes over, and ceases entirely by the end of week 12 **(fig. 29.8).**

The **placenta**[10] is the fetus's life-support system—a disc-shaped organ attached to the uterine wall on one side, and on the other, attached to the fetus by way of the **umbilical cord** **(fig. 29.9).** It is the fetus's source of oxygen and nutrients, and its means of waste disposal. The diffusion of nutrients from the mother's blood through the placenta into the fetal blood is called **placental nutrition.**

The placenta begins to develop about 11 days after conception, becomes the dominant mode of nutrition around the beginning of week 9, and is the sole mode of nutrition from the end of week 12 until birth. The period from week 9 until birth is called the **placental phase** of the pregnancy.

Figure 29.4 depicts the early development of the placenta, or *placentation.* The process begins during implantation, as extensions of the syncytiotrophoblast penetrate more and more deeply into the endometrium, like the roots of a tree penetrating into the nourishing "soil" of the uterus. These roots are the early chorionic villi. As they penetrate uterine blood vessels, they become surrounded by *lacunae,* or endometrial spaces filled with maternal blood (see fig. 29.4c). The lacunae eventually merge to form a single blood-filled cavity, the **placental sinus.** Exposure to maternal blood stimulates increasingly rapid growth of the villi, which

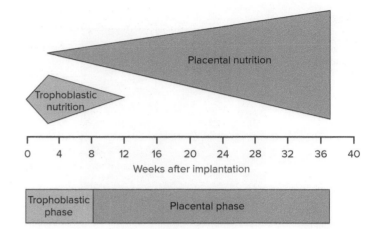

FIGURE 29.8 The Timetable of Trophoblastic and Placental Nutrition. Trophoblastic nutrition peaks at 2 weeks and ends by 12 weeks. Placental nutrition begins at 2 weeks and becomes increasingly important until birth, 37 weeks after implantation. The two modes of nutrition overlap up to the twelfth week, but the *trophoblast phase* is the period in which most nutrients are supplied by trophoblastic nutrition, and the *placental phase* is the period in which most (eventually all) nutrition comes from the placenta.

? *At what point do the two modes contribute equally to prenatal nutrition?*

become branched and treelike. Extraembryonic mesoderm grows into the villi and gives rise to the blood vessels that connect to the embryo by way of the umbilical cord.

When fully developed, the placenta is about 20 cm in diameter, 3 cm thick, and weighs about one-sixth as much as the newborn infant. The surface attached to the uterine wall is rough and consists of chorionic villi embedded in the endometrium. The surface facing the fetus is smooth and gives rise to the umbilical cord (fig. 29.9).

The umbilical cord contains two **umbilical arteries** and one **umbilical vein.** Pumped by the fetal heart, blood flows into the placenta by way of the umbilical arteries and then returns to the fetus by way of the umbilical vein. The chorionic villi are *filled with* fetal blood and *surrounded by* maternal blood (fig. 29.9a); the two bloodstreams don't mix unless there is damage to the placental barrier. The barrier, however, is only 3.5 μm thick—half the diameter of a red blood cell. Early in development, the villi have thick membranes that are not very permeable to nutrients and wastes, and their total surface area is relatively small. As the villi grow and branch, their surface area increases and the membranes become thinner and more permeable. This brings about a dramatic increase in *placental conductivity,* the rate at which substances diffuse through the membrane. Materials diffuse from the side of the membrane where they are more concentrated to the side where they are less so. Therefore, oxygen and nutrients pass from the maternal blood to the fetal blood, while fetal wastes pass the other way to be eliminated by the mother. Unfortunately, the placenta is also permeable to nicotine, alcohol, and other drugs that may be present in the maternal bloodstream.

---

[9]*decid* = falling off
[10]*placenta* = flat cake

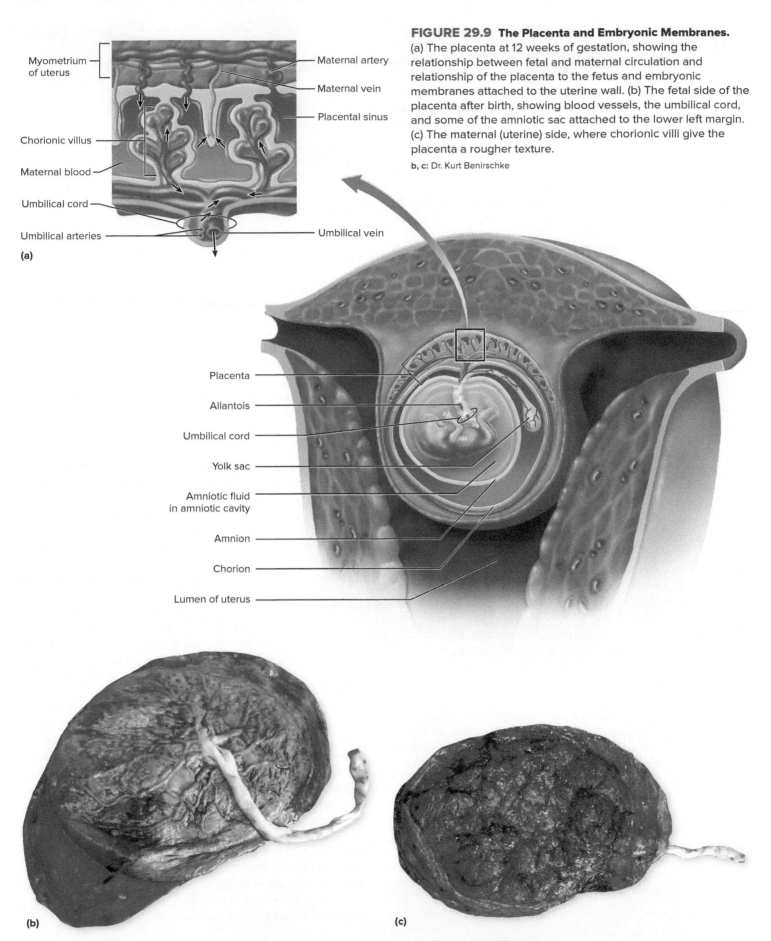

Myometrium of uterus

Chorionic villus

Maternal blood

Umbilical cord

Umbilical arteries

Maternal artery

Maternal vein

Placental sinus

Umbilical vein

(a)

FIGURE 29.9 The Placenta and Embryonic Membranes.
(a) The placenta at 12 weeks of gestation, showing the relationship between fetal and maternal circulation and relationship of the placenta to the fetus and embryonic membranes attached to the uterine wall. (b) The fetal side of the placenta after birth, showing blood vessels, the umbilical cord, and some of the amniotic sac attached to the lower left margin. (c) The maternal (uterine) side, where chorionic villi give the placenta a rougher texture.

b, c: Dr. Kurt Benirschke

Placenta

Allantois

Umbilical cord

Yolk sac

Amniotic fluid in amniotic cavity

Amnion

Chorion

Lumen of uterus

(b)

(c)

Table 29.4 summarizes the nutritional, excretory, and other functions of the placenta.

29.2d Fetal Development

By the end of 8 weeks, all of the organ systems are present, the individual is about 3 cm long, and it is now considered a **fetus** (see fig. 29.7d). The bones have just begun to calcify and the skeletal muscles exhibit spontaneous contractions, although these are too weak to be felt by the mother. The heart, beating since the fourth week, now circulates blood. The heart and liver are very large and form the prominent ventral bulge seen in figure 29.7c. The head is nearly half the total body length. The fetus is the final stage of prenatal development, from the start of the ninth week until birth. The organs that formed during the embryonic stage now undergo growth and cellular differentiation, acquiring the functional capability to support life outside the mother.

The circulatory system shows the most conspicuous anatomical changes from a prenatal state, dependent on the placenta, to the independent neonatal (newborn) state **(fig. 29.10).** The unique aspects of fetal circulation are the umbilical–placental circuit and the presence of three circulatory shortcuts called *shunts*. The internal iliac arteries give rise to the umbilical arteries, which pass on either side of the bladder into the umbilical cord. The blood in these arteries is low in oxygen and high in carbon dioxide and other fetal wastes; thus, they are depicted in blue in figure 29.10a. The arterial blood discharges its wastes in the placenta, loads oxygen and nutrients, and returns to the fetus by way of a single umbilical vein, which leads toward the liver. The umbilical vein is depicted in red because of its well-oxygenated blood. Some of this venous blood filters through the liver to nourish it. However, the immature liver is not capable of performing many of its postpartum functions, so it doesn't require a great deal of perfusion before birth. Most of the venous blood therefore bypasses it by way of a shunt called the **ductus venosus,** which leads directly to the inferior vena cava.

In the inferior vena cava, placental blood mixes with venous blood from the fetus's body and flows to the right atrium of the heart. After birth, the right ventricle pumps all of its blood into the lungs, but there is little need for this in the fetus because the lungs aren't yet functional. Therefore, most fetal blood bypasses the pulmonary circuit. Some goes directly from the right atrium to the left through the **foramen ovale,** a hole in the interatrial septum. Some also goes into the right ventricle and is pumped into the pulmonary trunk, but most of this is routed to the aorta by way of a short shunt called the **ductus arteriosus.** This occurs because the collapsed state of the fetal lungs creates high resistance and blood pressure in the pulmonary circuit, so blood in the pulmonary trunk takes a path of less resistance—through the ductus into the aorta, where the blood pressure is lower. The lungs receive only a trickle of blood, sufficient to meet their metabolic needs during development. Blood leaving the left ventricle enters the general systemic circulation, and some of this returns

TABLE 29.4	Functions of the Placenta
Nutritional roles	Permits nutrients such as glucose, amino acids, fatty acids, minerals, and vitamins to diffuse from the maternal blood to the fetal blood; stores nutrients such as carbohydrates, protein, iron, and calcium in early pregnancy and releases them to the fetus later, when daily fetal demand is greater than the mother can absorb from the diet
Excretory roles	Permits nitrogenous wastes such as ammonia, urea, uric acid, and creatinine to diffuse from the fetal blood to the maternal blood so the mother can excrete them
Respiratory roles	Permits O_2 to diffuse from mother to fetus and CO_2 from fetus to mother
Endocrine roles	Secretes estrogens, progesterone, relaxin, human chorionic gonadotropin, and human chorionic somatomammotropin; allows other hormones synthesized by the conceptus to pass into the mother's blood and maternal hormones to pass into the fetal blood
Immune roles	Transfers maternal antibodies (especially IgG) into the fetal blood to confer passive immunity on the fetus

to the placenta. This circulatory pattern changes dramatically at birth, when the neonate is cut off from the placenta and the lungs expand with air. Those changes will be described later.

Full-term fetuses have an average crown-to-rump length of about 36 cm (14 in.) and average weight of about 3.0 to 3.4 kg (6.6–7.5 lb). The fetus gains about 50% of its birth weight in the last 10 weeks.

Review table 29.3 and figure 29.7 for additional aspects of fetal development.

BEFORE YOU GO ON

Answer the following questions to test your understanding of the preceding section:

5. Distinguish between trophoblastic and placental nutrition.

6. Identify the two sources of blood to the placenta. Where do these two bloodstreams come closest to each other? What keeps them separated?

7. State the functions of the placenta, amnion, chorion, yolk sac, and allantois.

8. What developmental characteristic distinguishes a fetus from an embryo? At what gestational age is this attained?

9. Identify the three circulatory shunts of the fetus. Why does the blood take these "shortcuts" before birth?

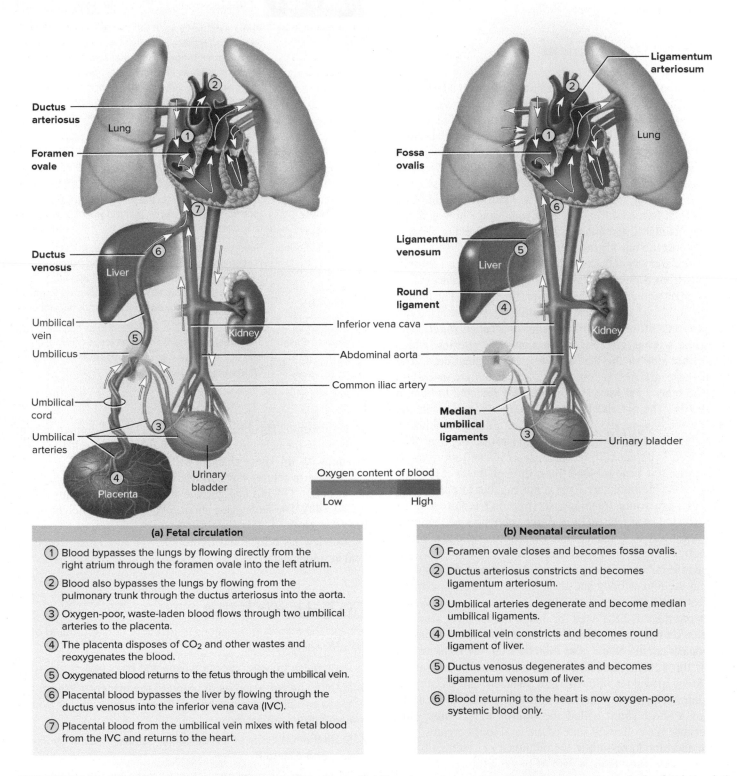

(a) Fetal circulation

1. Blood bypasses the lungs by flowing directly from the right atrium through the foramen ovale into the left atrium.

2. Blood also bypasses the lungs by flowing from the pulmonary trunk through the ductus arteriosus into the aorta.

3. Oxygen-poor, waste-laden blood flows through two umbilical arteries to the placenta.

4. The placenta disposes of CO_2 and other wastes and reoxygenates the blood.

5. Oxygenated blood returns to the fetus through the umbilical vein.

6. Placental blood bypasses the liver by flowing through the ductus venosus into the inferior vena cava (IVC).

7. Placental blood from the umbilical vein mixes with fetal blood from the IVC and returns to the heart.

(b) Neonatal circulation

1. Foramen ovale closes and becomes fossa ovalis.

2. Ductus arteriosus constricts and becomes ligamentum arteriosum.

3. Umbilical arteries degenerate and become median umbilical ligaments.

4. Umbilical vein constricts and becomes round ligament of liver.

5. Ductus venosus degenerates and becomes ligamentum venosum of liver.

6. Blood returning to the heart is now oxygen-poor, systemic blood only.

FIGURE 29.10 Blood Circulation in the Fetus and Newborn. Boldface terms in part (a) indicate the three shunts in the fetal circulation, which allow most blood to bypass the liver and lungs. Boldface terms in part (b) indicate the postpartum vestiges of fetal structures.

29.3 The Neonate

Expected Learning Outcomes

When you have completed this section, you should be able to

a. describe how and why the circulatory system changes at birth;

b. explain why the first breaths of air are relatively difficult for a neonate;

c. describe the major physiological problems of a premature infant; and

d. discuss some common causes of birth defects.

The period immediately following birth is a crisis in which the neonate suddenly must adapt to life outside the mother's body. The first 6 to 8 hours are a **transitional period** in which the heart and respiratory rates increase and the body temperature falls. Physical activity then declines and the baby sleeps for about 3 hours. In its second period of activity, the baby often gags on mucus and debris in the pharynx. The baby then sleeps again, becomes more stable, and begins a cycle of waking every 3 to 4 hours to feed. The first 4 weeks of life constitute the **neonatal period** and the infant at this stage is called a **neonate.**

29.3a Adapting to Life Outside the Uterus

The most dramatic and suspenseful event at birth is for the neonate to begin breathing on its own. Breathing, of course, is useless unless most or all of the blood circulates through the lungs to exchange gases there. Until birth, most blood has bypassed the lungs, so the onset of breathing also necessitates a radical change in blood circulation. The respiratory and circulatory systems therefore figure prominently in the neonate's adaptations to life outside the uterus, but other systems also must adapt to this new and challenging lifestyle.

Respiratory Adaptations

It is an old misconception that a neonate must be spanked to stimulate it to breathe. During birth, CO_2 accumulates in the baby's blood and strongly stimulates the respiratory chemoreceptors. Unless the infant is depressed by oversedation of the mother, it normally begins breathing spontaneously. It requires a great effort, however, to take the first few breaths and inflate the collapsed alveoli. For the first 2 weeks, a baby takes about 45 breaths per minute, but subsequently stabilizes at about 12 breaths per minute.

Circulatory Adaptations

When the lungs expand with air, resistance and blood pressure in the pulmonary circuit drop rapidly and pressure in the right heart falls below that in the left. Blood flows briefly from the left atrium to the right through the foramen ovale (opposite from its prenatal flow) and pushes two flaps of tissue into place to close this shunt. In most people, these flaps fuse and permanently seal the foramen during the first year, leaving a depression, the *fossa ovalis,* in the interatrial septum (see fig. 19.7). In about 25% of people, however,

the foramen ovale remains unsealed and the flaps are held in place only by the relatively high blood pressure in the left atrium. Pressure changes in the pulmonary trunk and aorta also cause the ductus arteriosus to collapse. It closes permanently around 3 months of age and leaves a permanent cord, the *ligamentum arteriosum,* between the two vessels.

After the umbilical cord is clamped and cut, the umbilical arteries and vein collapse and become fibrotic. The proximal part of each umbilical artery becomes the *superior vesical artery,* which remains to supply the bladder. Other obliterated vessels become fibrous cords or ligaments: The distal parts of the umbilical arteries become the *median umbilical ligaments* of the abdominal wall; the umbilical vein becomes the *round ligament (ligamentum teres)* of the liver; and the ductus venosus (a former shunt around the liver) becomes the *ligamentum venosum* on the inferior surface of the liver (fig. 29.10b).

Immunologic Adaptations

Cellular immunity begins to appear early in fetal development, but the immune responses of the neonate are still weak. Fortunately, an infant is born with a near-adult level of IgG acquired from the mother through the placenta. This maternal IgG breaks down rapidly after birth, declining to about half the initial level in the first month and to essentially none by 10 months. Nevertheless, maternal IgG levels remain high enough for 6 months to protect the infant from measles, diphtheria, polio, and most other infectious diseases (but not whooping cough). By 6 months, the infant's own IgG reaches about half the typical adult level. The lowest total (maternal + infant) level of IgG exists around 5 to 6 months of age, and respiratory infections are especially common at that age. The IgA in the colostrum also gives a breast-fed neonate immune protection against gastroenteritis.

Other Adaptations

Thermoregulation and fluid balance are also critical aspects of neonatal physiology. An infant has a larger ratio of surface area to volume than an adult does, so it loses heat more easily. One of its defenses against hypothermia is brown fat, a special adipose tissue deposited from weeks 17 to 20 of fetal development. The mitochondria of brown fat release all the energy of fatty acids as heat rather than using it to make ATP; thus, this is a heat-generating tissue. As a baby grows, its metabolic rate increases and it accumulates even more subcutaneous fat, thus producing and retaining more heat. Nevertheless, body temperature is more variable in infants and children than in adults.

The kidneys aren't fully developed at birth and can't concentrate the urine as much as a mature kidney can. Consequently, infants have a relatively high rate of water loss and require more fluid intake, relative to body weight, than adults do.

In addition, the liver is still not fully functional at birth, most joints aren't yet ossified, and myelination of the nervous system isn't completed until adolescence. Indeed, humans are born in a very immature state compared with other mammals—a fact necessitated by the narrow outlet of the female pelvis, which in turn was a product of the evolution of bipedal locomotion (see Deeper Insight 8.5).

DEEPER INSIGHT 29.3

CLINICAL APPLICATION

Neonatal Assessment

A newborn infant is immediately evaluated for general appearance, vital signs (temperature, pulse, and respiratory rate), weight, length, and head circumference and other dimensions; and it is screened for congenital disorders such as phenylketonuria (PKU). At 1 minute and 5 minutes after birth, the heart rate, respiratory effort, muscle tone, reflexes, and skin color are noted and given a score of 0 (poor), 1, or 2 (excellent). The total (0–10), called the *Apgar*[11] *score,* is a good predictor of infant survival. Infants with low Apgar scores may have neurological damage and need immediate attention if they are to survive. A low score at 1 minute suggests asphyxiation and may demand assisted ventilation. A low score at 5 minutes indicates a high probability of death.

29.3b Premature Infants

Infants born before the start of week 37 are generally considered **premature.** They have multiple difficulties in respiration, thermoregulation, excretion, digestion, and liver function. Neonates born at that age average about 2.6 kg (5.8 lb). Most neonates weighing 1.5 to 2.5 kg are viable, but with difficulty. Those weighing under 500 g rarely survive.

The respiratory system is adequately developed by 7 months of gestation to support independent life. Infants born before this have a deficiency of pulmonary surfactant, causing **infant respiratory distress syndrome (IRDS),** also called *hyaline membrane disease.* The alveoli collapse each time the infant exhales, and a great effort is needed to reinflate them. The infant becomes very fatigued by the high energy demand of breathing. IRDS may be treated by ventilating the lungs with oxygen-enriched air at a positive pressure to keep the lungs inflated between breaths, and by administering surfactant as an inhalant. Nevertheless, IRDS remains the most common cause of neonatal death.

A premature infant has an incompletely developed hypothalamus and therefore cannot thermoregulate effectively. Body temperature must be controlled by placing the infant in a warmer.

It is difficult for premature infants to ingest milk because of their small stomach volume and underdeveloped sucking and swallowing reflexes. Some must be fed by nasogastric or nasoduodenal tubes. Most of them, however, can tolerate human milk or formulas. Infants under 1.5 kg (3.3 lb) require nutritional supplements of calcium, phosphorus, and protein.

The liver is also poorly developed, and bearing in mind its very diverse functions (see table 26.6), you can probably understand why this would have several serious consequences. The liver synthesizes inadequate amounts of albumin, so the baby suffers hypoproteinemia. This upsets the balance between capillary filtration and reabsorption and leads to edema. The infant bleeds easily because of a deficiency of the clotting factors synthesized by the liver. This is true to some degree even in full-term infants, however,

because the baby's intestines are not yet colonized by the bacteria that synthesize vitamin K, which is essential for the synthesis of clotting factors. Vitamin K injections are now routine (but somewhat controversial) for newborns in the United States. Jaundice is common in neonates, especially premature babies, because the liver can't dispose of bile pigments such as bilirubin efficiently. A moderately elevated bilirubin level *(neonatal hyperbilirubinemia)* is normal and desirable in all infants, however. Bilirubin plays a valuable role as an antioxidant until the infant can develop its other antioxidant systems.

29.3c Birth Defects

A birth defect, or **congenital anomaly,**[12] is the abnormal structure or position of an organ at birth, resulting from a defect in prenatal development. The study of birth defects is called **teratology.**[13] Birth defects are the most common cause of infant mortality in North America. Not all of them are noticeable at birth; some are detected months to years later. Thus, by the age of 2 years, 6% of children are diagnosed with congenital anomalies, and by age 5 the incidence is 8% because of those that have made their presence known in the interim. The following sections discuss some known causes of congenital anomalies, but in 50% to 60% of cases, the cause is unknown.

Teratogens

Teratogens[14] are agents that cause anatomical deformities in the fetus. They fall into three major classes: drugs and other chemicals, infectious diseases, and radiation such as X-rays. The effect of a teratogen depends on the genetic susceptibility of the embryo, the dosage of the teratogen, and the time of exposure. Teratogen exposure during the first 2 weeks usually doesn't cause birth defects, mainly because the affected embryo doesn't survive to birth; most abort. Teratogens can exert destructive effects at any stage of development, but the period of greatest vulnerability is weeks 3 through 8. Different organs have different critical periods. For example, limb abnormalities are most likely to result from teratogen exposure at 24 to 36 days, and brain abnormalities from exposure at 3 to 16 weeks.

Perhaps the most notorious teratogenic drug is thalidomide, a sedative first marketed in West Germany in 1957. Thalidomide was taken by many women in early pregnancy to relieve morning sickness, and by others as a sleeping aid even before they knew they were pregnant. By the time it was removed from the market in 1961, it had affected an estimated 10,000 to 20,000 babies worldwide, many of them born with unformed arms or legs **(fig. 29.11)** and often with defects of the ears, heart, and intestines. The U.S. Food and Drug Administration never approved thalidomide for market, but many American women obtained it from foreign sources or by participation in clinical drug trials. Thalidomide has recently been reintroduced and used under more tightly controlled conditions for more limited purposes such as treating leprosy.

[12]*con* = with; *gen* = born; *a* = without; *nomaly* = evenness, regularity
[13]*terato* = monster; *logy* = study of
[14]*terato* = monster; *gen* = producing

FIGURE 29.11 Schoolboy Showing the Effect of Thalidomide on Upper Limb Development.
Time & Life Pictures/Getty Images

People in some Third World countries still take it in a misguided attempt to treat AIDS and other diseases, resulting in an upswing in severe birth defects. A general lesson to be learned from the thalidomide tragedy and other cases is that pregnant women should avoid all sedatives, barbiturates, and opiates. Even the acne medicine isotretinoin (Accutane) has caused severe birth defects. Many teratogens produce less obvious or delayed effects, including physical or mental impairment, inattention, hyperirritability, strokes, seizures, respiratory arrest, crib death, and cancer.

Alcohol causes more birth defects than any other drug. A pregnant woman taking even one drink a day can noticeably affect fetal and childhood development, with some effects not noticed until a child begins school. Alcohol abuse during pregnancy can cause **fetal alcohol syndrome (FAS),** characterized by a small head, malformed facial features, cardiac and central nervous system defects, stunted growth, and behavioral signs such as hyperactivity, nervousness, and a poor attention span. Cigarette smoking also contributes to fetal and infant mortality, ectopic pregnancy, anencephaly (failure of the cerebrum to develop), cleft lip and palate, and cardiac abnormalities. Diagnostic X-rays should be avoided during pregnancy because radiation can have teratogenic effects.

Infectious diseases are largely beyond the scope of this book, but it must be noted at least briefly that several microorganisms can cross the placenta and cause serious congenital anomalies, stillbirth, or neonatal death. Common viral infections of the fetus and newborn include herpes simplex, rubella, cytomegalovirus, and human immunodeficiency virus (HIV). Many infants were born in 2016, especially in Brazil, with *microcephaly* (abnormally small

heads) attributed to the mosquito-borne Zika virus. Congenital bacterial infections include gonorrhea and syphilis. *Toxoplasma,* a protozoan contracted from meat, unpasteurized milk, and house cats, is another common cause of fetal deformity. Some of these pathogens have relatively mild effects on adults, but because of its immature immune system, the fetus is vulnerable to devastating effects such as blindness, hydrocephalus, cerebral palsy, seizures, and profound physical and mental retardation. These diseases are treated in greater detail in microbiology textbooks.

Mutagens and Genetic Anomalies

Genetic anomalies are the most common known cause of birth defects, accounting for an estimated one-third of all cases and 85% of those with an identifiable cause. One cause of genetic defects is **mutations,** or changes in DNA structure. Among other disorders, mutations cause achondroplastic dwarfism (see Deeper Insight 7.2), cleft lip and palate (see Deeper Insight 29.4),

DEEPER INSIGHT 29.4

CLINICAL APPLICATION

Cleft Lip and Palate

Cleft lip and palate (CLP) is one of the most common congenital malformations, occurring in 1 or 2 out of 1,000 live births. Cleft palate (*palatoschizis,* PAL-ah-to-SKIZ-is) results from failure of the fetal maxillae to join on the midline, leaving a median fissure in the roof of the mouth between the oral and nasal cavities **(fig. 29.12).** It is often accompanied by an upper lip cleft (*cheiloschizis,* KY-lo-SKIZ-is) on one or both sides. A cleft palate makes it difficult for an infant to generate the suction needed for nursing, and may be accompanied by frequent ear infections, abnormal tooth development, and difficulties in hearing and speech. In recent years, at least 10 genes on 8 chromosomes have been identified that cause CLP, but it can also have environmental causes such as tobacco, alcohol, and corticosteroid use during pregnancy. Cleft lip and palate can be corrected by maxillofacial surgery with good cosmetic results, but may require follow-up speech therapy and dental surgery, often placing a heavy long-term burden on patients and families. Correction by 18 months of age can improve language acquisition and avoid the psychosocial problems often faced by school-age children with CLP.

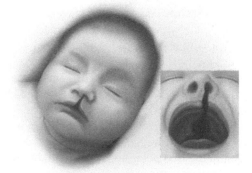

FIGURE 29.12 An Infant with Cleft Lip and Palate. (a) Cleft lip. (b) Cleft palate. Note the fissure between the oral and nasal cavities, which creates problems for nursing infants in suckling and swallowing.

microcephaly, stillbirth, and childhood cancer. Mutations can occur through errors in DNA replication during the cell cycle or under the influence of environmental agents called **mutagens,** including some chemicals, viruses, and radiation.

Some of the most common genetic disorders result not from mutagens, but from the failure of homologous chromosomes to separate during meiosis. Recall that homologous chromosomes pair up during prophase I and normally separate from each other at anaphase I (see section 27.4a). This separation, called *disjunction,* produces daughter cells with 23 chromosomes each.

In **nondisjunction,** a pair of chromosomes fails to separate. Both chromosomes go to the same daughter cell, which receives 24 chromosomes while the other cell receives 22. **Aneuploidy**[15] (AN-you-PLOY-dee), the presence of an extra chromosome or lack of one, is the most common cause of miscarriages, accounting for about 50% of cases. The lack of a chromosome, leaving one chromosome without a match, is called **monosomy,** whereas the presence of one extra chromosome, producing a triple set, is called **trisomy.** Aneuploidy can be detected prior to birth by **amniocentesis,** the examination of cells in a sample of amniotic fluid, or by **chorionic villus sampling (CVS),** the biopsy of cells from the chorion.

Figure 29.13 compares normal disjunction of the X chromosomes with some effects of nondisjunction. In nondisjunction, an egg may receive both X chromosomes. If it is fertilized by an X-bearing sperm, the result is an XXX zygote and a set of anomalies called the **triplo-X syndrome.** Some triplo-X females are infertile, have mild intellectual impairments, or both. If an XX egg is fertilized by a Y-bearing sperm, the result is an XXY combination and **Klinefelter**[16] **syndrome.** People with Klinefelter syndrome are sterile males, usually of average intelligence, but with undeveloped testes, sparse body hair, unusually long arms and legs, and enlarged breasts (*gynecomastia*[17]). This syndrome often goes undetected until puberty, when failure to develop the secondary sex characteristics may prompt genetic testing.

The other possible outcome of X chromosome nondisjunction is that an egg may receive no X chromosome (both X chromosomes are discarded in the first polar body). If fertilized by a Y-bearing sperm, it dies for lack of the indispensable genes on the X chromosome. If it is fertilized by an X-bearing sperm, however, the result

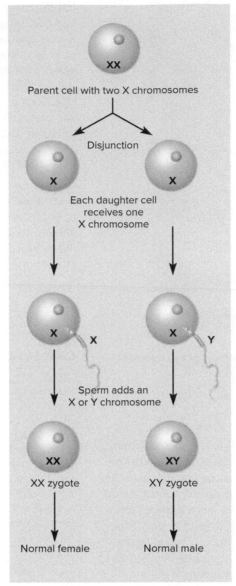

(a) Normal disjunction of X chromosomes

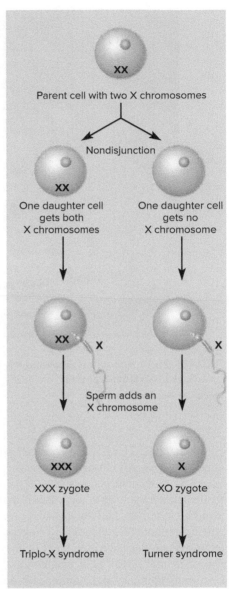

(b) Nondisjunction of X chromosomes

FIGURE 29.13 Disjunction and Nondisjunction. (a) The outcome of normal disjunction and fertilization by X- or Y-bearing sperm. (b) Two of the possible outcomes of nondisjunction followed by fertilization with an X-bearing sperm.

❓ *In the right half of the figure, what would the two outcomes be if the sperm carried a Y chromosome instead of an X?*

is a female with **Turner**[18] **syndrome,** with an XO combination (O represents the absence of one sex chromosome). About 97% of fetuses with Turner syndrome die before birth. Survivors show no serious impairments as children, but tend to have a webbed neck and widely spaced nipples. At puberty, secondary sex characteristics fail to develop **(fig. 29.14).** The ovaries are nearly absent, the girl remains sterile, and she usually has a short stature.

---

[15]*an* = not, without; *eu* = true, normal; *ploid,* from *diplo* = double, paired
[16]Harry F. Klinefelter Jr. (1912–90), American physician
[17]*gyneco* = female; *mast* = breast; *ia* = condition

[18]Henry H. Turner (1892–1970), American endocrinologist

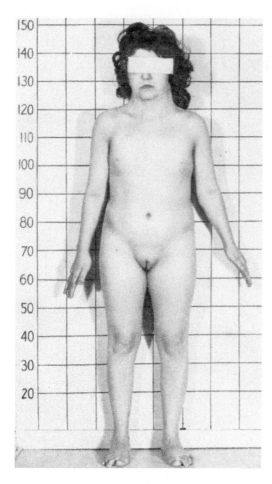

FIGURE 29.14 Turner Syndrome. A 22-year-old woman with Turner syndrome, with an XO karyotype (see figure 29.13, far right). Note her short stature (about 145 cm, or 4 ft 9 in.), lack of sexual development, webbed neck, and widely spaced nipples.

Courtesy Mihaly Bartalos

The other 22 pairs of chromosomes (the *autosomes*) are also subject to nondisjunction. Only three autosomal trisomies are survivable: those involving chromosomes 13, 18, and 21. The reason is that these three chromosomes are relatively gene-poor. In all other autosomal cases, trisomy gives the embryo a lethal "overdose" of genes. Even the nonlethal trisomies are the leading genetic cause of mental and developmental abnormalities.

Nondisjunction of chromosomes 13 and 18 results in *Patau syndrome (trisomy-13)* and *Edward syndrome (trisomy-18)*, respectively. Nearly all fetuses with these trisomies die before birth. Infants born with these syndromes are severely deformed, and fewer than 5% survive for 1 year.

The most survivable trisomy, and therefore the most common among children and adults, is **Down**[19] **syndrome (trisomy-21).** Down syndrome occurs in about 1 out of 700 to 800 live births in the United States. Its signs include impaired physical and

intellectual development; short stature; a relatively flat face with a flat nasal bridge; low-set ears; *epicanthal folds* at the medial corners of the eyes; an enlarged, protruding tongue; stubby fingers; and a short broad hand with only one palmar crease **(fig. 29.15).** People with Down syndrome tend to have outgoing, affectionate personalities. Cognitive impairment is common and sometimes severe, but doesn't always occur.

About 75% of fetuses with trisomy-21 die before birth, and 20% of infants born with it die before the age of 10 from such causes as immune deficiency and abnormalities of the heart or kidneys. For those who survive beyond that age, modern medical care has extended life expectancy to the 60s. After the age of 40, however, about 75% of these people develop early-onset Alzheimer disease, linked to a gene on chromosome 21.

Aneuploidy is far more common in humans than in any other species, and 90% of cases are of maternal rather than paternal origin. These facts seem to result from the extraordinarily long time it takes for human oocytes to complete meiosis—as long as 50 years. For various reasons, including defects in the mitotic spindle and in chromosomal crossing-over, aging eggs become less and less able to separate their chromosomes into two identical sets. This is evident in the statistics of Down syndrome: The chance of having a child with Down syndrome is about 1 in 3,000 for a woman under 30, 1 in 365 by age 35, and 1 in 9 by age 48.

BEFORE YOU GO ON

Answer the following questions to test your understanding of the preceding section.

10. How does inflation of the lungs at birth affect the route of blood flow through the heart?

11. Why is respiratory distress syndrome common in premature infants?

12. Define *nondisjunction* and explain how it causes aneuploidy. Name two syndromes resulting from aneuploidy.

29.4 Aging and Senescence

Expected Learning Outcomes

When you have completed this section, you should be able to

a. define *senescence* and distinguish it from aging;

b. describe some major changes that occur with aging in each organ system;

c. summarize some current theories of senescence; and

d. be able to explain how exercise and other factors can slow the rate of senescence.

Like Ponce de León searching for the legendary fountain of youth in Florida, people yearn for a way to preserve their youthful appearance and function. Our real concern, however, is not aging but senescence. The term **aging** is used in various ways but is taken here to mean all changes that occur in the body with the passage of time—including the growth, development, and increasing

---

[19]John Langdon H. Down (1828–96), British physician

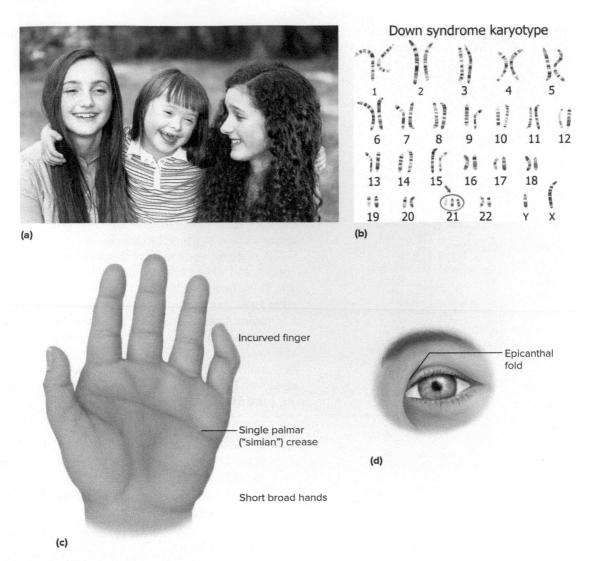

Down syndrome karyotype

FIGURE 29.15 Down Syndrome. (a) A child with Down syndrome (center) and her sisters, who are unaffected by the trisomy. (b) The karyotype (chromosomal chart) of a male with Down syndrome, showing the trisomy of chromosome 21 (oval with arrow). (c) Characteristics of the hand in Down syndrome. (d) The epicanthal fold over the medial commissure (canthus) of the left eye.

a: Denys Kuvaiev/Alamy; b: Zuzana Egertova/Alamy Stock Photo

❓ *What was the sex of the person from whom the karyotype in part (b) was obtained?*

functional efficiency that occur from childhood to adulthood, as well as the degenerative changes that occur later in life. **Senescence** is the degeneration that occurs in an organ system after the age of peak functional efficiency. It includes a gradual loss of reserve capacities, reduced ability to repair damage and compensate for stress, and increased susceptibility to disease.

Senescence is not just a personal concern but an important issue for health-care providers. In the early twentieth century, most Americans died before age 65, often from infectious diseases. Now, about three-quarters of deaths in the United States are at ages 65 and older, and one in seven living Americans is in that age bracket. As the average age of the population rises, health-care professionals find themselves increasingly occupied by the prevention and treatment of the diseases of age. The leading causes of death change markedly with age. Accidents, homicide, suicide,

and AIDS figure prominently in the deaths of people 18 to 34 years old, whereas the major causes of death after age 55 are clearly related to senescence of the organ systems: in descending order, heart disease, cancer, stroke diabetes, chronic obstructive pulmonary disease (COPD), and infectious lung diseases (pneumonia and influenza). The causes of senescence, however, remain as much a scientific mystery today as cancer was 50 years ago and heredity was 100 years ago.

As we survey the senescence of the organ systems, you should notice many points relevant not only to caring for an aging population but also to personal health and fitness practices that can lessen the effects of senescence and improve the quality of life in your own later years. In addition, the study of senescence calls for renewed attention to the multiple interactions among organ systems. As you will see, the senescence of one organ system typically contributes to the senescence of others. Your study of this topic will bring together many concepts introduced in earlier chapters of the book. You may find the glossary helpful in refreshing your memory of concepts revisited in the following discussion.

29.4a Senescence of the Organ Systems

Organ systems don't all degenerate at the same rate. For example, from ages 30 to 80, the speed of nerve conduction declines only 10% to 15%, but the number of functional glomeruli in the kidneys declines about 60%. Some physiological functions show only moderate changes at rest but more pronounced differences when tested under exercise conditions. The organ systems also vary widely in the age at which senescence becomes noticeable. There are forerunners of atherosclerosis, for example, even in infants; visual and auditory sensitivities begin to decline soon after puberty. By contrast, the female reproductive system doesn't show significant senescence until menopause and then its decline is relatively abrupt. Aside from these unusual examples, most physiological measures of performance peak between the late teens and age 30, then decline at a rate influenced by the level of use of the organs.

Integumentary System

Two-thirds of people age 50 and over, and nearly all people over age 70, have medical concerns or complaints about their skin. Senescence of the integumentary system often becomes noticeable by the late 40s. The hair turns grayer and thinner as melanocytes die out, mitosis slows down, and dead hairs are not replaced. The atrophy of sebaceous glands leaves the skin and hair drier. As epidermal mitosis declines and collagen is lost from the dermis, the skin becomes almost paper-thin and translucent. It becomes looser because of a loss of elastic fibers and flattening of the dermal papillae, which normally form a stress-resistant corrugated boundary between the dermis and epidermis. If you pinch a fold of skin on the back of a child's hand, it quickly springs back when you let go; do the same on an older person and the skinfold remains longer. Because of its loss of elasticity, aged skin sags to various degrees and may hang loosely from the arm and other places.

Aged skin has fewer blood vessels than younger skin, and those that remain are more fragile. The skin can become reddened as broken vessels leak into the connective tissue. Many older people exhibit **rosacea**—patchy networks of tiny, dilated blood vessels visible especially on the nose and cheeks. Because of the fragility of the dermal blood vessels, aged skin bruises more easily. Injuries to the skin are more common and severe in old age, partly because the cutaneous nerve endings decline by two-thirds from age 20 to age 80, leaving one less aware of touch, pressure, and injurious stimuli. Injured skin heals slowly in old age because of poorer circulation and a relative scarcity of immune cells and fibroblasts. Antigen-presenting dendritic cells decline by as much as 40% in the aged epidermis, leaving the skin more susceptible to recurring infections.

Thermoregulation can be a serious problem in old age because of the atrophy of cutaneous blood vessels, sweat glands, and subcutaneous fat. Older people are more vulnerable to hypothermia in cold weather and heatstroke in hot weather. Heat waves and cold spells take a disproportionate toll among elderly poor individuals who suffer from a combination of reduced homeostasis and inadequate housing.

These are all "normal" changes in the skin, or **intrinsic aging**—changes that occur more or less inevitably with the passage of time. In addition, there is **photoaging**—degenerative changes in proportion to a person's lifetime exposure to ultraviolet radiation. UV radiation accounts for more than 90% of the integumentary changes that people find medically troubling or cosmetically disagreeable: skin cancer; yellowing and mottling of the skin; age spots *(solar lentigines)* (len-TIJ-ih-neez), which resemble enlarged freckles on the back of the hand and other sun-exposed areas; and wrinkling, which affects the face, hands, and arms more than areas of the body that receive less exposure. A lifetime of outdoor activity can give the skin a leathery, deeply wrinkled, "outdoorsy" appearance **(fig. 29.16),** but beneath this rugged exterior is a less happy histological appearance. The sun-damaged skin shows many malignant and premalignant cells, extensive damage to the dermal blood vessels, and dense masses of coarse, frayed elastic fibers underlying the surface wrinkles and creases.

FIGURE 29.16 Senescence of the Skin. The skin exhibits both intrinsic aging and photoaging. The deep creases seen in the old woman's face result mainly from photoaging.

(young child): Stephen Flint/Alamy; (old person): Mark Girvan Portraits/Alamy

Senescence of the skin has far-reaching effects on other organ systems. Cutaneous vitamin D production declines as much as 75% in old age. This is all the more significant because the elderly spend less time outdoors; and because of increasing lactose intolerance, they often avoid dairy products, the only dietary source of vitamin D. Consequently, the elderly are at high risk of calcium deficiency, which, in turn, contributes to bone loss, muscle weakness, and impaired glandular secretion and synaptic transmission.

Skeletal System

After age 30, osteoblasts become less active than osteoclasts. This imbalance results in **osteopenia,** the loss of bone; when the loss is severe enough to compromise a person's physical activity and health, it is called *osteoporosis* (see Deeper Insight 7.4). After age 40, women lose about 8% of their bone mass per decade and men about 3%. Bone loss from the jaws is a contributing factor in tooth loss.

Not only does bone density decline with age, but the bones become more brittle as the cells synthesize less protein. Fractures occur more easily and heal more slowly. A fracture may impose a long period of immobility, which makes a person more vulnerable to pneumonia and other life-threatening infectious diseases.

People notice more stiffness and pain in the synovial joints as they age, and degenerative joint diseases affect the lifestyle of 85% of people over age 75. Synovial fluid is less abundant and the articular cartilage is thinner or absent. Exposed bone surfaces abrade each other and cause friction, pain, and reduced mobility. *Osteoarthritis* is the most common joint disease of older people and one of the most common causes of physical disability (see Deeper Insight 9.5). Even breathing becomes more difficult and tiring in old age because expansion of the thorax is restricted by calcification of the sternocostal joints. Degeneration of the intervertebral discs causes back pain and stiffness, but herniated discs are less common in old age than in youth because the discs become more fibrous and stronger, with less nucleus pulposus.

Muscular System

One of the most noticeable changes we experience with age is the replacement of lean body mass (muscle) with fat. The change is dramatically exemplified by CT scans of the thigh. In a young well-conditioned male, muscle accounts for 90% of the cross-sectional area of the midthigh, whereas in a frail 90-year-old woman, it is only 30%. Muscular strength and mass peak in the 20s; by the age of 80, most people have only half as much strength and endurance. Many people over age 75 can't lift a 4.5 kg (10 lb) weight with their arms; such simple tasks as carrying a sack of groceries into the house may become impossible. The loss of strength is a major contributor to falls, fractures, and dependence on others for the routine activities of daily living. Fast-twitch fibers exhibit the earliest and most severe atrophy, thus increasing reaction time and reducing coordination. Regular exercise, however, can remarkably preserve and restore muscle size and strength **(fig. 29.17).**

There are multiple reasons for the loss of strength. Aged muscle fibers have fewer myofibrils, so they're smaller and weaker. The sarcomeres are increasingly disorganized, and muscle

mitochondria are smaller and have reduced quantities of oxidative enzymes. Aged muscle has less ATP, creatine phosphate, glycogen, and myoglobin; consequently, it fatigues quickly. Muscles also exhibit more fat and fibrosis with age, which limits their movement and blood circulation. With reduced circulation, muscle injuries heal more slowly and with more scar tissue.

But the weakness and easy fatigue of aged muscle also stem from the senescence of other organ systems. There are fewer motor neurons in the spinal cord, and some muscle shrinkage may represent denervation atrophy. The remaining neurons produce less acetylcholine and show less efficient synaptic transmission, which makes the muscles slower to respond to stimulation. As muscle atrophies, motor units have fewer muscle fibers per motor neuron, and more motor units must be recruited to perform a given task. Tasks that used to be easy, such as buttoning the clothes or eating a meal, take more time and effort. The sympathetic nervous system is also less efficient in old age; consequently, blood flow to the muscles doesn't respond efficiently to exercise and this contributes to their rapid fatigue.

Nervous System

The nervous system reaches its peak development around age 30. After age 40, the brain loses about 5% of its mass every 10 years,

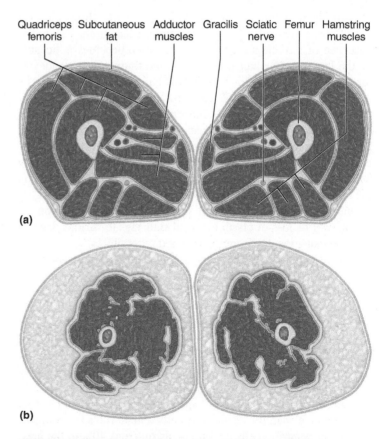

(a)

(b)

FIGURE 29.17 Muscle Senescence and Its Prevention. Drawings based on CT scans of cross sections of the thighs. (a) Thighs of a 74-year-old triathlete, showing how well muscle mass can be maintained in old age with exercise. (b) Thighs of a sedentary 74-year-old, showing extensive muscle atrophy and replacement by subcutaneous fat.

and possibly faster after age 70. The cerebral gyri are narrower, the sulci are wider, the cortex is thinner, and there is more space between the brain and meninges. The remaining cortical neurons have fewer synapses, and for multiple reasons, synaptic transmission is less efficient: The neurons produce less neurotransmitter, they have fewer receptors, and the neuroglia around the synapses is more leaky and allows neurotransmitter to diffuse away. The degeneration of myelin sheaths with age also slows down nerve conduction. The losses are not uniform throughout the brain, but fastest in the prefrontal cortex—the area concerned with abstract thought, judgment, planning, personality, and explicit memory—and in the hippocampus, the seat of memory formation.

Neurons exhibit less rough ER and Golgi complex with age, which indicates that their metabolism is slowing down. Old neurons accumulate lipofuscin pigment and show more neurofibrillary tangles—dense mats of cytoskeletal elements in their cytoplasm. In the extracellular material, plaques of fibrillar protein (amyloid) appear, especially in people with Down syndrome and Alzheimer disease (AD). AD is the most common nervous disability of old age (see Deeper Insight 12.4).

Not all functions of the central nervous system are equally affected by senescence. Motor coordination, intellectual function, and short-term memory decline more than language skills and long-term memory. Elderly people are often better at remembering things in the distant past than remembering recent events.

The sympathetic nervous system loses adrenergic receptors with age and becomes less sensitive to norepinephrine. This contributes to a decline in homeostatic control of such variables as body temperature and blood pressure. Many elderly people experience *orthostatic hypotension*—a drop in blood pressure when they stand, which sometimes results in dizziness, loss of balance, or fainting. Impaired balance and neuromuscular reflexes, slow baroreflexes, and fragile bones often combine tragically in a fall that breaks a hip and leads to death from pneumonia and other complications of immobility.

Sense Organs

Some sensory functions decline shortly after adolescence. Presbyopia (loss of flexibility in the lenses) makes it more difficult for the eyes to focus on nearby objects. Visual acuity declines and often requires corrective lenses at a young age. Cataracts (cloudiness of the lenses) are more common in old age. Night vision is impaired as more and more light is needed to stimulate the retina. This has several causes: There are fewer receptor cells in the retina, the lens and vitreous body becomes less transparent, and the pupil becomes narrower as the pupillary dilators atrophy. Even without cataracts, the retina receives only one-third as much light at age 60 as it does at age 20. Dark adaptation takes longer as the enzymatic reactions of the photoreceptor cells become slower. Changes in the structure of the iris, ciliary body, or lens can block the reabsorption of aqueous humor, thereby increasing the risk of glaucoma. Having to give up reading and driving can be among the most difficult changes of lifestyle in old age.

Auditory sensitivity peaks in adolescence and declines afterward. The tympanic membrane and the joints between the auditory ossicles become stiffer, so vibrations are transferred less effectively to the inner ear, creating a degree of conductive deafness. Nerve deafness occurs as the number of cochlear hair cells and auditory nerve fibers declines. The greatest hearing loss occurs at high frequencies and in the frequency range of most conversation. The death of receptor cells in the semicircular ducts, utricle, and saccule, and of nerve fibers in the vestibular nerve and neurons in the cerebellum, results in dizziness and impaired balance—another factor in falls and bone fractures.

The senses of taste and smell are blunted as the taste buds, olfactory cells, and second-order neurons in the olfactory bulbs decline in number. Food may lose its appeal, and declining sensory function can therefore be a factor in malnutrition.

Endocrine System

The endocrine system degenerates less than any other organ system. The reproductive hormones drop sharply and growth hormone and thyroid hormone levels decline steadily after adolescence. The pineal gland becomes increasingly calcified in old age and its melatonin output falls. Since melatonin is a sleep-inducing hormone, this may be a reason for the insomnia often experienced by the elderly. Other hormones continue to be secreted at fairly stable levels even into old age. Target-cell sensitivity declines, however, so some hormones have less effect. For example, the pituitary gland is less sensitive to negative feedback inhibition by adrenal glucocorticoids; consequently, the response to stress is more prolonged than usual. Diabetes mellitus is more common in old age, largely because target cells have fewer insulin receptors. In part, this is an effect of the greater percentage of body fat in the elderly. The more fat at any age, the less sensitive other cells are to insulin. Body fat increases as the muscles atrophy, and muscle is one of the body's most significant glucose-buffering tissues. Because of the blunted insulin response, glucose levels remain elevated longer than normal after a meal.

Circulatory System

Cardiovascular disease is a leading cause of death in old age. Senescence has multiple effects on the blood, heart, arteries, and veins. Anemia may result from nutritional deficiencies, inadequate exercise, disease, and other causes. The factors that cause anemia in older people are so complicated it's almost impossible to control them enough to determine whether aging alone causes it. Evidence suggests that there is no change in the baseline rate of erythropoiesis in old age. Hemoglobin concentration, cell counts, and other variables are about the same among healthy people in their 70s as in the 30s. However, older people don't adapt well to stress on the hematopoietic system, perhaps because of the senescence of other organ systems. As the gastric mucosa atrophies, for example, it produces less of the intrinsic factor needed for vitamin B_{12} absorption. This increases the risk of anemia. As the kidneys age and the number of nephrons declines, less erythropoietin is secreted. There may also be a limit to how many times the hematopoietic stem cells can divide and continue giving rise to new blood cells. Whatever its cause, anemia limits the amount of oxygen that can be transported and thus contributes to the atrophy of tissues everywhere in the body.

▶▶▶ **APPLY WHAT YOU KNOW**

Draw a positive feedback loop showing how anemia and senescence of the kidneys could affect each other.

Nearly everyone is affected to some degree in old age by arteriosclerosis and atherosclerosis (see the distinction in section 20.2a). Coronary atherosclerosis leads to the degeneration of myocardial tissue; angina pectoris and myocardial infarction become more common; the heart wall becomes thinner and weaker; and stroke volume, cardiac output, and cardiac reserve decline. Like other connective tissues, the fibrous skeleton of the heart becomes less elastic. This limits cardiac distension and reduces the force of systole. Degenerative changes in the SA and AV nodes and conduction pathways of the heart lead to a higher incidence of cardiac arrhythmia and heart block. Physical endurance is compromised by the drop in cardiac output.

Arteries stiffened by arteriosclerosis cannot expand as effectively to accommodate the pressure surges of cardiac systole. Blood pressure therefore rises steadily with age, although it is uncertain to what extent this is an inherent biological effect of aging versus an effect of culture and lifestyle. It doesn't occur in all societies. Atherosclerosis also narrows the arteries and reduces the perfusion of most organs. The effects of reduced circulation on the skin, skeletal muscles, and brain have already been noted. The combination of atherosclerosis and hypertension weakens the arteries and increases the risk of aneurysm and stroke.

Atherosclerotic plaques trigger thrombosis, especially in the lower limbs, where flow is relatively slow and the blood clots more easily. About 25% of people over age 50 experience venous blockage by thrombosis—especially people who don't exercise regularly.

Degenerative changes in the veins are most evident in the limbs. The valves become weaker and less able to stop the backflow of blood. Blood pools in the legs and feet, raises capillary blood pressure, and causes edema. Chronic stretching of the vessels often produces varicose veins and hemorrhoids. Support hose can reduce edema by compressing the tissues and forcing tissue fluid to return to the bloodstream, but physical activity is even more important in promoting venous return.

Immune System

The amounts of lymphatic tissue and red bone marrow decline with age; consequently, there are fewer hematopoietic stem cells, disease-fighting leukocytes, and antigen-presenting cells (APCs). Also, the lymphocytes produced in these tissues often fail to mature and become immunocompetent. Both humoral and cellular immunity depend on APCs and helper T cells, and therefore both types of immune response are blunted. As a result, an older person is less protected against cancer and infectious diseases. It becomes especially important in old age to be vaccinated against influenza and other acute seasonal infections.

Respiratory System

Pulmonary ventilation declines steadily after the 20s and is one of several factors in the gradual loss of stamina. The costal cartilages and joints of the thoracic cage become less flexible, the lungs have less elastic tissue, and the lungs have fewer alveoli. Vital capacity, minute respiratory volume, and forced expiratory volume fall. The elderly are also less capable of clearing the lungs of irritants and pathogens and are therefore increasingly vulnerable to respiratory infections. Pneumonia causes more deaths than any other infectious disease and is often contracted in hospitals and nursing homes.

The chronic obstructive pulmonary diseases (COPDs)—emphysema and chronic bronchitis—are more common in old age since they represent the cumulative effects of a lifetime of degenerative change. They are among the leading causes of death in old age, but are avoidable; they are much less common among nonsmokers than among smokers. Pulmonary obstruction also contributes to cardiovascular disease, hypoxemia, and hypoxic degeneration in all the organ systems. Respiratory health is therefore a major concern in aging.

Urinary System

The kidneys exhibit a striking degree of atrophy with age. From ages 25 to 85, the number of nephrons declines 30% to 40% and up to a third of the remaining glomeruli become atherosclerotic, bloodless, and nonfunctional. The kidneys of a 90-year-old are 20% to 40% smaller than those of a 30-year-old and receive only half as much blood. The glomerular filtration rate is proportionately lower and the kidneys are less efficient at clearing wastes from the blood. Although baseline renal function is adequate even in old age, there is little reserve capacity; thus, other diseases can lead to surprisingly rapid renal failure. Drug doses often need to be reduced in old age because the kidneys can't clear drugs from the blood as rapidly; this is a contributing factor in overmedication among the aged.

Water balance is more precarious in old age because the kidneys are less responsive to antidiuretic hormone and because the sense of thirst is sharply reduced. Even when given free access to water, many elderly people don't drink enough to maintain normal blood osmolarity. Dehydration is therefore common.

Voiding and bladder control become problematic for both men and women. About 80% of men over the age of 80 are affected by benign prostatic hyperplasia. The enlarged prostate compresses the urethra and interferes with emptying of the bladder. Urine retention may cause pressure to back up in the kidneys, aggravating the failure of the nephrons. Older women are subject to incontinence (leakage of urine), especially if their history of pregnancy and childbearing has weakened the pelvic muscles and urethral sphincter. Senescence of the sympathetic nervous system and nervous disorders such as stroke and Alzheimer disease can also cause incontinence.

Digestive System and Nutrition

Restaurants commonly offer a "seniors' menu" and reduced prices to customers over 60 or 65 years old, knowing that they tend to eat less. There are multiple reasons for this reduced appetite. Older people have lower metabolic rates and tend to be less active than younger people and, hence, need fewer calories. The stomach atrophies with age, and it takes less to fill it up. For many, food has less esthetic appeal in old age because of losses in the senses of smell, taste, and even vision. In addition, older people secrete less saliva, making food less flavorful and swallowing more difficult. Reduced salivation also makes the teeth more prone to caries. Dentures are an unpleasant fact of life for many people over 65 who have lost their teeth to caries and periodontitis. Atrophy of the epithelium of the oral cavity and esophagus makes these surfaces more subject to abrasion and may further detract from the ease of chewing and swallowing. Even the ability to chew declines; the muscles of mastication lose about 40% of their mass and the mandibular bone loses about 20% over the course of a lifetime.

The reduced mobility of old age makes shopping and meal preparation more troublesome, and with food losing its sensory appeal, some decide that it simply isn't worth the trouble. However, one's protein, vitamin, and mineral requirements remain essentially unchanged, so vitamin and mineral supplements may be needed to compensate for reduced food intake and poorer intestinal absorption. Malnutrition is common among older people and is an important factor in anemia and reduced immunity.

As the gastric mucosa atrophies, it secretes less acid and intrinsic factor. Acid deficiency reduces the absorption of calcium, iron, zinc, and folic acid. Heartburn becomes more common as the weakening lower esophageal sphincter fails to prevent the reflux of stomach contents into the esophagus. The most common digestive complaint of older people is constipation, which results from reduced muscle tone and weaker peristalsis of the colon. This seems to stem from a combination of factors: atrophy of the muscularis externa, reduced sensitivity to neurotransmitters that promote motility, less fiber and water in the diet, and less exercise. The liver, gallbladder, and pancreas show only slightly reduced function, but the drop in liver function reduces the rate of drug deactivation and can contribute to overmedication.

Reproductive System

In men, the senescent changes in the reproductive system are relatively gradual; they include declining testosterone secretion, sperm count, semen volume, and libido. By age 65, sperm count is about one-third of what it was in a man's 20s. Men remain fertile (capable of fathering a child) well into old age, but impotence (inability to maintain an erection) can occur because of atherosclerosis, hypertension, medication, and psychological reasons.

In women, the changes are more pronounced and develop more rapidly. Over the course of menopause, the ovarian follicles are used up, gametogenesis ceases, and the ovaries stop producing sex steroids. This may result in vaginal dryness, genital atrophy, and reduced libido and may make sex less enjoyable. With the loss of ovarian steroids, a postmenopausal woman has an elevated risk of osteoporosis and atherosclerosis.

29.4b Exercise, Senescence, and Life Expectancy

Other than the mere passage of time, senescence results from obesity and insufficient exercise more than from any other causes.

Conversely, good nutrition and exercise are the best ways to slow its progress.

People who exercise moderately for as little as 10 to 15 minutes a day have been found to live, on average, 3 years longer than sedentary people, although it is difficult to separate causation from correlation in such studies. That is, it remains unclear how much of this is an *effect* of the exercise and how much results from *correlation* with other healthy lifestyle choices. There is no question, however, that regular exercise maintains endurance, strength, and joint mobility, and reduces the incidence and severity of hypertension, osteoporosis, obesity, and diabetes mellitus. This is especially true if you begin a program of regular physical exercise early in life and make a lasting habit of it. If you stop exercising regularly after middle age, the body rapidly becomes deconditioned, although appreciable reconditioning can be achieved even when an exercise program is begun late in life. A person in his or her 90s can increase muscle strength two- or threefold in 6 months with as little as 40 minutes of isometric exercise a week. The improvement results from a combination of muscle hypertrophy and neural efficiency.

Resistance exercises may be the most effective way of reducing accidental injuries such as bone fractures, whereas endurance exercises reduce body fat and increase cardiac output and maximum oxygen uptake. A general guideline for ideal endurance training is to have three to five periods of aerobic exercise per week, each 20 to 60 minutes long and vigorous enough to reach 60% to 90% of your maximum heart rate. The maximum is best determined by a stress test but averages about 220 beats per minute minus one's age in years.

An exercise program should ideally be preceded by a complete physical examination and stress test. Warm-up and cool-down periods are especially important in avoiding soft tissue injuries and undue cardiovascular stress. Because of their lower capacity for thermoregulation, older people must be careful not to overdo exercise, especially in hot weather. At the outset of a new exercise program, it is best to "start low and go slow."

29.4c Theories of Senescence

Why do our organs wear out? Why must we die? There still is no general theory on this. The question actually comes down to two issues: (1) What are the mechanisms that cause the organs to deteriorate with age? (2) Why has natural selection not eliminated these and produced bodies capable of longer life?

Mechanisms of Senescence

Numerous hypotheses have been proposed and discarded to explain why organ function degenerates with age. Some authorities maintain that senescence is an intrinsic process governed by inevitable or even preprogrammed changes in cellular function. Others attribute senescence to extrinsic (environmental) factors that progressively damage our cells over the course of a lifetime.

There is good evidence of a hereditary component to longevity. Unusually long and short lives tend to run in families. Monozygotic (identical) twins are more likely than dizygotic

FIGURE 29.18 Progeria. This is a genetic disorder in which senescence appears to be greatly accelerated. The individuals here, from left to right, are 15, 12, and 26 years old. Few people with progeria live as long as the woman on the right.

Bettmann/Getty Images

twins to die at a similar age. One striking genetic defect called *progeria*[20] is characterized by greatly accelerated senescence **(fig. 29.18).** Symptoms begin to appear by age 2. The child's growth rate declines, the muscles and skin become flaccid, most victims lose their hair, and most die in early adolescence from advanced atherosclerosis. In Werner syndrome, caused by a defective gene on chromosome 8, people show marked senescence beginning in their 20s and usually die by age 50. There is some controversy over the relevance or similarity of these syndromes to normal senescence, but they do demonstrate that many of the changes associated with old age can be brought on by a genetic anomaly.

Knowing that senescence is partially genetic, however, doesn't answer the question about why tissues degenerate. Quite likely, no one theory explains all forms of senescence, but let's briefly examine some of them.

Replicative Senescence   Normal organ function usually depends on a rate of cell renewal that keeps pace with cell death. There is a limit, however, to how many times cells can divide. Human cells cultured in the laboratory divide 80 to 90 times if taken from a fetus, but only 20 to 30 times if taken from older people. After reaching their maximum number of divisions, cultured cells degenerate and die. This decline in mitotic potential with age is called **replicative senescence.**

Why this occurs is a subject of lively research. Much of the evidence points to the **telomere,**[21] a "cap" on each end of a chromosome analogous to the plastic tip of a shoelace. In humans, it consists of a noncoding nucleotide sequence CCCTAA repeated 1,000 times or more. One of its functions may be to stabilize the chromosome and prevent it from unraveling or sticking to other chromosomes. Telomeres also prevent a cell from falsely recognizing the ends of a chromosome as broken and activating DNA repair mechanisms that would do more harm than good. Also, during DNA replication, DNA polymerase can't reproduce the very ends of the DNA molecule. If there were functional genes at the end, they wouldn't get duplicated. The telomere may therefore provide a bit of "disposable" DNA at the end, so that DNA polymerase doesn't fail to replicate genes that would otherwise be there. Every time DNA is replicated, 50 to 100 bases are lost from the telomere. In old age, the telomere may be exhausted and the polymerase may then indeed fail to replicate some of the terminal genes. Old chromosomes may therefore be more vulnerable to damage, replication errors, or both, causing old cells to be increasingly dysfunctional. The long life of stem cells and "immortality" of cancer cells results from an enzyme called *telomerase,* lacking from healthy differentiated cells. Telomerase enables cancerous and stem cells to repair telomere damage and escape the limit on number of cell divisions.

DNA Damage Theory   Telomere damage and replicative senescence are clearly not the entire answer to why organs degenerate. Skeletal muscle fibers and brain neurons exhibit pronounced senescence, yet these cells are nonmitotic. Another leading theory of senescence is unrepaired DNA damage. DNA suffers an astonishing 10,000 to 100,000 damaging events per day in the average mammalian cell. Most of it is fixed by DNA repair enzymes, but this is not 100% efficient. Some damage persists and accumulates as cells age, especially nondividing cells like neurons, cardiomyocytes, and skeletal muscle fibers. Such cumulative damage has been shown to cause age-related decline in liver and kidney function; cardiac and muscular strength; and brain functions related to neuronal survival, synaptic plasticity, learning, and memory.

Cross-Linking Theory   About one-fourth of the body's protein is collagen. With age, collagen molecules become cross-linked by more and more disulfide bridges, thus making the fibers less soluble and more stiff. This is thought to be a factor in several of the most noticeable changes of the aging body, including stiffening of the joints, lenses, and arteries. Similar cross-linking of DNA and enzyme molecules could progressively impair their functions as well.

Other Protein Abnormalities   Not only collagen but also many other proteins exhibit increasingly abnormal structure in older

---

[20]*pro* = before; *ger* = old age

[21]*telo* = end; *mer* = piece, part, segment

tissues and cells. The changes are not in amino acid sequence—therefore not attributable to DNA mutations—but lie in the way the proteins are folded and other moieties such as carbohydrates are attached to them. This is another reason that cells accumulate more dysfunctional proteins as they age.

Autoimmune Theory Some of the altered macromolecules described previously may be recognized as foreign antigens and stimulate lymphocytes to mount an immune response against the body's own tissues. Autoimmune diseases do, in fact, become more common in old age.

Evolution and Senescence

If certain genes contribute to senescence, it raises an evolutionary question: Why doesn't natural selection eliminate them? In an attempt to answer this, biologists once postulated that senescence and death were for the good of the species—a way for older, worn-out individuals to make way for younger, healthier ones. We can see the importance of death for the human population by imagining that science had put an end to senescence and people died at an annual rate of only 1 per 1,000 regardless of age (the rate at which American 18-year-olds now die). If so, the median age of the population would be 163, and 13% of us would live to be 2,000 years old. The implications for world population, social order, and competition for resources would be staggering. Thus, it is easy to understand why death was once interpreted as a self-sacrificing phenomenon for the good of the species.

But this hypothesis has several weaknesses. One of them is the fact that natural selection works exclusively through the effects of genes on the reproductive rates of individuals. A species evolves only because some members reproduce more than others. A gene that doesn't affect reproductive rate can be neither eliminated nor favored by natural selection. Genes for disorders such as Alzheimer disease have little or no effect until a person is past reproductive age. Our prehistoric and even fairly recent ancestors usually died of accidents, predation, starvation, weather, and infectious diseases at an early age. Few people lived long enough to be affected by atherosclerosis, colon cancer, or Alzheimer disease. Natural selection would have been "blind" to such death-dealing genes, which would escape the selection process and remain with us today.

29.4d Death

Life expectancy, the average length of life in a given population, has steadily increased in industrialized countries. People born in the United States at the beginning of the twentieth century had a life expectancy of only 45 to 50 years; nearly half of them died of infectious disease. As of 2017, by contrast, the average boy born in the United States that year could expect to live 76.1 years and the average girl 81.1 years. This trend is due mostly to victories over infant and child mortality, not to advances at the other end of the life span. **Life span,** the maximum age attainable by humans, increased significantly from 1950 to 2010. As yet, however, there is no verifiable record of anyone living past the age of 122 years—Jeanne Calment (1875–1997) of Arles, France, whose fascinating story you can read on the Internet.

There is no definable instant of biological death. Some organs function for an hour or more after the heart stops beating. During this time, even if a person is declared legally dead, living organs may be removed for transplantation. For legal purposes, death was once defined as the loss of a spontaneous heartbeat and respiration. Now that cardiopulmonary functions can be artificially maintained for years, this criterion is less distinct. Clinical death is now widely defined in terms of **brain death**—a lack of cerebral activity indicated by a flat electroencephalogram for 30 minutes to 24 hours (depending on state laws), accompanied by a lack of reflexes or lack of spontaneous respiration and heartbeat.

Death usually results from the failure of a particular organ, which then has a cascading effect on other organs. Kidney failure, for example, leads to the accumulation of toxic wastes in the blood, which in turn leads to loss of consciousness, brain function, respiration, and heartbeat.

Ninety-nine percent of us will die before age 100, and there is little chance that this outlook will change within our lifetimes. We cannot presently foresee any "cure for old age" or significant extension of the human life span. The real issue is to maintain the best possible quality of life, and when the time comes to die, to be able to do so in comfort and dignity.

BEFORE YOU GO ON

Answer the following questions to test your understanding of the preceding section.

13. Define *aging* and *senescence*.

14. List some tissues and organs in which changes in collagenous and elastic connective tissues contribute to senescence.

15. Many older people have difficulty with mobility and self-maintenance tasks such as dressing and cooking. Name some organ systems whose senescence is most relevant to these limitations.

16. Explain why both endurance and resistance exercise are important in old age.

17. Summarize five cellular or biochemical mechanisms that may contribute to senescence.

DEEPER INSIGHT 29.5

CLINICAL APPLICATION

Assisted Reproductive Technology

Fertile heterosexual couples who have frequent intercourse and use no contraception have a 90% chance of conceiving within 1 year. About one in six American couples, however, is *infertile*—unable to conceive. For this and other reasons, individuals and couples often resort to clinical assistance to achieve parenthood. Reasons include avoidance of genetic defects when a parent is known to be a carrier of a harmful allele; male or female infertility; a history of repeated miscarriages; desire to store eggs or sperm for delayed parenthood or to preserve healthy gametes before undergoing chemotherapy, ovarian or testicular cancer surgery, or other procedures; and the desire for children among single persons and same-sex couples. In the United States alone, there are more than 140,000 trials and 55,000 births per year by the methods to be described here. *Assisted reproductive technology (ART)* is defined by the U.S. Public Health Service and World Health Organization as techniques in which both eggs and sperm are manipulated.

Intrauterine Insemination

Intrauterine insemination (IUI) was formerly called artificial insemination (AI). It technically lies outside the definition of ART, since it involves only sperm manipulation, but it is the oldest and least expensive clinical means of overcoming male infertility to achieve parenthood. If a man's infertility is only a matter of low sperm output (oligospermia[22]), he can achieve biological fatherhood by a process of pooling and storing sperm from multiple ejaculates, washing them to remove seminal fluid (which can inflame the female uterus), then introducing them into the uterus with a cervical catheter. If he produces no sperm at all (aspermia) or is at risk of transmitting a genetic defect, sperm from other donors is used. Men planning vasectomies sometimes donate sperm for storage as insurance against the death of a child, divorce and remarriage, or a change in family planning. AI was first performed in 1790, and for more than a century, the sperm donors were often the physicians themselves or medical students who donated sperm for pay. Cryogenic (frozen) storage of semen in liquid nitrogen was developed in 1953, techniques of insemination refined, and IUI became much more common. The first commercial sperm banks opened in 1970. Most women undergoing IUI use sperm from anonymous donors, but are able to select from a catalog that specifies the donors' physical and intellectual traits. The success rate for IUI ranges from 1 in 6 to 20 trials.

Oocyte Donation

The counterpart to sperm donation is *oocyte donation,* in which fresh oocytes are obtained from a donor, fertilized, and transplanted to the uterus of the client. A woman may choose this procedure for a variety of reasons: being past menopause, having had her ovaries removed, or having a hereditary disorder she doesn't want to pass to her children, for example. The donated oocytes are sometimes provided by a relative or may be left over from another woman's in vitro fertilization (see next section). The first baby conceived by oocyte donation was born in 1984. This procedure has a success rate of 20% to 50%.

In Vitro Fertilization

In vitro[23] *fertilization (IVF)* is an option for couples with such issues as male infertility and women whose uterine tubes cannot pass an egg or preembryo because of scars from pelvic inflammatory disease or other defects, but who have a healthy uterus. It is called *in vitro* for the fact that sperm and eggs are introduced to each other in a clinical vessel, with fertilization occurring there before the preembryo is introduced to the body. In preparation for IVF, a woman is treated with gonadotropins to induce the superovulation of multiple eggs. A physician views the ovary with a laparoscope and removes eggs by suction. These are placed in a solution that mimics the chemical environment of her reproductive tract, and sperm are added to the dish. In some cases, fertilization is assisted by piercing the zona pellucida before the sperm are added (*zona drilling*) or by injecting sperm directly into the egg through a micropipette **(fig. 29.19).** The latter method, called *intracytoplasmic sperm injection (ICSI),* is standard procedure in some clinics.

Preembryos reach the 8- to 16-cell stage about a day after fertilization. If there is a concern about parental chromosome abnormalities such as nondisjunction, one or two cells can be safely removed at this stage and inspected to ensure absence of defects. The clinician then introduces a preembryo into the uterus and monitors the woman's HCG level over the following days for signs of implantation. In cases where a woman has lost her ovaries to disease, the oocytes may be provided by another donor, sometimes a relative. Excess IVF preembryos may be donated to other infertile couples, frozen and used for later implantation attempts, or donated for such purposes as fertility and stem-cell research. One record pregnancy was achieved with an embryo that had been frozen 20 years earlier.

The chance of success in each IVF attempt is 20% to 35%—highest in younger women. IVF has been used in animal breeding since the 1950s, but the first child conceived this way was born (amid much controversy) in 1978. The practice grew rapidly after that, and at least 8 million babies conceived by IVF had been born by 2018. The inventor of IVF,

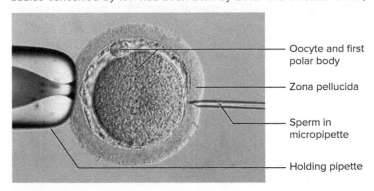

— Oocyte and first polar body

— Zona pellucida

— Sperm in micropipette

— Holding pipette

FIGURE 29.19 Intracytoplasmic Sperm Injection (ICSI). The egg is held with gentle suction on the pipette at left while a sperm is injected into its cytoplasm through the micropipette on the right.
Phanie/Alamy

---

[22]*oligo* = few

[23]*in vitro* = in glass

Robert Edwards, received the 2010 Nobel Prize for Physiology or Medicine for this achievement.

Surrogate Mothers

IVF is an option only for women who have a functional uterus. A woman who has had a hysterectomy or is otherwise unable to become pregnant or maintain a pregnancy may contract with a *surrogate mother* who provides a "uterus for hire." Some surrogates are both genetic and gestational mothers, and others gestational only. In the former case, the surrogate is artificially inseminated by a man's sperm and agrees to give the baby to the man and his partner at birth. In the latter case, oocytes are collected from one woman's ovaries, fertilized in vitro, and the preembryos are placed in the surrogate's uterus. This is typical of cases in which a woman has functional ovaries but no functional uterus. Several hundred babies have been produced this way in the United States. In at least one case, a woman carried the child of her infertile daughter, thus giving birth to her own granddaughter.

Gamete Intrafallopian Transfer

The limited success rate of IVF led to a search for more reliable and cost-effective techniques. *Gamete intrafallopian transfer (GIFT)* was developed in the mid-1980s on the conjecture that pregnancy would be more successful if the oocyte was fertilized and began cleavage in a more natural environment. Eggs are obtained from a woman after a weeklong course of ovulation-inducing drug treatment. The most active sperm cells are isolated from the semen, and the eggs and sperm are introduced into her uterine tube proximal to any existing obstruction. In a modification called *zygote intrafallopian transfer (ZIFT)*, fertilization occurs in vitro and the preembryo is introduced into the uterine tube. Traveling down the uterine tube seems to improve the chance of implantation when the conceptus reaches the uterus. The chance of success in both GIFT and ZIFT is about 22%.

Embryo Adoption

Embryo adoption is used when a woman has malfunctioning ovaries but a normal uterus. A man's sperm are used to artificially inseminate another woman. A few days later, the preembryo is flushed from the donor's uterus before it implants and is transferred to the uterus of the woman who wishes to have a child.

Issues in Choice of Method

Many issues, sometimes complicated, can enter into one's choice of ART options. The methods described here vary widely in success rates and cost. Expenses range from less than $1,000 for IUI to more than $20,000

for GIFT and ZIFT—and this is cost *per trial,* with as little as 15% to 35% chances of success. There is much variation in whether insurance policies or national health services will cover the costs.

Like many other advances in medicine, reproductive technology also has its own ethical and legal dilemmas, some of which are especially confounding. Perhaps the most common problem is the surrogate mother who changes her mind. Surrogates enter into a contract to surrender the baby to a couple at birth, but after carrying a baby for 9 months and giving birth, they sometimes feel differently. This raises questions about the definition of motherhood, especially if she is the gestational but not the genetic mother.

The converse problem is illustrated by a case in which the child had hydrocephalus and neither the contracting couple nor the surrogate mother wanted it. In this case, genetic testing showed that the child actually had been fathered by the surrogate's husband, not the man who had contracted for her service. The surrogate then accepted the baby as her own. Nevertheless, the case raised the question of whether the birth of a genetically defective child constituted fulfillment of the contract and obligated the contracting couple to accept the child, or whether such a contract implied that the surrogate mother must produce a healthy child.

In another case, a wealthy couple was killed in an accident and left frozen preembryos in an IVF clinic. A lawsuit was filed on behalf of the preembryos on the grounds that they were heirs to the couple's estate and should be carried to birth by a surrogate mother so they could inherit it. The court ruled against the suit and the preembryos were allowed to perish. In still another widely publicized case, a man sued his wife for custody of their frozen preembryos as part of a divorce settlement.

IVF also creates a question of what to do with the excess preembryos. Some people view their disposal as a form of abortion, even if the preembryo is only a mass of 8 to 16 undifferentiated cells. On the other hand, there are those who see such excess preembryos as a research opportunity to obtain information that can't be obtained in any other way. In 1996, an IVF clinic in England was allowed to destroy 3,300 unclaimed preembryos, but only after heated public controversy.

It is common for scientific advances to require new advances in law and ethics. The parallel development of these disciplines is necessary if we are to benefit from the developments of science and ensure that knowledge is applied in an ethical and humane manner.

STUDY GUIDE

▶ Assess Your Learning Outcomes

To test your knowledge, discuss the following topics with a study partner or in writing, ideally from memory.

29.1 Fertilization and the Preembryonic Stage

1. Why sperm must meet an egg near the distal end of the uterine tube; factors that may aid in sperm migration
2. Why freshly ejaculated sperm cannot fertilize an egg; the process in which they acquire that ability
3. The acrosomal reaction, barriers to fertilization, and why multiple sperm must collaborate to fertilize an egg
4. The term for fertilization of an egg by two or more sperm, and how the egg normally prevents this
5. Events that occur between penetration by a sperm and the mingling of sperm and egg chromosomes; the term for a fertilized egg
6. The division of pregnancy into three trimesters and into preembryonic, embryonic, and fetal stages
7. Duration of the preembryonic stage; the three major events that occur in this stage; and the end product of this stage
8. The meaning of *cleavage;* the term for the resulting cells; development and characteristics of the morula and blastocyst; and structural and functional distinctions between the trophoblast and embryoblast
9. The process of implantation; the cytotrophoblast and syncytiotrophoblast; and the role of the latter in implantation and nourishment of the conceptus
10. The source and function of human chorionic gonadotropin
11. The process of gastrulation; the formation and names of the three primary germ layers; and why the process is called embryogenesis

29.2 The Embryonic and Fetal Stages

1. Major events that occur in the embryonic stage and the developmental ages at which it begins and ends
2. Longitudinal and lateral folding of the embryo; how this gives rise to the body cavity and gut; and the term for the differentiation of the embryonic organs

3. Structure and function of the four extra-embryonic membranes associated with the embryo and fetus
4. The source and functions of amniotic fluid
5. How the conceptus is nourished prior to implantation
6. The mode of trophoblastic nutrition; what the trophoblast digests for its nourishment at this stage; the developmental age at which this yields to the placenta as the dominant mode of nutrition; and the age at which it ends entirely
7. When and how the placenta begins to form; the structure of the placenta; the method of transfer of nutrients and wastes between the maternal and fetal blood
8. Structure of the umbilical cord and the origin and termination of the umbilical blood vessels in the fetal body
9. When the individual is considered to be a fetus, and by what criterion
10. Developments that occur in the fetal stage; the meaning of *digital rays, meconium, lanugo, vernix caseosa, quickening,* and *vertex position*
11. Why the fetal circulatory system differs from the neonatal system, and names of the circulatory shunts in the fetus

29.3 The Neonate

1. What occurs in the neonate in the transitional period of 6 to 8 hours after birth; the duration of the neonatal period
2. What happens to the umbilical arteries and fetal circulatory shunts after birth; names of the adult remnants of the shunts
3. Why breathing is so difficult for the neonate
4. Sources of neonatal immunity; the age at which an infant produces ample amounts of antibody on its own
5. Why neonatal thermoregulation is so critical; the functional importance of brown fat in the neonate
6. Why the neonate needs more fluid intake relative to body weight than adults do
7. Why premature infants are at risk of infant respiratory distress syndrome, hypothermia, hypoproteinemia, edema, clotting deficiency, and jaundice
8. Four principal causes of congenital anomalies (birth defects)

9. Three classes of teratogens, with examples of each; why organ systems vary in age of maximum susceptibility to teratogenesis
10. Some of the more common and serious infectious diseases of the newborn
11. Nondisjunction and how it gives rise to triplo-X, Klinefelter, Turner, and Down syndromes; the signs of these syndromes; the term for any condition in which there are more or fewer than two sex chromosomes or two copies of each autosome

29.4 Aging and Senescence

1. The difference in meaning between *aging* and *senescence*
2. Differences in the leading causes of death in old age compared to those of young adulthood
3. Senescent changes in the integumentary system; differences between intrinsic aging and photoaging of the skin; and why integumentary senescence raises the risk of lactose intolerance, bone loss, muscle weakness, and poorer glandular secretion and synaptic transmission
4. Senescent changes in the skeletal system and how males and females differ in this respect
5. Senescent changes in the muscular system, and how they arise partially from nervous system senescence
6. Senescent changes in the nervous system and why this has especially widespread effects on homeostasis
7. Forms of declining sensory function in old age
8. The relatively slight senescence of most endocrine functions except for reproductive hormones; reasons for increased risk of diabetes mellitus as one ages
9. Senescent changes in the circulatory system including the blood, heart, and blood vessels; how circulatory system senescence contributes to atrophy in many other organs
10. Why senescent losses of immune function raise the risk and severity of infectious diseases and cancer
11. Senescent changes in the respiratory system, including the thoracic cage; why pneumonia and chronic obstructive pulmonary diseases become such prevalent causes of death

STUDY GUIDE

12. Senescent changes in the urinary system; how this affects fluid needs and drug therapy in old age; and reasons for increasing urine retention in elderly men and incontinence in elderly women
13. Senescent changes in the digestive system and their effects on nutrition
14. Senescent changes in the male and female reproductive systems and the hormonal effects of this senescence on other organ systems
15. The relative contributions of regular exercise to longevity and quality of life in old age, and disorders for which the risk is reduced by regular exercise
16. Theories of senescence including replicative senescence and the telomere theory; protein and DNA cross-linking; protein misfolding and other structural defects; and the autoimmune theory
17. The hereditary contribution to life expectancy; the reason natural selection cannot eliminate genes that cause the degenerative diseases of old age
18. The difference between life span and life expectancy, and why medical science has been able to extend one but not the other
19. Clinical and legal criteria of death and the issue of how clinical death differs from complete biological death

▶ Testing Your Recall

Answers in Appendix A

1. When a conceptus arrives in the uterus, it is at what stage of development?
   a. zygote
   b. morula
   c. blastomere
   d. blastocyst
   e. embryo

2. The entry of a sperm nucleus into an egg must be preceded by
   a. the cortical reaction.
   b. the acrosomal reaction.
   c. the fast block.
   d. implantation.
   e. cleavage.

3. The stage of the conceptus that implants in the uterine wall is
   a. a blastomere.
   b. a morula.
   c. a blastocyst.
   d. an embryo.
   e. a zygote.

4. Chorionic villi develop from
   a. the zona pellucida.
   b. the endometrium.
   c. the syncytiotrophoblast.
   d. the embryoblast.
   e. the corona radiata.

5. Which of these results from aneuploidy?
   a. Turner syndrome
   b. fetal alcohol syndrome
   c. nondisjunction
   d. progeria
   e. rubella

6. Fetal urine accumulates in the _____ and contributes to the fluid there.
   a. placental sinus
   b. yolk sac
   c. allantois
   d. chorion
   e. amnion

7. Cells may be limited in how many times they can divide because of shortening of the _____ of their chromosomes at each division.
   a. blastomeres
   b. centromeres
   c. telomeres
   d. life expectancy
   e. autosomes

8. Photoaging is a major factor in the senescence of
   a. the integumentary system.
   b. the eyes.
   c. the nervous system.
   d. the skeletal system.
   e. the cardiovascular system.

9. Which of these is *not* a common effect of senescence?
   a. reduced synthesis of vitamin D
   b. atrophy of the kidneys
   c. atrophy of the cerebral gyri
   d. increased risk of intervertebral disc herniation
   e. reduced pulmonary vital capacity

10. For the first 8 weeks of gestation, a conceptus is nourished mainly by
    a. the placenta.
    b. amniotic fluid.

    c. colostrum.
    d. decidual cells.
    e. yolk cytoplasm.

11. Viruses and chemicals that cause congenital anatomical deformities are called _____.

12. Aneuploidy is caused by _____, the failure of two homologous chromosomes to separate in meiosis.

13. The maximum age attainable by a member of the human species is called the _____.

14. The average age attained by humans in a given population is called the _____.

15. Fetal blood flows through growths called _____, which project into the placental sinus.

16. The enzymes with which a sperm penetrates an egg are contained in an organelle called the _____.

17. Stiffening of the arteries, joints, and lenses in old age may be a result of cross-linking between _____ molecules.

18. An enlarged tongue, epicanthal folds of the eyes, and mental retardation are characteristic of a genetic anomaly called _____.

19. The fossa ovalis is a remnant of a fetal shunt called the _____.

20. A developing individual is first classified as a/an _____ when the three primary germ layers have formed.

STUDY GUIDE

▶ Building Your Medical Vocabulary

Answers in Appendix A

State a meaning of each word element, and give a medical term from this chapter that uses it or a slight variation of it.

1. con-
2. decidu-
3. gero-
4. mor-
5. placento-
6. -ploid
7. senesc-
8. syn-
9. telo-
10. terato-

▶ What's Wrong with These Statements?

Answers in Appendix A

Briefly explain why each of the following statements is false, or reword it to make it true.

1. The ability of sperm to fertilize an egg declines sharply in the first 5 hours after ejaculation.

2. Fertilization normally occurs in the lumen of the uterus.

3. An egg is usually fertilized by the first sperm that contacts it.

4. The zygote begins dividing into multiple embryonic cells as soon as it reaches the uterus.

5. The conceptus is first considered a fetus when all three primary germ layers have formed.

6. As the placenta develops, the membranes of its chorionic villi become thicker and more selective with respect to what blood-borne substances it allows to pass through to the fetus.

7. The kidneys show significantly less senescence in old age than most other organs.

8. Fetal blood bypasses the nonfunctional liver by passing through the foramen ovale.

9. Blood in the umbilical vein has a lower P_{O_2} than blood in the umbilical arteries.

10. The gradual destruction of telomeres by telomerase is thought to be a major contributor to senescence and cell death.

▶ Testing Your Comprehension

1. Suppose a woman had a mutation resulting in a tough zona pellucida that did not disintegrate after the egg was fertilized. How would this affect her fertility? Why?

2. Suppose a drug were developed that could slow down the rate of collagen cross-linking with age. What diseases of old age could be made less severe with such a drug?

3. Some health-food stores market the enzyme superoxide dismutase (SOD) as an oral antioxidant to retard senescence. Explain why it would be a waste of your money to buy it.

4. In some children, the ductus arteriosus fails to close after birth—a condition that eventually requires surgery. Predict how this condition would affect (a) pulmonary blood pressure, (b) systemic diastolic pressure, and (c) the right ventricle of the heart.

5. Only one sperm is needed to fertilize an egg, yet a man who ejaculates fewer than 10 million sperm is usually infertile. Explain this apparent contradiction. Supposing 10 million sperm were ejaculated, predict how many would come within close range of the egg. How likely is it that any one of these sperm would fertilize it?

APPENDIX A

ANSWER KEYS

This appendix provides answers to questions in the figure legends and the end-of-chapter questions in the "Testing Your Recall," "Building Your Medical Vocabulary," and "What's Wrong with These Statements?" sections. Answers to "Apply What You Know" and "Testing Your Comprehension" questions are available to instructors on the text Connect site at www.mcgrawhillconnect.com.

CHAPTER 1

Figure Legend Questions

1.7 Vasodilation allows more blood to flow close to the body surface and to lose heat through the skin; thus, it cools the body.

1.9 Yes; one could say that pregnancy activates a series of events leading to childbirth, the termination of the pregnancy. Thus, it has the qualities of a negative feedback loop.

1.11 MRI is better than X-rays for visualizing nervous tissue, since X-rays do not penetrate bone very well. It also shows better contrast than X-rays in visualization of other soft tissues. X-rays are better than PET scans for visualizing bones, teeth, and other hard or dense tissues, as PET scans have relatively low resolution and do not serve well to visualize tissues with little regional variation in metabolic rate.

Testing Your Recall

1. a	8. c	15. homeostasis
2. e	9. d	16. set point
3. d	10. b	17. negative feedback
4. a	11. dissection	18. organ
5. c	12. gradient	19. stereoscopic
6. c	13. deduction	20. prehensile,
7. a	14. psychosomatic	opposable

Building Your Medical Vocabulary (Answers may vary; these are acceptable examples.)

1. listen—auscultation	6. nature—physiology
2. apart—dissection	7. cut—dissection
3. the same—homeostasis	8. to stay—homeostasis
4. change—metabolism	9. solid—stereoscopic
5. touch—palpation	10. to cut—tomography

What's Wrong with These Statements?

1. Auscultation means listening to body sounds, not inspecting the body by touch.
2. MRI does not involve ionizing radiation and has no known risk to a fetus.
3. Positive feedback is beneficial in limited cases, but more often it causes rapid departure from the homeostatic set point and may cause illness or death.
4. Each cell has many organelles, so organelles far outnumber cells.
5. Matter will move spontaneously down a gradient without the need for application of external energy.
6. Leeuwenhoek was a textile merchant who built microscopes to examine fabric.

7. A scientific theory is founded on a large body of evidence and summarizes what is already known.
8. Both the treatment and control groups consist of volunteer patients.
9. Evolutionary biologists do not believe humans evolved from monkeys, but that humans and apes evolved from the same ancestor.
10. Negative feedback is a self-corrective process with a beneficial effect on the body.

ATLAS A

Figure Legend Questions

A.4 Right lower quadrant (RLQ)

A.8 No, it is inferior to the peritoneal cavity, since the peritoneum passes over its superior surface.

Testing Your Recall

1. d	8. d	15. hand, foot
2. c	9. b	16. meninges
3. e	10. d	17. retroperitoneal
4. d	11. mesenteries	18. medial
5. d	12. parietal	19. inferior
6. a	13. mediastinum	20. cubital, popliteal
7. a	14. nuchal	

Building Your Medical Vocabulary (Answers may vary; these are acceptable examples.)

1. before—antebrachium	6. within—intraperitoneal
2. neck—cervical	7. wall—parietal
3. above—epigastric	8. around—peritoneum
4. below—hypochondriac	9. behind—retroperitoneal
5. groin—inguinal	10. arrow—sagittal

What's Wrong with These Statements?

1. A sagittal section could only pass between the lungs or through one lung, not through both of them.
2. A frontal section passes from left to right and could include both eyes.
3. The knee is proximal to the ankle (tarsal region).
4. The diaphragm is inferior to the lungs.
5. The esophagus is superior to the stomach.
6. The liver extends from the hypochondriac to the epigastric region, superior to the lumbar region.
7. The heart is enfolded by the pericardial cavity but not contained within it.
8. The kidneys are retroperitoneal.
9. The peritoneum lines the outside of the stomach and intestines.
10. The sigmoid colon is in the lower left quadrant.

CHAPTER 2

Figure Legend Questions

2.8 Because water molecules are attracted to each other, it requires more thermal energy for any one of them to break free and evaporate.

2.12 Decomposition

2.26 No, the amount of energy released is the same with or without an enzyme.

Testing Your Recall

1. a	9. b	16. -ose, -ase
2. c	10. d	17. phospholipids
3. a	11. cation	18. cyclic adenosine
4. c	12. free radicals	monophosphate
5. a	13. catalyst, enzymes	19. anaerobic
6. e	14. anabolism	fermentation
7. b	15. dehydration	20. substrate
8. c	synthesis	

Building Your Medical Vocabulary (Answers may vary; these are acceptable examples.)

1. not—atom	6. water—hydrolysis
2. oxygen—aerobic	7. part—polymer
3. both—amphipathic	8. one—monomer
4. heat—calorie	9. few—oligosaccharide
5. glue—colloid	10. loving—hydrophilic

What's Wrong with These Statements?

1. The monomers of a polysaccharide are monosaccharides (simple sugars).
2. ATP is not an energy-storage molecule. Most of our reserve energy is stored in fat.
3. Such molecules are called isomers, not isotopes.
4. Catabolism produces products with less energy than the reactants.
5. Peptide bonds join amino acids together, not sugars.
6. A saturated fat is one to which no more hydrogen can be added.
7. Enzymes, like all catalysts, are not consumed by the reactions they catalyze.
8. Above a certain temperature, enzymes denature and cease working.
9. These solutes have different molecular weights, so 2% solutions would not contain the same number of molecules per unit volume.
10. A solution with pH 8 has one-tenth the hydrogen ion concentration of one with pH 7.

CHAPTER 3

Figure Legend Questions

3.8 Adenylate cyclase is a transmembrane protein. The G protein is peripheral.
3.19 The Na⁺–K⁺ pump requires ATP, whereas osmosis does not. ATP is quickly depleted after a cell dies.
3.22 Transcytosis is a combination of endocytosis and exocytosis.
3.27 Large molecules such as enzymes and RNA must pass through the nuclear pores, but pores in the plasma membrane must be small enough to prevent such large molecules from escaping the cell.
3.33 A centriole is composed of a cylinder of nine groups of microtubules, but in a centriole, there are three microtubules in each group and in an axoneme there are only two. Also, an axoneme usually has a central pair of microtubules, whereas a centriole does not.

Testing Your Recall

1. e	9. d	16. exocytosis
2. b	10. b	17. Ribosomes,
3. d	11. micrometers	proteasomes
4. b	12. second messenger	18. smooth ER,
5. e	13. Voltage-gated	peroxisomes
6. e	14. hydrostatic	19. ligand-gated
7. a	pressure	channel
8. c	15. hypertonic	20. cistern

Building Your Medical Vocabulary (Answers may vary; these are acceptable examples.)

1. opposite—antiport	6. easy—facilitated
2. color—chromatin	7. spindle—fusiform
3. together—cotransport	8. study of—cytology
4. cell—cytoplasm	9. process—pinocytosis
5. into, within—endocytosis	10. eat—phagocytosis

What's Wrong with These Statements?

1. Osmosis does not require ATP, so it can continue even after cell death.
2. Some cells have two or more nuclei and some cells have none.
3. Second messengers activate enzymes in the cell; they are not transport proteins.
4. Peroxisomes are produced by the endoplasmic reticulum, not by the Golgi complex.
5. A channel could not move material from the outside of a cell to the inside unless it extended all the way across the membrane; it must be a transmembrane protein.
6. The plasma membrane consists primarily of phospholipid molecules.
7. The brush border is composed of microvilli.
8. Cells in hypertonic saline will lose water and shrivel.
9. Osmosis is not a carrier-mediated process and therefore not subject to a transport maximum.
10. Many ribosomes lie free in the cytosol, not attached to the ER or nucleus.

CHAPTER 4

Figure Legend Questions

4.1 The helix would bulge where two purines were paired and would be constricted where two pyrimidines were paired.
4.8 The ribosome would have no way of holding the partially completed peptide in place while adding the next amino acid.

Testing Your Recall

1. a	8. d	14. polyribosome
2. e	9. d	15. RNA polymerase
3. c	10. a	16. genome
4. c	11. cytokinesis	17. 46, 92, 92
5. e	12. cyclin-dependent	18. ribosome
6. b	kinases	19. growth factors
7. a	13. genetic code	20. autosomes

Building Your Medical Vocabulary (Answers may vary; these are acceptable examples.)

1. different—allele	6. nucleus—karyotype
2. finger—polydactyly	7. next in a series—metaphase
3. double—diploid	8. shape—polymorphism
4. half—haploid	9. change—mutation
5. different—heterozygous	10. many—polydactyly

What's Wrong with These Statements?

1. There are no ribosomes on the Golgi complex; they are on the rough ER.
2. There are no genes for steroids, carbohydrates, or phospholipids, but only for proteins.
3. RNA is half the weight of a DNA of the same length because it has only one nucleotide strand, whereas DNA has two.
4. Each amino acid is represented by a triplet, a sequence of three bases, not one base pair.
5. A single gene can code for multiple proteins.

6. This law describes the pairing of bases between the two strands of DNA, not between mRNA and tRNA.
7. Only about 2% of the human DNA codes for proteins.
8. Mutations can be harmful, beneficial, or neutral.
9. Males have only one X chromosome, but have two sex chromosomes (the X and Y).
10. Several RNA polymerase molecules at once can transcribe a gene.

CHAPTER 5

Figure Legend Questions

5.2 They are longitudinal sections. In a cross section, both the egg white and yolk would look circular. In an oblique section, the white would look elliptical but the yolk would still look circular.
5.12 The epithelia of the tongue, oral cavity, esophagus, and anal canal would look similar to this.
5.28 Gap junctions
5.30 Exocytosis
5.31 The sketch would look like one of the purple sacs in the middle figure, budding directly from the epithelial surface with no duct.
5.32 Holocrine glands, because entire cells break down to become the secretion, and these must be continually replaced.

Testing Your Recall

1. a	9. b	17. basement
2. b	10. b	membrane
3. c	11. necrosis	18. matrix (extracel-
4. e	12. mesothelium	lular material)
5. c	13. lacunae	19. multipotent
6. a	14. fibers	20. simple
7. b	15. collagen	
8. e	16. skeletal muscle	

Building Your Medical Vocabulary (Answers may vary; these are acceptable examples.)

1. away—apoptosis
2. cartilage—chondrocyte
3. outer—ectoderm
4. producing—collagen
5. tissue—histology
6. whole—holocrine
7. glassy—hyaline
8. dead—necrosis
9. formed—neoplasia
10. scale—squamous

What's Wrong with These Statements?

1. The esophageal epithelium is nonkeratinized.
2. All of them contact the basement membrane.
3. There are a few cases of skeletal muscles not attached to bones.
4. Glandular secretions are produced by cells of the parenchyma; the stroma is nonsecretory supportive connective tissue.
5. Adipose tissue is an exception; cells constitute most of its volume.
6. Adipocytes are also found in areolar tissue, either singly or in small clusters.
7. Tight junctions serve mainly to restrict the passage of material between cells.
8. Neoplasia is abnormal tissue growth, such as tumors; development of mature tissue types from nonspecialized tissues is called differentiation.
9. Excitability is characteristic of all living cells, but most highly developed in nerve and muscle cells.
10. Perichondrium is lacking from fibrocartilage and from hyaline articular cartilage.

CHAPTER 6

Figure Legend Questions

6.5 Keratinocytes
6.8 Cuticle
6.11 Asymmetry (A), irregular border (B), and color (C). The photo does not provide enough information to judge the diameter of the lesion (D).

Testing Your Recall

1. d	8. a	14. cyanosis
2. c	9. a	15. dermal papillae
3. d	10. d	16. earwax
4. b	11. Insensible	17. sebaceous glands
5. a	perspiration	18. anagen
6. e	12. arrector muscle	19. dermal papilla
7. c	13. debridement	20. third-degree

Building Your Medical Vocabulary (Answers may vary; these are acceptable examples.)

1. substance—melanin
2. white—albinism
3. skin—dermatology
4. through—diaphoresis
5. same—homograft
6. injure—lesion
7. black—melanoma
8. tumor—carcinoma
9. nail—eponychium
10. hair—piloerector

What's Wrong with These Statements?

1. Basal cell carcinoma is the most common form of skin cancer.
2. The number of melanocytes is about the same in all skin colors; dark skin results from the accumulation of melanin in keratinocytes.
3. Keratin is the protein of the epidermis; the dermis is composed mainly of collagen.
4. Vitamin D synthesis begins in the keratinocytes.
5. Epidermal cell multiplication occurs in the stratum basale.
6. Cells of the cortex are also dead; the only living hair cells are in and near the hair bulb.
7. The hypodermis is not considered to be a layer of the skin.
8. Different races have about the same density of melanocytes but different amounts of melanin.
9. A genetic lack of melanin causes albinism, not pallor. Pallor is a temporary, nonhereditary paleness of the skin.
10. Apocrine sweat glands develop at puberty.

CHAPTER 7

Figure Legend Questions

7.1 The wider epiphyses provide surface area for muscle attachment and bone articulation, while the narrowness of the diaphysis minimizes weight.
7.6 Places where bone comes close to the skin, such as the sternum and hips
7.7 Temporal bone, parietal bone, and several others
7.9 Humerus, radius, ulna, femur, tibia, fibula
7.10 An infant's joints are still cartilaginous.
7.12 The zones of cell proliferation and cell hypertrophy

Testing Your Recall

1. e	8. e	15. hypocalcemia
2. a	9. b	16. Osteoblasts
3. d	10. d	17. calcitriol
4. c	11. hydroxyapatite	18. osteoporosis
5. d	12. canaliculi	19. metaphysis
6. a	13. appositional	20. osteomalacia
7. d	14. solubility product	

Building Your Medical Vocabulary (Answers may vary; these are acceptable examples.)

1. calcium—hypocalcemia
2. destroy—osteoclast
3. softening—osteomalacia
4. marrow—osteomyelitis
5. straight—orthopedics
6. bone—osseous
7. bone—osteocyte
8. growth—diaphysis
9. dart—spicule
10. place—ectopic

What's Wrong with These Statements?

1. Flat cranial bones have a middle layer of spongy bone called the diploe.
2. Cartilage is removed and replaced by bone, not calcified and transformed into bone.
3. The most common bone disease is osteoporosis, not fractures.
4. Bones elongate at the epiphysial plate, not the articular cartilage.
5. Osteoclasts develop from stem cells in the bone marrow, not from osteoblasts.
6. Osteoblasts give rise only to osteocytes and are therefore unipotent.
7. Hydroxyapatite is the major mineral of bone; the major protein is collagen.
8. Osteons have blood vessels in their central canals, not in the canaliculi.
9. The major effect of vitamin D is bone resorption, though it also promotes deposition.
10. Parathyroid hormone indirectly promotes bone resorption, not deposition.

CHAPTER 8

Figure Legend Questions

8.10 Any five of these: the occipital, parietal, sphenoid, zygomatic, and palatine bones, and the mandible and maxilla
8.12 Any five of these: the frontal, lacrimal, and sphenoid bones, and the vomer, maxilla, and inferior concha
8.25 Rupture of this ligament allows the atlas to slip anteriorly and the dens of the axis to tear into the spinal cord.
8.35 The adult hand lacks epiphysial plates, the growth zones of a child's long bones.
8.41 The three cuneiforms and the cuboid bone of the tarsus are arranged in a row similar to the distal carpal bones (trapezium, trapezoid, capitate, and hamate), with the trapezium corresponding to the median cuneiform (proximal to digit I in each case). In the proximal row, the navicular bone of the tarsus is somewhat similar to the scaphoid of the carpus, being proximal to digit I and articulating with three bones of the distal row, but the calcaneus and talus are very different, being adapted to their load-bearing role.

Testing Your Recall

1. b
2. e
3. a
4. d
5. a
6. e
7. c
8. b
9. e
10. b
11. fontanelles
12. temporal
13. sutures
14. sphenoid
15. anulus fibrosus
16. dens
17. auricular
18. styloid
19. foramina
20. medial longitudinal

Building Your Medical Vocabulary (Answers may vary; these are acceptable examples.)

1. rib—intercostal
2. helmet—cranium
3. tough—dura mater
4. tongue—hypoglossa
5. little—ossicle
6. breast—mastoid
7. foot—bipedal
8. wing—pterygoid
9. above—supraorbital
10. ankle—metatarsal

What's Wrong with These Statements?

1. It passes out the jugular foramen.
2. Each hand and foot has 14 phalanges.
3. The female pelvis is wider and shallower than the male's.
4. The carpal bones are in the base of the hand, not the narrow wrist region.
5. Muscles of the infraspinous fossa are easily palpated on the back, inferior to the scapular spine.
6. You would be resting your elbow on the olecranon.
7. The lumbar vertebrae have transverse processes but no transverse costal facets.
8. The most frequently broken bone is the clavicle.
9. *Arm* refers to the region containing only the humerus; *leg* refers to the region containing the tibia and fibula.
10. These extra bones in the cranium are called sutural bones, not sesamoid bones.

CHAPTER 9

Figure Legend Questions

9.2 The gomphosis, because a tooth is not a bone
9.4 The pubic symphysis consists of the cartilaginous interpubic disc and the adjacent parts of the two pubic bones.
9.5 Interphalangeal joints are not subjected to a great deal of compression.
9.7 $MA = 1.0$. Shifting the fulcrum to the left would increase the MA of this lever, while the lever would remain first class.
9.19 The atlas (C1)

Testing Your Recall

1. c
2. b
3. a
4. e
5. c
6. c
7. a
8. d
9. b
10. d
11. synovial fluid
12. bursa
13. pivot
14. Kinesiology
15. gomphosis
16. serrate
17. extension
18. range of motion
19. articular disc
20. talus

Building Your Medical Vocabulary (Answers may vary; these are acceptable examples.)

1. away—abduction
2. joint—arthritis
3. characterized by—cruciate
4. letter X—cruciate
5. leg—talocrural
6. to lead—adduction
7. movement—kinesiology
8. moon—meniscus
9. to lay back—supination
10. to pull—protraction

What's Wrong with These Statements?

1. Osteoarthritis occurs in almost everyone after a certain age; rheumatoid arthritis is less common.
2. A kinesiologist studies joint movements; a rheumatologist treats arthritis.
3. Synovial joints are diarthroses and amphiarthroses, but never synarthroses.
4. There is no meniscus in the elbow.
5. This action involves hyperextension of the shoulder.
6. The cruciate ligaments are in the knee.
7. The round ligament is somewhat slack and probably does not secure the femoral head.
8. The knuckles are diarthroses.

9. Synovial fluid is secreted by the synovial membrane of the joint capsule and fills the bursae.
10. A tooth is not a bone.

CHAPTER 10

Figure Legend Questions

10.4 The brachialis and lateral head of the triceps brachii have direct attachments; the biceps brachii and long head of the triceps brachii have indirect attachments.
10.8 The zygomaticus major, levator palpebrae superioris, and orbicularis oris
10.16 Pectoralis minor, serratus anterior, and all three layers of the upper intercostal muscles
10.27 *Teres* refers to the round or cordlike shape of the first muscle, and *quadratus* refers to the four-sided shape of the second.
10.28 Part (c) represents a cross section cut too high on the forearm to include these muscles.
10.34 Climbing stairs, walking, running, or riding a bicycle
10.38 The soleus

Testing Your Recall

1. b	9. d	16. urogenital triangle
2. b	10. c	
3. a	11. buccinator	17. linea alba
4. c	12. fascicle	18. synergist
5. e	13. prime mover (agonist)	19. bipennate
6. e		20. sphincter
7. b	14. hamstring	
8. a	15. flexor retinacula	

Building Your Medical Vocabulary (Answers may vary; these are acceptable examples.)

1. head—splenius capitis
2. work—synergist
3. bundle—fascicle
4. lip—levator labii superioris
5. lower back—quadratus lumborum
6. mouse—muscle
7. muscle—perimysium
8. shoulder—omohyoid
9. feather—bipennate
10. third—peroneus tertius

What's Wrong with These Statements?

1. The connective tissue that encloses individual muscle fibers is endomysium.
2. The orbicularis was once thought to be a sphincter but is no longer interpreted as such.
3. The biceps brachii is fusiform.
4. A synergist aids an agonist in its function; it does not oppose the agonist.
5. Many skeletal muscles are innervated by cranial nerves (those in the head and neck).
6. Normally, no muscular effort is needed to exhale.
7. The hamstrings flex the knee and therefore would not aid in lifting the body to the next step.
8. The facial nerve innervates 16 of the facial muscles tabulated in this chapter. The trigeminal innervates 6 tabulated muscles, but they are muscles of chewing and swallowing, not facial expression.
9. The adductor pollicis is by far the strongest of the three listed muscles (important in the strength of the hand grip), but is not listed first.
10. They are on opposite sides of the tibia and act as antagonists.

ATLAS B

Figure Legend Questions

B.1 Orbicularis oris; trapezius

B.5 The lungs, heart, liver, stomach, gallbladder, and spleen, among others
B.8 Sternocleidomastoids
B.11 Posterior
B.13 Fat (adipose tissue)
B.18 Five: one tendon proximally (at the humerus) and four distally (in the hand)
B.19 The mark would belong close to where the leader for the styloid process of the radius ends in figure B.19b.
B.20 The mark would belong close to where the leader for the rectus femoris ends; the vastus intermedius is deep to this.
B.21 The fibula
B.24 There is no such bone; digit I (the great toe) has only a proximal and distal phalanx.
B.25 Answers to the muscle test are as follows:

1. f	11. x	21. k
2. b	12. m	22. d
3. k	13. n	23. f
4. p	14. e	24. b
5. h	15. g	25. a
6. y	16. v	26. u
7. z	17. f	27. j
8. w	18. c	28. i
9. c	19. x	29. g
10. a	20. w	30. q

CHAPTER 11

Figure Legend Questions

11.1 The striations distinguish it from smooth muscle; the multiple nuclei adjacent to the plasma membrane and the parallel fibers distinguish it from both cardiac and smooth muscle.
11.2 The electrical excitation spreading down the T tubule must excite the opening of calcium gates in the terminal cisterns.
11.13 ATP is needed to pump Ca^{2+} back into the sarcoplasmic reticulum by active transport and to induce each myosin head to release actin so the sarcomere can relax.
11.16 The gluteus maximus and quadriceps femoris
11.17 The muscle tension curve would drop gradually while the muscle length curve would rise.

Testing Your Recall

1. a	8. c	15. acetylcholine
2. c	9. e	16. myoglobin
3. b	10. b	17. Z discs
4. d	11. threshold	18. varicosities
5. c	12. oxidative	19. muscle tone
6. c	13. terminal cisterns	20. Isometric contraction
7. e	14. myosin	

Building Your Medical Vocabulary (Answers may vary; these are acceptable examples.)

1. weak—myasthenia
2. self—autorhythmic
3. abnormal—dystrophy
4. same—isometric
5. length—isometric
6. muscle—myocyte
7. flesh—sarcolemma
8. time—temporal
9. tension—isotonic
10. growth—dystrophy

What's Wrong with These Statements?

1. A motor neuron may supply 1,000 or more muscle fibers; a motor unit consists of one motor neuron and all the muscle fibers it innervates.
2. Somatic motor neurons do not innervate cardiac muscle.
3. Fast glycolytic fibers fatigue relatively quickly.
4. Thin myofilaments extend well into the A bands, where they overlap with thick myofilaments.
5. Thin and thick myofilaments do not shorten, but glide over each other.
6. Thick and thin myofilaments are present but not arranged in a way that produces striations.
7. Under natural conditions, a muscle seldom or never attains complete tetanus.
8. Even excitation would be impossible without ATP, because ATP drives the active transport (Na^+–K^+) pumps that maintain membrane potential and excitability.
9. A muscle produces most of its ATP during this time by anaerobic fermentation, which generates lactate; it does not consume lactate.
10. Autorhythmicity is limited to unitary smooth muscle.

CHAPTER 12

Figure Legend Questions

12.9 Its conduction speed is relatively slow, but it has a small diameter and contributes relatively little bulk to the nervous tissue.

12.25 One EPSP is a voltage change of only 0.5 mV or so. A change of about 15 mV is required to reach threshold and make a neuron fire.

12.30 The CNS interprets a stimulus as more intense if it receives signals from high-threshold sensory neurons than if it receives signals only from low-threshold neurons.

12.32 A reverberating circuit, because a neuron early in the circuit is continually restimulated

Testing Your Recall

1. e	9. d	16. myelin sheath gaps
2. c	10. b	
3. d	11. afferent	17. axon hillock, initial segment
4. a	12. conductivity	
5. c	13. absolute refractory period	18. norepinephrine
6. e		19. facilitated zone
7. d	14. dendrites	20. Neuromodulators
8. a	15. oligodendrocytes	

Building Your Medical Vocabulary (Answers may vary; these are acceptable examples.)

1. forward—anterograde
2. to touch—synapse
3. star—astrocyte
4. tree—dendrite
5. carry—afferent
6. knot—ganglion
7. to walk—retrograde
8. nerve—neuroglia
9. hard—sclerosis
10. body—somatic

What's Wrong with These Statements?

1. A neuron never has more than one axon.
2. Oligodendrocytes of the brain perform the same function as Schwann cells of the PNS.
3. The extracellular concentration of Na^+ is greater than its intracellular concentration.
4. Only a small fraction of the neuron's Na^+ and K^+ exchange places across the plasma membrane.

5. The threshold stays the same but an EPSP brings the membrane potential closer to the threshold.
6. The absolute refractory period sets an upper limit on firing frequency.
7. The effect of a neurotransmitter varies from place to place depending on the type of receptor present.
8. The signals travel rapidly through the internodal segments and slow down at each myelin sheath gap.
9. Learning involves modification of the synapses of existing neurons, not an increase in the neuron population.
10. Neurons cannot undergo mitosis to replace those that are lost, although limited replacement occurs through multiplication and differentiation of stem cells.

CHAPTER 13

Figure Legend Questions

13.5 If it were T10, there would be no cuneate fasciculus; that exists only from T6 up.

13.10 They are in the anterior horn of the spinal cord.

13.13 They are afferent, because they arise from the posterior root of the spinal nerve.

13.15 Severing one phrenic nerve paralyzes the diaphragm on the ipsilateral side; severing both of them paralyzes the entire diaphragm and causes respiratory arrest.

13.25 Motor neurons are capable only of exciting skeletal muscle (end-plate potentials are always excitatory). To inhibit muscle contraction, it is necessary to inhibit the motor neuron at the CNS level (point 6).

13.26 They would show more synaptic delay, because there are more synapses in the pathway.

Testing Your Recall

1. e	8. a	15. intrafusal fibers
2. c	9. e	16. phrenic
3. d	10. b	17. decussation
4. d	11. ganglia	18. proprioception
5. e	12. ramus	19. posterior root
6. c	13. spinocerebellar	20. tibial, common fibular
7. c	14. crossed extension	

Building Your Medical Vocabulary (Answers may vary; these are acceptable examples.)

1. spider—arachnoid
2. tail—cauda equina
3. opposite—contralateral
4. wedge—cuneate
5. same—ipsilateral
6. diaphragm—phrenic
7. tender—pia mater
8. oneself—proprioception
9. branch—ramus
10. roof—tectospinal

What's Wrong with These Statements?

1. The gracile fasciculus is an ascending (sensory) tract.
2. It terminates in the upper lumbar region of the vertebral column.
3. Each segment of the spinal cord has several rootlets.
4. All spinal nerves are mixed nerves; none are purely sensory or motor.
5. The dura is separated from the bone by a fat-filled epidural space.
6. The horns of the spinal cord are gray matter.
7. Corticospinal tracts are descending (motor) tracts, not sensory.
8. Dermatomes overlap each other by as much as 50%.
9. Some somatic reflexes are mediated primarily through the brainstem and cerebellum.
10. Many ipsilateral reflex arcs are also polysynaptic.

CHAPTER 14

Figure Legend Questions

14.9 Signals in the cuneate fasciculus ascend to the cuneate nucleus in part (c), and signals in the gracile fasciculus ascend to the nearby gracile nucleus. Both of them decussate together to the contralateral medial lemniscus in parts (b) and (a) and travel this route to the thalamus.

14.10 The reticular formation is labeled on all three parts of the figure.

14.14 Commissural tracts also cross through the anterior and posterior commissures shown in figure 14.2.

14.15 Dendrites; the axons project downward into the white matter.

14.22 Regions with numerous small muscles

Testing Your Recall

1. c
2. a
3. e
4. a
5. b
6. c
7. a
8. d
9. e
10. e
11. corpus callosum
12. ventricles, cerebrospinal
13. arbor vitae
14. vagus nerve
15. choroid plexus
16. precentral
17. frontal
18. association areas
19. categorical
20. Broca area

Building Your Medical Vocabulary (Answers may vary; these are acceptable examples.)

1. pain—neuralgia
2. head—hydrocephalus
3. brain—cerebrospinal
4. body—corpus callosum
5. brain—encephalitis
6. record of—electroencephalogram
7. island—insula
8. eye—oculomotor
9. pulley—trochlea
10. little—peduncle

What's Wrong with These Statements?

1. The optic nerve is purely sensory. Eye movements are controlled by the oculomotor, trochlear, and abducens nerves.
2. The cerebral hemispheres do not develop from neural crest tissue.
3. The midbrain is rostral to the pons.
4. The Broca and Wernicke areas are ipsilateral, both in the left hemisphere in most people.
5. The choroid plexuses produce only 30% of the CSF.
6. Hearing is a temporal lobe function; vision resides in the occipital lobe.
7. Respiration is controlled by nuclei in the pons and medulla oblongata.
8. The trigeminal nerve carries sensory signals from the largest area of the face.
9. The vagus nerve (cranial nerve X) innervates organs of the thoracic and abdominopelvic cavities.
10. The cerebellum contains more than half of all brain neurons.

CHAPTER 15

Figure Legend Questions

15.4 No; inhaling and exhaling are controlled by the somatic motor system and skeletal muscles.

15.5 The neurosoma of the somatic efferent neuron is in the anterior horn and the neurosoma of the sympathetic preganglionic neuron is in the lateral horn.

15.7 The vagus nerve

15.9 The pupils dilate because fear increases sympathetic output, which induces dilation.

Testing Your Recall

1. b
2. c
3. e
4. e
5. a
6. e
7. d
8. d
9. a
10. c
11. adrenergic
12. Dual innervation
13. Autonomic tone
14. vagus
15. enteric
16. norepinephrine
17. sympathetic
18. preganglionic, postganglionic
19. cAMP
20. vasomotor tone

Building Your Medical Vocabulary (Answers may vary; these are acceptable examples.)

1. pressure—baroreflex
2. dissolve—sympatholytic
3. wall—intramural
4. rule—autonomic
5. ear—otic
6. feeling—parasympathetic
7. kidney—adrenal
8. internal organs—splanchnic
9. together—sympathetic
10. internal organs—visceral

What's Wrong with These Statements?

1. Both systems are always simultaneously active.
2. Cutaneous blood vessels receive only sympathetic fibers.
3. In biofeedback and other circumstances, limited voluntary control of the ANS is possible.
4. The sympathetic division inhibits digestion.
5. The sympathetic division has a few cholinergic postganglionic fibers, although most are adrenergic.
6. Waste elimination can occur by autonomic spinal reflexes without necessarily involving the brain.
7. All parasympathetic fibers are cholinergic.
8. The sympathetic division has more neural divergence and therefore more widespread, less organ-specific, effects than the parasympathetic division.
9. The hypoglossal nerve carries no parasympathetic fibers.
10. They have antagonistic effects on the iris.

CHAPTER 16

Figure Legend Questions

16.1 Yes; two touches are felt separately if they straddle the boundary between two separate receptive fields.

16.9 The lower margin of the violet zone ("all sound") would be higher in that frequency range.

16.15 They are the outer hair cells, which function to "tune the cochlea" and improve discrimination between sounds of different pitches.

16.16 It would oppose the inward movement of the tympanic membrane and, thus, reduce the amount of vibration transferred to the inner ear.

16.24 This would prevent tears from draining into the lacrimal canals, resulting in more watery eyes.

16.25 Cranial nerve III, because it controls more eye movements than IV or VI.

16.30 It is the right eye. The optic disc is always medial to the fovea, so this has to be a view of the observer's left and the subject's right.

16.42 Approximately 68:20:0, and yellow

16.45 It would cause blindness in the left half of the visual field. It would not affect the visual reflexes.

Testing Your Recall

1. a
2. c
3. b
4. a
5. e
6. e
7. d
8. c
9. c
10. b
11. fovea centralis
12. ganglion
13. photopsin
14. otoliths
15. outer hair cells
16. stapes
17. inferior colliculi
18. basal cells
19. olfactory bulb
20. referred pain

Building Your Medical Vocabulary (Answers may vary; these are acceptable examples.)

1. two—binaural
2. cross over—hemidecussation
3. half—hemidecussation
4. tears—lacrimal
5. stone—otolithic
6. spot—macula sacculi
7. pain—nociceptor
8. dark—scotopic
9. infection—asepsis
10. hair—peritrichial

What's Wrong with These Statements?

1. These fibers end in the medulla oblongata.
2. They are perceived in the right hemisphere because of decussation.
3. Because of hemidecussation, each hemisphere receives signals from both eyes.
4. Chemoreceptors that monitor blood chemistry, for example, are interoceptors.
5. The posterior chamber, the space between iris and lens, is filled with aqueous humor.
6. Descending analgesic fibers block signals that have reached the dorsal horn of the spinal cord.
7. Cranial nerve VIII carries both auditory and equilibrium signals.
8. The tympanic cavity is filled with air.
9. Rods release glutamate in the dark and stop when they are illuminated.
10. The trochlear and abducens nerves control the superior oblique and lateral rectus, respectively.

CHAPTER 17

Figure Legend Questions

17.1 Heart, liver, stomach, small intestine, placenta (any three)
17.4 The posterior pituitary (neurohypophysis)
17.19 Steroids enter the target cell; they do not bind to membrane receptors or activate second messengers.
17.24 Such a drug would block leukotriene synthesis and thus inhibit allergic and inflammatory responses.

Testing Your Recall

1. b
2. d
3. a
4. c
5. c
6. c
7. d
8. c
9. a
10. e
11. adenohypophysis
12. tyrosine
13. acromegaly
14. cortisol
15. glucocorticoids
16. interstitial endocrine
17. negative feedback inhibition
18. hypophysial portal system
19. permissive
20. Up-regulation

Building Your Medical Vocabulary (Answers may vary; these are acceptable examples.)

1. gland—adenohypophysis
2. bile—cholecystokinin
3. flow through—diabetes
4. twenty—eicosanoid
5. yellow—luteinizing
6. resembling—thyroid
7. full of—glomerulosa
8. favoring—progesterone
9. turn—gonadotropin
10. urine—glycosuria

What's Wrong with These Statements?

1. Gonadotropin secretion would rise because of a lack of negative feedback inhibition from the testes.
2. Glycoproteins cannot enter the target cell; they bind to surface receptors of the plasma membrane.
3. Thyroglobulin can be synthesized, but it cannot be iodinated, so no thyroid hormone is produced.
4. Tumors can cause hypersecretion but can also destroy endocrine cells and lead to hyposecretion.

5. Hormones are also secreted by the heart, liver, kidneys, and other organs not generally regarded as glands.
6. Most cases of diabetes mellitus are caused by insensitivity to insulin, not a lack of insulin.
7. The pineal gland and thymus undergo involution with age; they are larger in children than they are later in life.
8. Without iodine, there is no thyroid hormone (TH); without TH, there can be no negative feedback inhibition.
9. The tissue at the center is the adrenal medulla.
10. There are also two testes, two ovaries, and four parathyroid glands.

CHAPTER 18

Figure Legend Questions

18.1 (Answering this requires labeling the illustration.)
18.4 The sunken center represents the former location of the nucleus.
18.5 Hemoglobin consists of a noncovalent association of four protein chains. The prosthetic group is the heme moiety of each of the four chains.
18.18 *Myelo-* refers to the bone marrow, where these cells develop.
18.19 Although numerous, these WBCs are immature and incapable of performing their defensive roles.
18.21 A platelet plug lacks the fibrin mesh that a blood clot has.
18.22 It would affect only the intrinsic mechanism.
18.23 In both blood clotting and hormonal signal amplification, the product of one reaction step is an enzyme that catalyzes the production of many more molecules of the next product. Thus, there is a geometric increase in the number of product molecules at each step and ultimately, a large final result from a small beginning.
18.25 The older theory of leeching was that many disorders are caused by "bad blood," which could be removed painlessly by medicinal leeches. The modern practice is to take advantage of the anticoagulants in the leech saliva to promote blood flow to a tissue or to dissolve and remove clots that have already formed.

Testing Your Recall

1. b
2. c
3. c
4. a
5. b
6. d
7. d
8. c
9. d
10. c
11. hematopoiesis
12. hematocrit (packed cell volume)
13. thromboplastin
14. agglutinogens
15. hemophilia
16. hemostasis
17. Sickle-cell disease
18. polycythemia
19. vitamin B_{12}
20. erythropoietin

Building Your Medical Vocabulary (Answers may vary; these are acceptable examples.)

1. without—anemia
2. producing—erythroblast
3. red—erythrocyte
4. aggregate—agglutination
5. blood—hemostasis
6. white—leukocyte
7. deficiency—leukopenia
8. vein—phlebotomy
9. formation—hemopoiesis
10. clot—thrombosis

What's Wrong with These Statements?

1. Most of the volume is usually plasma.
2. Hyperproteinemia causes retention of more water in the circulatory system and raises blood pressure.
3. Oxygen deficiency is the result of anemia, not its cause.
4. Clotting (coagulation) is one mechanism of hemostasis, but hemostasis includes other mechanisms (vascular spasm and platelet plug), so it is not synonymous with the other two terms.
5. He can be the father if he is heterozygous for type A *(I^Ai)*, the mother is heterzygous for type B *(I^Bi),* and both are heterzygous for

Rh type *(Dd)*. The baby could then inherit *ii* and *dd,* and have phenotype O–.

6. The most abundant WBCs are neutrophils.
7. Blood clotting requires Ca^{2+} at several steps.
8. Even platelets arise ultimately from hematopoietic stem cells.
9. The heme is excreted; the globin is broken down into amino acids that can be reused.
10. In leukemia, there is an excess of WBCs. A WBC deficiency is leukopenia.

CHAPTER 19

Figure Legend Questions

19.1   Both; they receive pulmonary arteries from the pulmonary circuit and bronchial arteries from the systemic circuit.
19.2   To the left
19.7   The trabeculae carneae
19.12   The right atrium
19.14   It ensures that wave summation and tetanus will not occur, thus ensuring relaxation and refilling of the heart chambers.
19.19   They prevent prolapse of the AV valves during ventricular systole.
19.20   This is the point at which the aortic valve opens and blood is ejected into the aorta, raising its blood pressure.

Testing Your Recall

1. d	9. a	16. T wave
2. b	10. c	17. vagus
3. d	11. systole, diastole	18. myocardial
4. a	12. systemic	infarction
5. a	13. atrioventricular	19. endocardium
6. d	(coronary) sulcus	20. cardiac output
7. d	14. Na^+	
8. c	15. gap junctions	

Building Your Medical Vocabulary (Answers may vary; these are acceptable examples.)

1. entryway—atrium	6. nipple—papillary
2. slow—bradycardia	7. semi—semilunar
3. heart—cardiology	8. fast—tachycardia
4. crown—coronary	9. vessel—vasomotor
5. moon—semilunar	10. belly—ventricle

What's Wrong with These Statements?

1. The coronary circulation is part of the systemic circuit; the other division is the pulmonary circuit.
2. There are no valves at the openings of the venae cavae.
3. The first two-thirds of ventricular filling occurs before the atria contract. The atria add only about 31% of the blood that fills the ventricles.
4. The vagus nerves affect heart rate but not contraction strength.
5. High CO_2 and low pH accelerate the heart rate.
6. The first heart sound occurs at the time of the QRS complex.
7. The heart has its own internal pacemaker and would continue beating; the nerves only alter the heart rate.
8. That would result from clamping the pulmonary veins, not the pulmonary arteries.
9. Cardiomyocytes do have a stable resting potential when they are at rest.
10. The ECG is a composite record of the electrical activity of the entire myocardium, not a record from a single myocyte. It looks much different from an action potential.

CHAPTER 20

Figure Legend Questions

20.2   Veins are subjected to less pressure than arteries and have less need of elasticity.
20.5   Endocrine glands, kidneys, the small intestine, and choroid plexuses of the brain
20.8   Veins have less muscular and elastic tissue, so they expand more easily than arteries.
20.10   Arterial anastomoses: the arterial circle of the brain, the celiac circulation, encircling the heads of the humerus and femur, and the arterial arches of the hand and foot. Venous anastomoses: the jugular veins, the azygos system, the mesenteric veins, and venous networks of the hand and foot. Portal systems: the hepatic portal system and (outside of this chapter) the hypophysial portal system. Answers may vary.
20.20   Nothing would happen if he lifted his finger from point O because the valve at that point would prevent blood from flowing downward and filling the vein. If he lifted his finger from point H, blood would flow upward, fill the vein, and the vein between O and H would stand out.
20.27   Aorta → left common carotid a. → external carotid a. → superficial temporal a.
20.36   The ovaries and testes begin their embryonic development near the kidneys. The gonadal veins elongate as the gonads descend to the pelvic cavity and scrotum.
20.39   Joint movements may temporarily compress an artery. Anastomoses allow for continued blood flow through alternative routes to more distal regions.
20.40   The cephalic, basilic, and median cubital vv.

Testing Your Recall

1. c	9. e	16. transcytosis
2. b	10. d	17. sympathetic
3. a	11. systolic, diastolic	18. baroreceptors
4. e	12. continuous	19. cerebral arterial
5. b	capillaries	circle
6. c	13. Anaphylactic	20. basilic, cephalic
7. e	14. thoracic pump	
8. a	15. oncotic pressure	

Building Your Medical Vocabulary (Answers may vary; these are acceptable examples.)

1. vessel—angiogenesis	6. belonging to—vasa vasorum
2. arm—brachiocephalic	7. standing—saphenous
3. abdomen—celiac	8. below—subclavian
4. window—fenestrations	9. chest—thoracoacromial
5. neck—jugular	10. bladder—vesical

What's Wrong with These Statements?

1. Blood can bypass capillaries by flowing through an arteriovenous anastomosis.
2. Blood drains from the brain by way of the internal jugular veins.
3. The longest blood vessel is the great saphenous vein.
4. Some veins have valves, but arteries do not.
5. By the formula $F \propto r^4$, the flow increases in proportion to the fourth power of radius, or 16-fold.
6. The femoral triangle is bordered by the inguinal ligament, sartorius muscle, and adductor longus muscle.
7. The lungs also receive blood from the bronchial arteries of the systemic circuit.
8. Most capillaries reabsorb only a portion (typically about 85%) of the fluid they filter; the rest is absorbed by the lymphatic system.

9. An aneurysm is a weak, bulging vessel that *may* rupture.
10. The response to falling blood pressure is a corrective vasoconstriction.

CHAPTER 21

Figure Legend Questions

21.2 There are much larger gaps between the endothelial cells of lymphatic capillaries than between those of blood capillaries.

21.3 There would be no consistent one-way flow of lymph. Lymph and tissue fluid would accumulate, especially in the lower regions of the body.

21.4 (1) Prevention of excess tissue fluid accumulation and (2) monitoring the tissue fluids for pathogens

21.5 Lymph flows from the breast to the axillary lymph nodes. Therefore, metastatic cancer cells tend to lodge first in those nodes.

21.13 Erythrocytes in the red pulp; lymphocytes and macrophages in the white pulp

21.15 Both of these produce a ring of proteins in the target-cell plasma membrane, opening a hole in the membrane through which the cell contents escape.

21.23 All three defenses depend on the action of helper T cells, which are destroyed by HIV.

21.26 The ER is the site of antibody synthesis.

Testing Your Recall

1. b	9. a	16. pyrogen
2. c	10. c	17. interleukins
3. a	11. pathogen	18. antigen-binding
4. a	12. lysozyme	site, epitope
5. d	13. Lymphadenitis	19. clonal deletion
6. b	14. diapedesis (emi-	20. autoimmune
7. e	gration)	
8. d	15. opsonization	

Building Your Medical Vocabulary (Answers may vary; these are acceptable examples.)

1. apart—anaphylactic	6. set in motion—cytokine
2. secrete—paracrine	7. water—lymphatic
3. outside—extravasated	8. enlargement—splenomegaly
4. arising—endogenous	9. disease—lymphadenopathy
5. freedom—immunology	10. fire—pyrogen

What's Wrong with These Statements?

1. Lysozyme is a bacteria-killing enzyme.
2. The principal birthplace of lymphocytes is the red bone marrow; T lymphocytes migrate from there to the thymus.
3. Interferons promote inflammation.
4. Helper T cells are also necessary to humoral and innate immunity.
5. Negative selection serves to eliminate or deactivate self-reactive T cells (not unresponsive ones), thus preventing immune attack on one's own tissues.
6. The thymus and spleen do not receive or filter any incoming lymph; only lymph nodes do this.
7. Only antibodies of the IgG and IgM classes employ complement fixation.
8. One can be HIV-positive without having AIDS. AIDS is defined by a low helper T cell count ($< 200/\mu L$), not by the presence of the virus.
9. Anergy is a loss of lymphocyte activity, whereas autoimmune diseases result from misdirected activity.
10. Plasma cells are antibody-synthesizing cells of the connective tissues that develop from B cells; they are not found in the blood plasma.

CHAPTER 22

Figure Legend Questions

22.3 The line would cross the figure just slightly above the trachea label.

22.4 Epiglottic, corniculate, and arytenoid

22.7 The right main bronchus is slightly wider and more vertical than the left, making it easier for aspirated objects to fall into the right.

22.8 To secrete mucus

22.17 Any airflow through the nose would not be registered by the spirometer, and the spirometer could not give a correct reading of pulmonary ventilation.

22.19 P_{O_2} drops from 104 to 95 mm Hg on its way out of the lungs because of some mixing with systemic blood. It drops farther to 40 mm Hg when the blood gives up O_2 to respiring tissues, and remains at this level until the blood is reoxygenated back in the lungs. P_{CO_2} is 40 mm Hg leaving the lungs and rises to 46 mm Hg when CO_2 is picked up from respiring tissues. It remains at that level until the blood returns to the lungs and unloads CO_2.

22.23 About 60%

22.25 In the alveoli, CO_2 leaves the blood, O_2 enters, and all the chemical reactions are the reverse of those in figure 22.23. The blood bicarbonate concentration will be reduced following alveolar gas exchange because bicarbonate is taken up by the chloride shift antiport and converted to CO_2 and water.

22.26 A higher temperature suggests a relatively high metabolic rate and, thus, an elevated need for oxygen. Comparison of these curves shows that for a given P_{O_2}, hemoglobin gives up more oxygen at warmer temperatures.

Testing Your Recall

1. c	10. a	17. compliance,
2. c	11. epiglottis	elasticity
3. a	12. bronchial tree	18. ventral respiratory
4. e	13. pulmonary	group
5. e	surfactant	19. ventilation–
6. c	14. atmospheric	perfusion coupling
7. b	15. Obstructive	20. alkalosis,
8. a	16. anatomical dead	hypocapnia
9. d	space	

Building Your Medical Vocabulary (Answers may vary; these are acceptable examples.)

1. imperfect—atelectasis	6. measuring device—spirometer
2. smoke—hypercapnia	7. nose—nasofacial
3. cancer—carcinoma	8. breathing—dyspnea
4. horn—corniculate	9. breath—spirometry
5. true—eupnea	10. shield—thyroid

What's Wrong with These Statements?

1. They also fire during expiration (although at a lower rate) to exert a braking action on the diaphragm.
2. The two lungs have a total of 18 segmental bronchi but only 5 lobes.
3. The most abundant cells are alveolar macrophages.
4. When volume increases, pressure decreases.
5. Atelectasis can have other causes such as airway obstruction.
6. The greatest effect is to lower the CO_2 level; accelerated breathing has little effect on blood O_2.
7. We inhale all the gases of the atmosphere, whether the body uses them or not; there is no way to separate one gas from another as we inhale.

8. In an average 500 mL tidal volume, 350 mL reaches the alveoli.
9. The lower the P_{CO_2}, the higher the pH.
10. Most blood CO_2 is transported as bicarbonate ions.

CHAPTER 23

Figure Legend Questions

23.2 Ammonia is produced by the deamination of amino acids; urea is synthesized from ammonia and carbon dioxide; uric acid is produced from nucleic acids; and creatinine is produced from creatine phosphate.
23.3 It would be in the dark space at the top of the figure, where the spleen, colon, and small intestine are shown.
23.10 The afferent arteriole is larger. The relatively large inlet to the glomerulus and its small outlet result in high blood pressure in the glomerulus. This is the force that drives glomerular filtration.
23.16 It lowers the urine pH; the more Na^+ that is reabsorbed, the more H^+ is secreted into the tubular fluid. This is seen at the Na^+–H^+ antiport along the right margin of the figure.
23.23 The relatively short female urethra is less of an obstacle for bacteria traveling from the perineum to the urinary bladder.

Testing Your Recall

1. a	9. c	16. transport
2. d	10. a	maximum
3. b	11. micturition	17. Antidiuretic
4. c	12. Renal autoregula-	hormone
5. b	tion	18. internal urethral
6. b	13. trigone	19. protein
7. d	14. macula densa	20. arcuate
8. e	15. podocytes	

Building Your Medical Vocabulary (Answers may vary; these are acceptable examples.)

1. nitrogen—azotemia
2. bladder—cystitis
3. ball—glomerulus
4. next to—juxtaglomerular
5. middle—mesangial
6. kidney—nephron
7. foot—podocyte
8. sagging—nephroptosis
9. pus—pyelonephritis
10. straight—vasa recta

What's Wrong with These Statements?

1. Calcium and sodium reabsorption by the PCT are influenced by parathyroid hormone and angiotensin II.
2. Urine contains more urea and chloride than sodium.
3. There is one renal corpuscle per nephron and many nephrons drain into each collecting duct, so renal corpuscles substantially outnumber collecting ducts.
4. "Tight" junctions of the renal tubule are quite leaky, and a substantial amount of tubular fluid passes through them to be reabsorbed by the paracellular route.
5. Diabetes insipidus shows no glucose in the urine.
6. Dilation of the efferent arteriole reduces resistance and thus lowers the glomerular blood pressure and filtration rate.
7. Angiotensin II stimulates aldosterone secretion and Na^+ reabsorption, thus reducing urine output.
8. Urine can be as dilute as 50 mOsm/L.
9. Normally there is abundant sodium but no glucose in the urine.
10. Micturition is caused by contraction of the detrusor.

CHAPTER 24

Figure Legend Questions

24.1 The tissue fluid compartment
24.8 Ingestion of water
24.10 It would decrease along with the pH.
24.13 Reverse both arrows to point to the left.

Testing Your Recall

1. c	9. d	16. hyperkalemia
2. a	10. b	17. hyponatremia
3. a	11. Na^+	18. respiratory
4. a	12. K^+ and Mg^{2+}	acidosis
5. d	13. metabolic water	19. limiting pH
6. c	14. cutaneous transpi-	20. osmolarity
7. e	ration	
8. b	15. fluid sequestration	

Building Your Medical Vocabulary (Answers may vary; these are acceptable examples.)

1. food—hyperalimentation
2. blood—hypoxemia
3. intestine—parenteral
4. potassium—hyperkalemia
5. sodium—hyponatremia
6. next to—parenteral
7. isolate—sequestration
8. breathing—transpiration
9. across—transpiration
10. volume—hypovolemia

What's Wrong with These Statements?

1. This is an effect of hypokalemia, not hyperkalemia.
2. Aldosterone has only a small influence on blood pressure.
3. Such injuries elevate the ECF potassium level.
4. Phosphate concentration is less critical than that of other electrolytes and can safely vary over a relatively broad range.
5. PTH promotes calcium absorption but phosphate excretion.
6. Protein buffers more acid than bicarbonate or phosphates do.
7. Increased sodium reabsorption increases urinary H^+ excretion and lowers the urine pH.
8. Alkalosis tends to cause a reduction of respiratory rate and pulmonary ventilation so the ECF pH will rise again.
9. More water than salt is lost in true dehydration, so the body fluids become hypertonic.
10. Oral wetting and cooling have only a short-term effect on thirst.

CHAPTER 25

Figure Legend Questions

25.6 The first and second premolars and third molar
25.7 The enamel is a secretion, not a tissue; all the rest are living tissues.
25.11 Blockage of the mouth by the root of the tongue and blockage of the nose by the soft palate
25.12 The muscularis externa of the esophagus has two layers of muscle, with skeletal muscle in the upper to middle regions and smooth muscle in the middle to lower regions. In the stomach, it has three layers of muscle, all of which are smooth muscle.
25.14 It exchanges H^+ for K^+ (H^+–K^+ ATPase is an active transport pump).
25.20 The hepatic artery and the hepatic portal vein
25.32 Lipids do not enter the hepatic portal system that leads directly to the liver. Dietary fats are absorbed into the lacteals of the small intestine, then would have to travel the following route, at a minimum, to reach the liver: intestinal trunk → thoracic duct → left subclavian vein → heart → aorta → celiac trunk → common hepatic artery → hepatic artery proper → hepatic arteries → liver.
25.33 The internal anal sphincter is composed of smooth muscle and therefore controlled by the autonomic nervous system. The external anal sphincter is composed of skeletal muscle and therefore controlled by the somatic nervous system.

Testing Your Recall

1.	b	8.	a	15.	vagus
2.	d	9.	a	16.	gastrin
3.	c	10.	a	17.	sinusoids
4.	e	11.	occlusal	18.	dipeptidase
5.	a	12.	amylase, lipase	19.	bile acids
6.	c	13.	parotid	20.	iron
7.	a	14.	enteric		

Building Your Medical Vocabulary (Answers may vary; these are acceptable examples.)

1. cavity—antrum
2. juice—chylomicron
3. little—micelle
4. vomiting—emetic
5. bridle—frenulum
6. liver—hepatocyte
7. dry—jejunum
8. gateway—portal
9. gateway—pyloric
10. S-shaped—sigmoid

What's Wrong with These Statements?

1. Fat digestion begins in the stomach.
2. Most of the tooth is dentin.
3. Hepatocytes secrete bile into the bile canaliculi.
4. The ileal papilla regulates the passage of residue from the ileum of the small intestine into the cecum of the large intestine.
5. The lacteals take up chylomicrons, not micelles.
6. Hepcidin inhibits iron absorption and prevents iron overload.
7. The small intestine absorbs not only glucose but also fructose and galactose.
8. Most of the water is absorbed by the small intestine.
9. Secretin stimulates the liver and pancreas to secrete bicarbonate and inhibits gastric secretion.
10. Water, glucose, and other nutrients pass between cells, through the tight junctions.

CHAPTER 26

Figure Legend Questions

26.4   A high HDL:LDL ratio indicates that excess cholesterol is being transported to the liver for removal from the body. A high LDL:HDL ratio indicates a high rate of cholesterol deposition in the walls of the arteries.

26.7   NADH and $FADH_2$

26.11   Acidosis, ketoacidosis, or metabolic acidosis

26.12   Amino acids → keto acids → pyruvate → glucose

Testing Your Recall

1.	a	8.	a	15.	liver
2.	c	9.	d	16.	insulin
3.	b	10.	d	17.	core temperature
4.	e	11.	incomplete	18.	arcuate
5.	b	12.	glycogenolysis	19.	cytochromes
6.	e	13.	gluconeogenesis	20.	ATP synthase,
7.	c	14.	urea		ATP

Building Your Medical Vocabulary (Answers may vary; these are acceptable examples.)

1. bag—ascites
2. bad—cachexia
3. color—cytochrome
4. producing—lipogenesis
5. sugar—hypoglycemia
6. like—ascites
7. thin—leptin
8. splitting—glycolysis
9. new—gluconeogenesis
10. push—chemiosmotic

What's Wrong with These Statements?

1. Leptin suppresses the appetite.
2. A nutrient is a dietary substance that is absorbed into the tissues and becomes part of the body; water meets this criterion and is considered a nutrient.
3. Fat has more than twice as many calories per gram as carbohydrate does.
4. Most of the cholesterol is endogenous, not dietary.
5. Excessive protein intake generates excess nitrogenous waste and can cause renal damage.
6. Excessive ketone production is an effect of high-fat diets.
7. The membrane reactions produce up to 28 ATP per glucose, whereas glycolysis and the matrix reactions produce only 4 ATP.
8. Gluconeogenesis is a postabsorptive phenomenon.
9. Brown fat does not generate ATP.
10. At 21°C, the body loses about 60% of its heat by radiation.

CHAPTER 27

Figure Legend Questions

27.1   Both disorders result from defects in hormone receptors rather than from a lack of the respective hormone.

27.5   The word *vagina* means "sheath." The tunica vaginalis partially ensheathes the testis.

27.10   An enlarged prostate compresses the urethra and interferes with emptying of the bladder.

27.11   A tunica albuginea would allow excessive pressure to build in the corpus spongiosum, compressing the urethra and interfering with ejaculation.

27.13   The crossing-over in prophase I results in a mixture of maternal and paternal genes in each chromosome.

27.14   The next cell stage in meiosis, the secondary spermatocyte, is genetically different from the other cells of the body and would be subject to immune attack if not isolated from the antibodies in the blood.

Testing Your Recall

1.	a	9.	d	15.	tunica albuginea
2.	a	10.	d	16.	seminal vesicles
3.	a	11.	mesonephric	17.	nurse
4.	c	12.	zinc	18.	secondary
5.	a	13.	pampiniform		spermatocyte
6.	d		plexus	19.	deep
7.	e	14.	secondary	20.	acrosome
8.	c		spermatocytes		

Building Your Medical Vocabulary (Answers may vary; these are acceptable examples.)

1. hidden—cryptorchidism
2. twins—epididymis
3. out—ejaculation
4. union—gamete
5. condition—cryptorchidism
6. reduction—meiosis
7. testis—cryptorchidism
8. network—rete testis
9. body—acrosome
10. sheath—tunica vaginalis

What's Wrong with These Statements?

1. Testosterone is secreted by the interstitial endocrine cells.
2. The sperm DNA is contained in the nucleus in the sperm head.
3. Meiosis II is completed before spermiogenesis, which is the conversion of the four spermatids to mature sperm.
4. Only the testes are primary sex organs; the penis is a secondary sex organ.

5. Female fetal development results from a low testosterone level, not from estrogen.
6. The seminal vesicles contribute about 60% of the semen.
7. The pampiniform plexus prevents the testes from overheating.
8. Sperm have no testosterone receptors; testosterone binds to androgen-binding protein in the seminiferous tubules.
9. There is no such phenomenon as male menopause, and sperm production normally continues throughout old age.
10. Erection is the result of parasympathetic stimulation of the blood vessels of the erectile tissues.

CHAPTER 28

Figure Legend Questions

28.4   To move the egg or conceptus toward the uterus
28.8   Paraurethral glands
28.9   They cause milk to flow from the acinus into the ducts of the mammary gland.
28.10 This results in a clearer image since the X-rays do not have to penetrate such a thick mass of tissue.
28.18 The rising ratio of estradiol to progesterone makes the uterus more irritable.

Testing Your Recall

1. a	8. b	15. corona radiata
2. d	9. c	16. antrum
3. c	10. c	17. climacteric
4. a	11. follicle	18. conceptus
5. e	12. endometrium	19. infundibulum,
6. b	13. menarche	fimbriae
7. b	14. corpus luteum	20. lochia

Building Your Medical Vocabulary (Answers may vary; these are acceptable examples.)

1. beginning—menarche
2. of—gravidarum
3. mound—cumulus
4. pregnancy—progesterone
5. uterus—hysterectomy
6. milk—lactation
7. to tie—tubal ligation
8. uterus—endometrium
9. egg—oogenesis
10. first—primipara

What's Wrong with These Statements?

1. Only the ovum and cumulus oophorus cells enter the uterine tube, not the whole follicle.
2. HCG is secreted by the placenta.
3. Meiosis II is not completed until after ovulation, and only if the egg is fertilized.
4. Such girls often have lower than average body fat and delayed menarche because of this.
5. Many eggs and follicles undergo atresia during childhood, so their number is greatly reduced by the age of puberty.
6. Prolactin is secreted during pregnancy but does not induce lactation then.
7. Colostrum is lower in fat than milk is.
8. Up to two dozen follicles mature to the secondary follicle stage in each cycle, but usually only one of them ovulates.

9. Progesterone inhibits uterine contractions.
10. Only the superficial (functional) layer is shed.

CHAPTER 29

Figure Legend Questions

29.2   An unfertilized egg dies long before it reaches the uterus.
29.8   About 8 weeks
29.13 XXY (Klinefelter syndrome) and YO (a zygote that would not survive)
29.15 Female, as seen from the two X chromosomes at the lower right

Testing Your Recall

1. b	8. a	15. chorionic villi
2. b	9. d	16. acrosome
3. c	10. d	17. collagen
4. c	11. teratogens	18. Down syndrome
5. a	12. nondisjunction	(trisomy-21)
6. e	13. life span	19. foramen ovale
7. c	14. life expectancy	20. embryo

Building Your Medical Vocabulary (Answers may vary; these are acceptable examples.)

1. with—congenital
2. falling off—decidual
3. old age—progeria
4. mulberry—morula
5. flat cake—placenta
6. double—aneuploidy
7. aging—senescence
8. together—syncytiotrophoblast
9. end—telomere
10. monster—teratogen

What's Wrong with These Statements?

1. The ability to fertilize an egg increases in the first 10 hours as sperm become capacitated.
2. Fertilization occurs in the uterine tube.
3. Several early-arriving sperm clear a path for the one that fertilizes the egg.
4. Early cell divisions occur while the conceptus is still in the uterine tube, about 2 days before arrival in the uterus.
5. The individual is considered an embryo then; it is not a fetus until all of the major organs have formed.
6. As they develop, the chorionic villi become thinner and more permeable.
7. The kidneys exhibit one of the greatest degrees of senescence, shrinking 60% to 80% by age 90.
8. The foramen ovale is a shunt in the heart by which blood bypasses the lungs; the shunt that bypasses the liver is the ductus venosus.
9. Blood in the umbilical vein is returning from the placenta, where it has picked up oxygen and thus has a high P_{O_2}.
10. Telomerase is a telomere-repairing enzyme that prolongs cell life, as in stem cells and cancer cells.

APPENDIX D

Table D.2 Question

Asn-Ile-Tyr-Val-Arg-Asp

APPENDIX B

SYMBOLS, WEIGHTS, AND MEASURES

Units of Length

m	meter
km	kilometer (10^3 m)
cm	centimeter (10^{-2} m)
mm	millimeter (10^{-3} m)
μm	micrometer (10^{-6} m)
nm	nanometer (10^{-9} m)

Units of Mass and Weight

amu	atomic mass unit
MW	molecular weight
mole	MW in grams
g	gram
kg	kilograms (10^3 g)
mg	milligrams (10^{-3} g)
μg	micrograms (10^{-6} g)

Units of Pressure

atm	atmospheres (1 atm = 760 mm Hg)
mm Hg	millimeters of mercury
P_X	partial pressure of gas X (as in P_{O_2})

Conversion Factors

1 in. = 2.54 cm	1 cm = 0.394 in.
1 fl oz = 29.6 mL	1 mL = 0.034 fl oz
1 qt = 0.946 L	1 L = 1.057 qt
1 g = 0.0035 oz	1 oz = 28.38 g
1 lb = 0.45 kg	1 kg = 2.2 lb
°C = (5/9)(°F − 32)	°F = (9/5)(°C) + 32

Units of Volume

L	liter
dL	deciliter (= 100 mL) (10^{-1} L)
mL	milliliter (10^{-3} L)
μL	microliter (= 1 mm³) (10^{-6} L)

Units of Heat

cal	"small" calorie
kcal	kilocalorie (Calorie; 1 kcal = 1,000 cal)
Cal	"large" (dietary) calorie (1 Cal = 1,000 cal)

Greek Letters

α	alpha
β	beta
γ	gamma
Δ	delta (uppercase)
δ	delta (lowercase)
η	eta
θ	theta
λ	lambda
μ	mu
π	pi

Units of Concentration

Chemical concentrations—the amounts of solute in a given volume of solution—are expressed in different ways for different scientific or clinical purposes. Some of these are explained here, particularly those used in this book.

WEIGHT PER VOLUME

A simple way to express concentration is the weight of solute in a given volume of solution. For example, intravenous (I.V.) saline typically contains 8.5 grams of NaCl per liter of solution (8.5 g/L). For many biological purposes, however, we deal with smaller quantities such as *milligrams per deciliter (mg/dL)*. For example, a typical serum cholesterol concentration may be 200 mg/dL, also expressed as 200 mg/100 mL or 200 milligram-percent (mg-%).

PERCENTAGES

Percentage concentration is also simple to compute, but it is necessary to specify whether the percentage refers to the weight or to the volume of solute in a given volume of solution. For example, if we begin with 5 g of dextrose (an isomer of glucose) and add enough water to make 100 mL of solution, the resulting concentration will be 5% weight per volume (w/v). A commonly used intravenous fluid is D5W, which stands for 5% w/v dextrose in distilled water.

If the solute is a liquid, such as ethanol, percentages refer to volume of solute per volume of solution. Thus, 70 mL of ethanol diluted with water to 100 mL of solution produces 70% volume per volume (70% v/v) ethanol.

MOLARITY

Percentage concentrations are easy to prepare, but that unit of measurement is inadequate for many purposes. The physiological effect of a chemical depends on how many molecules of it are present in a given volume, not the weight of the chemical. Five percent glucose, for example, contains almost twice as many sugar molecules as the same volume of 5% sucrose. Each solution contains 50 g of sugar per liter, but glucose has a molecular weight (MW) of 180 and sucrose has a MW of 342. Since each molecule of glucose is lighter, 50 g of glucose contains more molecules than 50 g of sucrose.

To produce solutions with a known number of molecules per volume, we must factor in the molecular weight. If we know the MW and weigh out that many grams of the substance, we have a quantity known as 1 *mole*. One mole of glucose is 180 g and 1 mole of sucrose is 342 g. Each quantity contains the same number of molecules of the respective sugar—a number known as *Avogadro's number,* 6.023×10^{23} molecules per mole.

Molarity (M) is the number of moles of solute per liter of solution. A one-molar (1.0 M) solution of glucose contains 180 g/L, and 1.0 M solution of sucrose contains 342 g/L. Both have the same number of solute molecules in a given volume. Body fluids and laboratory solutions usually are less concentrated than 1 M, so biologists and clinicians more often work with *millimolar* (mM, 10^{-3} M) and *micromolar* (μM, 10^{-6} M) concentrations.

OSMOLARITY AND OSMOLALITY

The osmotic concentration of body fluids has a great effect on cellular function, body water distribution, nutrient absorption, urinary water loss, the sense of thirst, and blood pressure. Thus, it is important to quantify osmotic concentrations in physiology and in clinical practice (as when giving I.V. fluid therapy). Physiologists and clinicians usually express osmotic concentration in *milliosmoles per liter* (mOsm/L).

One *osmole* is 1 mole of dissolved particles. If a solute does not ionize in water, then 1 mole of the solute yields 1 osmole (osm) of dissolved particles. A solution of 1 M glucose, for example, is also 1 osm/L. If a solute does ionize, it yields two or more dissolved particles in solution. A 1 M solution of NaCl, for example, contains 1 mole/L of sodium ions and 1 mole/L of chloride ions; 1 M calcium chloride ($CaCl_2$) would (if completely dissociated) yield 1 mole of calcium ions and 2 moles of chloride ions. All ions equally affect osmosis and must be separately counted in a measure of osmotic concentration. Thus,

$$1 \text{ M NaCl} = 2 \text{ osm/L, and}$$

$$1 \text{ M CaCl}_2 = 3 \text{ osm/L.}$$

Osmolality is the number of osmoles of solute per kilogram of water, and *osmolarity* is the number of osmoles per liter of solution. Most clinical calculations are based on osmolarity, since it is easier to measure the volume of a solution than the weight of water it contains. The difference between osmolality and osmolarity can be important in experimental work, but at the concentrations of human body fluids, there is less than 1% difference between the two, and the two are essentially interchangeable for clinical purposes.

All body fluids and many clinical solutions are mixtures of many chemicals. The osmolarity of such a solution is the total osmotic concentration of all of its dissolved particles.

A concentration of 1 osm/L is substantially higher than we find in most body fluids, so physiological concentrations are usually expressed in terms of milliosmoles per liter (mOsm/L) (1 mOsm/L = 10^{-3} osm/L). Blood plasma, tissue fluid, and intracellular fluid measure about 300 mOsm/L.

MILLIEQUIVALENTS PER LITER

Electrolytes are important for their chemical, physical (osmotic), and electrical effects on the body. Their electrical effects, which determine such things as nerve, heart, and muscle actions, depend not only on their concentration but also on their electrical charge. A calcium ion (Ca^{2+}) has twice the electrical effect of a sodium ion (Na^+), for example, because it carries twice the charge. In measuring electrolyte concentrations, one must take the charges into account.

One *equivalent* (Eq) of an electrolyte is the amount that would electrically neutralize 1 mole of hydrogen ions (H^+) or hydroxide ions (OH^-). For example, 1 mole (58.4 g) of NaCl yields 1 mole, or 1 Eq, of Na^+ in solution. Thus, an NaCl solution of 58.4 g/L contains 1 equivalent of Na^+ per liter (1 Eq/L). One mole (98 g) of sulfuric acid (H_2SO_4) yields 2 moles of positive charges (H^+). Thus, 98 g of sulfuric acid per liter would be a solution of 2 Eq/L.

The electrolytes in human body fluids have concentrations less than 1 Eq/L, so we more often express their concentrations in *milliequivalents per liter* (mEq/L). If you know the millimolar concentration of an electrolyte, you can easily convert this to mEq/L by multiplying it by the valence (charge) of the ion:

$$1 \text{ mM Na}^+ = 1 \text{ mEq/L}$$

$$1 \text{ mM Ca}^{2+} = 2 \text{ mEq/L}$$

$$1 \text{ mM Fe}^{3+} = 3 \text{ mEq/L}$$

ACIDITY AND ALKALINITY (PH)

Acidity is expressed in terms of pH, a measure derived from the molarity of H^+. Molarity is represented by square brackets, so the molarity of H^+ is symbolized $[H^+]$. pH is the negative logarithm of hydrogen ion molarity; that is,

$$pH = -\log [H^+].$$

In pure water, 1 in 10 million molecules of H_2O ionizes into hydrogen and hydroxide ions: $H_2O \rightleftharpoons H^+ + OH^-$. Pure water has a neutral pH because it contains equal amounts of H^+ and OH^-. Since 1 in 10 million molecules ionize, the molarity of H^+ and the pH of water are as follows:

$$[H^+] = 0.0000001 \text{ M} = 10^{-7} \text{ M}$$

$$\log [H^+] = -7$$

$$pH = -\log [H^+] = 7$$

The pH scale ranges from 0 to 14 and is logarithmic, so each integer up or down the scale represents a 10-fold difference in $[H^+]$. This is exemplified by the following three strongly acidic pH values:

If $[H^+] = 0.1$ M	$pH = -\log 10^{-1} = 1.0$
If $[H^+] = 0.01$ M	$pH = -\log 10^{-2} = 2.0$
If $[H^+] = 0.001$ M	$pH = -\log 10^{-3} = 3.0$

The less concentrated the H^+, the higher the pH. pH values below 7.0 are considered acidic. Above 7.0, they are basic or alkaline. The following three values lie at the basic end of the pH scale:

If $[H^+] = 0.000000000001$ M	$pH = -\log 10^{-12} = 12.0$
If $[H^+] = 0.0000000000001$ M	$pH = -\log 10^{-13} = 13.0$
If $[H^+] = 0.00000000000001$ M	$pH = -\log 10^{-14} = 14.0$

PERIODIC TABLE OF THE ELEMENTS

Nineteenth-century chemists discovered that when they arranged the known elements by atomic weight, certain properties reappeared periodically. In 1869, Russian chemist Dmitri Mendeleev published the first modern periodic table of the elements, leaving gaps for those that had not yet been discovered. He accurately predicted properties of the missing elements, which helped other chemists discover and isolate them.

Each row in the table is a *period* and each column is a *group* (*family*). Each period has one electron shell more than the period above it, and as we progress from left to right within a period, each element has one more proton and electron than the one before. The dark steplike line from boron (5) to astatine (85) separates the metals to the left of it (except hydrogen) from the nonmetals to the right. Each period begins with a soft, light, highly reactive *alkali metal,* with one valence electron, in family

IA. Progressing from left to right, the metallic properties of the elements become less and less pronounced. Elements in family VIIA are highly reactive gases called *halogens,* with seven valence electrons. Elements in family VIIIA, called *noble (inert) gases,* have a full valence shell of eight electrons, which makes them chemically unreactive.

Ninety-one of the elements occur naturally on earth. Physicists have created elements up to atomic number 118 in the laboratory, but the International Union of Pure and Applied Chemistry has established formal names only through element 112 to date.

The 24 elements with normal roles in human physiology are color-coded according to their relative abundance in the body (see table 2.1). Others, however, may be present as contaminants with very destructive effects (such as arsenic, lead, and radiation poisoning).

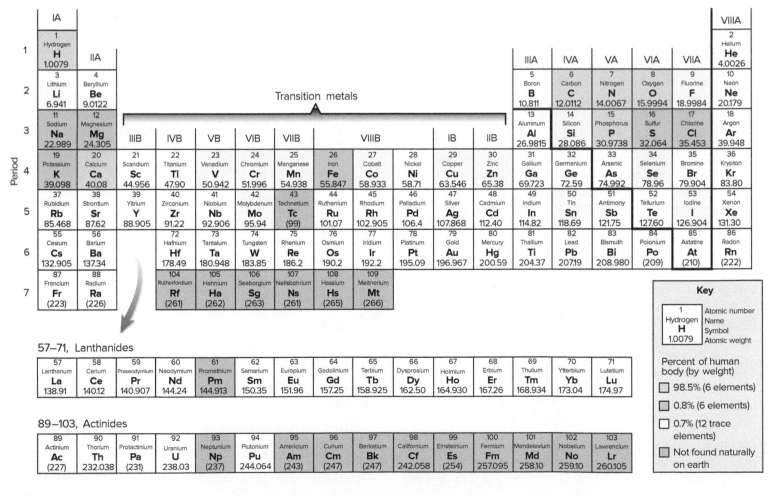

APPENDIX D

THE GENETIC CODE AND AMINO ACIDS

Table D.1 lists the 20 amino acids involved in protein structure, with the three-letter and one-letter symbols used in writing out amino acid sequences (as in fig. 2.25, for example). **Table D.2** is the genetic code, relating mRNA codons to the amino acids. To determine what amino acid is encoded by a given mRNA codon, choose the first letter of the codon from the column on the left, the second letter from the row across the top, and the third letter from the column on the right. The amino acid symbol is at the intersection of these three. For example, codon GCU codes for alanine (Ala) and CAC codes for histidine (His). Codons UAA, UAG, and UGA are *stop codons*, which do not code for any amino acid but indicate the end of the message to be translated, like the period at the end of a sentence.

TABLE D.1	The 20 Amino Acids and Their Symbols				
Alanine	Ala	A	Leucine	Leu	L
Arginine	Arg	R	Lysine	Lys	K
Asparagine	Asn	N	Methionine	Met	M
Aspartate	Asp	D	Phenylalanine	Phe	F
Cysteine	Cys	C	Proline	Pro	P
Glutamate	Glu	E	Serine	Ser	S
Glutamine	Gln	Q	Threonine	Thr	T
Glycine	Gly	G	Tryptophan	Trp	W
Histidine	His	H	Tyrosine	Tyr	Y
Isoleucine	Ile	I	Valine	Val	V

TABLE D.2	The Genetic Code				
First Position	Second Position				Third Position
	A	G	C	U	
A	Lys	Arg	Thr	Ile	A
	Lys	Arg	Thr	Met	G
	Asn	Ser	Thr	Ile	C
	Asn	Ser	Thr	Ile	U
G	Glu	Gly	Ala	Val	A
	Glu	Gly	Ala	Val	G
	Asp	Gly	Ala	Val	C
	Asp	Gly	Ala	Val	U
C	Gln	Arg	Pro	Leu	A
	Gln	Arg	Pro	Leu	G
	His	Arg	Pro	Leu	C
	His	Arg	Pro	Leu	U
U	STOP	STOP	Ser	Leu	A
	STOP	Trp	Ser	Leu	G
	Tyr	Cys	Ser	Phe	C
	Tyr	Cys	Ser	Phe	U

? *The following genetic code represents a well-known hormone, angiotensin II: UUU-CCC-CAC-AUA-UAU-GUA-AGG-GAC. The amino acid sequence represented by this code begins Phe-Pro. . . . Write the rest of the sequence. (Answer is found in appendix A.)*

H H$_2$N—C—COOH CH$_3$ **Alanine**	H H$_2$N—C—COOH (CH$_2$)$_3$ NH C=N$^+$H$_2$ NH$_2$ **Arginine**	H H$_2$N—C—COOH CH$_2$ H$_2$N—C=O **Asparagine**	H H$_2$N—C—COOH CH$_2$ COOH **Aspartic acid**
H H$_2$N—C—COOH CH$_2$ SH **Cysteine**	H H$_2$N—C—COOH CH$_2$ CH$_2$ COOH **Glutamic acid**	H H$_2$N—C—COOH CH$_2$ CH$_2$ H$_2$N—C=O **Glutamine**	H H$_2$N—C—COOH H **Glycine**
H H$_2$N—C—COOH CH$_2$ C—NH ‖ CH HC—N **Histidine**	H H$_2$N—C—COOH H—C—CH$_2$ CH$_2$ CH$_3$ **Isoleucine**	H H$_2$N—C—COOH CH$_2$ CH H$_3$C CH$_3$ **Leucine**	H H$_2$N—C—COOH (CH$_2$)$_4$ $^+$NH$_3$ **Lysine**
H H$_2$N—C—COOH CH$_2$ CH$_2$ S CH$_3$ **Methionine**	H H$_2$N—C—COOH CH$_2$ ⬡ **Phenylalanine**	H H$_2$N$^+$—C—COOH H$_2$C CH$_2$ C H$_2$ **Proline**	H H$_2$N—C—COOH CH$_2$ OH **Serine**
H H$_2$N—C—COOH H—C—OH CH$_3$ **Threonine**	H H$_2$N—C—COOH CH$_2$ C=CH NH ⬡ **Tryptophan**	H H$_2$N—C—COOH CH$_2$ ⬡ OH **Tyrosine**	H H$_2$N—C—COOH CH H$_3$C CH$_3$ **Valine**

MEDICAL WORD ROOTS AND AFFIXES

a- no, not, without (atom, agranulocyte)
ab- away (abducens, abduction)
acetabulo- small cup (acetabulum)
acro- tip, extremity, peak (acromion, acromegaly)
ad- to, toward, near (adsorption, adrenal)
adeno- gland (lymphadenitis, adenohypophysis)
aero- air, oxygen (aerobic, anaerobic)
af- toward (afferent)
ag- together (agglutination)
-al pertaining to (parietal, pharyngeal, temporal)
ala- wing (ala nasi)
albi- white (albicans, linea alba, albino)
algi- pain (analgesic, myalgia)
aliment- nourishment (alimentary)
allo- other, different (allele, allograft)
amphi- both, either (amphiphilic, amphiarthrosis)
an- without (anaerobic, anemic)
ana- 1. up, build up (anabolic, anaphylaxis)
    2. apart (anaphase, anatomy)
    3. back (anastomosis)
andro- male (androgen)
angi- vessel (angiogram, angioplasty, hemangioma)
ante- before, in front (antebrachium)
antero- forward (anterior, anterograde)
anti- against (antidiuretic, antibody, antagonist)
apo- from, off, away, above (apocrine, aponeurosis)
arbor- tree (arboreal, arborization)
artic- 1. joint (articulation)
    2. speech (articulate)
-ary pertaining to (axillary, coronary)
-ase enzyme (polymerase, kinase, amylase)
ast-, astro- star (aster, astrocyte)
-ata, -ate 1. possessing (hamate, corniculate)
    2. plural of -a (stomata, carcinomata)
athero- fat (atheroma, atherosclerosis)
atrio- entryway (atrium, atrioventricular)
auri- ear (auricle, binaural)
auto- self (autolysis, autoimmune)
axi- axis, straight line (axial, axoneme, axon)
baro- pressure (baroreceptor, hyperbaric)
bene- good, well (benign, beneficial)
bi- two (bipedal, biceps, bifid)
bili- bile (biliary, bilirubin)
bio- life, living (biology, biopsy, microbial)
blasto- precursor, bud, producer (fibroblast, osteoblast, blastomere)
brachi- arm (brachium, brachialis, antebrachium)
brady- slow (bradycardia, bradypnea)
bucco- cheek (buccal, buccinator)
burso- purse (bursa, bursitis)
calc- calcium, stone (calcaneus, hypocalcemia)
callo- thick (callus, callosum)
calori- heat (calorie, calorimetry, calorigenic)
calv-, calvari- bald, skull (calvaria)

calyx cup, vessel, chalice (glycocalyx, renal calyx)
capito- head (capitis, capitate, capitulum)
capni- smoke, carbon dioxide (hypocapnia)
carcino- cancer (carcinogen, carcinoma)
cardi- heart (cardiac, cardiology, pericardium)
carot- 1. carrot (carotene)
    2. stupor (carotid)
carpo- wrist (carpus, metacarpal)
case- cheese (caseosa, casein)
cata- down, break down (catabolism)
cauda- tail (cauda equina, caudate nucleus)
-cel little (pedicel)
celi- belly, abdomen (celiac)
centri- center, middle (centromere, centriole)
cephalo- head (cephalic, encephalitis)
cervi- neck, narrow part (cervix, cervical)
chiasm- cross, X (optic chiasm)
choano- funnel (choana)
chole- bile (cholecystokinin, cholelithotripsy)
chondro- 1. grain (mitochondria)
    2. cartilage, gristle (chondrocyte, perichondrium)
chromo- color (dichromat, chromatin, cytochrome)
chrono- time (chronotropic, chronic)
cili- eyelash (cilium, superciliary)
circ- about, around (circadian, circumduction)
cis- cut (incision, incisor)
cistern, cisterna reservoir (Golgi cistern, cisterna chyli)
clast- break down, destroy (osteoclast)
clavi- hammer, club, key (clavicle, supraclavicular)
-cle little (tubercle, corpuscle)
cleido- clavicle (sternocleidomastoid)
cnemo- lower leg (gastrocnemius)
co- together (coenzyme, cotransport)
collo- 1. hill (colliculus)
    2. glue (colloid, collagen)
contra- opposite (contralateral)
corni- horn (cornified, corniculate, cornu)
corono- crown (coronary, corona, coronal)
corpo- body (corpus luteum, corpora quadrigemina)
corti- bark, rind (cortex, cortical)
costa- rib (intercostal, subcostal)
coxa- hip (os coxae, coxal)
crani- helmet (cranium, epicranius)
cribri- sieve, strainer (cribriform, area cribrosa)
crino- separate, secrete (holocrine, endocrinology)
crista- crest (crista galli, mitochondrial crista)
crito- to separate (hematocrit)
cruci- cross (cruciate ligament)
-cule, -culus small (canaliculus, trabecula, auricular)
cune- wedge (cuneiform, cuneatus)
cutane-, cuti- skin (subcutaneous, cuticle)
cysto- bladder (cystitis, cholecystectomy)
cyto- cell (cytology, cytokinesis, monocyte)

de- down (defecate, deglutition, dehydration)
demi- half (demifacet, demilune)
den-, denti- tooth (dentition, dens, dental)
dendro- tree, branch (dendrite, oligodendrocyte)
derma-, dermato- skin (dermatology, hypodermic)
desmo- band, bond, ligament (desmosome, syndesmosis)
dia- 1. across, through, separate (diaphragm, dialysis)
    2. day (circadian)
dis- 1. apart (dissect, dissociate)
    2. opposite, absence (disinfect, disability)
diure- pass through, urinate (diuretic, diuresis)
dorsi- back (dorsal, dorsum, latissimus dorsi)
duc- to carry (duct, adduction, abducens)
dys- bad, abnormal, painful (dyspnea, dystrophy)
e- out (ejaculate, eversion)
-eal pertaining to (arboreal, pineal)
ec-, ecto- outside, out of, external (ectopic, ectoderm, splenectomy)
ef- out of (efferent, effusion)
-elle small (fontanelle, organelle, micelle)
electro- electricity (electrocardiogram, electrolyte)
em- in, within (embolism, embedded)
emesi-, emeti- vomiting (emetic, hyperemesis)
-emia blood condition (anemia, hypoxemia)
en- in, into (enzyme, parenchyma)
encephalo- brain (encephalitis, telencephalon)
enchymo- poured in (mesenchyme, parenchyma)
endo- within, into, internal (endocrine, endocytosis)
entero- gut, intestine (mesentery, myenteric)
epi- upon, above (epidermis, epiphysis, epididymis)
ergo- work, energy, action (allergy, adrenergic, synergist)
eryth-, erythro- red (erythema, erythrocyte)
esthesio- sensation, feeling (anesthesia, somesthetic)
eu- good, true, normal, easy (eupnea, aneuploidy)
exo- out (exopeptidase, exocytosis, exocrine)
facili- easy (facilitated)
fasci- band, bundle (fascia, fascicle)
fenestr- window (fenestrated)
fer- to carry (efferent, uriniferous)
ferri- iron (ferritin, transferrin)
fibro- fiber (fibroblast, fibrosis)
fili- thread (myofilament, filiform)
flagello- whip (flagellum)
foli- leaf (folic acid, folia)
-form shape (cuneiform, fusiform)
fove- pit, depression (fovea)
funiculo- little rope, cord (funiculus)
fusi- 1. spindle (fusiform)
    2. pour out (perfusion)
gamo- marriage, union (monogamy, gamete)
gastro- belly, stomach (gastrointestinal, digastric)
-gen, -genic, -genesis producing, giving rise to (pathogen, carcinogenic, glycogenesis)
genio- chin (geniohyoid, genioglossus)
germi- 1. sprout, bud (germinal, germinativum)
    2. microbe (germicide)
gero- old age (progeria, geriatrics, gerontology)
gesto- 1. to bear, carry (ingest).
    2. pregnancy (gestation, progesterone)
glia- glue (neuroglia, microglia)
globu- ball, sphere (globulin, hemoglobin)
glom- ball (glomerulus)

glosso- tongue (glossopharyngeal, hypoglossal)
glyco- sugar (glycogen, glycolysis, hypoglycemia)
gono- 1. angle, corner (trigone)
    2. seed, sex cell, generation (gonad, oogonium, gonorrhea)
gradi- walk, step (retrograde, gradient)
-gram recording of (electrocardiogram, sonogram)
-graph recording instrument (sonograph, electrocardiograph)
-graphy recording process (sonography, radiography)
gravi- severe, heavy (gravid, myasthenia gravis)
gyro- turn, twist (gyrus)
hallu- great toe (hallucis)
hemato- blood (hematology, hematopoiesis)
hemi- half (hemidesmosome, hemisphere)
-hemia blood condition (polycythemia)
hemo- blood (hemophilia, hemoglobin)
hetero- different, other, various (heterozygous)
histo- tissue, web (histology, histone)
holo- whole, entire (holistic, holocrine)
homeo- constant, unchanging, uniform (homeostasis, homeothermic)
homo- same, alike (homologous, homozygous)
hyalo- clear, glassy (hyaline, hyaluronic acid)
hydro- water (dehydration, hydrolysis, hydrophobic)
hyper- above, above normal, excessive (hyperkalemia, hypertonic)
hypo- below, below normal, deficient (hypogastric, hyponatremia, hypophysis)
-ia condition (anemia, hypocalcemia, osteomalacia)
-ial pertaining to (hypophysial, epiphysial)
-ic pertaining to (isotonic, hemolytic, antigenic)
-icle, -icul small (ossicle, canaliculus, reticular)
ilia- flank, loin (ilium, iliac)
-illa, -illus little (papilla)
-in protein, substance (trypsin, fibrin, melanin)
infra- below (infraspinous, infrared)
ino- fiber (inotropic, inositol)
insulo- island (insula, insulin)
inter- between (intercellular, intervertebral)
intra- within (intracellular, intraocular)
iono- ion (ionotropic, cationic)
ischi- to hold back (ischium, ischemia)
-ism 1. process, state, condition (metabolism, rheumatism)
    2. doctrine, belief, theory (holism, reductionism, naturalism)
iso- same, equal (isometric, isotonic, isomer)
-issimus most, greatest (latissimus, longissimus)
-ite little (dendrite, somite)
-itis inflammation (dermatitis, gingivitis)
jug- to join (conjugated, jugular)
juxta- next to (juxtamedullary, juxtaglomerular)
kali- potassium (hypokalemia)
karyo- seed, nucleus (megakaryocyte, karyotype)
kerato- horn (keratin, keratinocyte)
kine- motion, action (kinetic, kinase, cytokinesis)
labi- lip (labium, levator labii)
lacera- torn, cut (foramen lacerum, laceration)
lacrimo- tear, cry (lacrimal gland, nasolacrimal)
lacto- milk (lactose, lactation, prolactin)
lamina- layer (lamina propria, laminar flow)
latero- side (bilateral, ipsilateral)
lati- broad (fascia lata, latissimus dorsi)
-lemma husk (sarcolemma, neurilemma)
lenti- lens (lentiform)
-let small (platelet)

leuko- white (leukocyte, leukemia)
levato- to raise (levator labii, elevation)
ligo- to bind (ligand, ligament)
line- line (linea alba, linea nigra)
litho- stone (otolith, lithotripsy)
-logy study of (histology, physiology, hematology)
lucid- light, clear (stratum lucidum, zona pellucida)
lun- moon, crescent (lunate, lunule, semilunar)
lute- yellow (macula lutea, corpus luteum)
lyso-, lyto- split apart, break down (lysosome, hydrolysis, electrolyte, hemolytic)
macro- large (macromolecule, macrophage)
macula- spot (macula lutea, macula densa)
mali- bad (malignant, malocclusion, malformed)
malle- hammer (malleus, malleolus)
mammo- breast (mammary, mammillary)
mano- hand (manus, manipulate)
manubri- handle (manubrium)
masto- breast (mastoid, gynecomastia)
medi- middle (medial, mediastinum, intermediate)
medullo- marrow, pith (medulla)
mega- large (megakaryocyte, hepatomegaly)
melano- black (melanin, melanocyte, melancholy)
meno- month (menstruation, menopause)
mento- chin (mental, mentalis)
mero- part, segment (isomer, centromere, merocrine)
meso- in the middle (mesoderm, mesentery)
meta- beyond, next in a series (metaphase, metacarpal)
metabol- change (metabolism, metabolite)
-meter measuring device (calorimeter, spirometer)
metri- 1. length, measure (isometric, emmetropic).
    2. uterus (endometrium)
micro- small (microscopic, microcytic, microglia)
mito- thread, filament (mitochondria, mitosis)
mono- one (monocyte, monogamy, mononucleosis)
morpho- form, shape, structure (morphology, amorphous)
muta- change (mutagen, mutation)
myelo- 1. spinal cord (poliomyelitis, myelin)
    2. bone marrow (myeloid, myelocytic)
myo-, mysi- muscle (myoglobin, myosin, epimysium)
natri- sodium (hyponatremia, natriuretic)
neo- new (neonatal, gluconeogenesis)
nephro- kidney (nephron, hydronephrosis)
neuro- nerve (aponeurosis, neurosoma, neurology)
nucleo- nucleus, kernel (nucleolus, nucleic acid)
oo- egg (oogenesis, oocyte)
ob- 1. life (aerobic, microbe)
    2. against, toward, before (obstetrics, obturator, obstruction)
oculo- eye (oculi, oculomotor)
odonto- tooth (odontoblast, periodontal)
-oid like, resembling (colloid, sigmoid, ameboid)
-ole small (arteriole, bronchiole, nucleolus)
oligo- few, a little, scanty (oligopeptide, oliguria)
-oma tumor, mass (carcinoma, hematoma)
omo- shoulder (omohyoid, acromion)
onycho- nail, claw (hyponychium, onychomycosis)
op- vision (optics, myopia, photopic)
-opsy viewing, to see (biopsy, rhodopsin)
or- mouth (oral, orbicularis oris)
orbi- circle (orbicularis, orbit)
organo- tool, instrument (organ, organelle)

ortho- straight (orthopnea, orthodontics, orthopedics)
-ose 1. full of (adipose)
    2. sugar (sucrose, glucose)
-osis 1. process (osmosis, exocytosis)
    2. condition, disease (cyanosis, thrombosis).
    3. increase (leukocytosis)
osmo- push (osmosis, chemiosmotic)
osse-, oste- bone (osseous, osteoporosis)
oto- ear (otolith, otitis, parotid)
-ous 1. full of (nitrogenous, edematous)
    2. pertaining to (mucous, nervous)
    3. like, characterized by (squamous, filamentous)
ovo- egg (ovum, ovary, ovulation)
oxy- 1. oxygen (hypoxia, oxyhemoglobin)
    2. sharp, quick (oxytocin)
palli- pale (pallor, globus pallidus)
palpebro- eyelid (palpebrae)
pan- all (panhypopituitarism, pancreas)
panni- cloth, rag (pannus, panniculus)
papillo- nipple (papilla, papillary)
par- birth (postpartum, parturition, multiparous)
para- next to (parathyroid, parotid)
parieto- wall (parietal)
patho- 1. disease (pathology, pathogen)
    2. feeling (sympathetic)
pecto- 1. chest (pectoralis)
    2. comblike (pectineus)
pedi- 1. foot (bipedal, pedicle)
    2. child (pediatrics)
pelvi- basin (pelvis, pelvic)
-penia deficiency (leukopenia, thrombocytopenia)
penna- feather (unipennate, bipennate)
peri- around (periosteum, peritoneum, periodontal)
perone- fibula (peroneus tertius, peroneal nerve)
phago- eat (phagocytosis, macrophage)
philo- loving, attracted to (hydrophilic, amphiphilic)
phobo- fearing, repelled by (hydrophobic)
phor- to carry, bear (diaphoresis, electrophoresis)
phragm- partition (diaphragm)
phreno- diaphragm (phrenic nerve)
physio- nature, natural cause (physiology, physician)
-physis growth (diaphysis, hypophysis)
pilo- hair (piloerection)
pino- drink, imbibe (pinocytosis)
planto- sole of foot (plantaris, plantar wart)
plasi- growth (hyperplasia, neoplasia)
plasm- shaped, molded (cytoplasm, endoplasmic)
plasti- form (thromboplastin)
platy- flat (platysma)
pnea- breath, breathing (eupnea, dyspnea)
pneumo- air, breath, lung (pneumonia, pneumothorax)
podo- foot (pseudopod, podocyte)
poies- forming (hematopoiesis, erythropoietin)
poly- many, much, excessive (polypeptide, polyuria)
primi- first (primary, primipara, primitive)
pro- 1. before, in front, first (prokaryote, prophase, prostate)
    2. promote, favor (progesterone, prolactin)
pseudo- false (pseudopod)
psycho- mind (psychosis, psychosomatic)
ptero-, pterygo- wing (pterygoid)
-ptosis dropping, falling, sagging (apoptosis, nephroptosis)

puncto- point (puncta)
pyro- fire (pyrogen, antipyretic)
quadri- four (quadriceps, quadratus)
quater- fourth (quaternary)
radiat- radiating (corona radiata)
rami- branch (ramus)
recto- straight (rectus abdominis, rectum)
reno- kidney (renal, renin)
reti- network (reticular, rete testis)
retinac- retainer, bracelet (retinaculum)
retro- behind, backward (retroperitoneal, retrovirus)
rhombo- rhombus (rhomboideus, rhombencephalon)
rubo-, rubro- red (bilirubin, rubrospinal)
rugo- fold, wrinkle (ruga, corrugator)
sacculo- little sac (saccule)
sarco- flesh, muscle (sarcoplasm, sarcomere)
scala- staircase (scala tympani)
sclero- hard, tough (sclera, sclerosis)
scopo- see (microscope, endoscopy)
secto- cut (section, dissection)
semi- half (semilunar, semimembranosus)
sepsi- infection (asepsis, septicemia)
-sis process (diapedesis, amniocentesis)
sole- sandal, sole of foot, flatfish (sole, soleus)
soma-, somato- body (somatic, somatotropin)
spheno- wedge (sphenoid)
spiro- breathing (inspiration, spirometry)
splanchno- viscera (splanchnic)
spleno- 1. bandage (splenius capitis)
       2. spleen (splenic artery)
squamo- scale, flat (squamous, desquamation)
stasi-, stati- put, remain, stay the same (hemostasis, homeostatic)
steno- narrow (stenosis)
ster-, stereo- solid, three-dimensional (steroid, stereoscopic)
sterno- breast, chest (sternum, sternocleidomastoid)
stria- stripe (striated, corpus striatum)
sub- below (subcutaneous, subclavicular)
sulc- furrow, groove (sulcus)
supra- above (supraspinous, supraclavicular)
sura- calf of leg (triceps surae)
sym- together (sympathetic, symphysis)
syn- together (synostosis, syncytium)
tachy- fast (tachycardia, tachypnea)

tarsi- ankle (tarsus, metatarsal)
tecto- roof, cover (tectorial membrane, tectum)
telo- last, end (telophase, telencephalon)
tempo- time (temporal)
terti- third (tertiary)
theli- nipple, female, tender (epithelium, polythelia)
thermo- heat (thermogenesis, thermoregulation)
thrombo- blood clot (thrombosis, thrombin)
thyro- shield (thyroid, thyrohyoid)
-tion process (circulation, pronation)
toci- birth (oxytocin)
tomo- 1. cut (tomography, atom, anatomy)
        2. segment (dermatome, myotome, sclerotome)
tono- force, tension (isotonic, tonus, myotonia)
topo- place, position (isotope, ectopic)
trabo- plate (trabecula)
trans- across (transpiration, transdermal)
trapezi- 1. table, grinding surface (trapezium)
          2. trapezoidal (trapezius)
tri- three (triceps, triglyceride)
tricho- hair (trichosiderin, peritrichial)
trocho- wheel, pulley (trochlea)
troph- 1. food, nourishment (trophic, trophoblast)
         2. growth (dystrophy, hypertrophy)
tropo- to turn, change (metabotropic, gonadotropin)
tunica- coat (tunica intima, tunica vaginalis)
tympano- drum, eardrum (tympanic, tensor tympani)
-ul small (trabecula, tubule, capitulum, glomerulus)
-uncle, -unculus small (homunculus, caruncle)
uni- one (unipennate, unipolar)
uri- urine (glycosuria, urinalysis, diuretic)
utriculo- little bag (utriculus)
vagino- sheath (invaginate, tunica vaginalis)
vago- wander (vagus)
vaso- vessel (vascular, vas deferens, vasa recta)
ventro- belly, lower part (ventral, ventricle)
vermi- worm (vermis, vermiform appendix)
vertebro- spine (vertebrae, intervertebral)
vesico- bladder, blister (vesical, vesicular)
villo- hair, hairy (microvillus)
vitre- glass (in vitro, vitreous humor)
vivi- life, alive (in vivo, revive)
zygo- union, join, mate (zygomatic, zygote, azygos)

GLOSSARY

A

abdominal cavity The body cavity between the diaphragm and pelvic brim. fig. A.5

abduction (ab-DUC-shun) Movement of a body part away from the median plane, as in raising an arm away from the side of the body. fig. 9.13

absorption 1. Process in which a chemical passes through a membrane or tissue surface and becomes incorporated into a body fluid or tissue. **2.** Any process in which one substance passes into another and becomes a part of it. *Compare* adsorption.

acetylcholine (ACh) (ASS-eh-till-CO-leen) A neurotransmitter released by somatic motor fibers, parasympathetic fibers, and some other neurons, composed of choline and an acetyl group. fig. 12.22

acetylcholinesterase (AChE) (ASS-eh-till-CO-lin-ESS-ter-ase) An enzyme that hydrolyzes acetylcholine, thus halting signal transmission at a cholinergic synapse.

acid A proton (H+) donor; a chemical that releases protons into solution.

acidosis An acid–base imbalance in which the blood pH is lower than 7.35.

acinus (ASS-ih-nus) A sac of secretory cells at the inner end of a gland duct. fig. 5.30

actin A filamentous intracellular protein that provides cytoskeletal support and interacts with other proteins, especially myosin, to cause cellular movement; important in muscle contraction and membrane actions such as phagocytosis, ameboid movement, and cytokinesis. fig. 11.3

action The movement produced by contraction of a particular muscle, or its role in preventing an unwanted movement; the function of a muscle.

action potential A rapid voltage change in which a plasma membrane briefly reverses electrical polarity; has a self-propagating effect that produces a traveling wave of excitation in nerve and muscle cells.

active site The region of a protein that binds to a ligand, such as the substrate-binding site of an enzyme or the hormone-binding site of a receptor.

active transport Transport of particles through a selectively permeable membrane, up their concentration gradient, with the aid of a carrier that consumes ATP.

acute Pertaining to a disease with abrupt onset, intense symptoms, and short duration. *Compare* chronic.

adaptation 1. An evolutionary process leading to the establishment of species characteristics that favor survival and reproduction. **2.** Any characteristic of anatomy, physiology, or behavior that promotes survival and reproduction. **3.** A sensory process in which a receptor adjusts its sensitivity or response to the prevailing level of stimulation, such as dark adaptation of the eye.

adaptive immunity A system of pathogen-specific defenses, developed upon initial exposure to an antigen and entailing cellular memory and accelerated responses to the pathogen on later reexposure, thereby preventing or minimizing disease. Includes various T and B lymphocytes, plasma cells, and antibodies. *Compare* innate immunity.

adduction (ad-DUC-shun) Movement of a body part toward the median plane, such as bringing the feet together from a spread-legged position. fig. 9.13

adenosine triphosphate (ATP) (ah-DEN-oh-seen tri-FOSS-fate) A molecule composed of adenine, ribose, and three phosphate groups that functions as a universal energy-transfer molecule; yields adenosine diphosphate (ADP) and an inorganic phosphate group (Pi) upon hydrolysis. fig. 2.29a

adenylate cyclase (ah-DEN-ih-late SY-clase) An enzyme of the plasma membrane that makes cyclic adenosine monophosphate (cAMP) by removing two phosphate groups from ATP; important in the activation of the cAMP second-messenger system.

adipocyte (AD-ih-po-site) A fat cell.

adipose tissue A connective tissue composed predominantly of adipocytes; fat.

adrenergic (AD-ren-UR-jic) Pertaining to norepinephrine (NE) and epinephrine, as in adrenergic nerve fibers that secrete NE, adrenergic receptors that bind it, and adrenergic effects on a target organ.

adrenocorticotropic hormone (ACTH) A hormone secreted by the anterior pituitary gland that stimulates the adrenal cortex to secrete cortisol and other glucocorticoids; one of the stress hormones.

adsorption The binding of one substance to the surface of another without becoming a part of the latter. *Compare* absorption.

aerobic exercise (air-OH-bic) Exercise in which oxygen is used to produce ATP; endurance exercise.

aerobic respiration Oxidation of organic compounds in a reaction series that requires oxygen and produces ATP.

afferent (AFF-ur-ent) Carrying toward, as in a blood vessel that carries blood toward a tissue or a nerve fiber that conducts signals toward the central nervous system.

agglutination (ah-GLUE-tih-NAY-shun) Clumping of cells by antibodies.

albumin (al-BYU-min) A class of small proteins constituting about 60% of the protein fraction of the blood plasma; plays roles in blood viscosity, colloid osmotic pressure, and solute transport.

aldosterone (AL-doe-steh-RONE, al-DOSS-teh-rone) A steroid hormone secreted by the adrenal cortex that acts on the kidneys to promote sodium retention and potassium excretion.

alkalosis An acid–base imbalance in which the blood pH is higher than 7.45.

allele (ah-LEEL) Any of the alternative forms that one gene can take, such as dominant and recessive alleles.

alveolus (AL-vee-OH-lus) **1.** A microscopic air sac of the lung. **2.** A gland acinus. **3.** A tooth socket. **4.** Any small anatomical space.

amino acid A small organic molecule with an amino group and a carboxyl group; amino acids are the monomers of which proteins are composed, and function also as neurotransmitters and in other roles.

amnion A transparent sac that encloses the fetus and amniotic fluid.

amphipathic (AM-fih-PATH-ic) Pertaining to a molecule that has both hydrophilic and hydrophobic regions, such as phospholipids, bile acids, and some proteins.

ampulla (am-PULL-uh) A wide or saclike portion of a tubular organ such as a semicircular duct or uterine tube.

anabolism (ah-NAB-oh-lizm) Any metabolic reactions that consume energy and construct more complex molecules with higher free energy from less complex molecules with lower free energy; for example, the synthesis of proteins from amino acids. *Compare* catabolism.

anaerobic fermentation (AN-err-OH-bic) A reduction reaction independent of oxygen that converts pyruvate to lactate and enables glycolysis to continue under anaerobic conditions.

anastomosis (ah-NASS-tih-MO-sis) An anatomical convergence, the opposite of a branch; a point where two blood vessels merge and combine their bloodstreams or where two nerves or ducts converge. fig. 20.10

anatomical position A reference posture that allows for standardized anatomical terminology. A subject in anatomical position is standing with the feet flat on the floor, arms down to the sides, and the palms and eyes directed forward. fig. A.1

androgen (AN-dro-jen) Testosterone or a related steroid hormone. Stimulates bodily changes at puberty in both sexes, adult libido in both sexes, development of male anatomy in the fetus and adolescent, and spermatogenesis.

aneurysm (AN-you-rizm) A weak, bulging point in the wall of a heart chamber or blood vessel that presents a threat of hemorrhage.

angiogenesis (AN-jee-oh-GEN-eh-sis) The growth of new blood vessels.

angiotensin II (AN-jee-oh-TEN-sin) A hormone produced from angiotensinogen (a plasma protein) by the kidneys and lungs; raises blood pressure by stimulating vasoconstriction and stimulating the adrenal cortex to secrete aldosterone.

anion (AN-eye-on) An ion with more electrons than protons and consequently a net negative charge.

antagonist 1. A muscle that opposes the agonist at a joint. **2.** Any agent, such as a hormone or drug, that opposes another.

antagonistic effect 1. An effect in which two hormones, neurotransmitters, or divisions of the nervous system oppose each other and produce opposite effects on a target cell or organ. **2.** An effect in which a drug blocks or otherwise opposes the action of one of the body's own signaling mechanisms.

antebrachium (AN-teh-BRAY-kee-um) The region from elbow to wrist; the forearm.

anterior Pertaining to the front (facial-abdominal aspect) of the body; ventral.

anterior root The branch of a spinal nerve that emerges from the anterior side of the spinal cord and carries efferent (motor) nerve fibers; often called *ventral root*. fig. 13.2b

antibody A protein of the gamma globulin class that reacts with an antigen and aids in protecting the body from its harmful effects; found in the blood plasma, in other body fluids, and on the surfaces of certain leukocytes and their derivatives.

antidiuretic hormone (ADH) (AN-tee-DYE-you-RET-ic) A hormone released by the posterior lobe of the pituitary gland in response to low blood pressure; promotes water retention by the kidneys. Also known as *arginine vasopressin*.

antigen (AN-tih-jen) Any large molecule capable of binding to an antibody or immune cells and triggering an immune response; usually a protein, glycoprotein, or glycolipid.

antigen-presenting cell (APC) A cell that phagocytizes an antigen and displays fragments of it on its surface for recognition by other cells of the immune system; chiefly macrophages and B lymphocytes.

antiport A cotransport protein that moves two or more solutes in opposite directions through a cellular membrane, such as the Na⁺–K⁺ pump.

apical surface The uppermost surface of an epithelial cell, usually exposed to the lumen of an organ. fig. 3.4

apocrine Pertaining to certain sweat glands with large lumens and relatively thick, aromatic secretions and to similar glands such as the mammary gland; named for a mistaken belief that they form secretions by pinching off bits of apical cytoplasm.

apoptosis (AP-op-TOE-sis) Programmed cell death; the normal death of cells that have completed their function. *Compare* necrosis.

appendicular (AP-en-DIC-you-lur) Pertaining to the limbs and their supporting skeletal girdles. fig. 8.1

areolar tissue (AIR-ee-OH-lur) A fibrous connective tissue with loosely organized, widely spaced fibers and cells and an abundance of fluid-filled space; found under nearly every epithelium, among other places. fig. 5.14

arrector A smooth muscle associated with each hair follicle that serves to erect the hair. fig. 6.7

arteriole (ar-TEER-ee-ole) A small artery that empties into a metarteriole or capillary.

arteriosclerosis (ar-TEER-ee-o-sclair-O-sis) Stiffening of the arteries correlated with age or disease processes, caused primarily by cumulative free radical damage and tissue deterioration. *Compare* atherosclerosis.

articular cartilage A thin layer of hyaline cartilage covering the articular surface of a bone at a synovial joint, serving to reduce friction and ease joint movement. fig. 9.5

articulation A skeletal joint; any point at which two bones meet; may or may not be movable.

aspect A particular view of the body or one of its structures, or a part that faces in a particular direction, such as the anterior aspect.

atherosclerosis (ATH-ur-oh-skleh-ROE-sis) A degenerative disease of the blood vessels characterized by the presence of lipid deposits; often leading to calcification of the vessel wall and obstruction of coronary, cerebral, or other vital arteries. *Compare* arteriosclerosis.

atrioventricular (AV) node (AY-tree-oh-ven-TRIC-you-lur) A group of autorhythmic cells in the interatrial septum of the heart that relays excitation from the atria to the ventricles.

atrioventricular (AV) valves The mitral (left) and tricuspid (right) valves between the atria and ventricles of the heart; the left AV valve was formerly known as the *bicuspid valve*.

atrophy (AT-ro-fee) Shrinkage of a tissue due to age, disuse, or disease.

autoantibody An antibody that fails to distinguish the body's own molecules from foreign molecules and thus attacks host tissues, causing autoimmune diseases.

autoimmune disease Any disease in which antibodies fail to distinguish between foreign and self-antigens and attack the body's own tissues; for example, systemic lupus erythematosus and rheumatic fever.

autolysis (aw-TOLL-ih-sis) Digestion of cells by their own internal enzymes.

autonomic nervous system (ANS) (AW-toe-NOM-ic) A motor division of the nervous system that innervates glands, smooth muscle, and cardiac muscle; consists of sympathetic and parasympathetic divisions and functions largely without voluntary control. *Compare* somatic nervous system.

autoregulation The ability of a tissue to adjust its own blood supply through vasomotion or angiogenesis.

autosome (AW-toe-some) Any chromosome except the sex chromosomes. Genes on the autosomes are inherited without regard to the sex of the individual.

avascular Devoid of blood vessels, as in epithelia and cartilage.

axial (AC-see-ul) Pertaining to the head, neck, and trunk; the part of the body excluding the appendicular portion. fig. 8.1

axillary (ACK-sih-LERR-ee) Pertaining to the armpit.

axon terminal The swollen tip at the distal end of an axon; the site of synaptic vesicles and neurotransmitter release. fig. 12.21

axoneme The central core of a cilium or flagellum, composed of microtubules; these are arranged in a circular array of nine microtubule pairs, and in flagella and mobile cilia, another microtubule pair at the center of the circle.

B

baroreceptor (BER-oh-re-SEP-tur) A cardiovascular pressure sensor that triggers autonomic reflexes in response to fluctuations in blood pressure; baroreceptors are located in the heart, aortic arch, and carotid sinuses.

basal surface The lowermost surface of an epithelial cell, attached to either a basement membrane or an underlying epithelial cell. fig. 3.4

base 1. A chemical that binds protons from solution; a proton acceptor. **2.** Any of the purines or pyrimidines of a nucleic acid (adenine, thymine, guanine, cytosine, or uracil) serving in part to code for protein structure. **3.** The broadest part of a tapered organ such as the uterus or heart or the inferior aspect of an organ such as the brain.

basement membrane A thin layer of glycoproteins, collagen, and glycosaminoglycans beneath the deepest cells of an epithelium, serving to bind the epithelium to the underlying tissue. fig. 5.33

basophil (BAY-so-fill) A granulocyte with coarse cytoplasmic granules that produces heparin, histamine, and other chemicals involved in inflammation. table 18.6

belly The thick part of a skeletal muscle between its origin and insertion. fig. 10.4

bicarbonate buffer system An equilibrium mixture of carbonic acid, bicarbonate ions, and hydrogen ions ($H_2CO_3 \rightleftharpoons HCO_3^- + H^+$) that stabilizes the pH of the body fluids.

bicarbonate ion An anion, HCO_3^-, that functions as a base in the buffering of body fluids.

biogenic amines A class of chemical messengers with neurotransmitter and hormonal functions, synthesized from amino acids and retaining an amino group; also called *monoamines*. Examples include epinephrine and thyroxine.

bipedalism The habit of walking on two legs; a defining characteristic of the family Hominidae that underlies many skeletal and other characteristics of humans.

blood–brain barrier (BBB) A barrier between the bloodstream and nervous tissue of the CNS that is impermeable to many blood solutes and thus prevents them from affecting the brain tissue; formed by the tight junctions between capillary endothelial cells, the basement membrane of the endothelium, and the perivascular feet of astrocytes.

B lymphocyte A lymphocyte that functions as an antigen-presenting cell and, in humoral immunity, differentiates into an antibody-producing plasma cell; also called a *B cell*.

body 1. The entire organism. **2.** Part of a cell, such as a neuron, containing the nucleus and most other organelles. **3.** The largest or principal part of an organ such as the stomach or uterus; also called the *corpus*.

brachial (BRAY-kee-ul) Pertaining to the arm proper, the region from shoulder to elbow.

bradykinin (BRAD-ee-KY-nin) An oligopeptide produced in inflammation that stimulates vasodilation, increases capillary permeability, and stimulates pain receptors.

brainstem The stalklike lower portion of the brain, composed of the medulla oblongata, pons, and midbrain. fig. 14.8

bronchiole (BRON-kee-ole) A pulmonary air passage that is usually 1 mm or less in diameter and lacks cartilage but has relatively abundant smooth muscle, elastic tissue, and a simple cuboidal, usually ciliated epithelium.

bronchus (BRONK-us) A relatively large pulmonary air passage with supportive cartilage in the wall; any passage beginning with the main bronchus at the fork in the trachea and ending with segmental bronchi, from which air continues into the bronchioles.

brush border A fringe of microvilli on the apical surface of an epithelial cell, serving to enhance surface area and promote absorption. fig. 5.6

bursa A sac filled with synovial fluid at a synovial joint, serving to facilitate muscle or joint action. fig. 9.6

C

calcification The hardening of a tissue due to the deposition of calcium salts.

calorie The amount of thermal energy that will raise the temperature of 1 g of water by 1°C. Also called a *small calorie* to distinguish it from a dietary Calorie (capital *C*), or kilocalorie.

Calorie *See* kilocalorie.

canaliculus (CAN-uh-LIC-you-lus) A microscopic canal, as in osseous tissue. fig. 7.4

capillary (CAP-ih-LERR-ee) The narrowest type of vessel in the cardiovascular and lymphatic systems; engages in fluid exchanges with surrounding tissues.

capillary exchange The process of fluid transfer between the bloodstream and tissue fluid through the walls of the blood capillaries.

capsule The fibrous covering of a structure such as the spleen or a synovial joint.

carbohydrate A hydrophilic organic compound composed of carbon and a 2:1 ratio of hydrogen to oxygen; includes sugars, starches, glycogen, and cellulose.

carbonic anhydrase An enzyme found in erythrocytes and kidney tubule cells that catalyzes the decomposition of carbonic acid into carbon dioxide and water or the reverse reaction ($H_2CO_3 \rightleftharpoons CO_2 + H_2O$).

carcinogen (car-SIN-oh-jen) An agent capable of causing cancer, including certain chemicals, viruses, and ionizing radiation.

cardiac output *(CO)* The amount of blood pumped by each ventricle of the heart in 1 minute.

cardiomyocyte A cardiac muscle cell.

cardiovascular system An organ system consisting of the heart and blood vessels, serving for the transport of blood. *Compare* circulatory system.

carpal Pertaining to the wrist (carpus).

carrier 1. A protein in a cellular membrane that performs carrier-mediated transport. **2.** A person who is heterozygous for a recessive allele and does not exhibit the associated phenotype, but may transmit this allele to his or her children; for example, a carrier for sickle-cell disease.

carrier-mediated transport Any process of transporting materials through a cellular membrane that involves reversible binding to a transport protein.

catabolism (ca-TAB-oh-lizm) Any metabolic reactions that release energy and break relatively complex molecules with high free energy into less complex molecules with lower free energy; for example, digestion and glycolysis. *Compare* anabolism.

catecholamine (CAT-eh-COAL-uh-meen) A subclass of biogenic amines that includes epinephrine, norepinephrine, and dopamine. fig. 12.22

cation (CAT-eye-on) An ion with more protons than electrons and consequently a net positive charge.

caudal (CAW-dul) **1.** Pertaining to a tail or narrow tail-like part of an organ. **2.** Pertaining to the inferior part of the trunk of the body, where the tail of other animals arises. *Compare* cranial. **3.** Relatively distant from the forehead, especially in reference to structures of the brain and spinal cord; for example, the medulla oblongata is caudal to the pons. *Compare* rostral.

celiac (SEEL-ee-ac) Pertaining to the abdomen.

central nervous system (CNS) The brain and spinal cord.

centriole (SEN-tree-ole) An organelle composed of a short cylinder of nine triplets of microtubules, usually paired with another centriole perpendicular to it; origin of the mitotic spindle; identical to the basal body of a cilium or flagellum. fig. 3.33

cephalic (seh-FAL-ic) Pertaining to the head.

cerebellum (SER-eh-BELL-um) A large portion of the brain posterior to the brainstem and inferior to the cerebrum, responsible for equilibrium, motor coordination, and memory of learned motor skills. fig. 14.11

cerebrospinal fluid (CSF) (SERR-eh-bro-SPY-nul, seh-REE-bro-SPY-nul) A liquid that fills the ventricles of the brain, the central canal of the spinal cord, and the space between the CNS and dura mater.

cerebrum (seh-REE-brum, SERR-eh-brum) The largest and most superior part of the brain, divided into two convoluted cerebral hemispheres separated by a deep longitudinal fissure.

cervical (SUR-vih-cul) Pertaining to the neck or a narrow part (cervix) of certain organs.

cervix (SUR-vix) **1.** The neck. **2.** A narrow or necklike part of an organ such as the uterus and gallbladder. fig. 28.3

channel protein A transmembrane protein that has a pore through it for the passage of materials between the cytoplasm and extracellular fluid. fig. 3.7

chemical bond A force that attracts one atom to another, such as their opposite charges or the sharing of electrons.

chemical synapse A meeting of a nerve fiber and another cell with which the neuron communicates by releasing neurotransmitters. fig. 12.21

chemoreceptor An organ or cell specialized to detect chemicals, as in the carotid bodies and taste buds.

chief cells The majority type of cell in an organ or tissue such as the parathyroid glands or gastric glands.

cholecystokinin (CCK) (CO-leh-SIS-toe-KY-nin) A polypeptide employed as a hormone and neurotransmitter, secreted by some brain neurons and cells of the digestive tract. fig. 12.22

cholesterol (co-LESS-tur-ol) A steroid that functions as part of the plasma membrane and as a precursor for all other steroids in the body.

cholinergic (CO-lin-UR-jic) Pertaining to acetylcholine (ACh), as in cholinergic nerve fibers that secrete ACh, cholinergic receptors that bind it, or cholinergic effects on a target organ.

chondrocyte (CON-dro-site) A cartilage cell; a former chondroblast that has become enclosed in a lacuna in the cartilage matrix. figs. 5.19 to 5.21

chorion (CO-ree-on) An embryonic membrane external to the amnion; forms part of the placenta and has diverse functions including fetal nutrition, waste removal, and hormone secretion. fig. 29.7f

chromatin (CRO-muh-tin) Filamentous material in the interphase nucleus, composed of DNA and associated proteins.

chromosome A complex of DNA and protein carrying the genetic material of a cell's nucleus. Normally there are 46 chromosomes in the nucleus of each cell except germ cells. fig. 4.5

chronic 1. Long-lasting. 2. Pertaining to a disease that progresses slowly and has a long duration. *Compare* acute.

chronic bronchitis A chronic obstructive pulmonary disease characterized by damaged and immobilized respiratory cilia, excessive mucus secretion, infection of the lower respiratory tract, and bronchial inflammation; caused especially by cigarette smoking. *See also* chronic obstructive pulmonary disease.

chronic obstructive pulmonary disease (COPD) Certain lung diseases (chronic bronchitis and emphysema) that result in long-term obstruction of airflow and substantially reduced pulmonary ventilation; one of the leading causes of death in old age.

cilium (SILL-ee-um) A hairlike process, with an axoneme, projecting from the apical surface of an epithelial cell; often motile and serving to propel matter across the surface of an epithelium, but sometimes nonmotile and serving sensory roles. fig. 3.10

circulatory shock A state of cardiac output inadequate to meet the metabolic needs of the body.

circulatory system An organ system consisting of the heart, blood vessels, and blood. *Compare* cardiovascular system.

circumduction A joint movement in which one end of an appendage remains relatively stationary and the other end is moved in a circle. fig. 9.16

cirrhosis (sih-RO-sis) A degenerative liver disease characterized by replacement of functional parenchyma with fibrous and adipose tissue; causes include alcohol, other poisons, and viral and bacterial inflammation.

cistern (SIS-turn) A fluid-filled space or sac, such as the cisterna chyli of the lymphatic system and cisterns of the endoplasmic reticulum and Golgi complex. fig. 3.28

climacteric A period in the lives of men and women, usually in the early 50s, marked by changes in the level of reproductive hormones; a variety of somatic and psychological effects; and, in women, cessation of ovulation and menstruation (menopause).

clone A population of cells that are mitotically descended from the same parent cell and are identical to each other genetically or in other respects, such as a B- or T-cell clone.

coagulation (co-AG-you-LAY-shun) The clotting of blood, lymph, tissue fluid, or semen.

coenzyme (co-EN-zime) A small organic molecule, usually derived from a vitamin, that is needed to make an enzyme catalytically active; acts by accepting electrons from an enzymatic reaction and transferring them to a different reaction chain.

cofactor A nonprotein such as a metal ion or coenzyme needed for an enzyme to function.

cohesion The clinging of identical molecules such as water to each other.

collagen (COLL-uh-jen) The most abundant protein in the body, forming the fibers of many connective tissues in places such as the dermis, tendons, and bones.

colloid An aqueous mixture of particles that are too large to pass through most selectively permeable membranes but small enough to remain evenly dispersed through the solvent by the thermal motion of solvent particles; for example, the proteins in blood plasma.

colloid osmotic pressure (COP) A portion of the osmotic pressure of a body fluid that is due to its protein. *Compare* oncotic pressure.

column *See* funiculus.

columnar A cellular shape that is significantly taller than it is wide. fig. 5.6

commissure (COM-ih-shur) 1. A bundle of nerve fibers that crosses from one side of the brain or spinal cord to the other. fig. 14.2 2. A corner or angle at which the eyelids, lips, or genital labia meet; in the eye, also called the *canthus*. fig. 16.23

complement 1. To complete or enhance the structure or function of something else, as in the coordinated action of two hormones. 2. A system of plasma proteins involved in defense against pathogens.

computerized tomography (CT) A method of medical imaging that uses X-rays and a computer to create an image of a thin section of the body; also called a *CT scan*.

concentration gradient A difference in chemical concentration from one point to another, as on two sides of a plasma membrane.

conception The fertilization of an egg, producing a zygote.

conceptus All products of conception, ranging from a fertilized egg to the full-term fetus with its embryonic membranes, placenta, and umbilical cord. *Compare* embryo, fetus, preembryo.

condyle (CON-dile) A rounded knob on a bone serving to smooth the movement of a joint. fig. 8.2

conformation The three-dimensional structure of a protein that results from interaction among its amino acid side groups, its interactions with water, and the formation of disulfide bonds.

congenital Present at birth; for example, an anatomical defect, a syphilis infection, or a hereditary disease.

conjugated A state in which one organic compound is bound to another compound of a different class, such as a protein conjugated with a carbohydrate to form a glycoprotein.

connective tissue A tissue usually composed of more extracellular than cellular volume and usually with a substantial amount of extracellular fiber; forms supportive frameworks and capsules for organs, binds structures together, holds them in place, stores energy (as in adipose tissue), or transports materials (as in blood).

contractility 1. The ability to shorten. 2. The amount of force that a contracting muscle fiber generates for a given stimulus; may be increased by epinephrine, for example, while stimulus strength remains constant. 3. The amount of force that a contracting heart chamber generates for a given preload.

contralateral On opposite sides of the body, as in reflex arcs in which the stimulus comes from one side of the body and a response is given by muscles on the other side. *Compare* ipsilateral.

cooperative effect Effect in which two hormones, or both divisions of the autonomic nervous system, work together to produce a single overall result.

corona A halo- or crownlike structure, as in the corona radiata of the brain and ovaries, coronary circulation of the heart, and coronal suture of the skull.

corona radiata **1.** An array of nerve tracts in the brain that arise mainly from the thalamus and fan out to different regions of the cerebral cortex. **2.** The first layer of cuboidal cells immediately external to the zona pellucida around an egg cell.

coronal plane *See* frontal plane.

coronary circulation A system of blood vessels that serve the wall of the heart. fig. 19.10

corpus **1.** Body or mass, such as the corpus callosum and corpus luteum. **2.** The main part of an organ such as the stomach or uterus, as opposed to such regions as the head, tail, or cervix.

corrosion cast *See* vascular corrosion cast.

cortex The outer layer of some organs such as the adrenal glands, kidneys, cerebrum, lymph nodes, ovaries, and hairs; usually covers or encloses tissue called the *medulla*.

corticosteroid (COR-tih-co-STERR-oyd) Any steroid hormone secreted by the adrenal cortex, such as aldosterone, cortisol, and sex steroids.

costal (COSS-tul) Pertaining to the ribs.

cotransport A form of carrier-mediated transport in which a membrane protein transports two solutes simultaneously or within the same cycle of action by either facilitated diffusion or active transport; for example, the sodium–glucose transporter and the Na⁺–K⁺ pump.

countercurrent A situation in which two fluids flow side by side in opposite directions, as in the countercurrent multiplier of the kidney and the countercurrent heat exchanger of the scrotum.

cranial (CRAY-nee-ul) **1.** Pertaining to the cranium of the skull. **2.** In a position relatively close to the head or a direction toward the head. *Compare* caudal.

cranial nerve Any of 12 pairs of nerves connected to the base of the brain and passing through foramina of the cranium.

crista (plural, *cristae*) An anatomical crest, such as the crista galli of the ethmoid bone or the crista of a mitochondrion.

cross section A cut perpendicular to the long axis of the body or an organ.

crural (CROO-rul) Pertaining to the leg proper or to the crus (leg) of a organ.

crus (pronounced cruss; plural, *crura*) **1.** A leglike extension of an organ such as the penis or clitoris. figs. 27.10b, 28.8 **2.** The leg proper (crural region, from knee to ankle) of the lower limb.

cuboidal (cue-BOY-dul) A cellular shape that is roughly like a cube or in which the height and width are about equal; typically looks squarish in tissue sections. fig. 5.5

current A moving stream of charged particles such as ions or electrons.

cusp **1.** One of the flaps of a valve of the heart, veins, and lymphatic vessels. **2.** A conical projection on the occlusal surface of a premolar or molar tooth.

cutaneous (cue-TAY-nee-us) Pertaining to the skin.

cyanosis (SY-uh-NO-sis) A bluish color of the skin and mucous membranes due to ischemia or hypoxemia.

cyclic adenosine monophosphate (cAMP) A cyclic molecule produced from ATP by the enzymatic removal of two phosphate groups; serves as a second messenger in many hormone and neurotransmitter actions. fig. 2.29b

cytolysis (sy-TOL-ih-sis) The rupture and destruction of a cell by such agents as complement proteins and hypotonic solutions.

cytoplasm The contents of a cell between its plasma membrane and its nuclear envelope, consisting of cytosol, organelles, inclusions, and the cytoskeleton.

cytoskeleton A system of protein microfilaments, intermediate filaments, and microtubules in a cell, serving in physical support, cellular movement, and the routing of molecules and organelles to their destinations within the cell. fig. 3.24

cytosol A clear, featureless, gelatinous colloid in which the organelles and other internal structures of a cell are embedded.

cytotoxic T cell A T lymphocyte that directly attacks and destroys infected body cells, cancerous cells, and the cells of transplanted tissues.

D

daughter cells Cells that arise from a parent cell by mitosis or meiosis.

deamination (dee-AM-ih-NAY-shun) Removal of an amino group from an organic molecule; a step in the catabolism of amino acids.

decomposition reaction A chemical reaction in which a larger molecule is broken down into smaller ones. *Compare* synthesis reaction.

decussation (DEE-cuh-SAY-shun) The crossing of nerve fibers from the right side of the central nervous system to the left or vice versa, especially in the spinal cord, medulla oblongata, and optic chiasma.

deep Relatively far from the body surface; opposite of *superficial*. For example, most bones are deep to the skeletal muscles.

degranulation Exocytosis and disappearance of cytoplasmic granules, especially in platelets and granulocytes.

denaturation A change in the three-dimensional conformation of a protein that destroys its enzymatic or other functional properties, usually caused by extremes of temperature or pH.

dendrite Extension of a neuron that receives information from other cells or from environmental stimuli and conducts signals to the soma. Dendrites are usually shorter, more branched, and more numerous than the axon and are incapable of producing action potentials. fig. 12.4

dendritic cell An antigen-presenting cell of the epidermis and mucous membranes. fig. 6.3

denervation atrophy The shrinkage of skeletal muscle that occurs when the motor neuron dies or is severed from the muscle.

dense connective tissue A connective tissue with a high density of fiber, relatively little ground substance, and scanty cells; seen in tendons and the dermis, for example.

depolarization A shift in the electrical potential across a plasma membrane to a value less negative than the resting membrane potential; associated with excitation of a nerve or muscle cell. *Compare* hyperpolarization.

dermal papilla A bump or ridge of dermis that extends upward to interdigitate with the epidermis and create a wavy boundary that resists stress and slippage of the epidermis.

dermis The deeper of the two layers of the skin, underlying the epidermis and composed of fibrous connective tissue.

desmosome (DEZ-mo-some) A patchlike intercellular junction that mechanically links two cells together. fig. 5.28

diabetes (DY-uh-BEE-teez) Any disease characterized by chronic polyuria of metabolic origin; diabetes mellitus unless otherwise specified.

diabetes insipidus (in-SIP-ih-dus) A form of diabetes that results from hyposecretion of antidiuretic hormone; unlike other forms, it is not characterized by hyperglycemia or glycosuria.

diabetes mellitus (DM) (mel-EYE-tus) A form of diabetes that results from hyposecretion of insulin or from a deficient target-cell response to it; signs include hyperglycemia and glycosuria.

diaphysis (dy-AF-ih-sis) The shaft of a long bone. fig. 7.1

diarthrosis (DY-ar-THRO-sis) *See* synovial joint.

diastole (dy-ASS-toe-lee) A period in which a heart chamber relaxes and fills with blood; especially ventricular relaxation.

diastolic pressure (DY-ah-STAHL-ic) The minimum arterial blood pressure measured during the interval between heartbeats

diencephalon (DY-en-SEFF-uh-lon) A portion of the brain between the midbrain and corpus callosum; composed of the thalamus, epithalamus, and hypothalamus. fig. 14.12

differentiation Development of a relatively unspecialized cell or tissue into one with a more specific structure and function.

diffusion Spontaneous net movement of particles from a place of high concentration to a place of low concentration (down a concentration gradient).

diploid (2n) In humans, having 46 chromosomes in 23 homologous pairs, with one member of each chromosome pair coming from each parent.

disaccharide (dy-SAC-uh-ride) A carbohydrate composed of two simple sugars (monosaccharides) joined by a glycosidic bond; for example, lactose, sucrose, and maltose. fig. 2.16

disseminated intravascular coagulation (DIC) Widespread clotting of the blood within unbroken vessels, leading to hemorrhaging, congestion of the vessels with clotted blood, and ischemia and necrosis of organs.

distal Relatively distant from a point of origin or attachment; for example, the wrist is distal to the elbow. *Compare* proximal.

disulfide bond A covalent bond that links two cysteine residues through their sulfur atoms, serving to join one peptide chain to another or to hold a single chain in its three-dimensional conformation.

diuretic (DY-you-RET-ic) A chemical that increases urine output.

dominant 1. Pertaining to a genetic allele that is phenotypically expressed in the presence of any other allele. **2.** Pertaining to a trait that results from a dominant allele.

dopamine (DOE-puh-meen) An inhibitory catecholamine neurotransmitter of the central nervous system, especially of the basal nuclei, where it acts to suppress unwanted motor activity. fig. 12.22

dorsal Toward the back (spinal) side of the body; in humans, usually synonymous with *posterior*.

dorsal root *See* posterior root.

dorsiflexion (DOR-sih-FLEC-shun) A movement of the ankle that reduces the joint angle and raises the toes. fig. 9.22

duodenum (DEW-oh-DEE-num, dew-ODD-eh-num) The first portion of the small intestine extending for about 25 cm from the pyloric valve of the stomach to a sharp bend called the *duodenojejunal flexure;* receives chyme from the stomach and secretions from the liver and pancreas. fig. 25.25

dynein (DINE-een) A motor protein involved in the beating of cilia and flagella and in the movement of molecules and organelles within cells, as in retrograde transport in a nerve fiber.

E

eccrine (ECK-rin) Pertaining to gland cells that release their product by exocytosis; also called *merocrine.*

ectoderm The outermost of the three primary germ layers of an embryo; gives rise to the epidermis and nervous system.

ectopic (ec-TOP-ic) In an abnormal location; for example, ectopic pregnancy and ectopic pacemakers of the heart.

edema (eh-DEE-muh) Abnormal accumulation of tissue fluid resulting in swelling of the tissue.

effector A molecule, cell, or organ that carries out a response to a stimulus.

efferent (EFF-ur-ent) Carrying away or out, as in a blood vessel that carries blood away from a tissue or a nerve fiber that conducts signals away from the central nervous system.

elastic fiber A connective tissue fiber, composed of the protein elastin, that stretches under tension and returns to its original length when released; responsible for the resilience of organs such as the skin and lungs.

elasticity The tendency of a stretched structure to return to its original dimensions when tension is released.

electrical synapse A gap junction that enables one cell to stimulate another directly, without the intermediary action of a neurotransmitter; such synapses connect the cells of cardiac muscle and single-unit smooth muscle.

electrolyte A salt that ionizes in water and produces a solution that conducts electricity; loosely speaking, any ion that results from the dissociation of such salts, such as sodium, potassium, calcium, chloride, and bicarbonate ions.

elevation A joint movement that raises a body part, as in hunching the shoulders or closing the mouth.

embolism (EM-bo-lizm) The obstruction of a blood vessel by an embolus.

embolus (EM-bo-lus) Any abnormal traveling object in the bloodstream, such as agglutinated bacteria or blood cells, a blood clot, or an air bubble.

embryo A developing individual from the sixteenth day of gestation when the three primary germ layers have formed, through the end of the eighth week when all of the organ systems are present. *Compare* conceptus, fetus, preembryo.

emphysema (EM-fih-SEE-muh) A degenerative lung disease characterized by a breakdown of alveoli and diminishing surface area available for gas exchange; occurs with aging of the lungs but is greatly accelerated by smoking or air pollution.

endocrine gland (EN-doe-crin) A ductless gland that secretes hormones into the bloodstream; for example, the thyroid and adrenal glands. *Compare* exocrine gland.

endocytosis (EN-doe-sy-TOE-sis) Any process in which a cell forms vesicles from its plasma membrane and takes in large particles, molecules, or droplets of extracellular fluid; for example, phagocytosis and pinocytosis.

endoderm The innermost of the three primary germ layers of an embryo; gives rise to the mucosae of the digestive and respiratory tracts and to their associated glands.

endogenous (en-DODJ-eh-nus) Originating internally, such as the endogenous cholesterol synthesized in the body in contrast to the exogenous cholesterol coming from the diet. *Compare* exogenous.

endometrium (EN-doe-MEE-tree-um) The mucosa of the uterus; the site of implantation and source of menstrual discharge.

endoplasmic reticulum (ER) (EN-doe-PLAZ-mic reh-TIC-you-lum) An extensive system of interconnected cytoplasmic tubules or channels; classified as rough ER or smooth ER depending on the presence or absence of ribosomes on its membrane. fig. 3.28

endothelium (EN-doe-THEEL-ee-um) A simple squamous epithelium that lines the lumens of the blood vessels, heart, and lymphatic vessels.

enteric (en-TERR-ic) Pertaining to the small intestine, as in enteric hormones and enteric nervous system.

eosinophil (EE-oh-SIN-oh-fill) A granulocyte with a large, often bilobed nucleus and coarse cytoplasmic granules that stain with eosin; phagocytizes antigen–antibody complexes, allergens, and inflammatory chemicals and secretes enzymes that combat parasitic infections. table 18.6

epidermis A stratified squamous epithelium that constitutes the superficial layer of the skin, overlying the dermis. fig. 6.3

epinephrine (EP-ih-NEFF-rin) A catecholamine that functions as a neurotransmitter in the sympathetic nervous system and as a hormone secreted by the adrenal medulla; also called *adrenaline.* fig. 12.22

epiphysial plate (EP-ih-FIZ-ee-ul) A plate of hyaline cartilage between the epiphysis and diaphysis of a long bone in a child or adolescent, serving as a growth zone for bone elongation. figs. 7.9, 7.11

epiphysis (eh-PIF-ih-sis) **1.** The head of a long bone. fig. 7.1 **2.** The pineal gland (epiphysis cerebri).

epithelium A type of tissue consisting of one or more layers of closely adhering cells with little intercellular material and no blood vessels; forms the coverings and linings of many organs and the parenchyma of the glands. Also known as *epithelial tissue*.

erectile tissue A tissue that functions by swelling with blood, as in the penis and clitoris and inferior concha of the nasal cavity.

erythrocyte (eh-RITH-ro-site) A red blood cell.

erythropoiesis (eh-RITH-ro-poy-EE-sis) The production of erythrocytes.

erythropoietin (eh-RITH-ro-POY-eh-tin) A hormone that is secreted by the kidneys and liver in response to hypoxemia and stimulates erythropoiesis.

estrogens (ESS-tro-jenz) A family of steroid hormones known especially for producing female secondary sex characteristics and regulating various aspects of the menstrual cycle and pregnancy; major forms are estradiol, estriol, and estrone.

evolution A change in the relative frequencies of alleles in a population over a period of time; the mechanism that produces adaptations in human form and function. *See also* adaptation.

excitability The ability of a cell to respond to a stimulus, especially the ability of nerve and muscle cells to produce membrane voltage changes in response to stimuli.

excitation–contraction coupling Events that link the synaptic stimulation of a muscle cell to the onset of contraction.

excitatory postsynaptic potential (EPSP) A partial depolarization of a postsynaptic neuron or muscle cell in response to a neurotransmitter, making it more likely to reach threshold and produce an action potential.

excretion The process of eliminating metabolic waste products from a cell or from the body. *Compare* secretion.

exocrine gland (EC-so-crin) A gland that secretes its products into another organ or onto the body surface, usually by way of a duct; for example, salivary and gastric glands. *Compare* endocrine gland.

exocytosis (EC-so-sy-TOE-sis) A process in which a vesicle in the cytoplasm of a cell fuses with the plasma membrane and releases its contents from the cell; used in the elimination of cellular wastes, in the release of gland products and neurotransmitters, and for the replacement of membrane removed by endocytosis.

exogenous (ec-SODJ-eh-nus) Originating externally, such as exogenous (dietary) cholesterol; extrinsic. *Compare* endogenous.

expiration 1. Exhaling. **2.** Dying.

extension Movement of a joint that increases the angle between articulating bones (straightens the joint). fig. 9.12 *Compare* flexion.

extracellular fluid (ECF) Any body fluid that is not contained in the cells; for example, blood, lymph, and tissue fluid.

extrinsic (ec-STRIN-sic) **1.** Originating externally, such as extrinsic blood-clotting factors; exogenous. **2.** Not fully contained within a specified organ or region but acting on it, such as the extrinsic muscles of the hand and eye. *Compare* intrinsic.

F

facilitated diffusion The process of transporting a chemical through a cellular membrane, down its concentration gradient, with the aid of a carrier that does not consume ATP; enables substances to diffuse through the membrane that would do so poorly, or not at all, without a carrier.

facilitation Making a process more likely to occur, such as the firing of a neuron, or making it occur more easily or rapidly, as in facilitated diffusion.

fascia (FASH-ee-uh) A layer of connective tissue between the muscles or separating the muscles from the skin. fig. 10.1

fascicle (FASS-ih-cul) A bundle of muscle or nerve fibers ensheathed in connective tissue; multiple fascicles bound together constitute a muscle or nerve as a whole. figs. 10.1, 13.9

fat 1. A triglyceride molecule. **2.** Adipose tissue.

fatty acid An organic molecule composed of a chain of an even number of carbon atoms with a carboxyl group at one end and a methyl group at the other; one of the structural subunits of triglycerides and phospholipids.

fenestrated (FEN-eh-stray-ted) Perforated with holes or slits, as in fenestrated blood capillaries and the elastic sheets of large arteries. fig. 20.5

fetus In human development, an individual from the beginning of the ninth week when all of the organ systems are present, through the time of birth. *Compare* conceptus, embryo, preembryo.

fibrin (FY-brin) A sticky fibrous protein formed from fibrinogen in blood, tissue fluid, and lymph; forms the matrix of a blood clot.

fibroblast A connective tissue cell that produces collagen fibers and ground substance; the only type of cell in tendons and ligaments.

fibrosis Replacement of damaged tissue with fibrous scar tissue rather than by the original tissue type; scarring. *Compare* regeneration.

fibrous connective tissue Any connective tissue with a preponderance of fiber, such as areolar, reticular, dense regular, and dense irregular connective tissues.

filtration A process in which hydrostatic pressure forces a fluid through a selectively permeable membrane (especially a capillary wall).

fire To produce an action potential, as in nerve and muscle cells.

fix 1. To hold a structure in place; for example, by fixator muscles that prevent unwanted joint movements. **2.** To preserve a tissue by means of a fixative such as formalin.

flexion A joint movement that, in most cases, decreases the angle between two bones. fig. 9.12 *Compare* extension.

fluid balance A state in which average daily water gains (by intake and synthesis) equal water losses, and water is properly distributed among the body's fluid compartments. *Also called* water balance.

fluid compartment Any of the major categories of fluid in the body, separated by selectively permeable membranes and differing from each other in chemical composition. Primary examples are the intracellular fluid, tissue fluid, blood, and lymph.

follicle (FOLL-ih-cul) **1.** A small space, such as a hair follicle, thyroid follicle, or ovarian follicle. **2.** An aggregation of lymphocytes in a lymphatic organ or mucous membrane.

follicle-stimulating hormone (FSH) A hormone secreted by the anterior pituitary gland that stimulates development of the ovarian follicles and egg cells in females and sperm production in males.

foramen (fo-RAY-men) (plural, *foramina*) A hole through a bone or other organ, in many cases providing passage for blood vessels and nerves.

formed element An erythrocyte, leukocyte, or platelet; any cellular component of blood or lymph as opposed to the extracellular fluid component.

fossa (FOSS-uh) A depression in an organ or tissue, such as the fossa ovalis of the heart, cranial fossa of the skull, or olecranon fossa of the elbow.

fovea (FO-vee-uh) A small pit, such as the fovea capitis of the femur or fovea centralis of the retina.

free energy The potential energy in a chemical that is available to do work.

free radical A particle derived from an atom or molecule, having an unpaired electron that makes it highly reactive and destructive to cells; produced by intrinsic processes such as aerobic respiration and by extrinsic agents such as chemicals and ionizing radiation.

frenulum (FREN-you-lum) A fold of tissue that attaches a movable structure to a relatively immovable one, such as the lip to the gum or the tongue to the floor of the mouth. fig. 25.4

frontal plane An anatomical plane that passes through the body or an organ from right to left and superior to inferior, dividing the body or organ into anterior and posterior portions; also called a *coronal plane.* fig. A.1

fundus The base, the broadest part, or the part farthest from the opening of certain viscera such as the stomach and uterus.

funiculus (few-NICK-you-lus) A bundle of nerve fibers in the spinal cord, arranged in three pairs constituting the spinal white matter; subdivided into tracts (fasciculi). fig. 13.3

fusiform (FEW-zih-form) Shaped like the spindle of a spinning wheel; elongated, thick in the middle, and tapered at both ends, such as the shape of a smooth muscle cell or a muscle spindle.

G

gamete (GAM-eet) An egg or sperm cell.

gametogenesis (geh-ME-to-JEN-eh-sis) The production of eggs or sperm.

ganglion (GANG-glee-un) A cluster of nerve cell bodies in the peripheral nervous system, often resembling a knot in a string.

gangrene Tissue necrosis resulting from ischemia.

gap junction A junction between two cells consisting of a pore surrounded by a ring of proteins in the plasma membrane of each cell; allows solutes to diffuse from the cytoplasm of one cell to the next; functions include cell-to-cell nutrient transfer in the developing embryo and electrical communication between cells of cardiac and smooth muscle. *See also* electrical synapse. fig. 5.28

gastric Pertaining to the stomach.

gate A protein channel in a cellular membrane that can open or close in response to chemical, electrical, or mechanical stimuli, thus controlling when substances are allowed to pass through the membrane. May occur in the plasma membrane as well as the membranes of cytoplasmic organelles.

gene An information-containing segment of DNA that codes for the production of a molecule of RNA, which in most cases goes on to play a role in the synthesis of one or more proteins.

gene locus The site on a chromosome where a given gene is located.

genome (JEE-nome) All the genes of one individual, estimated at about 20,000 genes in humans.

genotype (JEE-no-type) The pair of alleles possessed by an individual at one gene locus on a pair of homologous chromosomes; strongly influences the individual's phenotype for a given trait.

germ cell A gamete (sperm or egg) or any precursor cell destined to become a gamete, such as a primary oocyte or spermatogonium.

germ layer Any of the first three tissue layers of an embryo: ectoderm, mesoderm, or endoderm.

gestation (jess-TAY-shun) Pregnancy.

globulin (GLOB-you-lin) A globular protein such as an enzyme, antibody, or albumin; especially a family of proteins in the blood plasma that includes albumin, antibodies, fibrinogen, and prothrombin.

glomerular capsule (glo-MERR-you-lur) A double-walled capsule around each glomerulus of the kidney; receives glomerular filtrate and empties into the proximal convoluted tubule. fig. 23.7

glomerulus (glo-MERR-you-lus) **1.** A spheroidal mass of blood capillaries in the kidney that filters plasma and produces glomerular filtrate, which is further processed to form the urine. fig. 23.7 **2.** A spheroidal mass of nerve endings in the olfactory bulb where olfactory neurons from the nose synapse with mitral and dendritic cells of the bulb. fig. 16.7

glucagon (GLUE-ca-gon) A hormone secreted by alpha cells of the pancreatic islets in response to hypoglycemia; promotes glycogenolysis and other effects that raise blood glucose concentration.

glucocorticoid (GLUE-co-COR-tih-coyd) Any hormone of the adrenal cortex that affects carbohydrate, fat, and protein metabolism; chiefly cortisol and corticosterone.

gluconeogenesis (GLUE-co-NEE-oh-JEN-eh-sis) The synthesis of glucose from noncarbohydrates such as fats and amino acids.

glucose A monosaccharide ($C_6H_{12}O_6$) also known as blood sugar; glycogen, starch, cellulose, and maltose are made entirely of glucose, and glucose constitutes half of a sucrose or lactose molecule. The isomer involved in human physiology is also called *dextrose.*

glucose-sparing effect An effect of fats or other energy substrates in which they are used as fuel by most cells, so that those cells do not consume glucose; this makes more glucose available to cells such as neurons that cannot use alternative energy substrates.

glycocalyx (GLY-co-CAY-licks) A layer of carbohydrate molecules covalently bonded to the phospholipids and proteins of a plasma membrane; forms a surface coat on all human cells.

glycogen (GLY-co-jen) A glucose polymer synthesized by liver, muscle, uterine, and vaginal cells that serves as an energy-storage polysaccharide.

glycogenesis (GLY-co-JEN-eh-sis) The synthesis of glycogen.

glycogenolysis (GLY-co-jeh-NOLL-ih-sis) The hydrolysis of glycogen, releasing glucose.

glycolipid (GLY-co-LIP-id) A phospholipid molecule with a carbohydrate covalently

bonded to it, found in the plasma membranes of cells.

glycolysis (gly-COLL-ih-sis) A series of anaerobic oxidation reactions that break a glucose molecule into two molecules of pyruvate and produce a small amount of ATP.

glycoprotein (GLY-co-PRO-teen) A protein molecule with a smaller carbohydrate covalently bonded to it; found in mucus and the glycocalyx of cells, for example.

glycosaminoglycan (GAG) (GLY-co-seh-ME-no-GLY-can) A polysaccharide composed of modified sugars with amino groups; the major component of a proteoglycan. GAGs are largely responsible for the viscous consistency of tissue gel and the stiffness of cartilage.

glycosuria (GLY-co-SOOR-ee-uh) The presence of glucose in the urine, typically indicative of a kidney disease, diabetes mellitus, or other endocrine disorder.

goblet cell A mucus-secreting gland cell, shaped somewhat like a wineglass, found in the epithelia of many mucous membranes. fig. 5.33a

Golgi complex (GOAL-jee) An organelle composed of several parallel cisterns, somewhat like a stack of saucers, that modifies and packages newly synthesized proteins and synthesizes carbohydrates. fig. 3.29

Golgi vesicle A membrane-bounded vesicle pinched from the Golgi complex, containing its chemical product; may be retained in the cell as a lysosome or become a secretory vesicle that releases the product by exocytosis.

gonad The ovary or testis.

gonadotropin (go-NAD-oh-TRO-pin) A pituitary hormone that stimulates the gonads; specifically FSH and LH.

G protein A protein of the plasma membrane that is activated by a membrane receptor and, in turn, opens an ion channel or activates an intracellular physiological response; important in linking ligand–receptor binding to second-messenger systems.

gradient A difference or change in any variable, such as pressure or chemical concentration, from one point in space to another; provides a basis for molecular movements such as gas exchange, osmosis, and facilitated diffusion, and for bulk movements such as the flow of blood, air, and heat.

gray matter A zone or layer of tissue in the central nervous system where the neuron cell bodies, dendrites, and synapses are found; forms the cerebral cortex and basal nuclei; cerebellar cortex and deep nuclei; nuclei of the brainstem; and core of the spinal cord. fig. 14.6c

gross anatomy Bodily structure that can be observed without magnification.

growth factor A chemical messenger that stimulates mitosis and differentiation of target cells that have receptors for it; important in such processes as fetal development, tissue maintenance and repair, and hematopoiesis; sometimes a contributing factor in cancer.

growth hormone (GH) A hormone of the anterior pituitary gland with multiple effects on many tissues, generally promoting tissue growth.

gustation (gus-TAY-shun) The sense of taste.

gyrus (JY-rus) A wrinkle or fold in the cortex of the cerebrum or cerebellum.

H

hair cell Sensory cell of the cochlea, semicircular ducts, utricle, and saccule, with a fringe of surface microvilli that respond to the relative motion of a gelatinous membrane at their tips; responsible for the senses of hearing, body position, and motion.

hair follicle An epidermal pit that contains a hair and extends into the dermis or hypodermis.

half-life (T$_{1/2}$) 1. The time required for one-half of a quantity of a radioactive element to decay to a stable isotope (*physical half-life*) or to be cleared from the body through a combination of radioactive decay and physiological excretion (*biological half-life*). **2.** The time required for one-half of a quantity of hormone to be cleared from the bloodstream.

haploid (*n*) In humans, having 23 unpaired chromosomes instead of the usual 46 chromosomes in homologous pairs; in any organism or cell, having half the normal diploid number of chromosomes for that species.

helper T cell A type of lymphocyte that performs a central coordinating role in humoral and cellular immunity; target of the human immunodeficiency virus (HIV).

hematocrit (he-MAT-oh-crit) The percentage of blood volume that is composed of erythrocytes; also called *packed cell volume*.

hematoma (HE-muh-TOE-muh) A mass of clotted blood in the tissues; forms a bruise when visible through the skin.

hematopoiesis (he-MAT-o-poy-EE-sis) Production of any of the formed elements of blood.

hematopoietic stem cell (HSC) A cell of the red bone marrow that can give rise, through a series of intermediate cells, to erythrocytes, platelets, various kinds of macrophages, and any type of leukocyte.

heme (pronounced "heem") The nonprotein, iron-containing prosthetic group of hemoglobin or myoglobin; oxygen binds to its iron atom. fig. 18.5

hemoglobin (HE-mo-GLO-bin) The red gas transport pigment of an erythrocyte.

heparin (HEP-uh-rin) A polysaccharide secreted by basophils and mast cells that inhibits blood clotting.

hepatic (heh-PAT-ic) Pertaining to the liver.

hepatic portal system A network of blood vessels that connect capillaries of the intestines to capillaries (sinusoids) of the liver, thus delivering newly absorbed nutrients directly to the liver.

heterozygous (HET-er-oh-ZY-gus) Having nonidentical alleles at the same gene locus of two homologous chromosomes.

high-density lipoprotein (HDL) A lipoprotein of the blood plasma that is about 50% lipid and 50% protein; functions to transport phospholipids and cholesterol from other organs to the liver for disposal. A high proportion of HDL to low-density lipoprotein (LDL) is desirable for cardiovascular health.

hilum (HY-lum) A point on the surface of an organ where blood vessels, lymphatic vessels, or nerves enter and leave, usually marked by a depression and slit; the midpoint of the concave surface of any organ that is roughly bean-shaped, such as the lymph nodes, kidneys, and lungs. Also called the *hilus*. fig. 22.9b

histamine An amino acid derivative secreted by basophils, mast cells, and some neurons; functions as a paracrine secretion and neurotransmitter to stimulate effects such as gastric secretion, bronchoconstriction, and vasodilation. fig. 12.22

histology 1. The microscopic structure of tissues and organs. **2.** The study of such structure.

homeostasis (HO-me-oh-STAY-sis) The tendency of a living body to maintain relatively stable internal conditions in spite of greater changes in its external environment.

homologous (ho-MOLL-uh-gus) **1.** Having the same embryonic or evolutionary origin but not necessarily the same function, such as the scrotum and labia majora. **2.** Pertaining to two chromosomes with identical structures and gene loci but not necessarily identical alleles; each member of the pair is inherited from a different parent.

homozygous (HO-mo-ZY-gus) Having identical alleles at the same gene locus of two homologous chromosomes.

hormone A chemical messenger that is secreted by an endocrine gland or isolated gland cell, travels in the bloodstream, and triggers a physiological response in distant cells with receptors for it.

host cell Any cell belonging to the human body, as opposed to foreign cells introduced to it by such causes as infections and tissue transplants.

human chorionic gonadotropin (HCG) A hormone of pregnancy secreted by the chorion that stimulates continued growth of the corpus luteum and secretion of its hormones. HCG in urine is the basis for pregnancy testing.

human immunodeficiency virus (HIV) A virus that infects human helper T cells and other cells, suppresses immunity, and causes AIDS.

hyaline cartilage (HY-uh-lin) A form of cartilage with a relatively clear matrix and fine collagen fibers but no conspicuous elastic fibers or coarse collagen bundles as in other types of cartilage.

hyaluronic acid (HI-ul-yur-ON-ic) A glycosaminoglycan that is particularly abundant in connective tissues, where it becomes hydrated and forms the tissue gel.

hydrogen bond A weak attraction between a slightly positive hydrogen atom on one molecule and a slightly negative oxygen or nitrogen atom on another molecule, or between such atoms on different parts of the same molecule; responsible for the cohesion of water and the coiling of protein and DNA molecules, for example.

hydrolysis (hy-DROL-ih-sis) A chemical reaction that breaks a covalent bond in a molecule by adding an —OH group to one side of the bond and —H to the other side, thus consuming a water molecule.

hydrophilic (HY-dro-FILL-ic) Pertaining to molecules that attract water or dissolve in it because of their polar nature.

hydrophobic (HY-dro-FOE-bic) Pertaining to molecules that do not attract water or dissolve in it because of their nonpolar nature; such molecules tend to dissolve in lipids and other nonpolar solvents.

hydrostatic pressure The physical force exerted against a surface by a liquid such as blood or tissue fluid, as opposed to osmotic and atmospheric pressures.

hypercalcemia (HY-per-cal-SEE-me-uh) An excess of calcium ions in the blood.

hypercapnia (HY-pur-CAP-nee-uh) An excess of carbon dioxide in the blood.

hyperextension A joint movement that increases the angle between two bones beyond 180°. fig. 9.12

hyperglycemia (HY-pur-gly-SEE-me-uh) An excess of glucose in the blood.

hyperkalemia (HY-pur-ka-LEE-me-uh) An excess of potassium ions in the blood.

hypernatremia (HY-pur-na-TREE-me-uh) An excess of sodium ions in the blood.

hyperplasia (HY-pur-PLAY-zhuh) The growth of a tissue through cellular multiplication, not cellular enlargement. *Compare* hypertrophy.

hyperpolarization A shift in the electrical potential across a plasma membrane to a value more negative than the resting membrane

potential, tending to inhibit a nerve or muscle cell. *Compare* depolarization.

hypersecretion Excessive secretion of a hormone or other gland product; can lead to endocrine disorders such as Addison disease or gigantism, for example.

hypertension Excessively high blood pressure; criteria vary but it is often considered to be a condition in which systolic pressure exceeds 140 mm Hg or diastolic pressure exceeds 90 mm Hg at rest.

hypertonic Having a higher osmotic pressure than human cells or some other reference solution and tending to cause osmotic shrinkage of cells.

hypertrophy (hy-PUR-truh-fee) The growth of a tissue through cellular enlargement, not cellular multiplication; for example, the growth of muscle under the influence of exercise. *Compare* hyperplasia.

hypocalcemia (HY-po-cal-SEE-me-uh) A deficiency of calcium ions in the blood.

hypocapnia (HY-po-CAP-nee-uh) A deficiency of carbon dioxide in the blood.

hypodermis (HY-po-DUR-miss) A layer of connective tissue deep to the skin; also called *superficial fascia, subcutaneous tissue,* or when it is predominantly adipose, *subcutaneous fat.*

hypoglycemia (HY-po-gly-SEE-me-uh) A deficiency of glucose in the blood.

hypokalemia (HY-po-ka-LEE-me-uh) A deficiency of potassium ions in the blood.

hyponatremia (HY-po-na-TREE-me-uh) A deficiency of sodium ions in the blood.

hyposecretion Inadequate secretion of a hormone or other gland product; can lead to endocrine disorders such as diabetes mellitus or pituitary dwarfism, for example.

hypothalamic thermostat A nucleus in the hypothalamus that monitors body temperature and sends afferent signals to hypothalamic heat-promoting or heat-losing centers to maintain thermal homeostasis.

hypothalamus (HY-po-THAL-uh-muss) The inferior portion of the diencephalon of the brain, forming the walls and floor of the third ventricle and giving rise to the posterior pituitary gland; controls many fundamental physiological functions such as appetite, thirst, and body temperature and exerts many of its effects through the endocrine and autonomic nervous systems. fig. 14.12b

hypothesis An informed conjecture that is capable of being tested and potentially falsified by experimentation or data collection. *See also* theory.

hypotonic Having a lower osmotic pressure than human cells or some other reference solution and tending to cause osmotic swelling and lysis of cells.

hypoxemia (HY-pock-SEE-me-uh) A deficiency of oxygen in the bloodstream.

hypoxia (hy-POCK-see-uh) A deficiency of oxygen in any tissue.

I

immune system A system of diverse defenses against disease, including leukocytes and other immune cells, defensive chemicals such as antibodies, physiological processes such as fever and inflammation, and physical barriers to infection such as the skin and mucous membranes; not an organ system in itself but an inclusive term for defensive components of multiple organ systems. *See also* adaptive immunity; innate immunity.

immunity The ability to ward off a specific infection or disease by means of any of the body's innate or adaptive immune mechanisms.

immunoglobulin (IM-you-no-GLOB-you-lin) *See* antibody.

implantation The attachment of a conceptus to the endometrium of the uterus.

inclusion Any visible object in the cytoplasm of a cell other than an organelle or cytoskeletal element; usually a foreign body or a stored cell product, such as a virus, dust particle, lipid droplet, glycogen granule, or pigment.

infarction (in-FARK-shun) 1. The sudden death of tissue from a lack of blood perfusion. 2. An area of necrotic tissue produced by this process; also called an *infarct.*

inferior Lower than another structure or point of reference from the perspective of anatomical position; for example, the stomach is inferior to the diaphragm.

inflammation A complex of tissue responses to trauma or infection serving to ward off a pathogen and promote tissue repair; recognized by the cardinal signs of redness, heat, swelling, and pain.

inguinal (IN-gwih-nul) Pertaining to the groin.

inhibitory postsynaptic potential (IPSP) Hyperpolarization of a postsynaptic neuron in response to a neurotransmitter, making it less likely to reach threshold and fire.

innate immunity Nonspecific defenses against infection or disease that are present and functional from birth, work equally against multiple disease agents, do not require prior exposure, and do not possess immune memory. Includes epithelial barriers, natural killer cells, other leukocytes, macrophages, antimicrobial proteins, and the processes of inflammation and fever. *See also* adaptive immunity.

innervation (IN-ur-VAY-shun) The nerve supply to an organ.

insertion Traditionally, the attachment of a skeletal muscle to a bone or other structure that moves when the muscle contracts. This term is now being abandoned by authorities in human anatomy. *Compare* origin.

inspiration 1. Inhaling. 2. The stimulus that resulted in this book.

integral protein A protein of the plasma membrane that penetrates into or all the way through the phospholipid bilayer. fig. 3.6

integration A process in which a neuron receives input from multiple sources and their combined effects determine its output; the cellular basis of information processing by the nervous system.

intercalated disc (in-TUR-ka-LAY-ted) A complex of fascia adherens, gap junctions, and desmosomes that join two cardiac muscle cells end to end, microscopically visible as a dark line that helps to histologically distinguish this muscle type; functions as a mechanical and electrical link between cells. fig. 19.11

intercellular Between cells.

intercostal (IN-tur-COSS-tul) Between the ribs, as in the intercostal muscles, arteries, veins, and nerves.

interdigitate (IN-tur-DIDJ-ih-tate) To fit together like the fingers of two folded hands; for example, at the dermal–epidermal boundary, intercalated discs of the heart, and foot processes of the podocytes in the kidney. fig. 23.10b

interleukin (IN-tur-LOO-kin) A hormonelike chemical messenger from one leukocyte to another, serving as a means of communication and coordination during immune responses.

interneuron (IN-tur-NEW-ron) A neuron that is contained entirely in the central nervous system and, in the path of signal conduction, lies anywhere between an afferent pathway and an efferent pathway.

interosseous membrane (IN-tur-OSS-ee-us) A fibrous membrane that connects the radius to the ulna and the tibia to the fibula along most of the shaft of each bone. fig. 8.34

interphase That part of the cell cycle between one mitotic phase and the next, from the end of cytokinesis to the beginning of the next prophase.

interstitial (IN-tur-STISH-ul) 1. Pertaining to the extracellular spaces in a tissue. 2. Located between other structures, as in the interstitial cells of the testis and interstitial (extracellular) fluid of the tissues.

intervertebral disc A cartilaginous pad between the bodies of two adjacent vertebrae.

intracellular Within a cell.

intracellular fluid (ICF) The fluid contained in the cells; one of the body's major fluid compartments.

intravenous (I.V.) 1. Present or occurring within a vein, such as an intravenous blood clot. **2.** Introduced directly into a vein, such as an intravenous injection or I.V. drip.

intrinsic (in-TRIN-sic) **1.** Arising from within, such as intrinsic blood-clotting factors; endogenous. **2.** Fully contained within a specified organ or region, such as the intrinsic muscles of the hand and eye. *Compare* extrinsic.

involuntary Not under conscious control, including tissues such as smooth and cardiac muscle and events such as reflexes.

involution (IN-vo-LOO-shun) Shrinkage of a tissue or organ by autolysis, such as involution of the thymus after childhood and of the uterus after pregnancy.

ion A chemical particle with unequal numbers of electrons or protons and consequently a net negative or positive charge; it may have a single atomic nucleus as in a sodium ion or a few atoms as in a bicarbonate ion, or it may be a large molecule such as a protein.

ionic bond The force that binds a cation to an anion.

ionizing radiation High-energy electromagnetic rays that eject electrons from atoms or molecules and convert them to ions, frequently causing cellular damage; for example, X-rays and gamma rays.

ipsilateral (IP-sih-LAT-ur-ul) On the same side of the body, as in reflex arcs in which a muscular response occurs on the same side of the body as the stimulus. *Compare* contralateral.

ischemia (iss-KEE-me-uh) Insufficient blood flow to a tissue, typically resulting in metabolite accumulation and sometimes tissue death.

isometric Pertaining to a form of muscle contraction in which internal tension increases but the muscle does not change length or move a resisting object.

isotonic 1. Having the same osmotic pressure as human cells or some other reference solution. **2.** Pertaining to a form of muscle contraction in which a muscle changes length but maintains a constant amount of tension.

J

jaundice (JAWN-diss) A yellowish color of the skin, corneas, mucous membranes, and body fluids due to an excessive concentration of bilirubin; usually indicative of a liver disease, obstructed bile secretion, or hemolytic disease.

K

ketone (KEE-tone) Any organic compound with a carbonyl (C=O) group covalently bonded to a two-carbon backbone.

ketone bodies Certain ketones (acetone, acetoacetic acid, and β-hydroxybutyric acid) produced by the incomplete oxidation of fats, especially when fats are being rapidly catabolized. *See also* ketosis.

ketonuria (KEE-toe-NEW-ree-uh) The abnormal presence of ketones in the urine; a sign of diabetes mellitus but also occurring in other conditions that entail rapid fat oxidation.

ketosis (kee-TOE-sis) An abnormally high concentration of ketone bodies in the blood, occurring in pregnancy, starvation, diabetes mellitus, and other conditions; tends to cause acidosis and to depress the nervous system.

kilocalorie The amount of heat energy needed to raise the temperature of 1 kg of water by 1°C; 1,000 calories. Also called a *Calorie* or *large calorie*. *See also* calorie.

kinase Any enzyme that adds an inorganic phosphate (P_i) group to another organic molecule. Also called a *phosphokinase*.

L

labium (LAY-bee-um) A lip, such as those of the mouth and the labia majora and minora of the vulva.

lactate A small organic acid produced as an end product of the anaerobic fermentation of pyruvate; called *lactic acid* in its nonionized form.

lacuna (la-CUE-nuh) (plural, *lacunae*) A small cavity or depression in a tissue such as bone or cartilage; called a *cavernous space* in erectile tissues of the penis and clitoris.

lamella (la-MELL-uh) A little plate, such as a lamella of bone. fig. 7.4

lamina (LAM-ih-nuh) A thin layer, such as the lamina of a vertebra or the lamina propria of a mucous membrane. fig. 8.22

lamina propria (LAM-ih-nuh PRO-pree-uh) A thin layer of areolar tissue immediately deep to the epithelium of a mucous membrane. fig. 5.33a

larynx (LAIR-inks) A cartilaginous chamber in the neck containing the vocal cords; colloquially called the voicebox.

latent period The interval between a stimulus and response, especially in the action of nerve and muscle cells.

lateral Away from the midline of an organ or median plane of the body; toward the side. *Compare* medial.

law A verbal or mathematical description of a predictable natural phenomenon or of the relationship between variables; for example, Boyle's law of gases and the law of complementary base pairing in DNA.

lesion A circumscribed zone of tissue injury, such as a skin abrasion or myocardial infarction.

leukocyte (LOO-co-site) A white blood cell.

leukotriene (LOO-co-TRY-een) An eicosanoid that promotes allergic and inflammatory responses such as vasodilation and neutrophil chemotaxis; secreted by basophils, mast cells, and damaged tissues.

libido (lih-BEE-do) Sex drive; psychological motivation to engage in sex.

ligament A collagenous band or cord that binds one organ to another, especially one bone to another, and serves to hold organs in place; for example, the cruciate ligaments of the knee, broad ligament of the uterus, and falciform ligament of the liver.

ligand (LIG-and, LY-gand) A chemical that binds reversibly to a receptor site on a protein, such as a neurotransmitter that binds to a membrane receptor or a substrate that binds to an enzyme.

ligand-gated channel A channel protein in a plasma membrane that opens or closes when another chemical (ligand) binds to it, enabling the ligand to determine when substances can enter or leave the cell.

light microscope (LM) A microscope that produces images with visible light.

linea (LIN-ee-uh) An anatomical line, such as the linea alba of the abdomen or linea aspera of the femur.

lingual (LING-gwul) Pertaining to the tongue, as in lingual papillae.

lipase (LY-pace) An enzyme that hydrolyzes a triglyceride into fatty acids and glycerol.

lipid A hydrophobic organic compound composed mainly of carbon and a high ratio of hydrogen to oxygen; includes fatty acids, fats, phospholipids, steroids, and prostaglandins.

lipoprotein (LIP-oh-PRO-teen) A protein-coated lipid droplet in the blood plasma or lymph, serving as a means of lipid transport; for example, chylomicrons and high- and low-density lipoproteins.

load 1. To pick up a gas for transport in the bloodstream. **2.** The resistance acted upon by a muscle.

lobule (LOB-yool) A small subdivision of an organ or of a lobe of an organ, especially of a gland.

locus The site on a chromosome where a given gene is located.

long bone A bone such as the femur or humerus that is markedly longer than wide and that generally serves as a lever.

longitudinal Oriented along the longest dimension of the body or of an organ.

loose connective tissue *See* areolar tissue.

low-density lipoprotein (LDL) A lipoprotein of the blood plasma that is about 80% lipid (mainly cholesterol) and 20% protein; functions to transport cholesterol to target cells. A high proportion of LDL to high-density lipoprotein (HDL) is a risk factor for cardiovascular disease.

lumbar Pertaining to the lower back and sides, between the thoracic cage and pelvis.

lumen (LOO-men) The internal space of a hollow organ such as a blood vessel or the esophagus, or a space surrounded by secretory cells as in a gland acinus.

luteinizing hormone (LH) (LOO-tee-in-ize-ing) A hormone secreted by the anterior pituitary gland that stimulates ovulation in females and testosterone secretion production in males.

lymph The fluid contained in lymphatic vessels and lymph nodes, produced by the absorption of tissue fluid.

lymphatic system (lim-FAT-ic) An organ system consisting of lymphatic vessels, lymph nodes, the tonsils, spleen, and thymus; functions include tissue fluid recovery and immunity.

lymph node A small organ found along the course of a lymphatic vessel that filters the lymph and contains lymphocytes and macrophages, which respond to antigens in the lymph. fig. 21.11

lymphocyte (LIM-fo-site) A relatively small agranulocyte with numerous types and roles in innate, humoral, and cellular immunity. table 18.6

lysosome (LY-so-some) A membrane-bounded organelle containing a mixture of enzymes with a variety of intracellular and extracellular roles in digesting foreign matter, pathogens, and expired organelles.

lysozyme (LY-so-zime) An enzyme found in tears, milk, saliva, mucus, and other body fluids that destroys bacteria by digesting their cell walls. Also called *muramidase.*

M

macromolecule Any molecule of large size and high molecular weight, such as a protein, nucleic acid, polysaccharide, or triglyceride.

macrophage (MAC-ro-faje) Any cell of the body, other than a leukocyte, that is specialized for phagocytosis; usually derived from a blood monocyte and often functioning as an antigen-presenting cell.

macula (MAC-you-luh) A patch or spot, such as the macula lutea of the retina and macula sacculi of the inner ear.

malignant (muh-LIG-nent) Pertaining to a cell or tumor that is cancerous; capable of metastasis.

mast cell A connective tissue cell, similar to a basophil, that secretes histamine, heparin, and other chemicals involved in inflammation; often concentrated along the course of blood capillaries.

matrix 1. The extracellular material of a tissue. **2.** The fluid within a mitochondrion containing enzymes of the citric acid cycle. **3.** The substance or framework within which other structures are embedded, such as the fibrous matrix of a blood clot. **4.** A mass of epidermal cells from which a hair root or nail root develops.

mechanoreceptor A sensory nerve ending or organ specialized to detect mechanical stimuli such as touch, pressure, stretch, or vibration.

medial Toward the midline of an organ or median plane of the body. *Compare* lateral.

median plane The sagittal plane that divides the body or an organ into equal right and left halves; also called *midsagittal plane.* fig. A.1

mediastinum (MEE-dee-ah-STY-num) The thick median partition of the thoracic cavity that separates one pleural cavity from the other and contains the heart, great blood vessels, esophagus, trachea, and thymus. fig. A.5

medulla (meh-DULE-uh, meh-DULL-uh) Tissue deep to the cortex of certain two-layered organs such as the lymph nodes, adrenal glands, hairs, and kidneys.

medulla oblongata (meh-DULL-uh OB-long-GAH-ta) The most caudal part of the brainstem, immediately superior to the foramen magnum of the skull, connecting the spinal cord to the rest of the brain. figs. 14.2, 14.8

meiosis (my-OH-sis) A form of cell division in which a diploid cell divides twice and produces four haploid daughter cells; occurs only in gametogenesis.

melanocyte A cell of the stratum basale of the epidermis that synthesizes melanin and transfers it to the keratinocytes.

meninges (meh-NIN-jeez) (singular, *meninx*) Three fibrous membranes between the central nervous system and surrounding bone: the dura mater, arachnoid mater, and pia mater. fig. 14.5

merocrine (MERR-oh-crin) *See* eccrine.

mesenchyme (MES-en-kime) A gelatinous embryonic connective tissue derived from the mesoderm; differentiates into all permanent connective tissues and cardiac and smooth muscle.

mesentery (MESS-en-tare-ee) A serous membrane that binds the intestines together and suspends them from the abdominal wall; the visceral continuation of the peritoneum. fig. 25.3

mesoderm (MES-oh-durm) The middle layer of the three primary germ layers of an embryo; gives rise to muscle and connective tissue.

metabolism (meh-TAB-oh-lizm) Chemical reactions within a living organism.

metabolite (meh-TAB-oh-lite) Any chemical produced by metabolism.

metaplasia Transformation of one mature tissue type into another; for example, a change from pseudostratified to stratified squamous epithelium in an overventilated nasal cavity.

metastasis (meh-TASS-tuh-sis) The spread of cancer cells from the original tumor to a new location, where they seed the development of a new tumor.

microtubule An intracellular cylinder composed of the protein tubulin, forming centrioles, the axonemes of cilia and flagella, and part of the cytoskeleton.

microvillus An outgrowth of the plasma membrane that increases the surface area of a cell and functions in absorption and some sensory processes; distinguished from cilia and flagella by its smaller size and lack of an axoneme.

milliequivalent One-thousandth of an equivalent, which is the amount of an electrolyte that would neutralize 1 mole of H^+ or OH^-. Electrolyte concentrations are commonly expressed in milliequivalents per liter (mEq/L).

mitochondrion (MY-toe-CON-dree-un) An organelle specialized to synthesize ATP, enclosed in a double unit membrane with infoldings of the inner membrane called cristae.

mitosis (my-TOE-sis) A form of cell division in which a cell divides once and produces two genetically identical daughter cells; sometimes used to refer only to the division of the genetic material or nucleus and not to include cytokinesis, the subsequent division of the cytoplasm.

moiety (MOY-eh-tee) A chemically distinct subunit of a macromolecule, such as the heme and globin moieties of hemoglobin or the lipid and carbohydrate moieties of a glycolipid.

molarity A measure of chemical concentration expressed as moles of solute per liter of solution.

mole The mass of a chemical equal to its molecular weight in grams, containing 6.023×10^{23} molecules.

monocyte (MON-oh-site) An agranulocyte specialized to migrate into the tissues and transform into a macrophage. table 18.6

monomer (MON-oh-mur) **1.** One of the identical or similar subunits of a larger molecule in the dimer to polymer range; for example, the glucose monomers of starch, the amino acids of a protein, or the nucleotides of DNA. **2.** One subunit of an antibody molecule, composed of four polypeptides.

monosaccharide (MON-oh-SAC-uh-ride) A simple sugar, or sugar monomer; chiefly glucose, fructose, and galactose.

motor neuron A neuron that transmits signals from the central nervous system to any effector (muscle or gland cell); its axon is an efferent nerve fiber.

motor protein Any protein that produces movements of a cell or its components owing to its ability to undergo quick repetitive changes in conformation and to bind reversibly to other molecules; for example, myosin, dynein, and kinesin.

motor unit One motor neuron and all the skeletal muscle fibers innervated by it.

mucosa (mew-CO-suh) A tissue layer that forms the inner lining of an anatomical tract that is open to the exterior (the respiratory, digestive, urinary, and reproductive tracts). Composed of epithelium, connective tissue (lamina propria), and often smooth muscle (muscularis mucosae). fig. 5.33a

mucous membrane See *mucosa*.

multipotent Pertaining to a stem cell that has the potential to develop into two or more types of fully differentiated, functional cells, but not into an unlimited variety of cell types.

muscle fiber One skeletal muscle cell; a myofiber.

muscle tone A state of continual, partial contraction of resting skeletal or smooth muscle.

muscular system An organ system composed of the skeletal muscles, specialized mainly for maintaining postural support and producing movements of the bones.

muscularis externa The external muscular wall of certain viscera such as the esophagus and small intestine. fig. 25.2

muscularis mucosae (MUSK-you-LERR-iss mew-CO-see) A layer of smooth muscle immediately deep to the lamina propria of a mucosa. fig. 5.33a

mutagen (MEW-tuh-jen) Any agent that causes a mutation, including viruses, chemicals, and ionizing radiation.

mutation Any change in the structure of a chromosome or a DNA molecule, often resulting in a change of organismal structure or function.

myelin (MY-eh-lin) A lipid sheath around a nerve fiber, formed from closely spaced spiral layers of the plasma membrane of a Schwann cell or oligodendrocyte. fig. 12.8

myelin sheath gap A short unmyelinated segment between Schwann cells of a myelinated nerve fiber; site of action potential generation during saltatory conduction; also called *node of Ranvier*. fig. 12.4

myocardium (MY-oh-CAR-dee-um) The middle, muscular layer of the heart.

myoepithelial cell An epithelial cell that has become specialized to contract like a muscle cell; important in dilation of the pupil and ejection of secretions from gland acini.

myofilament A protein microfilament responsible for the contraction of a muscle cell, composed mainly of myosin or actin. fig. 11.2

myoglobin (MY-oh-GLO-bin) A red oxygen-storage pigment of muscle; supplements hemoglobin in providing oxygen for aerobic muscle metabolism.

myosin A motor protein that constitutes the thick myofilaments of muscle and has globular, mobile heads of ATPase that bind to actin molecules; also serves contractile functions in other cell types. fig. 11.3

N

necrosis (neh-CRO-sis) Pathological tissue death due to such causes as infection, trauma, or hypoxia. *Compare* apoptosis.

negative feedback A self-corrective mechanism that underlies most homeostasis, in which a bodily change is detected and responses are activated that reverse the change and restore stability and preserve normal body function.

negative feedback inhibition A mechanism for limiting the secretion of a pituitary tropic hormone. The tropic hormone stimulates another endocrine gland to secrete its own hormone, and that hormone inhibits further release of the tropic hormone.

neonate (NEE-oh-nate) A newborn infant up to 4 weeks old.

neoplasia (NEE-oh-PLAY-zhuh) Abnormal growth of new tissue, such as a tumor, with no useful function.

nephron (NEF-ron) One of approximately 1 million blood-filtering, urine-producing units in each kidney; consists of a glomerulus, glomerular capsule, proximal convoluted tubule, nephron loop, and distal convoluted tubule. fig. 23.8

nerve A cordlike organ of the peripheral nervous system composed of multiple nerve fibers ensheathed in connective tissue.

nerve fiber The axon of a single neuron.

nerve impulse A wave of self-propagating action potentials traveling along a nerve fiber.

nervous tissue A tissue composed of neurons and neuroglia.

net filtration pressure A net force favoring filtration of fluid from a capillary or venule when all the hydrostatic and osmotic pressures of the blood and tissue fluids are taken into account.

neural pool A group of interconnected neurons of the central nervous system that perform a single collective function; for example, the vasomotor center of the brainstem and speech centers of the cerebral cortex.

neural tube A dorsal hollow tube in the embryo that develops into the central nervous system. fig. 14.3

neuroglia (noo-ROG-lee-uh) All cells of nervous tissue except neurons; cells that perform various supportive and protective roles for the neurons.

neuromuscular junction A synapse between a nerve fiber and a muscle fiber; also called a *motor end plate*. fig. 11.7

neuron (NOOR-on) A nerve cell; an electrically excitable cell specialized for producing and conducting action potentials and secreting chemicals that stimulate adjacent cells.

neuropeptide A peptide secreted by a neuron, often serving to modify the action of a neurotransmitter; for example, endorphins, enkephalin, and cholecystokinin. fig. 12.22

neurotransmitter A chemical released at the distal end of an axon that stimulates an adjacent cell; for example, acetylcholine, norepinephrine, or serotonin.

neutrophil (NEW-tro-fill) A granulocyte, usually with a multilobed nucleus, that serves especially to destroy bacteria by means of phagocytosis, intracellular digestion, and secretion of bactericidal chemicals. table 18.6

nitrogenous base (ny-TRODJ-eh-nus) An organic molecule with a single or double carbon–nitrogen ring that forms one of the building blocks of ATP, other nucleotides, and nucleic acids; the basis of the genetic code. fig. 4.1

nitrogenous waste Any nitrogen-containing substance produced as a metabolic waste and excreted in the urine; chiefly ammonia, urea, uric acid, and creatinine.

nociceptor (NO-sih-SEP-tur) A nerve ending specialized to detect tissue damage and produce a sensation of pain; pain receptor.

norepinephrine (NE) (nor-EP-ih-NEF-rin) A catecholamine that functions as a neurotransmitter and adrenal hormone, especially in the sympathetic nervous system. fig. 12.22

nuclear envelope A pair of membranes enclosing the nucleus of a cell, with prominent pores allowing traffic of molecules between the nucleoplasm and cytoplasm. fig. 3.27

nucleic acid (new-CLAY-ic) An acidic polymer of nucleotides found or produced in the nucleus, functioning in heredity and protein synthesis; of two types, DNA and RNA.

nucleotide (NEW-clee-oh-tide) An organic molecule composed of a nitrogenous base, a monosaccharide, and a phosphate group; the monomer of a nucleic acid.

nucleus (NEW-clee-us) **1.** A cell organelle containing DNA and surrounded by a double membrane. **2.** A mass of neurons (gray matter) surrounded by white matter of the brain, including the basal nuclei and brainstem nuclei. **3.** The positively charged core of an atom, consisting of protons and neutrons. **4.** A central structure, such as the nucleus pulposus of an intervertebral disc.

nurse cell A supporting cell in the seminiferous tubules of the testes, acting to enfold and protect developing germ cells and promote the production of sperm; also called *Sertoli cell; sustentacular cell.*

O

olfaction (ole-FAC-shun) The sense of smell.

oncotic pressure (on-COT-ic) The difference between the colloid osmotic pressure of the blood and that of the tissue fluid, usually favoring fluid absorption by the blood capillaries. *Compare* colloid osmotic pressure.

oocyte (OH-oh-site) In the development of an egg cell, any haploid stage between meiosis I and fertilization.

oogenesis (OH-oh-JEN-eh-sis) The production of a fertilizable egg cell through a series of mitotic and meiotic cell divisions; female gametogenesis.

opposition A movement of the thumb in which it approaches or touches any fingertip of the same hand.

orbit The eye socket of the skull.

organ Any anatomical structure that is composed of at least two different tissue types, has recognizable structural boundaries, and has a discrete function different from the structures around it. Many organs are microscopic and many organs contain smaller organs, such as the skin containing numerous microscopic sense organs.

organelle Any structure within a cell that carries out one of its metabolic roles, such as mitochondria, centrioles, endoplasmic reticulum, and the nucleus; an intracellular structure other than the cytoskeleton and inclusions.

origin Traditionally, the relatively stationary attachment of a skeletal muscle to a bone or other structure. This term is now being abandoned by authorities in human anatomy. *Compare* insertion.

osmolality (OZ-mo-LAL-ih-tee) The molar concentration of dissolved particles in 1 kg of water.

osmolarity (OZ-mo-LERR-ih-tee) The molar concentration of dissolved particles in 1 L of solution.

osmoreceptor (OZ-mo-re-SEP-tur) A neuron of the hypothalamus that responds to changes in the osmolarity of the extracellular fluid.

osmosis (oz-MO-sis) The net flow of water through a selectively permeable membrane, resulting from either a chemical concentration difference or a mechanical force across the membrane.

osmotic pressure The amount of pressure that would have to be applied to one side of a selectively permeable membrane to stop osmosis; proportional to the concentration of nonpermeating solutes on that side and therefore serving as an indicator of solute concentration.

osseous (OSS-ee-us) Pertaining to bone.

ossification (OSS-ih-fih-CAY-shun) Bone formation.

osteoblast Bone-forming cell that arises from an osteogenic cell, deposits bone matrix, and eventually becomes an osteocyte.

osteoclast Macrophage of the bone surface that dissolves the matrix and returns minerals to the extracellular fluid.

osteocyte A mature bone cell formed when an osteoblast becomes surrounded by its own matrix and entrapped in a lacuna.

osteon A structural unit of compact bone consisting of a central canal surrounded by concentric cylindrical lamellae of matrix. fig. 7.4

osteoporosis (OSS-tee-oh-pore-OH-sis) A degenerative bone disease characterized by a loss of bone mass, increasing susceptibility to spontaneous fractures, and sometimes deformity of the vertebral column; causes include aging, estrogen hyposecretion, and insufficient resistance exercise.

ovulation (OV-you-LAY-shun) The release of a mature oocyte by the bursting of an ovarian follicle.

ovum Any stage of the female gamete from primary oocyte until fertilization; a primary or secondary oocyte; an egg.

oxidation A chemical reaction in which one or more electrons are removed from a molecule, lowering its free energy content; opposite of reduction and always linked to a reduction reaction.

P

pancreatic islet (PAN-cree-AT-ic EYE-let) A small cluster of endocrine cells in the pancreas that secretes insulin, glucagon, somatostatin, and other intercellular messengers; also called *islet of Langerhans.* fig. 17.12

papilla (pa-PILL-uh) A conical or nipplelike structure, such as a lingual papilla of the tongue or the papilla of a hair bulb.

papillary (PAP-ih-lerr-ee) **1.** Pertaining to or shaped like a nipple, such as the papillary muscles of the heart. **2.** Having papillae, such as the papillary layer of the dermis.

paracrine (PAIR-uh-crin) **1.** A chemical messenger similar to a hormone whose effects are restricted to the immediate vicinity of the cells that secrete it; sometimes called a *local hormone.* **2.** Pertaining to such a secretion, as opposed to *endocrine.*

parasympathetic nervous system (PERR-uh-SIM-pa-THET-ic) A division of the autonomic nervous system that issues efferent fibers through the cranial and sacral nerves and exerts cholinergic effects on its target organs.

parathyroid hormone (PTH) A hormone secreted by the parathyroid glands that raises blood calcium concentration by stimulating bone resorption by osteoclasts, promoting intestinal absorption of calcium, and inhibiting urinary excretion of calcium.

parenchyma (pa-REN-kih-muh) The tissue that performs the main physiological functions of an organ, especially a gland, as opposed to the tissues (stroma) that mainly provide structural support.

parietal (pa-RY-eh-tul) **1.** Pertaining to a wall, as in the parietal cells of the stomach and parietal bone of the skull. **2.** Pertaining to the outer or more superficial layer of a two-layered membrane such as the pleura, pericardium, or glomerular capsule. *Compare* visceral. fig. A.6

pathogen Any disease-causing microorganism.

pedicle (PED-ih-cul) A small footlike process, as in the vertebrae and renal podocytes; also called a *pedicel.*

pelvic cavity The space enclosed by the true (lesser) pelvis, containing the urinary bladder, rectum, and internal reproductive organs.

pelvis A basinlike structure such as the pelvic girdle of the skeleton or the urine-collecting space near the hilum of the kidney. figs. 8.36, 23.4

peptide Any chain of two or more amino acids. *See also* polypeptide, protein.

peptide bond A group of four covalently bonded atoms (a —C=O group bonded to an —NH group) that links two amino acids in a protein or other peptide. fig. 2.23b

perfusion The amount of blood supplied to a given mass of tissue in a given period of time (such as mL/g/min.).

perichondrium (PERR-ih-CON-dree-um) A layer of fibrous connective tissue covering the surface of hyaline or elastic cartilage.

perineum (PERR-ih-NEE-um) The region between the thighs bordered by the coccyx, pubic symphysis, and ischial tuberosities; contains the orifices of the urinary, reproductive, and digestive systems. figs. 27.6, 28.8

periosteum (PERR-ee-OSS-tee-um) A layer of fibrous connective tissue covering the surface of a bone. fig. 7.1

peripheral nervous system (PNS) A subdivision of the nervous system composed of all nerves and ganglia; all of the nervous system except the central nervous system.

peripheral protein A protein of the plasma membrane that clings to its intracellular or extracellular surface but does not penetrate into the phospholipid bilayer.

peristalsis (PERR-ih-STAL-sis) A wave of constriction traveling along a tubular organ such as the esophagus or ureter, serving to propel its contents.

peritoneum (PERR-ih-toe-NEE-um) A serous membrane that lines the peritoneal cavity of the abdomen and covers the mesenteries and viscera.

perivascular (PERR-ih-VASS-cue-lur) Pertaining to the region surrounding a blood vessel.

phagocytosis (FAG-oh-sy-TOE-sis) A form of endocytosis in which a cell surrounds a foreign particle with pseudopods and engulfs it, enclosing it in a cytoplasmic vesicle called a *phagosome*.

phalanx (FAY-lanks) (plural, *phalanges*) Any of the bones in the fingers or toes; there are two in the thumb and great toe and three in each of the other digits.

pharynx (FAIR-inks, FAR-inks) A muscular passage in the throat at which the respiratory and digestive tracts cross.

phospholipid An amphipathic molecule composed of two fatty acids and a phosphate-containing group bonded to the three carbons of a glycerol molecule; composes most of the molecules of the plasma membrane and other cellular membranes.

phosphorylation Addition of an inorganic phosphate (P_i) group to an organic molecule.

piloerector *See* arrector.

pinocytosis (PIN-oh-sy-TOE-sis) A form of endocytosis in which the plasma membrane sinks inward and imbibes droplets of extracellular fluid.

plantar (PLAN-tur) Pertaining to the sole of the foot.

plaque A small scale or plate of matter, such as dental plaque, the fatty plaques of atherosclerosis, and the amyloid plaques of Alzheimer disease.

plasma The noncellular portion of the blood; its liquid matrix, usually constituting slightly over one-half of its volume.

plasma membrane The membrane that encloses a cell and controls the traffic of molecules in and out of the cell. fig. 3.5

platelet A formed element of the blood derived from a megakaryocyte, known especially for its role in stopping bleeding, but with additional roles in dissolving blood clots, stimulating inflammation, promoting tissue growth and blood vessel maintenance, and destroying bacteria.

pleura (PLOOR-uh) A double-walled serous membrane that encloses each lung.

plexus A network of blood vessels, lymphatic vessels, or nerves, such as a choroid plexus of the brain or brachial plexus of nerves.

pluripotent Pertaining to a stem cell of the inner cell mass of a blastocyst that is capable of developing into any type of embryonic cell, but not into cells of the accessory organs of pregnancy.

polymer A molecule that consists of a long chain of identical or similar subunits, such as protein, DNA, and starch.

polypeptide Any chain of more than 10 or 15 amino acids. *See also* protein.

polysaccharide (POL-ee-SAC-uh-ride) A polymer of simple sugars; for example, glycogen, starch, and cellulose. fig. 2.17

polyuria (POL-ee-YOU-ree-uh) Excessive output of urine.

popliteal (pop-LIT-ee-ul) Pertaining to the posterior aspect of the knee.

positron emission tomography (PET) A method of producing a computerized image of the physiological state of a tissue using injected radioisotopes that emit positrons.

posterior Near or pertaining to the back or spinal side of the body; dorsal.

posterior root The branch of a spinal nerve that enters the posterior side of the spinal cord and carries afferent (sensory) nerve fibers; often called *dorsal root*. fig. 13.2b

postganglionic (POST-gang-glee-ON-ic) Pertaining to a neuron that conducts signals from a ganglion to a more distal target organ.

postsynaptic (POST-sih-NAP-tic) Pertaining to a neuron or other cell that receives signals from the presynaptic neuron at a synapse. fig. 12.19

potential A difference in electrical charge from one point to another, especially on opposite sides of a plasma membrane; usually measured in millivolts.

preembryo A developing individual from the time of fertilization to the time, at 16 days, when the three primary germ layers have formed. *Compare* conceptus, embryo, fetus.

preganglionic (PRE-gang-glee-ON-ic) Pertaining to a neuron that conducts signals from the central nervous system to a ganglion.

presynaptic (PRE-sih-NAP-tic) Pertaining to a neuron that conducts signals to a synapse. fig. 12.19

primary germ layers The ectoderm, mesoderm, and endoderm; the three tissue layers of an early embryo from which all later tissues and organs arise.

prime mover The muscle that produces the most force in a given joint action; agonist.

programmed cell death *See* apoptosis.

prolactin (PRL) A hormone secreted by the anterior pituitary gland that stimulates the mammary glands to secrete milk.

pronation (pro-NAY-shun) A rotational movement of the forearm that turns the palm downward or posteriorly. fig. 9.18

proprioception (PRO-pree-oh-SEP-shun) The nonvisual perception, usually subconscious, of the position and movements of the body, resulting from input from proprioceptors and the vestibular apparatus of the inner ear.

proprioceptor (PRO-pree-oh-SEP-tur) A sensory receptor of the muscles, tendons, and joint capsules that detects muscle contractions and joint movements.

prostaglandin (PROSS-ta-GLAN-din) An eicosanoid with a five-sided carbon ring in the middle of a hydrocarbon chain, playing a variety of roles in inflammation, neurotransmission, vasomotion, reproduction, and metabolism. fig. 2.21

prostate (PROSS-tate) A male reproductive gland that encircles the urethra immediately inferior to the bladder and contributes to the semen. (Avoid the mispronunciation "prostrate.") fig. 27.10

protein A large polypeptide; while criteria for a protein are somewhat subjective and variable, polypeptides over 50 amino acids long are generally classified as proteins.

proteoglycan (PRO-tee-oh-GLY-can) A large molecule composed of a bristlelike arrangement of glycosaminoglycans surrounding a protein core in a shape resembling a bottle brush. Binds cells to extracellular materials and gives the tissue fluid a gelatinous consistency.

proximal Relatively near a point of origin or attachment; for example, the shoulder is proximal to the elbow. *Compare* distal.

pseudopod (SOO-doe-pod) A temporary cytoplasmic extension of a cell used for locomotion (ameboid movement) and phagocytosis.

pseudostratified columnar epithelium A type of epithelium with tall columnar cells reaching the free surface and shorter basal cells that do not reach the surface, but with all cells resting on the basement membrane; creates a false appearance of stratification. fig. 5.7

pulmonary circuit A route of blood flow that supplies blood to the pulmonary alveoli for gas exchange and then returns it to the heart; all blood vessels between the right ventricle and the left atrium of the heart.

pyrogen (PY-ro-jen) A fever-producing agent.

R

ramus (RAY-mus) An anatomical branch, as in a nerve or in the pubis.

receptor 1. A cell or organ specialized to detect a stimulus, such as a taste cell or the eye. **2.** A protein molecule that binds and responds to a chemical such as a hormone, neurotransmitter, or odor molecule.

receptor-mediated endocytosis A process in which certain molecules in the extracellular fluid bind to receptors in the plasma membrane, these receptors gather together, the membrane sinks inward at that point, and the molecules are incorporated into vesicles in the cytoplasm. fig. 3.21

receptor potential A variable, local change in membrane voltage produced by a stimulus acting on a receptor cell; generates an action potential if it reaches threshold.

recessive 1. Pertaining to a genetic allele that is not phenotypically expressed in the presence of a dominant allele. **2.** Pertaining to a trait that results from a recessive allele.

reduction 1. A chemical reaction in which one or more electrons are added to a molecule, raising its free energy content; opposite of *oxidation* and always linked to an oxidation reaction. **2.** Treatment of a fracture by restoring the broken parts of a bone to their proper alignment.

reflex A stereotyped, automatic, involuntary response to a stimulus; includes somatic reflexes, in which the effectors are skeletal muscles, and visceral (autonomic) reflexes, in which the effectors are usually visceral muscle, cardiac muscle, or glands.

reflex arc A simple neural pathway that mediates a reflex; involves a receptor, an afferent nerve fiber, often one or more interneurons, an efferent nerve fiber, and an effector.

refractory period 1. A period of time after a nerve or muscle cell has responded to a stimulus in which it cannot be reexcited by a threshold stimulus. **2.** A period of time after male orgasm when it is not possible to reattain erection or ejaculation.

regeneration Replacement of damaged tissue with new tissue of the original type. *Compare* fibrosis.

renin (REE-nin) An enzyme secreted by the kidneys in response to hypotension; converts the plasma protein angiotensinogen to angiotensin I, leading indirectly to a rise in blood pressure.

repolarization Reattainment of the resting membrane potential after a nerve or muscle cell has depolarized.

residue Any one of the amino acids in a protein or other peptide.

resistance 1. A force that opposes the flow of a fluid such as air or blood. **2.** A force, or load, that opposes the action of a muscle or lever.

resting membrane potential (RMP) A stable voltage across the plasma membrane of an unstimulated nerve or muscle cell.

reticular cell (reh-TIC-you-lur) A delicate, branching phagocytic cell found in the reticular connective tissue of the lymphatic organs.

reticular fiber A fine, branching collagen fiber coated with glycoprotein, found in the stroma of lymphatic organs and some other tissues and organs.

reticular tissue A connective tissue composed of reticular cells and reticular fibers, found in bone marrow, lymphatic organs, and in lesser amounts elsewhere.

ribosome A granule found free in the cytoplasm or attached to the rough endoplasmic reticulum or nuclear envelope composed of ribosomal RNA and enzymes; specialized to read the nucleotide sequence of messenger RNA and assemble a corresponding sequence of amino acids to make a protein.

risk factor Any environmental factor or characteristic of an individual that increases one's chance of developing a particular disease; includes such intrinsic factors as age, sex, and race and such extrinsic factors as diet, smoking, and occupation.

rostral Relatively close to the forehead, especially in reference to structures of the brain and spinal cord; for example, the frontal lobe is rostral to the parietal lobe. *Compare* caudal.

ruga (ROO-ga) (plural *rugae,* ROO-jee) **1.** An internal fold or wrinkle in the mucosa of a hollow organ such as the stomach and urinary bladder; typically present when the organ is empty and relaxed but not when the organ is full and stretched. **2.** Tissue ridges in such locations as the hard palate and vagina. fig. 25.12

S

saccule (SAC-yule) A saclike receptor in the inner ear with a vertical patch of hair cells, the macula sacculi; senses the orientation of the head and responds to vertical acceleration, as when riding in an elevator or standing up. fig. 16.20

sagittal plane (SADJ-ih-tul) Any plane that extends from anterior to posterior and cephalic to caudal and that divides the body into right and left portions. *Compare* median plane.

sarcomere (SAR-co-meer) In skeletal and cardiac muscle, the portion of a myofibril from one Z disc to the next, constituting one contractile unit. fig. 11.5

sarcoplasmic reticulum (SR) The smooth endoplasmic reticulum of a muscle cell, serving as a calcium reservoir. fig. 11.2

scanning electron microscope (SEM) A microscope that uses an electron beam in

place of light to form high-resolution, three-dimensional images of the surfaces of objects; capable of much higher magnifications than a light microscope.

sclerosis (scleh-RO-sis) Hardening or stiffening of a tissue, as in multiple sclerosis of the central nervous system or atherosclerosis of the blood vessels.

sebum (SEE-bum) An oily secretion of the sebaceous glands that keeps the skin and hair pliable.

secondary active transport A mechanism in which solutes are moved through a plasma membrane by a carrier that does not itself use ATP but depends on a concentration gradient established by an active transport pump elsewhere in the cell.

second messenger A chemical that is produced within a cell (such as cAMP) or that enters a cell (such as calcium ions) in response to the binding of a messenger to a membrane receptor, and that triggers a metabolic reaction in the cell.

secretion 1. A chemical released by a cell to serve a physiological function, such as a hormone or digestive enzyme. **2.** The process of releasing such a chemical, often by exocytosis. *Compare* excretion.

selectively permeable membrane A membrane that allows some substances to pass through while excluding others; for example, the plasma membrane and dialysis membranes.

semicircular ducts Three ring-shaped, fluid-filled tubes of the inner ear that detect angular accelerations of the head; each is enclosed in a bony passage called the semicircular canal. fig. 16.21

semilunar valve A valve that consists of crescent-shaped cusps, including the aortic and pulmonary valves of the heart and valves of the veins and lymphatic vessels. fig. 19.8

semipermeable membrane *See* selectively permeable membrane.

senescence (seh-NESS-ense) Degenerative changes that occur with age.

sensation Conscious perception of a stimulus; pain, taste, and color, for example, are not stimuli but sensations resulting from stimuli.

sensory nerve fiber An axon that conducts information from a receptor to the central nervous system; an afferent nerve fiber.

serosa (seer-OH-sa) A thin epithelial membrane composed of a simple squamous epithelium overlying a thin layer of areolar tissue; covers the external surfaces of viscera such as the lungs, stomach, and intestines, and forms membranes such as the peritoneum, pleura, and pericardium, or a portion of such membranes. Also called *serous membrane.*

serous fluid (SEER-us) A watery, low-protein fluid similar to blood serum, formed as a filtrate of the blood or tissue fluid or as a secretion of serous gland cells; moistens the serous membranes.

serous membrane A membrane such as the peritoneum, pleura, or pericardium that lines a body cavity or covers the external surfaces of the viscera; composed of a simple squamous mesothelium and a thin layer of areolar connective tissue. Also called *serosa*. fig. 5.33b

sex chromosomes The X and Y chromosomes, which determine the sex of an individual.

shock 1. Circulatory shock, a state of cardiac output that is insufficient to meet the body's physiological needs, with consequences ranging from fainting to death. **2.** Insulin shock, a state of severe hypoglycemia caused by administration of insulin. **3.** Spinal shock, a state of depressed or lost reflex activity inferior to a point of spinal cord injury. **4.** Electrical shock, the effect of a current of electricity passing through the body, often causing muscular spasm and cardiac arrhythmia or arrest.

sign An objective manifestation of illness that any observer can see, such as cyanosis or edema. *Compare* symptom.

simple epithelium An epithelium in which all cells rest directly on the basement membrane; includes simple squamous, cuboidal, and columnar types, and pseudostratified columnar. fig. 5.3

sinuatrial node The pacemaker of the heart; a patch of autorhythmic cells in the right atrium that initiates each heartbeat.

sinus 1. An air-filled space in the cranium. **2.** A modified, relatively dilated vein that lacks smooth muscle and is incapable of vasomotion, such as the dural sinuses of the cerebral circulation and coronary sinus of the heart. **3.** A small fluid-filled space in an organ such as the spleen and lymph nodes. **4.** Pertaining to the sinuatrial node of the heart, as in *sinus rhythm.*

sodium–glucose transporter (SGLT) A symport that simultaneously transports Na$^+$ and glucose into a cell.

sodium–potassium (Na$^+$–K$^+$) pump An active transport mechanism in the plasma membrane that uses energy from ATP to expel three sodium ions from the cell and import two potassium ions into the cell for each cycle of the pump; used to drive secondary active transport processes, regulate cell volume, maintain an electrical charge gradient across the plasma membrane, and generate body heat.

somatic 1. Pertaining to the body as a whole. **2.** Pertaining to the skin, bones, and skeletal muscles as opposed to the viscera. **3.** Pertaining to cells other than germ cells.

somatic nervous system A division of the nervous system that includes efferent fibers mainly from the skin, muscles, and skeleton and afferent fibers to the skeletal muscles. *Compare* autonomic nervous system.

somatosensory 1. Pertaining to widely distributed *general senses* in the skin, muscles, tendons, joint capsules, and viscera, as opposed to the *special senses* found in the head only; also called *somesthetic.* **2.** Pertaining to the cerebral cortex of the postcentral gyrus, which receives input from such receptors.

somite One segment in a linear series of mesodermal masses that form on each side of the neural tube and give rise to trunk muscles, vertebrae, and dermis. fig. 29.7

spermatogenesis (SPUR-ma-toe-JEN-eh-sis) The production of sperm cells through a series of mitotic and meiotic cell divisions; male gametogenesis.

spermatozoon (spur-MAT-oh-ZO-on) A sperm cell.

sphincter (SFINK-tur) A ring of muscle that opens or closes an opening or passageway; found, for example, in the eyelids, around the urinary orifice, and at the beginning of a blood capillary.

spinal nerve Any of the 31 pairs of nerves that arise from the spinal cord and pass through the intervertebral foramina or through the gap between the spine and cranium.

spindle 1. An elongated structure that is thick in the middle and tapered at the ends (fusiform). **2.** A football-shaped complex of microtubules that guide the movement of chromosomes in mitosis and meiosis. fig. 4.15 **3.** A stretch receptor in the skeletal muscles. fig. 13.24

spine 1. The vertebral column. **2.** A pointed process or sharp ridge on a bone, such as the styloid process of the cranium and spine of the scapula.

splanchnic (SPLANK-nic) Pertaining to the digestive tract.

squamous (SKWAY-mus) **1.** Thin and flat. **2.** A cellular shape that is flat or scaly; pertains especially to a class of epithelial cells. figs. 5.4, 5.12

stem cell Any undifferentiated cell that can divide and differentiate into more functionally specific cell types such as blood cells and germ cells.

stenosis (steh-NO-sis) The narrowing of a passageway such as a heart valve or uterine tube; a permanent, pathological constriction as opposed to physiological constriction of a passageway.

steroid (STERR-oyd, STEER-oyd) A lipid molecule that consists of four interconnected carbon rings; cholesterol and several of its derivatives.

stimulus A chemical or physical agent in a cell's surroundings that is capable of creating a physiological response in the cell; especially agents detected by sensory cells, such as chemicals, light, and pressure.

strain The extent to which a body, such as a bone, is deformed when subjected to stress. *Compare* stress.

stratified epithelium A type of epithelium in which some cells rest on top of others instead of on the basement membrane; includes stratified squamous, cuboidal, and columnar types, and urothelium. fig. 5.3

stress 1. A mechanical force applied to any part of the body; important in stimulating bone growth, for example. *Compare* strain. **2.** A condition in which any environmental influence disturbs the homeostatic equilibrium of the body and stimulates a physiological response, especially involving the increased secretion of certain adrenal hormones.

stroke volume The volume of blood ejected by one ventricle of the heart in one contraction.

stroma The connective tissue framework of a gland, lymphatic organ, or certain other viscera, as opposed to the tissue (parenchyma) that performs the physiological functions of the organ.

subcutaneous (SUB-cue-TAY-nee-us) Beneath the skin.

substrate 1. A chemical that is acted upon and changed by an enzyme. **2.** A chemical used as a source of energy, such as glucose and fatty acids.

substrate specificity The ability of an enzyme to bind only one substrate or a limited range of related substrates.

sulcus (SUL-cuss) A groove in the surface of an organ, as in the cerebrum or heart.

summation 1. A phenomenon in which multiple stimuli combine their effects on a cell to produce a response; seen especially in nerve and muscle cells. **2.** A phenomenon in which multiple muscle twitches occur so closely together that a muscle fiber cannot fully relax between twitches but develops more tension than a single twitch produces. fig. 11.15

superficial Relatively close to the surface; opposite of deep. For example, the ribs are superficial to the lungs.

superior Higher than another structure or point of reference from the perspective of anatomical position; for example, the lungs are superior to the diaphragm.

supination (SOO-pih-NAY-shun) A rotational movement of the forearm that turns the palm so that it faces upward or forward. fig. 9.18

surfactant (sur-FAC-tent) A chemical that reduces the surface tension of water and enables it to penetrate other substances more effectively. Examples include pulmonary surfactant and bile acids.

sympathetic nervous system A division of the autonomic nervous system that issues efferent fibers through the thoracic and lumbar nerves and usually exerts adrenergic effects on its target organs; includes a chain of paravertebral ganglia adjacent to the vertebral column, and the adrenal medulla.

symphysis (SIM-fih-sis) A joint in which two bones are held together by fibrocartilage; for example, between bodies of the vertebrae and between the right and left pubic bones.

symport A cotransport protein that moves two solutes simultaneously through a plasma membrane in the same direction, such as the sodium–glucose transporter.

symptom A subjective manifestation of illness that only the ill person can sense, such as dizziness or nausea. *Compare* sign.

synapse (SIN-aps) **1.** A junction at the end of an axon where it stimulates another cell. **2.** A gap junction between two cardiac or smooth muscle cells at which one cell electrically stimulates the other; called an *electrical synapse.*

synaptic cleft (sih-NAP-tic) A narrow space between an axon terminal and the membrane of the postsynaptic cell, across which a neuro-transmitter diffuses. fig. 12.21

synaptic vesicle A spheroidal organelle in an axon terminal containing neurotransmitter. fig. 12.21

syndrome A suite of related signs and symptoms stemming from a specific pathological cause.

synergist (SIN-ur-jist) A muscle that works with the prime mover (agonist) to contribute to the same overall action at a joint.

synergistic effect An effect in which two agents working together (such as two hormones) exert an effect that is greater than the sum of their separate effects. For example, neither follicle-stimulating hormone nor testosterone alone stimulates significant sperm production, but the two of them together stimulate production of vast numbers of sperm.

synovial fluid A lubricating fluid similar to egg white in consistency, found in the synovial joint cavities and bursae.

synovial joint A point where two bones are separated by a narrow, encapsulated space filled with lubricating synovial fluid; most such joints are relatively mobile. Also called *diarthrosis.*

synthesis reaction A chemical reaction in which relatively small molecules are combined to form a larger one. *Compare* decomposition reaction.

systemic (sis-TEM-ic) Widespread or pertaining to the body as a whole, as in the systemic circulation.

systemic circuit All blood vessels that convey blood from the left ventricle to all organs of the body and back to the right atrium of the heart; all of the cardiovascular system except the heart and pulmonary circuit.

systole (SIS-toe-lee) The contraction of any heart chamber; ventricular contraction unless otherwise specified.

systolic pressure (sis-TOLL-ic) The peak arterial blood pressure measured during ventricular systole.

T

target cell A cell acted upon by a nerve fiber, hormone, or other chemical messenger.

tarsal Pertaining to the ankle (tarsus).

T cell A type of lymphocyte involved in innate immunity, humoral immunity, and cellular immunity; occurs in several forms including helper, cytotoxic, and suppressor T cells and natural killer cells.

tendon A collagenous band or cord associated with a muscle, usually attaching it to a bone and transferring muscular tension to it.

tetanus 1. A state of sustained muscle contraction produced by temporal summation as a normal part of contraction; also called *tetany.* **2.** Spastic muscle paralysis produced by the toxin of the bacterium *Clostridium tetani* or other causes.

thalamus (THAL-uh-muss) The largest part of the diencephalon, located immediately inferior to the corpus callosum and bulging into each lateral ventricle; a point of synaptic relay of nearly all signals passing from lower levels of the CNS to the cerebrum. figs. 14.8, 14.12a

theory An explanatory statement, or set of statements, that concisely summarizes the state of knowledge on a phenomenon and provides direction for further study; for example, the fluid-mosaic theory of the plasma membrane and the sliding filament theory of muscle contraction. *See also* hypothesis.

thermogenesis The production of heat, for example, by shivering or by the action of thyroid hormones.

thermoreceptor A neuron specialized to respond to heat or cold, found in the skin and mucous membranes, for example.

thermoregulation Homeostatic regulation of the body temperature within a narrow range by adjustments of heat-promoting and heat-losing mechanisms.

thorax A region of the trunk between the neck and the diaphragm; the chest.

threshold 1. The minimum voltage to which the plasma membrane of a nerve or muscle cell must be depolarized before it produces an action potential. **2.** The minimum combination of stimulus intensity and duration needed to generate an afferent signal from a sensory receptor.

thrombosis (throm-BO-sis) The formation or presence of a thrombus.

thrombus A clot that forms in a blood vessel or heart chamber; may break free and travel in the bloodstream as a thromboembolus. *Compare* embolus.

thyroid hormone Either of two similar hormones, thyroxine and triiodothyronine, synthesized from iodine and tyrosine.

thyroid-stimulating hormone (TSH) A hormone of the anterior pituitary gland that stimulates the thyroid gland; also called *thyrotropin.*

thyroxine (thy-ROCK-seen) The thyroid hormone secreted in greatest quantity, with four iodine atoms; also called *tetraiodothyronine.* fig. 17.17

tight junction A region in which adjacent cells are bound together by fusion of the outer phospholipid layer of their plasma membranes; forms a zone that encircles each cell near its apical pole and reduces or prevents flow of material between cells. fig. 5.28

tissue An aggregation of cells and extracellular materials, usually forming part of an organ and serving some discrete aspect of that organ's function; all tissues belong to one of the four primary classes—epithelial, connective, muscular, and nervous tissue.

totipotent Pertaining to a stem cell of the early preembryo, prior to development of a blastocyst, that has the potential to develop into any type of embryonic, extraembryonic, or adult cell.

trabecula (tra-BEC-you-la) A thin plate or layer of tissue, such as the calcified trabeculae of spongy bone or the fibrous trabeculae that subdivide a gland. fig. 7.4

trachea (TRAY-kee-uh) A cartilage-supported tube from the inferior end of the larynx to the origin of the main bronchi; conveys air to and from the lungs; colloquially called the *windpipe.*

translation The process in which a ribosome reads an mRNA molecule and synthesizes the protein specified by its genetic code.

transmembrane protein An integral protein that extends through a plasma membrane and contacts both the extracellular and intracellular fluid. fig. 3.6

transmission electron microscope (TEM) A microscope that uses an electron beam in place of light to form high-resolution, two-dimensional images of ultrathin slices of cells or tissues; capable of extremely high magnification.

triglyceride (try-GLISS-ur-ide) A lipid composed of three fatty acids joined to a glycerol; also called a *triacylglycerol* or *neutral fat*. fig. 2.18

trunk 1. That part of the body excluding the head, neck, and appendages. **2.** A major blood vessel, lymphatic vessel, or nerve that gives rise to smaller branches; for example, the pulmonary trunk and spinal nerve trunks.

T tubule Transverse tubule; a tubular extension of the plasma membrane of a muscle cell that conducts action potentials into the sarcoplasm and excites the sarcoplasmic reticulum. fig. 11.2

tunic (TOO-nic) A layer that encircles or encloses an organ, such as the tunics of a blood vessel or eyeball.

tympanic membrane The eardrum.

U

ultrastructure Fine details of tissue and cell structure, as far down as the molecular level, revealed by the electron microscope.

ultraviolet radiation Invisible, ionizing, electromagnetic radiation with shorter wavelength and higher energy than violet light; causes skin cancer and photoaging of the skin but is required in moderate amounts for the synthesis of vitamin D.

unipotent Pertaining to a stem cell that has the potential to develop into only one type of fully differentiated, functional cell, such as an epidermal stem cell that can become only a keratinocyte.

unmyelinated (un-MY-eh-lih-NAY-ted) Lacking a myelin sheath. fig. 12.9

urea (you-REE-uh) A nitrogenous waste produced from two ammonia molecules and carbon dioxide; the most abundant nitrogenous waste in the blood and urine. fig. 23.2

urothelium A type of stratified epithelium that lines much of the urinary tract, characterized by domed *umbrella cells* at the surface, protecting underlying cells from the acidity and hypertonicity of urine. Also called *transitional epithelium*. fig. 5.11

uterine tube A duct that extends from the ovary to the uterus and conveys an egg or conceptus to the uterus; also called *fallopian tube* or *oviduct*.

utricle (YOU-tri-cul) A saclike receptor in the inner ear with a nearly horizontal patch of hair cells, the macula utriculi; senses the orientation of the head and responds to horizontal acceleration, as when accelerating or decelerating in a car. fig. 16.20

V

van der Waals force A weak attraction between two atoms occurring when a brief fluctuation in the electron cloud density of one atom induces polarization of an adjacent atom; important in association of lipids with each other, protein folding, and protein–ligand binding.

varicose vein A vein that has become permanently distended and convoluted due to a loss of competence of the venous valves; especially common in the lower limb, esophagus, and anal canal (where they are called hemorrhoids).

vas (vass) (plural, *vasa*) A vessel or duct.

vascular Pertaining to blood vessels.

vascular corrosion cast A technique for visualizing the blood vessels of organs and tissues, especially the microvasculature, by flushing blood from the vessels, injecting a resin and letting it solidify, then digesting the actual tissue away with a corrosive agent, leaving only the resin cast; this is then viewed with a scanning electron microscope. figs. 20.1b, 23.10a

vasoconstriction (VAY-zo-con-STRIC-shun) The narrowing of a blood vessel due to muscular contraction of its tunica media.

vasodilation (VAY-zo-dy-LAY-shun) The widening of a blood vessel due to relaxation of the muscle of its tunica media and the outward pressure of the blood exerted against the wall.

vasomotion Collective term for vasoconstriction and vasodilation; any change in the diameter of a blood vessel.

vasomotor center A nucleus in the medulla oblongata that transmits signals to the blood vessels and regulates vessel diameter.

ventral Pertaining to the front of the body, the regions of the chest and abdomen; anterior.

ventral root *See* anterior root.

ventricle (VEN-trih-cul) A fluid-filled chamber of the brain or heart.

venule (VEN-yule) The smallest type of vein, receiving drainage from capillaries.

vertebra (VUR-teh-bra) One of the bones of the vertebral column.

vertebral column (VUR-teh-brul) A posterior series of usually 33 vertebrae; encloses the spinal cord, supports the skull and thoracic cage, and provides attachment for the limbs and postural muscles. Also called *spine* or *spinal column*.

vesicle A fluid-filled tissue sac or an organelle such as a synaptic or secretory vesicle.

vesicular transport The movement of particles or fluid droplets through the plasma membrane by the process of endocytosis or exocytosis.

viscera (VISS-er-uh) (singular, *viscus*) The organs contained in the body cavities, such as the brain, heart, lungs, stomach, intestines, and kidneys.

visceral (VISS-er-ul) **1.** Pertaining to the viscera. **2.** The inner or deeper layer of a two-layered membrane such as the pleura, pericardium, or glomerular capsule. *Compare* parietal. fig. A.6

visceral muscle Unitary smooth muscle found in the walls of blood vessels and the digestive, respiratory, urinary, and reproductive tracts.

viscosity The resistance of a fluid to flow; the thickness or stickiness of a fluid.

voluntary muscle Muscle that is usually under conscious control; skeletal muscle.

vulva The female external genitalia; the mons, labia majora, and all superficial structures between the labia majora.

W

water balance An equilibrium between fluid intake and output or between the amounts of fluid contained in the body's different fluid compartments.

white matter White myelinated nervous tissue deep to the cortex of the cerebrum and cerebellum and superficial to the gray matter of the spinal cord. fig. 14.6

X

X chromosome The larger of the two sex chromosomes; males have one X chromosome and females have two in each somatic cell.

X-ray 1. A high-energy, penetrating electromagnetic ray with wavelengths in the range of 0.1 to 10 nm; used in diagnosis and therapy. **2.** A photograph made with X-rays; radiograph.

Y

Y chromosome Smaller of the two sex chromosomes, found only in males and having little if any genetic function except development of the testis.

yolk sac An embryonic membrane that encloses the yolk in vertebrates that lay eggs and serves in humans as the origin of the first blood and germ cells.

Z

zygomatic arch An arch of bone anterior to the ear, formed by the zygomatic processes of the temporal, frontal, and zygomatic bones; origin of the masseter muscle.

zygote A single-celled, fertilized egg.

INDEX

Matrix
of bone tissue, 202–203
extracellular, 138, 141
hair, 184, *184*
of HIV, 817, *817*
of mitochondria, 103, *103*
of nail, 187, *187*
Matrix reactions, in aerobic
respiration, 988–989, *989,*
992t
Maturation phase, of tissue repair,
167
Mature ovarian follicle, *1040, 1051,*
1052–1053, 1056*t*
Maxillary sinus, 227, *230*
Maximum oxygen uptake (VO₂max),
406
Maximum voluntary ventilation
(MVV), 847
Mean arterial pressure (MAP), 734,
878
Mean corpuscular hemoglobin
(MCH), 678
Mean corpuscular volume (MCV),
678
Meatus
acoustic
external, *228, 229,* 231*t,* *232,*
233, 578, 579
internal, *228, 229,* 233, *233*
of bone, *226,* 226*t*
nasal cavity, *828,* 829
Mechanical advantage (MA), *274,*
274–275
Mechanical digestion, 926, 933
Mechanical junctions, in cardiac
muscle, *700,* 701
Mechanical stress, bone adaptation
to, 205, *205,* 210
Mechanically gated channels, 81
Mechanoreceptors, 566, 568
Meconium, 1067, 1086*t*
Medial, 29, 29*t*
Medial excursion, of mandible, 283,
284
Medial (internal) rotation, *277,* 281,
281
Medial lemniscus, *467,* 503, *505*
Medial longitudinal arch of foot,
261, *261, 380, 381, 382*
Median aperture, *500,* 501, *501*
Median forebrain bundle (MFB), 520
Median plane, 28
Mediastinal surface, of lung, 833,
834
Mediastinum, 32, *32,* 691
Medical art
evolution of, 4, *4*
Gray's Anatomy, 5
Vesalius atlas, 5
Medical history
anesthesia, 608
"animal electricity," 401
blood banking, 668

double helix, 110–112
flight of the Zenith, 849
homeostasis demonstration, 16
insulin, 649–650
man with hole in stomach, 969
nerve growth factor, 432
radiation, 43
radioactive bones, 203
word origins, 20
Medical imaging, 2, *22,* 22–23
Medical terminology, 19–20
Medications. *See* Drugs
Medicine
evolutionary, 11
genomic, 110, 115
modern, birth of, 3–6
origins of, 3–6
revolution in, 6
terminology of, 19–20
Medieval medicine, 3–4
Medina, Lina, 1048
Medium arteries, *727,* 727–728
Medium veins, *727,* 732
Medium-wavelength (M) cones,
605, *606*
Medroxyprogesterone, 1070, 1070*t*
Medulla
of adrenal glands. *See* Adrenal
medulla
of hair, 184, *184*
of kidney, 870, *871, 872, 874*
of lymph node, 790–791, *791*
of ovary, 1038, *1040*
of thymus, 789, *790*
Medulla oblongata, *494,* 495, *496,*
503, *504, 508*
in autonomic control, 558
in blood pressure control, 738
cardiac centers of, 503, 507, 713
in digestion control, 941, 944
emetic center of, 942
in hearing, 585
in pain modulation, 572
respiratory centers of, 503,
839–841, *840*
in taste, 574
vasomotor center of, 503, 507,
736, 737–739
Medullary cavity, 200, *200*
Medullary cone, 461, *461*
Medullary cords, of lymph node,
790–791, *791*
Medullary ischemic reflex, 738
Medullary sinus, of lymph
node, *791*
Megacolon, 553
Megakaryoblasts, 679
Megakaryocytes, 679, *679*
Megavitamins, 985
Meiosis, 128
in oogenesis, 1050, *1051*
in spermatogenesis, 1023–1025,
1024
Meiosis II, 1078

Melanin, 131, 180–182, *181,* 185,
185, 423, 594
Melanocortin, 977, *978*
Melanocyte(s), 177, *177,* 180, 190,
1097
Melanocyte-stimulating hormone
(MSH), 190
Melanoma, 132, 190–191, *191*
Melanopsin, 601, 607
Melanosomes, 177
Melatonin, 518, 624, 631*t,* 633*t,*
633–634
synthesis of, 635
Membrane(s), 31–34, 32*t,* 163, 165,
165. See also specific
types
Membrane attack complex (MAC),
797–798, *799*
Membrane potentials, 93, 157. *See*
also Action potentials
local, 434–435, 435*t*
resting, 93, 394, *433,* 433–434
Membrane proteins, *80, 81,*
81–82, *82*
Membrane reactions, in aerobic
respiration, 988, 992*t*
Membrane skeleton (terminal web),
79, 84, 97, *98*
Membrane transport, 87–96, 96*t*
active, 87, 91–92, 96*t*
carrier-mediated, 87, 90–93, 96*t*
by filtration, 87, 96*t*
osmolarity and tonicity in, 89–90
by osmosis, 88–89, *89,* 96*t*
passive, 87
by simple diffusion, 87–88, 96*t*
vesicular, 93–95, 96*t*
Membranous labyrinth, 580, *581*
Membranous organelles, 97
Membranous urethra, 893, 1017,
1018
Memory, 451–453, 519–520
aging and, 1099
Alzheimer disease and, 453, 1099
brain lesions and, 520
emotional, 452, 520
explicit (declarative), 452, 519
forgetting, 453
frontal lobe and, 511
hippocampus and, 520
hypothalamus and, 510
immediate, 452
immune, 803, 810, 811–812, *812*
implicit, 452, 519
long-term, 452
olfaction and, 576
short-term, 452
sleep and, 519
working, 452
Memory B cells, *812,* 814*t*
Memory consolidation, 519
Memory T cells, 808, *809,* 810, 814*t*
Memory trace, 452
Menarche, 1049

Mendel, Gregor, 110
Mendelian genetics, 110
Meningeal layer, of dura mater, 497,
499
Meninges, 32, 231
brain, 497–498, *499*
spinal cord, *461,* 461–463, *462*
Meningitis, 487*t,* 499, 580
Meniscal injuries, 292, *292*
Meniscus (menisci), 273, 290, *291,*
292, *292,* 299
Menopause, 1038, 1049, 1101
evolution of, 1049
hirsutism in, 186
hot flashes in, 1049
Menses, 1056
Menstrual cycle, 1042, 1050, *1054,*
1055–1056, *1057*
anovulatory, 1049
disorders of, 1068*t*
ischemic phase of, 1056
menstrual phase of, *1054,* 1056
pheromones and, 576
premenstrual phase of, *1054,*
1056
proliferative phase of, *1054,*
1055, *1057*
secretory phase of, *1054,* 1056,
1057
Menstrual fluid, 1056
Menstrual phase, *1054,* 1056, *1057*
Menstruation. *See also* Menstrual
cycle
cessation of. *See* Menopause
first, 1049
Mental cleft, 312*t*
Mental protuberance, *226,* 238, *238*
Mental region, *364*
Mental spines, *228*
Mental symphysis, 238
Mentolabial sulcus, *364*
Mentum (chin), *364*
Mercury, millimeters of, 842
Merocrine (eccrine) glands, 162,
164, 188, 189, 190*t*
Mesangial cells, 879, *879*
Mesencephalon, 495, *498,* 503
Mesenchymal cells, 139, 1081
Mesenchyme, 139, 148, 206–207,
1081
Mesenteric lymph nodes, *784,* 792,
792
Mesenteries, 34, *34, 374, 375,*
928–929, *929*
anterior (ventral), 34, 928
posterior (dorsal), 34, *34,* 928,
1083
Mesocolic lymph nodes, *792*
Mesocolon, 34, 929, *929, 964,* 965
Mesoderm, 139, 1076, 1080–1081,
1081, 1082, 1083, 1083*t,*
1087
Mesometrium, *1041,* 1042
Mesonephric duct, 1010, *1011*